LAND TENURE

ꙅꙅꙅꙅꙅ LAND TENURE

Edited by

KENNETH H. PARSONS, RAYMOND J. PENN, AND PHILIP M. RAUP

Proceedings of the

World
(International) Conference on Land Tenure (and Related) Problems.

University of
(in World Agriculture Held at Madison,) Wisconsin, 1951

Madison, Wisconsin, 1956

THE UNIVERSITY OF WISCONSIN PRESS

Published by

 THE UNIVERSITY OF WISCONSIN PRESS
811 STATE STREET, MADISON 5

MANUFACTURED IN THE UNITED STATES OF AMERICA BY THE
WILLIAM BYRD PRESS, INC., RICHMOND, VIRGINIA

LIBRARY OF CONGRESS CATALOG CARD NUMBER 55-8486

§§§§   PREFACE

THIS VOLUME presents the proceedings of the conference on world land tenure problems which convened October 7, 1951, on the campus of the University of Wisconsin at Madison, Wisconsin. The papers included are mainly those read at the general sessions of the conference; but a few supplementary articles are included, principally contributions to and summaries of the working party seminars.

These papers are essentially by-products of the conference. Consequently, the contributions can be appreciated best by noting them in the context in which they were produced. The conference was the principal part of a project which included the conference, a training program, and a considerable number of field trips. Two different groups from foreign countries participated in the proceedings as delegates and trainees. Approximately fifty of the participants were senior men—administrators and mature scholars. There were three or four administrators to every academic person. These persons were called delegates, but their participation in the conference was solely as experts and students of the problem. They spoke for themselves and not as officials of their countries. The trainees, a group of twenty-five younger men, participated in the conference on the same basis. For them, the conference was the first phase of a one-year training program centering on the analysis of land tenure problems in relation to economic and social development. About seventy-five American scholars and administrators also participated in the conference, principally as the chairmen of meetings or as consultants. A few major papers were read by the American participants on some aspect of American history, policy, or experience. Consequently, this volume is composed principally of contributions from the foreign participants, especially the delegates.

It is noteworthy that these proceedings are not the product of a group of men gathered together for the primary purpose of reading papers to each other; rather, these proceedings are the written record, mostly composed at Madison, left by a group of earnest men living, working, and growing together as they discussed their common problems. They were motivated by a sense of the supreme importance of equitable tenure arrangements for the peace and productivity of the free world.

The conference was a co-operative project in a number of dimensions. It was sponsored jointly by several agencies of the Federal government and the University of Wisconsin. The conference was conducted as a project in the technical assistance programs of the Technical Cooperation Administration of the Department of State and the Economic Cooperation Administration, now succeeded by the Foreign Operations Administration, and the principal expenses were borne by these agencies. The program was planned by two committees: one was composed of representatives of the University of Wisconsin and of the above mentioned agencies, together with representatives of the Departments of Agriculture, Interior, and Labor; another program committee was constituted from representatives of several of the Land Grant colleges who have been co-operating on land tenure research through the regional land tenure committees sponsored by the Farm Foundation of Chicago. Early in November, 1951, the conference group traveled through eight states in the Midwest and the Southeastern states and had the privilege of the hospitality on that trip of the Farm Foundation at

Chicago, Purdue University, the University of Kentucky, and Berea College; the University of Tennessee and the T.V.A.; Clemson College, North Carolina State College, and Virginia Polytechnic Institute. The closing sessions of the conference were held in Washington, where the conference group had the privilege of visiting the several U.S. agencies participating in the program. In the summer of 1952 the trainee group took an extensive field trip through the upper Midwest area; here they were the guests of North Dakota, South Dakota, Colorado, Nebraska, and Iowa. Representatives of the Food and Agriculture Organization and the General Secretariat of the United Nations and the Caribbean Commission participated in the conference proceedings.

The conference was experimental and exploratory. It was organized in the belief that administrators and scholars from all over the world, who have responsibilities for, as well as intellectual and moral commitments to, the understanding and resolution of land tenure problems, could make a substantial contribution to genuine progress in dealing with these problems, by discussions, intensive study, the presentation and criticism of papers, and by an exchange of views. As an experiment in international intellectual co-operation, it was projected in the belief that technical discussions of these difficult economic and social issues could prepare and smooth the way for constructive programs of both the individual countries and by international agencies. Fundamentally, the conference was intended as an effort in technical co-operation on a world scale designed to think through and better understand tenure problems and adjustments. The explorations in the conference, the worldwide network of acquaintances established, the instruction, inspiration, and encouragement that came to the participants—all these, it was hoped, would help pave the way for specific and constructive action at the program level. This was our faith as the conference was projected.

The University of Wisconsin assumed full responsibility for the conduct of the program, and the University had the fullest co-operation from scores of other agencies and institutions. The vigor and freedom of the discussions reflected fully the value of an atmosphere of academic freedom in stimulating frank expression of views. Special library facilities and assistance were made available to the conference participants. The Library of the U.S. Department of Agriculture contributed substantially to the library collections.

The conference may be viewed as an experiment, also, in a functional, or problem, approach to technical and intellectual co-operation on a world scale. As we move forward attempting to find the most effective ways to draw upon the talent, resources, and facilities of our present colleges and universities, there are many questions about how such uses should be organized—by countries, by problems, how? Only time and experience demonstrate the better and worse ways of university participation in this world effort. In this conference we tried a problem approach to a group of some forty countries. The assumption that countries in different parts of the world had similar problems in land tenure adjustments seems substantiated by the conference discussions. Of even more importance, the programs undertaken by any country were generally agreed to have valuable lessons for many other countries who have even grossly similar tenure, land use, population, or institutional patterns.

A steering committee was organized early in the conference with the dual responsibility of giving guidance to the day-by-day policy decisions of the conference and formulating suggestions as to whether and how the work and experience of the conference might be carried forward. The formal report of the steering committee is published at the conclusion of this volume. Only time and further developments can determine the degree to which the recommendations of the committee can be made operative. It is noteworthy, however, that both the appraisal of the experience and the recommendations for the future were solely the work of the delegate committee. This statement is eloquent testimony to the value of pooling intellectual resources on a world scale on problems of common interest. This committee was headed by Akram El-Ricaby of Syria as chairman; other members were Jose E. Velmonte of the Philippines, M. L. Dantwala, Bombay, India, Albert Costa of France, and Claudio Romero of Paraguay.

The conference program is so deeply indebted to people everywhere that it is scarcely possible to acknowledge these obligations adequately. In a very real sense this was path-breaking effort, and special credit is due to many officials in Washington, both for the wholehearted support which they gave it and the unqualified approval accorded the University for the full responsibility for the conduct of the program. The late Dr. H. G. Bennett, Administrator of the Technical Cooperation Administration, gave the project inspiring support; likewise, Dr. Dennis FitzGerald, Deputy Director of the Economic Cooperation Administration, Undersecretary of Agriculture Clarence J. McCormick, and the office of Secretary of State, especially Assistant Secretary Willard Thorp, not only gave the conference vigorous support but presented the opening papers at the conference. Scores of colleagues of these men worked indefatigably over many weeks on the organization and arrangements for the conference. Twenty-three staff members of nine different U.S. agencies appeared on the program as experts on different phases of the tenure and development problems.

Professors from seventeen American universities other than Wisconsin participated in the program on the Madison campus. Each of these persons is a recognized authority, and this group contributed greatly to the understanding of the problems. It is to be noted that the American participants and visitors were rarely in attendance for more than a day or a week. In the aggregate they were numerous but at any one time they were relatively few. In addition, twelve colleges or universities were hosts to all or a part of the conference group. In state after state a series of remarkably effective programs were presented; through these trips firsthand and expertly interpreted visits were made to scores of farms and ranches.

Finally, the limitless contributions of the staff of the University are to be acknowledged. There is no way to estimate the effort which the faculty and staff of the University of Wisconsin put into this project. Hundreds of persons in more than a score of departments contributed to the organization and operation of the conference. Most of them must remain nameless here. The facilities and generous hospitality of the Memorial Union gave the conference a home which we shall long remember.

The teamwork in the University community was nothing less than a rediscovery by those of us participating in the conference of the true meaning of a university. When a special talent was needed, there it was. But especial tribute is due to two groups of people: our colleagues in the language departments and the secretarial staff. The conference was conducted in three languages—English, French and Spanish—with simultaneous translation through private communication systems. Our colleagues, especially in the French Department under the leadership of Professor André C. Lévêque, and in the Spanish Department under the leadership of Professor Renato I. Rosaldo, did the impossible and earned the gratitude of everyone. The task of translating and interpreting into several other languages was also done with friendly expertness as the need arose.

In the operation of the conference it was early discovered that a distribution of texts of the papers was essential for fruitful discussions in the general sessions. Time after time translators worked through the night getting the texts ready for duplication. Always the secretarial staff under the talented leadership of Miss Dena Dworsky and Mrs. Gretchen Pfankuchen managed to get the manuscript typed or the stencils cut in time for the numerous sessions. Somehow, too, the duplicating office in the Department of Agricultural Journalism succeeded in running the thousands of pages of copy every day.

In the preparation of the manuscript for publication, Professor Wyn F. Owen has contributed generously to the final editing.

THE EDITORS

ACKERMAN, JOSEPH. *Farm Foundation, Chicago, Illinois*

AKHTAR, S. M. *Chairman, Department of Economics, University of the Punjab, Lahore, Pakistan*

AKIB, SALIM. *Junior Agricultural Officer, Department of Agriculture, Government of Malaya, Kedah, Federation of Malaya*

ALAM, ASSADOLLAH. *Chamberlain to His Imperial Majesty's Court; Former Minister of Agriculture, Government of Iran, Teheran, Iran*

ALAMUDDIN, NAJIB. *Member, Superior Economic Council of Lebanon; President, Near East Resources, Beirut, Lebanon*

ARCA-PARRÓ, ALBERTO. *Technical Adviser to the Director-General of Statistics, Ministry of Development, Government of Venezuela, Caracas, Venezuela*

ASTORGA, JOSÉ RAMÓN. *Under-Secretary, Ministry of Agriculture, Republic of Chile, Santiago, Chile*

BACHMAN, KENNETH J. *Head, Production, Income, and Costs Section, Agricultural Research Service, Department of Agriculture, Washington, D. C.*

BAKKEN, HENRY H. *Professor of Agricultural Economics, University of Wisconsin, Madison, Wisconsin*

BASCOM, WILLIAM. *Professor of Anthropology, Northwestern University, Evanston, Illinois*

BELTRÁN, GREGORIO. *Assistant Technical Adviser, National Agricultural Institute, Caracas, Venezuela*

BENNETT, HENRY G. [*deceased*]. *Former Administrator, Technical Cooperation Administration, United States Department of State, Washington, D. C.*

BERNAL, PEDRO. *Former General Manager,* *Agricultural Credit Bank, Bogota, Colombia*

BEUSCHER, JACOB H. *Professor of Law, University of Wisconsin, Madison, Wisconsin*

BONDURANT, JOHN H. *Economist in Farm Economics, University of Kentucky, Lexington, Kentucky*

BONNÉ, ALFRED. *Professor of Regional Economics and Sociology, Hebrew University, Jerusalem, Israel*

BUNCE, ARTHUR [*deceased*]. *Former Chief, Far Eastern Section, Division of International Finance, Federal Reserve Board, United States Government, Washington, D. C.*

CARROLL, THOMAS F. *Food and Agriculture Organization, United Nations, Rome, Italy*

CASE, H. C. M. *Head, Department of Agricultural Economics, University of Illinois, Urbana, Illinois*

CHAPMAN, DANIEL A. *Area Specialist, United Nations Secretariat, New York City, New York*

CLARK, NOBLE. *Associate Director, Agricultural Experiment Station, University of Wisconsin, Madison, Wisconsin*

CLAWSON, MARION. *Former Director, Bureau of Land Management, United States Department of Interior, Washington, D. C.*

COCHRAN, DOROTHY. *Information Staff, North American Regional Office, Food and Agriculture Organization, United Nations, Washington, D. C.*

COSTA, ALBERT ALEXANDRE. *Civil Administrator, Ministry of Agriculture, Republic of France, Paris, France*

DANTWALA, M. L. *Professor of Economics, University of Bombay, Bombay, India*

DeSouza, João Gonçalves. *President, National Institute of Immigration and Colonization, Rio de Janeiro; Brazilian Delegate, Food and Agriculture Organization, United Nations*

Dietze, Constantin C. von. *Professor of Economics, University of Freiburg, Freiburg, Germany*

Durán, Marco Antonio. *Director of Credit, National Agricultural and Livestock Credit Bank, Mexico City, Mexico*

El-Ricaby, Akram. *Secretary-General, Syrian Ministry of Agriculture, Damascus, Syria*

Ezzat, Mohamed Abdel Wahab. *Higher Committee on Land Reform, Ministry of Agriculture, Cairo, Egypt*

Fakher, Hossein. *Ministry of Foreign Affairs, Government of Iran, Teheran, Iran*

FitzGerald, Dennis A. *Deputy Director, Foreign Operations Administration, Washington, D. C.*

Flores, Edmundo. *Office of National Finance, Mexico City, Mexico*

Fred, Edwin B. *President, University of Wisconsin, Madison, Wisconsin*

Gaballah, Elsayed. *College of Agriculture, Cairo University, Cario, Egypt*

Galbraith, John K. *Professor of Economics, Harvard University, Cambridge, Massachusetts*

Ghavam, Mohammad Reza. *Head, Economic and Supervisory Department, Ministry of Labor, Government of Iran, Teheran, Iran*

Groves, Harold M. *Professor of Economics, University of Wisconsin, Madison, Wisconsin*

Hambidge, Gove. *United States Representative, Food and Agriculture Organization of the United Nations, United States Department of Agriculture, Washington, D. C.*

Harrington, Earl G. *Chief, Division of Cadastral Engineering, Bureau of Land Management, United States Department of Interior, Washington, D. C.*

Harris, J. S. *Senior Officer, Department of Trusteeship, United Nations, New York City, New York*

Harris, Marshall. *Agricultural Economist, Agricultural Research Service, United States Department of Agriculture, Washington, D. C.*

Hendrix, William E. *Assistant Professor of Economics, University of Chicago, Chicago, Illinois*

Herskovits, Melville J. *Professor of Anthropology, Northwestern University, Evanston, Illinois*

Hill, George W. *Coördinator, Department of Sociology and Cultural Anthropology, Central University of Venezuela, Caracas, Venezuela*

Hill, John Stuart. *Chief Land Commissioner, Ministry of Agriculture and Fisheries, Her Majesty's Government, London, England*

Hsiao, Tseng. *Director, Chinese Research Institute of Land Economics; President, Chinese Land Reform Association, Taipeh, Formosa*

Hyodo, Setsuro. *Secretary-Official, Ministry of Agriculture and Forestry, Government of Japan, Tokyo, Japan*

Jha, Aditya Nath. *Secretary, Ministry of Agriculture and Cooperation, Lucknow, U.P., India*

Kanel, Don. *Assistant Professor of Agricultural Economics, University of Nebraska, Lincoln, Nebraska*

Kelso, Maurice M. *Dean of Agriculture, Montana State College, Bozeman, Montana*

Kolb, John H. *Professor of Rural Sociology,*

University of Wisconsin, Madison, Wisconsin

LADEJINSKY, WOLF I. *Foreign Operations Administration, Washington, D. C.; Former Agricultural Attaché, United States Government, Tokyo, Japan*

LICHAUCO, LUIS. *Chairman, Board of Directors, Land Settlement and Development Corporation, Manila, Philippine Islands*

LLOVET, EDUARDO. *Director, National Institute of Colonization, Montevideo, Uruguay*

McCORMICK, CLARENCE J. *Former Under-Secretary, United States Department of Agriculture, Washington, D. C.*

MacGREGOR, JAMES J. *Department of Forestry, University of Oxford, Oxford, England*

McNALL, PRESTON E. *Professor of Agricultural Economics, University of Wisconsin, Madison, Wisconsin*

MADDOX, JAMES G. *American International Association for Economic and Social Development, New York City, New York*

MARIÑO, CRISTINA. *Assistant Technical Adviser, National Agricultural Institute, Caracas, Venezuela*

MENON, M. S. *Research Officer, Ministry of Food and Agriculture, Government of India, New Delhi, India*

MORTON, WALTER A. *Professor of Economics, University of Wisconsin, Madison, Wisconsin*

MOTHERAL, JOE R. *Agricultural Research Service, United States Department of Agriculture, Washington, D. C.*

MURRAY, WILLIAM. *Head, Department of Economics and Sociology, Iowa State College, Ames, Iowa*

NATARAJAN, B. *Economic Adviser and Joint Secretary to the Government of Madras, Madras, India*

NEALE-SILVA, EDUARDO. *Professor of Spanish,*

University of Wisconsin, Madison, Wisconsin

NELSON, LOWRY. *Professor of Sociology, University of Minnesota, St. Paul, Minnesota*

OWADA, KEIKI. *Ministry of Agriculture and Forestry, Government of Japan, Tokyo, Japan*

PALMER, SIEGFRIED H. *Chief Administrative Adviser, Federal Ministry for Food, Agriculture, and Forestry, West German Government, Bonn, Germany*

PAPAGEORGIOU, EUTHYMIOS. *Professor of Agricultural Economics and Policy, University of Salonica, Salonica, Greece*

PARSONS, KENNETH H. *Professor of Agricultural Economics, University of Wisconsin, Madison, Wisconsin*

PELZER, KARL. *Associate Professor of Geography, Yale University, New Haven, Connecticut*

PENN, RAYMOND J. *Chairman, Department of Agricultural Economics, University of Wisconsin, Madison, Wisconsin*

PETROVICH, MICHAEL B. *Assistant Professor of History, University of Wisconsin, Madison, Wisconsin*

PIHKALA, KAARLO UOLEVI. *Professor of Agricultural Policy, University of Helsinki, Helsinki, Finland*

PONCE DE LEÓN, FRANCISCO. *Deputy, National Congress of Peru, Lima, Peru*

POSADA, ANTONIO. *Inter-American Statistical Institute, Pan American Union, Washington, D. C.*

PRONIN, DIMITRI. *Instructor in Agricultural Engineering, University of Wisconsin, Madison, Wisconsin*

PROVINSE, JOHN. *Assistant Commissioner of Indian Affairs, United States Department of Interior, Washington, D. C.*

RAUP, PHILIP M. *Professor of Agricultural Economics, University of Minnesota, St. Paul, Minnesota*

RICHE, J. E. LE. *Agricultural Official, Ministry of Agriculture, Government of Libya, Tripolitania, Libya*

ROCHE, JEAN. *Chief Engineer, Rural Engineering Service; Chief, Technical Section on Land Consolidation, Ministry of Agriculture, Republic of France, Paris, France*

RODRÍGUEZ-CABRERA, MANUEL. *Farm Appraiser, Agricultural and Industrial Bank of Cuba, Havana, Cuba*

ROGERS, CHARLES E. *Information Consultant; Formerly with the Food and Agriculture Organization, 2651 16th Street, N.W., Washington, D. C.*

ROMERO, CLAUDIO. *Director, Department of Plans, Agrarian Reform Institute, Asunción, Paraguay*

ROSSI-DORIA, MANLIO. *Professor of Agricultural Economics, University of Naples, Naples, Italy*

SAN ROMÁN, MANUEL M. DE. *Chief, Agrarian Department, Ministry of Agriculture, Government of Costa Rica, San José, Costa Rica*

SANTOS, LUIS RIVERA. *Executive Director, Social Programs Administration, Department of Agriculture and Commerce, Government of Puerto Rico, Santurce, Puerto Rico*

SARGUT, IBRAHIM ATIF. *Under-Secretary of Agriculture, Ministry of Agriculture, Government of Turkey, Ankara, Turkey*

SCHAARS, MARVIN A. *Professor of Agricultural Economics, University of Wisconsin, Madison, Wisconsin*

SCHEER, CORNELIS D. *Head, Economics Section, Horticultural Division, Ministry of Agriculture, Fisheries, and Food, Government of The Netherlands, The Hague, Netherlands*

SCHICKELE, RAINER. *Chief, Land and Water Use Branch, Food and Agriculture Organization, United Nations, Rome, Italy*

SCHILLER, OTTO. *Director, Institute of Agricultural Policies and Food Economy, College of Agriculture, Stuttgart-Hohenheim, Germany*

SEMTHITI, THEB. *Chief Co-operative Officer, Department of Cooperatives, Ministry of Agriculture, Government of Thailand, Bangkok, Thailand*

SHARP, LAURISTON. *Chairman, Department of Sociology and Anthropology, Cornell University, Ithaca, New York*

STERLING, HENRY S. *Associate Professor of Geography, University of Wisconsin, Madison, Wisconsin*

STEWART, CHARLES L. *Professor of Agricultural Economics, University of Illinois, Urbana, Illinois*

SUFI, M. H. *Deputy Secretary, Ministry of Agriculture, Government of Pakistan, Karachi, Pakistan*

TAEUBER, CONRAD. *Assistant Director, Bureau of the Census, United States Department of Commerce, Washington, D. C.*

TAEUBER, IRENE B. [MRS. CONRAD TAEUBER]. *Research Associate, Office of Population Research, Princeton University, Princeton, New Jersey*

TAMAYO, ARMANDO. *Minister of Agriculture and Animal Husbandry, Government of Venezuela, Caracas, Venezuela*

TANG, HUI-SUN. *Chief, Land Reform Division, Joint Commission on Rural Reconstruction, Taipeh, Formosa*

TANNOUS, AFIF. *Head, Middle East Division, Foreign Agricultural Service, United States Department of Agriculture, Washington, D. C.*

TAPIA, ANTONIO. *National Agricultural and Livestock Credit Bank, Mexico City, Mexico*

TAYLOR, CARL C. *Consultant in Community Development, Foreign Agricultural Service, United States Department of Agriculture, Washington, D. C.*

TAYLOR, HENRY C. *Former Professor of Agricultural Economics, University of Wisconsin; First Chief of the Bureau of*

Agricultural Economics, United States Department of Agriculture, Indian-Queen-on-the-Potomac, 7809 Fort Foote Road, Washington, D. C.

THEIN, BA. *Assistant Director of Agriculture, Department of Agriculture, Government of Burma, Rangoon, Burma*

THORP, WILLARD L. *Professor of Economics, Amherst College, Amherst, Massachusetts; Former Assistant Secretary for Economic Affairs, United States Department of State*

TIMMONS, JOHN F. *Professor of Economics, Iowa State College, Ames, Iowa*

VAN ROSSEM, JAN M. *Junior Officer, Ministry of Agriculture, Government of The Netherlands, The Hague, Netherlands*

VANDERPOL, PHILINE R. [PHILINE VANDERPOL LACHMAN]. *International Monetary Fund, Washington, D. C.*

VELMONTE, JOSE E. *Dean, College of Business Administration, University of the Philippines, Quezon City, Philippine Islands*

VOLIN, LAZAR. *Special Assistant, Foreign Agricultural Service, United States Department of Agriculture, Washington, D. C.*

WELCH, FRANK J. *Dean, College of Agriculture, University of Kentucky, Lexington, Kentucky*

YOUTH, TEP. *Chief, Cadastral Service, Ministry of Agriculture and Animal Husbandry, Government of Indo-China, Cambodia, Indo-China*

YTTBERBORN, G. R. *Deputy Director-General, Royal Board of Agriculture, Government of Sweden, Stockholm, Sweden*

TABLE OF CONTENTS

CONTENTS　　　　　　　　　　　　　　　　　　　xvii

𝒮𝒮𝒮𝒮   LIST OF TABLES

xxiii

∂∂∂∂   FIGURES

You certainly are people of great courage, of great patience, and of great fortitude to be willing to face the extraordinary magnitude and complexity of problems of land use and land tenure as they exist throughout the world. I salute you for that courage.

WALTER J. KOHLER
Governor, State of Wisconsin

THIS conference will be a demonstration of international co-operation and a lesson in the value of the peaceable approach to the solution of a common problem. It should prove a source of encouragement for those who are working—in the laboratories, in the fields, and at the conference—toward that end.

EDWIN B. FRED
President, University of Wisconsin

Part I INTRODUCTION

LAND REFORM AND AGRICULTURAL DEVELOPMENT

Kenneth H. Parsons

THE RISING concern for the improvement of land tenure conditions in world agriculture is based upon the insights and the belief that present tenure arrangements are stifling the economic development of agriculture in many countries. It is the purpose of this introductory essay to try to think through the general question of the relation of land reform to the development of agriculture. To the extent that this effort succeeds it should help tie together the more specific contributions in the proceedings,[1] by identifying certain basic issues which cut across cultural and national boundaries.

The free world is searching for ideas and methods for developing democratically satisfying and productive economies for people now suffering from insecurity, poverty, ill health, and inertia. Our sense of freedom and our appreciation of the dignity of man require that the development process enlist the participation of the people on a voluntary basis. Since the plain people of the world are mostly tillers of the soil, a program of development which enlists the willing participation of these people must be one which makes sense to them and meets their basic aspirations. Nothing less than a significant hold on the land will satisfy most of these people. As we search for solid foundations upon which to build enduring and just programs of economic and social development we are compelled to try to understand the present and prospective unrest on the land; and if we are wise, we shall strive to honor the aspirations of

peasants and use their stirring hopes as energy for economic and social development.

If land tenure problems are as important in world affairs as the participants in this conference believe them to be, it is essential that we discuss these problems until thoughtful people all over the world can see how the tenure problems of their own countries are significantly similar to or uniquely different from those of other peoples. What is needed ultimately is such understanding of the possible relations of tenure adjustments to genuine economic, political, and social progress that tenure policy can become an integral part of constructive national and international policies for peace and development. We need clearly marked pathways through the jungle of tenure difficulties in world agriculture over which thought can travel from problems to constructive policies. These pathways must be marked out by scholarship and statesmanship devoted to the understanding and solution of tenure problems. This is what the tenure conference was about.

The Context

Land tenure relations are social relations, central to which is man's relation to man in the use of land. This strategic relationship is more than a mere contractual agreement between landlord and tenant. Through ownership of land, property relations not only define the status of the owner by defining the duties with reference to the use

3

of land which all other persons must honor but also define the limits within which the owner's will is supreme with reference to the use and disposition of land. Within this property context fall the formal and legally enforceable agreements of landlord and tenant. But beyond these legal sanctions, customary arrangements may have even more compelling force; religious principles may explicitly define tenure and inheritance practices. It is evident, therefore, that the tenure arrangements may actually define the social and economic status of individuals in an agrarian economy—of which feudalism is the classical example in the history of the West. Also, the tenure terms upon which land is held actually define the use-relations of the land to the farm as an economic unit; the terms of tenure define the price or performance required for the use of land, which stipulations in turn greatly influence the incentives to energetic effort, the adoption of new agricultural techniques, and the care of the soil.

Land reform in this context is considered to be the aggregate of programs for resolving tenure problems. Agricultural development is taken to include changes in status of farm people which influence their effective participation in the farm economy as well as the improvement in farm production and land use practices. The particular requirements of reform as an improvement depend not only upon understanding the real difficulties in the situation in which reform is attempted but depend also upon what can be done within the limits of the actual potentialities for improvement. These vary greatly from one country to another.

Land tenure relations have significant local histories everywhere. There are certain similarities of practices in man's dealing with man over the use of land which can be noted. But the uniqueness of country and area features remain for significant identification and consideration in public policy and programming. Nevertheless, the basic similarities in tenure problems among very diverse areas are much greater than might be supposed upon first thought. This evidently is due both to the similiar practices which develop in the natural economies of men living on the land and to the similarity of paths toward economic and social development. The requirements of commerce, the advantages of market specialization and trade, the development and enforcement of contracts, and the individualization of economic activity under market stimulus all move in the direction of developing out of the more unique local practices property and business relations more in accordance with the general needs of modern marketing activities. Consequently it would seem that the tenure problems of each country, and in fact those of several different sectors of the economy of many countries, can be compared and understood primarily in terms of the stage of development of the economy in relation to antecedent circumstances. A vast amount of research is needed before we can really understand in an economy the essential nature of structural changes which are correlative to development and among which land tenure adjustments are strategic. The general directions of these historical movements, which are easier to discern than the nature of structural changes, depend on many factors: the nature of the early or primitive organization, the incidence of Western ideas, laws and markets, the basic policy drives toward market orientation, investment, social control, and the philosophies of communalism, the welfare state, communism, or the many shades of capitalism.

If one were to reduce this to simplest terms and use a single scale for measuring variations, perhaps the best one for interpreting tenure problems would be that transition from a subsistence agrarian economy of status to a market economy in which varying proportions of the gainfully employed are engaged in agriculture. In the Western experience since the Middle Ages, this is the transition from feudalism to the present varieties of market-oriented agricultural economies.

On this scale, the direction of the West has been toward a market-investment economy in agriculture as well as in other phases of economic life. The direction of movement has been toward the separation of social, economic, political, and religious organization. Land tenure forms gradually evolved as the required personal services for the use of land became commuted into money rents and the farmers became freemen, as civil and religious organizations became separated, as citizenship became more secure, and as property and contracts gradually evolved from the prerogatives of rulers and the customs of the people.

On this conceivable scale of social, economic, and political differentiation, economies fall naturally, as a secondary classification, on a scale of population density; the pressure of people upon agricultural land is a major factor in defining tenure relations.

A few brief characterizations of tenure situations by major geographical regions may give perspective to the discussion which follows. In the Middle East, population pressure is heavy in relation to land in Egypt, Lebanon, Jordan, and Israel. Water is the limiting factor in virtually all of the area; the margin for expansion in the agricultural area is set by the availability of water. Most of the area has emerged in recent times from the suzerainty of the Ottoman Empire. Of all the countries in the Middle East, perhaps Iran shows most clearly the lack of population pressure on the land. In most of the area there are serious problems in agricultural credit. None of the countries are industrially developed, although Israel is becoming so and Turkey

has for at least a generation been moving in this direction.

In terms of ownership of land, the farmers of Egypt, Lebanon, and Turkey are predominantly land owners, although in Egypt, at least, there has long been a very uneven distribution of land ownership.[2] In Syria perhaps half and in Iran less than a fifth of the farmers own land.

In terms of land programs, there is strong emphasis in this region upon the irrigation and development of land not now under cultivation, as the several papers in this volume suggest. In Iran and Egypt there are initial programs of land redistribution—in Iran a voluntary program for crown lands and in Egypt a government program of redistribution of large estates.

Moving eastward, the Indian subcontinent, now Pakistan and India, is still from the point of view of tenure and development virtually a constellation of small economies —and the problems vary greatly from one area to another. The population of most of India and East Pakistan is dense; the development of new land through irrigation is still being undertaken on an extensive scale, especially in the northwest parts of the subcontinent. But the general rule is a dense population, with the market orientation of agriculture limited principally to the cash and export crops, sugar, cotton, tea, and jute. The consequences of Western colonialism are many, with the development of peculiar tenure forms as discussed in the papers from these countries.

In terms of historical development, the stability of the Indian culture is impressive. In part, at least, an explanation of this may be found in the fact that the increasing market orientation of the economy has been facilitated by the relatively high degree of functional economic specialization built into the traditional caste system. But in the aggregate, the pressure of population is very great and is a heavy weight against both agricultural improvement and effective land reforms. Particularly is there a great number of landless, or near landless, workers who must depend for a living upon employment in agriculture. Some 30 per cent of the rural people in India are in this group, an extent perhaps without parallel anywhere else in the world. The village is the center of agricultural life, as it is elsewhere throughout the old world, but in India, again perhaps uniquely, the proposals for and programs of rural development including land reform in these countries are village-oriented and include an abiding hope, by many people, in the development of village co-operatives in agriculture. Money lending and agricultural credit have been recognized as serious problems for three-quarters of a century, at least, but the problems persist.

Southeast Asia, from Burma to the Philippines, is principally a rice economy, with critical population pressures limited to Java and parts of the Philippines. Plantation economies under foreign auspices are frequent, particularly in Malaya, Indo-China, and formerly in Indonesia. The peasant peoples are relatively poor even in the absence of population pressure on the land, due in part to the limitations of the technology of production. The percentage of ownership varies greatly over the region. Agricultural credit is very limited, and farm-to-market roads are greatly needed for development of agriculture. Taken as a whole this region is rich with potentialities but has suffered greatly from the disorganizing influence of markets since the opening of the Suez Canal, from long occupation by foreign powers, from political instability, from the lack of a native middle class, and from population pressure in certain areas.

Japan stands as a unique case of development in the Far East. This is well known and needs no comment. In terms of land tenure adjustments, a comprehensive land reform has been carried out, and it is dis-cussed fully in the conference proceedings. But two or three points may be worth special notation.

Japan, like China, is a densely populated old country. Prior to reform the holdings of land with hundreds of acres were relatively few. The rural society remained strongly feudalistic, with onerous taxes on agriculture and a lack of social equality in the rural villages. The land distribution converted the great majority of tenants into owners of small farms (the modal size of which was about one hectare); absentee landlordism was abolished. The land reform programs of Japan were long in the making and came about only after active farmer movement agitation for several decades. A unique set of circumstances, military occupation and inflation, permitted both the transfer of land to tenants and the payment therefor in a relatively short period of time. Local committees carried much of the responsibility of administration, and this experience seems to have valuable lessons for other countries. Land reform in Japan came late in the historical process of development; the adjustments incident to the redistribution of property were made much easier by the availability of urban occupations and the excellent system of transportation. There was virtually no landless farm laborer class in rural Japan at the time of land redistribution.

On the mainland of China the land reform program is proceeding under communist auspices. What might be called the first stage of land reform seems to have been achieved, namely, a wide distribution of land among the peasants. If the reform follows the usual pattern in communist countries, this is only a stage on the road to collectivization of agriculture.

On Formosa the principal emphases on land reform have been the rent reduction program and the distribution of public lands. More recently, privately owned lands above individual holdings of approximately five acres of paddy rice land and ten acres of dry land are being purchased by the government and sold to tenants.

Land tenure in Africa presents the whole range of problems from those of communal holding of land to the most commercial type of market specialization. Great changes are going on now as the native peoples and their communal systems of tenure are being drawn into the market economy. The native communal tenures are a part of a system of extensive land utilization with the shifting cultivation and pastoral methods appropriate for a meager population. Gradually the original tenures are giving way to individual holdings of a peasant type or to the plantation type of operation for the production of cash crops. Foreign or nonnative ownership of land is considerable, particularly in the "crown" lands, but there are now laws and administrative rules against the acquisition of land by anyone except natives. The ownership and use of land is naturally one of the most controversial issues that is emerging, whereby this vast area is being gradually developed through mining activities and commercialized agriculture.

In Latin America the characteristic tenure pattern is a pattern of few large holdings embracing the major part of the privately owned land and a countless number of tiny holdings, many of which have an insecure and indefinite squatter-rights tenure. The present pattern results from the transplantation in earlier centuries of a feudal tenure from the Iberian peninsula of Europe. This was superimposed upon a native population. Where these natives had a vigorous society and survived, the "Indian" tenures are a problem. Some of the countries—among them notably Brazil—are moving toward a peasant or family-size type of holding. Mexico has gone through a violent revolution on the land which replaced the ha-

ciendas with a village type of communal holding; but here, too, a middle-size kind of individual holding is growing. The most frequent type of land program in these countries is that of development and settlement, largely from public domain lands. Characteristically, in these countries there is ferment and political instability, and as a result there are relatively slow rates of economic development—except for the specialized productions of coffee, sugar, and, more recently, cotton—especially in the Caribbean. An unbalanced and inadequate food production leads to nutritional deficiencies. There is still a continuing struggle for the peasants up from feudalism to a more meaningful status and secure citizenship. Agriculture is insulated from market influences partly by the suffocation of old tenure relations and partly by a lack of transportation. In these countries most of the terrain is very broken.

In Europe there are all stages of adjustment from feudalism to a nearly pure investment form of land holding. The agrarian revolutions of the sixteenth century to the nineteenth century broke the old feudal pattern of England and western Europe. In England the peasants were swept into industry before the economic revolution of land enclosures and industrialization. On the continent the peasants survived but became specialized producers for the urban markets. In the Scandinavian countries, especially, a commercial type of family farming developed very similar in organization to that of the new world. In eastern Europe, as in Russia, the freeing of the peasants came late; and the unrest of peasants over land has been exploited by the communist revolutions.

In the United States, and quite similarly in Canada, the land tenure pattern has developed as a part of fluid industrializing economy in a virtually empty continent, with a premium on labor as the scarce factor. The results are notorious. A horde of land-hungry native pioneers and European immigrants became land owners. The slave base of the original cotton and tobacco economy of the southern states gave way to share cropping and tenancy; but there were always large numbers of independent farmers over all but the very best of southern cotton lands. Gradually the sharecropper economy is dissolving in the market economy of the twentieth century. Poverty and small farms in considerable numbers persist, especially in the southeastern states. The continental climate with heavy rains brings erosion and soil losses which a more adequate tenure system would prevent. Changes wrought by new technologies and mechanization are pressing for modification of earlier leasing forms. Capital and credit are persistent problems which threaten to grow more acute, although the improvements since 1920 in the mechanics and terms of agricultural credit extension—especially amortized loans of longer term—have wrought a silent revolution for the greater security of tenure on the land. Although the commercialization of agriculture is extensive, productive farms in great numbers are kept in the same family of cultivators for many generations. The family farm persists over most of the country, due primarily to the basic economic advantages of family operation and the shrewd financial management of the successful families. Agricultural legislation and publicly sponsored credit programs have favored the family type farm, but the leading principle of land tenure in America is essentially the freedom to invest in land. Accordingly, numerous programs are being tried to protect the public interest in private land use by zoning and land-use regulations under the peculiarly American "police power," by conservation districts, and by the demonstration that conservation is good private economy.

In this very hasty and superficial review we have tried to sketch the relevant characteristics of the different regions of the world where tenure problems are considered critical. All of these problems are discussed more fully in the conference papers which follow. The differences between countries are obvious and great; yet all countries are caught up in this entangling web of development and production for market which works such great changes in the structure of economies. We now turn to the task of working out interpretations which may put the seemingly diverse problems into the perspective of a few central issues.

Opportunities on the Land

It has been suggested that the tenure context in which a farmer or peasant works influences his performance, or productivity. A more analytical consideration of this point is essential. The issues and problems of land tenure become clearer if we distinguish first between the dimensions of opportunity in farming—of which the use of land is the principal item—and the status or degrees of freedom of the individual to exercise his abilities. The ability of farm people is the product of development—investment in and the training of people. The status of people is an expression of their place in the total social scheme and defines, approximately, the zones of freedom of choice or discretion which are open to the individual. The status of farm people, generally speaking, has long been defined principally by their relationship to the ownership and use of land and by their place in the kinship or family group. In recent times their citizenship in the state has become increasingly important.

Land tenure problems arise fundamentally from the contests over the control and use of land. It has become commonplace to refer to the threat to political and economic stability posed by poverty and starvation in the overpopulated and underdeveloped areas of the world, where land tenure problems are most acute. But it is doubtful whether this is the most fundamental explanation. Rather, it seems more instructive to interpret the revolutionary ferment in the old world as an expression of a new, emerging sense of citizenship or perhaps a groping toward citizenship. The experiences of poverty and starvation, while intensified in recent decades, run back as far as the memory of man; but the promises of the possibilities of citizenship are as new as the emerging nationalism of nations from recent colonies and mandatories. In a very deep sense tenure problems are power problems, problems of disparity in economic, social, and political power. Here it is suggested that the new thing that has been added to the old power problems over the use and control of land is the emerging sense of citizenship.

That land is equivalent to economic opportunity in an agrarian society is almost axiomatic. But opportunity has other dimensions which need to be noted if we are to understand the land tenure problems of our times. The right to use the land on whatever terms is essentially a production opportunity. But the right to dispose of the product of the land is a market opportunity. Almost equally important is the access to credit, which permits the purchase of adequate seeds, fertilizers, and supplies. From the opportunity perspective, then, there are really three dimensions of opportunity which are also potential sources of economic power: control of land use, control of markets, and control of credit.

An exhaustive analysis of these issues of control would lead to a critical examination of the relevant conceptions of property. Here we merely note that in a subsistence economy the right to use the land to produce subsistence is the major concern of the peasant. His struggle there is to secure a large enough share in the village lands to keep together the bodies and souls of his family. This leads essentially to a physical or corporeal sense of property. But to the extent that farm people are producing for the market with purchase of household needs and production requisites, land as property takes on a different character; access to market becomes valuable; and land as property comes to be more of an intangible property reflecting this market access. Correlatively this value of market access creates an asset which can be pledged for debt. There then evolves a new form of property rights in land—incorporeal property, which rests upon a right-duty relationship, wherein the right is valuable to the creditor because the payment of debt is a duty of the borrower enforceable by the state.

It seems that the peasants of the old cultures think principally in the concrete terms of corporeal property, of physical things for the use of their families. They have found the more abstract property relations of intangible and incorporeal property difficult to comprehend. As a consequence of the spread and dominance of modern (and principally Western) ideas of laws, property, contracts, markets, individualism, and justice, the native populations found themselves with a capacity to make contracts "willingly" for debts which they may have only dimly understood but which permitted the immediate consumption of the intangible value of the land. In consequence, foreclosures occurred, and peasants gradually sank into the debt and despair of landlessness or into the servitude of debt.

Many inferences may be drawn from these changing conceptions of property and the correlative status of people on the land. They may be regarded as exploitation and injustice or even as necessary steps to development. All of these inferences are relevant to the issues presented by land tenure problems. But, it is suggested, at the core of these interpretations is the objective and strategic fact of the changing conception of property and the correlative relationships to markets.

The whole tradition of non-Marxian Western economies from Adam Smith and John Locke to the present supports the view that economic development in a free society requires an extension of market operations in the economy. But the subtle interconnections between liberty-property and markets have not been clearly understood. The original conception of "natural liberty" gradually developed into an absolute view of freedom as the nature and significance of property, and the relations of property to liberty were neglected by economists. It remained for the late Professor John R. Commons in the twentieth century[3] to again direct economic analysis back to a fundamental understanding of the significance of property in relation to liberty, market structures, and economic power.

This brief comment on so vast a subject is intended only to place certain issues about tenure status and tenure relations into proper historical, analytical, and structural context. The issues cannot be explored fully here, but it will be obvious that it is at this level of analysis that issues can be joined with the neo-Marxian viewpoints in their interpretations of exploitation and their insistence upon revolutionary solutions.

Characteristically in the old agrarian countries, the controls over opportunities have gravitated to the hands of a relatively few people. Any one of these may be quite strategic; but they form a complex which fits together. It is for this reason that land reform, which provides only land to the tiller, is of minor significance without access to markets and adequate credit. It is the control over the different dimensions of opportunity to make a living from the land that characterizes the "feudalism" found in Asia in recent times. In China, for example,

in recent decades, the land was not owned in huge estates, as in Hungary, but the peasant nevertheless had very limited opportunities, partly because of his numbers and partly because the marketing and credit channels were likely controlled even when the peasant might own his bit of land.

This interdependence of controls suggests why the communist land reforms in Eastern Europe and in North Korea, where land has been allotted to individual holders and not yet collectivized, remain such hollow victories for the peasants. "Co-operatives" rigidly control the markets "in and out"— control the supplies acquired and products disposed of. In Russia, the tractor stations have become a further engine of control through the rationing of machinery services to Russian collectives and the associated charges.

The agrarian revolutions of the West in the era of the French revolutions were revolts against the concentrated controls of land. The philosophy of natural liberty of Adam Smith had a profound influence on the middle class revolutions of eighteenth-century Europe. The transformation of Western Europe into nations of freeholding farmers and free tenants was, of course, a long process. The recognition of these basic similarities in tenure problems between the underdeveloped areas of today and the presently industrialized West of earlier centuries may give us several clues as to how Western experience may provide significant lessons for other areas. This is particularly true when reference is made to the disturbing and energizing influence of an emerging citizenship as the hitherto voiceless peasants gradually become clothed with the power of sovereignty.

But if there are similarities there are also profound differences between the East today and the eighteenth-century West— especially differences in the density of population. Here again the concept of opportunities to make a living from the land may be illuminating. Distinction should be made in thinking about tenure problems between what we may call physical opportunity on the land and the terms upon which these physical opportunities are occupied. Not only is there a vast difference in the kind of public policies which can be directed effectively toward the expansion of total physical opportunities on the land and those policies concerned with the access to those opportunities but the strategy of land reform policies in promoting economic development appears to consist primarily in achieving an efficacious balance between these two complementary approaches to opportunities on the land.

Consideration of the density of population points initially to questions regarding the physical dimensions of opportunity on the land. There are at least three relevant and distinguishable dimensions to physical opportunities on the land: (1) the physical ratios of population to the land measured in terms of population density per acre of used land, size of farm, etc., (2) the degree of dependence upon agriculture in the economy, and (3) the degree of technological development in agriculture.

Measures of population density, size of farms, etc. give a first approximation to a statement of the kind of obstacles which are faced in any economy in trying to create a tolerable degree of productivity. There are countries where population pressure is not considered to present real problems in agricultural development—as for example in the "rice bowl" countries of the mainland of Southeast Asia and in parts of Latin America. In such areas the "land problems" emphasized are those of reclamation, development, and settlement—in other words, ways of expanding total physical production opportunities in a country. The extension of irrigation facilities is another problem. All of these problems are important and are

being pushed in virtually all parts of the world. It is noteworthy that developments of improved techniques for earth moving and disease control have drastically altered the feasibility of land reclamation, irrigation, and settlement in many areas in recent years.

Nevertheless, taking the world as a whole the prospect is very limited for a reduction of the pressure of population on the land through the development of "new" lands and the correlative migration of peoples. Where such developments are possible and the costs within reason, there are great "tenure problems" in the distribution and ownership of these new lands and waters. For the great majority of countries the expansion of physical opportunities is primarily not so much a matter of clearing new lands as of applying improved techniques to presently cultivated areas or of shifting the balance in the economies toward greater industrialization.

The degree of dependence upon agriculture as a means of making a living is only the obverse of the extent of industrialization. But at least two aspects of this relative dependence are important here. There may be rather definite limits to the potentialities of either agriculture or industry in any country. This is not the place to argue the issues of limitations to industrialization. But it is generally recognized that effective economic development will leave some countries primarily agricultural and perhaps leave no two countries with precisely the same balance between agriculture and other forms of industry. What is important here in terms of the dimensions of opportunity is that the possibilities for the expansion of opportunities in agriculture seem necessarily much more limited than in industry. So far, the control over natural processes in agriculture is relatively minor when compared with the tremendous power available to industry through the control of chemical and physical processes. In terms of opportunity this means that the power of science and technology to create new opportunities is much less in agriculture than in mechanical and chemical industries. In terms of national economies this means that there may be rather definite limits to what agricultural technology can do to alleviate poverty. However, in all countries today there are wide margins of unutilized technological potentials in agriculture.

The connections between the expansion of physical, or production, opportunities on the land and tenure problems are both direct and complex. The question always arises as to how the benefits as well as the costs are to be distributed. Furthermore the prospective participation in the benefits of technological improvement in farm operations seems largely to determine the rates of adoption of new technologies; the terms of sharing in such benefits are a part of the terms of land tenure of individual farms. Nevertheless, there are obvious advantages for the strategy of dealing with tenure problems through the expansion of total production opportunities on the land. Any land reform program means that economic opportunities will be reapportioned to some degree. In terms of the possibilities of peaceful and progressive changes, it is eminently clear that an expansion of total opportunities on the land and elsewhere in the economy may create the possibilities of making these transitions with a minimum of conflict.

The full implications of the relation between the use of technology to expand physical opportunities on the land and the more controversial matters of property and access to the land must await the fuller examination of the latter questions. But even this consideration of the physical dimensions of opportunity on the land should indicate quite clearly that the two aspects of the tenure adjustment are complementary to each other. The technological approach to

agricultural development may make much easier the decisions and policies on the more controversial issues of tenure and property rights, but sooner or later the two aspects of the questions must be considered together.

Population Pressure and Rent

The significance of the ratio of people to the land varies, of course, with the degree of dependence upon land as a means of making a living. The ratio of farm population to land is a direct measure of the average opportunity in farming relative to the productivity of the land. With a relatively fixed area of land and within the limits of feasible improvements and advanced technology, the numbers of people determine the average opportunities. In this sense the rates of growth of population and densities of population set one of the limits to what can be done in land reform.

This is not to say, however, that the pressure of population must prevent an improvement or expansion of opportunities on the land even though the immediate result of health and medical improvements is an increase in people. The overriding principle seems to be that rates of population growth are checked, if at all, only as a part of economic and social development. With the limited total opportunities available in the old cultures the individual families on the land seem to have their relative productivity determined by the number of children. In these viciously competitive situations a large family may ensure relatively higher family income even as the total weight of the population drives all down toward greater poverty. Also, it is widely recognized that a rise in the status of women, with their peculiar concern for the welfare of their children, and a consciously increased standard of living have the consequence of smaller families. There are numerous instances of farm families limiting the size of their families to fit the available land—in France and Czarist Russia, for example. But the general rule of the subtle connections between land tenure status and birth rates in the densely settled agrarian countries may well be found in the comment of John Stuart Mill a century ago regarding the Irish cottier: "he can scarcely be either better or worse off by any act of his own."[4] Improved tenure status should bring some increased measure of responsible action and with it a greater probability of the recognition that the numbers of children in a family will affect the quality of their opportunities.

Obviously, the pressure of population results in a bidding up of price of the land. The usual procedure is for the rent of land to gradually move upward. Under pressure of necessity the peasants in the densely populated old countries bid for the right to use the land until the rent is pushed up from such long-accustomed shares of one-half up towards 75 to 80 per cent in extreme cases. There is no point here in enlarging upon the well-known miseries of the tenants. The outcome of population pressure on inadequate farming opportunities is for the rent to vary directly with the quality of the land, with the "natural" tendency for the tenant's share to approximate a subsistence wage return. Correlatively, the reduced standard of living gets capitalized into higher land values.

All this is familiar; yet it is of the greatest importance in the current land tenure situation of the world. Much is being attempted to improve the relative position of the tenant. Legislation increasing the share of the tenant has been enacted in many countries. But it is extremely difficult to force rentals down by sheer regulation alone where the discrepancy in bargaining power between landlord and tenant is great. It requires not only a very strong will on the part of public officials to make rent reduction effective but also some special procedure or set of circumstances which neutralizes the great disparity in bargaining power between landlords and tenants. These problems of achieving equitable tenancy arrangements come up in virtually all countries with any freedom of investment, and the questions were given extensive consideration by the tenure conference. But the problem of landlord-tenant relations is most acute in densely settled countries. It is here that strenuous efforts are currently being made to improve the condition of the tenants. To cite one example, the reduction in land rent to 37.5 per cent of the rice crop has been achieved in Formosa in recent years; the effort failed for many years on the mainland of China.

Degrees of Freedom in Tenure Status

We may conveniently begin this phase of the discussion by reference to the time honored scale of tenure rights ranging from the landless laborer through tenancy to indebted owner and unencumbered ownership. Although this is a classification solely in terms of the "demanders" of land without reference to the conditions of supply, it is nevertheless a meaningful array. This scale has been put to two principal uses in the West—especially in the United States—in discussions of tenure policy: (a) it is conceived of as a "ladder" up which aspiring and successful farmers climb, and (b) it has been used as a reference point, as a rough statement of the problem of achieving security in the job and general "social security" for farm workers and security of occupancy for tenants.

There is no disposition to argue with these formulations. There are certain deficiencies in this simple scaling, however, if one attempts to discuss the varieties of tenure status found in different cultures, including both the East and the West. Since one of the purposes of the conference discussions was to find common ground for the understanding of tenure problems, we undertake here a very brief outline of a somewhat more comprehensive classification. Essentially this statement attempts to consider the breadth of opportunity and the social relations within the structure of land opportunities in relation to the more specific tenure arrangements by indicating in some detail the degrees of freedom permitted to the occupant of land.

One gets better perspective on the tenure problems of world agriculture by recognizing at the outset that the "natural" state of most people on the land appears to have long been that of poverty, indebtedness, and servitude. This is simply to set a bench mark for gauging the nature and significance of problems. The reader may turn almost at random to the papers presented at the conference from the countries currently called "underdeveloped"—Latin America, Africa, Middle East or Far East—and find there described situations in which the occupants of the land are poor peasants, although virtually all other persons in the rural economy enjoy a more favorable status as landholders, creditors, purchasers of farm commodities, etc. There is characteristically a very small middle class, families are the basic social units, and the better and more fortunate families appear to experience cumulative gains over the generations even as the pressure of population and the accumulation of debts gradually push the peasant people down the tenure scale.

The simplest characterization of these situations is that of a great disparity of economic, social, and political power in the hands of the few in contrast to the traditional impotence and even inertness of the many. It is this disparity which becomes so obvious once the peasants begin to think about these things—whether or not that thinking is spontaneous or stimulated by education or propaganda. Once the

traditional equilibrium is disrupted the challenge to leadership is to direct this new "force" to constructive ends. Historically, in Western Europe (including Britain) the forces of peasant unrest were channelled toward the construction of a society of greater freedom, equality, and productivity. And it was the freemen of these cultures who occupied the new world. From Eastern Europe on east through Russia and China the power of this yearning by the peasants for land and independence has been channelled into totalitarian economic systems, which may be productive but certainly are not free. As the work of Professor Mitrany[5] shows so clearly, the urban-minded liberals of Europe of the past century failed to comprehend the significance of the peasants' aspirations and, consequently, their power was not used to strengthen democratic political and economic procedures. The chance to really understand the peasant mind and the great political power which they are destined to hold in the second half of the twentieth century seems to be open still for the free world. The central question of world tenure policy therefore is this: Will the revolution on the land which is building up over so much of the world go the way of the West toward freedom—roughly the way of the French Revolution—or the way of the Marxist-Russian revolution?

The contemporary interest and faith in economic and social development are expressions of belief, or hope, that "It Can Be Done," to use the title of Secretary McCormick's paper. Taking a world view, if one compares our times with the period of the sixteenth to eighteenth centuries in the history of the West, there are certain debits: we lack the "empty" space of good land which the westerners exploited; we have a greater pressure of population on land than in the earlier centuries; and the adjustments must essentially be made on a global scale. On the credit side the free world has the scientific and industrial revolutions as resources, as demonstrated achievements of free societies; a new and powerful system of national and international finance with great powers for creating and molding economic opportunities; a vast experience interpreted by honest historians and other social scientists; and the incomparable demonstration of the power of institutions which promote productivity through security, freedom, and equality.

In relation to all this, what difference does it make whether a family is an owner-cultivating family, a tenant family, or farm-laborer family?

If we begin at the lower end of the scale, it is clear that the landless laborers are completely at the mercy of the situation when there is a high ratio of people to land and little or no mobility and no alternative employment. This is to say that the laborer has virtually no effective will of his own. Those who have the jobs for hire can only ration out the limited employment. It seems that the relationship must be one of command and obedience—of superior and inferior—almost regardless of the tolerance of either party or both.

As thought moves up the scale to tenants, what do we find? In terms of physical opportunities which the tenant may occupy, he is limited in most parts of the world to the area his family can cultivate by its own hands or its own labor perhaps implemented by a few simple tools including a possible equity in draft animals. Anyone who has heard peasants argue about whether it required the labor of three or four men with their families to keep a pair of oxen in full use must have been impressed by relative dearness of draft animals in comparison with human labor. With the primitive technology in use a tenant family can scarcely cultivate more than two to five acres where rice is an important crop or slightly higher

acreages in other cropping patterns. At any rate the maximum allotment of land which a tenant can get is the area which his family can cultivate. What he does get within that maximum is a matter of his persuasiveness or bargaining power, which is influenced by his ability as a farmer, the competition for land, and so on.

But this is only the beginning: the rental transaction not only determines the area he may cultivate but the terms upon which the land is worked. Where many seek land and there is strong competition for it, the terms of tenant performance may be very onerous.

When this is cast in terms of status, however, it is clear that the tenant likely has privileges as well as opportunities not open to the laborer. To some degree he is his own boss; he has the privilege of exercising his own will with reference to the land. During his term of tenancy he has some rights which the landlord honors. It would take a whole volume to sketch out in detail the variation found in any country in the kinds and degrees of rights the tenant enjoys and the correlative duties which the landlord accepts to secure the tenant's performance. But common to all of them there are a few dimensions: the gross value of the right is measured by the physical productivity of the opportunity to cultivate the land; the net value of the right to cultivate is the residual after meeting the rent payment or performance requirements (the influence of prices and market values upon these opportunities depends upon the degree to which farming is more than a means to self-subsistence); within this context and during the time of the renting the tenant may be his own boss—he may exercise his own will, make the decisions of management for himself, his family, and his employees, if any.

One may say that in terms of status the tenant acquires a degree of independence for a while, but the rights which the family enjoys during the term of lease are always running out into a nearly full exposure to the decisions of the landlord unless some protection of occupancy in law or custom is granted the tenant. In short, the tenant characteristically achieves an assured but limited freedom of action for only limited periods of time within his temporary domain.

With an owner it is different. For the limited space on the earth which he can call his own, he is the master of his domain as long as his ownership shall run. Where the ownership of land carries the right of bequest or inheritance, the owner's will with reference to the use of the land may be effective beyond his own lifetime—as our legal name of "a will" for making a bequest so eloquently reports. Again, ownership is not something fixed and invariable; but the rights to use for the possessor and his heirs in perpetuity are the essential point. The privilege of free sale and alienation is often a limited right. The degree of family control over land ownership is extremely important; but this involves essentially the question of the degree to which the family or the individual shall exercise its will over the use and disposition of the land.

Once a family can say this land is "ours" they are their own masters, within the limits of the opportunities represented by the land. Even so, the ownership of land can be only a nominal right if debts are sufficiently onerous or if the freedom to market is a sufficiently restricted or inaccessible alternative.

Consequently, the question of tenure status is not only a matter of income or degree of poverty; it is also a matter of human dignity and the privilege of exercising one's own will. When one rates tenure status on the scale of degrees of freedom for the human will it is evident that it varies from something like zero in the usual status of farm laborers through a zone of freedom of discretion by tenants which has a time limit of the length of lease and a spatial limit for natural opportunity and a value limit of subsistence and market income to an ownership which is limited only by the size of the opportunity. In terms of the exercise by the owner-cultivator of his will within that domain it is qualified necessarily only by the impacts of consequences upon other persons. Net income measures the degree of freedom from want, but the kind and extent of rights measure the degree of freedom from arbitrary and wilful acts of other persons.

It is a fact of the greatest significance that there is virtually no evidence that a more efficient economic unit of farming has been devised than the family unit. Obviously units can become so small that the returns to labor and management may be grossly inadequate. But this is a stubborn, natural fact, and it is one which even technological advantages of scale rarely surmount. But generally speaking, as Brewster has so effectively pointed out, the temporal and biological nature of farm production requires that the unit of farming remain relatively small if economy is to be achieved. The family unit has numerous advantages, particularly if it is also the owner of the land.[6]

When all such considerations of status, independence, and incentives for production are interpreted together, the reasons are obvious for the emergence of the ideal of the owner-operated family farm in the aspirations of farm people and in social and public policy. There are difficulties at every turn and countless frustrations in the attempts of rural families to have efficient-size farms of their own. But where opportunities are reasonably open, as in the New World, we are finding that a family-size farm is an efficient form of economy, as appropriate technologies and credit policies have been devised. The rights of investment may need to be qualified to fit the investment capacities of farm families. It is significant that programs for improving landlord-tenant relations usually do owner-operatorship the honor of taking the latter as a criterion of achievement. The contributions of an independent farming people to political stability are impressive even when the excesses of more enthusiastic claims are discounted. All this is only to say that the ideal of a family farm is the outcome of a complex of social judgments in the experience of man, not a mere prejudice of farm people.

It must be recognized, however, that circumstances in many countries so limit the possibilities of farm size and economic progress generally as to warrant the attempts to organize agriculture on other bases. Families by the millions all over the industrialized parts of the world have worked out a blend of part-time farming with other employments. Experiments in co-operative farming are being tried in a number of countries; compelling arguments are advanced for the possibilities of better utilizing improved technologies through co-operative farming, especially in circumstances of difficult weed control or peculiar crop requirements. There are, however, many problems of achieving a tolerable degree of independent status, initiative, and incentive by the participants. The experiments in co-operative farming over the world are of great significance, and they are discussed at length in the proceedings.

The statement so far has not attempted to relate debt status to the degrees of freedom secured by tenure status. Although debts are in fact independent obligations, they are closely interrelated with tenure status and may greatly limit the degree of freedom of tenure status.

It is important to note that debts are obligations: the debtor is in the position of being forced to meet his duty to pay debts. Consequently, the duties assumed under debts may actually cancel out or even exceed the rights which the cultivator achieves in tenure status. Where the borrower has land, a pledging of land for debt may result in loss of ownership, or it may result only in a sharing of income. The tenant who assumes a debt may pledge his crop for security, with the correlative provision that the crop be marketed through the creditor. But with the laborer with no ownership of either land or crop, he has only his own services to pledge; consequently, the "security" for the loan may really turn out to be a pledging of future "labor power" to the creditor. This leads in the extreme cases of the assumption of the father's debts by the sons to a virtually inherited servitude.

Reform: Kinds and Characteristics

Land reform is a very ancient idea which has gradually taken different forms as the economies have grown toward market specialization with stronger financial institutions and as the people have been clothed with the attributes of sovereignty. In ancient China, revolution on the land was a recognized right of the people. Every few centuries the land was redivided and the people were set out on a new footing of equality. In ancient times in the eastern Mediterranean area and elsewhere, land was redivided among the families every seven years or so. These are rather simple programs for dividing up land according to obvious need. One can almost read these experiences to say that land should be distributed so that each pair of hands would have a reasonably equal chance to feed one mouth.

This elementary idea is still present in our thinking about land reform, but if one studies land reform proposals he will find that they have been extended in two directions from this primitive notion: (a) to include an idea of freedom of status, and (b) to improve farm people's position with reference to market or money income. This is perhaps inevitable as the position of the individual becomes more clearly defined and differentiated, in the family or kinship group, as a citizen in politcal affairs and as a participant in a market economy. In the West, as the individual farmer and his family have become differentiated as citizens from the larger social group their lives have become more closely integrated with the farm as a business concern. The independent farmer of modern times is dependent upon both government and markets. These relations will be clearer as we classify and characterize the various kinds of land reform proposals. It is well to remember that reform means literally *re*-form; consequently, what is under review are proposals to change the form of rural society and economy with reference to right of land use and possession within the framework and principles of free societies.

Land consolidation.—Programs for the consolidation of fragmented holdings are among the least controversial of land reform programs. Within any total size of farm, the land may be divided up into many parcels; where fragmentation has progressed far it makes a small farm smaller and a bigger farm inefficient. Fragmentation is common throughout the Old World —from Europe to Asia, wherever a village type settlement of farmers is found. Characteristically it results from a literal interpretation of equality in landholding; if any landholder in the village is to share proportionally in the lands of different quality and distance from the village he will usually have something like five pieces of land. Where inheritance practice follows this same literal principle, the inheritance of land may lead over a few generations to the fragmentation of a few hectare farm into from fifty to one hundred pieces.

The causes, we may say, are attempts to distribute widely the opportunities of land ownership in a society where there are few employment opportunities alternative to agriculture. The leading principle of remedial action is consolidation of holdings to reduce nature's resistance to man's efforts to use land. This may require the assertion of the inherent public or social interest in the individual property holding. The procedures followed are varied in the extreme. They differ in both technical procedure and degree of democratic or voluntary participation permitted the citizens. The processes are difficult and controversial, but the conflicts of interest are relatively superficial. The desired end is a potential solvent of all conflicts of interest over consolidation to insure the well-being of all citizens.

Settlement and colonization.—These new land programs are also ways of extending man's dominion over physical nature. Especially where the lands to be occupied are public lands, the problems of "reform" may be difficult technically, but politically the issues are likely to be those of expense and settler success.

Programs to improve the relative position of small or family farms in the economy.—Land reform proposals almost inevitably extend to a series of proposals to make the opportunities to use land more secure or rewarding through reducing hazards or handicaps in the relation of the farm to the marketing and credit structure. In these proposals the farms as business units are recognized as the instrument, or even another dimension, of the family unit in a finance and market economy. Such programs follow necessarily from the fact that land is the full measure, or dimension, of economic opportunity only in a subsistence economy. The proposals extend therefore to agricultural credit and to co-operative marketing, both sales and service, and emphasize the principles of co-operative credit as a means of maximizing self-help. Closely related are the various kinds of co-operative arrangements for the use of farm equipment.

Such proposals or programs all have the common purpose of making the relations of the farm as a business unit to the total economy more secure and equitable. Such programs may be pursued independently of any proposals to change the size of farm. In terms of property, they do not effect the character of land as physical, or corporeal, property; rather, they are designed to make this physical object more valuable to the user by making the market and financial relations more valuable.

Landlord-tenant relations.—Rent regulation programs direct the terms upon which land shall be rented.

In the industrialized countries of Great Britain and western Europe, regulations of rental arrangements have gone a long way toward giving tenants security of expectations concerning occupancy and compensation for disturbance; landlords are similarly protected against careless husbandry and destruction of property. This approach has great, demonstrated usefulness under such circumstances. Whether such regulations can be made comparably effective in underdeveloped countries is doubtful; at a minimum there would be much greater administrative difficulties in countries without secure property relations and economic arrangements.

In the old and densely settled countries, the typical proposal is that of stipulating that rents shall not exceed some specified percentage of the crop, such as took place in the reduction of rent to 37.5 per cent of the crop in pre-communist China and in Formosa, or such as legislation effected in reducing the rent to one-third of the crop in certain states of India.

The regulations of the rental relation between landlord and tenants, like the more generalized programs previously discussed for modifying market and credit relations, have the merits and defects of possible gradualness of incidence. In principle, the regulation of landlord-tenant relations is based upon the partial separation of control from the ownership of land. In the highly organized Anglo-American economies, the judicial power to regulate and even void certain kinds of contracts is a great safety valve and the evident key to social progress without revolution. Some social equivalent to this means of gradually relieving tensions seems essential for any stable economy. However, it must be recognized that in a revolutionary era such as our own such questions of gradual adjustment as rent regulation must be ultimately appraised by the contribution to the preservation of public order. The situation may demand more drastic measures—to the long-time advantage of all groups, including the propertied classes.

Co-operative farming.—The co-operative organization of farm production is advocated in many countries as a way of introducing quickly the major advantages of new agricultural technology and improved methods of management. In the areas where co-operatives have been tried extensively, in India, Pakistan and Israel, there are also strong social foundations for co-operative groups and numerous opportunities for experiments in resettlement projects. General adoption of a co-operative type of farm organization in India and Pakistan is advocated by many intellectual leaders who see in this form of economy an opportunity to revive the village as an effective economic and political unit; it is also expected that economies of scale and improved technologies may be realized through village management of land use and strategic farm operations. However, co-operative farming remains largely a possible rather than an active method of achieving land reforms in the free world. The so-called co-operative farming programs of the communist countries are characteristically state dominated rather than voluntary and are essentially ways of exercising controls over farm production, grain collection, and income distribution.

Redistribution of land.—The redistribution of land is the most controversial of all reform questions. The ultimate purpose is usually to establish the cultivators as owner-occupiers, either by making them new entrepreneurs or by increasing the size of previously held small units. Characteristically such programs come about in situations where there are long-standing grievances and great poverty of the cultivators. By reducing the prospective return from rents the regulation of rentals may be an intermediate step. Land distribution is the "hot" core of the land reform problem.

Clearly a land redistribution program is a very serious undertaking in any country. In a sense the inauguration of such a program is a recognition that serious inequities and maladjustments have accumulated in the economy. Yet it is a fact that very great pressures have been built up in country after country until some program of land redistribution appears to be the lesser evil of several alternatives. Characteristically, landlordism comes under a social blight in the political processes which build up the pressure for redistribution. The fact that landlords generally have performed very little, if any, productive function in the underdeveloped countries adds fuel to the flames. In its deeper meaning a passionate drive for land distribution, such as gripped France in the eighteenth century and Mexico a generation ago, is more than an effort to share the land. Such revolutions are mass gropings for greater equality.

The interpretation of the situation in each individual country would be different according to particular circumstances and histories. But the great unrest and agitation in recent years has dampened investment in agriculture in many countries which have neither undergone communist revolutions nor active redistribution programs. The consequence is undoubtedly a substantial impediment to investments in improved agricultural facilities and to agricultural production and economic development generally.

This is not a new story. The feudalism of Western Europe was swept away by revolution. It is the task of modern statesmanship to make the transition to more productive and more equitable societies without the horrible costs of revolution. Land tenure adjustments appear essential in many countries to facilitate the development of the economies. Yet it must be recognized that land reform is not a cure-all and that it can be productive of social and economic benefits only as a part of comprehensive programs of development.

Issues in Tenure and Productivity

In trying to understand such controversial issues as land reform and get a perspective on them, we will do well to anchor to a few main ideas. The overriding principle seems to be that economy and justice are more likely to be achieved at less social cost if the country can be kept functioning as a political and economic going concern. When a society dissolves into anarchy and revolution, incalculable losses occur. In this context, then, the questions of land reform really turn out to be questions of whether and of how adjustments can be made within the structure of economic and political arrangements, so that violent revolution is avoided, tension relieved, conflicts mitigated, and the economy kept going while the rate of productivity is increased. >

In the strategy of development of most underdeveloped countries an increase in food production is absolutely essential. An impressive proportion of the underdeveloped countries must import food to meet minimum needs at the cost of scarce foreign exchange. Food has become, since World War II, an important weapon of politics. Hunger beyond a certain point is not only inhumane but leads to unrest, and it is readily exploited politically by political agitators. The margin for saving for development can be created in many countries only by increasing food production in the aggregate and per capita.

One of the great challenges in the strategy of economic development is to devise procedures for development that do not exploit the peasants in the process. Much of the load of economic development in the recently developing countries, such as Japan and Russia, has rested upon the backs of the peasants. In the economic development of England in earlier centuries the peasants were ruthlessly swept aside by the upsurge of market enterprises. It is gravely to be doubted whether political stability could be maintained in the presently underdeveloped areas of the world if development attempted to depress the standard of living of peasants beyond present levels. It is this awful prospect which makes so urgent the introduction of improved technologies and, in many countries, the dampening down of rates of population increase. A marketable surplus of agricultural produce must be produced in the countryside if capital formation is to occur. The development of market systems of trading and financing is likewise essential to development.

As economists review history and the economic ideas that have been derived from Western experience, the subtle interconnections within the process of economic development among technology, productivity, the emergence of a marketable surplus, the generation of demand, balance growth, taxation and monetary policy, savings, capital formation, and international trade are

becoming clear. But Western thinking has long dealt with market and job oriented conduct wherein individuals make calculations to a considerable extent in terms of money and respond to money payments. In short, Western man is a product of and has been shaped by a propertied, industrialized, and monetized society. In this same process persons as citizens have become distinct from property; the social, economic, and political status of individuals has been derived from the less differentiated societies of earlier eras. Consequently, when Western economic analysis is brought to bear upon the problems of economic development in the underdeveloped areas, the incentives and responses presupposed do not work in the same degree as in our Western societies. People are not market, job, and investment minded in our sense because their experience has been so different.

⟨ It is here that the significance of land reform for economic development is noteworthy. Granted that an increase in agricultural production is essential to the development of most underdeveloped countries, how is it to be stimulated or induced? If voluntarily, how?⟩If not voluntarily then the communistic collective farm with coerced performance becomes a natural alternative. But how voluntarily?

⟨The peasants will respond voluntarily only on their terms, so-to-speak. As a minimum this means that a situation must be created wherein they receive a reasonable reward for their efforts, i.e., there must be a reasonable ratio between their share in the effort and costs of production and their share in the crops produced.⟩The margins for subsistence are so slight that peasants can afford little risk; any innovation in production practice that goes wrong may lead to near starvation for the family; they must have a sufficient sense of security so that they can plan production programs over a period of years; there must be a realizable possibility that they can actually improve their life by their own efforts.

The tremendous outburst of energy released in Denmark after individual holds were created and bondage was abolished in 1788 has been noted by Jensen. A literal renaissance of agriculture occurred. "An enormous amount of hard labor was applied in the following 50 years . . . The peasants were like pioneers in a new country, and the farm labor and the new methods of the time were utilized much more fully than when the peasants' labor had to a large degree been wasted on the demesne land . . . In 30 years, crops for the country as a whole increased 100 per cent."[7]

< This is what land reform is about: to change the pattern of securities, incentives, and inducements for farm people. >The peasants of the world have indicated, more-or-less accurately, the price of their energetic participation in the economy. That price is a hold on the land in a way that meets their deep desires and their long-standing judgments. Furthermore, the political destiny of country after country is being placed in the hands of the peasants as the new national independence gives the ballots to the people.

Can the price be paid for peasant participation without wrecking the economies and the societies of the underdeveloped countries? The answer would seem to be clearly yes, if the problems are faced resolutely and the international community really understands the nature of the difficulties confronting developing countries. We have vast experiences of experimentation that need careful study and appraisal. We have great advances in technology to exploit. We have new and powerful financial institutions which may serve as a means for avoiding many of the bitter and bloody struggles over the land of earlier centuries. We have the demonstrated productivity which comes from secure economic and political citizenship in free societies. There is no doubt that development requires greater equality than many old societies now enjoy; but through development we can avoid making that equality merely an equality of poverty.

Part II SIGNIFICANCE OF TENURE ADJUSTMENTS
FOR ECONOMIC AND SOCIAL DEVELOPMENT

LAND AND THE FUTURE

ഗ഻ഗ഻ഗ഻ഗ഻ *Willard L. Thorp*

IN ALL probability, there have never before been so many dissatisfied people in the world. This is not because there is more starvation, more pain, or more misery than at other times. The facts are quite to the contrary. The rising discontent is rather because of knowledge—the increased knowledge of how other people live. When people lived in isolated communities completely ignorant of the world beyond the horizon they had only local standards of comparison. But today they have information, and misinformation, about the delights of distant green pastures. This becomes the basis of resentment against their lives and their surroundings. The resulting discontent is responsible for much of today's political instability and economic unrest.

The answer lies in large part in further increasing the flow of knowledge. If greater knowledge contributes to the creation of discontent, it can also be an instrument for dealing with it. The discontent also creates an opportunity. Periods of complacency are never periods of progress. Given a desire for improvement, streams of knowledge can flow back to these people in many countries, and they can benefit from the experience of others who have made greater progress.

In this general context, no one can possibly overstate the importance of the problems which you have come to Madison to consider, those relating to land and the people on the land. You will be talking

about two-thirds of the world's population. There are many countries where more than three-fourths of the people are on the land. In no country can their problems and attitudes be disregarded. In many countries, the future will depend in large part on their future. The conference on world land tenure problems, and each of you individually, can contribute greatly to the development and flow of knowledge so essential to the process of economic and social betterment.

There are tremendous differences in the lives and productivity of the people on the land throughout the world. Let me describe the kind of situation which presents the greatest problems. Let us consider a farmer who has to support his family of six on the produce of less than two acres. He does not own the land. He rents it from an absentee landlord who takes two-thirds of the crop for rent. He has no security of tenure. He doesn't know how long he can work on this farm. Another tenant may come along next year and offer even higher rent. This farmer has had to borrow money from a professional money-lender. He pays 40 per cent interest, and his debt is bigger now than it was a year ago. He has friends who pay 60 per cent interest. One of his friends borrows at 80 per cent.

This farmer of ours is tired and discouraged. He has to farm on worn-out soil with the most primitive tools. He can never allow any land to be fallow, and he has never even heard of commercial fertilizer. He uses seed saved from his own crop of the year before. His two acres are divided into three plots, all widely scattered. It takes him almost two hours to go from his home to the nearest plot. That part of his crop which he sells he takes to market on the back of a donkey. And when he gets it to market, he must take whatever price is offered—he has no method of storage. Last year he had nothing to market. He gave all his surplus to the money-lender in partial payment of his interest charges. I need not describe his standard of living—it can hardly be called subsistence.

The problem of this farmer is not that he does not work hard enough, although his energies may be sapped by bad health conditions and malnutrition. As a matter of fact, he works from dawn to dark. His difficulty is that he is enmeshed in an archaic economic and social system. He is the victim of a state of technological ignorance and of the absence of the help which might be provided by capital, equipment, marketing organization, and the like.

Some persons have suggested that the best solution for a country where such conditions prevail is to disregard the situation of farmers like this and place emphasis upon industrial development. I do not wish to decry the importance of industrial development, but it is a tragic conclusion to insist that it is the exclusive path to economic betterment. Surely the improvement of agriculture must be a prime objective of economic development.

In the development of the United States, agriculture has been one of the strongest contributors. Until 1870, we imported more foodstuffs than we exported. However, our own production expanded rapidly and was the basis for the rapid development of internal trade within the country. In more recent years our exports of foodstuffs have been an important element in our balance of payments. In fact, agriculture has always been a major component in our economic strength.

Today, we have about 5.5 million farms in the United States, with a farm population of about 25 million people. The real estate, livestock, machinery, crop inventory, and other financial assets in our agriculture represent a capital accumulation of about 130 billion dollars. The net equity is 115 billion dollars. Total income from agriculture represents almost 10 per cent of our national income. In terms, therefore, of jobs, national income, foreign trade, capital accumulation, and even of scientific management and application of modern technology, agriculture is a major element in our economy. Add to this the processing industries which flow out of agriculture—milling, slaughtering, canning, refining, and the like—and the role of agriculture is even more impressive.

Land and its related institutions are significant to a country not merely for economic reasons. They are also important in terms of the character of individuals which is developed, which in turn, bears upon the nature of the prevailing political institutions. There can be no doubt that in the United States the extent of land ownership in the form of small, individually-owned farms has had much to do with strengthening the notions of freedom and democracy. The owner of a farm has a stake in the community. He is concerned with the quality and behavior of his government. He belongs to that great middle class, those individuals who are relatively independent yet not able to control any important operation and who are so essential in any democracy. It is interesting to note that in the United States most of our so-called progressive political movements have arisen and have had their principal strength in the heart of our farming country.

But we must not limit our assessment of the importance of these problems even to

economic and political terms, important as
they may be. We must remember that we
are not discussing statistical units or mass
phenomena. We are talking about individual human beings and their very real
and pressing problems. We cannot disregard poverty and misery wherever it may
be. It is in terms of human values, of the
effort to extend personal opportunity and
security, that we find the ultimate justification of this conference and of your efforts.

A general program to alleviate land problems is frequently—though not always—
referred to as "land reform." This assembly is called a "conference on world land
tenure problems." The United Nations General Assembly and the Economic and Social
Council have used the label "land reform"
in their resolutions on the subject. I do not
wish to quibble over words, but sometimes
labels are misleading, and I wish to sound
a note of caution. In some parts of the
world, the term "land reform" has been
widely used as a cover for the ruthless confiscation of the land by the state and the
liquidation of private holdings and often of
private holders as well. The propaganda
appeal of the label is strong, but such a
process is not land reform in any sense. It
begins with the promise of land to the
farmer. Very quickly it becomes merely the
transfer of ownership from private owners
to the state. There is no improvement in the
status of the worker on the land. Instead, in
many instances harsh production quotas
and delivery deadlines make the farmer's
condition worse—often desperate. A story
in *The New York Times,* September 26,
1951, confirms this fact. It tells of desperate
Soviet farmers who have resorted to steal-
ing from the collective farms. As a result,
new regulations have had to be established
requiring that the books and accounts of
collective farms be audited six times a year
by Communist party and government officials.

This is not land reform. Nothing can be
called land reform which does not have
as its basic and primary concern the improved welfare of the man who works the
land. The economic and social institutions
surrounding his life on the farm must be
improved to bring him a higher standard
of living and increased psychological satis-
factions.

There are many who think of land reform primarily as redistribution of the
land—as the breaking up of large land
holdings into small ones. This may be a
part of a land reform program but certainly
only one part—and not the most important
one at that. In fact, there are certain crop
and land conditions where large-scale enterprises may be the most efficient, although
there still may be opportunities for economic and social improvement.

The United Nations Economic and Social
Council at its recent meeting in Geneva
adopted a resolution which indicates quite
clearly the broad range of objectives that
must be sought in a genuine land reform
program. This resolution, which was introduced and strongly supported by the United
States, covers efficient size of farm units,
security of tenure on the land, the right to
ownership of land by the man who works
it, clear titles to land and water, adequate
credit at reasonable rates, more efficient
marketing methods, and equitable taxes on
land and its produce. The resolution also
suggests the development of farm co-operatives for cultivating, marketing, and processing agricultural products.

These recommendations relate directly to
agricultural matters. But there are other
problems which do not arise from defects
in the agrarian structure itself. These too
must be remedied if the strictly agricultural
programs are to succeed. The Economic and
Social Council recognized this important
fact in its resolution. It recommended diversification of economies so that agricul-

ture might be better integrated into general economic development. It recommended the establishment of small-scale and cottage industries. It urged nations to develop literacy programs, to engage in research, and to extend education through extension services. It might well also have noted the relevance of public health programs.

These many elements in a genuine land reform program must of course be spelled out in much greater detail. They will vary in their form and applicability from country to country. However, in one respect they will be similar everywhere—they often will require political action. In a number of countries there are many competent persons who understand the economics of land reform. There are many who know the techniques. But frequently these talents cannot be put to work. The required legislation may be lacking. Necessary funds are not appropriated. Substantial progress often requires political decisions, and there are often strong vested interests which stand in the way. And there is always inertia, the dead hand of custom and tradition.

This problem may have to be solved before considerable economic benefits can be realized. Where this is true, a long and careful educational program may have to be instituted. Widespread public education through discussion may be necessary. The benefits of an improved land system will have to be made clear at every level—national, state, and local—in the cities as well as on the farms.

This is a difficult problem, but one not without hope of solution. Each one of us has within our own governmental structure the means of solution through our own established processes. It requires work and imagination, but it can be done. In fact, it must be done.

The United States has been actively engaged in improving the lot of the farmer on the land—land reform, if you will—since the very beginning of its national existence. We recognize, of course, that our land problems have been different from those of many other countries. In many respects they have been less acute. We were most generously endowed with fertile soil. We have never experienced severe population pressure on the land. We have had large areas of public lands to dispose of. But nevertheless we have had land problems to solve. In common with others, we will continue to have problems. This is not a reason for complaint. It is the pattern of any evolving and progressive society.

For ourselves, we in the United States have been firm believers in the farmer-owned–family-size farm. We consider it one of the bulwarks of a healthy agriculture and a vigorous democracy. For this reason we began very early in our national life to make it relatively easy for farmers to purchase government-owned lands in parcels of moderate size. Back as far as 1800 public lands were sold at 2 dollars an acre. And this liberal tendency continued through the passage of the Homestead Act of 1862. This act gave without charge 160 acres to anyone who would reside upon and cultivate the land for 5 years. As a matter of fact, we made purchase of these lands too easy. Out of this policy arose one of our most difficult problems—the careless and wasteful utilization of land.

It soon became clear to us that *ownership* and *proper size* of farm unit were not in themselves enough for a sound land policy. A happy and prosperous farmer and a healthy agriculture could be assured only with the addition of agricultural education and research, adequate financial and marketing arrangements, good transportation at reasonable rates, a fair tax structure, and so on. In 1862 our Congress passed a law giving public lands to each state to endow and support a college where instruction was to be given in agriculture and the mechanical arts. In 1887 another act provided funds for the establishment of agricultural experiment stations in the various state colleges. Additional programs have provided funds for distribution among the state agricultural colleges for short-term winter courses, correspondence courses, lectures, and publications dealing with land and related problems.

Agricultural education was augmented by the creation of a Federal Commissioner of Agriculture to collect and disseminate agricultural information among the people of the United States. This bureau later became a government department whose head, the Secretary of Agriculture, is a member of the President's Cabinet.

We have had to pass laws to provide credit for the farmer. Some needed money to buy lands, others needed funds to tide them over from one crop to another. Ordinary commercial banks did not meet this need; so in 1916 we established a system of Federal Land Banks. Later we organized the Farm Credit Administration which provides a co-ordinated system for the extension of both short- and long-term credit to farmers. This was helpful to the established family farmer, but it didn't solve the problem of the farm tenant or the hired farm worker who wanted to buy a farm. To encourage this development, we enacted legislation to authorize loans which could be repaid over a period of forty years. Small farmers can get loans to enlarge their farms or to build them up with livestock and equipment.

These then are some of the things we have done to improve the position of the farmer on the land in the United States. These, together with others such as encouragement and aid to co-operatives and the Interstate Commerce Act to assure fair and nondiscriminatory freight rates, constitute our "land reform" program. We still have problems, especially those involving the ten-

ant farmer, the sharecropper, the hired farm worker, and, more recently, the migratory farm worker. We are still struggling with these problems, but even in such difficult fields, substantial progress has been made.

Our interest in solutions to land problems has not only persisted through the years but has extended to the problems of our neighbors in the world community. This is indicated in part by our strong support last fall of the United Nations General Assembly Resolution on Land Reform and of our active role in promoting the Land Reform Resolution adopted by the Economic and Social Council in Geneva this summer.

It has been further demonstrated in Japan where under the Allied occupation we encouraged the Japanese government to initiate and assisted it in the execution of extensive land reform measures. This program, which I understand will be discussed in detail during the course of this conference, achieved notable changes in a centuries-old, uneconomic and antidemocratic land system. It brought substantial benefits to 3 million Japanese farmers, 50 per cent of the total. Only 30 per cent of Japanese farmers were full owners of the land which they cultivated before land reform. Today approximately 85 per cent are full owners of the land they work. The percentage of land operated by full tenants has been reduced from 46 per cent to 12 per cent. Absentee ownership has almost completely disappeared. All of this was done in a little more than two years in a thoroughly orderly and democratic way.

There are other examples of active land reform programs in other countries, most of which you will be discussing later in the conference—India, the Philippines, Italy, Turkey, and many others. We can all learn much from each other's experience. All of them deserve our closest study and friendly encouragement.

I have spoken at some length about the experience of the United States with land problems. I do wish to make it clear, however, that I am not suggesting that the *form* and *structure* of American land institutions and practices provide the solution to the problems of other countries. Certainly forms and structures suitable to the American economy may not be suitable to others. Each nation must find solutions to its own problems within the framework of its own cultural and institutional background. United States experience will be helpful principally as it can be modified and adapted to other situations.

But while we hold no special brief for American *form and structure,* we do feel a sense of pride in the *motives* and *methods* of land reform as applied by the United States and by other nations of the free world. We feel this because, in both motives and methods, there is a critical difference between land reform as practiced in the free world and what has been improperly called "land reform" in the Soviet-dominated world. With respect to the motives, we seek the economic and social welfare of the farmer, rather than the consolidation of the power of the state. With respect to method, we have followed an orderly constitutional process rather than rely upon the confiscation of property and the liquidation of land owners, with all its attendant hardship. The results of our motives and methods have been just as revolutionary, but they have achieved the goal of genuine improvement in a thoroughly practical and democratic way.

The report on land reform by the United Nations Secretary-General, published in June of this year, is an important new document in this field. It reveals land problems of almost frightening proportions. It shows the terrific job ahead of us. In another sense, however, the report presents a picture of promise. It records that a large number of

countries have recognized the importance of their land problems and have set about to solve them. It reveals what amounts to a world-wide movement to improve the life and output of the farmer on the land.

The important question is: how can this movement toward land reform be encouraged? Again there must be national answers. It is basically the job for the people of each nation. They must want it. They must see the importance of land problems to their own national development. They must become aware of the promise which land reform holds for their future. They must define their own goals and shape their programs in the light of their own institutional backgrounds. They must set about the task of training their own technicians. They must create a political environment favorable to the development of an improved land system.

It is only upon this foundation that the encouragement and assistance of others can be built. The United Nations and its agencies can render great assistance. The FAO, UNESCO, the ILO—each within its own field of special competence—can help by accumulating technical "know-how" and by making it available to interested nations. They should be requested to do so. The United Nations and its agencies can and should be urged to arrange their meetings to assure the full exchange of land experience among nations.

Great good and much encouragement can come from nongovernmental conferences like this one. I can visualize regional conferences of this kind being organized in the future—one in Asia, one in Latin America, another in Europe, still another in the Middle East. Wider participation throughout the area and a sharper focus on the problems discussed would provide mutual assistance of immense value.

The United States has no special responsibility for and no unique competence in solving land problems the world over. Solutions to these problems do not lie in the heads or hands or pockets of any one nation. We have, however, encouraged and supported the land reform programs of other nations. We will continue that encouragement and support. You may be sure that we will continue, as we have in the past, to support land reforms through international organizations such as the General Assembly, the Economic and Social Council, and the Food and Agriculture Organization.

We want to do more than this to encourage genuine land reform. In the past the United States government has provided technical aid in connection with problems of economic and social organization, as well as the technological problems involved in land tenure and related fields. We have provided both technical and financial assistance to drain, irrigate, and otherwise reclaim lands not under cultivation. We have provided technical and financial aid to industrialization and other worthy projects which have also served the purpose of providing employment for surplus farm populations. We will continue to do these things. We will do whatever else we can appropriately do to encourage and assist programs which show promise of bringing lasting benefits to farm people and of enhancing the role of agriculture in the national economy.

I have great hopes for this conference, as I am sure each of you have. We do not, of course, expect final solutions to the problems or even to segments of problems. Land problems arise only in part from the land itself. They arise more from the relationship of people to the land, the dependence of people upon the land, and their attitudes toward it. As one goal is reached or approached, another goal emerges. The solution to one problem sows the seed of still other problems. The continuous quest for a better life itself creates fresh problems.

Likewise it is true that the solution of one problem contributes to the solution of the next. Through an increase in the productivity of the land under cultivation, the whole economy is rendered stronger and more prosperous, and more attention can be paid to improving agriculture. More food often means stronger and healthier farm workers who can then produce more food. Improved agricultural conditions mean more purchasing power and expanded opportunities for industrial development. In short, no economy can be stronger than its parts, and its parts can and will weaken or reinforce each other.

You have undertaken to explore a problem of tremendous significance. Undoubtedly it is a major contributor to the the unrest so prevalent in the world today. The problem is difficult and complex. The stakes are high. The rewards of a successful attack upon the problem are immeasurable. They will come in terms of a happier and more humane life, a more efficient economy, a more vigorous democracy, and a stable and lasting peace. On behalf of my government I welcome you to Madison; I am happy to extend to you our very best wishes for a successful and fruitful conference.

IT CAN BE SOLVED

Clarence J. McCormick

THE PURPOSE of this conference may be summed up in something that was said by the ancient Roman philosopher Seneca about two thousand years ago. "A hungry people," he said, "listens not to reason, nor cares for justice, nor is he bent by any prayers." It is really in recognition of that fundamental fact that we who represent many nations are here today.

While I know that we are here to explore a general world problem, I hope that to the greatest extent possible the discussions of this conference will be concrete in nature, rather than overly general. When concrete problems confront us—and surely the problems of food and land are concrete—we can deal with them best by talking in specific terms.

That is one of *my* aims now. Many of my remarks will concern agriculture and land tenure as they exist in the United States today. I am going to try to show where the United States stands today in respect to agriculture and land tenure— as well as the road we traveled to reach our present position—and what we are trying to do about the problems that loom ahead of us.

But I want to stress one thing above all— one thought that is fundamental in everything I am going to say here. I am calling it to your attention, underlining it in this way, because unless this one point is made clear the whole meaning of the conference may be misunderstood. This thought that I want to stress is that I, personally, and the other speakers from this country as well, have no intention whatsoever of trying to tell the representatives of any other country how to solve their problems. We are not so presumptuous. We have plenty to keep us occupied tending to our own business.

But, at the same time, we are more than ready to co-operate with any of you in exchanging ideas, talking over methods, outlining spheres of action, and extending any other help that is appropriate.

As Mr. Thorp, the Assistant Secretary for Economic Affairs, has indicated, land tenure and land reform are part of the world problem of food. The world problem of food in turn is tied up with peace, with security, with human dignity. Hunger and peace are poles apart—so much so that peace can have only an uncertain existence so long as the world is part well-fed and part starved. I know that this is the kind of topic that lends itself to fine words, and I am not given to fine words. But I am sure that the greatest economic problem in the world today is the scarcity of food. I believe the great hope of the world is the knowledge that something *can be done,* not tomorrow but *now,* to increase food supplies and lessen world hunger.

I hope that all of you share my feelings about the importance of this conference— about the fact that we are approaching a point in human affairs that has been the aim of mankind through the centuries. We are approaching a point at which, by sharing skill and knowledge, equipment and capital, by making better use of the world's land resources, enough food can be produced to feed the world's people adequately.

I do not think that is being over-optimistic. Scientists in the FAO, in our own Department of Agriculture, and scientists in other organizations and other countries agree that there is enough "know-how" to produce much, much more food than is now being produced in the world. Yet we all recognize that it is one thing to have the theoretical knowledge of how to produce and quite another thing to apply it and make production a reality. What takes place at this conference should have a tremendous effect on the world's ability, eventually, to translate knowledge of production into actual food and fiber.

Throughout the records of human history we see a continual hungering of mankind for food and the land resources and ownership that would provide food. Primitive peoples, even those who live by hunting or those who are a step higher in the economic ladder and who follow a pastoral life, generally have their well-defined territories in which they hunt or in which they move with their flocks and herds. We know how the Jewish people of Biblical times longed for the promised land, the land of milk and honey.

Land tenure problems have existed in every age and among every people. But today the problems that exist are probably more acute than ever before because today people in the disadvantaged regions know better than they ever did before that such problems as hunger, exorbitant rentals and rates of interest, huge land holdings that are poorly used, do not have to continue. They are not laws of nature. They can be changed—and the people *want* to change them. Three-fourths of the people of the world get their living by tilling the land or grazing it with livestock. Consequently, their hope for a rising standard of living is centered in a more productive agriculture.

But the obvious fact is that agricultural institutions in many countries raise a barrier to higher farm output and higher standards of living. In this country we know something about this problem through experience, and few would contend that we have completely licked it. Now it is significant that a century and a half ago, most of the economic problems of the United States were also rural problems—much the same kind of problems, in a broad sense, as farmers in many parts of the world are confronted with today. Our agriculture was on a largely self-sufficing basis. In other words, production was largely for home use rather than for a commercial market. It was relatively unmechanized. There were many hand tools in use; but the plows, harrows, and wooden-wheeled wagons of the period were very crude.

However, there is one point of very considerable difference. Whereas in many areas of the world today a very large proportion of farmers do not own the land they work, in this country we have built our agriculture on individual ownership of the land. Our agricultural pattern is the family farm pattern—a family living on the farm, making a home there, getting most or all of its income from the farm, doing most of the work on the farm, combining in the farm both home and business. The men who shaped the early governmental structures of our nation had strong feelings about this kind of agricultural pattern. Thomas Jefferson, Andrew Jackson, Daniel Webster, Thomas Hart Benton, Abraham Lincoln—they all thought it necessary to democratic strength that the man who tills the land ought to own it, ought to have security in the possession of the land. From the early beginnings of the nation, public land was made available to farmers on very liberal terms. In the mid-part of the nineteenth century, the public lands of the West were opened up to settlement, so that farmers could get title to 160 acres of land just by claiming it and living and working on it for a few years. Thus, the great majority of farms in the United States have from the beginning been owned by the families who operated them.

Farmers were aided in other ways. There were land-grant colleges and experiment stations to carry on research and provide information on good farming methods. Means for gathering useful statistical information that would be helpful to farmers were set up. Thirty-five years ago the Federal Land Bank system was started to establish a farm mortgage credit system.

For a long time, this country proceeded on the apparent assumption that outside of ownership of the land by the individual operating farmer not much else was needed in the way of land tenure policy. Gradually, it became evident that ownership alone was not enough. And by the time the early 1930's arrived, it was extremely clear that unless governmental steps were taken to deal with the farm problems that had arisen, even the pattern of individual operator-ownership was in grave danger.

At that time, the nation's farmers were in a very serious economic plight. Farmers had lost much of their foreign market. They were producing more of some commodities than they could sell at fair prices. They were heavily in debt. The total farm mortgage debt in 1930 was estimated at more than 20 per cent of the value of all farms. Whereas in the 1800's about three farms out of four had been owner-operated, in 1930 about 42 per cent were operated by tenants. There were nearly 800,000 share-croppers in our farm economy. We were suddenly awakened to the fact that a small farmer who was without money or credit resources —even though he owned his farm—was just about as insecure on the land as was the tenant.

We were suddenly made aware also that a condition of widespread ownership did not in itself mean that the land would be properly used and safeguarded against erosion and depletion of organic matter. Not only did the average farmer need more information on *how* to take care of the land, he needed, above all, a fair price for his products so he would not be forced to mine the soil to keep his family alive. We realized, too, that a great many farm families were not sharing in the advances that city people, at least the great majority of them, had come to accept as commonplace.

In the past two decades the United States has made a determined effort to strengthen its agriculture on many fronts. Essentially, what this country has been seeking is the preservation of human resources on the land as well as the improvement of the land itself. There were a number of essential actions that had to be taken. Something had to be done to bring production into reasonable balance with demand. This problem was attacked by means of the Agricultural Adjustment Acts of 1933, 1938, and by later related legislation. These measures provided not only for production adjustment, for marketing limitations that farmers could impose on themselves by a two-thirds vote, and for price supports: under them, there was established also a system of county and community farmer committees elected by the farmers. These committees give American farmers a more direct voice in farm policy and its application.

There was a need for more adequate credit, both long-term and short-term, to enable farmers to buy farms, or to enlarge them, or to get better equipment. This has been provided through the Farm Credit Administration and the Farmers Home Administration and the agencies which preceded it. The special purpose of FHA and its preceding agencies was to provide credit for small farmers, tenants, and others who could not get credit through other channels.

There was a need for soil conservation. In 1935, Congress set up a Soil Conservation Service within the Department of Agriculture to administer a long-time program to combat erosion and to conserve land and water resources. In 1936, Congress passed the Soil Conservation and Domestic Allotment Act which provided financial assistance to farmers in carrying out approved soil and water conservation practices.

There was a need to bring electric power

to rural areas. In 1935 only about 11 per cent of the nation's farms had electric power line service. In 1935 the Rural Electrification Administration came into existence to make loans to co-operatives for providing power to rural areas. Last year a rural telephone loan program was established to be administered by REA.

There was a need for an expanded research program. Under the Bankhead-Jones Act of 1935, Congress took steps to point agricultural research more directly toward practical farm problems. In 1938, four great regional research laboratories were authorized. In 1946, the Research and Marketing Act gave still more emphasis to production and distribution research.

There were a number of other programs also: insurance of crops against loss caused by drought, flood, and other natural damage; a school lunch program; flood control projects; an expansion of price supports; and a farm housing loan program.

There is no time now to describe the operations of our farm programs in detail. But I would like to point out some of their results. Whereas in the early 1930's more than 42 per cent of the nation's farms were tenant-operated, only about one-fourth of our farms are operated by tenants today. This change has been brought about by many factors, but the credit programs have certainly played a big part.

Agricultural credit agencies supervised in the Farm Credit Administration have made more than 5 million loans totalling roughly 18 billion dollars in the last 17 years. As of June 30, 1950, these agencies currently had outstanding some 622,000 loans totalling a little less than 2 billion dollars. The Federal Land Banks have gradually retired their government capital and now are completely farmer-owned. The production credit associations are making rapid strides in the same direction. A large number of these also are now wholly member-owned.

About two million small farmers have been helped by the loan programs under the Farmers Home Administration. But the real test is not found in the number of loans or repayments. The primary objective of this supervised credit is to help family-type farmers to better living through successful farming. National surveys have shown large gains in these borrowers' incomes, operating capital, and net worth.

I have mentioned that in the 1930's before the Rural Electrification program began only about one-tenth of the nation's farms had powerline electric service. Today approximately 85 per cent of the farms have electricity. This has been a big factor in increasing farm efficiency as more and more uses are found for electricity in farm production. It has also meant that farm homes can now have the convenience and comforts that electric power makes possible. I want to point out here that the repayment record of these lending programs is excellent. Payments of rural electrification loans are almost 100 per cent on schedule. A substantial proportion of the loans are being paid up ahead of the due dates.

A stupendous job is being done in soil conservation. Nearly one and one-quarter billion acres are now covered in the more than 2,300 soil conservation districts which draw upon technical help of the Soil Conservation Service and other Department of Agriculture facilities. Meanwhile, about 50 per cent of all farms co-operated in the agricultural conservation program in 1950. The savings in land resources are beyond calculation.

The nation has had impressive returns on its agricultural research. You all know the effect of hybrid corn. The additional return that is due to hybrid corn has been estimated at about 1 *billion* dollars a year. The research costs amounted to about 10 *million* dollars. Disease-resistant cereals developed in recent years add about one-half billion dollars each year to farm income from cereal crops. Phenothiazine, a remedy for internal parasites of livestock, saves the nation about 10 *million* dollars a year in livestock losses. The research to develop it cost 10 *thousand* dollars! I could cite a great many other research achievements. All of these results depend not only on research and technical knowledge in the laboratories but on dissemination of *information,* on *education* of the farm people so that they will know about these advances and will make use of them.

Let me sum up the results of the past few decades of agricultural progress in this country by saying that they have helped bring about a big improvement in rural living standards. Farm families have made good use of the economic advantages of recent years. Many of them have put modern conveniences in their homes—for kitchens, for laundry, for living room, for bath. They have improved their schools. They are making farming communities more attractive and inviting.

All this in turn helps to make farm people better informed citizens, increasingly awake to national and world events. It makes them strong in their love of democracy. More than this, the increased purchasing power of our farm people has been passed on to workers and business and professional people in the cities and has increased their standard of living.

One of the most vital effects of the farm programs, however, has been the part it has played in increasing the productivity of our agriculture. Farmers in the United States have been producing about two-fifths more food and fiber than they did in the prewar 1935–39 period. This year, because of the need for still further increases in production, we expect a new all-time record output.

Our agriculture is producing at this very high level with a considerably smaller working force and not much more acreage under cultivation than we had in the prewar period. Actually less than one-sixth of our population is now on farms, and only one working person out of eight is employed in agriculture. This is a fact that is full of meaning in view of the manpower and energies that are thus released, whether for defense or for peacetime production.

We are proud of this progress, and I think justly so. It has been a test of the ability of a free people to develop constructive programs to restore their land and their agriculture to health and to maintain them in a healthy condition. Yet we know that all the programs we have do not serve our family-farm agriculture as effectively as we should like them to. So we are on the lookout for ways to improve them. For several months now we have had in progress a family-farm policy review. We want to find out how well our programs are now serving the needs of our family farms. We know that these family farms are the backbone of our way of life. We know that the family farms can give us most of the production increases we need now and will need in the years ahead.

In co-operation with farm organizations, with the land-grant colleges, with church and civic groups and, most of all, in co-operation with individual farmers all over the country, we have stimulated widespread discussion of present farm programs and activities. We want the people who are most interested—the taxpayers, the consumers, and the farmers—to speak up plainly and say where the programs are doing a good job, where they are falling short, and what improvements they feel should be made.

You will note that we are asking not for compliments—we want criticism and, most of all, constructive suggestions.

There are plenty of problems still to be solved in this country. Despite the progress of recent years, farmers as a group are not yet sharing fully in the national income and the material advantages that are available to city people as a group. There are still many needs to be met in conservation, research, price protection, electrification, and credit.

As we look to the future we expect our population to continue its growth. In 1960, we may have a population of 170 millions or more. In 1975 we may have about 200 millions. We may also have heavy demand from abroad. That means we must continue to increase farming efficiency. We must use more fertilizer and use it wisely. We will need more farm machinery, better buildings, less waste, improved control of insects and diseases, new varieties of plants and seeds, and better methods of distribution.

I have been outlining for you some of the experiences of the United States in land tenure and agricultural policy. I have not done this in a spirit of boastfulness; nor have I done it because of any illusions that our pattern will necessarily fit the needs of any other country. I have made my remarks rather in the belief that every people can profit from the problems and experiences of others.

Our experience in this country indicates that a good system of land tenure depends upon many conditions—not on ownership alone, not just on fair dealing between owners and tenants, not on government policies alone. A good system of land tenure depends upon the productivity of farms, upon good markets and fair prices, education, credit, farm organizations, farm co-operatives, and governmental institutions that are responsive to the will of the people. A land tenure system to be satisfactory to the people must reflect a condition of freedom. When reforms are needed, freedom itself is likely to produce them.

Just as charity covers a multitude of sins, so land policy covers a multitude of things. That is why I hesitate to use the phrase "land reform." It is not only because the Soviets and their satellites have given that name an unfortunate meaning—a meaning that begins with confiscation and division of large holdings and ends in collectivization—so that the people, who expected better things, find out that the last stage of Soviet land reform is worse than the original system.

Such misuse of the term land reform is bad enough, but what may be even worse in the long run is the notion that land reform means only changing the owners of the land. If you have time, some of you might want to consider at this conference whether there is a new name to take the place of land reform.

The point I am making, in any event, is that good land policy eventually requires improvement in social and economic conditions. It implies a good tax system, a good credit system; it implies co-operatives and co-operation on a broad front among farmers and people as a whole.

I would like to end my discussion on two notes. The first is a note of encouragement. The problem of land, which in the last analysis is the problem of food, *can* be solved. There are a great many indications that this is the plain truth. The progress that has been made in this country in increasing agricultural production may be matched or even exceeded by world progress in the years ahead. I understand that over a large area of Europe farm production since 1947 has increased by about 25 per cent. I have seen, on my brief trip to Europe, some of the advances that are being made in consolidating scattered land holdings and the interest in the problem of land tenure. Our Secretary of Agriculture visited in Europe last summer, and he came home very much impressed with the methodical efforts being made to pursue the problems of agricultural rehabilitation and expansion of production.

Many of us know what has taken place in Japan since the war ended. We know that much progress was being made in Korea before the invasion in June, 1950. That's the first of my two closing notes—progress *can* be made, progress *is* being made, progress *will* be made, I am sure, if we set our minds to it.

The second note is that we in the United States are not only willing to help—*we want to help*. We supported vigorously the resolution on land reform adopted by the General Assembly of the United Nations last November. We also advocated that land problems in trust territories be studied by a committee of the Trusteeship Council.

The Secretary of Agriculture, still more recently, asked that greater attention be given land tenure conditions in the long-term program of the Food and Agriculture Organization.

These actions indicate our earnest wish to co-operate in lessening land tenure problems. I hope that at this conference there will be much discussion as to just what a nation like the United States can do to help. We have welcomed many agricultural, civic, and government leaders here from abroad. They have studied our methods. Not all of our methods are suited to other nations, but you are welcome to any help that can come from that source.

Within limits which will be determined by the course of the world in the years ahead, we may be able to extend credit to other nations. The extent to which we may do so is determined by the Congress. In our own nation, we have had programs of credit by which farmers who do not own their land may come to own it. Some people have suggested that we underwrite similar programs in other nations. If we were to do so, there would still be a question as how best to do it. For example, should the United States isolate her credit, or should she lend money in conjunction with other nations through existing or new agencies? And if such credit is provided, what about the many other things we have come to learn are involved in land tenure reforms along with financing—what should be done about encouraging farm co-ops, about more extension education, about farm management guidance on the borrower's farms? Perhaps this conference can contribute the answers to some of those questions.

As you know, I am an administrative official of this country. I do not make the laws. Therefore, I cannot commit the nation to this course or that. But I know I speak for the people when I say that we are interested in the progress of freedom and human dignity throughout the world. We will welcome your searching studies of the ways in which the problems of land tenure may be solved. And I promise you the full support of the United States Department of Agriculture.

LAND AND INDEPENDENCE—AMERICA'S EXPERIENCE

 Henry G. Bennett

IT IS A pleasure and an honor to address this international gathering—a pleasure because I have been privileged to visit twenty-nine of the countries represented here today, and I can now welcome you to mine. It is an honor to take part in a conference which serves the cause of human welfare and world peace.

We are here to consider problems of land tenure, which affect the lives of almost every man, woman, and child on this earth.

The Technical Cooperation Administration, which I head in the Department of State, carries on the Point Four Program. This is the program which President Truman first proposed in his Inaugural Address of January, 1949. This is the program through which the United States is now sharing the services of its technicians and specialists with other countries in a cooperative effort to help other peoples increase production, improve health, promote education, and create a decent life for themselves. Because three-fourths or more of the people in the country concerned live on the land, we and they together are concentrating our efforts in the Point Four Program on improving the economic and social conditions of rural life.

We are putting major emphasis on agriculture because we know it is fundamental. The land is the primary source of all material life on this earth. From it we derive our sustenance and our wealth. Most wealth comes from earth and rock in the form either of minerals, coal, petroleum, and the like, or in the form of vegetable matter. The few inches of top soil are the most prolific and universal source of wealth that we have. Agriculture is the world's largest and most indispensable business. So we believe the Point Four Program must be concerned first and foremost with agriculture and especially with man's ability to produce more food.

The Point Four Program is usually thought of in terms of demonstrating and teaching better techniques and practices. Indeed we believe this is the way we Americans can make our greatest contribution. But techniques and methods are only means to an end. Our purpose is to help dignify agriculture so that the millions of people who live on and work the land will not only produce abundantly but enjoy the fruits of their labor as well.

We recognize that techniques of production and distribution are not the only fac-

tors that shape the relationship of the farmer to the land and to the society of which he is a part. We recognize the vital importance of the legal, economic, and social conditions under which the farmer uses the land he tills. That is why we in the Point Four Program have joined in sponsoring this conference on world land tenure problems. We are grateful to the University of Wisconsin for making it possible to meet here in these pleasant and hospitable surroundings.

I should like to use this occasion to discuss with you some of our own experiences with land tenure problems in the United States. I fully realize the danger of implied comparisons. Much of our experience with land problems cannot, and should not, be considered applicable in *your* countries. Happily, no two peoples have the same history or geography. In diversity we find the riches and glory of our free society of nations.

In the early years of the history of my country, the major challenge was to settle an almost empty continent, to tame a wilderness, and to clear and cultivate vast tracts of land. Ours was just the reverse of the problem in many other countries where population presses on available land resources. The family-size farm under conditions prevailing in the United States may be 160 acres or more; in other countries it may be three, five, or fifty acres.

However, there are certain general principles that can be adapted and applied to different situations. Certainly there is much that we can learn from each other as we exchange views and experiences at this conference. So in discussing some of our experiences with land tenure problems in the United States, I do not intend to imply that our land policies and practices are perfect or ideal.

As you travel around this country—and I hope you will have a chance to do so—you will observe the many imperfections in our own land policies. I hope you will observe, also, that we are striving to correct them. To me, the most hopeful thing about our land policy in the United States is that it is continuously developing and improving. Our history is, in large part, the story of a continuing land reform movement. Progress has been faster and more perceptible at some times than at others. But over the 175 years of our independent nationhood, there has been a sense of life and forward movement. This sense of progress has characterized the growth of our nation.

The thinking of our political philosophers has both shaped and reflected our history at different stages. The primarily agrarian nature of society at the time of the founding of the Republic is reflected in the thinking of our great liberal President Thomas Jefferson, who declared that "the small landholders are the most precious part of a state." Today, that opinion might be contested by labor, industry, and other groups.

About a hundred years later, in a time of increasing industrialization and pressure of population on the land in the older states, another philosopher, Henry George, championed the "single tax" on land. George declared that "what is necessary for the use of land is not its private ownership, but the security of improvements. It is not necessary to say to a man 'this land is yours,' in order to induce him to cultivate or improve it. It is only necessary to say to him, 'whatever your labor or capital produces on this land shall be yours.'"

The touchstone of our attitude toward the land, however, has remained constant. You will find it expressed in our Declaration of Independence, which asserts that man is endowed with certain inalienable rights, that "among these are life, liberty, and the pursuit of happiness." To translate those rights—in which we deeply believe—into reality is the basic purpose of our land policy and of all our national policies. We have struggled to create and to maintain a land tenure system that would best serve man's enjoyment of "life, liberty, and the pursuit of happiness," the fundamental rights to which we believe he is entitled.

Today many people think of land reform exclusively in terms of land ownership. The ideal situation, of course, would be for every man to own the land he tills. I have no quarrel with that ideal. I think all of us would like to see our societies come as close as possible to realizing that ideal. But progress toward an ideal must recognize the limitations of the practical. We must go forward one step at a time, and it is not practical at this time in any country, including the United States, for every farmer to own the land he works.

What is practical and attainable for every farmer, either as owner or as tenant, is the opportunity to work the land under conditions that provide him with *the incentive and the means* to farm efficiently, to conserve and improve the soil, and to obtain a fair share of the fruits of his labor for himself and his family. I believe this is a practical objective. I am convinced that the means of reaching it are varied and flexible enough to be applied in all countries and under all conditions.

It seems to me, then, that there are three essential principles that underlie a just and equitable land system. First, the farmer must be able to own land or to use the land he tills under fair conditions and terms of tenure. Second, the farmer must have access to credit on reasonable terms, to enable him to farm efficiently whether as owner or tenant. Third, he must have access to the knowledge and techniques that will make his efforts productive and profitable to him and to society.

These are the goals toward which we have been struggling in the United States, with varying success. These are the goals toward which we still are striving in the evolution of our national land policy. What have we done and achieved in relation to these basic principles?

The hunger for land, which, like the yearning for freedom, is universal, was one of the strongest motives in the settlement of North America. The restlessness of an increasing number of families without land was one of the factors that led to the American Revolution. The colonies had inherited the land laws of the mother country. Large holdings passed from father to first son, and vast estates were kept intact by entailment. The manorial system persisted until the colonies won their independence. Individual colonists of poor or moderate means found it hard to buy land. Among the first results of the Revolution was the confiscation of large Royalist estates. Feudalistic quitrents were abolished, and laws that protected large estates were repealed. This sharp break with the past enabled the young nation to create a new legal framework for land ownership. Men who served in the Revolutionary armies were offered free land. In fact, the practice of helping our war veterans to start life again as farmers has persisted to this day. In 1785, even before the adoption of our present Constitution, Congress passed laws providing for the sale of land to new settlers in the region west of the Appalachian mountains. The price per acre was low, but many settlers found it hard to make the first cash payment. They demanded cheaper land and more liberal terms. So the laws were changed to make it easier to own land. My own grandfather held land under an act signed by President Andrew Jackson. And on that land I was born.

The cry for cheap land grew until it became a cry for free land. And eventually free land came. The year 1862 was a landmark in American agriculture. In the midst of a terrible Civil War which threatened to destroy our nation, President Lincoln signed three great agricultural laws. The first of these laws was a new and more liberal Homestead Act. It gave any citizen, or immigrant planning to become a citizen, clear title to 160 acres of public land, provided he settled on it and worked it for five years.

The second law, the Morrill Act, offered each state 30,000 acres of public lands for each Senator or Representative it had in Congress. The proceeds from the land were to be used to establish and maintain colleges for the teaching of agricultural and mechanical arts. Thus education came to agriculture, and thus began our great land-grant colleges, of which the University of Wisconsin is an outstanding example.

The third law signed by President Lincoln established a Department of Agriculture as an independent agency of the Federal government.

With progress in the laws affecting agriculture came remarkable changes on the farm itself. In the early days of our Republic, the American farmer developed his farm mainly with his own strength and resourcefulness. He cut down the virgin forest with an ax. He turned the soil with a rude wooden plow drawn by a horse or an ox. He might use a crude harrow made of logs with wooden spikes. He sowed by broadcasting seed by hand from a sack slung over his shoulder or stooped to plant seeds in hills. If he cultivated, it was with a hoe. He harvested with a sickle or a scythe, threshed with a flail, and winnowed by tossing straw before the wind.

Henry Adams, one of our historians, was moved to remark that "the Saxon farmers of the eighth century enjoyed most of the comforts known to American farmers of the eighteenth."

But as waves of new settlers pushed the frontier westward, the farmer developed better tools and practices, became a producer for market instead of just for home consumption. One basic improvement was the replacement of the unwieldy wooden plow of the colonial period with the steel turning plow. It was still animal-drawn, but it raised the farmer's efficiency and was within his means to buy.

With the invention of a practical reaper at the close of the 1840's came the beginning of the machine age in American agriculture. Harvesting is the most time-consuming part of grain production, and often the crop would be damaged by weather before the harvesting could be completed. For that reason, the reaper is sometimes called the greatest invention of the early machine age in agriculture.

The reaper, which later became a binder and a thresher as well, is mainly responsible for cutting the time it took to plant, grow, harvest, and thresh an acre of wheat from sixty man-hours in the nineteenth century to four man-hours in the twentieth century.

It has taken me only a minute to describe something that took a hundred years to accomplish—the mechanization of American agriculture, which is still far from complete today. We are apt to forget that it came step by step—a long, slow, and arduous progress, accompanied by a long, slow process of education, both theoretical and practical. Today, other societies are trying to telescope this progress, to jump a century in a generation. I believe it can and will be done, but only step by step, and only with a prodigious effort to educate farmers.

The period between 1862 and 1900 saw one of the greatest migrations in human history. More than 14 million people came to the United States from other countries. Free land and the pressure of population in our eastern states sent a wave of humanity rolling across the continent to people the area of the Great Plains. One of the most exciting episodes of the land rush happened in my home state of Oklahoma. On April 22, 1889, a large section of Oklahoma was opened to homesteaders. Thousands of prospective farm owners crowded to the border. As a signal was given at noon, they charged across the line like an invading army to claim the land they wanted!

It was in that period and in the Great Plains area that a grievous mistake was made in land policy—a mistake that did not become clearly apparent until years later. It had tragic consequences. That mistake has been pointed out by Professor Benjamin H. Hibbard of this very University. Professor Hibbard, one of the leading authorities on our public land policies, tells us that the Homestead Act was unsound—at least as applied to the Great Plains area. The land unit of the Homestead Act was 160 acres—a unit considered the proper "family-size" farm. But the Great Plains region has an average annual rainfall of 10 to 18 inches. Droughts lasting for a season or several years are not uncommon. These conditions called for special kinds of farming—either dry land farming, cattle grazing, or intensive farming with the aid of irrigation. But 160 acres was too small a tract for dry farming or grazing and too large for irrigated farming. Widespread erosion and the dust storms of the 1930's were part of the price the nation paid and is still paying for these mistakes.

Aside from this basic error, the law was sometimes badly administered. It is significant that the platform of the Republican party in 1872 included the statement: "We are opposed to further grants of the public lands to corporations and monopolies, and demand that the national domain be set apart for free homes for the people." And the platform of the Democratic party the same year said the same thing.

Mistakes in policy helped to bring on a farm depression. Since the Civil War, farm prices had been falling while the prices of other things were rising. The American farmer was competing with new producers in Russia, Australia, Argentina, and Canada. About 1895, American farm prices fell to disastrous levels. Many farmers began to mortgage or sell their farms. In 1880, when free land was plentiful, three out of every four farmers were owners or part owners of the land they worked. For the first thirty years after 1900, ownership declined and tenancy increased until only about half the farmers owned their land.

The people and the government of the United States were discovering that something more than the provision of free land was needed to create a productive and prosperous agriculture.

Even during this period of general decline, however, some progress was made. In 1887, Congress passed the Hatch Act. It provided Federal aid to the states for experimentation and research in agriculture, to be conducted by the land-grant colleges. The creation of experiment stations was a great forward step—almost as important as the land-grant colleges themselves.

In 1902, Congress passed the first Reclamation Act, which allowed the Federal government to put money into irrigation. In 1914 came the Smith-Lever Act establishing our national farm extension service.

The extension service in America is personified by the county agent. He is the man who takes scientific knowledge from the land-grant college classroom and experiment station direct to the farmer on the land. The county agent works side by side with the farmer, demonstrating the best seeds, the best in new livestock practices, the best in new equipment and new techniques. The Smith-Lever Act has put a farm demonstration agent within reach of every rural county. These agents are the key to putting scientific agriculture into practice and making farm credit effective. They show the farmer how to get the most out of his money and his skill.

In 1917, Congress gave the Federal government power to support agricultural and vocational education in secondary schools. Since then, American boys and girls have been able to get good training in agriculture even if they are not able to go to college.

I have said little so far about farm credit. Our government was slow in waking up to its importance. The Federal Farm Loan Act of 1916 gave the farmer his first reliable source of credit at rates less than 10 per cent. Under the Act, farmers could obtain loans for five to forty years, at 6 per cent interest or less, with land, buildings, or farm improvements as security. In 1923, short-term credit was made available. The Intermediate Credit Act provided for loans for six months to three years, with crops and livestock as security.

These measures were basic to our long-range agricultural program. But except during the sharp, brief rise in farm prices during the first world war, the American farmer was sliding down the slippery slope toward depression. By 1929—when the great industrial and financial crash came—he was already in a depression. The farm population, one-quarter of the nation, was earning only 7 per cent of the national income. Between 1927 and 1932, 10 per cent of our farms were forfeited because of mortgages.

At that low point in our fortunes, we began a drastic overhauling of our agricultural system, including farm credit. The Farm Credit Administration was established in 1933 as the basis of our farm credit structure. It remains so today. I will outline its three main features.

First, farmers can get credit for a number of purposes. A farmer can borrow to pay off other debts, buy land, or improve his land and get equipment. He can get short-term, intermediate, and long-term loans at low interest rates.

Second, farmers can get technical advice they need to operate their farms efficiently. This combination of easy credit and technical advice is what we call "supervised credit." Along with the loan, the farmer receives help in planning to spend it wisely and to repay it systematically out of increased earnings.

Third, the credit program uses private capital through public institutions. The government derives part of the capital for these loans by selling government securities to banks, insurance companies, or individual investors.

Another agency of the Department of Agriculture, the Farmers Home Administration, provides supervised credit for poor farm families unable to get help from any other source. These families get very long-term loans at very low interest and pay them back in small installments. Trained agents work closely with the borrowers in planning and carrying out their farm improvements. Thousands of small farmers, many of whom had been tenants all their lives, have become prosperous farm owners with this help.

I spoke earlier of the tragic consequences of plowing up the dry lands of the Great Plains. You have heard of the Dust Bowl of the 1930's. You probably have seen moving pictures of it. I lived through the Dust Bowl—although sometimes I doubted that I would. I have been in dust storms that shut out the sun at midday and made it almost impossible to breathe. I never want to go through that experience again. Neither does our nation—and we do not intend to.

A few thoughtful Americans began years ago to warn us to conserve our soil and water—our most precious natural assets. But we did not listen to them soon enough. Not until our topsoil began to blow away and take the livelihood of many farmers with it did we really get busy on soil conservation. The Soil Conservation Service was estab-

lished in the Department of Agriculture in 1935. In five years, one-fourth of the nation's farmers were doing something to stop erosion and to conserve their soil. This program is growing. We are determined at last to stop the abuse of our soil and save our land to pass on to our children.

So far I have been talking mainly about the land, the credit, and the services that our government has provided for farmers. From what I have said you might conclude that in recent years, at least, American farmers have stood passive and with open hands waiting for their government to help them. That would be a wrong conclusion. I could spend much time telling what our farmers have done and are doing for themselves. Time does not permit me to do this, but I do want to say a few words about our agricultural co-operatives. As the name suggests, these are organizations in which farm people voluntarily band together for mutual benefit. These organizations are of various kinds—some are purchasing co-operatives through which farmers save money by buying fertilizer, equipment, and other supplies in large quantities. Others are marketing co-operatives through which producers process, store, and sell their products jointly, economically, and profitably.

Most of these co-operatives started small —just a few farm families putting together their personal resources. Today, the co-operative movement has grown big, strong, and healthy in this country. I mention the co-operatives to show you that government assistance has not made our farmers weaker or sapped their initiative. In fact, it has had the opposite effect of putting the farmers in a better position to help themselves and each other.

These, then, are some of the efforts we have made in our long history of independence to enable the American farmer to enjoy "life, liberty, and the pursuit of happiness," and thus to dignify him in his way of life. We have come a long, hard way, and we still have far to go. But I think the basic principles I stated earlier are still sound and will not lead us far astray: first, ownership of land, or its use under fair and equitable conditions of tenure; second, access to credit on reasonable terms; and third, access to modern knowledge and techniques for efficient production and decent living.

As regards ownership, it must be remembered that we Americans are blessed with an abundance of good land. Yet, I think it is fair to say that our policies and laws have encouraged independent ownership and fair distribution. The decline in land ownership that lasted from about 1880 to after 1930 has been reversed, and now at least two-thirds of all American farmers own land. We have not always had laws that adequately protected and gave incentive to tenant farmers, and we have not always firmly enforced the laws we had. But we believe that much progress has been made and that most of the tenancy arrangements we now have are generally fair to both tenant and landlord.

As I have said, one of the discoveries we made was that land-ownership, or satisfactory tenancy conditions, in themselves, are not enough. The establishment of the land-grant colleges freed our educational system from its classical mold and gave farm families the opportunity for higher education. For the first time, agriculture took its rightful place in education as a science to be learned and an art to be cultivated, rather than a rude craft practiced by the ignorant and the lowly. The addition of experiment stations enabled the land-grant colleges to advance scientific knowledge in agriculture. Extension agents took the benefits of that knowledge to the farmer on the land.

One element remained to be added to this program—the education of farm women

as equal partners in farm improvement. I cannot overstate the importance of this element. It gave a dynamic push to American agricultural progress and did perhaps more than anything else to make our farms the livable places they are today. The doors of the land-grant colleges were opened to women. Home economics took its place as a course of study entitled to a degree. From the colleges went home demonstration agents to help the farm wife become a contributing member of the farm enterprise. Still later, our young people organized themselves into 4-H clubs and Future Farmers of America. Thus the idea took shape that all members of the farm family can work together in creating new opportunities for a good life.

As regards credit, we were curiously slow in recognizing its importance as a practical means of enabling farmers to acquire land and to translate modern technology into more profitable farming. But since we recognized that fact, we have worked diligently to provide adequate credit facilities for farmers on a practical and economical basis. In fact, we have now taken an important further step in the direction of combining all three of these essential elements in an integrated program which encourages farm ownership and efficient, profitable farming.

In the last analysis, it is up to the American farmer himself to take full advantage of what is now available to him. I have faith in his initiative, and in like fashion I have faith in the initiative, the sound sense, and the independent spirit of farmers I have known all over the world.

We are attending this conference in their interest. But we know full well that their interest is ours, and that all of us are bound together in a common destiny. In that knowledge, let us work together here for a better world, in which we can live in peace and in dignity as good neighbors.

As Administrator of the Technical Co-operation Administration I greet you, and on behalf of my Government and its President I extend to you a cordial welcome. I assure you he holds each of your governments in high regard.

LAND REFORM AND ECONOMIC DEVELOPMENT

Dennis A. FitzGerald

IN COMING to the University of Wisconsin for the international conference on land tenure and related problems, I am reminded of the rich history and tradition of Wisconsin in the field of land tenure. This University has had a prominent place in the study of the development of American land tenure systems and of needed measures and institutional adjustments that make for desirable relationships between people and the land. It is most appropriate, therefore, that land tenure specialists from all over the free world should be gathered here to discuss problems of mutual concern and interest and jointly to work toward their solutions. Economic Cooperation Administration is happy to participate and to extend its support to such a worthwhile undertaking.

It may be convenient if I begin my remarks by defining, or perhaps the better word would be describing, what we in this country mean by "land tenure" and "land reform." We like to use the words "land tenure" to describe all those arrangements by which farmers or others hold or control land and that condition its use and occupancy. In this context land tenure covers much more than mere rights in land; it encompasses agricultural economic institutions generally, including agricultural land ownership and tenancy, land rents, taxation of agricultural land or income from land, and even rural credit facilities. We conceive of the term "land reform" as covering the changes in these agricultural economic institutions which improve the economic, social, and political status of the individual occu-

pier of land and in so doing contribute to general economic development.

Back of this concept is a fundamental belief in the individual liberty of man and his right to own and control property. Throughout history land has been considered almost synonymous with property. In the free world a wide diffusion of rights in property and in the opportunity to acquire such rights is a basic tenet of democracy. The wide diffusion of rights in property is, in our opinion, almost synonymous with individual freedom and liberty.

Economic development, upon which rests the hope of the mass of the people for better living in the broadest sense of the term, is at once an essential prerequisite to land reform and a partial consequence of it. In this country we have a saying—and I am sure most of you have a comparable saying in yours—for which nobody has a concise answer, namely, "Which comes first, the hen or the egg?" But we do not need to have an answer to this academic question in order to improve our poultry population and to increase both the quantity and quality of our egg production. Similarly, we do not need to answer the question of which comes first, economic development or land reform.

If, for purposes of simplification, we classify all areas in two groups—first, those in which land resources are limited in relation to the existing agricultural population, and second, those in which it is not— the interrelationship between land reform and economic development becomes more apparent. In areas with heavy "population pressure," the agricultural situation is characterized by an inadequacy of agricultural resources in relation to the farming population. Small, inefficient farms tend to be the rule, although a scattering of large estates is not uncommon. With a surplus of farmers competing actively for the use of land—for an opportunity to employ their principal resource, labor—land owners frequently may be able to retain a disproportionate share of the returns from the land. Social discontent and political unrest breed easily in such a fertile soil. Even in these circumstances much can be done to improve the economic conditions of the land occupiers, and, of course, everything that can be done should be done. The lasting solution, however, must rest upon the gradual development of nonagricultural resources and the orderly transfer of people from agricultural to nonagricultural pursuits. Only in this way can a more efficient balance be obtained between land resources and the agricultural population. Generally speaking, therefore, the development of manufacturing, the processing of agricultural products, and an expansion of trade activities should be encouraged. History has demonstrated conclusively that it is through such developments that the pressure of population on the land is lessened and opportunity provided for the efficient use of labor-saving tools and techniques. Most important, such economic developments invariably have led to increased food production and higher standards of living for all. In such a setting, agricultural adjustment programs—including land reforms—can progress more easily in bringing about improved relationships of people to land resources.

Under the second of the assumed situations, that is, those areas where, in relation to the agricultural population, there is an adequacy of agricultural resources, even though undeveloped, the problem and, therefore, its solution is probably much simpler. The possibility of developing economic farming units which will provide a reasonable level of living for the operator is much greater, and essential government investment probably can be confined more largely to public services such as transportation and educational and health facilities.

In the United States we have been singularly fortunate in having both comparatively abundant land resources in relation to population, even though that population has been growing rapidly, and in having even more rapid economic development in nonagricultural activities. As a consequence, the proportion of our population engaged in agriculture has declined steadily throughout most of our history. And since 1916 the absolute number of persons engaged in agriculture has been falling while agricultural production has continued to expand. Simultaneously, of course, the economic progress of this country has permitted a rapid increase in the capital investment in agriculture and in output per agricultural worker. Between 1900 and 1950 the per capita production of agricultural workers in the United States more than doubled.

Economic development rests, in the last analysis, upon the accumulation of capital and its investment in productive uses. In many areas of the world capital accumulation is impeded by the inability of the individual to save anything from his already inadequate income, and frequently, when he does, the savings are hoarded rather than invested.

A second, and in the past a most important, source of investment capital in any given area is from other parts of the world where economic development is more advanced and where the custom of saving and opportunity to save for investment is more highly developed. Today there appears to be increasing difficulties to be overcome before such investment flow can be counted upon, and in any event it cannot be a complete substitute for domestic savings.

The most important single incentive to a flow of either private or public capital from abroad, it seems to me, is the investment climate in the country or area desiring such investments. Unfortunately, in my opinion, the investment climate in many areas today is not conducive to attracting outside venture capital. This is attributable in considerable part to the generally unsettled external political and social conditions over which any individual country may have little control. But this is by no means the whole story. Many countries, no doubt for what they consider to be laudable efforts to improve or protect the economic conditions of their people, actually inhibit the free investment of foreign capital. Elimination of such misguided "nationalism" would appear to be an essential prerequisite to obtaining the very real benefits which can grow out of effective foreign capital investment.

In addition to developing the right climate for attracting foreign capital it is of course equally necessary to encourage in every way possible both domestic savings and the investment of those savings in productive activities. The steps which a government can take to achieve this objective will vary immensely. In all, however, internal political and economic stability stand out as of prime importance to optimum domestic investment in agriculture just as they do in providing an attractive climate for foreign investment.

One of the most constructive features of this conference is the emphasis being placed upon the workshop-seminar approach. In addition to the exchange of views and experiences dealing with land reform as such it affords an unexcelled opportunity for all of us to explore ideas and exchange experiences in the collateral problems of economic development as they affect or are affected by land reform. We all recognize immediately that conditions vary tremendously between countries and even between areas within a country, and what may have worked effectively under one set of conditions would be completely inapplicable in another. Nevertheless, the rich experience collectively represented by the participants at this conference can but contribute to the knowledge and understanding of each one of us and thereby better prepare us to develop more adequate solutions to the problems that we as individuals and our respective countries face.

In commenting as I have upon the importance of economic development generally, I do not want to minimize for a moment the value of land reform itself. A wide range of improvements in agricultural economic institutions themselves is possible without excessive capital investment. Substantial progress in agricultural production can be made through technological developments—use of improved seed varieties, insecticides, optimum application of fertilizers, and introduction of improved types of tools and machines—and through further development of land already in farms. The opening up of new land remains a promising possibility in some areas.

In many instances, however, land reform is necessary for the full development and use of modern science and technology in agriculture. The most pressing needs therefore may be for an improved tenure system, the development of credit facilities for both short- and long-term credit under favorable terms and at reasonable rates of interest, expanded and redirected educational programs, and the enactment of necessary legislation for an organization setup suitable to carry on land development programs, including essential public works for land reclamation, roads, and public facilities.

An extension of property interests in land can be brought about through change in land ownership patterns, better landlord-tenant arrangements, and through the elimination of oppressive controls and burdens where they exist. Institutional improvements in this direction affect the productivity of the farmer and this productivity vitally affects the over-all economic development of a nation. Institutional changes of this particular kind may be politically most difficult even though relatively inexpensive. This is particularly true in instances in which large estates or holdings should be divided into family operating units. At the other end of the scale are instances in which small units need to be consolidated because of inadequate size or because of their scattered nature.

In the United States I suspect we have a land ownership pattern that is less troubled by these situations than that found in most other parts of the world. The most consistent phase of our land policy has been the establishment and improvement of family farms. We have found that, for most types of farming, the family farm is a highly efficient and productive type of organization, from both an individual and a social viewpoint. Ideally we believe such a family farm should be a unit that can be operated by the labor of the family or with the employment of very little outside labor and that provides an income sufficient for a good family living, including sufficient savings for farm maintenance and improvement. Unfortunately, in areas where population pressure is great, the tendency is for the units to be so small that deterioration rather than improvement is the more likely. Under these circumstances farmers are in no position to maintain their land resources, improve their economic status, or lend support to the stability of political institutions.

If the farms are too small, it may be necessary to produce high income-yielding crops per unit of land even though national interest, market outlets, or other conditions may call for the production of more extensive crops. Under these conditions, land redistribution merely for the purpose of vesting ownership and operation in a greater number of individuals may be a disservice both to the individuals concerned and to the country.

Another aspect of land reform which does not necessarily require a large initial investment is land consolidation—the regrouping of scattered ownership parcels. This is one of the pressing land reforms needed, and to some extent it is under way in many parts of Western Europe. For example, in western Germany in 1950, of 223,000 farms of from 2 to 3 hectares in size, 23 per cent consisted of between 6 and 10 separate parcels, 24 per cent between 11 and 20 parcels, and 7 per cent between 21 and 30 parcels.

Through the consolidation of scattered parcels, it is possible to increase substantially agricultural production and at the same time reduce farm operating cost. Potential production increases are estimated as high as 25 to 30 per cent and unit cost decreases from 10 to 15 per cent. Of equal significance is the fact that the land tenure patterns following land consolidation provide an incentive for improved land use and conservation practices and a basis for more effective agriculture-wide planning and program operations.

In some parts of the world farmers typically rent the land they operate. This is true in much of Southeast Asia, in the countries of the Middle East, and in several South American countries. Tenancy in itself is not to be deplored where the rentals are not exorbitant and where the tenant has a reasonable degree of security and stability, especially if it is of a form which does not preclude the acquiring of land ownership. However, where rentals take the major part of the income from land and land is held as a closed investment, tenants have little, if any, economic incentive or opportunity to increase the productive capacity of the land or to improve their own well-being. Legislation providing for more equitable sharing out of the returns from land may be a partial solution but, in the long run, the eventual solution must be to bring about a better balance between the agricultural population and land resources.

More or less parenthetically, I should like to mention one source of investment funds for land reform and related purposes that has been available in the last three years. This source is the local currency which Marshall Plan countries have been depositing in their central banks in an amount equivalent to the dollar grants-in-aid provided by the United States. The Italian government, for example, proposed and the United States readily concurred in the use of a considerable amount of the Italian lira counterpart for land reclamation, drainage, and irrigation and for the establishment of a source of credit for small farmers at reasonable interest rates. Again, the Netherlands has used guilder counterpart funds for the rehabilitation and recovery of lands flooded with sea water during World War II. Several European countries have used some of this local counterpart currency for establishing or expanding agricultural advisory services.

The United States program of economic aid to countries in Southeast Asia has been in operation only for a year or so in most instances, but it is quite clear that these countries will want to use at least part of the local counterpart currencies growing out of this assistance for carrying forward various land reform and related activities.

One collateral matter affecting both land reform and economic development generally to which I should like to refer briefly is that of the relation of population to economic resources, including land resources. The population of the world has increased

approximately fourfold in the last three centuries, from about 545 million in 1650 to 2 billion 450 million in 1950. In the last hundred years the world's population has almost doubled. One of the most disturbing aspects is that today about one-half of the world's population lives in countries which have a diet of less than 2,500 calories a day. In fact, the majority probably have diets in the neighborhood of 2,000 calories per person per day. This low level of food consumption, combined with poor health conditions generally, results in a high incidence of disease and a high death rate. But generally birth rates continue high and disease control methods have become more widely used, so that population continues to grow and to press upon resources generally.

Excessive pressure of population upon resources, including land resources, in many parts of the world must be reckoned as a hard fact. Unless there is a decline in the rate of population growth in these areas, progress in achieving desirable levels of production, nutrition, and economic development will be seriously obstructed. I have no pat solution to this problem and, indeed, it is extraordinarily difficult and complex. Experience seems to suggest that declining birth rates are associated with economic development and social progress and without the latter little progress can be made in achieving the decline in birth rates which will, as economic resources increase, bring about a gradual improvement in the economic status of the individual.

While the population problem may prove to be the most intractable, I recognize that many direct land reform measures will also be most difficult—particularly those that involve a change in property rights. But all are highly important. The feasibility of different measures must be studied, new ways of overcoming obstacles developed, and courses of action determined upon and executed with vigor. This requires courageous but tactful leadership and a framework within which such leadership can effectively make itself felt. There is no easy road to land reform, and conditions demand that progress be made. This is our challenge.

With this final observation, I sincerely wish the members of this conference a very profitable and enjoyable stay in the United States.

ISSUES IN THE BACKGROUND OF THE CONFERENCE

Philip M. Raup

THROUGHOUT the nineteenth century and well into the twentieth century the people of the United States devoted a major part of their energies to the development and carrying out of land policies on a heroic scale. The tasks of settling a continent, dividing up its land, and of creating a system of farms owned predominantly by the people who farm them have played a major role in United States history.

The development of the American land tenure sysem has been part of a long history of world-wide struggle for land tenure reforms—a struggle whose roots lie deep in antiquity and a struggle that still plagues the world today. In this century two world wars have brought in their wake a succession of revolutions and reforms centered in an impressive number of cases around land tenure issues. The nineteenth century was characterized by the rapid reorganization of feudal systems of land tenure in most of Western Europe; there remain major portions of the world where the adjustment of the land tenure system to the techniques and institutions of a modern age has yet to take place. Midcourse in the twentieth century—the age of the machine, of the city, of industrial civilization, and of atomic power—the brute fact remains: land tenure problems lie at the root of some of the most perplexing problems that disturb the peace of our world.

Can these problems be solved peaceably? Can they be solved in a manner that con-

forms with the desires of widely differing peoples for a better life? It has been done in Denmark. In England a quiet revolution over the years has effected a major transformation in the British land tenure system. In Ireland the farmer today is the owner of his land—a status that he has achieved by struggle but which in the main has been reached without loss of his freedom as an individual or sacrifice of his democratic way of life. These and other items are for the credit side, but they are too few. Recent events in China, the Philippines, Italy, and Iran, and the threat of upheaval in many other troubled spots all combine to force our attention upon world land tenure problems today. The struggle is still with us.

There has been an impressive awareness of this fact since the end of World War II. It runs as a continuing thread through a number of significant documents of American policy and through a variety of statements of lay and governmental officials and organizations. It is the purpose of this paper to document these statements since the end of the last war and to relate them to the conference on world land tenure problems.

As World War II drew to a close, there was a flurry of activity in the United States in drafting statements of policy to guide military commanders in their roles as occupying authorities, particularly in Germany and, somewhat later, in Japan. Several guides to policy were prepared and directed specifically to the need for postwar land tenure reforms in occupied territories. For Germany, one of the early guides to policy was contained in a War Department pamphlet, *Agricultural Holdings and the Law of Hereditary Estates in Germany*. Referring to the 3 per cent of the population that owned 20 per cent of the land of Germany, a group roughly characterized as the Junkers, this pamphlet declared:

> This group has formed the kernel of political and social reaction in Germany . . . Under the Weimar Republic, the majority of the Junkers supported and encouraged all movements aiming at the overthrow of the Republic. They comprised the most reactionary and anti-democratic group of Germany in that period . . . Incontrovertible political considerations will necessitate the dissolution of the Junker holdings. Their continuation would constitute one of the most formidable obstacles to the establishment of a lasting democracy in Germany, for the holders of these estates have been consistent and active opponents of democratic government.[1]

This policy recommendation was reinforced by a later study that emphasized the need for a dissolution of landed estates[2] as a precondition for German democratic development.

> The concentration of large estates in Eastern Germany has resulted in a feudal society of poorly educated, poorly paid, and ill-housed farm labor population and an educated and powerful land owning "elite." This naturally has affected unfavorably the development of family farms. It has retarded the education of farm laborers and the participation in self-government of both farm laborers and family farmers.[3]

The formal statement of these policy recommendations was contained in the basic *Directive to Commander in Chief of U.S. Forces of Occupation Regarding the Military Government of Germany,* item 28 of which read:

> You will direct the German authorities to utilize large landed estates and public lands in a manner which will facilitate the accommodation and settlement of Germans and others or increase agricultural output.[4]

For Japan, the basic statement of United States policy regarding land tenure reform came a few months later. In October, 1945, the State Department had supplied General MacArthur with a detailed study of the Japanese farm tenancy situation recommending a basic land tenure reform. About the same time the *Basic Directive for Post Surrender Military Government in Japan Proper* was issued. It set forth in clear though general terms the policies which should govern the military occupation in democratizing labor and industrial and agricultural institutions in Japan.[5] "Thus within a few weeks General MacArthur received on the one hand full authority for correcting undemocratic economic arrangements in Japan, and on the other hand, a documented indictment of the undemocratic land tenure system."[6]

It is beyond the scope of this survey to attempt any account or analysis of the implementation of U.S. land tenure policies in Germany and Japan.[7] The policy statements cited here are important in their own right, for they are the points of departure in an account of the development of United States attitudes and policy toward programs of land tenure changes in foreign countries in the recent past. Prior to the defeat of Germany and Japan the United States had had no occasion to develop policies of this nature. Leaving aside at present the question of the success or failure in policy implementation, the policies as stated put the United States on record in favor of land tenure reforms in countries in which the United States had direct responsibilities.

A second development toward the close of World War II is also of importance in this account. In August, 1944, while the war was yet on, a conference was held in

Puerto Rico to discuss the land tenure problems of the Caribbean area. At that meeting representatives were assembled from Cuba, Haiti, and the Dominican Republic, and from the Caribbean possessions of the United Kingdom, the Netherlands, and the United States.

Devoting its attention to the technical phases of land tenure problems, this conference underlined the dominant roles that agriculture and the tenure of agricultural land play throughout the Caribbean area. Land is the most important productive factor. Faced with a staggering and increasing pressure of people on the land resources, the Caribbean countries are struggling with a farm economy in which the common unit of production takes two forms: the large plantation and the tiny subsistence farm. Usually absentee-owned, producing often for a single export market, the Caribbean plantation emerges as an unstable and trouble-breeding tenure institution. The small holdings, on the other hand, are too small to provide the security and level of living desired by the farm and plantation-worker families that till them. In this setting the 1944 conference was a significant event. It provided the first opportunity for a systematic survey of these Caribbean tenure problems, and it set an example for subsequent efforts at a common approach to the study of international land tenure problems.[8]

Two further important conferences on land tenure problems took place soon after the end of the war. The first occurred in February, 1946, when the Farm Foundation and the University of Chicago sponsored a conference on family farm policy. Hampered though it was by the dislocations of travel and communications that immediately followed the war, this conference nevertheless managed to include on its agenda a discussion of land tenure and family farm problems in an impressive number of countries in addition to the United States. Much valuable exploratory work came out of this conference, particularly with regard to the definition of issues and the relation of land tenure problems to the social, economic, and political fabric in which they occur.[9]

Three months later, in May, 1946, an international conference on the rural church and farm land tenure was called together in New York City under the sponsorship of a number of church organizations having world-wide interests and missions.[10] The importance of this conference lay in the fact that it mobilized and gave voice to the growing concern of a wide variety of church and lay religious leaders over land tenure and agrarian reform problems. The war had forced the return to the United States of a number of agricultural missionaries, religious workers, and leaders from the far corners of the world. In summarizing their deliberations at this conference, John H. Reisner, Executive Secretary, Agricultural Missions, Inc., pointed out:

The total well-being of rural people everywhere is dependent upon an early and just solution of these land tenure problems. The political stability of many areas is closely related to economic inequalities and related injustices. These matters are of grave concern to religious people in all countries. It is difficult to nurture spiritual growth among rural people who must struggle "to keep body and soul together." It is recognized that the work of local religious leaders is handicapped seriously by these unstable conditions and disconcerting influences. . . . Church leaders and people in political power are gradually awakening to their moral responsibilities in these matters.[11]

The three conferences cited here played an important role in focusing the attention of a number of organizations and professional workers in the field of land tenure on the disruptive forces inherent in world land tenure problems. They were important steps in the development of a widespread conviction that a solution to world land tenure problems was vital to the peace that had failed to come, even after the exhausting experience of two world wars.

Events in the political sphere soon reinforced this conviction. Of primary significance in this context was Yugoslavia's break with Russia and with the Cominform states in 1948. Although the reasons for Yugoslavian disaffection are complex, there seems to be general agreement that Tito's unwillingness to follow the Russian timetable for land tenure change was one of the basic causes of the split. The Russian-inspired programs for farm collectivization were too much for the Yugoslav peasants. Unique among the Russian satellite countries of Eastern Europe, Tito's Yugoslavia was in a position to resist. The Yugoslav action dramatized the major importance which land tenure policies play in the Russian Communist programs for revolt and the seizure of power.

The threat of Communism to Americans has generally been associated with industrial unrest and with programs of revolt that have been centered in urban and industrial areas. It has been a difficult lesson to learn that for most of the world outside the United States, Canada, Britain, and several Western European countries, the threat of Communism has revolved around agrarian issues. Tito's action underlined this fact.

This lesson was driven home with finality by the fall of China. Though recriminations over the failure of Chinese policy still fill newspaper headlines, little doubt can remain that a fundamental reason for China's fall was the repeated failure of the Kuomintang regime to carry out basic land tenure reforms.[12]

Communist programs, in China as elsewhere, may aim at industrialization in the future and may be vitally dependent on it. The hard fact remains that most of the countries of the world which face a Communist threat of revolt are overwhelmingly agrarian, and in those countries the likeliest vehicle for Communist aggression is the promise of land tenure reform.

Recognition of this fact has been particularly evident in the United States within the past eighteen months and especially since the outbreak of the Korean war. A succession of reports by United States officials, observers, and by newspaper correspondents from China, from Korea, and from elsewhere have reiterated the fundamental role that inequitable land tenure systems are playing in the unrest that grips so many countries today.[13]

Official recognition of this fact was made in President Truman's broadcast from San Francisco upon his return from the Wake Island conference with General MacArthur in October, 1950. The President said:

We know that the peoples of Asia have problems of social injustice to solve. They want their farmers to own their land and to enjoy the fruits of their toil. That is one of our great national principles also. We believe in the family-size farm. That is the basis of our agriculture and has strongly influenced our form of government.[14]

The President's statement was one of a number of official and semi-official statements in the fall of 1950 which drew attention to the need for land tenure reforms. Just before leaving for Wake Island the President had been handed the report by the Economic Survey Mission to the Philippines, which he had appointed at the request of the President of the Philippine Republic. This document, popularly referred to as the Bell Report, was explicitly critical of the lack of progress in land tenure improvement. It stated:

Land is the most important source of wealth in the Philippines and its concentration or distribution is the primary factor that affects the social and economic well-being of the people. . . . The land problem remains the same or worse than four years ago and the dissident trouble has spread to wider areas. . . . The Philippine farmer is between two grindstones. On top is the landlord, who often exacts an unjust share of the crop in spite of ineffective legal restrictions to the contrary. Beneath is the deplorably low productivity of the land he works. The farmer cannot see any avenue of escape. He has no credit except at usurer's rates. There is no counsel to which he can turn with confidence. He is resistant to change for fear of losing the meager livelihood he and his family possess. The incentive to greater production dies aborning when what he regards as an unjust share of the harvest of his work goes to the landlord.[15]

Several weeks later Secretary of Agriculture Charles F. Brannan addressed the annual U.S. Department of Agriculture Outlook Conference in Washington, D.C., and observed:

American people are greatly disturbed by what is happening in other countries of the world. They realize that a part of the unrest in many countries can be traced to insecure and inequitable land tenure. Under those conditions farm people do not feel that they have a stake in the land, or that they are receiving an equitable share of the produce of the land. This brings us to a greater realization that widespread land ownership, security of tenure, and equitable landlord-tenant arrangements are part of the basic fabric of our democratic institutions.

In this setting, perhaps we need to look for possible improvements in our own situation. Are we setting a good example as a free Nation? How can we make further advances toward the goal of family farm ownership?[16]

At the same time, but in another setting, Senator John Sparkman of Alabama was voicing a similiar expression of the interest of the United States in world land tenure problems. Speaking as the United States delegate before Committee 2 of the General Assembly of the United Nations, Senator Sparkman set forth in specific terms the interest of the United States government in proposals for land tenure reforms. He said:

In the United States we believe strongly in farm ownership, individual farm ownership. We believe that the land that a man and his family works and on which they make a living ought to belong to him and to his family. It is that objective toward which we have been working during the last many years, and it is that kind of a program or a similar program that we envisage may very well be encouraged by this General Assembly and by this committee, and might very well be undertaken in many parts of the world. That is the reason, Mr. Chairman, that we wholeheartedly support this kind of a program, and that is the reason we ask for the amendment that would particularly provide for helping small farmers, individual farmers, to own and operate the land out of which they and their families make a living.[17]

This was a theme to which the Secretary of Agriculture returned on November 16, 1950, in an address before the annual meeting of the Association of Land Grant Colleges and Universities. Mr. Brannan devoted a major portion of that speech to a discussion of the roots of unrest in peasant countries.

All over Asia, communists are spreading the word that the land is to be divided up. "Join with us," they say, "and the land you farm will be yours. Help us overthrow the present authorities, and you will immediately be a land owner. This is the only way you can ever hope to have your own farm." . . .

Among at least half of the world's people, the misery of the peasant is a basic obstacle to peace because it provides the "soil" in which communism or some other form of totalitarianism breeds. . . .

We should by all means make clear that our country has had experience in dealing with such problems as are faced by the farm people of Asia, the Middle East, Africa, South America—problems of land tenure.

Those looking toward Russia for a tenure pattern are looking in the wrong direction. . . . The worst error that could be made . . . would be to look to American democracy as merely the center of productive genius and to Russian communism as the spiritual center in the field of social organization. The communist pattern offers only degradation. The democratic pattern conforms with the most deeply felt desires of mankind. . . .

The greatest thing we have to export is hope.[18]

The Secretary of Agriculture continued discussion of this subject in speeches before the annual meeting of the National Grange at Minneapolis;[19] before the North Dakota Farmers Union, at Bismarck;[20] and, as Chairman of the United States Delegation, before the Fourth Inter-American Conference on Agriculture at Montevideo, Uruguay.[21] Throughout these speeches, Secretary Brannan placed parallel emphasis on the land tenure roots of world unrest and emphasized the importance which the family farm and the widespread ownership of farm land has had for the development of American democracy. A large part of the history of America is the history of a "land reform" continent-wide in scope. We must see to it, he repeatedly emphasized, that we protect and improve our land tenure system at home, if we are to be of greatest aid to other peoples.

Two administrative actions were the outgrowth of this interest in land tenure at home and abroad. The first was the establishment, within the Department of Agriculture, of a systematic review of all current programs and activities to determine how they now contribute or can be made to contribute to the support of the family farm.[22]

Coincident with the review of domestic family farm policy was the systematic study, by an inter-departmental committee, of

United States policy with regard to land tenure reforms in other countries. Under-Secretary of Agriculture Clarence J. McCormick undoubtedly had this policy study in mind in a recent speech before the Twelfth Food and Agriculture Organization Council Session in Rome, Italy. After reviewing the continued strong interest of the United States in the work of the FAO, he continued:

Land reform in its broadest interpretation deeply affects security in the world today. . . . We in the United States regard land reform in the broad terms of improvement of all economic and social institutions surrounding farm life. . . . We recognize . . . that specific land reform measures will have to be evaluated in relationship to the conditions peculiar to each region and country, and that the individual cultural patterns of many countries may have differing constructive contributions to offer toward the same basic objective.

In support of this policy which we as a nation have affirmed, the United States Government intends giving encouragement and assistance to land reform when and wherever it will substantially contribute to promoting the objectives I have enumerated.

We shall do so in both planning and administration of our foreign economic and technical assistance program, and we will also lend other practical assistance to desirable land reforms in addition to the economic and technical assistance programs. We shall also actively encourage and assist in carrying forward land reforms in non-self-governing territories under United States administration, and upon request, will work with other governments in connection with desirable land reform in such territories under their administration. Furthermore, we shall take every opportunity to support and encourage desirable land reform programs through all appropriate international agencies.[23]

These policy statements form the backdrop for the Wisconsin conference on world land tenure problems. There is no illusion on the part of those who planned the conference that land tenure reforms can alone be the touchstone for solution to the problems of agrarian and underdeveloped areas. No panaceas will be sought at the conference; the emphasis will be on a group effort to work together and think together to the end that each participant will be strengthened in the task of improving the tenure arrangements in his own country in a manner suitable to his country's institutions and compatible with the hopes, aspirations, and needs of his people.

Part III — THE ROLE OF INTERNATIONAL AGENCIES IN LAND TENURE IMPROVEMENTS

OPENING REMARKS BY THE CHAIRMAN

Noble Clark

IN THE past years, we have thought of an international agency as having its activities pretty directly confined to those things which involve joint action by several nations. International officials have traditionally been men who spent most of their time and efforts on political matters. They usually were careful to confine these political activities to relationships between nations, and they avoided doing anything which might properly be considered as interfering in the internal affairs of a friendly nation. By and large, this policy is today being followed by the central organization of the United Nations. I presume all of us, from whatever nation we may come, would not like to see officials of the United Nations try to influence the elections of our home country or in other ways exercise direct influence on political matters which we and our fellow citizens believe are primarily national and not international in character.

But if we are realistic and are honest with ourselves, we will have to admit that by far the most of the distressed people of the world owe their distress to factors which are primarily local and national, not international. Hunger, illiteracy, ill health and disease, lack of individual opportunity to benefit promptly and in large measure from the constant stream of new findings in science and technology—these and many other matters of local and national responsibility and authority are much the most important

causes of human misery, human discouragement, and human frustration.

I might say, parenthetically, most of our land tenure problems are primarily local and national, not international. Even if the diplomats in the foreign services of our countries were able to carry forward to successful conclusion all of their international activities involving joint efforts by many nations, the hundreds of millions of underprivileged people now in the world would still not have their welfare greatly improved unless simultaneously the respective nations took equally constructive steps in correcting and improving such basic problems as an adequate food supply, the provision of a basic education for all citizens, and the making available of health and medical services that will protect people from preventable diseases and enable them to live out their full span of years in vigor and in strength.

When the United Nations was organized in 1945, people throughout the world hoped they were creating an agency which could and would preserve peace and prevent war. They also hoped this new international organization with its associated specialized agencies would find ways of reducing the hunger, the ill-health, and the other underlying causes of human distress which make people desperate enough so that war no longer is renounced but instead is accepted as the lesser of two evils because it promises to bring with it material benefits to the victor.

Tonight, we are going to hear from representatives of the United Nations and the Food and Agriculture Organization of the United Nations. They are to tell us of the achievements and of the hopes and plans of their agencies as regards improvements in land tenure situations in different parts of the world. I also hope they tell us of their own difficulties and their problems, particularly as to how they can get the sovereign nations of the world to respond favorably when an international agency calls attention to undesirable and unfortunate situations within the individual nations which only the individual nations themselves can correct.

I have the conviction that preservation of world peace depends directly on the rapidity and the effectiveness of the programs of relieving hunger, providing universal education, making available at least a reasonable minimum of medical services, and in furnishing the other basic human needs. These are largely technical matters, not political matters. Likewise, they have always been regarded as lying inside the jurisdiction of the individual sovereign nation. They are critically urgent problems that cannot safely wait long for our effective attention. We may not have too much time. We know that some of the nations will need outside help in attacking these internal problems. This help will consist largely of learning what tools and what procedures have proved most useful to others. They can and will want to do the necessary tasks very largely for themselves. There is a growing realization throughout the world of the need for extending such help.

I am sure all of us tonight will listen with interest to our speakers when they tell us how their agencies, created to facilitate international programs, are proposing to persuade and to aid the individual nations to carry forward promptly the enormously important internal or national responsibilities for improvements in human nutrition, in health, in education, and general welfare of the people.

ECONOMIC AND SOCIAL IMPROVEMENTS THROUGH INTERNATIONAL CO-OPERATION

Gove Hambidge

I AM supposed to talk to you tonight about what the international agencies can do in relation to land tenure improvement. Actually, I am not really going to talk to you about that subject at all. I feel that each of you here is a specialist in your own field—economics mainly—concerned with very basic questions in the world today. What I would like to do would be to tell you something of how I feel about the whole broad picture of which this land reform element is a part—the whole broad picture, as I, as an international servant, a citizen of the world very much concerned with the problems that face all of us today, see it. With that introduction, I am going into some remarks about the work of the Food and Agriculture Organization.

This movement in which you are engaged here is a basic segment of what I think is perhaps the most important development of the time that we live in. Perhaps it will turn out to be one of the most important developments in history. This movement is taking place over a very large segment of the world, covering maybe two-thirds of the world's population. It is doing things that have not been done before and enabling that huge segment of the world's population to catch up with things that they have not caught up with before. That movement is essentially an agrarian movement; it is concerned with agriculture and with food, and the problems that you are dealing with when you get right back to the basis of them are problems of food and the production of food. They are basic because food is the first need of the human being.

I am reminded of a statement that our Director-General prepared recently for the Commission on Human Rights. His fundamental point was: "Yes, human rights are extremely important. All the things that the Commission on Human Rights covers are important. But they apply first of all to living human beings, and unless the human being is alive, human rights don't mean much. And he cannot be alive unless he has enough food to live."

So the first human right is enough food to sustain life. And a lot of people of the world today have just barely enough food. Certainly they don't have enough food to live any normal life span or any really healthy life. There is far too little food, in other words, and the situation is not really getting any better.

There has been a good deal of recovery since the war, but the surveys that the Food and Agriculture Organization has made indicate that the per capita supplies of food are now a little bit worse in the areas that were poorly fed before the war. This is true in spite of the progress in recovery and in spite of the enormous progress that has been made in the United States and other highly developed countries.

The second thing that makes this question extremely basic is the fact that food is produced by farmers and of course in part by fishermen. By far the largest number of people in the world are farmers.

And finally there is the fact that industrialization of underdeveloped areas, which is an extremely important business today, can come only if we are able to draw workers from agriculture and put them into industry, and that requires the development of agriculture for greater production and the development of greater agricultural efficiency.

So the net result is that if there is to be any progress in the world today of the sort that we all hope for, certainly food and agricultural problems are absolutely basic to that progress. They are going to play a big part, perhaps the biggest part. We are also coming to realize more and more that no lasting peace is possible in a world in which so large a proportion of mankind is hungry all the time. The food and agriculture movement which started some years ago has been growing on us, and it is now really taking hold and is becoming a big movement.

I would like to go back very briefly into a little of the history of the past few years. I feel that the Food and Agriculture Organization of the United Nations has been a catalyst in this business. I do not mean that it was the only organization involved or that it was the first. I think that the Hot Springs conference called by President Roosevelt in 1943 was a prime mover in a lot of developments that have occurred since. Right in the middle of the war President Roosevelt brought the representatives of about forty-three governments together under very difficult circumstances to deal with problems of food which, he realized, were going to be very acute after the war and which were acute at that time during the war. He brought these people together to see what could be done about the problems, and as a result, the Food and Agriculture Organization was set up two years later, in 1945.

It was a pretty small beginning. We managed to work up a budget of 5 million dollars for this organization which was to handle food and agricultural problems all over the world, and it got under way. The reason it got under way was not only because it was in response to certain social pressures in the world which existed at that time and have become more intense since. (Perhaps the last war itself was an expression of those pressures.) Another reason was that production knowledge had grown to such an extent that we knew everybody could produce far more food in the world than they were at the time. Another was that nutrition knowledge had developed to the point where we knew what the needs of the human being are for food, what he has to have to maintain himself in health and to live a decent kind of a life and a decent length of life. A tremendous advance had been made in the more highly developed countries because they knew there were tools and materials available to do these things. In underdeveloped counties, pressures were set up because enormous numbers of the world's people just are not content to stay disadvantaged knowing that things can be done today that have never been done in the past.

There were obstacles in the way, but they were not technical obstacles. Fundamentally, they were obstacles of an economic, social, and institutional nature, and one of them is this whole question in which you are involved, the question of land reform.

Well, the Food and Agriculture Organization made its modest beginning. It developed eventually into a membership of sixty-six member nations. But since it was set up in 1945, there has been a tremendous growth of this idea. The United States government started its Point Four program, made very large appropriations for this kind of work. The ECA operations spread from the idea of aid and recovery in Europe into also working in the Far East in un-

derdeveloped areas. The Technical Co-operation Administration was set up.

The United Nations agencies were involved in special Point Four programs which, by the way, have doubled the budget of the Food and Agriculture Organization so that we now have about 5 million dollars devoted to technical assistance projects in addition to our regular budget of about 5 million dollars.

The British Commonwealth countries got together on a similar kind of plan—the Colombo Plan—for the development of areas in Southeast Asia, which involved a great deal of money and a good deal of technical skill. Switzerland started in a modest way to give some technical assistance where it could, and the idea has been spreading pretty well over the world and is becoming a really big movement. It is scattered afar; the efforts are here and there. You have heard it from a number of people here—from Dr. Bennett of the Technical Assistance Administration, Mr. Thorp of the State Department, and from others who were involved in this same kind of thing from other angles.

It is beginning to add up. All of these agencies, including the Food and Agriculture Organization, other United Nations agencies, and the bilateral organizations are beginning to work together, and we can see it shaping up into a really significant world movement that can have profound effects. In this movement are included not only these governmental and intergovernmental organizations but quite a number of private groups who are doing the same kind of thing—adding their efforts to ours and we to theirs. There are religious groups of various kinds and a number of private foundations which are doing outstanding work. They are doing a number of things that are very worth-while. The whole thing begins to make a pattern of thinking which is, I think, characteristic of the times in which we live and which all of us might pay a good deal of attention to from the standpoint of trying to see it as a pattern of thinking, as a constructive movement over and against the destructive forces which occupy so much of our attention today.

Back of it, of course, is something based on the need for food. It is based on the simple, basic, physiological needs of the human being, and therefore it is very, very fundamental. But there is something even deeper, and that is the spiritual needs of the human being. I mean that back of a man's ability to own and operate his farm is his desire to get food and health and education for his family. Those things are expressions of a desire to really express the true dignity and worth of the peoples and nations and, above all, of individuals. Those are the things that I think are back of this movement.

Now I would like to give you a very brief picture of the work of FAO in this field. I think we are doing a fundamental job. FAO is six years old this fall. We have done things that I am sure you are familiar with in the way of economic and statistical studies and publications, technical studies and publications, and surveys of agricultural and forestry and fishery needs in various countries. And now we have the technical assistance program in operation. Our reports show that as of August we have some 213 technical experts working in some 35 different countries on technical assistance projects, which is not a bad record for a comparatively small organization. We are working on all kinds of projects that governments ask us to do. I don't have time to go into any detail. I might, however, just mention one outstanding example—Pakistan, where we have a very, very broad program which covers everything from economic and statistical assistance down to improvement in poultry production and large scale irrigation and drainage projects.

In this irrigation and drainage project we are salvaging about a million and a half acres of land that went bad because salts accumulated in the soils and the water table rose to the point where crops could no longer be grown on them.

We have a nice little project in Ecuador which pleases me very much. One of our people went in there to live among the Indians in the mountains, and he found that in Ecuador, where they raise many sheep, they import a good deal of their woolen garments and clothing. He found that some weaving was being done there on looms that had been used for several hundred years without any improvement at all and that the people made something like eighty cents a day by selling their woven products made on these crude implements. Our man worked with them, a group of thirty thousand of them. He brought in some improved looms from American Indians and found that the Ecuadorean weavers took hold of them and just simply loved them. They very quickly learned how to use them and raised their earnings in a short time from eighty cents a day to something like three dollars a day. Our adviser there is now in the process of organizing a co-operative setup to maintain these gains and to see that the native weavers themselves keep them and see that they are not exploited.

Well, those are two random examples. One further example is the control of rinderpest throughout the whole Far East, which is one of the most difficult and important jobs that we have engaged in. We are getting countries together on a kind of co-operative basis to take hold of the terrible livestock disease which kills off the buffalo and cows and oxen in areas where the farmers are absolutely dependent upon them for cultivating their land. When the disease takes hold it kills off enormous quantities of them. Through the development of a new vaccine, which is very cheap, we have been getting rinderpest under control and will probably succeed in eliminating it before too long throughout the whole of Africa and the Far East where it now is a terrible devastating drag on production.

In this work we are co-operating with the other United Nations agencies in a whole range of activities. We are involved with the International Bank, which in some cases goes out with us on surveys of agricultural needs and helps to supply the funds that are necessary. With the World Health Organization we have co-operative projects involved in malaria control and increase in agricultural production. With UNESCO we are working on projects of fundamental education. UNESCO and FAO have a fundamental education center down in Mexico right now. We have close relationships with the bilateral agencies, too, in a sense of checking projects, trying to see that we do not duplicate and overlap any more than is really legitimate and necessary and trying to see that our efforts add up to something that is significant as a total effort. That is a very difficult thing to do, and I think that this whole business is new enough so that I don't think any of us need be ashamed of the progress that has been made so far in the way of getting together. But at the same time, it is one of the most difficult things to work out in detail on a day-to-day basis.

The place of land tenure and the problems relating to land tenure in that whole picture are extremely fundamental. The experience of our technical people and our economists shows over and over again that you come up against this question of land tenure systems as a bottleneck in land conditions in pushing forward and developing production, in producing more food, and in bringing about the kind of improvements that we all know technically can be made. We had a rather specific and interesting example of that recently in Rome, where we were going over a document that included some material on improvements in agricultural production as possible practicable targets for production. I do not remember the figures, but we will say that in a given area there was a terrific deficit of certain kinds of foods. The figure was given, for example, that in ten years you could, say, double production of that particular foodstuff, or increase it by one-third, or whatever it was. And some of the economists were talking about this and said, "No, you cannot do that because if you extrapolate your curve of what has occurred during the past fifty or seventy-five years, you will find that the production is actually going down and not up." Well, to be sure, it is. But actually when you talk to your technicians about the problem, they say, "Yes, you can do that; you can double the production of that product within that period of time. But you cannot do it unless you have the economic conditions that enable you to do it."

Technically, it is feasible, but you must have credit for your farmers; you must have incentives for production; you must have prices of products that enable them to keep on producing. You must have some kind of security of tenure. You must have a little larger holding so that they can use better implements and can afford better oxen or whatever it may be—a team of oxen that can actually do a day's work instead of a team that can only do a third of a day's work—and enough food for them to keep them up, and that kind of thing. So those problems are your bottlenecks and those are the things we must tackle.

Now all those things can be done. Technically we can do an enormously better job in the world today than we have been doing. But we cannot do it unless people are willing to get down and really get to work and solve some of these social and economic problems in which land conditions are particularly important—and that includes industrialization. In addition to solving problems of land tenure, I would include the whole process of cottage industry development and other industrialization. Those are the things we really must tackle, and those are the things you have been talking about. It is your work. It is the only thing that can make possible the full technical improvements that we are capable of making today.

Now there is one other thing I want to bring in. That is the question of information and education in relation to the problems that you are dealing with. I, myself, feel, because so much of my work has been in that field, that education and information is really the key of the whole thing in a way. I mean you can work all those things out, but you must first persuade people that they need to and want to make changes. And, second, you must inform them on how to make the changes—that is, the everyday people out in the country. But then in addition to that, you must persuade many government officials and others that changes need to be made and can be made, and you must persuade many people who are holding privileged positions in the world today that it is going to be necessary to make changes—or else! And that is pretty important, too. I mean by "or else" that you make changes of very bad conditions voluntarily and in a peaceful way or we are going to see them made violently and by revolution. However you look at it, the job of information is basic. The average technical person I have known is not against information, but he just tends to neglect it. He does not know much about it, and he often has some feeling of inferiority about it, I found. I think that every technician ought to have as part of his own education some kind of training in the importance of information and in how to go about stating

the things he needs to state in such a way that other people will be convinced of the need for them and will understand what he is talking about and what needs to be done. That phase of the work is going to receive some attention here at this meeting. It is a thing about which Food and Agriculture Organization is concerned. We can help governments in developing techniques for information. Problems are different, and the approach must be different in different countries as in all the things we are talking about in this conference of yours. A good many tools and techniques are available— from the radio, motion pictures and slide films, to simple things such as posters, pamphlets, books, village talks, and things that are suitable for people who are illiterate. Professor C. E. Rogers is here with you, and he will be conducting your workshop on information techniques.

Now as to the role of the international agencies in the picture, there are many bilateral agencies with a lot more money than the international agencies concerned with technical problems. They are doing yeoman's service. And so are we, and we all fit together. Now they can do certain things extremely well, and I think from the standpoint of resources they are able to throw more resources into a given problem than the international agencies are. But we also have a place in there that is, I think, significant.

A great many of the people in this room represent governments that are members of the Food and Agriculture Organization. We belong together. I mean, the organization that I belong to is you people in this room —it is your government's, at least, your Food and Agriculture Organization, your country's Food and Agriculture Organization. You set this organization up among you to help you do a certain kind of a job. We all have a lot to learn from each other, both on the kind of problems we face and how to work them out. And that is what this organization is really for and what it is all about. We are going at a job together co-operatively. We are learning how to do it as we go along. We are engaged in some extremely noble and wonderful experiments, I think, and if we keep on, we can do some very big things. Even though the international agencies have a relatively small role in some ways, they have an advantage in the fact that every country which is a member of that agency is a voting partner in the agency, and that has a certain kind of significance that is worth-while.

Then, too, the Food and Agriculture Organization and the World Health Organization and others, because of the breadth of membership, are able to send out teams of experts that come from a good many different countries. We may throw experts from as many as ten different countries into one country to help solve the country's problems. I mention that because I do not think it is a thing that is too widely understood today. I was talking to one of the editors of one of the dailies in this country recently. He asked me: "Well, what is the advantage of the Food and Agriculture Organization in all this business? Why can't we do everything through the American agencies?" Well, that is a fine viewpoint for an American, and it is quite understandable. When I explained to him what I am just telling you, he said: "Well, I didn't think of it that way. I think you really have something in your favor."

It is this business, the feeling of partnership, the feeling that we are all pulling together on this thing, that is the real essence of the work that we may be able to do in this field.

I have tried to give you a little picture of what I think is a tremendously big, dynamic movement today and in which a whole lot of things play a part. They have all got to work together, all kinds of technical aspects of the subject and all kinds of countries pulling together on the job. I think it is a commonplace to say that the time is short, the problems are difficult, but I think it is true. But *if* we can keep ahead of disaster, I honestly think we have some wonderful possibilities ahead of us, and in spite of the pessimists I really think we can produce enough food to keep ahead of the needs of the population of the world today and in the future.

THE UNITED NATIONS AND LAND REFORM

ᔑᔑᔑᔑ   *J. S. Harris*

THERE IS no need in an address to an audience composed of specialists on problems of land tenure and land reform to emphasize their fundamental importance in the world today. Indeed, this conference on world land tenure problems is itself a heartening recognition of their significance and at the same time a recognition of the importance of international co-operation in this field.

As this conference and its members will contribute, through their work on problems of land tenure and agrarian reform, to economic development and to rising standards of living, so will this conference contribute also to human dignity and freedom and to social and political stability. This conference deserves the important success I am confident it will achieve.

I propose tonight to outline briefly for you the role of the United Nations in the field of land tenure and land reform. It will not be possible for me in this paper to discuss the important activities of the United Nations specialized agencies, such as the FAO, UNESCO, and the ILO in this field. I am pleased, however, that the work of the Food and Agriculture Organization, which has important and direct responsibilities for these international problems, has been described for you by Mr. Hambidge of the FAO and that further details will be given to you by Mr. Carroll of that organization.

References to the need for land reform and for changes in the agrarian structure of many underdeveloped countries have been made at various times in the debates of United Nations organs concerned with the development of such countries. Such references may be noted in the early discussions, for example, of the Economic and Social Council and of the Trusteeship Council as well as in the General Assembly's Special Committee on Information Transmitted under Article 73(e) of the Charter—the Committee on Non–Self-Governing Territories. Recently, a U.N. report, "Measures for the Economic Development of Under-Developed Countries," has emphasized the need for land reform in many of these countries.[1]

It was at the Fifth Session of the General Assembly, however, in 1950, that the debates became more precisely concerned with land problems. The result was the adoption of a series of resolutions on this specific question.

Perhaps the most important and certainly the most comprehensive of these resolutions was that on land reform. This resolution, based on a draft submitted by the Polish delegation and unanimously adopted by the General Assembly, recommended that the Secretary General of the United Nations should, in co-operation with the Food and Agriculture Organization, prepare and submit to the Economic and Social Council an analysis of the degree to which unsatisfactory forms of agrarian structure and, in particular, systems of land tenure in the underdeveloped countries impede economic development and thus depress the standards of living especially of agricultural workers and tenants and of small and medium-size farmers. The resolution further requested the Economic and Social Council to consider the analysis and to prepare recommendations to the General Assembly with a view to the improvement of the conditions of agricultural populations.

The resolution based on the Polish draft proposal was amended by Cuba, Egypt, Haiti, the United States, the United Kingdom, and Yugoslavia. The discussion in the Assembly, which brought out clearly the basic importance of the question and its great complexity, emphasized that the redistribution of land would not by itself improve the condition of farmers, unless accompanied by the provision of credit, technical assistance and machinery, the organization of co-operatives, and the framing of suitable fixed policies. The need for parallel industrial development was also stressed.

The report on land reform prepared by the United Nations Secretariat in co-operation with the Food and Agriculture Organization and published in September, 1951—a few weeks ago—is based on a recognition of the complexity of the issues involved. Because of limitations of time and data the report is not an exhaustive survey either of agrarian structures in all countries or of all aspects of the agrarian structure of any one country or small group of countries. The report describes the main features of agrarian structure in underdeveloped countries by means of examples and deals with the size and layout of farms, the various conditions of tenancy, agricultural credit, settlement of legal title to land and to water rights, communal tenure, and the special problems presented by estates and plantations. The last two chapters provide a study of the relations between the agrarian structure and economic development, together with a summary and a statement of certain conclusions.

The substantive nature of this report—which, I hope, all members of this conference will have an opportunity to study—will be discussed by Mr. Carroll of the FAO, who immediately follows me on this platform.

The Economic and Social Council discussed the report on land reform at its Thirteenth Session in Geneva, a few weeks ago, September 3–7, 1951. Both the United States and the Polish delegations submitted draft resolutions. An amendment to the Polish draft was submitted by Czechoslovakia, while Belgium, Canada, Chile, France, India, Pakistan, Poland, the Philippines, Sweden, and the United Kingdom submitted amendments to the United States draft.

The resolution, based on a revised United States draft, was adopted by a vote of fourteen to zero, with four abstentions (Czechoslovakia, Mexico, Poland, and the U.S.S.R.).

The resolution recognizes the diversity of agricultural conditions and recommends that governments institute appropriate reforms. It then outlines a series of measures.

These measures include: assurance of security of tenure to cultivators and opportunities to acquire ownership of land; the organization of landholdings into farms of efficient size, whether by dividing unduly large holdings or combining fragmented units; the provision of agricultural credit at reasonable interest rates and legislative or administrative measures to reduce agricultural indebtedness; legislation to prevent exorbitant rentals on agricultural land; the elimination of inequitable tax loads; promotion of co-operative organizations for cultivating, marketing, and processing agricultural products and purchasing farm supplies

and equipment; encouragement to the diversification of agriculture and rational diversification of the economy to develop agriculture as part of an integrated economic development program; establishment of industries in rural areas, especially those using indigenous agricultural products as their raw materials; establishment of workshops or factories for making, repairing, and servicing essential agricultural machinery and storing spare parts; expansion and development of rural literacy, general, and technological education programs; engagement in adequate agricultural research; and improvment of the economic, social, and legal status of agricultural laborers on plantations and other large estates.

In addition, all governments, including those for non–self-governing territories, should ensure that the interests of populations not economically advanced are fully protected by policies and laws relating to the transfer of land.

The Council further recommended that the specialized agencies give high priority to the land reform problem in their technical assistance programs, focus attention on the urgent need for land reform in many areas, give high priority to the recruitment of professional staff to advise governments, and place particular emphasis on assisting governments which wish to adopt land reform measures.

The Secretary-General of the United Nations was requested to give assistance to governments on matters falling outside the field of specialized agencies, particularly on measures to improve fiscal systems and prevent the imposition of inequitable taxes and other assessments on land cultivators. At least once every three years he should report with recommendations to the Council on land reform measures, on the basis of a special questionnaire to governments.

Another aspect dealt with in the resolution was that of the possibilities which free and voluntary agricultural co-operation offered of meeting the needs for technical and economic progress in agriculture while preserving individual rights and freeedoms. The Secretary-General was asked to analyze the results of such co-operation in various countries for a future Council session.

The General Assembly, it was finally recommended, should consider this subject periodically to enable all member governments to participate in discussions on developments in this field.

This recent recommendation of the Economic and Social Council will be transmitted to the General Assembly which meets for its Sixth Session in Paris next month.

There were two other resolutions adopted by the General Assembly at its Fifth Session to which I should like to refer briefly.

The resolution on the development of arid land was proposed by the representative of Egypt, and this resolution, also adopted unanimously by the General Assembly, called attention to the fact that one of the basic reasons for the low standard of living in certain underdeveloped countries was the inadequate extent of the areas at present under cultivation. It recommended that the Secretary-General, in collaboration with the competent specialized agencies, prepare a report on the practical measures adopted to study the problems of arid zones. This report, now in preparation, will be examined by the Economic and Social Council at its next session with a view to facilitating and encouraging the development of arid land.

The last resolution on land problems to which I should like to refer tonight is that on the rural economic development of the Trust Territories. This resolution, presented jointly by the delegations of Denmark, Mexico, the Philippines, Syria, and the United States, and amended by India, was adopted by the General Assembly at its

Fifth Session by a vote of fifty-four to zero, with two abstentions.

This resolution recognized that the equitable distribution and the proper utilization of the land together constituted one of the essential conditions in ensuring, maintaining, and promoting the economic and social advancement of inhabitants of Trust Territories. It recommended that the Trusteeship Council study the prevailing policies, laws, and practices relating to land, land utilization, and the alienation of land in the Trust Territories, taking into account the present and future needs of the indigenous inhabitants from the standpoint of the basic objectives of the Trusteeship system and the territories' future economic requirements, as well as the social and economic consequences of the transfer of land to non-indigenous inhabitants. The resolution also asked the Council, in the light of its study, to make such recommendations to the administering authorities as might be conducive to the economic and social development of the people of the territories.

As many of you know, there are eleven Trust Territories with a population of some 18 million peoples under the International Trusteeship system for which the United Nations has supervisory responsibilities. Seven of these Territories are in Africa: Tanganyika, the Cameroons, and Togoland under British Administration; Ruanda Orundi under Belgian administration; Somaliland under Italian administration, and Togoland and the Cameroons under French administration. The remaining four territories are in the Pacific: Western Samoa under New Zealand administration; New Guinea under Australian administration; the Pacific Islands under American administration, and the tiny but important phosphate island of Nawm under joint British, Australian, and New Zealand administrative responsibility.

The vast bulk of the population of these

territories is in Africa; Tanganyika alone has a population of 7.5 millions. Because African land tenure and attendant problems have certain distinct characteristics it may be of interest to this audience to hear part of the United Nations report on the general background of land tenure and some of the broad problems as they exist in the African trust territories south of the Sahara.[2]

In Africa south of the Sahara communal tenure in which control over land is exercised through a social group is the most widespread form of agrarian structure. According to the U.N. report:

In this region communal tenure exists in a variety of forms, with certain fundamental features in common. Land is held on a tribal, village, kindred or family basis, and individuals have definite rights in this land by virtue of their membership in the relevant social unit. Hence, title to land has a communal character and it is usufructuary, rather than absolute. A chief, for example, may be the custodian of the land but he is not its owner. The normal unit of land ownership is generally the extended family or kindred group, and once the land is granted to such a group, it remains its property. In theory, land may be pledged and redeemed, but only in such manner that it will not be permanently lost.

Though different physical conditions result in a variety of forms of cultivation in various parts of Africa, communal tenures have been most frequently associated with shifting subsistence agriculture. Shifting cultivation in any of its forms implies a relatively plentiful supply of land in relation to population. As the area of land in relation to population declines, more intensive methods of cultivation become necessary. This has already happened in many parts of Africa as a result of a number of closely related factors, including population increases, the introduction of commercial crops and the alienation of land either on a concession basis or to immigrant settlers. Soil deterioration and soil erosion, already serious problems in these areas, further reduce the available land. New techniques of agriculture are thus

imperative, not only for the purposes of commercial cropping and subsistence production, but also for maintaining the fertility of the soil and for reconditioning land already eroded.

Under the pressure of these influences, traditional systems of land tenure are necessarily being adjusted. Frequently, however, conflicts of interest arise between the development of commercial cropping, and the requirements of farming methods designed to prevent loss of soil fertility, since overcropping for commercial reasons is a common danger and may contribute seriously to soil deterioration. Moreover, commercial crops may be developed at the expense of local food crops. New methods also frequently involve some capital expenditure—for example, for the fencing of pasture lands, for fertilizer and new agricultural implements. In many instances, the lack of proved experience tending to show that the additional returns justify new forms of effort and expenditure may be more important obstacles to change than the existing form of land tenure.

Indeed, available data suggest that the communal systems of land tenure in Africa have not proved in themselves so inflexible as to prevent adaptation to new conditions. In certain parts of Africa, for example in the Gold Coast and Uganda [and in some areas of the Trust Territories of Tanganyika and Togoland under British Administration], the traditional communal land system has been changing rapidly to one of individual private holdings in land, mainly in response to the desire to exploit land for commercial purposes. In other areas of Africa, the communal system has been less completely modified. In the Belgian Congo [and in the Trust Territory of Ruanda-Urundi under Belgian administration] commercial and subsistence crops have been developed under government direction, without fundamentally affecting the customary system of land tenure in force. . . . The question of the influence of land tenure in Africa is therefore not whether traditional systems present *per se* a powerful obstacle to economic development, but rather whether the new forms arising from the increasing invasion of subsistence economy by an economy based on exchange will lead to economic development, without in the long run destroying much of the land for agricultural production, or resulting in abuses detrimental to the social and economic welfare of the community.

. . . .

The communal system is also affected by the expansion of the demand for labor. Production for export of agricultural and mining products has given rise to a demand for labor which has transformed increasing numbers of Africans from subsistence agriculturists into agricultural and industrial wage earners. . . . There are many aspects to this question; what is relevant here are the profound effects which the more or less prolonged absence of male workers may have upon indigenous agriculture. Where shifting agriculture prevails and trees and bush have to be cut down in order to prepare fallow land for production, the absence of male workers is particularly serious. In the Belgian Congo, for example, recruitment of African workers for wage-earning employment far from their villages led to a decline in local food production, necessitating restrictions or recruitment and the development of a policy for a stabilized labour force in mining and industry.

Economic development thus implies profound changes in agricultural society. As the increasing demand for labour attracts still larger numbers into industrial employment, indigenous subsistence agriculture is subjected to ever increasing pressures. [Certain African areas] are becoming increasingly unable to maintain the levels of food production necessary to support their own populations. Also, the production of cash crops for export is, in certain instances, taking place at the expense of food production for local consumption. All these developments point to the necessity for increasing the production of food for local consumption at a time when the proportion of the total population engaged in agriculture is declining and pressure on the land calls for more intensive agriculture.

The alienation of land, either in the form of large-scale concessions granted to non-indigenous persons for purposes of commercial development or in the form of land acquired by permanent immigrant settlers, has been another force disrupting the traditional system. [In certain areas of Africa—but not in the Trust Territories—land alienation has given rise to the reserve system with its attendant evils and problems. The problem in these non-Trust Territories of East and South Africa is in general less one of land tenure systems than of government policy in regard to land areas available for occupation, agricultural improvement and industrial development. In many instances the reserved areas have proved insufficient for the needs of an expanding population.] One aspect of this system is seen in the increase in the numbers of migrant laborers coming from the reserves.

It is evident that in these conditions the role of government must be crucial. The problems arising from the changes taking place in African rural society have involved all the administrations concerned in measures to control and direct agricultural development. These measures deal, for example, with such diverse matters as pest and disease control, soil erosion, irrigation and regulation of land tenure. The rapid extension of cash cropping and the growing influence of a money economy have led to a more intensive use of land and thus given rise to the need for improved techniques of agriculture. These developments are exerting a profound influence on indigenous agricultural society and on land usage. The relatively high price of primary products in recent years has quickened the tempo of change, which in turn has increased the need for administrative guidance and action. In this respect mention may be made of the marketing boards [such as those set up for British Nigeria and the Cameroons, British Gold Coast and Togoland], whereby crops are purchased by the boards from producers at guaranteed prices and sold on the market at higher prices. The funds thus accruing to the boards are used to stabilize prices over a period of time and to assist in the general improvement of crop production in the areas concerned.

In some cases administrations have sought to encourage development by providing for registration of titles to land in accordance with the principles of European land laws. A conspicuous example of this process is found in French West Africa.

Included in the Trust Territory is the Cameroons under French administration. The problem of the settlement of communal title is a complex and delicate one; recently, the Trusteeship Council received petitions from Africans in the French Cameroons alleging certain inequities arising from the registration system.

There have been several efforts in Africa to adapt indigenous agriculture and land tenure to modern conditions. Two of the best known are the Niger Development Project in French West Africa and the Gezira Scheme in the Sudan. A description of these two projects and similar schemes lie outside the scope of this paper.

I have tried to give you some idea of the partial background of land facts and problems which are being considered by the Trusteeship Council's committee in its study of rural economic development in the Trust Territories.

The committee is now at work. Its first task has been to establish the existing situation. It will then proceed to examine its implications against the background of land utilization policies and analyze the opportunities for and obstacles to progress so that recommendations may be made looking to the most beneficial use of the land in the Trust Territories from the standpoint of the basic objectives of the International Trusteeship System. Among these objectives are the promotion of the political, economic, social, and educational advancement of the inhabitants of the Trust Territories and their progressive development toward self-government or independence.

In the ways I have just mentioned and in numerous other ways the United Nations is striving to create conditions of stability and well-being not only in the political field but, as importantly, through the promotion of higher standards of living, full employment, and conditions of economic progress and development through the solution of international economic problems and of national and of local economic problems through international co-operation. In this context, problems of land tenure, land reform, and rural economic development now have high priority.

WORLD LAND TENURE PROBLEMS AND
THE FOOD AND AGRICULTURE ORGANIZATION

Thomas F. Carroll

SECRETARY Thorp said at the Tuesday banquet that land reform was "improving the lot of the farmer on the land." This puts the Food and Agriculture Organization of the United Nations squarely into the largest world-wide land reform business. Ever since October, 1945, FAO has been helping the world's farmers toward growing more food and fiber and toward developing a more satisfactory level of living. By collecting information, by preparing and disseminating technical publications, by bringing people from different nations together in meetings and conferences, and, finally, by carrying "know-how" directly into the field in the form of professional assistance, FAO has compiled an impressive record of accomplishments as the "extension agent" of the world.

FAO's work falls into three main fields. First, the gathering, analyzing, and dissemination of information. You are all familiar with our publications, which are printed in three languages and which have a wide international circulation. Under this category falls the compilation of up-to-date statistical material, the preparation of food balance sheets on the basis of which national plans and programs can be made, and the preparation of our many special technical reports on agricultural, nutritional, economic, forestry, and fisheries topics.

The second category of FAO's activities is international consultation. An example of work under this heading is the establishment of an international rice commission in the Far East. This commission is carrying forward an integrated program of improving rice varieties throughout the region where rice is the major crop. Another type of program involves the sponsoring of training centers on such subjects as better agricultural statistics and extension methods.

The third major field of our activities may be described as direct technical aid. FAO staff members and others under contract with FAO cover the globe on assignments ranging from fighting potato blight in Chile to helping to organize irrigation projects in Pakistan. During the past year these field activities of FAO have been stepped up to huge proportions due to the availability of funds under the United Nations Expanded Technical Assistance Program for Economic Development. What is happening is that scientists and technicians are being drawn from field and forest and seaside, from universities and experiment stations and government departments in countries all over the world. These experts travel to other countries where they stay for periods ranging from a few months to perhaps two years working out practical methods on the spot for increasing production, improving distribution, enlarging research and experimental work, reorganizing government agencies, and, in general, getting people acquainted with better ways of doing things. We now have some 180 experts stationed in 38 countries. The total number of experts called for in signed agreements with member countries is 340.

Only one-third of these people are from the United States; 33 other nations are represented among them.[1]

Turning now to FAO's activities more specifically in the field of land tenure, let me report to this conference that two of our divisions are more directly concerned with the subject. The Agriculture Division, of which I am a member, and our Economics Division both have resources to deal with land tenure problems. We have issued several significant publications related to land tenure, and our technicians have dealt with actual land tenure situations in the field in several countries. Among the special subjects covered are inheritance systems, laws relating to land and water rights, the fragmentation of holdings, land settlement, agricultural credit, co-operation, and, more recently, land reform.

As an illustration, I want to give you an account of our recent activities in the field of farm credit in Central America. Some years ago FAO, with the co-operation of the Economic Commission for Latin America surveyed the credit needs in the Central American Republics. This FAO-ECLA survey has had practical results in stimulating interest, in improving credit conditions, and especially in developing what is commonly called supervised credit for small-scale farmers not in a position to provide the collateral required by ordinary credit sources. Supervised credit consists in general of funds granted, usually by a government agency and at low interest, mainly on the basis of the character of the borrower and his possibilities for using them to better his economic situation; and the supervision consists of help given to him by extension workers or other experts in making good use of the funds to better his living conditions and economic position.

Experience has demonstrated that a sound system of supervised agricultural credit is perhaps the most effective approach for raising the living standards of rural people. Actually, however, the problem is not one of credit alone. To be really effective, supervised credit must be tied in with such programs as those for extension work, marketing, development of co-operatives, improvements in land tenure, the settlement of new agricultural areas, and regional economic development.

Late last year we carried out a study of the system of supervised credit established in Paraguay under the guidance of the Servicio Technico Interamericano de Cooperación Agricole (STICA) because of its possible usefulness in other Latin American countries; and we are now publishing the report.

In April and May of this year we collaborated with the United Nations in a survey of living conditions among the rural people of Guatemala. As an outcome of this survey a plan for rural betterment through a system of supervised credit has been prepared.

We are now preparing a general paper on supervised agricultural credit in Latin America, and additional field studies are envisaged for 1952 in other countries, possibly Venezuela, Brazil, Mexico, and Costa Rica. In 1952 or 1953 the time will be ripe for a regional meeting on this subject, which has been suggested by many member governments, and FAO is co-operating with ECLA in arrangements for such a meeting.[2]

I now want to call your attention to three important FAO publications directly related to the theme of this conference. I will summarize the subject of the first two briefly and describe the contents of the third in somewhat more detail.

The first of these documents is *Land Settlement for Agriculture*. It outlines the process of agricultural settlement and resettlement, it describes the various considerations and difficulties which may arise in connection with these operations, and suggests some ways in which these difficulties may be met.

Settlement and resettlement are expensive and difficult operations which should not be undertaken lightly or casually. Every agricultural settlement runs the risk of being a failure or of proving far more expensive than was expected. Even the best plans may go awry. A few bad seasons at the beginning of a settlement may be disastrous both financially and psychologically. Mistakes in estimating the capabilities of the land or water supply may easily be made; expected markets may fail; unexpected diseases may attack crops and settlers. The most careful deliberation and inquiry should precede a decision to proceed with operations and the most careful preparations should be made before the actual operations are begun.

When a decision has been taken, however, the operations should be pursued with the utmost diligence and vigor and every effort should be made to instil and maintain in the settlers an enthusiasm which will evoke such diligence and vigor. An important means to this end will be to see to it that they remain mentally serene and that no avoidable feeling of unfairness or frustration develops. This paper has inevitably been written largely from the point of view of efficient farming, but farming is more than an occupation; it is a way of life, and farmers are men and individual personalities before they are economic units. Due attention to this fact may make all the difference between success and failure.

The second report is another major contribution to the literature of land reform. It is called *The Consolidation of Fragmented Agricultural Holdings*. About half of this report deals with the general problem of fragmentation, including its types, effects, prevention, and possible remedies. The remainder treats four important consolidation programs actually carried out under different kinds of conditions in four different countries. The evils of fragmentation are relatively easily comprehended, and many people have the impression that consolidation is one of the easiest forms of land reform. The material in this bulletin, however, is convincing evidence that the difficulties besetting formation of more economic layout of farms are numerous indeed.

The third report that I want to recommend to you is the joint FAO-UN study on agrarian structures *Land Reform—Defects in Agrarian Structure as Obstacles to Economic Development.* This study is not an exhaustive treatise on all aspects of agrarian institutions as they affect economic development, but it is the best available published work calling the world's attention to those very problems which form the *raison d'etre* of this conference. I am going to sketch for you the high lights of this study in somewhat greater detail, because I believe they are most relevant to your daily deliberations here at Madison.

The report begins by stating that faults in agrarian institutions, such as fragmentation, insecurity, insufficient credit, inflexible and unprogressive taxation, are features of the agriculture of all countries of the world, no matter what stage of development. While such defects, therefore, may have considerable deleterious effects in even the more highly developed countries, they are usually the major limiting factors in the economic and social advancement in the less developed world areas.

Inventory is then taken of the most unsatisfactory conditions, which are highlighted by examples from various countries. The report goes on to say that the most common problem of the agrarian structure throughout the world is the uneconomic size of farms. Only a relatively small percentage of farms is adjusted in size to the efficient use of labor, the requirements of farm families, and needs of national food and fiber production. Judged by such criteria, most farms are either too small or too large. In many countries large numbers of farms are even too small to provide a subsistence minimum for the cultivator and his family. The average size of a farm in Japan is two and one-half acres and in India between three and four acres. Even in the sparsely populated regions of the world a large majority of holdings is too small to offer a farmer full employment and sufficient income. In most of the same areas the bulk of the land is taken up by very large holdings.

Concentration of land ownership in large holdings might mean, as it does in most of Asia and the Middle East, the leasing out of parts of large estates to small independent tenants. In other areas, such as Latin America, large farms are owned and operated as single units. When there are many small tenants as part of the large estates, the chief difficulties in the way of development are exorbitant and inflexible rents, great insecurity of tenure without any legal protection, small cash returns to the tenant leaving no margin for investment, and, generally, little incentive to increase output and to make improvements. Under such conditions the existence of large-scale property ownership does not secure any of the advantages of large-scale operation and investment. The landlord incurs few of the costs of production, while the tenant gets few of the benefits expected from improved techniques of work.

Where large farms are operated as single units we have to distinguish between estates farmed extensively in areas of sparse population with much idle land and intensively worked plantations existing in regions of great shortage of land and excess of labor. Both types offer the farm population unsatisfactory conditions of employment, no degree of responsibility or initiative in management, and very little income. In Latin America fully one-half of the agricultural land is in holdings of over 15,000 acres. The ownership of these estates is concentrated in the hands of 1.5 per cent of the farmers.

The largest bulk of the rural population consists of small tenants and landless laborers. In most countries, where extensively farmed large estates exist side by side with many self-sufficient farms, agricultural production is generally not adapted to the demand for food. Foods of high nutritional value and important for their protective function are especially scarce. Such estate economies might permit the accumulation of wealth in a few hands, but they universally fail to provide a broad basis of purchasing power for those people who work and live on the land. Concentration of estates on the best farming land often forces small farmers to cultivate poor areas on steep slopes where the danger of soil erosion is great.

Plantation economies occur in areas of heavy population pressure. In the West Indies, for instance, where there are thirty to fifty people in agriculture for every one hundred acres of cultivated land, large extensively worked plantations are common. Some of these estates might be considered efficient in purely business terms. But, from the point of view of a nation's food supply and economic development, they invariably give rise to serious problems. The explicit need in most countries for a more equal distribution of income and for greater opportunities of social advancement are pressing heavily on the plantation system. In most places where agriculture is dominated by plantations, one-crop or few-crop economies geared to export have an adverse effect on economic stability and internal development.

Closely related to these fundamental defects in the agrarian structure in underdeveloped countries is the basic need for the settlement of land titles and water rights. A legal system which does not fix such rights firmly and justly is not only not conducive to efficient agricultural practices but leads to continuous disputes over resources, perpetuates insecurity, and encourages the waste of land, water, and manpower.

Among the many facilities and services which farmers need in order to produce, none is more important than an adequate provision of credit. Shortage of production credit may be both a cause and effect of poverty, but even in countries of low capital accumulation the inadequacy of existing credit agencies appears to be a major obstacle to the expansion of production. Small farmers generally suffer more from lack of credit or from unfavorable conditions of credit than large landowners. The examination of the agrarian credit structure in key underdeveloped countries shows that unreasonably high interest rates prevail. In India large landowners pay between 9 per cent and 12 per cent interest, while the bulk of the debtors, who are small farmers, must pay between 12 per cent and 50 per cent and sometimes, on unsecured loans, as much as 300 per cent. In many other countries exorbitant interest rates and the lack of long-term credit facilities result in widespread rural indebtedness. In most cases a high rate of farm debts does not indicate a high level of investment, but occurs from the habit of financing consumption. More than half the farmers in China are burdened with debts incurred through consumption needs. In Ceylon 73 per cent of the farmers are in debt, and 90 per cent of the rural debts were contracted for nonproductive purposes.

Unwise taxation policies are having detrimental effects on farm production. In many underdeveloped regions of the world a rigid system resting upon an improperly selected and infrequently revised tax base is in effect. Such taxation is disproportionate to the level of incomes, especially when prices change. Taxes are exorbitant during depressions and light during booms. Where tenancy is prevalent, there is a tendency for landlords to shift the burden of taxation to tenants. Unreasonably high taxes for small farmers, directly or indirectly assessed, contribute to chronic rural indebtedness and reinforce the trend toward mortgaging and selling farms to large landowners. Many forms of taxation affect primarily consumption. It is estimated that in the underdeveloped countries such taxes in various forms account for from one-half to one-third of the total fiscal revenue. The heaviest burden of taxation usually affects articles of mass consumption. The combined effect of heavy assessment of land and of agricultural products frequently results in farmers getting taxed much more heavily than urban dwellers and receiving fewer services in return.

While it is relatively easy to diagnose the faults in agrarian institutions everywhere, it is very difficult to propose specific solutions. Although the experience of several countries is available, it is even harder to put already existing remedies into operation. Most of the problems mentioned previously are highly interdependent. The effectiveness of reforms often depends on concerted action in many interrelated spheres of activity. Certain features of the agrarian structure, such as high rents, excessively small farms, or large plantations, affect large world areas, but their influence is different in every country and in every region. For this reason no universal prescription is possible.

The report analyzes the experience of some countries which have carried out extensive land reform measures. Certain of the possible reforms are relatively straightforward, single-purpose measures which may be introduced in most places without fundamentally changing the economic and social fabric of agriculture. Among these are the consolidation of fragmented holdings to insure greater efficiency in management; the registration of titles of land and water; the reform of the taxation system

to put it on a more equitable and on a less burdensome basis; the provision of long-term credit at reasonable rates; and the strengthening of rural educational and advisory services. Although carrying out programs of this sort is by no means simple, there is sufficient experience available to give such reforms, when intelligently tackled, a good chance of success.

In many places where economic and social problems are most pressing, more fundamental, and therefore much more difficult, reforms seems to be indicated. Most of them involve the transfer of ownership from large landowners to cultivators. During the past few decades several countries have undertaken comprehensive reforms of this type. The scale of these changes might be indicated by noting that in China agrarian reforms completed by 1950 affected 145 million people; in India by January, 1950, 4.5 million acres (over a third of the cultivated land), has been transferred into the hands of owner-farmers, and 3 million cultivators have purchased land under the new laws; in Mexico, where the *latifundia* system was radically changed between 1922 and 1945, nearly half of the total cultivated area (17.5 million acres), has been transferred to village-ownership under the *ejido* system.

It is extremely difficult to judge the effect of these reforms not only because of their great complexity but because most of them have taken place very recently and few of the desired data are available. In general, it can be said that in areas where there is much land and where market conditions are favorable there is good reason to expect that a changeover from large estates to smaller-scale and more intensive farming will have beneficial social and economic effects. Where additional land can be brought under cultivation and where the newly established farms can be provided with helpful services in the form of well-designed new institutions there is a good chance for eventually raised incomes, fuller employment, increased and qualitatively better food supply, and a stimulus for industrial development. Where large owner-operated farms already practice intensive farming, subdivision of large units can easily lead to a decline in production, unless the transfer is made in such a way that the economic efficiency of the system is somehow preserved or replaced. The role of co-operatives in this connection may be crucial, and the need for ancillary services to the small farmer becomes paramount.

An entirely different situation prevails in countries where the population pressure is great and where there is no new land to be redistributed. A change in the status of tenants toward full ownership may have highly beneficial effects by improving the cultivators' income and by raising farm production. There are also important social gains to be made by the creation of responsible and independent owners. But in such conditions land reform is not likely to enlarge the already often too small farms and will not remove the fundamental defect of too many people on the land. To secure economic development in such circumstances will require a broader range of measures with specific emphasis on intensification and diversification of production.

The introduction and strengthening of farmers' production and marketing co-operatives appears to be a most important way to improve the existing agrarian structure in many countries. Certain types of co-operative farming also show promise in helping to establish new types of institutions following land reform. Farmers' co-operatives are most successful where peasant proprietorship is already well established. Co-operatives offer their members economies of large-scale procurement and marketing; they promote specialization and standardization and thereby increase efficiency; and

they can help farmers to offset their weak bargaining position.

Most types of fundamental land reforms bring with them a change in scale and type of production. In many areas of adverse natural conditions, especially in arid and tropical climates, it is hard to establish new forms of agrarian structures involving small independent farms without special assistance from governments. In such areas land reform measures must be part-and-parcel of broad development schemes in the nature of integrated regional development programs, large-scale investment, co-ordinated efforts for land and water use, the control of soil erosion, large-scale irrigation projects, and the expansion of transportation.

In the overpopulated regions of the world diversified production might take the form of small-scale, labor-intensive types of decentralized activities, such as cottage industries. These measures accompanying land reform are important, because full economic development must be induced on a broad front. If agrarian reforms are undertaken in isolation, their effect might be easily cancelled out, unless simultaneous attention is paid to the other sectors of the economy. But conversely, it cannot be expected that industrial development (now so high on the agenda of most underdeveloped countries) can be successful as long as the level of living in the countryside does not rise and as long as any additional income generated by industrialization is absorbed by agricultural rents and interest. It is well to keep in mind that agrarian reforms by changing the distribution of income and raising farm production will allow industrial expansion to generate its own purchasing power and to create its own market. In this way, the reform of a defective agrarian structure is, above all, an essential building block in the intricate construction for economic and social progress.

It is clear from this survey of the world

agrarian structure that a tremendous need for improvement exists. For the first time in history the nations of the world have been made collectively conscious of the grave rural institutional problems that underly misery, famine, and low human welfare. It has been and it is now within the scope of the FAO to tackle these problems with the aid of other international and national organizations created to assist the less developed portions of the globe. The exact nature of FAO's program in this field will not be available until the Sixth Session of the FAO Conference, to be held in November, 1951.[3] But in the meantime members of the FAO Council (which is a smaller policy-forming body) making recommendations to the Conference agreed in June, 1951, that "FAO should encourage member governments to ask Technical Assistance for aid in the development of programs of rural reform; and that the experts provided by Technical Assistance should have extensive experience in dealing with the problems in underdeveloped countries." The Council also went on record to suggest that when FAO defines its future specific program of land tenure it should:

(1) take further steps to make all member nations increasingly conscious of the problem, (2) encourage the use of expert advice, and (3) assist countries to secure the finances often needed to carry through programs of rural reform.

Whatever the exact nature of our future program, in addition to the activities FAO is already carrying on to improve the world agrarian structure, it will substantially depend on the member governments themselves. FAO is essentially a service organization, and we operate on request of governments. So far under the Expanded Technical Assistance Program we have not received a single official request from any country for assistance in connection with land tenure problems. We are ready to honor such

requests, and hope that a number will be forthcoming in the near future. In the meantime we will continue to keep as much of this vast field as possible under surveillance and to carry on our basic function of analysis, education, and facilitation of international co-operation. I personally envisage further tenure meetings, possibly organized along regional lines and maybe incorporating the training center idea which has worked so well in other fields. There is also the expectation for more international studies, one of which is scheduled to appear in 1952. A compilation of water laws in various countries is now under way.

Some of us believe that although much is known about land tenure matters, most of the available information has not been collected with an eye to contributing to the solutions of the problems which form the substance of this conference. Much of this data presents inadequate and misleading descriptions and does not allow for the analysis of causative factors and insights into functional economic and social relationships. We feel that the development of conceptual tools and methodological devices in the field of land tenure are also badly needed. This conference can make important contributions in this direction.

In conclusion, I hope that I could indicate to you FAO's deep interest in what you have come here to discuss. Land reform is our business. FAO is now assisting and is ready to assist further your governments in their efforts toward economic and social development. Please get acquainted with our people and our facilities. You will find in FAO an atmosphere of sincere concern and professional competence. As a representative of the Director General of the Food and Agriculture Organization of the United Nations, I wish you a happy and successful conference.

IN PREPARING these notes for publication in

the conference Proceedings, the writer wishes to supplement his remarks by two Appendices, which contain material developed after the Madison sessions. The first of these is the summary of discussions and the text of Resolution No. 8 of the Sixth Session of the FAO Conference, and the second is the text of FAO's special program of work in response to this resolution. It is essential to read these documents along with the above paper in order to get a reasonably up-to-date picture of FAO's role in land reform as an expression of international concern.

APPENDIX A

REPORT AND RESOLUTION ON AGRARIAN STRUCTURES BY THE SIXTH SESSION OF THE FAO CONFERENCE

Reform of Agrarian Structures

The subject of agrarian reform aroused a large number of interested comments by the delegates. There was general agreement that the reform of the agrarian structure was a proper topic for FAO to consider in endeavoring to fulfill the general aims of the organization: To increase agricultural production, and to promote better rural living. There was also general acceptance of the theme of the joint FAO/UN study presented to the Twelfth Session of the Council, which brought to light the various ways in which certain defects in the agrarian structure, such as small and fragmented holdings, insecurity of tenure, lack of registration of titles to land and water, scarcity of credit, unfair rentals, or inequitable taxes against the interest of sound economic and social use of land, seriously impede economic development. There was explicit and implicit concurrence among the delegates on the need for concerted action to remedy these defects in order to raise food production, in line with the exposition of Director-General in which he outlined the serious world food situation.

The Conference noted the resolution on land reform of the Economic and Social Council, which called upon FAO to assume a major responsibility in dealing with this problem of agrarian structures, and it agreed that the Organization should accept this challenge.

The Conference considered that the elimination of defective features from existing agrarian structures is not only essential to economic progress, but that such measures would materially contribute to human freedom and dignity and consequently would secure social stability and further peaceful democratic development. The Conference emphasized the importance of country-wide enthusiasm for the rational utilization of natural resources developed through scientific knowledge to their maximum potential, in order to assure to the farmer a decent standard of living.

The Conference calls upon Member Governments to examine their own agrarian structure in the light of the ECOSOC resolution and to promote to the fullest, the exchange of information and the spread of education to further popular understanding of rural betterment.

It is clear that agrarian reform is a manifold and complex operation, involving not only such measures as listed above, but closely tied in with most other aspects of economic and social life. In line with the main conclusions of the joint FAO/UN study, the Conference concurred in the view that the reform of the agrarian structure must be part and parcel of the general program of economic development. Consequently, many delegates felt that FAO should not treat agrarian reform in isolation, but integrate it with other projects in its program related to economic development in the broadest sense. For instance, it is recognized that the resource characteristics of different agricultural regions have a decisive effect on such features of rural institutions as the optimum size of holdings and the pattern of land utilization.

The Conference recognizes that in final

analysis the basic measures in this field must be taken by the governments themselves, as part of their national programs. However, FAO, charged with the responsibility of promoting world agricultural production and rural living, should be able to assist Member Nations in carrying out rural reform programs.

If FAO is to carry out such a program of assistance, the Secretariat must have available extensive and continuous information on land tenure and all related matters. The Conference therefore requests the Director-General to make appropriate arrangements for the collection and analysis of this information with the view to maximum benefit to Member Countries. The Conference calls upon Member Governments to give to the Secretariat full and detailed information and documentation on these subjects.

As emphasized in the discussion, several countries have already valuable experience in many fields of agrarian reform, which they are willing to put at the disposal of other Member Governments. Certain delegations, on the other hand, expressed great interest in measures put into effect in other countries, because of the rural reforms now being planned or in the process of execution in their own countries. The Conference therefore requested the Director-General to make the experience of individual countries in the field of specific reform measures available to all interested governments. To this end, FAO should initiate analytical studies in co-operation with Member Governments, and also assist selected Member Nations in the appraisal of the effectiveness of current measures of land reform in the field.

For the purpose of periodical exchange of information and experience among experts in this field, the Conference recommended the organization of regional meetings on problems of agrarian structure. A number of member governments have already expressed their willingness to be hosts to such meetings.

It is evident that the Expanded Technical Assistance Program can serve as an appropriate framework for carrying out some of FAO's work on rural reform. Delegates commented on the desirability of giving high priority within ETAP to projects dealing with agrarian reform. The Conference called on Member Govern-

ments engaged in planning economic development projects which involve changes in the agrarian structure, to request FAO for help under the Expanded Technical Assistance Program, either in dealing with particular aspects of their rural institutional structure such as credit, fragmentation, etc., or in planning a general attack on all phases of the problem. It was pointed out that in countries where large programs of technical assistance are now under way, changes in agrarian structures should be considered as an essential supplementary activity, because the effectiveness of many of the technological measures depends on the improvement of existing institutional structures. In this connection, it has been suggested that instead of one expert working in isolation, there ought to be "land tenure teams" tackling simultaneously various aspects of agrarian reform in a problem area. Governments might want to give this matter consideration, when they submit requests for assistance.

In accordance with suggestions made during the debate, the Conference recommended the establishment of training centers in the field of agrarian structures, particularly land tenure, as similiar centers have already been successfully organized on a number of technical subjects. Such centers are to broaden the training and experience of men, who would work on problems connected with agrarian reform in their own countries. These prospective centers might concentrate on the question of methodology (i.e. how to attack land tenure problems), because instruction in the fundamentals of research and analysis seems to be most badly needed. It is recommended that such training centers be associated with practical demonstrations in which projects featuring sound agrarian structure are stressed. It is hoped that in the operation of such centers full advantage will be taken of possible co-operation between FAO, other international agencies, and the technical assistance organizations of Member Nations.

Since agrarian reform cannot be accomplished without adequate capital inputs and consequently considerable costs, the problem of the internal and external financing of agrarian reform programs is a very essential one. The Conference, having heard a statement by the Representative of the International Bank for Reconstruction and Development, agreed that FAO, in co-operation with the United Nations and its appropriate Specialized Agencies, should explore the possibility of the provision of more effective methods of financing, both through mobilization of the internal resources of the countries concerned and through international institutions, already existing or organized for this purpose, which would provide loans or grants as referred to in the appropriate resolution of the ECOSOC (F/2107).

In conclusion, the Conference felt that the reform of agrarian structure is such an important factor in carrying out the broad objectives of FAO and those which specifically confront this Conference, as presented in the Director-General's opening statement for Commission I, that agrarian reform should be an important part of the Program of Work of the Organization for the next years to come. The Conference adopted the following resolution:

RESOLUTION No. 8

Reform of Agrarian Structures

The Conference—

Having examined the Report on "Defects in Agrarian Structures as Obstacles to Economic Development," the Resolution of the ECOSOC thereon, and the Director-General's "Statement on Reform of Agrarian Structures" (C 51/I-3),

Considers (a) that in many countries the agrarian structure has most serious defects, in particular the uneconomic size of farms, the fragmentation of holdings, the maldistribution of landed property, excessive rents, inequitable systems of taxation, insecurity of tenure, perpetual indebtedness or the lack of clear titles to land and water; (b) that these defects prevent a rise in the standard of living of small farmers and agricultural laborers and impede agricultural development; (c) that reform of agrarian structure in such countries is essential to human dignity and freedom, and to the achievement of the aims of FAO;

Endorses the Resolution of the ECOSOC of September 7 insofar as it applies to FAO; and

Urges Member Governments (a) to take immediate steps to implement that resolution, and to co-operate with FAO in supplying information and participation in such investigations as FAO may undertake; (b) to request the assistance of FAO to carry out reform of their agrarian structure;

Requests the Director-General to:

1. assemble in co-operation with other appropriate organizations on a continuing basis at FAO Headquarters information on land tenure, land reform and allied subjects, with a view to analyzing and making it available to interested Member Governments and institutions;

2. co-operate with Member Nations in the appraisal of the effectiveness of past and current measures of reform of agrarian structure;

3. take the leadership in organizing with other entities of the United Nations such interagency arrangements as may be useful and appropriate to enable each UN agency to make its fullest contribution to implementing the ECOSOC Resolution, to provide assistance to governments on all aspects of reform of agrarian structure, and to arrange for the preparation of reports on progress achieved as called for in the ECOSOC Resolution;

4. review the Program of Work of FAO with a view to insuring a high priority and an integrated approach to those projects in the various divisions which are related to the problems of reform of agrarian structure in the broadest sense in order to keep member nations informed of all aspects of the problem under review and to be fully prepared to give assistance to governments in the development of their programs;

5. be prepared to assist governments by provision of technical assistance on programs designed to promote desirable reforms including land tenure, agricultural credit, agricultural co-operatives, and agricultural extension services and rural industries;

6. seek the co-operation of other international organizations, Member Governments and private bodies on investigations of problems of reform of agrarian structure including the

analysis and promotion of methods of external and internal financing of agrarian reform programs;

7. promote the organization of regional conferences or training centers combined with demonstration projects on reform of agrarian structures in co-operation with other national and international organizations and governments of the regions concerned; and

8. report to the Council, as soon as practicable, on initial progress made in implementing those recommendations, on obstacles encountered, and on further possibilities uncovered, and subsequently to report fully to the next regular Conference on progress achieved.

Rome, December 1951

𝔖𝔖𝔖𝔖 APPENDIX B

THE FAO NEW PROGRAM OF WORK ON LAND

TENURE AND RELATED SUBJECTS

1. The Conference of the Food and Agriculture Organization of the United Nations at its Sixth Session examined the United Nations Report on "Defects in Agrarian Structure as Obstacles to Economic Development" and the Resolution of the Economic and Social Council of the United Nations thereon (No. 6 of the 7th September 1951) and passed a comprehensive Resolution on agrarian reform. The object of the present paper is to outline the new program of work proposed in order to give full implementation to this Resolution. In the earlier discussions on this subject the term "agrarian structure" was used. This term has a very wide, and somewhat vague, content, since it includes the whole legal, customary, and institutional framework within which agriculture is carried out. Prompt and effective action clearly demands some initial limitation of the field of work, and it is doubtless for this reason that the FAO Conference described its Resolution as one on "agrarian reform," and that the Economic and Social Council of the United Nations confined its principal recommendation to the Specialized Agencies (in par. 5 of its Resolution) to "land reform" and to measures directly necessary to the success of such reform. With the same object the present paper deals primarily with land tenure and those aspects of agrarian reform that are closely and directly related to land tenure. This does not, of course, mean that other aspects of the problems of agrarian reform will be neglected,

nor does it imply the omission of any part of the FAO Program of Work for 1952–53 presented to the Conference, which includes important projects on co-operatives, credit, extension and some aspects of land use. It merely means that in the new work, planned in implementation of the Conference's Resolution and made possible by the additional funds allotted for that purpose, emphasis will first be placed on land tenure and subjects directly related thereto.

2. Considerable work has already been done on land tenure and related subjects. Papers have been published by the FAO on the consolidation of fragmented agricultural holdings, on essential steps in national agricultural development, and on agricultural credit, especially supervised agricultural credit, in various Latin-American countries and in Libya. The Food and Agriculture Organization also collaborated with the United Nations in the preparation of the Report on Land Reform cited above. Technical meetings have been held on co-operatives in the Caribbean area and in Southern Asia and the Far East, and a regional meeting on land utilization has been held in Ceylon. In addition, a paper on general aspects of the provision of agricultural credit for the small farmers is in the press. Under the Expanded Technical Assistance Program, field work on agricultural credit is in progress in Libya, Iran, Honduras, and Jamaica, on agricultural co-operatives in Mexico (Fundamental Education Center) and

Thailand. A regional training center on co-operatives for the Near East and a seminar on agricultural credit for Latin America are in preparation. An inquiry has also begun, in collaboration with the Fiscal Division of the United Nations, into the effect on agricultural development of duties and regulations imposed on the rural population through taxation and other fiscal measures.

3. It is intended that the new program in the field of land tenure and agrarian reform should include general studies, functional monographs, field studies of particular situations, regional seminars, and demonstration projects. These various items are to be regarded as complementary to one another, and as far as possible work in the field and at headquarters will be carried out simultaneously with the object of gradually accumulating a body of general and local information which will facilitate the preparation of reports to the Economic and Social Council of the United Nations and to the Council and Conference of the FAO and will provide a proper basis for advice and assistance to Member Governments under the Expanded Technical Assistance Program. The success of the program will depend largely on close and effective co-operation between the FAO staff and the governments and technicians of Member Countries. Indeed, work done in the field can only be carried out with the approval and assistance of the Member Governments concerned. The items enumerated below indicate the general scope of the work proposed and are not to be regarded as constituting a rigid program, the development of which, at this stage, is neither practicable nor desirable, since the precise matters dealt with and the order of priority must inevitably depend largely on external factors, including the wishes and needs of Member Governments.

A. *General Studies:*
 a) Definition of terms;
 b) Bibliography;
 c) Criteria for evaluating systems of land tenure;
 d) Methods of conducting field inquiries into local agrarian situations;

 e) The relation of land tenure and agrarian reform to agricultural development;
 f) The influence of land tenure systems on the manner in which the capital, management, and labor required for farming are provided and applied.
 g) The effect of land tenure systems on the standard of life of the agricultural producer and his family, the amenities of rural life and the social conditions of agricultural communities.

B. *Functional Monographs on Specific Aspects of Land Tenure Systems in General:*
 a) Descriptions of the main features of different systems of land tenure and analysis of their advantages and disadvantages to agriculture:
  1) Tenancy;
  2) Cultivation by the landowner;
  3) Large, centrally-operated estates including "plantations";
  4) Communal tenure;
  5) Co-operative tenure and collectives;
  6) Mixed tenures;
  7) Public lands.
 b) Studies on:
  1) Methods of financing land reform measures;
  2) Water rights in land tenure;
  3) Public control and limitation of private rights in land;
  4) Cadastral surveys and registration of rights in land;
  5) Management of forests in relation to types of ownership.

C. *Country Studies.*—These will be studies of actual tenure situations as revealed by local inquiry. Such studies will naturally cover a much wider field than land tenure alone, since any satisfactory appreciation of a particular tenure situation must necessarily be based on a view of the agrarian situation as a whole. Three types of study are contemplated and will include, where possible, discussion of the effects of any changes that may have been introduced:

a) Studies based on actual requests by Member Governments for an examination of a system believed to be unsatisfactory but on which little or no remedial action has been attempted;

b) Studies in countries where measures of land reform have already been introduced; and

c) Studies in countries where changes in the agrarian system are actually taking place.

D. *Regional Seminars* of the type contemplated in paragraph 7 of the 7th Resolution of the Sixth Conference of the Food and Agriculture Organization of the United Nations. These seminars will be organized for the exchange of knowledge and ideas on problems of land utilization and land tenure and related subjects within the region concerned and not for the study of particular projects. If the regions are carefully selected, it is thought that the problems of the various countries will be found to have many common features. The seminars will assist the solution of regional problems not only by clarifying the issues but also by providing convenient means for the dissemination of information or remedial measures proposed or undertaken, the application of such measures, the difficulties encountered, and the results obtained from them.

E. *Demonstration Projects.*—A "demonstration project" is an actual experiment in agrarian reform conducted in a limited area with the object (a) of gaining practical knowledge and experience of the effects of a measure of land reform before applying it generally or (b) of demonstrating the advantages of a measure to the people. The scope for such experiments varies greatly with local political and social conditions: in some countries the expenditure of public money on what is *prima facie* to the advantage of a particular group of the population may not be tolerated; in others experiments of this kind have in fact been car-

ried out without serious opposition. If such projects are to succeed, they must provide not only for the satisfactory administration of the measure of reform to which the experiment is directed but also for such improvements in the public services provided as may be necessary to the success of the scheme. Adequate advisory and technical services, credit, improvements in communications, water supplies, and marketing facilities, the registration of rights in land and reformed taxation systems designed to facilitate rather than impede agricultural development are examples of activities which must often be associated with land reforms if success is to be achieved.

4. Work in connection with country studies, regional seminars and demonstration projects has to be carried out within the territories of Member Countries. The success of such projects—and indeed their very possibility—depends, therefore, primarily on requests and invitations received from Member Governments and on the facilities and co-operation provided by these governments and by universities and other institutions within their territories. Much can, however, be done by officers of the Organization working in the field to stimulate such requests and invitations. As an example, the response to a suggestion for holding a regional seminar on land utilization and land tenure in Latin America has been very encouraging, and it seems that several member countries would be willing to act as hosts to such a seminar. A further obvious limitation is placed on the FAO program by the amount of funds from time to time available to the Organization or allotted by Member Governments. Subject to these limitations, it is the intention of the FAO to make every effort to provide advice and assistance to Member Governments on all aspects of agrarian reform falling within the field of the Organization's activities, and, to this end, to collaborate closely with Member Governments and universities, charitable foundations and other national institutions, with the United Nations Organization and with other specialized agen-

cies concerned. An obvious immediate field for such collaboration is the preparation of the questionnaires and reports on the reform of agrarian structures and on agricultural co-operatives called for by the Economic and Social Council's Resolution on Land Reform.

5. The success of collaborative work, whether the collaboration is with Member Countries or with other international bodies, depends on careful preparation, on close co-ordination of effort from the earliest stages of the work, and on clear agreements as to the division of work and responsibility between the collaborating bodies. The need to make the best use of limited and separately controlled funds also points in the same direction. The practical problems of satisfactory collaboration are per-

haps greatest in regard to work in which several international agencies are jointly interested. The Food and Agriculture Organization therefore intends, in the spring or early summer of 1952, to invite the United Nations Organization and the specialized agencies concerned in this matter to send representatives to participate in a meeting to discuss the best method of achieving effective collaboration and the most profitable employment of the staff and funds available. It is expected that such *ad hoc* meetings will be necessary from time to time as the program develops in order to maintain effective co-ordination.

22 February 1952

Part IV   THE LAND TENURE
SITUATION IN THE MIDDLE EAST

OPENING REMARKS BY THE CHAIRMAN

ᏇᏇᏇᏇ   *Afif Tannous*

YOU HAVE observed from the program that we have put a group of countries together to discuss the land tenure system and problems. So my first remark, a very brief one, is to explain why we have put these countries together. There is no political reason for this. But there are economic, social, and traditional reasons. We have together the countries of Iran and the Arab-speaking countries of the Near East. In all of these countries, including Egypt, Libya, Syria, Lebanon, Iraq, Jordan, Saudi Arabia, and Iran, too, which is not an Arab country— in all of these there are great similarities in their background of the tenure system. An old system of land ownership prevails, remote in its origins, literally going back to the dawn of human history. In all of these countries, the Islamic religion, or way of life, predominates. It is not only a religion, it is really a total way of life permeating various aspects of the culture of these countries, including in its influence the land

tenure system that we know now exists. This whole system, briefly stated, is characterized by absentee ownership of the land. That is a predominant and very important feature. At the same time we observe that the great majority of the peasants are either very small owners of land or altogether landless. This system is also characterized by a peculiar type of farming, of share-cropping, of tenancy.

All of these points will be discussed in detail by the various leaders who are going to present the case for each one of these countries. But it would do us well as delegates to look at the Near East, the group of countries I mentioned, as a whole and to think of the system as one for all, with a few differences here and there, and to keep in mind that suggested solutions for these problems for any one of these countries might do quite well with some modifications for the other countries, too.

LAND TENURE IN SYRIA

ᏇᏇᏇᏇ   *Akram El-Ricaby*

BEFORE going into the subject of land tenure, I would like to acquaint you with my country. Syria is situated in the northwestern corner of the Arabian peninsula. It is one of the Arab states of the Middle East; it is a small country with great poten-

tialities. Its population is well over 3.5 millions, three-fourths of whom live directly on agriculture. Agriculture is the backbone of our economic existence. The country is run as a democratic republic with a parliament elected once every four years.

84

The area is about 18.5 million hectares; at present the farmed lands stretch over 8 million hectares, while the remaining 10.5 million hectares include forests, grazing lands, and areas in need of development schemes. A little more than half of this area extends over the Syrian Steppe desert, which provides excellent grazing for sheep usually kept by the Bedouin tribes and forms our main source of meat and wool.

Our rivers draw their waters from the mountainous regions. The rivers Orontes, Farfar, and the Abana of the Bible draw their waters from the Ante-Lebanon mountains, and the Tigris, the Euphrates, and the Khabour draw from the Anatolian mountains.

Syria, and especially Damascus, was the cradle of ancient civilizations. Later it was the center of the Omayad civilization that radiated in all directions. With its strategic position in the Middle East and the energy of its people it withstood different waves of invasions which destroyed large areas of its forest and agriculture. Its history was closed down by the Ottoman conquest from the north five hundred years ago. About 1908 Damascus and Cairo became the center of the propagation of Arab national movements; and during the first world war Syria took an active part in the Arab revolt against the Ottomans and regained its short-lived independence, which was destroyed by another invasion from the West. This invasion lasted twenty-five years and ended in 1945, when our independence was won again.

Our main crops are wheat, barley, cotton, rice, hemp, tobacco, and olive oil. We export wheat and cotton. Our tobacco—especially the smoked variety of Latakia—and olive oil are among the main items exported exclusively to the United States, with which we have a growing trade. We also grow and export vegetables and fruits, and we have good mineral and other re-sources. We are working very hard to stimulate our agriculture and industries and to expand our irrigated areas to strengthen our economic structure—whence we hope we shall be able to contribute to the general welfare of a democratic world.

The land laws and regulations in Syria are by origin a mixture of traditions and rules, some of which date back to the time of the Ottoman rule, some of which are of more recent introduction by the French mandatory administration, and, lastly, some of which were promulgated and amended since Syria became independent. These laws and regulations were subjected to many additions and amendments as time went on.

The original tradition came from the Califs, who paid salaries to their soldiers. Their successors, the Seltchouks, followed this rule; the rule was later discontinued, and, instead, lands were granted to the soldiers. In this way all army salaries and expenses were met out of the land revenues. This granting of land required the beneficiary to dwell on the land itself and develop it.

The Ottomans, who came after the Seltchouks, were also a military dynasty, and, therefore, their military laws and regulations included articles concerning the land laws. This was due to the close relations that existed between mobilization and the land.

In all countries conquered by the Ottomans, a general survey of the lands was carried out and the tithes (one-tenth) revenues assessed. A census was carried out in each village, and the number of inhabitants marked down; the woodlots, the forests, and the grazing lands were also defined. Finally, according to its revenues (or crop production) the land was divided into four categories:

1. Khas (private) lands, which were reserved by the Sultan, who might grant them to a prince or minister or a personality of

that rank or to his favorites. The revenue of such Khas lands was estimated as not over 100,000 aktches. (One aktche was one one-hundredth of a Turkish gold pound. Each gold pound equals at today's rates thirteen dollars, and one aktche is equal to thirteen cents.)

2. Zaameh or Leadership lands, which were given to the keeper of the Sultan's purse or to heads of batallions or commanders of fortresses or influential notables or persons of similar rank. The revenue of such lands varied from 20,000 to 100,000 aktches.

3. Timar lands, which were given to gallant soldiers. The revenue of such lands varied from 3,000 to 20,000 aktches.

4. Wakf, or lands dedicated to charity or educational institutions.

Further, it was ruled that for every 5,000 aktches of revenues from lands under the first two categories and 3,000 aktches from lands under the third category one fully armed man had to be supplied in times of war.

Upon the death of one of the above beneficiaries his rights and obligations went to his son; if the son was a minor, a fully armed substitute had to be sent for him until he became of age. When no heir existed, the right went back to the state, and the land was given to another worthy soldier upon the recommendation of Emir ul Umera, or Commander-in-Chief.

An interesting point in this connection was that those to whom the revenues of such lands were granted had to dwell on the land itself. They were called "owners of the land" and were entitled to collect the tithes from crops raised by the "tenants," who were not permitted to cede their tenancy to others without permission from the land owners. The newcomer, however, had to pay to the "owner" a "seniority right." On the other hand, no owner of the land was permitted to acquire for himself the tenants' utilization rights or to give them to the inhabitants of another district. This precaution was taken to prevent owners from holding both ownership rights and tenancy rights and to guard against a possible shortage of land which villagers (or dwellers on the same lands) might suffer at a future date.

This type of land ownership and tenant rules went on in a satisfactory manner up to the year 1584. After this date a departure from these rules was observed. The result of this departure was the corruption of the whole system. This was due to the fact that the favorite Seigneurs or Aghas of the Sultan's palace, or of the Grand Vizirs or ministers, began to pass such rights of ownership in turn to their own men and favorites regardless of their worthiness, efficiency, and capability in war or in working the lands. It will be remembered that previously such rights were given only to men-of-the-sword, or warriors. These favorites lived in Istanbul or big towns instead of dwelling on the land itself as was the rule previously. These new owners enjoyed the protection of their masters and introduced contractors to exploit their rights for them. These contractors went too far in collecting the rights of their employers and robbed the people of their money.

From this period onward a new practice was established by these favorites. While putting the contractors to collect their revenues from the tenants (agrarian people), the favorites themselves lived in towns, increasing their contacts with the Wali (governor) and the government officials and using the influence of their masters and protectors to protect and assist their protégé-contractor, thus bringing to the state a bad reputation. This situation continued up to the year 1839, when the "New Reforms" were declared whereby the Timar and Zaame rights were cancelled and, instead, a lifetime salary was given to previous "owners." These salaries were made proportionate with the previous revenues they enjoyed; and the tithe (one-tenth) rights were collected directly by the state. In 1848, however, all former Timar and Zaameh owners were sent on half-pay pension, and in 1858 a law was passed whereby the management of old rights was taken up by the finance officers.

In 1859 the first Tapu, or land and right, registration system was introduced, and in 1874 Defter Khakani, or land registrars, and tapu clerks were employed. These officials were considered land owners and were designated to issue ownership and usufruct (tenancy, land utilization, or Tasarrouf) documents (deeds). From this date onward no one could acquire any utilization (Tasarrouf) rights without written permission from the land registrars.

The utilizers (state tenants or Tasarrouf holders) of the state domain, or miri lands, were in reality tenants who paid rents in advance against the utilization right and also a deferred rent in the form of a tithe equivalent to one-fifth of the crop grown each year.

The Ottoman land laws divided the lands into five categories:

1. Mulk, or lands held in absolute ownership.

2. Emiri lands, the ownership of which basically belongs to the state; the right of utilizing it may be given by the state to individuals.

3. Wakf, or lands dedicated to certain educational or charity institutions or purposes.

4. Public lands, which are left to be used by the public, such as roads, squares, parks, public markets, etc. Their title belongs to the state.

5. Dead lands or vacant lands, which are not owned or used by anybody and are situated at a distance of one and one-half miles from buildings and from which a man's loud voice could not be heard. However, one must not be misled by the definition of this category of land which covers extended areas in Syria. A fair percentage of it may be well developed and easily utilized.

With regard to mulk lands, or those held in absolute ownership, the neck of the land (to use the Arabic term), or the holding right, what is on the land and in it together with its exploitation and utilization rights belong to its owner.

In the Emiri lands the neck, or holding right, belongs to the state, but the utilization, or Tasarrouf (usufruct), right belongs to its owner, but under certain conditions.

Should the occupant (user) tenant neglect the land or fail to crop it for five years he loses his right, and the land reverts to the state.

The state as owner of the neck collects one-tenth of the crops and can give the right of utilization (tenancy) to someone else when the lands fall free. This transfer is subject to the payment of certain registration fees.

Tasarrouf, or utilization, right to cultivate the land is given to peasants (tenants) who exploit the lands and who are given tapu, or ownership, documents. (The tithes of such lands were given in old times to holders of Timar and Zaama rights.)

When an owner of a freehold—land held in absolute ownership—dies without heirs the neck of the land passes to the state.

When, by order of the Sultan, Tasarrouf, or utilization, rights are given to someone, the neck is kept by the state.

As time went on, ownership of the land or of tenancy rights was fragmented following the death of the owner, thus causing the multiplication of the number of shares on the land. However, the increasing population of the villages reduced the absorptive capacity of the village lands, and the task of farming a small strip of land became very difficult. The insecurity which prevailed at that time also forced villagers to farm one part of the village lands at a time, collectively dividing this land by the rope or the rod. The number of strips allocated to each person varied according to his share of ownership and the type of the soil. This type of "common field" helped villagers to co-operate in protecting their crops. Each year the common field was moved to another side of the village lands. This practice meant fallowing the land for two or three years according to the area of the village lands and the number of its owners.

This practice of farming the property jointly with a common frame brought into existence what was called "Musha lands." Musha means undefined share in a common property. Such a partnership was optional when a number of persons bought a piece of land and shared its profits, or it was compulsory when partnership was gained by inheritance.

On lands situated close to densely populated localities, such as villages or towns where the number of owners was high, it was not easy to split or parcellate the lands into economically farmable areas; consequently a grouping of one family's shares of the land had to be adopted, and thus the "common family property" came into being. This developed a feudal or regalian property in which the ownership, or neck, of the land belonged to the proprietors (the family) and the right of its use (tenancy) remained in the hands of its users. The peasant (tenant), however, paid a share of his crop to the proprietors (of the neck). The feudal system has withered away, but some of its relics are sometimes seen in certain parts of the country.

The Musha's (common share) ownership of the land has greatly retarded development, decreased fertility, and exposed the land to the effect of soil erosion. The establishment of good order and security,

the high prices of agricultural products, etc., have all induced people to shower the land department with applications for settling their rights and consolidating their property, whereby they may be enabled to exploit their land at will.

Mention was made of the fragmentation of the land by inheritance. Inheritance in Syria is of two kinds.

1. Land held in absolute ownership (Mulk) is inherited in accordance with the Moslem inheritance rule; that is, the female heir inherits half the share of the male heir.

2. In miri lands, where the ownership (neck) belongs to the state, children of both sexes inherit equal shares; the wife gets one-fourth of the property if she has children; in the absence of children the wife inherits one-half of the property—the other half going to the next of kin (the same applies to the husband when inheriting his wife's share); and grandchildren inherit their deceased father's share.

These laws of inheritance are followed and accepted by all the inhabitants of Syria of all religions. It may be of interest to mention here that in accordance with our traditions, regardless of religion, all females and elderly persons or disabled members of the family, so long as they live, enjoy the protection and support of the male, who takes this duty voluntarily.

Prior to 1909, the trees of Emiri lands were treated as an absolute property of the person who planted them and were subjected to the Moslem inheritance rule, while the land was left subject to the miri inheritance rule. In 1909 a law was passed whereby the trees were considered as part of the land and subject to the same miri inheritance rule.

The Ottoman land laws and regulations were subjected to many additions and amendments which rendered them complicated. With the liberation of Syria at the end of 1918, and later in 1920, the new independent government was given no time to make changes in these laws. The French occupied the country and the mandatory regime was established. However, the French High Commissioner had to make amendments to these laws. He promulgated many decisions. The most important was Decision No. 3339, dated November 13, 1930, which regulated the rights of (immovable) ownership. This decision amended the Ottoman land laws and the tapu rules. It considered the Wakf, or the dedication of the land, a temporary or causal measure having nothing to do with the definition and classification of the land. Further, it divided the leftover lands and brought them under one category of the public and dead lands and subjected them both to the state domain laws.

The categories of land under the Ottoman laws listed above have, therefore, been changed by Declaration No. 3339 as follows:

1. Property held in absolute ownership and situated within built-up areas or within administrative (municipal) boundaries.

2. Emiri lands, the neck of which remains in the hands of the state, but whose use and exploitation rights are owned by other persons.

3. Leftover or vacant and unprotected properties. Their areas and merits have been defined and limited in accordance with local practice and tradition. The ownership of such lands is acquired by those who occupy and farm them continuously without dispute.

4. Leftover but protected lands. These lands belong to the state or the municipalities and are partly considered as state domains.

5. Vacant (deserted) and dead lands. These areas are considered Emiri lands, they are unoccupied and their boundaries are undefined, but they can be occupied and utilized by permission of the state, and the priority rights may be acquired in accord-

ance with the state domain laws and regulations.

While these amendments promoted better means for the development and improvement of the land, they nevertheless paved the way for certain political and drastic measures which were intended to be taken by the mandatory, had this regime survived. Later in 1941, following the evacuation of the Vichists from Syria by the British, the mandatory position was extremely weakened, and in order to strengthen their hold and create partisans the French passed a decree whereby "desert Bedouin boundaries" were laid down in favor of Bedouin chiefs. These boundaries included vast areas of agricultural lands which normally should be treated as state domains.

The French civil and military administrations encouraged their Bedouin friends to lay their hands on sparsely populated large fertile state domain lands. This was a serious abuse of the existing law, ruling out the control of the domains administration. The country with its parliament is, therefore, faced with two serious problems: (1) finding a solution to the problem of this Bedouin entity created by the French, which makes Bedouin settlement difficult, and (2) revision of the redistribution of such lands in order to provide land to the landless.

In accordance with the new Syrian constitution and civil code, redistribution takes into account the following points.

A maximum limit of ownership (area) and tenancy has to be defined by laws. Such areas vary according to the local conditions prevailing in each district. These laws are not retroactive.

Laws should be passed with the object of encouraging the small and medium ownerships.

The state domains should be distributed among those who have no utilization (tenancy) rights against a small fee payable in installments, and the area of such lands should be adequate to insure these occupiers good living.

Laws should be passed to protect the peasant and raise his standard of living.

Should a miri land be neglected and left unutilized (unfarmed) for a period of five years, the ownership rights are to be cancelled and the land is to revert to the state.

Members of one family for their mutual benefit could agree among themselves in writing to develop a common family property for a period not exceeding fifteen years (such a property may have been acquired by inheritance or purchase).

Priority rights on a state domain land may be obtained if the occupier can prove that during three years he has constructed a dwelling, planted trees, and improved the land. In this case, the utilization (tenancy) rights are registered in his name free of any fee, on condition that he loses his rights if the land is neglected for three years following the date of registration.

Recently two draft laws were submitted to parliament for defining a maximum limit of ownership as expressed in the constitution, for distributing state domain lands, and for reconsidering how the rights over very large areas of state domain lands were obtained under certain circumstances. These draft laws are the subject of serious discussions in parliament, which is alive to the fact that the land should become an instrument of work and a center of human activity, not a means of oppression and an instrument of servitude.

The State Domains

The state-owned domains are of two kinds: (1) public property that cannot be sold and on which no right can be acquired even with the lapse of time limitation (public buildings, roads, squares, etc.), and (2) special state domains (rural), which are not public property, the neck of which remains with the state, and which the state treats as an absolute property. The right to use and exploit special state domains may be given to persons in accordance with certain rules conforming with the local habits and administrative regulations.

Originally, most of the fertile state domain lands were owned by the Sultan Abdulhamid and administered by a special department called "Saniya," or privy administration, which was attached directly to the Sultan's person. The expenses of this administration were met from the land exploitation (cropping) revenues, and the excess balance went to the Sultan's private treasury. The Saniya administration had a secret function of reporting to the Sultan directly.

In 1909 when the Sultan abdicated and the new constitution came into being, the Sultan was forced to cede the ownership of his Saniya lands to the state. They were then termed Mudawara, or transferred domains, and later on in accordance with Article 60 of the Lausanne Treaty each state which was formerly a part of the Ottoman empire was given possession of the transferred domains situated within its boundaries. These lands were annexed to the state domains administration.

The state domains administration has branches all over the country where these lands exist, and these lands are administered as follows: (1) by lease, (2) by lease with a promise of sale, and (3) by sale.

In cultivated lands, leasing a state domain land is concluded, first, by public auction. Notice is served in accordance with the law. The terms of this type of lease cannot exceed four years. Under very special circumstances such lands may be leased by private agreements. Second, state domain land is leased by short-term leases entered into by a contract concluded before the beginning of the agricultural year (season).

In uncultivated lands, lease with a promise of sale is concluded by private agreement or by auction for a period not exceeding fifteen years for a long-term lease and ten years for shorter leases. Such a contract is concluded in accordance with the general and special terms conforming with the special regulations and obligations. The value of such lands is decided upon by the authorities and local committees concerned. The value is payable in fifteen or ten yearly installments, and the annual rent is fixed at a figure equivalent to three one-thousandths of the sales value. A reduction of 1 per cent is allowed for advance or cash payment on large exploitations and 10 per cent in the case of small exploitations. However, the obligations include punctual payment of the installments and rents, exploitation of the land by the tenant himself, obtaining permission before transferring tenancy rights to others, construction of the necessary buildings on the land, and planting of trees as may be ruled in the contract.

In both cases of leasing cultivated state domain land the main object is that the tenant himself should farm the land, and priority of obtaining the land is given to the inhabitants of the area.

Leasing uncultivated, vacant, or free lands includes hunting lands situated within boundaries of state forests. The contract here also is concluded by private agreement or auction, provided the terms of the contract do not exceed fifteen years. These contracts expire either when the tenant becomes owner or when he gives up his tenancy prior to the expiration of his contract. If, however, the state domains administration for any reason finds it necessary to terminate the contract, the administration pays the tenant an indemnity to cover the estimated value of buildings and trees.

Table 1 shows the extent of state domain lands in Syria, exclusive of the lands within Bedouin tribal boundaries.

TABLE 1

STATE DOMAIN LANDS IN SYRIA

District	Area (in hectares)	Number of Villages
Damascus	24,520	12
Hauran	10,902	85
Homs	535,526	164
Hama	269,177	63
Latakiah	8,025	61
Aleppo	462,835	600
Euphrates	5,560	36
Jezireh	26,578	93
Total	1,343,123	1,114

The Rural Lands

CADASTRAL WORK

When the Ottomans evacuated Syria, most of the properties were left unregistered; and in 1920 when the short-lived independent government of Syria was just on the verge of changing the laws to adapt them to the new ideas, needs, and circumstances, the French occupation of the country took place. It was long after the establishment of their mandatory administration that the French took the necessary measures for solving the prevailing disputes on lands and boundaries and rights on the Musha, or common share of the lands. Such measures were imperative for the development of the rural property.

For this purpose, in 1933 the French government in Syria entered into a contract with a person named Mr. Derafour for carrying out cadastral work in the states subjected to the French mandatory administration, which then included the territories of Syria, Lebanon, Alawites, and Alexandretta. In accordance with this contract, Derafour submitted bills of his expenditures, which were paid by the French and debited to the accounts of the *Intérêts Communs Administration*. Derafour was to charge for himself 10 per cent over all the total values of his bills. He provided the instruments and recruited the necessary local staff.

After 1940, with the British occupation of Syria, the Syrian government tried to rid itself of this very expensive burden. The death of Mr. Derafour took place about this time, the contract was terminated, and the whole cadastral system was incorporated in the lands department (*Services Foncières*) as an independent administration, and its work continued as before, with the necessary number of foreign experts being employed.

As time went on, the tempo of the cadastral work slowed down owing to certain limiting factors that might be grouped as follows: (1) the increasing flow of applications for land settlement and consolidation, (2) budgetary limitations affecting the number of staff and the purchase of instruments, and (3) shortage of trained personnel.

The solving of disputes and the *lotissement et remembrement* have really led to the development of the settled areas in most parts of Syria (with the exception of large areas in the Jeziret and parts of the Euphrates) where the Musha, or common ownership, was given an end. The boundaries between properties that belonged to villagers and nonvillagers were definitely cleared, and land owners and tenants prospered. Such results caused the flooding of the land department with applications for opening the cadastral and rural improvement operations in the various districts.

The special circumstances that have prevailed in Syria since 1943 and 1945 have not permitted the government to allocate all the necessary funds required for expanding the work and purchasing instruments, although they have been quite alive to the benefit resulting from and necessity of allocating generous funds for this purpose. The present instruments are becoming quite difficult to use. They need replacement and additional quantities need to be purchased to cope with the increasing demands for settlement work.

The shortage of staff is becoming a serious problem, since a number of the old staff have retired or passed away or have found better-paid employment with other local and foreign companies. It is hoped, however, that when circumstances permit, a training center will be organized for recruiting and training the necessary staff.

The late Mr. Derafour followed the Swiss system of cadastre, and it is followed still by the Syrian land department. This system follows Topography, Geodesie, and Triangulation as a basis for the cadastral operations, the main object being to define clearly the boundaries of every property.

The rural lands development operations aim at the just distribution and parcellation of the lands consistent with the rights held thereof and according to the type of soils and their productivity; consequently, the classification of the lands and sites is made in such a way that each owner is given a reduced number of possibly adjacent, larger fields instead of his numerous shares in numerous plots.

We know that in Talliseh Village, one person was recorded as having owned shares in sixty-seven Musha plots, the width of each plot not exceeding one and one-half meters. After the settlement operations, this same person owned three fields that he could farm or let easily and freely. The plan of Gando Village shows clearly the position of the distribution of property before and after the operations.

The operations of the rural land settle-

TABLE 2

CLASSIFICATION OF LAND IN SYRIA

	Hectares
Areas most unsuited for farming without applying special development schemes	10,709,771
Area surveyed and consolidated	3,524,732
Area to be surveyed and consolidated	4,213,383
Total area of Syria	18,447,886

ment and improvement are carried out as follows.

In the area declared open for the operations, a local committee is formed, composed of the following members: the Agricultural Officer (or Inspector) of the area, the head of the village (Mukhtar), and two experts selected jointly by the owners of lands. This committee is headed by the land magistrate in charge of the operations. The duties of this committee are the classification and evaluation of the land and the consideration of factors affecting use of the land.

The classification of the land is taken as a basis for the redistribution (*remembrement et lotissement*) work. (See tables 2 and 3.)

The evaluation of the land takes into consideration its productivity and other factors for establishing an "equivalence." In consultation with the local people, the members of the committee decide among themselves that (taking all factors into consideration) the field under reference could be divided into five categories, each being marked down and enumerated very carefully on a provisional map brought by the cadastre officers. These defined areas are carefully measured and a value thereof is

TABLE 3

PRIVATE LANDHOLDINGS IN SYRIA

DISTRICT	SMALL (less than 10 hectares)		MEDIUM (10–100 hectares)		LARGE (over 100 hectares)		PERCENTAGE OF STATE-OWNED LAND
	Number	Percentage of Area	Number	Percentage of Area	Number	Percentage of Area	
Damascus	178,000	21	288,000	34	348,000	42	3
Aleppo	265,000	13	646,000	30	745,000	35	22
Homs	38,000	4	130,000	12	157,000	15	69
Hama	8,000	1	145,000	24	195,000	31	44
Hauran	195,000	46	188,000	45	27,000	6	3
Euphrates	133,000	15	286,000	32	246,000	28	40
Jezireh	56,000	5	528,000	52	343,000	34	20
Latakiah	175,000	28	340,000	38	207,000	33	5
Sweida (Jebel Druz)	110,000	33	175,000	53	45,000	14	..
Total	1,158,000	15	2,726,000	33	2,353,000	29	23

given by the committee; also, the values of the shares held by each owner are calculated and compared. They decide, for instance, that plot number 1 is worth one and one-half times plot number 2 and that plot number 1 is worth four times plot number 3; a convenient coefficient is established, and each owner given a definite plot in a definite site, the value of which should be consistent with the original value of his share. Each owner's choice of neighbors is given a positive consideration. A married couple or brothers or friends may wish to become neighbors. The fields are arranged accordingly.

The draft classification and evaluation is declared open for criticism within twenty days, and each owner can bring his objections, if he has any, to the committee. If his request is accepted, the necessary adjustments are made with the aid of local experts selected by the land magistrate and the file is sent to the technical department for further calculations.

The establishment of roads to give access to each owner is also the subject of careful examination and layout.

The irrigation canals are seriously considered when dealing with irrigable lands, and the magistrate marks down these canals so that each field should be able to draw water from the main canal. Priority right is registered in favor of lands situated at the farthest end of the main canal whereby owners can draw their share (ration) of the irrigation water first.

Once the foregoing operations reach this stage, the land magistrate decides that the necessary formalities should be completed for concluding the work. He sets up a list of owners and their neighbors (whose rights are finally defined) and the documents are sent to the technical department for completing the distribution. The final draft settlement project is then put to notice for thirty days and applications are invited only

for ascertaining whether the allocated fields are equivalent to the owner's shares and for determining whether the owners were satisfied with their neighbors. No objection as to the evaluation or classification is entertained at this stage, since an opportunity was given previously for this purpose. The completion of these formalities (transactions) marks the end of the operations. The land is handed over to its owner, and a registration document is given to him in accordance with the existing legislation.

EVALUATION

In evaluating land, the following factors are taken into consideration and calculated: (1) crop production and soil type and fertility, (2) local sales values per unit area, (3) local practice and experience when comparing, exchanging, or selling land by villagers (dwellers) among themselves, and (4) labor availability and requirements.

TAXATION

Taxation in Syria is very much simplified. All agricultural products are subjected to a tax of 7 per cent of their value when moved for consumption. The total amount of this tax collected in 1950 was approximately 8 million dollars. All town properties pay 7 per cent of their value as estimated by the proper departments of the ministry of finance.

However, the Syrian parliament is considering the possibility of imposing a heavy progressive taxation system on rural land in order to apply an automatic area restriction.

CREDIT

The Agricultural (State) Bank, with a capital of about eight million dollars, extends loans on short and long terms against mortgaging a settled property at an interest of 6 per cent. On granting loans, only 60 per cent of the value of arable lands and 40 per cent of the value of lands under trees are considered. The payments of long-term loans are extended over ten yearly installments.

A proposed draft law is in parliament aiming at facilitating loans to small farmers, accepting the mortgage of unsettled Musha shares, and opening current and other accounts in favor of small and medium farmers and co-operative societies.

This credit facility is not adequate, and small farmers and tenants have to pay a heavy and greedy interest either to wealthy landlords or to local lenders. It is hoped that when circumstances permit, the government will be enabled to increase the capital and activities of the Agricultural Bank. Syria enjoys a positive trade balance and a good national income. Since three-fourths of its population are interested in farming, the provision of credit facility will greatly relieve the rural population.

LANDLORD AND TENANT

Land in Syria is worked by a written lease between landlord and tenant for a limited period, by the share system, and by direct operation of the landlord.

In the share system, if the landlord provides the land and habitation only he gets about 30 per cent of the produce. If, in addition, the landlord plows the land with a tractor and pays 50 per cent of the expense of clearing water canals, etc. he gets 50 per cent of the produce. The cost of manure is borne equally by landlord and tenant. All other farm operations are carried out by the farmer.

In direct operations, the landlord farms his land and employs laborers and pays a foreman a salary ranging from $250 to $300 per annum, plus about 400 kilograms of grain for his bread. When there are fruit trees, the tenant gets, in addition, 25 per cent of the value of the fruit but is required to look after the trees in accordance with the directions given him.

When the landlord keeps milking cows, the usual custom is for the landlord and tenant to share the yield equally. Sometimes the tenant pays 50 per cent of the value of the cows and becomes a share owner. Then expenses are shared equally. This practice varies according to district and to local practice.

THE LAND TENURE SITUATION IN IRAN

§§§§   *Assadollah Alam*

FIRST OF ALL, I should like to thank the University of Wisconsin and those agencies of the United States government which have provided this opportunity to us, as delegates from Iran, to express our views and difficulties in connection with land tenure questions.

Iran is predominantly agricultural. Its agricultural products are different kinds which reflect the wide variety in soil and climate. The over-all land area has been estimated at 164 million hectares. About 16 million hectares of these are classified as crop lands. But no more than approximately 4 million hectares out of the 16 million hectares of crop land are under actual cultivation every year. Another 30 million hectares has been estimated potentially cultivable. Therefore it can easily be seen what a large potentially cultivable area has been left unused in Iran due to undeveloped irrigation and lack of capital. In addition to the crop land, 10 million hectares of forest and 15 million hectares of pasture land are also in the list of estimated figures.

As far as land tenancy is concerned, the

cultivated, or cultivable, lands in Iran can be classified under two major categories, namely:

1. The land which is owned by land owners but is cultivated by someone else, the landlord receiving an annual fixed income or a share of the crop. This category constitutes the major part of the farms in Iran and includes the lands owned by the State, by the Crown, and the lands endowed for certain charity purposes (tithed lands).

2. The second category is composed of lands which are owned and cultivated by the same person—the farmer.

After this classification, in order to realize the essential land tenure position in Iran we must consider the question of land tenancy in connection with the other major elements working on the land, regardless of the legal ownership, in order to constitute a farm and to produce a crop. Generally speaking, for this purpose we can name in Iran five major elements, which are: land, water, seed, labor (labor usually produced by the farmer), and equipment. Equipment includes all tools necessary for cultivation and housing.

Generally, all the five major elements are considered equally important in raising crops. Therefore, whoever possesses any one, or any combination, of these elements is entitled to the same proportion of the crop raised. This is the general principle. However, if we travel within the country we will see that not only the possession of any, or any combination, of these major elements by one person varies from one region to another but also the relative value of these elements and accordingly the share of their possessor from the crop vary from one section to another. In most cases we see that the land and water belong to the land owner and that the seed, the labor, and equipment are provided by the farmer. In this combination, if the water is to be supplied through certain expensive ways, for example, by

kanat, which is an old Iranian device to drain the underground water to the lower surface, then the possessor of the land and water takes two shares out of five of the crop and the remainder belongs to the farmer who has provided the other three elements, namely, labor, seed, and equipment. Contrary to this, if the crop is rain-fed and the water is not so difficult to get, then the land owner does not get more than one-fifth of the crop or its equivalent in money. In some regions where there is no water supply and the crop depends completely on the rain to grow farming involves great risk because of irregularity of the rainfall. In these regions the land owner does not get more than one-tenth of the crop. These three general examples show the varying value of the major elements of farming in Iran and their respective shares from the product.

Now, in referring to the land alone, we must admit that land ownership in Iran is highly concentrated in the hands of a small number of individuals among whom absenteeism is frequent and who are not often well prepared to utilize the law in its best way or to invest substantial amounts of capital in new lines of agricultural economy. Side by side with these are a large number of undersized holdings which cannot be considered efficient and economic units. This situation in the rural areas is both one of the major causes and one of the results of incredible poverty and low hygienic and educational levels.

Now, I must say that in this situation the Iranian Government, especially during the last two decades, has not completely failed to take effective measures to better the situation; in fact, I must say that it has been successful to some extent. It has been the policy of most of the governments who have come to power in Iran during the last two decades to encourage the development of small land ownership through distributing the state-owned lands among farmers and extending credits to them from the Agricultural Bank.

Fifteen years ago the late King H.I.M. Reza Shah Pahlavi issued an order according to which a considerable area of high quality state-owned crop lands of Sistan province was distributed among the farmers, who were required to pay off the price of their allocated land during ten years. Recently an independent irrigation corporation has been set up by the government to supply water for the present potentially cultivable lands. The various departments of the Ministry of Agriculture, of which I was in charge for some time, are working to help out the land owners as well as the farmers with their problems and difficulties. This ministry carries out a very important task of combatting livestock and plant diseases and pests. The fight against the locust is also one of the major tasks of this ministry.

Gentlemen, in most of our deliberations and experiences with regard to the land tenancy questions as well as other agricultural economic problems we have come to this conclusion: that land tenancy is not the only problem, though it is one of the most important ones. Especially is this true in Iran, where, as I mentioned before, the farmer does not always possess all the elements of farming, such as seed and equipment. Therefore, even if the farmer is given the legal ownership of the land, still this must be supplemented by the establishment of certain types of co-operatives and management agencies to help them out with day-by-day problems and financial difficulties. This task has been carried out in most parts of Iran by the land ownership institution for centuries past. These supplementary land reform projects need capital and leadership.

Iran, perhaps like many other countries, lacks this capital for the time being, and this seriously affects the success of any land reform project. I will come to the concrete example of this type of failure when I speak of two major economic development projects initiated during recent years.

One of these projects is the one called the Seven Year Plan. This plan was, under the order of the Council of Ministers, made by Morrisson Knudson Corporation, which is an American institution. The project embraces a wide range of governmental activities and co-ordinates them into a single program. As far as the agricultural aspect of the plan is concerned, it is intended to develop the cultivation of certain main products by mechanizing agriculture, combatting plant pests, providing the growers with technical assistance and advance payments, making available some facilities for importing agricultural machinery, and giving the growers proper instructions. Therefore, an essential principle has been taken into consideration—that apart from endeavoring to solve the problems related to land tenancy in favor of efficiency and democracy, an attempt must also be made to increase the productivity of the land, regardless of who ultimately benefits from the result. Of course there is no doubt that if a farm does not produce an economic amount of crop it will not help its farmer, even if he becomes the owner of the land.

The Seven Year Plan was supposed to be financed by loans from the International Bank and from the United States and by revenue from the oil industry of Iran.[1] But unfortunately the loans from the International Bank for Reconstruction and Development and from the United States have not been received. After considerable discussion and expenditure of money from the empty purse of Iran, these loans still have not been made available, and our revenue from the oil has been held by the former Anglo-Iranian Oil Company because of the recent dispute over the nationalization act of the Parliament.

The second major land reform project in Iran has been initiated by His Imperial Majesty the Shah Mohamad Reza Shah Pahlavi. His Majesty, being greatly concerned with the well-being of the farmers, issued an order in February, 1951, that all crown lands were to be distributed among the farmers against reasonable long-term payments. There has been set up an *ad hoc* royal commission to supervise the execution of this order. I have the honor of being a member of this commission as well as the inspecting director of the Crown Land Office.[2]

The importance of these land reform projects of His Imperial Majesty may be appreciated when we see that about three thousand villages out of a total of forty-five thousand existing in Iran are subject to His Majesty's order.

The form of dividing the crown lands among the farmers, of course, varies according to the domestic conditions of each region of the country in which the land is located. However, I can formulate the general provisions of such a distribution as follows:

1. The lands are to be divided among those who are actually occupying or who will be occupying the same land.

2. The size of the land allotted to each farmer is to be not less than a minimum size to provide a fair standard of living for its cultivator's family.

3. The price of the allocated land to each farmer is to be paid on a long-term basis during twenty-five years.

4. The total amount of the price of the land is determined as approximately ten times the annual land owner's share of the crop. Moreover, His Majesty, being kind to his people, has ordered a 20 per cent reduction from the whole amount of the price as estimated in the above-mentioned formula. Therefore, what a farmer actually will pay annually as the price of his allocated land is equal to about one-third of his annual payment which would have been paid to the land owner in the past as his share of the crop.

5. The farmer has no right to transfer the purchased land to anyone else as long as he has not paid off all his annual payment in due time.

6. The annually collected money from the farmers is to be invested for public economic and social welfare. This money can also be employed as credit for certain banking institutions as explained below.

7. An Agricultural Bank is to be established as a mother agency for the co-operative institutions in the crown's villages thus distributed. These co-operative institutions are designed to provide any kind of technical, financial, and social help that the farmers used to receive in the past from the Crown Land Office. Moreover, these co-operative institutions will provide, on reasonable terms, the farmers with the modern home and farm utilities and will help them in marketing their crops. Therefore, the farmer who receives land under His Majesty's above-mentioned order will not only be the owner of his farm but also he will have access to certain co-operative institutions established in his community, institutions which are not common in any of the Iranian agricultural communities up to the present time.

Thus, Gentlemen, as you see here in this very last analysis His Majesty does not sell his lands to the farmers but rather he gives them to the farmers as a gift in the form of land to each individual farmer and in the form of credit for the co-operative institutions of the community.

Of course, I must also mention certain serious difficulties which have arisen in executing His Majesty's order to divide the Crown lands among the farmers. These difficulties, generally speaking, are the following:

1. The effect of the inheritance law upon the matter. This will certainly lead to uneconomic subdivision of land allocated to one farmer at the present time as an economic-size farm. This question becomes more serious when we see that life expectancy in Iran is low and that thus the farms become more often subject to the application of the inheritance law than in some other countries such as the United States in which the expectancy of life is high.

2. The number of applicants for land in most villages is far greater than the amount of land available for distribution. Therefore, the land in its minimum economic size must be given to the qualified farmers. But, as you know, the qualifications may disappear as time passes, especially if the farmer dies, since no one can be sure that his usual legal successor will possess the same qualifications.

3. As I mentioned before, we must determine the minimum economic size available in each village for each farmer. On the other hand, we know that a size of land which may be considered minimum economic size today may not be so tomorrow, because of the changing conditions of life and agricultural science.

4. The payment, as the price of the land, is split up for twenty-five years. If during this period the farmer who has bought the land dies, there will be left a considerable complication about the responsibility of his descendants for the rest of the payment.

5. In some regions of Iran, besides the land owner and the actual farmer some other person has acquired in one way or another certain rights in connection with the land. Therefore, the transfer of complete legal ownership of the land to the actual farmer affects that third party's right unless some sort of mutual agreement is worked out.

6. Finally, the establishment of the bank and the co-operative institutions to replace the Crown Land Office in assisting the farmers requires, in the beginning, a considerable amount of capital. The Crown Land Office is not able for the time being to provide such capital, nor is any other available agency within the country. Therefore, from this point of view the execution of such a helpful and well-devised project of land reform in Iran has been seriously affected and in fact may come to a standstill.

This is why I feel obliged to call the attention of the United States authorities who deal with the Point Four and other technical and financial assistance programs to this serious problem which faces Iran in carrying out its so-necessary land reform program. I may just add another point in this connection—that should His Majesty's land reform plan in Iran (the largest and most important plan of its kind in the country's history) fail because of lack of capital within the country and because of the lack of financial aids from other democratic countries it will certainly be a serious blow to the confidence of those individuals, especially farmers, who believe in democratic procedure in agricultural economic reforms in Iran, as well as in neighboring states. This must be given more attention, especially when you consider that our country has been geographically located in the front row of the free world.

In spite of the above-mentioned difficulties, the Crown Land Office and the *ad hoc* Royal Commission have used all their possibilities to execute His Majesty's order. In the short time since the decision has been taken by His Majesty they have been able to divide one large village among the farmers and are in the process of dividing three others (which may be already divided, when I am speaking to you). Meanwhile, in doing so they are collecting experience for their future steps.

In the last minute of my time, Gentlemen, I should like also to call your attention to the close connection of the land tenure question with that of security, whether it is internal or external. In the present world, one can find many concrete examples where all the major elements of cultivation are available to one person but still social and political circumstances do not allow him to work out his long-term plans and his ways and means to provide a better living for himself, for his family, and for his fellow man.

THE LAND TENURE SYSTEM OF EGYPT

Mohamed Abdel Wahab Ezzat

EGYPT IS predominantly an agricultural country with 75 per cent of the population depending for their livelihood on agriculture. Although the total area of Egypt is about 386,000 square miles, only about 13,500 square miles are cultivable. This productive area is approximately 8 million acres, of which 6 million acres were under cultivation in 1947. In the same year the population of the country exceeded 19 million people; and 99 per cent of the population lived in the cultivable area of the Delta and the Nile Valley, which represents about 3 per cent of the total area of the country.

Egypt is one of the most highly congested population areas in the whole world. In 1947 it had an average of 1,210 persons per square mile dependent upon agricultural land. Probably nowhere else in the world is there so large a population per square mile that is dependent solely upon agriculture as in Egypt.

Thanks to the perennial irrigation system which makes possible the production of two or even three crops per year from the same piece of land, the crop area of the country far exceeds the cultivable area. In 1948 the crop area was about 9.1 million acres, while the cultivable area was only 5.8 million acres. The supply of land could be increased only by huge irrigation and drainage projects, but the increase would by no means be large.

The main crops of Egypt are cotton, cloves, corn, wheat, sugar cane, and barley. On cotton the economy of the country revolves, and cotton usually occupies about 10 per cent of the crop area.

Although the death rate is very high in Egypt, especially among infants, it will certainly decline with the spread of the medical services to the rural areas, which are only now securing the benefits of medical science. The birth rate, on the other hand, is also very high, and for cultural reasons is not likely to drop as fast as the death rate. The result will be a rapid increase of the country's population. In the absence of rapid industrialization, this means more population pressure on the land.

The man-land ratio is high, reaching three persons per acre in some of the provinces, which necessarily means a very low standard of living.

The present concept of private property rights was not developed in Egypt until the second half of the nineteenth century. The inequality of opportunity for getting land which prevailed under Turkish rule and continued to prevail with some modifications during more recent history is responsible for the present concentration of land ownership in a few hands.

In 1890 the total number of holdings was 767,000. By 1945 this number had increased to 2,606,000. This increase in the number of landed properties is accounted for by the increase in the number of very small holdings which are often too small to provide their operators with even a minimum subsistence level of living. Holdings of less than 5 acres numbered 611,000 in 1890 and 2,447,000 in 1945, while the holdings of 5 to 50 acres increased slightly from 144,000 in 1890 to 147,000 in 1945. The number of holdings of 50 acres and up was 12,000 in both 1896 and 1945.

In 1945 holdings of less than 1 acre accounted for 71 per cent of the total, those of 1 to 2 acres for 13 per cent, and those of 2 to 5 acres for 10 per cent of the total number of holdings. This means that holdings of less than 5 acres accounted for 94 per cent of the total number of holdings. Holdings of 5 to 50 acres were 5.5 per cent of the total, and only .5 per cent of the holdings were above 50 acres in size.

In terms of area the picture was different. The group of holdings of less than 5 acres occupied 34 per cent of the total area and averaged .8 acre per holding; the group of 5 to 50 acres occupied 30 per cent of the total area and averaged 12 acres per holding; and the group of holdings of more than 50 acres occupied 36 per cent of the area and averaged 179 acres in size.

The average size of farm in Egypt in 1947 was 6 acres. But the majority of the farms were far smaller than the average. Farms of less than 1 acre represented 37 per cent of the total; those of between 1 and 2 acres, 20 per cent; and those of less than 5 acres represented more than 80 per cent of the total number of farms. Those of between 5 and 50 acres accounted for 18 per cent and those of above 50 acres for about 1 per cent of the farms.

Besides the very small size of the Egyptian farms, most of them are made up of numerous tracts, sometimes of very impractical size and sometimes at great distance from each other and from the farmer's house.

Inheritance is the principal way by which land is acquired. The available data on tenure groups in Egypt are probably not completely reliable but do indicate that landless agricultural laborers outnumber the owner-operators and the renters combined. The number of landless laborers has increased rapidly; the increase was 121 per cent in the 10 years between 1927 and 1937.

Comparison of average wage rates and land values in Egypt and the United States for 1945 shows that an average acre of farm land in the United States was worth the equivalent of less than 10 days of the average farm worker's wages. In Egypt an equivalent farm land area claimed a price equal to about 20 years of the average Egyptian worker's wages.

The investigation of the Peasants' Department of the Egyptian Ministry of Social Affairs has revealed that on the big estates where records are kept and where some of the land is operated by the owner and some of it is rented out the rents charged were in some cases higher than the net output obtained from the land operated by the owner. This shows that tenants in Egypt frequently are little better off than the agricultural laborers. Actually, their rental payments in many cases absorb part of their income as laborers and operators, as well as the full economic rent due to land.

Farm credit facilities available in Egypt do not help either the agricultural laborers or the tenants in climbing the agricultural ladder. Land owners, however, are given short-term production credit and long-term reclamation credit if they are able to offer the needed security.

As to costs, returns, and efficiency on different sizes of farms in 1947, about 81 per cent of the Egyptian farms were of small size, with an average of 1.4 acres and average gross output of 35.4 Egyptian pounds per acre; 18 per cent were of medium size (5 to 50 acres), with an average size of 12.4 acres and an average gross output of 39.9 Egyptian pounds per acre; and only 1 per cent of the farms were of large size (over 50 acres), with an average size of 173.4 acres and an average gross output of 36.9 Egyptian pounds per acre. The medium-size farms in the 5 to 10 acres size group had the highest average gross income—an average of 41.4 Egyptian pounds per acre.

According to a survey undertaken in 1938, the most productive and the most efficient size of farm was found to be around 5 acres. This means that the breakdown of the large estates into medium-size farms and the elimination of the very small could lead to an increase in total productivity and in the national agricultural output.

The land tenure system affects the national agricultural production in two ways: (1) The system favors production of particular crops which suit either the owners of small parcels of land or the absentee landowners. While the value of the national agricultural output could be increased through a shift in crop production, the land tenure system does not permit such shifts. (2) The number of medium-size farms, the most efficient size in Egypt, is very small compared with that of the very small and the large farms.

The land tenure system in Egypt results in the existence of a very large group of landless agricultural laborers who, because of limited industrial activities, are forced to rely on agriculture for their livelihood. Because of their large number and the concentration of land in a few hands, they are forced to accept very low wages which do not permit an acceptable standard of living. Second, the large tenant class and their weak bargaining position as compared with that of the landlords leads to rack renting. Instead of making something out of their work, most tenants live miserable lives and deprive themselves in order to be able to pay their high rents. Third, the standard of living for the majority of the farm people is very low.

Forms of rent payments in Egypt include cash rent, share rent, rent in kind, and rent in kind and cash at the same time.

Length of leases in Egypt varies from one crop only to three years or even more. But the year-to-year lease is the most common. This kind of lease does not give the tenant any security of tenure and makes it impossible for him to plan his operations over a period of years.

The political power of the landowners in Egypt was such that it was difficult to enact any legislation that would have an adverse effect on their traditional rights. Measures for improving the tenure system fall into two categories: direct and indirect.

Direct Measures

Direct measures include steps to secure the following:

Increases in the land area under cultivation.—The government is studying different schemes for making the utmost use of the water of the River Nile. The Nile floods highly during three months of the year, during which a good part of its rich water goes to the sea. The schemes involve the erection of a number of dams and reservoirs, some of which are not located in Egyptian territory. This needs on the one hand huge amounts of money and on the other hand an agreement with the neighboring countries. These schemes are likely to add to the already cultivated area an additional area of 4 million acres.

More equitable distribution of landholdings.—Three years ago State Domains Administration (Ministry of National Economy) reclaimed a part of its land. It has been divided into units of 5 acres each. Small houses of two rooms and utilities for each unit have been built in modern villages each containing 200 houses, a rural school, a mosque, a small hospital; all other services are provided. These units were given to the landless people chosen by the Ministry of Social Affairs from the over-populated provinces. For the first 10 years there is a contract of lease, at the end of which the farmer automatically becomes the owner. The price of the land will be paid on an installment basis during a period of 40 years. It should be the policy of the government to distribute all the newly reclaimed land on this basis.

More efficient size of units.—This step involves putting a ceiling on land ownership as well as preventing fragmentation of holdings.

More equitable landowner-tenant relations.—The Ministry of Social Affairs is seriously considering this problem with the objective of organizing the landlord-tenant relationship.

Indirect Measures

Indirect measures for improving the tenure system include the following:

Education.—Since 1950 free education has been provided in Egypt up to the stage of high schools. The number of schools is rapidly increasing.

Industrialization.—Although industrialization is always mentioned whenever the advancement and progress of the economically underdeveloped countries are discussed, it is not as easy an objective to achieve as many people are inclined to think. In order to succeed, industrialization must be based on a sound economic basis, and many prerequisite conditions must be present. Some of the prerequisites of industrialization are present in Egypt; others are not. However, there has been some progress in this respect in Egypt since the first world war. The number of industrial laborers in 1950 totalled 600,000. The generation of the hydroelectric power from the Asswan Dam and other dams will certainly accelerate industrialization to some extent.

Migration.—This is mainly a political issue.

Birth Control.—Spread of education and industrialization will be effective in this matter.

All these measures are complementary, and no single one can solve the problem by itself. It is only through a well-planned, carefully integrated program of action involving these proposed measures that the tenure system in Egypt can be improved.

PRACTICAL PROPOSALS FOR THE SOLUTION OF LAND TENURE PROBLEMS IN LEBANON

Najib Alamuddin

HAVING COME at the tail end of the Middle East caravan, my task has been made very simple. My able colleagues have exposed to you the land tenure problems in many of the Arabic speaking countries. These problems are common to all of our countries. The historical background, the cultural patterns, the grass roots, all were ably exposed. I shall not, therefore, take your time by duplicating what has been said. I shall follow a simple procedure of first introducing my country, second, exposing briefly our land tenure problems in Lebanon, and third, proceeding to follow what Dr. Tannous has accused me of doing, and that is to follow my own way of humbly submitting to this conference a few suggestions which I believe may be of value.

Lebanon is a very small country. Unfortunately, its land tenure problems are not proportional to its size. They are as serious, as real, and as grave as the land tenure problems in any of the other Middle East countries. My friend Dr. Tannous started on the physical description of Lebanon. I wish he had finished that description. Lebanon is a very beautiful country. It is called the Switzerland of the Middle East, and it is a summer and winter resort to the various Middle East countries. Its area is only 10,400 square kilometers, about 4,000 square miles. Of that area we have only 270,000 hectares under cultivation. The rest is pasture land and forest land. Some of the mountainous land is completely waste land. There is no possibility of a considerable increase in the land under cultivation. It is estimated that only around 80,000 hectares could be added to the land already under cultivation in Lebanon. Of the 270,000 hectares under cultivation, only 44,000 are under irrigation. This area, however, could be increased considerably with the introduction of irrigation projects which are quite possible. The population of Lebanon is about 1,200,000 people, 70 to 75 per cent of whom are farming people. Making a few manipulations in arithmetic, one can easily see that we have 115 persons per square kilometer—384 per square mile. On cultivated land, with 75 per cent of the population farmers, we have 333 persons per square kilometer, or about 832 per square mile.

Our chief exports from Lebanon are citrus products, olive oil, onions, some cereals, and emigrants. Our trade is not balanced. We balance our trade through invisible sources of revenue. As a tourist country, as a country that has a free currency market, as a country that serves the hinterland with transit trade, we have indirect or invisible sources of revenue. We also have a very important source of revenue, that is, the money sent back to the home country by our emigrants.

That, in brief, is a description of Lebanon. I shall not go into a political description, since we are not supposed to touch on politics.

Now, the land tenure problem in Lebanon is, as I have said, similar to the problems in the various Arab countries. The other night when I sat down to listen to the Undersecretary of State, Mr. Thorp, describing a distressed farmer I could believe that Mr. Thorp was describing the farmers of Lebanon. When I later heard many of my colleagues in this conference, I became convinced that they, too, probably considered Mr. Thorp's statement to apply to their farmers. I think I would like to repeat the statement of Mr. Thorp for the purpose of emphasizing the condition and the state of farmers in many parts of the world. Mr. Thorp said: "Let me describe the kind of situation which presents the greatest problems. Let us consider a farmer who has to support his family of six on the produce of less than two acres. He does not own the land. He rents it from an absentee landlord who take two-thirds of the crop for rent. He has no security of tenure. He does not know how long he can work on this farm. Another tenant may come along next year and offer even higher rent. This farmer has had to borrow money from a professional money lender. He pays 40 per cent interest, and his debt is bigger now than it was a year ago. He has friends who pay 60 per cent interest; one who borrows at 80 per cent."

I believe Mr. Thorp was conservative in the description of this farmer if the description is applied to Lebanon. Our farmer does not only pay 40, 60, or 80 per cent interest on his loans; usually he pays 10 per cent per month, making it 120 per cent per annum at compound interest. Sometimes he pays 300 per cent. Our farmer's land is not only divided into three plots, widely scattered, it is divided into many times more plots. Fortunately the government is attempting the consolidation of these fragments. I may say that in one village the number of parcels is 32,000, the number of parcels per property is 56, and the area of each parcel is about 0.06 hectare. The width of each parcel is a few meters and the length is a few kilometers. It is estimated that 30 per cent of efficiency is lost because of this fragmentation, 10 per cent because of the distance, 10 per cent due to the loss of land, and 10 per cent due to excessive seeding. As for the size of holding in Lebanon, I will mention that 171 properties represent half the area of the cultivated land. In other words, 0.2 per cent of the proprietors own 50 per cent of the land. Mr. Thorp said that his farmer was tired and discouraged. Our farmer is tired, discouraged, desperate, and helpless. He is in a complete state of apathy. Many writers have misunderstood this state of apathy in our part of the world and have erroneously called it fatalism. Fatalism is not the cause of the distress of our farmer. We have fatalism, but it is not the cause of the distress of our farmer. His distress is caused by the various land tenure problems we have had. The hundreds of thousands of Lebanon farmers who have emigrated from Lebanon to the various parts of the world have certainly proved that they were not deterred by fatalism. They have proved that they are just as hard-working and industrious as their fellow men. Secretary Thorp said that a farmer carried his crop to the market on the back of a donkey. Well, our farmer, in many cases, does not even own that donkey. He carries the crop to the market on his own back, and when he reaches there not only does he have to accept the prices offered but he is usually cheated on weights of his crop and on the prices he can get.

As a result of the great population pressure on the land, a great number of our Lebanon farmers emigrated from Lebanon to countries generous enough to accept them. I can safely state that in North and South America alone we have as many Lebanese as we have in Lebanon. As a result of the pressure of population on the land and, also, the inflation caused by the last war, the price of land soared beyond economic levels. It costs over two thousand dollars to purchase an acre of irrigated land suitable for fruit tree planting and over fifteen hundred dollars to purchase an acre suitable for citrus planting.

Gentlemen, the situation I exposed is not unique and confined to Lebanon. It is common to all countries in the Middle East and to many countries also outside of the Middle East.

We did not come to this conference only to listen to stories of sadness and distress. We came to this conference because we believed it is the first constructive step towards finding solutions to land tenure problems. We are anxious to exchange ideas, to learn and to take back with us what we have learned. I am not the best qualified in this gathering to offer suggestions. I am quite sure many of my learned colleagues are more qualified than I. I shall, however, humbly offer a few suggestions of what I think this conference may do.

To begin with, I think that the suggestion by the University of Wisconsin that all these speeches and all the literature should be compiled into one volume is a remarkable suggestion and a very useful one, but I am going to go a step further. I am going to suggest that this conference need not die by the time its set period expires. It must go on, and in order to go on it must have extension activities—things that we cannot accomplish in five or six weeks, things that spring from this conference and can be accomplished as extension activities of this conference.

The first is the project of compiling into

one volume the technical aspects of the various problems we have heard and will hear, the situation of land tenure in the various countries, the projects under consideration and development and execution in the various countries, and also the suggestions given by delegates of the various countries as to the possible methods of procedure in an attempt at the solution of these problems. These should be compiled into a volume which we could take back or could be sent back to us as a practical and constructive result of this conference.

A second suggestion, which is of great value to the Arab countries, is the formulation of a model land code. We are going to go back to our countries, and we are going to interest people in land reform. This will definitely mean legislation to meet the various problems of land reform. In many Arab countries we have legislation; in some we have no legislation; but we feel we do not have the experience and the talent for adequate, efficient legislation on land reform. We like to be helped and assisted, and I suggest as an extension activity of this conference that perhaps a survey of the situation be made in the Arab Middle East. Some wise men from this country should meet with some wise men from our countries, purely on an academic and technical level, and exchange ideas and experiences. With the wise men of this country giving their experiences on land reform legislation and with the wise men of our country guiding them through our national and religious laws they might jointly produce a model guide for legislation on land reform in the Arab world. That guide will not be imposed on anybody. It would be used as a reference for those interested. It would also serve as a constructive, positive project which might give interested leaders and interested people the germ of a seed for some kind of land reform. I am proposing that the University

of Wisconsin sponsor this project for the Arab world as an extension activity of this conference.

My third suggestion was touched upon by my able colleague from Egypt. In Lebanon we have population pressure on the land. So far, we are lucky in having countries accept our surplus population. There will come a time when this will no more be available to us. Doors of various countries will be closed to immigration from other countries. We are going to be attempting reform, especially improvement of sanitary conditions with its consequent effect on mortality rates. As a result we shall have a surplus population which will constitute a grave danger. Something ought to be done. We may introduce industrialization, we may acquire more land, redeem more land in the country. We may introduce agricultural irrigation projects, but that is not enough. The time will come, and is coming, when people have to consider adjustment and control of population through family limitation. It will be very appropriate as an extension activity of this conference that a project, and possibly research, be speeded up for better and more acceptable methods of family limitation.

I proceed from these suggestions as to what the conference may possibly do to some more suggestions, but these are based on a completely different aspect. I have to introduce certain facts before I proceed with my coming suggestions.

First, the Honorable Dean Acheson, Secretary of State of the United States government, made a statement on this conference now held in Wisconsin which was the subject of a press release dated October 9, 1951. I am quoting only a very small, relevant part of that release. Secretary Acheson said: "I would like to express *our interest in and support for* a significant event which opened yesterday at the University of Wisconsin."

My second fact is as follows. You all

heard Undersecretary of State Willard L. Thorp in his speech give the following statement: "We want to do more than this to encourage genuine land reform." He was talking about the help the United States government has already contributed to international organizations on land reform. "We want to do more than this to encourage genuine land reform. In the past, the United States government has provided technical aid in connection with problems of economic and social organization, as well as the technological problems involved in land tenure and related fields. We have provided both technical and financial assistance to drain, irrigate, and otherwise reclaim lands not under cultivation. We have provided technical and financial aid to industrialization and other worthy projects which have also served the purpose of providing employment for surplus farm populations. We will continue to do these things. We will do whatever else we can appropriately do to encourage and assist programs which show promise of bringing lasting benefits to farm people and of enhancing the role of agriculture in the national economy."

Likewise, may I here quote two relevant passages from the talk given to this conference by the Undersecretary of Agriculture, Mr. McCormick? He said: "We have plenty to keep us occupied tending to our business, but at the same time we are more than ready to co-operate with any of you in exchanging ideas, talking over methods, outlining spheres of action, and extending any other help that is appropriate." Then he further said: "We in the United States are not only willing to help, *we want to help.* . . . I hope that at this conference there will be a great deal of discussion as to just what a nation like the United States can do to help."

My last fact here along this line is a very realistic item of news. Most of you have read in the papers that the President of the United States has just signed a bill for nearly 7.5 billion dollars to be spent in aiding foreign countries. Now, these four facts are very significant.

Likewise, I would like to mention that we heard also from the platform of the conference and in private people who told us that land tenure problems are national and not international, people who told us that we nationals must attempt to solve our problems. This was heard from the platform, and this was heard in private conversation. That, gentlemen, is quite true. And giving credit to all our governments in the Middle East I would like to state that all of them are conscious of the necessity and urgency of land tenure reform. There are only two questions, two elements, that are of great significance. One is the element of time, and the other is the element of method of procedure. No problem that has ever faced the world has not been solved. We can solve our problems as nationals, but it will probably take us a much longer time than is anticipated in this grave international situation. Also, we may solve our problems, but the methods of solution may be different from what we expect.

The clear and definite promises and pledges made to this conference by members of the United States government are very sincere and very real. These gentlemen have done their share, in my opinion, as far as this conference goes. It is up to us now to do our share. Let us assume that they are not going to impose on us and on our countries their technical aid programs and their various other aid programs. Let us assume that such aid programs are not given to us as charity. Let us assume that they will not introduce anything which will clash with our national dignity and integrity and with our existing religious laws and traditions. Once we assume that, let us, gentlemen, proceed to tell these generous and sincere friends how they can help us. Let us point out to them the difficulties they will encounter in our countries if they attempt such programs and show them how they can overcome these difficulties. Let us put to them some concrete projects. Now, we know that in certain cases we have no concrete projects because we do not have the technical know-how to formulate these projects in a way that they can be directly executed. Let us, therefore, begin by asking for technical assistance which will help us in formulating some of these projects. I, for one, am going to ask for one at the present time. I will leave it to my other colleagues and countrymen to ask for more. I want the establishment of an organization in Lebanon to offer the farmer credit facilities at reasonable rates of interest. It is no use attempting to solve land tenure problems without credit facilities being made available to the farmer. We may take large estates from feudal landlords, divide them up, distribute them to the farmers, and if we stop at that, in five years' time these small units will revert to the money lender. All we would have achieved is changing a feudal landlord and substituting a merchant money lender in his place. I prefer the merciful feudal landlord. There is no use attempting any land tenure reform unless we adopt the basic factor that the farmer must, himself, obtain the maximum compensation for his efforts on the land. That cannot be done without credit facilities, adequate credit facilities, made available to all the farmers who need financial assistance. I shall not take your time by exposing to you the details of this project which is very near to my heart and on which I have worked for over ten years. All of you have worked out similar projects in your minds and in your experience. All I am saying is that I am accepting the challenge of these gentlemen to offer a concrete project.

A last and final suggestion comes from the end of the statement by Undersecretary McCormick I quoted. He said: "I hope that at this conference there will be a great deal of discussion as to just what a nation like the United States can do to help." In my humble way, I am going to submit a thought to our friends in Washington in response to their challenge. I am going to use land tenure language. I am going to tell my friends in Washington that absentee management and fragmentation of responsibilities are as harmful in aid programs as their equivalents in land tenure. I am going to suggest that their field representatives be qualified to make recommendations from the field and that their recommendations be taken seriously. I am going to suggest that they explain to us matters of great confusion in my mind—the various organizations that are supposed to be giving aid—FAO, TCA, ECA, Point Four. There are many organizations we hear of. I, personally, am not very clear in my mind as to what these organizations can do, what they are willing to do, and how they will be able to correlate their desire to help with our desire to tell them what help we need. I understand that technical service will be made available in the Middle East region. This is a very wise and constructive step. It is possible that similar arrangements can be set up in other parts of the world.

Gentlemen, these are my very humble suggestions to this conference. But I would like to end my talk by reminding you that when I introduced myself at the beginning of this conference, I told Professor Parsons and the conference as a whole that I would reserve the expression of my thanks until the end of the conference. I cannot wait until then. I would like to express my sincere thanks to the University of Wisconsin, to the professors who are giving us all their time, and also to the representatives of the United States government agencies present with us for the excellent way they have convinced us of their sincerity in tackling this very grave and serious problem. Thank you.

THE SIGNIFICANCE OF SOME ASPECTS OF ISLAMIC CULTURE FOR TENURE ADJUSTMENTS: A COMMENT

Elsayed Gaballah

IN THE opening address of this conference Secretary Thorp emphasized that attention should be given to the culture of each country so that solutions to tenure problems would be consistent with the values held by the people. In the Middle Eastern countries many of the values held are deeply rooted in religious origins. It seems to me that they have to be considered, even though we treat them as many economists do—as data. Furthermore, the economic content of Islamic social policy is clearly defined, even though the economic content is treated only as a means to higher values. Should economists be misled by attempts at objectivity and quantification of data and ignore these values and the social relationships leading thereto, they will not be able to formulate the tenure problems of this area.

The economic content of Islamic social policy is clearly defined. It stresses (1) maximum of production and efficiency—and I would stress that efficiency is itself a value commensurable with other moral values, (2) wide distribution of wealth, (3) earning of additional income only through work, (4) security for the underprivileged. Not only are the economic measures prescribed for the realization of the aims of social policy but there is a legal system which enforces some of them. The Western mind cannot understand economic performance in this culture if it ignores these values which have been held by tradition and enforced for centuries through a legal and educational system.

The economic measures are partly speci-

fied, partly to be realized through a democratic way of performance. On the production side, freedom of economic decisions on the part of individuals is stressed; on the exchange side, the exchange of equivalents is stressed. In taxation, a policy of the redistribution of property and income is called for. In inheritance, succession laws aim for a wide distribution of property within the family and among related families, as well as for the promotion of charitable and educational purposes. The economic system, which is supposed to operate wholly as a means to higher ends—allowing for the operation of such forces and the realization of such contents—is based upon private property, competitive pricing, and the banning of an interest rate. The latter requires that savings should go directly to equity investment, rather than be loaned out.

The values have been maintained and sustained through effective religious education and other measures. Furthermore, the failure to realize these values is considered to be due to the lack of enforcement of necessary measures. The only economic measures now fully enforced are those implemented through the laws of succession. It is to be noted that inheritance, the use of wills, etc., has a strong bearing on land tenure questions.

Among the maxims honored by many very wealthy people and institutions is the maxim requiring that they not lend surplus cash at interest. This is very important. Many of the big land owners who have surplus cash could invest it in land. Beyond this, surplus cash tends to be wasted in luxurious consumption or hoarded; the absentee ownership of land and specialization on exportable cash crops work in this direction also. But the population pressure on the land is very great, and those who are forced by their poverty to borrow must pay exorbitant interest rates. It is also important to note that the aspirations of the masses for better and freer living have been raised tremendously, stimulated both from within and without.

Now in terms of principle, we have to make certain basic reconciliations. First, the principle of technical efficiency conflicts with the principle of wide distribution of wealth—for wide distribution in a stationary economy must eventually result in an extreme subdivision of wealth. And I repeat that this very efficiency is held to be a moral value. Second, this very efficiency frustrated the desire for security through some land tenure systems, particularly the trust system known as waqf. Third, there is the reconciliation of the aloofness of lending surplus cash with economic expansion. Fourth, with most cash holders willing to invest in new lands possible of reclamation we must find a way to reconcile such investment with the popular demands for the lessening of concentration of ownership of land. Fifth, there is the necessity of expansion and the desire for wider distribution and thereby more immediate consumption in underdeveloped economies. These are the principles that conflict with each other in the operation of the economic and social systems of the Middle East.

The question of succession is closely related to land tenure. Of peculiar interest is the practice of waqf land. Waqf is some sort of trust system in which the title to the property vanishes, leaving only title to use by beneficiaries. This system insulates and freezes wealth by taking it out of circulation. Also, this is a one-way proposition; once the property goes in, it cannot be sold. Over the centuries, large areas have been absorbed in this system of tenure. If you were going through Egypt and found a farm depleted, with buildings falling down, you would be 90 per cent correct to say: "This is waqf." The system was introduced to provide security, and it helps the purpose of security. But it comes in conflict with efficiency over a period of generations and ultimately defeats the purpose of security itself which it was aimed for. I leave to your reflection and imagination what other defects this system would have. But at least it encourages laziness of the beneficiaries. With the administration of their wealth in other hands, they can go nowhere except through courts or much legislation, and when his share in the property becomes as little as one two-hundredth a person really has no interest in the land at all.

To understand the situation in the Middle East it is important to remember that the mass of the people consider the failure to realize the economic goals of the Islamic social system to be due to the lack of enforcement. The people do not expect a wide distribution of wealth in the sense of complete or near-complete equality. They realize that there would be the very rich and the very poor even with all the measures enforced. But they know, and all of us know, that if the whole Islamic system of economic measures were put into operation the outcome would automatically result in a lessening of inequality. The masses of the people are thinking in terms of what can be done within their own systems without comparing them with other systems. Consequently their political aspirations naturally center upon the enforcement of these Islamic measures.

MAJOR ASPECTS OF LAND TENURE AND
RURAL SOCIAL STRUCTURE IN ISRAEL

Alfred Bonné

My subject this evening is land tenure and the social organization of rural settlements in Israel, both closely related aspects of the new rural society in that country. You will appreciate that I am not able to give you more than an outline of these problems, but I shall feel well rewarded if my paper succeeds in rousing your interest in a further study of the subjects treated by me.

Land Tenure Conditions

Each new society enjoys a unique situation when it starts to develop an economic, social, and legal system of its own: it is free from the hampering legacy of old and frequently outworn institutions. Modern social and political thought has aptly demonstrated the significance and power of resistance of vested interests, particularly in a period of transition. We have become aware of the extent to which these interests in the old and new world are apt to frustrate even moderate attempts for economic and social betterment if these attempts are likely to affect the distribution of national income that is adjusted to those established interests. Such grave obstacles to a progressive development do not exist when a new society comes into formation, as was the case with Israel. For this reason many of the social devices and institutions which are operated or developed in Israel labor under relatively favorable auspices. Certainly it holds true with respect to land tenure conditions and to the social organization of the rural settlements.

In the sphere of land tenure a remarkable form of nationalization of land has developed. I use the term of nationalization for the acquisition and administration of land not by the state but by a special institution, the Jewish National Fund; and while land is regarded as the property of the nation, it is leased out to the individual tenant farmers with a view to promoting a bond of attachment between him and his piece of land.

I wish, however, to make two points clear from the beginning: the nationalization of land in Israel comprises only part of the total area of the country. There exist large tracts which are privately owned. A second point is that the concept of nationalization goes back about fifty years; it has, through continuous thought and improvement, succeeded in becoming an important aspect in the economic and social life of the community.

When the Zionist movement started its activities in Palestine about seventy years ago, the forms of land tenure which existed then in the country were found altogether unsuitable for the new settlers—absentee ownership, a shocking division of the crop, and a lack of fundamental equality between tenant and landowner. In addition to these practical considerations, ideological motifs played a role. The Zionist movement was imbued with Biblical notions which placed great emphasis on a free, undisturbed relation between man and his plot of land. The need of the first settlers to enjoy progressive land tenure conditions was thus forcefully supported by religious tradition. Conditions of ancient Oriental agriculture with respect to crop-sharing, accumulation of land in the hands of a few great landowners were not so different from those prevailing on the contemporary scene. The social conscience of the Bible has reacted with the admonition that God is the supreme owner of the land ("then mine is the land"); that the fate of the tiller of the soil is a primary concern of society ("you shall dwell in the land in safety"); and that "the land shall not be sold for ever."

This ideological heritage has been fully incorporated into the program of the Jewish National Fund which developed into the central institution of the Zionist movement for the acquisition and administration of land. The new settlers did not become the owners of the land; they acquired the status of tenants in hereditary lease on public land. In a sense the concept thus implemented has much in common with the ideas of the earlier land reformers: Henry George in the United States and Adolf Damashke in Germany who fought against what they regarded as the basic evil of modern society—the monopolistic character of uncontrolled private land ownership. Some of the writings of these reformers, which were widely inspired by the Bible, served as sources for the Zionist theoreticians who developed the principles of the Jewish National Fund.

How does the Fund work, and how is the land obtained? In the past it was bought on the market and paid for from the revenue of the Fund collected from voluntary contributions of Jews from all over the world. The annual income amounts now to many millions of pounds; the area owned by the Fund exceeds two million dunams (500,000 acres). The Fund has recently been endowed by the Israeli Parliament with a special legal status under the Development Authority Act. This Act grants the right to purchase abandoned land to two bodies, namely, the State of Israel and the Jewish National Fund. The position of the Fund has considerably grown by this new status which will greatly facilitate the further acquisition of land.[1]

The allocation of the land to settlers is based on several principles, the first of which is the national (or public) ownership of the land itself. This principle implies a prohibition of resale of land and a right of control through the Fund if the usufruct passes from one tenant to another. The lease is contingent upon the annual payment of rent, which means at the same time that the National Fund retains its position as land owner and the tenant acknowledges his status as tenant with all the rights and duties involved. The tenant is subject to certain obligations and restrictions; thus the land is protected against over-utilization; if there is a rise in land values, a new evaluation may take place and lead to a higher fixation of the rent. If by changes in the technique of cultivation the size of the farm proves to be too large —which happened frequently in the past with the spread of irrigation—the tenant has to consent to a reduction of the area allotted to him.

In the lease contracts the use of the land is always specified: for agricultural cultivation, for the establishment of a factory, for a house or school building, etc. These terms cannot be changed without the permission of the Fund. Likewise, the tenant cannot transfer his rights to another tenant if the Fund is not agreeable. The contract is made for a period of reasonable length (forty-nine years) in order to create a sense of confidence in the heart of the tenant and to encourage him to invest. If a tenant reaches the final year stipulated in the contract, he can ask for another forty-nine years' prolongation, which means that the property may be easily held in one family for generations.

The annual rent depends on the value of the estate. In the case of agricultural land it is usually 2 per cent; for urban land the rate is 4 per cent. As mentioned above, there are, however, from time to time, new assessments, and the tenant may have to accept a higher burden if the general conditions justify the rise.

If there are no cogent reasons against it, the tenant may, with the approval of the Fund, transfer this right to somebody else, either by sale or by sublease; he may likewise mortgage rights on the land or dispose of them in favor of his heirs. This form of lease approximates, therefore, the right of disposal exerted by an owner of land proper.

Owing to the hectic developments in recent years, some of the original devices failed to prevent, for instance, a certain degree of speculation with the rights of usufruct; the general rise of land prices affected also the value of the lease and led to a strong demand for lease contracts. In a number of cases, the former tenants yielded to the temptation to sell their rights at a considerable profit. The lease contracts are, however, likely to be amended and there is reason to assume that such misuses will in the future cease or be reduced to cases of minor importance.

Of the 524 Jewish villages which existed at the end of 1950, 460, or 84 per cent, were on land owned by the Jewish National Fund.[2] Nationalized land has become the basic form of land ownership in Jewish agriculture. The main results of the development are the following. Farmers and settlements on national land are in secure possession of their land and are interested in the improvement of their farms as much as settlers on private land. The land is allotted to each farmer in equal portions, the size varying in accordance with the requirements of cultivation in different zones. (About six acres for irrigated farms and twenty-five to thirty acres for dry farming.) The use of land is under control. No accumulation of such land by wealthy owners is possible. The last point is of particular importance in a tiny country where a large increase of population is likely to encourage speculation in land.

Social Organization of Settlements

The aspect of nationalized land finds its counterpart in the social organization of the new settlements. The social structure of the settlements is again an original device to solve the complicated problems which presented themselves with the realization of the Zionist goals, namely, to settle on the land essentially urban people who came into surroundings very different from the countries of their origin in their physical, economic, and social configurations. The paucity of capital, the lack of skill and experience, the decision to return to the soil and to stay on the land, and a certain utopian urge for an improved social order were all responsible for the development of the new collective and co-operative types of settlement.[3] The co-operative and collective settlements, however, do not represent all the types of Zionist settlement; there are, as we shall presently see, no less than six different social forms. The freedom to develop such different forms of living in accordance with the preferences and choice of the inhabitants is a significant feature of the social climate of Israel.

At the close of 1951, there were 707 rural settlements in Israel, divided, as shown in Table 4, into the following types: Moshavat (rural), Kibbutzim, Moshvei Ovdim, Moshavim, Moshavim Shitufim, settlements of new immigrants (including independent Maabaroth), training farms, schools, and various rural settlements, and Arab villages (excluding Bedouins). What are the specific features of these settlements?

Moshavot (singular, Moshava) are private villages. They are ordinary rural villages based on private land ownership and private enterprise. The population of the villages of this group is rising rapidly, owing to the establishment of new immigrant centers (Maabarot) in the village area.

In Kvutzot or Kibbutzim (singular,

TABLE 4

RURAL SETTLEMENTS IN ISRAEL,
DEC. 31, 1951

Settlements	Number	Population
Moshavot	29	49,658
Kibbutzim	217	68,156
Moshvei Ovdim	191	60,810
Moshavim	42	24,974
Moshavim Shitufiim	28	4,024
Settlements of new immigrants (incl. independent Maabaroth)	68	76,731
Training farms, schools, and various rural settlements	30	26,546
Total non-Arab settlements	605	310,899
Arab villages (excluding Bedouins)	102	108,000

Kvutzah or Kibbutz) settlements not only land but all means of production and the whole range of domestic appliances, including kitchen and clothing supplies, are owned collectively; production and consumption are organized on behalf of the community on a collective basis. Domestic and social services are likewise provided communally. The privacy enjoyed by the members of the settlement is the individual living quarter. A general assembly which comprises all the members governs the Kibbutz through elected delegates. Most of the Kibbutzim are predominantly agricultural, though important industrial enterprises have been added to the farm activities in many settlements. The oldest collective settlement Deganiah was founded in 1909.[4]

Moshvei Ovdim (singular, Moshav Ovdim), or workers' co-operative smallholders settlements, are founded on the principles of mutual aid and equality of opportunity between the members. All farms are equal in size. Hired labor is, in principle, prohibited, as each individual farm is to be worked by the member and his family.[5] The settlement is completely co-operative in that all the produce of farms is sold through a central co-operative, and all purchases for the requirements of the village are undertaken co-operatively. Certain types of agricultural equipment are owned by the settlement as a whole and operated co-operatively.

Moshavim (singular, Moshav), or smallholders settlements, are smallholders' settlements and resemble in many ways the Moshvei Ovdim but do not have the same rigid ideological basis. Hired labor, for example, is permitted. Villages of this group are normally called "middle class" settlements to differentiate them from the Moshvei Ovdim of the Labor movement. There is no completely standard type within this group. In some cases, they are established on privately-owned land, in others on nationally-owned land.

Moshav Shitufi (plural, Moshavim Shitufiim) is a settlement based on collective ownership of property and collective (pooled) work as in the kibbutz. Each family, however, as in the Moshav Ovdim, has it own house and is responsible for its own domestic services, such as feeding, laundry, and care of the children. Payment is based on the principle: "to each according to his needs and from each according to his capacities"—each family, for example, receiving money in accordance with the size of the family.

Maabarot (singular, Maabarah) are transitory villages, or settlements of new immigrants. The independent Maabarot and work villages established for the absorption of new immigrants are intended to become permanent agricultural settlements and will, in time, conform to the pattern of one or another type of established settlement. In addition to twenty-three work villages more than one hundred Maabarot with over 65,000 inhabitants have been set up in the vicinity of established urban and rural centers and for the most part are considered administratively as belonging to these centers. In some cases, however, the association will be only temporary.

The training farms and schools have a special significance for the training of young farmers in view of the lack of agricultural knowledge and practice among most of the new immigrants. Many of these schools and farms have extended facilities for agricultural instruction in all branches of farming, including auxiliary occupations such as repair shops.

Problems of Collective Settlements

It is quite natural for the attention of outside observers to be focused primarily on the collective settlements and their specific features. Their external characteristics are the division of the settlements into community buildings such as dining hall, kitchen, farm buildings, libraries, and schools, on the one hand, and living quarters consisting of small housing units, on the other. Children live in special quarters and are cared for by those members who are trained for the job. The community is governed by means of a "general meeting," in which every member has the right to participate and vote on matters of general concern. On questions which require more specialized knowledge, numerous committees supervise or even decide the activities of the community. Everyone who is able to work must work, men and women, though the latter are employed as much as possible in the garden, kitchen, nursery, and children's quarters.

Recent American social history also knows experiments in collective living, but in America settlements were either converted to individualistic types of settlement or had a short-lived existence only—apart from those where an ideology with genuine favor and moral power worked as a unifying bond. As I have already mentioned, the Zionist communal settlements succeeded where individual colonization failed, owing to the extremely discouraging conditions which prevailed in the earlier colonies at the end of the nineteenth century and beginning of the twentieth century. The communal structure of production and consumption was the result of economic necessity no less than of ideological preference.

There was a time when a fierce controversy raged within and without as to the merits and viability of the Zionist collective settlements. Today, after nearly thirty years' experience with the larger settlements, the discussion has abated. It is now generally admitted that a number of economic advantages derive from communal production and communal living: reduced investment per capita in production equipment and housekeeping appliances, more efficient use of labor and skill required for large-scale production branches and for household activities, and in general a more efficient organization of the productive and nonproductive activities which a large-scale unit makes possible.

There is no doubt that economically the collective settlements have proved their viability and have shown not only a remarkable resistance to all kinds of difficulties but have, particularly in critical times, excelled in various services and in producing a number of national leaders—political, military, and social.

In judging the future prospects of these settlements, one has to be aware of the changed background in the country, which may somewhat influence the relatively stable conditions of growth which existed in the past. The immigrants now pouring into the country are less attracted by the opportunities of collective living than their predecessors. Many of them do not care for the socialist element embodied in the communal settlement and prefer the individualist types which are usually less exacting in their demands on the individual. The collective settlement needs a largely homogeneous composition and outlook in order to maintain the fundamental functions of joint production and communal living. Thus the present changes in the composition of the population following the mass immigration from widely different countries and the political dissensions in the country are not conducive to a quick or a proportional growth of the collective settlements. Ardent believers in socialist ideals regret the present decrease in the influence of collective settlements and the inner difficulties they experience as a result of the changes in the social climate of the country. They fear that the other types of settlement do not as easily produce and maintain the pioneering spirit which is so vital to the success of the nation's efforts.

Recent conferences convened by the collective settlements indeed confirmed the general feeling that these groups are passing through a critical stage in their existence. They recognize that the weakening of their ideological appeal and the reduction in their relative position in the community cannot be explained only by the easier conditions of living the newcomers find in town and in private villages. It has to do with the fundamental attitudes of communal settlements towards authority.

The collective settlements were in the past marked by a detached, if not distrusting, relationship toward government. True, the Mandatory government was not a national government elected by the people and did not show particular interest or sympathy for these new ventures in social progress. But the antagonism stemmed from deeper roots. The radical departure

from established and traditional social patterns, which is such an essential feature of the communal settlements, implied also an attitude of dissent towards established forms of rule. A reform movement highly critical of many institutions of existing society which it wants to rebuild on new foundations can not suddenly overcome its suspicion of authority because a new state with a national government has now come into existence. Moreover, political conditions in the new state frequently produced a government coalition of conservative and moderate socialist elements, certainly not an ideal association from the viewpoint of radical reformers.

Yet an attitude of negation and hostility toward the state was also impossible since the recognition of the revolutionary nature of the establishment of the new state was general and its impact on the realization of political essentials and of time-honored national hopes was obvious.

It is a situation which compels the leaders and members of the Kibbutz movement to find new answers and formulas for spiritual and political adjustment. In a society where newcomers have such a strong numerical position and obtain immediately after arrival all civil rights, their adoption of this or that pattern of life can decide the strength and even the fate of a well-rooted social movement.

Yet whatever the preferences of the newcomers may be, there is no compulsion to decide in favor of this or that form of settlement. The collective settlements are voluntary establishments spontaneously developed in a community of free people who voluntarily decide their way of life by means of democratic social planning.

This freedom of action is not automatically preserved; it needs cultivation and education. The present mass immigration has placed an extremely heavy burden on the shoulders of the resident population. Many developments are taking place under hectic and improvised conditions. It scarcely could be otherwise since the population of Israel rose in three years from 600,000 to 1,400,000 inhabitants. Great strains have been put on the available human and material resources. It is difficult to predict what will be the outcome of the present efforts to master an admittedly difficult situation. All I can say now is that there is a confident hope that the creative forces which have in the past found answers to challenging conditions and issues and developed new forms of land tenure and social organization will be able to find solutions to the issues of today and tomorrow.

THE PROGRAM OF AGRICULTURAL DEVELOPMENT IN TURKEY

Ibrahim Atif Sargut

SINCE I do not know English, I will not be able to present this report to you myself, and for this I ask your forgiveness. My dear friend Orhan Nebioglu has kindly consented to read the report to you for me. I wish to thank the sponsors of this conference, the government of the United States, the Economic Cooperation Administration, and the University of Wisconsin for this helpful conference. I am one of those who strongly believe that conferences of this kind will bring about better relationships among nations.

General Information about Turkey

Turkey is a republican nation and has a democratic regime. Turkey is composed of two peninsulas, one part being in Europe and the other in Asia. These two peninsulas are separated by two straits: the Bosphorus and the Dardanelles. Turkey is surrounded by sea on three sides. On the north is the Black Sea, on the west the Aegean, and on the south the Mediterranean. Turkey's land neighbors are Bulgaria and Greece on the west, Russia and Iran on the east, and Iraq and Syria on the south.

Turkey possesses a variety of characteristics as regards her climate. These characteristics make possible several different climatic sections where many different crops can be raised, as will be mentioned a little later.

Turkey is 776,980 square kilometers in area. Her population according to the general census of 1950 is 20,934,670. Of this number 5,267,695 live in cities and 15,666,975 in villages. The average population per square kilometer is 27. This number is 277 in the most concentrated area and 5 in the least concentrated area.

Eighty-two per cent of the population are farmers. Thus Turkey has acquired the characteristics of an agricultural nation. The country's geographical, topographical, and ecological nature have a lot to do with this fact, as shown by the figures in Table 5.

The Agriculture of Turkey

As mentioned before, 82 per cent of the nation's population makes its living by farming. Therefore, the only way to rehabilitate Turkey in the economic field is to increase the productive and purchasing power of this absolute majority. Through this the standard of living will rise in Turkey.

All of the rehabilitation programs in Turkey have the following objectives: to have a better standard of living in Turkey and to sell the excess products to needy countries to help them solve their food

TABLE 5

LAND UTILIZATION IN TURKEY, 1951

Kind of Land Use	Sq. Km.	Per cent
Fields	154,960	20.20
Cereals	88,810	11.58
Vegetables	4,180	0.54
Industrial plants	10,930	1.43
Others	2,030	0.26
Fallow (land left to rest for a year)	49,010	6.39
Meadows and Pasturages	368,060	47.98
Meadows	36,760	4.79
Pasturages, pasturages in the mountains	27,150	3.54
Pasturages	304,150	39.65
Vineyards and Gardens	15,293	1.99
Vegetable gardens	1,510	0.19
Fruit gardens	5,440	0.71
Vineyards	5,500	0.72
Olive yards	2,840	0.37
Rose gardens	3	......
Forests	104,180	13.58
Unfertile lands	124,626	16.25
Lakes, swamps	9,510	1.24
Other	115,116	15.01
Total	767,119	100.00

problem. I would like to emphasize the following point: Turkey, which is side by side with a consumer continent, Europe, is in a position to greatly increase its agricultural production. Turkey's potential for agricultural production, by the roughest estimates, can be doubled in a short time. Our objective is even to exceed this estimate.

Turkey has a great variety of products. The main ones are cereals, vegetables, tobacco, potatoes, cotton, flax, sugar beets, opium, citrus, nuts, figs, grapes, pistachios, various kinds of animal products, fish, and a great variety of fruits.

The abundance of production in our country today is greatly due to the aid of the Marshall Plan. As a result of this help our farmers possess machinery and tools necessary for agriculture. This equipment has enabled our farmers to cultivate their land in a broader and more scientific way, with the result that our production is better in quality and greater in quantity. Marshall Plan aid has also played an important role in modernizing the agricultural procedures.

The very core and foundation of Turkey's economic policy is the agricultural development of the nation, because, as is well understood, the total development and prosperity of Turkey is directly dependent on the rehabilitation and prosperity of the Turkish farmer. Therefore, it is very important that our farmers be supplied with technical knowledge, modern equipment and devices, and aids through credits which will help to yield bigger and cheaper production. This is the basis of our economic plans. At the top of our basic policies are the ways that will lead the farmers to prosperity through the quickest means. Plans have been prepared for all subjects that will lead us to economic rehabilitation. Some of these are: agricultural investigations, agricultural education and its spread throughout the country, agricultural organization, and economic provisions. A good number of these plans have actually been put into practice.

The items that have been taken into account and put into practice first, before others, will be mentioned very briefly. These include mechanization, both through local manufacture of animal-drawn grain drills, steel plows, cultivators, and harrows, and through seed cleaners, seed treaters and swathers, as well as by importation of tractors, combines, trucks, and heavy tillage implements not now manufactured locally.

New land is being added daily to the cultivated acreage by clearing, drainage, water development for irrigation, and in presently waterless areas by water development for domestic use, as well as by making available mechanized equipment which permits farmers to handle larger acreages.

Land productivity is being increased by pasture and forage seeding, fertilizer application, use of mechanical seeders, improved irrigation, availability of better seed varieties, including hybrid corn, and by improved tillage methods.

Animal production is being increased through better winter feeding, improved pastures, control of parasites, and a breeding program using both local and imported sires. In this connection, artificial insemination has already made great strides in Turkey.

We are starting a program to obtain maximum returns from our forest land, in terms of fuel, timber, grazing, and recreation.

Fruit and vegetable production is being increased for both home consumption and marketing, and educational work in preservation methods is under way.

A very important field in which we are just now getting started is home economics. While we have not yet gone very far, we believe that human nutrition and home improvement are among our most important projects.

In these programs we are using the experience and research work of our own country as well as that which we can gather from all parts of the world. Both our research and educational facilities in agriculture are being strengthened. New lines of research are being instituted where pressing problems exist. As information becomes available, from any source, our educational system makes such information available to farmers through the extension service,

provincial agricultural directors, agricultural schools, and research stations.

With the hope that it will be of special interest to the land tenure conference, I would like to discuss more fully three items which we have started putting into practice for the improvement of our agriculture; namely, (a) settlement, (b) giving land to farmers, and (c) cadastre and title-deed.

Settlement, Distribution, Registration

SETTLEMENT PROBLEMS

One of the problems that the government of Turkey has to tackle today is the problem of recent migration from Bulgaria. In the lands that are now outside the Turkish territory there are large Turkish minorities. In Bulgaria, the number is 723,000, in Rumania, 172,000, and in some other countries the numbers are not far below the latter figure.

The Turkish minorities in foreign countries, especially those in Bulgaria, are no longer in a position to take on the heavy burdens they are faced with. Our problem now is to settle these refugees in the very near future in a way contributory to our economic standing. From 1934 to 1949, or in a period of 16 years, the migration numbered 240,000. From the beginning of 1950 up to now, in a period of less than a year, the number of refugees from Bulgaria alone is 180,000. It is expected that this number will exceed 200,000 by the end of this year. These refugees, who have been living under most pitiful conditions, were forced to leave their homes in a very short time. We are now face to face with the problem of the settlement of these Bulgarian Turks. But with the provisions taken in time by the government and through the traditional hospitality of our people this huge bulk of immigrants have been settled and saved from hunger and lack of shelter.

The problem of settlement is created not only by migration. In and around our wooded lands there are about 80,000 to 100,000 families who are there because of the absence of land good enough for agriculture. They have a hard time making a living and have to be moved to areas where production may be possible. On the eastern coast of the Black Sea, the population is concentrated on a very small area. Our countrymen in those areas are making a request to move to more fertile lands. Their number is about 10,000 families. According to the minimum estimate, the costs for settling one migrant family amount to 3500 Turkish liras, or 1,250 dollars, as shown in Table 6.

TABLE 6
Cost of Settling One Migrant Family in Turkey

Item	Cost*
Construction	1,200
One year's board	1,200
Transportation	50
Clothing	50
Medical care	20
Room and fuel	180
Equipment and credit	800
Total	3,500†

*In Turkish liras. One lira equals 35.7 cents.
†Equals $1,250.

Our aim is to solve our settlement problems in a way that will cope with the economic as well as social conditions of Turkey. We find a close relationship between the settlement problems and our economic rehabilitation. Therefore, the lands that we select for settlements are the ones which have not been used for agriculture because of lack of water or other reasons. In keeping with the present laws, the amount of land given to a family of two which is to be settled varies with the location of the land, as shown in Table 7.

TABLE 7
Amount of Settlement Land Given to a Family of Two in Turkey*

	Dry Lands	Low Lands	Irrigable Lands
IN REGIONS WHERE AVERAGE RAINFALL IS BELOW 500 MM. A YEAR			
Fertile land	160	80	20
More fertile	110	60	14
Most fertile	60	40	8
IN REGIONS WHERE AVERAGE RAINFALL IS OVER 500 MM. A YEAR			
Fertile land	60	30	14
More fertile	44	24	12
Most fertile	24	16	8

*In Turkish dönüms. One dönüm equals approximately 1,000 square meters.

For a family of two to five members, an allotment of land of 50 per cent per person more than the allotment granted a family of two is made. For more than five members, an additional 10 per cent is granted over what is allotted to five members. These 10 per cent additional allotments are not allowed to exceed 50 per cent of what is given to a five-member family.

Again according to the laws regarding settlement, the transportation of the settlers and their possessions is taken care of by the government free of charge as far as the stations nearest to the areas of settlement. Medical care is also given free of charge. The following are also given to each immigrant, but only once: a house or land for the building of a house, land, draft animals, equipment and seeds; and to the artisan, equipment and a place to work in or enough capital to build one. If for some reason the immigrant decides to move to another location, he is not entitled to these things in his new location but is on his own. Because the problem of settlement is a vital issue, the government is aware of its importance and is taking measures to improve the conditions.

LAND DISTRIBUTION

Giving land to landless peasants is not only important because of its economic implications but it is important also because it is among the basic national functions that result in social gains. This fact has been recognized in the law passed in 1945, through which land distribution is being effected. There are a good number of peasants in our country who either have no land or very little. Most of them try to make their living as sharecroppers, tenants, and farm laborers; however, they are far from attaining any prosperity. Formerly some land that belonged to the government was given away to the peasants by a special commission; but because equipment was not granted, the land was not cultivated and was lost by the peasants. The new land law supplies the farmer with provisions that enable him to receive the fruits of his endeavors.

The main objectives of the Land Law can be summarized as follows:

1. To supply those farmers who have no land or not enough land with sufficient land to utilize their working capacities and provide the family with a decent living.

2. To provide those with enough land but not equipment with sufficient capital, farm equipment, and livestock to cultivate and manage a farm.

3. To render possible the cultivation of the country's soil on a long-range basis.

Land is divided into three categories according to size: small, medium and large. A piece of land up to 500 dönüms is called "small land"; from 500 to 5000 dönüms, "medium land"; and 5000 dönüms or more, "large land."

In the distribution of land this is the order that is being observed:

1. Those who do not have any land nor have any members of their families that possess land and consequently have to work on other people's land as sharecroppers and tenants.

2. Those who do not possess enough land.

3. Graduates of the departments of agriculture and veterinary medicine in the universities, or those who have completed agriculture courses recognized by the government, who do not have any or enough land.

4. Those over 18 years of age who wish to work independently of their families.

5. Those who make their living as agricultural laborers.

6. Nomads who are farmers.

The Republic of Turkey Agricultural Bank has opened credit for those who will found new farms, buildings, and establishments, make additions or repairs, and for the management of the farm. This is made possible in accordance with the new law. Establishment and enlargement credits are on a twenty-five-year basis, and management credit is on a three-year basis. The value of the land distributed is set at a minimum of one Turkish lira a dönüm and is payable on the basis of installments. No installments are necessary for the first five years, and from the sixth to the twentieth year this debt can be paid back in equal installments, free of interest. The land given has to be cultivated by the recipient and his family. Partnership and subleasing are illegal.

Since the enactment of the Land Law

2,000,000 dönüm of land has been distributed to 42,000 families and the title deeds
registered. There were 12,305 families who
obtained establishment, enlargement, and
repair credits from the middle of 1947 to
the end of 1950; they received 3,144,850
Turkish liras; and for production credits
1,027,570 Turkish liras have been distributed.

In order to speed up the distribution of
land this year, the number of the committees responsible for this job has been increased to fifty-one. The distribution of
land, which is so important in increasing
agricultural production, is given great significance, and speedy action is taken for
its completion.

TITLE-DEED AND CADASTRE LAWS

Land ownership disputes which have
such a close bearing on agricultural production are being solved through the new title-
deed and cadastre laws. Title deeds that
are concerned with land and other property
ownerships are being given special attention.

With a law that has recently been passed,
title-deed procedures have been shortened.
Formerly 400,000 tracts of land were registered in twenty years. With the new law,
300,000 tracts of land have been registered
in a matter of a year and a half. This
activity is going to spread throughout the
country, and in a short time a few tracts
of land that have not yet been registered
will also be registered, and there will not
be a single tract of unregistered land left.

I HOPE that with this brief information we
have given you some idea about the main
trends in the rehabilitation of agriculture
in Turkey. I would like to take this opportunity again to thank this organization for
kindly inviting us to speak.

Part V   THE LAND PROBLEM IN SOUTH ASIA

CONDITIONS OF FARMING IN PAKISTAN

M. H. Sufi

THERE WAS a time in my country when farming was regarded as the noblest of professions. Even today, land owning is a mark of respectability and position in society, but not so the actual job of farming. A man will take pride in the fact that he owns an estate comprising hundreds of acres, but ordinarily he will not admit in public that either he or any near relation of his is actually engaged in farming. This is because in the context of our social values, developed under foreign political domination, manual work of any kind has come to be considered derogatory to a man's dignity and social status. Operative farmers are therefore relegated to a position much inferior to that of nonoperating landlords and the townspeople engaged in industry or commerce. For the purpose of this statement, I have used the term "farmers" for all those who obtain their living from agriculture and cultivate the soil themselves. Those who possess large estates and operate them through hired labor or tenants I have referred to as "zamindars."

Pakistan, with an estimated population of 77 millions, is the fifth largest country in the world. Geographically it is divided into two parts. East Pakistan, which comprises the province of East Bengal, receives a heavy rainfall of over 100 inches in the year and grows crops such as rice, jute, sugar cane, tobacco, oil seeds, pulses, and tea. West Pakistan consists of the provinces of Sind, the Punjab, and Northwest Frontier Province; the centrally administered areas of Baluchistan and Karachi; and several princely states—Bahawalpur, Kalat, Khairpur, Swat, and others. The main crops of this region are wheat, cotton, rice, oil seeds, sugar cane, maize (corn), tobacco, millets, and fruits (both citrus and deciduous). Since rainfall is scanty, artificial irrigation is necessary and is done by means of either canals or wells.

Agriculture is the main industry of Pakistan. Eighty-five per cent of the people depend for their livelihood on farming. The resultant pressure on available land is so great that holdings are becoming progressively uneconomic. In West Pakistan the average holding is not more than five or six acres, and in East Bengal, where the density of population is still greater, the size of the average holding is reduced to about two acres only. This, of course, does not mean that there are no big estates. In Sind, East Bengal, and parts of the Punjab and the Frontier Province a large percentage of land is held by big zamindars who rent it out to share croppers in small parcels. Under these conditions farming tends to be of a subsistence character. The first consideration with every farmer is to grow his own food. He will also grow a little extra food or a small cash crop so that he may be able to buy consumer goods which he cannot produce himself. In normal circumstances this farm economy, delicately balanced as it is, ensures adequate supply of food, mostly in the form of cereals, and a small cash income to pay off debts which are inevitable for the sake of obtaining supplies and services not available in the village. Occasionally, however, this balance is disturbed by some natural calamity like floods, hailstorms, or epidemic among the livestock. In that event the farmer has to resort to heavy borrowing from which he may or may not be able to absolve himself during his lifetime.

Whether in debt or out of it, the farmer does not enjoy a high standard of living. He has a very simple home consisting of two or three rooms which he also uses as a storehouse. His food, though adequate, is lacking in variety. Fortunately in Pakistan the majority of farmers are accustomed to keeping a cow or a buffalo which supplies milk for the family. This habit of taking milk and milk products helps to balance the cereal diet to a considerable extent. Fruit is generally unobtainable in rural areas, except in the villages of the Frontier Province. Meat is considered a luxury, and forms part of the menu only on festive occasions or when a guest is to be specially entertained. The farmers of the Frontier Province are, however, an exception to this. They are heavy meat eaters.

The clothing used by farmers is of the simplest kind. Normally each member of the family has only one set of clothes which is renewed on the occasion of Ramzan Id or some such festival. Shoes are provided by the village shoemaker who is paid in kind every six months. In East Bengal, farmers generally go barefooted.

So much for the farmer's home. His farm is in still greater need of improvement. The farm has been exploited continuously for years and now its fertility is almost depleted. Successive generations of farmers have taken their food and fiber out of the land without giving anything back to renew its strength and vitality. The farmer hasn't got the means to buy commercial fertilizers. Farmyard manure is used but in very small quantity. Cow dung is burned as fuel, because no other fuel is available. The farmer is aware of the improved varieties of seeds which give better yields, but these require ready cash which may not be forthcoming. So he uses the seed from his old crop which he has specially preserved for this purpose. He knows very little about the methods of controlling insect pests and plant diseases; and even if he does, he is not in a position to put them into practice for want of funds. His farm is too small to be mechanized. Besides, machines are used to save labor. Our farm families have more labor than they can put to optimum use. They are not fully employed except at the time of sowing or harvesting. When farming is done under these conditions it is hardly surprising that the yields are low and the farmer gets a very poor return from his farm. This creates a vicious circle. The farmer does not use improved cultural practices; so he gets low returns; and since he gets low returns, he cannot afford to introduce new and improved practices. This vicious circle will have to be broken before agriculture in Pakistan can make any real progress.

The small farm is liable to a variety of other hazards. There is, for instance, the ever-increasing threat of waterlogging in areas where canal irrigation is done. It is estimated that every year about 40,000 acres of land are going out of cultivation on account of the rising of the subsoil water table. Several farmers have been ruined as a result of this. Again, there is the evil of fragmentation. A family holding may be large enough to provide adequate living for one generation, but when the head of the family dies, the farm is divided equally among his sons and daughters. This subdivision, which extends to each field of the farm, renders the resultant parcels of land quite uneconomical, and in consequence the standard of living of the new families is greatly depressed. This is actually happening in a large number of cases of farm families of the present generation. Fragmentation can be halted only if we promote a system of mixed economy under which agriculture and industry will balance and support each other, so that industry can absorb the surplus population from farms and the remaining farmers can grow enough food and raw materials to meet the requirements of the expanding industry. This is in fact one of the first things which the government of Pakistan decided to do. We have embarked upon a slow but steady program of industrial development, which by providing alternative occupations to people from rural areas will gradually relieve pressure on land and thus help in checking fragmentation of holdings.

Another very important step which the government of Pakistan has taken and which has a direct bearing on the purpose for which this conference has been called is the appointment of a commission on land reforms. Dr. Akhtar has referred to some of the tenancy legislation which has been enacted over a period of years by various provinces of Pakistan. The Central government, however, feels that these measures do not go far enough. Our Prime Minister, Mr. Liaquat Ali Khan, addressing the Food and Agriculture Committee at Karachi on December 4, 1950, said: "The question of

land reform is of very great importance to the future of Pakistan. I can hardly emphasize fully the close connection between a healthy development of agriculture and an enlightened land reform policy." He then announced the decision of his government to appoint a commission to go into the whole question of land tenure and expressed the hope that the labors of the commission would ultimately lead to the amelioration of the lot of the people engaged in agriculture.

The third measure we propose to adopt, with a view to increasing the farmer's income and raising his standard of living, is to strengthen the system of informal education of the farm people, which is popularly known in the United States as Extension Service. A group of five officials, including myself, came to this country four months ago to make an intensive study of the co-operative extension service which in America has done so much to encourage the application of science and technology on farms and in rural homes. It is our intention to reorganize our agricultural extension services so as to bring the fruits of research to the farmer's doorstep. In this way we hope to change farming from a mere profession, as it is now, into a businesslike proposition for our farmers.

THE LAND TENURE SITUATION IN PAKISTAN

S. M. Akhtar

THE SYSTEM of land tenure in a country determines the legal or customary relationship between the land, the cultivator, and the other parties having interests in such land. Thus, land tenure gives answer to such questions as: Who owns the land and what is the nature of its ownership? On what terms and conditions is the land culti-

vated and by whom—the owner or one of the varieties of tenants? What is the position of the state as regards ownership rights and rights in the share of the produce as a contribution to its finances? Even to pose such questions is to indicate the fundamental importance of the system of land tenure for a country. It is obvious that land tenure determines the size of the unit of ownership, the magnitude of the unit of cultivation, and, thus, indirectly the technique of farming used, the share of the cultivator in the product of the soil, and, consequently, the incentive imparted to the actual worker engaged in agricultural operation. Thus it has both a production and a distribution aspect. It not only influences the total production that could be obtained from a given area but it also determines whether the production is equitably or inequitably shared among the parties concerned. A defective system of land tenure can create overworked, underpaid, and oppressed peasantry along with an opulent, lazy, and parasitical class of land magnates. It can lead to demoralization generally associated with extremes of riches and poverty existing side by side. It can be a most effective barrier in the way of economic progress, because such a system kills incentive both in the landlord and in the cultivator for additional effort. Apart from its economic and social consequences, in fact as a corollary to them, it can cause political instability which may under conditions of internal and external pressure lead to the destruction of the entire existing pattern of society. Such an upheaval may sweep away in its trail the most cherished values and institutions painfully evolved through the experience of ages.

The potential dangers of a situation created by unjust and inequitable land tenure have increased incalculably in the context of modern economic and political developments. The days of the old isolated local economies have gone never to return. The world is fast becoming one economic unit. The telegraph, telephone, the radio, and the aeroplane have made the world communities members of one, though regretfully disunited, household. Developments in techniques and in ideas in one part of the world have immediate repercussion in every other part. No social or political institution can be kept like a hothouse plant from the sweeping drafts attacking it from all sides. A new consciousness of their fundamental rights is swaying the minds even of the so-called backward masses. There is a strong struggle for existence of ideas and attitudes and only those will survive that will serve the creative purposes of humanity. Every social and political system must justify itself through its utility in the best sense of the word or be prepared to recede to the limbo of things forgotten. Hence it is that the reform of unequitable and inadequate institutions like some of the land tenure systems of the world are no longer the concern alone of the individual countries in which such systems exist. It is the concern of the whole world because stupid behaviour in one quarter of the globe can involve in its consequences the whole of mankind. The time is approaching fast when no problem will remain local, at any rate no fundamental problem; it will require solution at the hands of the growing world community. Land tenure is one such problem, and the University of Wisconsin has done a great service to the cause of international peace and security by affording this opportunity of free discussion on a problem of such basic significance. I wish on behalf of my country to congratulate this University for taking this initiative.

Criteria of Judgment

Before I pass on to the discussion of the actual systems of land tenure existing in Pakistan and the problems created by them, I wish to lay down certain criteria of judgment which should help us in evaluating particular land tenure systems. To my mind a satisfactory land tenure system must satisfy three fundamental conditions.

1. It must give full scope to the application of the latest and most efficient technique of farming evolved by science for the

environment concerned. In other words, it should lead to the most economical and productive use of the resources of the country.

2. It must help in the apportionment of award to effort. This is not only necessary in the interest of maintaining adequate incentive from the point of view of productivity but it is also imperative to meet the demands of equity and social justice so necessary for the material, moral, and spiritual welfare of the agricultural worker.

3. It must ensure adequate finances for the state, especially in those communities in which the state budget has to depend mainly on the taxes derived from agricultural incomes.

It is clear from the above that we cannot lay down any definite pattern to which a land tenure system must conform. It is the end that we can define; the means will vary according to the environment—social, political, and historical—in which such end will be achieved. For instance, tenancy farming has produced excellent results in Great Britain, where landlords and capitalist farmers have traditions of looking to the welfare of the worker and maintaining high cultivation standards. Such a system has failed in most other countries, including Pakistan. Peasant ownerships have been very successful in the United States, but they have led to poverty and primitive agriculture in India, Pakistan, and elsewhere. Collective farming has succeeded in Russia, where the passion for land ownership has been weakened through certain political developments; it may hopelessly fail in countries in which ownership is still greatly desired as a hallmark of social prestige. When we think of solutions, therefore, we must not lose the sense of relativity and historical necessity. And this attitude fits well with those of the countries gathered here who believe in working through the method of growth from below rather than that imposed from above.

Introducing Pakistan

For the benefit of some members of the audience it may be necessary to give a few background facts about Pakistan and its economy so that the land tenure system may be seen in its true perspective. Pakistan came into existence by the division of what was the Indian Empire under the British rule before August 15, 1947. Predominantly Muslim majority areas contiguous to each other were separated to form Pakistan, the rest of the Empire forming India. The result is that the new state has two portions, one on the eastern and the other on the western frontiers of India, separated by about 1,000 miles of Indian territory. Excluding the disputed territory of Kashmir, which has a 92 per cent Muslim majority, of the rest of the Indian subcontinent Pakistan got about 23 per cent of the area and 18 per cent of the population. But on the basis of cultivated land Pakistan was worse off, the per capita cultivated area in Pakistan being six-tenths of an acre compared with seven-tenths of an acre in India. As regards the two wings of Pakistan, East Pakistan, or the Province of East Bengal, has a density of 780 persons and West Pakistan a density of 105 persons per square mile. The disparity, however, is not so great when we consider cultivated area per head. It is .45 acre of cultivated land per capita in East Pakistan and .79 acre per capita in West Pakistan. Thus, the pressure of population on land in Pakistan is quite high, though at the moment because of the fertility of its soil and excellent irrigation systems, especially in West Pakistan, the country in normal years produces a food grain surplus, mainly wheat, amounting to 500,000 tons a year. The main staple food grain of East Pakistan is rice and that of West Pakistan wheat.[1] The main cash crop of West Pakistan is cotton, mainly the long staple American variety, a high proportion of which is exported. Other crops are tea in East Pakistan and oil seeds in West Pakistan. Further, a variety of crops are produced for the use of the peasant's own household, such as sugar cane, chilies, vegetables, tobacco, etc. Thus, apart from the few cash crops, the other products of agriculture are for household use or for the use of the nearby town, if any. There is little of dairy farming and less of livestock raising. Agriculture thus is far from being a business for the peasant. In most cases, especially when prices are not abnormally high, the agriculturist hardly gets normal wages of his locality after meeting his cost of production. Farming is on a small scale, the majority of the holdings being of uneconomic size. The peasant is prone to get into debt and is liable to be exploited by the landlord, money lender, and middleman trader. As a consequence of small holdings and primitive methods of agriculture used, the living standards of the masses, about 80 to 85 per cent of whom depend upon agriculture, are unbelievably low. With poverty goes undernourishment, ill health, high incidence of disease, high death rate, especially among infants, and low life expectancy. To cover it all, there is almost universal illiteracy—as high as 30 per cent of the population. Conditions, however, have been improving since the coming of independence.

Land Tenure Systems of Pakistan

Due to historical reasons a variety of land tenures have developed in various parts of Pakistan. Therefore we cannot present any fixed or uniform pattern which could be true even of one particular province, not to speak of the country as a whole. The various existing systems, however, may be classified as follows.

State landlordism.—Here the ownership of land is claimed by the state. The system, however, is only of minor importance. The proprietary rights of the state exist only in what are called "crown lands." The proprietary rights of these lands have not yet been conferred on private individuals. These are usually waste lands gradually brought under cultivation by the extension of canals. Rights in them can be purchased by or conferred upon private individuals under certain conditions.

Private landlordism.—Here the proprietary rights are vested in private individuals. This system again is of two kinds: Permanent Settlement Estate System, where the land revenue claim of the state is fixed in perpetuity as in the East Bengal province (East Pakistan); and Temporary Settlement Estate System, where the land revenue charge is revised periodically, usually after thirty years. This system is found in all the provinces (and states) of West Pakistan and also in some areas of East Pakistan.

The system embraces not only big landed estates but also village communities of small peasant proprietors, as in parts of the Punjab and Northwest Frontier province of West Pakistan. When applied to such communities the system is called the Mahalwari (Mahal meaning a village) system in the Punjab and Bhaichara (brotherhood) system in the Northwest Frontier province. The distinguishing feature of this system of proprietorship is that the land revenue is fixed on the basis of the village of small peasants who are individually and collectively responsible for its payment. From the economic point of view the small ownerships stand on a footing different from the large estates because they are normally cultivated by the owners themselves, while larger estates involve cultivation by tenants. More of this later.

Ryotwari System.—This system stands between state landlordism and private landlordism, having certain common features of both. Some writers regard it akin to state landlordism because the ryot, or occupant, is free to give up a piece of land if he thinks it is not worth cultivating. In that case he is not liable to the land revenue charge, and the land reverts to the state. The ownership of "Commons" or "Shanni-lat" rests not in the village community, as is the case under the Mahalwari System considered above, but in the state. On the other hand, for all practical purposes the ryot, or occupant, is the proprietor of the land as long as he continues to pay the land revenue to the state. His rights are heritable and transferable. The system prevails in the province of Sind where the ryot, or occupants, are large estate holders, and its practical effect is the same as that of the large proprietary estates of the Punjab and North-west Frontier province.

Historical Evolution of Land Tenures

Before we pass on to the economic implications of the systems of land tenure as they now exist in Pakistan, it would be instructive to review their historical development. The oldest is the system of Permanently Settled Landed Estates called the Zamindari System of East Bengal. This is the oldest system because the areas included in the Province of Bengal were the first to be possessed by the British East India Company when, in 1765, Emperor Shah Alam granted the Dewani (right of collecting revenue) of Bengal and some other areas to the Company. The Company first tried to collect revenue through its own officials, but when this method proved unsuccessful they began to auction the rights of collection from 1772 onwards. These revenue collectors, however, did not become proprietors until after the permanent settlement of Bengal in 1793 by Lord Cornwallis.

Under this arrangement hereditary proprietary rights were conferred on the revenue collectors, who thus became Zamindars (or owners of land). The only condition to which they were subjected was that they paid the fixed amount of revenue. The reve-nue was fixed in cash in perpetuity at ten-elevenths of the rents realized by the Zamindars at the time, one-eleventh being left to the latter as their share. This charge had to be paid within the fixed limit, failing which the estate could be sold by auction.

It should be noted that the persons on whom the proprietary rights were conferred were never owners of those lands. Actually the rights of ownership had always belonged to the cultivators from time immemorial, but such rights had very little value in those times and were never pressed. Now they were conferred on the revenue collectors, who were mistaken for landlords in the English sense due to misunderstanding of the conditions in this country.

The revenue charge fixed was fairly heavy at the time, but later the value of land gradually rose, due to increased security and higher prices, and the charge became very light. This enabled the Zamindars to increase their rents, since no legal limitations had been put in the enhancement of rents by the regulation enforcing the settlement. On the other hand, subsequent regulations (in 1794, 1797, and 1822) and later an act in 1885, authorized the proprietors to increase their rents on certain grounds. Thus, the Zamindars' income increased at the expense of both the tenant and the state.

As the margin between the claim of the state and the economic rent of the land increased, another vicious development took place in the permanently settled areas. This is known by the name of subinfeudation. By subinfeudation is meant the emergence of a large number of rent-receiving interests between the cultivator and the state. Through the process of subletting of land, subinfeudation to some extent exists even in the temporarily settled areas of Pakistan, but its most serious manifestation has been in Bengal under permanent settlement. The basic reason for this development, as already noted, has been the existence of a big margin between the economic rent of an estate and the land revenue demand of the government. This margin has enabled a large number of rent-receiving interests to squeeze themselves between the state and the tiller of the soil, each having his share represented by the difference between what he received from the one below and what he pays to the one above him. The Simon Commission observed in 1926 that in some cases as many as fifty or more intermediary interests existed between the Zamindar at the top and the cultivator at the bottom. Similar observations were made by the Banking Enquiry Committee in 1930 and the Bengal Land Revenue Commission in 1940. Such a system, apart from creating conflicts between the various interests, is devoid of all incentive for agricultural development. A recent law aims at abolition of this system.

By the middle of the nineteenth century the evils of the system were already apparent. The peasantry was being exploited, a large number of interests in land were created, and the state was losing its due share of the revenue. As the dominion of the British extended to other parts of the subcontinent the system of Temporary Settlement was adopted. As regards ownership rights, they were adapted according to the conditions prevailing in each area or according to the view taken by the particular settlement officer. For instance, in the Punjab and Northwest Frontier province some large estate holders had established their proprietary rights during the period of political unsettlement. These rights were recognized. Other large estates were awarded to those who had lent a helping hand in the conquest. Where village communities of small peasants existed, as in the Eastern and Central Punjab, the Mahalwari System was introduced. In Sind, which was a part of the Bombay Presidency until quite late, the Ryotwari System was introduced in conformity with the pattern evolved in South

and West India. Here the main reason was the superfluity of infertile land and the scarcity of cultivators. The state kept the proprietary rights because these were not regarded as of much value by the occupants. It was, in fact, a concession to the cultivators rather than to the state. If full ownership had been conferred on the cultivators, they would have been liable to pay land revenue whether they cultivated a particular plot or not. Later, in Sind, with the coming in of the canals, land values rose and a situation analogous to large landlords of the Punjab and Northwest Frontier province was created. The occupants became, to all intents and purposes, absentee landlords.

Tenancy Farming

So much for the point of view of ownership. From the point of view of cultivation, two systems have resulted from this state of affairs: tenancy cultivation, with its concomitant absentee landlordism, and peasant proprietorship.

To take the tenancy cultivation first, it may be noted that broadly there are two kinds of tenants in Pakistan—the occupancy tenants and the tenants-at-will. The former pay a nominal rent to the landowner and cannot be ejected from their holdings so long as they pay this rent and do not misuse the land. Such tenants are practically like the owners, though socially their status is inferior to the land owning class. The most important class, however, are the tenants-at-will. This is the most oppressed and exploited class of peasantry. Beginning in 1859 in Bengal, legislative measures have been passed by the various provinces to protect the interests of these tenants. The aim has been to ensure to them fixity of tenure, fair rents, and the abolishment of all kinds of illegal exactions imposed on them by the landlords. One cannot say with confidence, however, that these measures, well intentioned as they are, have been able to accord adequate protection to the tenant. Many of the laws have loopholes which can be taken advantage of by the clever landlord. In addition, the poverty, ignorance, illiteracy, and entire dependence of the tenant on his landlord stand in the way of his getting the advantage of this legal protection.

The extent of tenancy cultivation varies from province to province in Pakistan, but roughly one may say that at least half of the total cultivated area of the country is cultivated by tenants-at-will and is owned by absentee landlords. Taking the provinces individually, the tenants-at-will cultivate about 80 per cent of the total area in Sind, over 50 per cent in the Punjab, 47 per cent in the Frontier province, and 50 per cent in the state of Bahawalpur. In Babuchisten they vary from tehsil to tehsil from 16 per cent to 40 per cent. In East Bengal they cultivate about 30 per cent of the total area, but this does not include the occupants who are practically peasant proprietors, though legally tenants of superior landlords.

The most usual system of tenancy is what is called "batai," or crop sharing on a fifty-fifty basis. It has been widely recognized that the tenants are still rack-rented in spite of the tenancy laws.

But the economic consequences of tenancy cultivation are serious, especially from the point of view of the optimum utilization of land and labor resources. Tenancy farming, as noted above, is carried on under the crop sharing system. Under this system the rent of land is paid in the form of one-half to one-third (according to circumstances) of the gross produce. Almost the entire cost of production is met by the tenant from his share. The government demand is paid by the landlord. Of such a system, Marshall observed as follows: "When the cultivator has to give to his landlord half of the return to each dose of capital and labor that he applied to the land, it will not be to his interest to apply any dose, the total return from which is less than twice enough to reward him."[2] This is what exactly has been happening in the Punjab. Speaking about the tenancy cultivation in the Punjab, Calvert wrote: "They generally take less care in preparing the land, plough less often, manure it less, and use fewer implements upon it, than owners. They grow less valuable crops, especially avoiding those requiring the sinking of capital in the land; they make little or no effort for improving their fields. They often keep a lower type of cattle; they avoid perennials and bestow no care on trees."[3] Thus, the system fails to afford adequate incentive to the cultivator.

As regards the landlord, the landlord in Pakistan takes very little interest in the improvement of the soil. He is concerned only with realizing as much rent through his corrupt agents as he possibly can. According to Calvert, "most Punjab landlords would spend practically nothing on the land."[4] What is true of the Punjab applies to other provinces as well. The system, therefore, is outmoded, and no amount of mere tenancy legislation will meet the situation. More radical measures are indicated.

Another peculiar feature of tenancy in Pakistan is that even where the ownership units consist of large estates they are given by the landlord to tenants in small parcels. Thus, advantage is not taken of the economic size of the proprietary holding. Small-scale, primitive agriculture prevails whatever the size of the owned area. The uneconomic size of the unit of cultivation is quite obvious in the case of small peasant proprietorships, which is the other form of cultivation.

Peasant Proprietorships

The extent of owner cultivated land varies from province to province. If we regard the small percentage of the total land under occupancy by tenants as practically held by owners, about half the total area in Pakistan is cultivated by owners. But the vast majority of these holdings are of uneconomic size. In the Punjab it was estimated that 20 per cent of the proprietors held less than one acre of land and that only one-third of the holdings in 1939 were of economic size. The number of uneconomic holdings has presumably increased with the passage of time and the working of the law of inheritance. Punjab is the most important province of peasant proprietors. Their condition elsewhere is no better, if it is not actually worse. They may be slightly better off than the tenant farmers because of the greater incentive to work on an ownership holding, but on the whole they do not live much above the subsistence level. In the past their ownerships have only facilitated their capacity to get into unproductive debt more deeply than the creditless tenant. Further, on account of the working of the law of inheritance, the proprietor's small patrimony not only tends to become smaller but more and more fragmented and hence less and less capable of being operated economically. Attempts have been made for consolidation of holdings, but due to the expense involved, lack of staff, and the inertia of the people, only a negligible proportion of the land has been tackled in this way. The capital resources of the peasant are too meager to enable him to adopt even those measures—such as better seed and more adequate manure—which could be adopted on his tiny holdings.

The Problem

We are now in a position to state the problem facing the country. Pakistan possesses fertile soil and an irrigation system which is among the best in the world. Although the country is producing surplus food grains in a normal year, compared to more advanced countries of the world it does not get adequate returns from the soil and from other resources invested in the land. With increased productivity per acre, the present production could be obtained from one-third to one-half of the present area under cultivation and greater variety could be imparted to agricultural products. Conventional methods of increasing production by way of better seed, more manure, and adequate water have not yielded significant results, nor has extension of cultivation to new lands kept pace with the increase in population. Though there are considerable possibilities of bringing new lands under the plough through the building of expensive canals in West Pakistan and measures of drainage in East Pakistan, the main resort in the country must be upon getting more out of the area already under cultivation through the application of the more scientific methods of farming.

The failure of measures of intensive farming in the past has been only partly due to the conservatism of the cultivator; mainly it has been the result of the systems of land tenure in the country, which have kept the unit of cultivation very small. Further, it has, on the one hand, created a parasitic class of absentee landlords, who have no interest in the development of agriculture, and, on the other hand, a resourceless and oppressed class of tenants, who have neither the incentive nor the opportunity of taking to more scientific methods of farming. Where small holdings are owned by the cultivator himself, his power of capital investment is extremely low, even when he has a desire for it. The result is a colossal waste of manpower and national resources. Apart from the economic waste there are the political and social repercussions of a system which keeps the major portion of the masses of a country ill-fed, ill-clad, ill-housed, and ill-cared for in every way. In a fast changing world such a state of affairs can be fraught with disastrous potentialities.

The problem before the country, therefore, is how to make agriculture more productive and the agriculturist more prosperous. This is a problem of production as well as of distribution, and on its solution depends further economic progress through greater capital formation for which land is the only important source. Thus, so far as production is concerned conditions must be created under which the land, material resources, and labor power of the country are utilized in the most efficient manner. This will involve two things: (1) The unit of cultivation must be extended so that more scientific methods of production can be applied to agriculture. (2) The cultivator as a human factor must be allowed to work under conditions which give him maximum incentive to put forth his best into the land and to be free of all exploitation by any agency whatsoever. Moreover, he must be saved from the uncertainties of fluctuations of national and international markets. If conditions mentioned under point 2 are created, the problem of distribution will be automatically solved. You cannot create proper incentive for work unless you can ensure that the fruit of labor will adequately compensate the efforts and sacrifices undergone by those who have undertaken that labor. Measures ensuring economic security and stability will also ensure equitable distribution of the fruits of agriculture among the participants in the enterprise. The first and the most important step to achieve these ends is the reform of the land system. Thus, the reform of the system of land tenure may be regarded as the prerequisite of agricultural development, in fact, of all economic development in Pakistan. Several lines of reform can be suggested in this connection, but the most hopeful to my mind is the introduction by adequate stages of a system of co-operative farming in the country—a subject to which we shall return at a later session of the conference.

In the meantime, the state has tackled the problem of improving conditions of tenancy in several ways. Several legislative measures have been passed by the various provincial governments since the partition. In the West Pakistan provinces these measures have chiefly aimed at abolition of all Jagirs, or claims, to land revenue on the part of private individuals granted in the past for various reasons; conferment of proprietary rights on occupancy tenants in return for compensation to the landlords; enlargement of the share of the tenant in the produce, thus decreasing rent; abolition of a variety of illegal exaction such as free service and other contributions imposed by the landlord on his tenants; prohibition of ejectment of tenants except under specified circumstances.

In East Pakistan a more radical measure has been passed and is now being implemented. Under it all intermediary interests between the state and the cultivator will be acquired by the state and the present owners of such interests will be compensated according to a given scale. The cultivator will thus become a tenant of the state instead of a private individual. Since tenancy rights will be transferable and rent reasonable, the measure practically amounts to a grant of ownership of land.

These steps are all in the right direction, but they do not completely meet the situation for reasons already mentioned. The ideal position will be the complete abolition of absentee landlordism, conferment of full proprietary rights on the cultivator, and application of the co-operative principle to the various processes of farming and agriculture in general.

PROBLEMS IN COUNTRIES WITH HEAVY PRESSURE
OF POPULATION ON LAND: THE CASE OF INDIA

M. L. Dantwala

PROBLEMS OF ownership of land and the social nexus arising out of these problems in countries with a heavy pressure of population on land are qualitatively different from those in countries where land is not so desperately sought. In such countries, agriculture is more a problem of relationship between men and men than between men and land. The struggle between men assumes a greater poignancy than the struggle against nature. No wonder in these countries the problem is charged with tensions and emotions unfamiliar to people under more fortunate circumstances. Centuries of injustice and exploitation have given rise to a situation which is intellectually indefensible and ethically wrong. Land is scarce; yet it is concentrated in a few hands. Yields are low, but rents are high. Farmers are poor, but farms are expensive. It will be my endeavor in this paper to unravel the various facets of the problem of land tenure in a predominantly agricultural and industrially underdeveloped country.

I may be pardoned if I begin at the end. Though I agree with the poet who said that what matters is the journey and not the journey's end, I think most of us would like to know the destination to which we are being carried. I, therefore, wish to highlight the conclusions which I am likely to reach through arguments I shall place before you. These conclusions I present in the form of a ten-point program of agrarian reforms for India.

1. Abolition of all intermediaries between the state and the tiller, with a rehabilitation allowance for the displaced intermediary.

2. Ceiling on individual ownership and redistribution of the excess—as well as the newly reclaimed land—in favor of uneconomic cultivators or landless laborers or co-operative farming societies.

3. Encouragement of owner-operated farming on fair-size farms and prevention of subletting in the future.

4. Occupancy rights for all existing tenants and actual cultivators. Fair rent and security of tenure.

5. Expansion of co-operative credit, marketing, processing, etc.

6. Full-fledged rehabilitation program for the low income farms on the lines of the Farm Security Administration.

7. Co-operative joint farming for palpably uneconomic farms.

8. Extension of nonfarm employment and transfer of population to it.

9. Check on low agricultural wages in the remote and depressed rural areas.

10. Abolition of serfdom or quasi-serfdom of landless laborers.

While examining problems of land tenure in India, I shall endeavor to establish the case for the above ten-point land reform program and, incidentally, show the inadequacy or the impracticability of competing alternatives. But before I do so, I wish to raise an academic issue.

Factors Determining Land Tenure

What determines the content of land tenure? Does the determination of land tenure policy depend upon our social values, attitudes, and ideology, or is its ultimate molding conditioned, if not governed, by objective economic facts? Or perhaps neither of these factors but sheer political expediency reflecting the power pulls of various groups in contemporary society determines the content of tenures. I submit that this is a basic question and a study of land tenures at different periods and in different countries yield results which are, in a way, not flattering to scientists. For, in the ultimate analysis, the politician in total or partial disregard of the sociologist and the economist has had the final say in the matter. This realization is somewhat of a damper for a conference of this nature. Our only consolation is that in the long run economic facts must assert themselves and human values must prevail and determine even the fate of the politician.

The query as to what determines the content of tenures would make a fascinating subject for research and one very germane to our discussion. In this paper, however, I wish to confine myself to examining the influence of economic realities on the determination of land tenures. Though all the facts I present relate to India, I think it would be legitimate to hold that they reflect conditions in countries in Southeast Asia and to a great extent in all industrially underdeveloped and predominantly agricultural countries with an excessive pressure of population on land.

The Economic Background

I propose to present these basic data only under four main headings: (1) size and composition of the agricultural population; (2) the ladder experience of tenure, as it is called in the United States; (3) size of holdings and the state of fragmentation; and (4) income and standard of living of various classes of agricultural population.

THE AGRICULTURAL POPULATION

Nearly 65 per cent of India's gainfully employed population depends for its livelihood on agriculture. On the basis of the 1951 census, this amounts to something like 100 millions. If we add to this the number of persons who indirectly depend on agri-

culture for livelihood, the number increases by at least another 10 per cent.

It would, however, be erroneous to believe that this constitutes a homogeneous group of persons. This group consists of, on the one hand, zamindars and talukdars holding thousands of acres of land, whose incomes would be liable to super-tax but for the exemption of agricultural income from income tax and, on the other hand, landless laborers who in many parts of the country have a status no better than serfs. Detailed figures of composition of the agricultural population are as of 1931, but it can be safely assumed that basically this pattern has remained unchanged. If anything, there has been some slipping down the ladder. The composition of the gainfully occupied agricultural population in British India in 1931 is shown in Table 8.

TABLE 8
AGRICULTURAL POPULATION IN
BRITISH INDIA, 1931

Group	Number
Noncultivating owners	4,151,000
Cultivating owners	28,397,000
Tenants	36,239,000
Agricultural laborers	33,523,000
Total	102,310,000

The figures in Table 8 reveal that nearly 70 per cent of persons employed in agriculture do not own land. It must be further remembered that even among those who "own" land, 50 to 80 per cent in various regions possess less than five acres and are thus owners only in name. They derive large portions of their livelihood by working as farm laborers on someone else's farm.

REGRESSION IN TENURE

What is more disturbing, however, is

the continuous regression on the agricultural ladder. There is a marked tendency for the land to pass into the hands of noncultivating owners. Thus, in the state of Bombay (which is a ryotwari, that is, peasant farming state) between the years 1916/17 and 1947/48, the percentage of noncultivating holders to the total increased from 9.3 per cent to 22.6 per cent and the percentage of area held by them increased from 12 per cent to 30 per cent. On the other hand, the number of landless laborers is continually on the increase. In 1882, the number of landless day laborers in agriculture was estimated at 7.5 millions. It increased to 21.5 millions in 1921 and 33 millions in 1931. Two subsequent estimates by the International Labor Organization are available. The one for 1933 puts the figure at 35 millions, and the 1944 figure is 68 millions. The latter figure obviously covers all low-income groups such as artisans, small landholders, tenants with all varieties of rights and interests in the land, and also wage labor working on land and on such casual jobs as road repairs. Table 9 shows the deterioration in the composition of agritural population.

TABLE 9

COMPOSITION OF AGRICULTURAL
POPULATION IN INDIA

Category	Number in Millions		Percentage Increase or Decrease
	1911	1931	
Noncultivating landlords	3.7	4.1	+10.8
Cultivators (owners or tenants)	74.6	65.5	−12.2
Agricultural laborers	21.7	33.3	+53.4

Demographic data suggest a regression from tertiary and secondary industries to primary industries. Thus, the percentage of the working population gainfully employed in industries in the whole of India has declined from 11 per cent in 1911 to 9.6 per cent in 1941. The 1931 census reveals that 64 per cent of the rural artisans were compelled to give up their traditional occupations and take to agriculture. The percentage of low-income farmers is also continuously rising. Even if we take Bombay state which, due to its comparatively higher degree of industrialization, has a better record of the size of holdings, etc., we find that between the years 1916/17 and 1947/48 the proportion of palpably uneconomic farms (below five acres) increased from 46.5 per cent to 52.0 per cent.

Intensive village surveys have amply corroborated all these facts. In a survey of a few typical villages in the Konkan region of the Bombay state, random sampling revealed that during three successive generations the percentage of owner-cultivators among the population earning livelihood from agriculture declined from 57 per cent to 41 per cent and then to 30 per cent. Another survey of 268 families in the Gujarat region showed that in one generation the percentage of owner-cultivators declined from 46.5 per cent to 31 per cent.

SIZE OF HOLDINGS

It is probably well known that the size of holdings is extremely small in India. Eighty-two per cent of holdings in Madras, 81 per cent in United provinces, 79 per cent in Orissa, 71 per cent in Bengal, 64 per cent in the Punjab, and 66 per cent in Assam are below five acres. In the state of Bombay, which has the highest average size of holdings among the states of the Indian Union, a recent survey conducted by the government Bureau of Economics and Statistics shows that 42 per cent of the total number of cultivators have holdings below five acres. The percentiles quoted below bring out the skewness of the distribution. Ten per cent of holdings are below 0.71 acres in size, 30 per cent below 2.97 acres, and 50 per cent below 6.80 acres. Most of these holdings are, of course, fragmented, and the same inquiry showed that the higher the size of holding, the larger the number of fragments. Not only are the holdings small, they are rapidly becoming smaller. An investigation by the Punjab Board of Economic Enquiry showed that between 1928 and 1939 the number of holdings below three acres increased from 43.4 per cent to 48.8 per cent. In Madras, Pattas paying land revenue of 10 rupees or less formed 69.5 per cent of the total number twenty years ago. They amounted to about 87.65 per cent at the time of the Famine Enquiry Commission (1945). According to the Hyderabad Agrarian Reforms Committee (1949), the average size of holdings had decreased from twenty-three acres in 1880 to fourteen acres in the 1945-46 period.

LIVING CONDITIONS

As for the incomes and standard of living, the picture is really depressing. The paragraph quoted below covers a wide focus of the condition as it existed before World War II.

In the Punjab a study of the farm accounts of 29 holdings revealed, in 1938–39, that where the capital and land were owned by the farmer and the permanent workers were from his family, receipts, on an average, showed an excess over expenditure of Rs. 28.21, but where land had to be rented, capital borrowed and labour hired, there was actually a loss, on an average, of Rs. 1.41. The highest farm income under the former conditions was no more than Rs. 72.63 per year, and under the latter no more than Rs. 29.09. Enquiries in other parts of the country have resulted in similar findings. In the U.P., an examination of the accounts of 122 cultivators in 13 typical villages revealed that the average "net" income, including wages of family labour, was as low as Rs. 2.94 per acre. The Gokhale Institute Survey of Farm Business in Wai Taluka in the Bombay Presidency in 1937–38 has to report that, if interest is allowed at three per cent per annum on the total capital investment and if the wage of family labour is calculated at Rs. 9 per month per adult workers, the net result for the average farm business is a loss for the year of Rs. 99. Conditions down South are no better. In the wet-land village of Nerur in Trichinopoly District, the average gross income per villager in 1936 was Rs. 38, out of which the dues to Government, landlords and money-lenders had to be paid. Under such conditions, the wages of agricultural labourers cannot but be the lowest. Generally speaking, the daily wages may be said to range from 3 to 6 annas a day for men, 2 to 4 annas for women, and 1.5 to 2 annas for children. Employment, of course, is not available all the year round, even at these wages.[1]

A word may be said about the influence of the recent high prices on rural incomes. The data on this subject are too inadequate to establish a conclusive trend. Intensive field surveys undertaken recently, however, go to show that whereas a small percentage of farmers at the top, in possession of economic and supra-economic farms, improved their position, as revealed by reduction in debts and addition to assets, a large majority of farmers experienced no such change in their status and that there was a marked decline in the position of those at the lowest rung of the economic ladder. An inquiry into the rural indebtedness in the state of Madras revealed that whereas the indebtedness of the big farmer was reduced by as much as 40 per cent between 1939 and 1945 that of tenants and landless laborers actually increased by 4.1 per cent and 45.6 per cent, respectively. The Ministry of Labor of the government of India recently conducted a survey of the conditions of agricultural laborers. Reports of three of these surveys are by now published. In these three villages the percentage of families with deficit budgets ranged from 67 per cent to 88 per cent, the extent of deficit varying from Rs. 10 to Rs. 190 per family.

The Indian Society of Agricultural Economics conducted two rural surveys in the postwar period. One was in a village—Bhuvel—which had under irrigation 33 per cent of its cultivated land, on which a remunerative crop of tobacco was grown. The village has a first-rate co-operative society. Yet in this village only 17 per cent of cultivators had a surplus budget. The other survey was conducted in a region which has had a network of really first-rate multipurpose co-operatives for more than twenty-five years. The survey analyzed the change in the economic conditions of the members of the co-operative society and found that whereas the big landholder had increased his holding during his membership, both the medium and small cultivators had actually smaller holdings than what they had when they joined the society.

TENANT FARMING HAS NO PLACE

What are the implications of these economic facts for the problem of ownership of land? I think one conclusion is almost inevitable. When the most frequent size of holding is less than five acres and there is no prospect of any substantial increase in the same in the near future, it is obvious that tenancy has no place in the agrarian setup of India. Probably not more than 5 per cent of farms are of a size which will admit of double interest of the owner and the tenant. The units are too small even for the owner-operator to eke out a decent living. Tenancy under the circumstance must result in the exploitation of the tenant and mining of the agricultural land. Theoretically, if the rent is no more than interest on the value of land and equipment on it,

the tenancy arrangements may not be considered exploitative. But in countries where land hunger is so acute, rents are always extortionate.

Yet, in contrast to what is desirable, probably more than two-thirds of the land under cultivation in India is tenant-cultivated and rents certainly represent returns higher than interest on investment by the landlord. Tenancy legislation under the circumstances can at best be ameliorative—except to the extent it provides for the buying up of land by the tenant and prevents further extension of the area under tenancy. The ultimate ideal of land tenures in India must be, subject to what is said below, the owner-operated farm. "Land to the tiller" is not just an idealistic political slogan; it represents a basic economic necessity.

PATHOLOGY OF PEASANT FARMING

Now it is an accepted principle of owner-operated family farming that unless the size of holding and auxiliary resources are adequate, it will exhibit pathological symptoms, making it thoroughly unacceptable as a mode of farming. Professor Medici of Italy gave an excellent diagnosis of the pathological type of peasant farming in a paper read at the Seventh International Conference of Agricultural Economists at Stresa.

The pathological symptoms that usually accompany the more typical manifestations of peasant farming are well known and we shall merely list them here. They are:

1. Malnutrition, accompanied by typical scarcity diseases,
2. High death rate accompanied by a high birth rate,
3. Illiteracy,
4. Tiny holdings, almost always insufficient to yield enough for assuring a decent standard of living to the peasant,
5. Splitting up of the small holdings into a great number of parcels of land, often at a distance one from the other,

6. Primitive and often insanitary farm dwellings,
7. Scanty use of mechanical and animal power and abundant use of human muscular energy,
8. Keen competition among the peasants seeking land accompanied by a land monopoly held by the great landowners,
9. High ground rents paid to the landowners and to numbers of middlemen who come between the landowner and the peasant; and
10. Selfishness and backwardness of the peasantry, often leading to excessively hard child labour.

All this indicates the necessity of avoiding an uncritical acceptance of peasant farming as the most desirable form of man-land relationship. It is of no use to recommend it for adoption unless we are sure that we shall be able to provide land and auxiliary resources in economic units to the majority of farmers. As the data presented above show, this cannot be done in India. In India, on top of pathological peasant farming we have an oppressive landlord-tenant nexus. I know that friends from the United Kingdom find it difficult to appreciate our dislike of tenant farming and friends in the United States our skepticism of peasant farming. The picture of agrarian economy as I have given above will lead, I hope, to a better appreciation of our attitudes on these issues.

Limitations of Accepted Remedies

A question may be asked: Can we not elevate the pathological type into an ideal one? The pattern of devices for achieving this is more or less well set: (1) breakup of big farms and their redistribution among landless or low-income class, (2) reclamation of what we in India call "culturable waste" and settlement of pathological groups on them, (3) provision of irrigation and other facilities which will make a smaller size of holding economic, (4) removal of—pushing out and pulling out—"surplus" farm population into "industrial" occupations, and (5) migration.

REDISTRIBUTION OF LAND

We may not think in terms of alternatives to peasant farming until we have explored the possibilities of progress on these lines. Redistribution of land is often suggested as a remedy for augmenting the size of uneconomic farms. At present, in the Indian Union some 90 million persons are gainfully occupied in agriculture, and the net sown area amounts to approximately 235 million acres. Assuming that we distribute this land more or less equally among all those actively engaged in agriculture, the per capita size of their farm will be just a little more than 2.5 acres; surely not an ideal size for peasant farming.

The Uttar Pradesh Zamindary Abolition Committee commenting on the efficacy of this device observes:

It will be seen that [in U.P.] 118 lakh [11.8 million] acres of land is required for bringing all the holdings of a size between 0.5 acre and 10 acres to the standard size. If all holdings exceeding 25 acres, whether in the cultivatory possession of the landholder or the tenant, were reduced to 10 acres we shall have about 6.7 lakh [.67 million] acres of land at our disposal. If we acquire only the *Sir* and *Khudkast* of the landlords in excess of 25 acres we get only 2.8 lakh acres which in either case is far too small to meet our requirements. Figures collected go to show that if the *Sir* and *Khudkast* holdings of the proprietors alone, below the standard size, were raised to the standard size of 10 acres, we should need no less than 16.76 lakh acres of land, which is a little less than twice the land which we can obtain by acquiring all land in excess of 25 acres whether held in cultivation by a landlord or tenant. If we fix the area of the maximum of *Sir* and *Khudkasht* holdings at 50 acres, we shall get no more than 1.9 lakh acres of land.[2]

These figures show that the cutting down of all holdings above twenty-five acres will have only a negligible effect on the agricultural economy and will not appreciably reduce the number of uneconomic holdings.

In Bombay state, if ownership holdings above one hundred acres are broken up and the land in excess of one hundred acres is pooled, it will release 1.3 million acres of land. If this is distributed only among the below five-acre group, it will raise the per capita ownership of land by cultivators in this group by not more than one acre. If a lower ceiling is put, say at twenty-five acres, the addition for the below five-acre group will not be more than three acres.

This, however, does not mean that the redistribution of land as a measure of agrarian reform must be given up. The above discussion leads to only one conclusion—that redistribution will not solve the question of adequate size of holdings on the basis of peasant farming. The measure has sociological and psychological aspects which make it a very significant plank in any program of agrarian reforms.

The trend of opinion on the question is inconclusive. The Agrarian Reform Committee appointed by the President of the Indian National Congress in 1947 under the chairmanship of an eminent Gandhian thinker Shri J. C. Kumarappa states: "We feel that to avoid social injustice there should be a reasonable relation between the economic holding and the maximum size of a holding which an individual peasant can be allowed to cultivate. . . . We, therefore, recommend that very large holdings should not continue. A ceiling to land holdings should be fixed and according to our considered views it should not be higher than three times the size of the economic holding. The surplus above the maximum should be acquired by the appropriate authority under the Land Commission on payment of compensation at graduated multiples of the assessment, to be determined by an impartial tribunal."

The *Harijan*, which was founded by Mahatma Gandhi, in an editorial dated September 1, 1951, quotes a letter from Shri Vinoba Bhave on the question of agrarian unrest in Telangana (Hyderabad Dn.) which, as some of you may know, was a scene of large-scale communist violence. Shri Vinoba in his letter states: "I know that the Hyderabad Government have enacted a law for the protection of tenants and that is good so far as it goes. But along with it another law limiting the maximum holding by an individual is necessary. Unnecessary time should not be wasted in debating the issue. If we want to solve the problem, let us realize its gravity and urgency." And he added: "To my mind, every son of the soil, that is every man must have a right and claim on mother earth in the same way as he has over air and water."

The Socialist party in its recently published election platform strongly advocates redistribution of land. Their brochure *We Build for Socialism* states:

The Socialist Party, intent on establishing social justice and working towards economic equality and anxious to release the pent-up energies of millions of our primary producers, will redistribute land so as to achieve these ends. No peasant family will be allowed to possess land more than three times the size of an economic holding, or roughly 30 acres of land of average productivity, and no one who does not personally participate in the processes of cultivation would be allowed to possess land. The land will belong to the tiller and intermediaries between him and the State will be abolished.

Proprietors of land possessing more than 30 acres will receive for lands over that limit (but only up to a maximum holding of 100 acres), an annuity for ten years calculated on the basis of fair rent. Effort would be made to ensure as soon as possible that no cultivating family has less than an economic holding, that is, an area of land that would afford a reasonable standard of living. Redistribution of land will be accompanied with consolidation of fragmented holdings.[3]

The First Five Year Plan just released by the Planning Commission—it is yet not adopted by the government—however rejects redistribution as a measure of agrarian reform. Its contention is as follows:

The second course is sometimes advocated and its implications need to be analyzed. The proposal to limit existing holdings raises important problems of finance, administration and management. Whether the States give compensation, or under another name, rehabilitation grants, the task is likely to be far beyond their resources. The available administrative machinery is in no position to cope in any systematic manner with the problems of acquisition on the vast scale which appears to be contemplated. The distribution of the land acquired from individual owners among various classes of claimants—small owners, tenants and landless labourers will present numerous practical problems involving basic social conflicts. Moreover, the land which is acquired will consist as a rule of fields scattered over the whole village and generally it will not be possible effectively to organise either collective farming or State management. On the larger farms, production will fall and, for a period at any rate, on other farms also, it may well be that the decline in production may have a serious effect on the well-being and stability of rural society as a whole. It is possible that any large-scale and sudden attempt to break up existing holdings may give rise to such organised forces of disruption as may make it extremely difficult to bring about the very transformation in the organisations of agriculture which is needed. In the conditions of India, peaceful and democratic change is likely to be the most lasting. It is, therefore, necessary to ponder carefully over the practical results of a policy of ceilings on individual holdings.[4]

On the question of the decline in production, however, I may be permitted to quote from Dr. Volin's article in the September, 1951, issue of *Foreign Agriculture:*

The fear that is sometimes expressed, that land reform in the under-developed countries would spell a disastrous decline of production, is largely unjustified. In most of these countries it is not necessary to split up into small, possibly uneconomic units large and efficiently operated farms, as was done in parts of Europe. It is simply a matter of change in legal status, which would entitle the small farmer, who already cultivates the land as a tenant or a sharecropper, to a larger share of the product of his labour and in the end would make it possible for him to become the owner of the land. Determined measures for reform of the existing system of land tenure not only would be of great significance politically, but in time would also have favourable economic effects because they would stimulate the personal interest of the tiller of the soil.[5]

Though the Planning Commission has rejected the device of redistribution, the trend of state legislation appears to have accepted the desirability of it in one form or another.

The U.P. Zamindary Abolition Act (1950) provides that in the future no sales of land should be made which will vest in the buyer an ownership of more than thirty acres of land (new and old together). The Bombay Tenancy and Agricultural Lands Act (1948) prevents a landlord from resuming land given on lease if he has already under personal cultivation fifty acres of land and entitles a tenant to compel the landlord to sell to him land which is leased out to him, at a price determined by a Land Tribunal, provided such a sale does not reduce the landlord's holding below fifty acres. The Hyderabad Tenancy and Agricultural Lands Act and legislation in a few other states have a similar provision.

LAND RECLAMATION

The contribution of land reclamation in augmenting the availability of land is capable of more precise evaluation. According to published statistics there are some 87 million acres of wasteland in the Indian Union, but not more than 20 to 25 million acres are economically capable of being brought under cultivation. In addition, there are nearly 10 million acres infested with deep-rooted weeds. Most of the "culturable waste" land is situated in malarious tracts and is infested with wild animals. It is covered by thick jungle growth or by tall grass.

During the last few years, under the Grow More Food plan and other measures, schemes of reclamation have been in operation all over the Union. Table 10 gives the extent of achievements and expectation.

TABLE 10
LAND RECLAMATION PROGRESS IN INDIA

Year	Amount*
1948	32.5
1949	72.0
1950	80.0
1951 (anticipated)	225.0
1952 (and for 7 years)	280.0

*In thousands of hectares.

It is estimated that during the next seven years the rate of annual reclamation will amount to 280,000 acres. Thus, as a result of schemes of reclamation, by 1960 the addition to cultivable land would amount to a little over 2 million acres or less than 1 per cent of the land under cultivation in 1950. The First Five Year Plan also estimates that by 1957 1.5 million acres will be reclaimed by the Central Tractor Organization and an additional 4 million acres of fallow land will be brought under cultivation.

It will be evident that land reclamation will not materially alter the position regarding the availability of land.

NONAGRICUTURAL EMPLOYMENT

This is considered the pièce de résistance of agrarian reform. Remove the population from primary to secondary and tertiary industries and not only will the per capita income and standard of living increase but rationalization of agrarian relations will become easier. This certainly is an over-simplification of the problem confronting an underdeveloped country. An analysis of factors responsible for accelerating or retarding the transfer of population is extremely complicated. First, the nature and extent of "surplus" population needs patient understanding. As is often pointed out, there are two distinct categories constituting the "surplus"—visible unemployment and underemployment or disguised unemployment. As the group of experts appointed by the Secretary General to the United Nations to report on measures for the economic development of underdeveloped countries observe:

The significance of the term "disguised" is that it is applied only to persons who are not normally engaged in wage employment. The disguised unemployed are those persons who work on their own account and who are so numerous, relative to the resources with which they work, that if a number of them were withdrawn for work on other sectors of the economy, the total output of the sector from which they are withdrawn would not be diminished even though no significant reorganisation occurred in this sector, and no significant substitution of capital. The term is not applied to wage labour; presumably employers will not employ a labourer for wages unless his labour increases the total product. The use of the word "unemployment" in this connection is, therefore, somewhat misleading, since it is more often confined to wage-labourers whose status is recorded in unemployment statistics. We prefer to use, hereafter, the less precise but more familiar term, "under-employment," which is used in our terms of reference.[6]

A two-pronged approach to this problem is necessary. One is to create more continuous employment within agriculture itself for the "underemployed" group. Provision of perennial irrigation, consolidation of holdings, and extension of marketing facilities are steps in that direction. For the unemployed group, nonfarm opportunities and employment within and without the village may be created. A warning may be uttered here. The impact of such transfers on the need for seasonal demand for labour within agriculture must not be lost sight of. If some of the nonfarm employment is complementary to the seasonal needs of agriculture and within the village itself, this requirement would be satisfied. But this raises a number of sociological and economic issues into which it is not possible to enter here.

Coming down to brass tacks, what is the exact scope of absorption of surplus population through industrialization? Can the past experience provide any indication? Table 11 gives the changing occupational pattern of Indian population from decade to decade. Industrialization in India no doubt was retarded by a complexity of socio-political problems. Yet India today ranks seventh or eighth in the scale of industrialization. Undoubtedly, the levels of consumption are depressingly low. However, Table 11 clearly proves that as an instrument of population transfer, industrialization has limited potentialities. This, however, does not mean that efforts need not be made to maximize industrial employment.

For obvious reasons the problem of migration need not detain us.

The Way Out

We have explored the potentialities of recognized devices for relieving the pressure of population on land, which, it is admitted, is a major handicap in the way of

TABLE 11

CHANGING OCCUPATIONAL PATTERN OF THE POPULATION OF INDIA*

	1911	1921	1931	1941
Total population	315	319	353	389
Working population	149	146	154	170
Persons employed in industry	17.5	16.7	15.3	16.3
Percentage of workers in industry to working population	11.0	11.0	10.3	9.6
Percentage of workers in industry to total population	5.5	4.9	4.3	4.2

*Numbers in millions and as percentages of totals.

putting agrarian relations on an economically efficient and socially just basis. Our conclusion is that while maximum use should be made of all these devices, the assessment of their potentiality indicates that for some time to come the land tenure policy must take the existing situation for granted and try to make the best of a bad situation. Ready-made panaceas based on ideological preferences and inadequate appreciation of basic economic situations will not only fail but may prove dangerous.

FARMING ON ECONOMIC UNITS

The basic economic conditions and the efficacy of a dynamic change being as stated above, what can one do to put agrarian relations on a just and equitable basis? Our first submission is that though the basic principles of a tenure policy must be uniform, intelligent application of those principles to a varying set of economic conditions may result in a multiple tenurial pattern. Thus, we may at once agree that all those farmers who possess the requisite resources—land, cattle, credit, etc.—in economic units may be, subject to conditions mentioned below, allowed to continue as owner-operators. To this may be added those who are submarginal today but whose status could be brought up to the margin by an application of what may be called supplementary co-operative or state aid.

The conditions governing individual ownership should be: ceiling on maximum individual holding, prevention of transfer of land to nonagriculturists, absentee rent-receiving class. Sales should be subject to the approval of land tribunal especially in regard to price; sub-leasing should be prohibited, and reasonable remuneration should be given to wage-paid labor.

CO-OPERATIVES FOR FARMERS

What pattern would we suggest for those millions who do not fall into either of the above two categories? First and foremost, the state should undertake a very comprehensive program of rehabilitation on the lines of the Farm Security Administration. But it is our firm conviction that it would be impossible to rehabilitate these millions on an individual basis. A very extensive application of co-operative principles will become imperative. It is true that co-operative pooling of resources does not increase the per capita availability, but inasmuch as the working of resources in economic units will result in efficiency, the community as well as the individuals forming the co-operative will derive distinct economic gains.

We are not oblivious to the numerous difficulties of co-operative management, but our submission is that the merits as well as the demerits of the proposals must be assessed in terms of alternatives. If we remind ourselves of the limitations of the oft-proffered remedies, we are left with only two other alternatives: status quo with dwarf farms and collective farming. No one

will obviously and openly advocate the status quo, but it is not unlikely that, for all practical purposes, the state may write off the submerged sections as beyond redemption and concentrate on sections with high potential. The other alternative of herding all uneconomic farmers into a collective farm and converting them into farm laborers really involves questions of social values and attitude on which it is fruitless to argue. I shall content myself with expressing a strong preference for co-operatives and against the collective. The picture of land ownership as it emerges from the above discussion seems to be owner-operation on economic units and co-operative ownership and management for the patently subeconomic.

Summary of Progress

As I draw to the close of my remarks, I should like to summarize briefly the progress which India has made on agrarian reform. Our problems have vast dimensions, but this has not deterred us from taking firm steps in the right direction.

Abolition of zamindari.—First and foremost is the question of doing away with the obsolete system of zamindari (absentee landlords). Legislation has now been passed in all states in which land is owned under zamindari tenure to abolish it. It is estimated that the legislation will cover 127 million acres of land and that the compensation to the landlords will amount to Rs. 450 crores.[7] The amount of compensation is based on a multiple of the annual rent received by the landlord either at a flat rate with a rehabilitation grant to the smaller landlords or on a graduated scale and is payable partly in cash and partly in negotiable or non-negotiable bonds.

Tenancy legislation.—Every state has enacted tenancy legislation for the protection of tenants. It provides for fair rent and for security of tenure with full-fledged occupancy rights. Some acts contain provision for enabling the tenants to buy land from their landlords at reasonable prices. Restrictions are also placed on sale of land to nonagriculturists and on subletting.

Agricultural laborer.—The Minimum Wages Act was passed by the Federal Legislature in 1948. It provides that three years after enactment minimum wages should be fixed for the agricultural laborer. This period has now been extended by two years.

Land reclamation.—The Central Tractor Station had reclaimed 400,000 acres of gunsee and kans infested land by the end of 1950. According to the present plans the tractor organization will reclaim 280,000 acres of land per year for the next seven years.

Irrigation.—The Five Year Plan of the government of India published recently provides for irrigating 16.3 million acres of land through major and minor irrigation works during the next five years. Investment of Rs. 450 crores is provided for this purpose. It may be noted that in the Five Year Plan 43 per cent of the total investment of Rs. 15 billion has been earmarked for agricultural and rural development, irrigation, and power.

Agricultural co-operation.—In 1950, there were 173,000 co-operative societies with a membership of 12.6 million and a working capital of Rs. 233 crores in the Indian Union.

Consolidation.—This is a major plank in land reform. Most of the states have legislation for this purpose. The achievements are of a varying order. In Madhya Pradesh consolidation of 2.5 million acres has taken place, reducing 4.5 million blocks to 900,000.

Community development projects.—Another notable line of development is the launching of some fifty urban-cum-rural community projects under the Indo-U.S. Technical Cooperation Agreement entailing an expenditure of Rs. 380 million over a period of three years. Half the expenditure will be met by the United States government. The projects will cover 16,600 villages and a population of 12 million people. The projects will be undertaken with the object of developing to the fullest possible extent the human and the material resources of the area. Special attention will be paid to the encouragement of the co-operative endeavor by the people themselves.

Fertilizer factory.—The state owned and operated fertilizer factory at Sindri, one of the biggest in Asia, has commenced production. It will soon produce 1,000 tons of Ammonium Sulphate per day. The potential demand of Indian farmers for fertilizers of this type is estimated at 2 to 3 million tons per year. The factory has been set up at a cost of Rs. 230 million.

Concluding Remarks

Will the land reform retard production and efficiency, which a backward country particularly cannot afford to sacrifice? Our answer is, yes, if it is too little and too late. A cold-blooded, static, and bureaucratic approach must take the antithesis between economic efficiency and social justice for granted. It is the task of leadership to see that a reform is viewed not as an end but as a beginning. Every victory generates a mood of relaxation and, perhaps, of complacency. It is for leadership to convert victories into higher struggles.

Before concluding, I must express my appreciation and my country's appreciation for the efforts of the American people to acquire an understanding of the problems of the people, as distinct from those purely of governments—if I may make such a distinction without being misunderstood. You understand a people better when you understand their difficulties, not so much in regard to the dramatic issues of international tensions but in regard to their everyday life. In my humble opinion, such an understanding is a better befriender and has more winning powers than financial and military assistance.

In its deepest analysis, the land problem in an old and under-developed country like ours is a problem of bestowing self-respect and human dignity on millions of submerged people. And that, once again in an ultimate analysis, is the most powerful bulwark against war and for peace.

AGRARIAN REFORM IN THE STATE OF
UTTAR PRADESH, INDIA

Aditya Nath Jha

THE SALIENT features of the Uttar Pradesh Zamindari Abolition and Land Reforms Act, 1951, are the acquisition of the interests of all the intermediaries on land on the payment of compensation amounting to eight times their net income to all the zamindars and of rehabilitation grants at a graded rate, ranging from twenty to two, to all the smaller zamindars paying annual land revenue not exceeding Rs. 5,000.

The Act seeks to evolve a new, simple, and uniform system of land tenure which combines the wholesome features of peasant proprietorship with the development of self-governing village communities in whom will be vested the ownership of all common lands and powers of land administration and management. In order to remedy the inefficiency and waste involved in the cultivation of the existing uneconomic holdings, the Act makes provision for the encouragement and rapid growth of co-operative farming suited to our conditions.

To overcome financial and legal difficulties, the tenants have been asked to make voluntary contributions of ten times their rent. This will provide finance for the speedy abolition of zamindari, check inflation, and utilize the peasant's savings for a productive purpose. The tenants who make this contribution will be entitled to transferable rights in their holdings and will pay as land revenue only 50 per cent of their existing rent. They will be classed as bhumidhars along with the intermediaries, who will also be given bhumidhari rights in groves and land cultivated by them.

The other class of tenants who do not contribute to the Zamindari Abolition Fund will be called sirdars. They will have a permanent and heritable interest in their holdings but will not be allowed to use them for any purpose other than agriculture, horticulture, or animal husbandry. The Act further protects the interests of these cultivators who do not at present enjoy any permanent rights in land but whose displacement would lead to social injustice and grave economic difficulties. The general body of tenants-of-sir to whom hereditary rights do not accrue and of the existing subtenants will be given security of tenure for a period of five years, after which they can, on payment of fifteen times the hereditary rate or the rent of their tenant-in-chief, acquire bhumidhari rights.

To prevent the re-emergence of the landlord-tenant system, the Act restricts the right of letting only to disabled persons, such as minors, widows, and persons suffering from physical or mental infirmity. To avoid accumulation of large holdings and the consequent exploitation of labor, no person will be permitted to acquire by sale or gift a holding of more than thirty acres.

The measure coming in the wake of the Panchayat Raj Act, which makes the village a small republic, is intended to facilitate economic and social development and to encourage the growth of social responsibility and community spirit leading to the establishment of a co-operative democracy.

It is proposed to extend the provisions of the bill to government estates. Separate legislation is under contemplation in respect of agricultural areas lying within the limits of municipalities, cantonments, notified areas, and town areas. The question of scaling down the debts of intermediaries whose rights will be acquired will also be dealt with by a separate enactment.

Acquisition of Intermediaries' Interests

It is now widely recognized that without a radical change in the existing land system no co-ordinated plan of rural reconstruction can be undertaken to ensure agricultural efficiency and increased food production, to raise the standard of living of the rural masses, and to give opportunities for the full development of the peasant's personality. The landlord-tenant system established by the British for reasons of expediency and administrative convenience should give place to a new order which restores to the cultivator the rights and the freedom which were his and to the village community the supremacy which it exercised over all the elements of village life.

The Act accordingly provides that with effect from a date to be notified by the government all the interests of the intermediaries including their interest in cultivated land, groveland, pathways, habitation sites, wastelands, forests, fisheries, ferries, public wells, tanks, water channels, markets, bazaars, mines and minerals and other subsoil rights shall be vested in the government free from all encumbrances.

The intermediaries shall however continue in possession of land in their own cultivation, trees upon such land, trees belonging to them in the habitation sites, groves, and their private wells.

All the persons living in the villages, whether zamindars, tenants, or landless, will become the owners of their houses and house sites.

Compensation

The Act provides for the acquisition of intermediaries' rights on payment of compensation at eight times their net assets. It will yield an income to the bigger zamindars sufficient for a reasonable standard of living. For rehabilitation of the smaller zamindars, who constitute the overwhelming majority, it further provides for the payment of a graded rehabilitation grant ranging from twenty to two times the net assets, being largest for low incomes and smallest for those with comparatively large incomes.

The compensation will be determined on the basis of entries in the record-of-rights by the courts of Compensation Officers specially appointed for the purpose. The revenue records will be regarded as conclusive, but provision has been made to protect the rights of persons who claim a title to land which is not recorded or who dispute the correctness of any entry in the records. Clerical or obvious errors may be corrected by the Compensation Officer himself; other errors may be corrected in proceedings for mutation or correction of khewat under the Land Revenue Act or by the order of a civil court. The civil courts have also been empowered to attach the compensation money if a claim or dispute about title is pending.

The Compensation Officer will first prepare a draft compensation assessment roll showing in respect of every estate the gross and net assets of each intermediary having a share in the estate. The gross assets will be calculated by taking the mahal or the village as the unit and will be the aggregate of rents including cesses and local rates payable to the proprietors of the estate by the inferior proprietors or tenants. Where the rent has not been determined, it will be determined at hereditary rates. Gross assets will also include income accruing to an intermediary on account of mines and minerals. In short, the gross assets of a mahal will consist of all the income that actually accrues to the proprietors of the mahal. The gross assets of a mahal thus obtained will be distributed amongst all the co-sharers of the mahal in proportion to their share and the gross assets of each intermediary will thus be obtained. From the gross assets thus obtained deductions will be made to arrive at his net assets. These deductions will consist of (1) any sum payable by the intermediary as land revenue, rent, cess or local rate, (2) cost of management and irrecoverable arrears of rent calculated at the rate of 15 per cent of the gross assets, (3) an amount computed at ex-proprietary rates in respect of the land in the personal cultivation of the intermediary, which after the acquisition will be left with the intermediary, (4) income tax paid in respect of income from royalties on account of mines and minerals, (5) 95 per cent of the gross income from a mine if the intermediary was directly working it, the reason for this deduction being that the intermediary will be allowed to continue to work the mine to his benefit even after the acquisition, and (6) any agricultural income-tax paid by the intermediary.

Provision has been made to counter steps which may have been or may hereafter be taken by intermediaries to defeat the provisions of this Act. If any intermediary has, after July 1, 1948, given new leases at low rent by taking heavy premiums, the rents of such holdings may be enhanced to hereditary level. No transfer by way of sale or gift made after July 1, 1948, would be recognized; and generally contracts or agreements made by an intermediary having the effect directly or indirectly of relieving a sirdar from the liability of payment of revenue or of entitling the intermediary to receive a higher rehabilitation grant than he would otherwise get have been declared to be void.

For the purpose of assessment of compensation every intermediary shall be regarded as a separate unit. In the case of joint Hindu families, father and sons shall be treated as one and other members of the family as separate units. To counter steps to break up large estates into smaller units with the intention of obtaining higher amounts on abolition of zamindari transfer by sale or gift between fathers and sons or husbands or wives, etc. made after August 8, 1948, shall be disregarded.

Compensation will be due from the date on which an estate is acquired and will bear interest at the rate of 2.5 per cent, but if its determination takes more than nine months interim compensation will be paid to avoid hardship.

Rehabilitation Grant

In addition to compensation, every intermediary whose aggregate land revenue does not exceed Rs. 5,000 will be entitled to a rehabilitation grant according to the schedules shown in Table 12.

The amount of compensation payable to an intermediary will be determined in respect of each estate separately. The rehabilitation grant, on the other hand, takes into account the economic circumstances of an individual. Those with small incomes necessarily need larger grants for adjusting themselves to changed conditions. The Rehabilitation Grants Officer will therefore determine the grant on the basis of the aggregate net assets and the aggregate land revenue of all the estates belonging to an intermediary.

Waqfs, Trusts, and Endowments

Private waqfs and trusts whose income is

TABLE 12

REHABILITATION GRANTS TO
INTERMEDIARIES IN INDIA*

Categories According to Land Revenue	Multiple of Net Assets Awarded
0–25	20
25–50	17
50–100	14
100–250	11
250–500	8
500–2,000	5
2,000–3,500	3
3,500–5,000	2

*In rupees.

meant only for the benefit of individuals will be treated like ordinary zamindari for the purposes of assessment and payment of the compensation and the rehabilitation grant.

Waqfs and trusts or parts thereof devoted wholly to charitable or religious purposes will be assured an annual income equal to their present income. This will be done in two stages: first, payment of compensation at the usual rate, secondly, payment of an annuity which added to the annual income on the compensation will be equal to the present annual income of the waqf or trust.

New Land System

The scheme of the new land system may be divided broadly into three parts: (1) the establishment of village communities or Gaon Samaj, (2) land tenures, and (3) development of co-operative farming.

VILLAGE COMMUNITIES

A village community shall include all the cultivators as well as all the residents of the village. All common lands in a village not included in a holding, all forests within the village boundaries, all trees other than trees in a holding, grove or abadi, public wells, tanks, water channels, habitation sites and pathways, private ferries, fisheries, markets and bazaars, shall vest in the village community. The Gaon Sabha, acting through the Gaon Panchayat as constituted under the Panchayat Raj Act, will exercise the powers and discharge the duties conferred or imposed by this Act. The Gaon Panchayat will thus be charged with the general superintendence, management, and control of all lands vesting in the village community. It shall ensure that the conditions of tenure prescribed by this Act are not violated. It will also be its duty to take measures for the development and improvement of agriculture and cottage industries. If the government so directs, the Gaon Panchayat will also collect and realize the land revenue. A committee of the Gaon Panchayat, consisting of the representatives of that village, will be formed for each village to deal with the settlement of vacant lands and discharge other functions relating to land management.

NEW LAND TENURES

There will be two main classes of tenure-holders, namely, Bhumidhars and Sirdars, and two minor classes, namely, Asamis and Adhivasis.

Bhumidhars.—All the intermediaries will be given bhumidhari rights in respect of their sir, khudkasht, and groves. All the tenants, who become sirdars, will have the right, on payment of ten times of their rent, to become bhumidhars. A bhumidhar will have a permanent, heritable, and transferable right in his holding and the right to use his land for any purpose whatsoever. He shall not be liable to ejectments.

Sirdars.—Sirdari rights will be conferred on all tenants with a right of occupancy. Sirdars will have a permanent and heritable interest in their holdings but will not be allowed to use them for any purpose other than agriculture, horticulture, or animal husbandry.

Asami.—Asami rights will be conferred upon tenants or subtenants of grove land, tenants' mortgagees, nonoccupancy tenants of pasture lands or lands covered by water, lands set apart for afforestation, land in the bed of river and used for casual or occasional cultivation, and tracts of shifting and unstable cultivation, and persons to whom leases are subsequently given in accordance with the provisions of this Act.

Asami rights will be heritable, but will generally not be permanent. Provisions have been made, however, to give them such security as is consistent with the conditions of their tenure. Bhumidhars and sirdars will, in the future, be allowed to let their land only when they are unable to cultivate it themselves, i.e., in cases of a minor or a widow, a person incapable of cultivation by reason of physical or mental infirmity or because he is in the military service or is under imprisonment. Where the land has been so let the asami will continue in possession until the disability has ceased or until the bhumidhars or sirdar wishes to cultivate the land himself.

Adhivasis.—A large class of cultivators have no stable rights in land. This includes tenants-of-sir and subtenants. It has been considered necessary to protect their rights and to give them security of tenure. They have been given the right to continue to hold their lands for five years from the commencement of this Act. After the expiry of this period, they may, on payment of fifteen times the hereditary rate in case of tenants-of-sir and fifteen times the rent of the tenant-in-chief in case of subtenants, acquire bhumidhari rights. If they do so, the rights of their landholders will be extinguished. Provision has been made for the payment of equitable compensation to the bhumidhars or sirdars whose rights will thus be acquired.

The acquisition of permanent rights by Adhivasis might lead to the further diminution of holdings in areas where they are particularly small. In such areas attempts will be made to give the tenants-in-chief as well as the sir holders some land out of the available vacant or cultivable land to make their holdings economic. Tenants-of-sir or subtenants will be liable to ejectment only in cases where this cannot be done and where the landholder wishes to bring the land under his personal cultivation.

GENERAL CONDITIONS OF TENURE

Bhumidhars and sirdars will in future pay land revenue and asamis and adhivasis rent. The adhivasis is only a transitional form of land tenure which will eventually disappear.

The table of devolution laid down in the Uttar Pradesh Tenancy Act has been maintained with only minor changes in order to prevent excessive subdivision of holdings. A bhumidhar shall, however, have the right to bequeath his land in accordance with his personal law. Subdivision of holdings will be permitted only if all the parts so subdivided are not less than an economic holding, i.e., six and one-fourth acres.

Bhumidhars will be free to transfer their holdings or part thereof to anyone except a person who would as a consequence of the transfer have a holding exceeding thirty acres. Where the aggregate of land held by any person along with his minor son, husband, or wife, or other dependent and the land acquired exceeds thirty acres, the acquisition shall be deemed illegal and he shall be liable to ejectment from the land acquired. This measure is intended to prevent the accumulation of large properties in the hands of a single individual. To prevent letting of land in the guise of a mortgage, the bhumidhars will not be allowed to mortgage their land with possession. If they do so, the mortgagee will be deemed to have purchased the land and will acquire the rights of a bhumidhar.

CO-OPERATIVE FARMS

There will be two kinds of co-operative farms: (1) small co-operative farms of fifty acres or more constituted by voluntary agreement among ten or more cultivators, and (2) a co-operative farm comprising all the uneconomic holdings in a village. The latter type can be established if two-thirds of the holders of uneconomic holdings in a village apply for the registration of such farm; on their doing so the remaining one-third will have to join.

As soon as a co-operative farm has been established consolidation proceedings will be taken up. The members of the co-operative farm will retain their individual rights in the land contributed by them. Model bylaws will be framed by the government to provide for the management of co-operative farms, maintenance of accounts, distribution of produce, and other details. As co-operative farming is regarded as the most effective method by which maximum use can be made of land it is intended to organize a drive for the encouragement of co-operative farms. A large number of facilities will be given to such farms, which may include exemption (partial or total) from agricultural income tax, reduction in land revenue, priority in irrigation, the right to acquire suitable areas of vacant lands, financial aid in the form of loans or subsidies, and technical advice from government experts.

Land Revenue

All bhumidhars and sirdars will be jointly and severally responsible for the land revenue assessed on the village.

In the case of land under the personal cultivation of an intermediary on the date of vesting, the land revenue shall be equal to the present land revenue and local rates on such land. In the case of a sirdar who acquires bhumidhari rights it shall be equal to half his rent. A sirdar who does not acquire bhumidhari rights will pay land revenue equal to the rent he was hitherto paying.

A new settlement, i.e., reassessment of land revenue, will not take place for the next forty years, and the interval between the succeeding settlements will again be forty years. When a settlement takes place the Settlement Officer shall have regard to the estimated average surplus produce remaining after deducting the ordinary cultivation expenses of the cultivator, and the revenue shall be such percentage of the surplus produce as may be fixed by a resolution of the Uttar Pradesh Legislature passed after the proposals of the government have been published in the Gazette as well as in the assessment circle concerned. The percentage of revenue to the surplus produce shall vary according to a graduated scale being largest on holdings, with the highest surplus produce and smallest on holdings with the lowest surplus produce. The percentage applicable to a bhumidhar shall not in any case exceed one-half of the percentage applicable to a sirdar.

The Act passed by the legislature of the State of Uttar Pradesh is intended to secure for the actual producer only primary justice, to help the vast masses of cultivators lead a better life, and to create conditions in which may develop a true sense of social responsibility and community spirit.

There is a terrific upheaval in almost all of Asia. Many people talk of the spread of Communism and think that the remedy lies in suppressing the so-called disruptive forces. That is true, so far as it goes, but unless there is a constructive and positive approach to the land problem, Communism cannot be warded off merely by acts of oppression. Those who desire peaceful progress, and particularly persons who have vested interest must naturally be foremost amongst them, must remember that in order to fight totalitarianism in any form, the aspirations and wishes of the common man must be respected and, to the extent possible, fulfilled.

The Act strives to maintain the *cultivating* rights of every person, whether he be a landlord, tenant, or subtenant.

Part VI

LAND AND POPULATION IN SOUTHEAST ASIA

LAND TENURE AND AGRARIAN PROBLEMS OF BURMA

Ba Thein

BURMA IS A typical model of an under-developed country, according to the definition of the United Nations Economic and Social Council, with "defects in agrarian structure as obstacles to economic development." She has plenty of natural resources and potentialities still remaining unexplored and undeveloped. With proper guidance and management, there is still ample scope to improve her economy, which received a severe battering in the last world war. In this task the country will need the concerted efforts of the administrators and the citizens and the technical help and guidance of the more advanced countries and the international bodies. If these are forthcoming in the measure required, the future of Burma is still bright, and the traditional land of pagodas and shrines can still hope to be flowing with milk and honey. Before going into further details, it might be necessary to indicate the situation of Burma on the world map. Although she has one of the most ancient civilizations Burma joined the family of nations as an independent state only on January 4, 1948. She was comparatively obscure and unknown to the outside world until the Burma-China Road was completed in 1941, just before World War II, and she became a theater of war for three years, from 1942 to 1945.

Population Density

Burma is situated in the Northern Tropics, touching Tibet at a point beyond 28 degrees north latitude, with China on the north, India and Pakistan on the west, Indo-China and Thailand on the east and southeast, and the Bay of Bengal bordering the south and southwestern coasts. She has an area of about 621,000 square miles, roughly corresponding to the northeast corner of the United States from Ohio to Maryland. The population of about 17 millions is made up of 88 per cent Burmans including all indigenous races, 4 per cent Hindus, 4 per cent Muslims, 3 per cent Chinese, and 1 per cent Europeans and other nationals. Burma's population density is the lowest in the East, with only 72 persons per square mile, as against 247 for India, 250 for China, and 496 for Japan. (These figures are for the years 1939–41). The population is fairly evenly distributed, so that she has no problem of population pressure as in many other Asian countries. In fact, she is still underpopulated. In the fertile plains of Lower Burma, as in the alluvial lowlands of Thailand and Cambodia, the population density averages less than 250 persons per square mile. This contrasts greatly with similar alluvial plains in adjacent India and China where rural people are as numerous as 1,000 or more per square mile.

Distribution of Occupations

Burma is predominantly rural, with 66.5 per cent of her working population engaged directly in agriculture and a large proportion of the remainder dependent in one way or another on the agricultural industry. The figures in Table 13, taken from the census of 1941, show the distribution of occupations.

TABLE 13

Occupational Distribution of the
Population of Burma, 1941

Occupation	Per cent
Agriculture	66.5
Industry	10.7
Trade	9.0
Transport	3.6
Professional and liberal arts	3.2
Animal husbandry	2.3
Forestry	0.8
Public administration	0.7
Domestic service	0.7
Exploitation of minerals	0.6
Police, etc.	0.5
Rentiers	0.1
Unproductive	1.3
	100.0

The figures for "industry" in Table 13 include a great many persons who actually belong to farm families but who spend part of their time in spinning, weaving, or other cottage industries (handicrafts). Hence agriculture is even more important than is indicated by these statistics. The economic importance of forestry and mining, on the other hand, is probably greater than the figures would indicate, for these industries produce materials which provide a disproportionate amount of business for the transport industries.

Cultivated Area

The total occupied area in Burma was 19,149,100 acres as shown in the Revenue Administration Report of 1935–36, comprising 12,790,497 acres occupied by agriculturists and 6,358,603 by nonagriculturists. Out of this total occupied area, about 18 million acres were cultivated and were devoted to the following major crops: 12 million acres under paddy (rice), 3 million under peanuts, sesame, millet, and cotton, 1 million under peas and beans, 1 million under fruit gardens and vegetables, and the remainder under various other crops. According to the Season and Crop Report, 1940–41, it was estimated that there were about 19 million acres of culturable waste which can be brought under cultivation by clearing the jungle and by reclaiming land lying on the seaward margin of the Delta. Since Lower Burma has such a relatively sparse population compared to her neighbors, it is to be expected that considerable areas of cultivable land have not yet been taken up for cultivation. As a matter of fact, we are still striving hard to reach the prewar level of 12 million acres under paddy, since most of the paddy land had to be abandoned during the war years. It will be a long time before it becomes necessary to open up new virgin soils.

Seasons

The rainfall comes almost entirely with the southwest monsoon, which lasts from late May to the end of October. The northeast monsoon is very weak and brings little or no rain. There is consequently a rainy season of five months during which period all the precipitation occurs, and a season of about seven months almost without rain. The incidence of rainfall varies from over 250 inches in the south to 25 inches or less in the center, rising again in the north to 150 inches or more. This diversity of rainfall entails a corresponding diversity in the crops grown. The heavy rainfall of the coastal districts and the delta of the Irrawaddy River makes it possible to raise only paddy as monoculture, with some rubber, coconut, betelnut, and fruit gardens. The absence of rain for nearly seven months makes winter-cropping difficult in these areas except on the inundated areas along the permanent river banks, where winter-cropping of peas and beans, tobacco, and peanuts is now being introduced and encouraged.

The "dry zone" of central Burma has a rainfall varying from below 25 inches to about 40 inches, but the distribution is very irregular, and droughts are common. In this area, paddy is a precarious crop unless irrigated. Canals were constructed by the Burmese kings as early as 1044 and are being very well maintained. Under the British regime these canals were improved, and new canals were built. This network of irrigation systems now feeds some 1.5 million acres of paddy land in the dry zone area which otherwise could not produce paddy. Although it is true that the paddy crop of the dry zone does not enter into any export trade, yet it does affect the trade in that it provides almost enough food for its own population in some districts of Upper Burma, thereby releasing a corresponding amount from Lower Burma for export.

Importance of Paddy Crop

Out of the total cultivated area of 18,800,-000 acres in 1941, about 12,500,000 acres, i.e., roughly two-thirds of the acreage, were under paddy. The figures change little from year to year, since there is no practical alternative to rice for most of the soil. The monsoon is so reliable that only relatively unimportant marginal areas are in danger of crop failure through lack of rain, mainly those in the rain-fed areas in the central dry zone region. The existence of a large dry zone, however, where other crops are invariably grown in the absence of irrigation, prevents the Burma paddy crop from occupying as large a proportion of the total acreage as in Thailand or Indo-China, as may be seen in Table 14.

Burma's economy is greatly dependent on

TABLE 14
PADDY CROP PRODUCTION IN
SOUTHEAST ASIA

Area	Percentage of Cultivated Area	Total Production (in tons)
Thailand	95.0	2,711,000
Indo-China	80.0	3,945,000
Burma	65.0	4,940,000
Java	45.0	4,007,000
Malaya	7.5	341,000
Total		15,944,000

her export of rice, which occupies about two-thirds of the total cropped area and represents half the value of the total exports of Burma. The normal paddy crop was over 7 million tons, of which a little over one-third is required for home consumption, leaving the remaining two-thirds available for export. The surplus rice supplied more than half of the total annual exports of Southeast Asia, or nearly two-fifths of the rice which entered international trade in the years preceding the war. India is our best customer, and she takes more than half of our total export of rice. Ceylon, Malaya, China, and Japan come next in order, and a good portion also goes to European markets. This indicates the important part played by paddy in the economy of Burma.

Agricultural Department

Although Burma is fairly rich in other mineral resources, she is particularly lacking in iron ore and coal to support the heavy industries which are generally recognized to be the foundation of successful industrialization. It seems probable that she must therefore remain predominantly an agricultural country. Naturally, therefore, it became imperative that measures should be taken to improve her agricultural conditions and the financial status of the agriculturists by giving not only financial aid but also technical advice. The latter was furnished by the Agricultural Department, which was established early in this century with a nominal staff and gradually expanded. At first the agricultural graduates were given training in Poona, India, until the Agricultural College and Research Institute was opened in Mandalay in 1924. This college had to be closed during the depression of the 1930's, but it was started again as a constituent college of Rangoon University in 1939. The work of the Department is manifold, consisting not only of research and experiments but also of extension service, as it is termed in the United States. Unfortunately, the Department is very much understaffed and the allotment of funds is so small that it is hardly possible to cope with various items of agricultural improvements. Among them are improved methods of cultivation to reduce cost and insure against crop failures; improved strains of seed that can resist disease, give higher yields, suit particular soils and localities, encourage growing of crops most suitable to the land, and promote the introduction of new crops, double cropping, mixed cropping, rotation, etc.; improved implements—for example, seed drills, row-crop cultivators, harvesters, tractors—in short, mechanization of farm operations as far as practicable; use of fertilizers and manures; proper layout of holdings and soil conservation; and, last but not least, the important extension services.

Crops.—Burma is divided into eight agricultural divisions, each having a central experimental station dealing in a particular crop characteristic of the area, seed farms for multiplication of improved seeds, and a number of demonstration holdings on which the results of research and experiment are demonstrated and disseminated to the farmers. The Department has evolved many improved strains of paddy, cotton, peanuts, sesame, beans, gram (chick-peas), wheat, and sugar cane, and the work in this direction is proceeding. We are fairly well advanced in this field of research, although more remains to be done in devising improved implements.

Implements.—Many of the indigenous bullock-drawn implements have been remodelled and designed for higher efficiency, and some new implements have been imported, chiefly from Britain and the United States. The use of tractors, however, has been less successful. By 1932, about sixty tractors had been imported; these, however, have not been a success as far as agricultural operations are concerned. The rice lands become swampy during the rains, and the heavy tractors tend to bog down. Paddy lands can be ploughed by tractors only in the dry season before the monsoon sets in and when the soil is baked hard like cement. Under this condition, the depreciation charges of the implement become prohibitive as compared with the normal cost of cultivation by indigenous bullock-drawn implements in the early rains when the soil condition is favorable. The feasibility of the use of small tractors adapted to the monsoon condition of the area, such as are being employed in Japan, remains to be explored. Petrol and other types of fuel are very expensive and spare parts are not easily available. Servicing thus becomes difficult, especially since there is a dearth of technical personnel.

Tractors.—The advances made in tractor design since 1932, when almost the last of the tractors was imported, make it possible to hope that the reintroduction of tractors may not be as dismal a failure as the first trials. A number of improved light-weight tractors were imported after World War II and are being experimented with and demonstrated in the dry zone area with appreciable success. The small and scattered nature of holdings and the diversity of crops grown tend to make tractor ploughing uneconomical. It will be necessary to consolidate some of the holdings and rearrange the cropping scheme in such a way that there will be fair-size blocks under the same crop, permitting agricultural operations to be done simultaneously and economically before we can think of mechanizing agriculture on any considerable scale. All farm operations and harvesting are now being done by manual labor. Considering the fact that the population of Burma in relation to its land is relatively small, the future of Burmese cultivation would seem to lie in the direction of increased use of machinery in agriculture if her resources are to be exploited in full. Even at the present stage of development, the use of small labor-saving devices would be advantageous. There would seem to be scope for research and experimentation in the evolution of the best type of machinery that could be used for the purpose. With certain alterations and adaptations, small harvesters for cotton, peanuts, millet, and paddy are likely to prove very successful for Burma and perhaps also for many other underdeveloped countries with similar conditions.

Mechanization.—The high efficiency of farming in America and the West has been made possible by mechanization. No doubt there are many limiting factors and unfavorable conditions prevailing in the East which prevent the complete mechanization of farming. Nevertheless, steps should be taken to introduce suitable types of farm machinery and other essential improvements stage by stage as the general organization and institutional framework become more progressive. During the course of my study of the rural economy of the United States, I have noticed a very remarkable feature.

The efficiency of farm labor has been highly developed and the production per capita correspondingly increased. Whereas a farmer with one pair of bullocks can work only 10 to 15 acres of land, the American farmer works 120 to 200 acres with the tractor.

Fertilizers.—The average yield of paddy in Burma is about 1,250 pounds per acre. On the best soil, the yield increases to about 2,250 or 2,500 pounds per acre; yet this is very poor compared to the yields in Japan, where the average yield is nearly three times as high. Considerable research work has been undertaken to find out the effect of various kinds of fertilizers, viz., nitrates, sulphates, phosphates, potash, and compost, on paddy and other crops and their economic maximum applications under different soil and climatic conditions. From the results obtained, it can be safely concluded that the application of fertilizers is very beneficial and that yields can be increased by over 50 per cent. But the question arises as to the availability of these fertilizers and their relative prices. At present, what little we are using has to be imported from India and Great Britain. The heavy freight charges limit the widespread application of fertilizers. We must, therefore, rely on natural manures—for example, manure, guano, prawn-dust (made from shrimp), etc. Unlike India, where cow dung is burned as fuel, we conserve cow dung, compost it, and utilize it to better advantage as manure. The Agricultural Department has been widely demonstrating the proper methods of composting and storage of farmyard manure. This is not enough. Commercial fertilizers have to be manufactured locally if the full needs of the country are to be met. How and when this can be done would depend on a number of related factors—finance, technical know-how, etc.

Livestock.—Unlike the more densely populated areas of Japan, China, Indo-

China, and India, where hand labor predominates, Burma normally relies chiefly upon cattle and water buffalo for draft purposes. A single team of oxen is normally sufficient for 10 to 15 acres of paddy land. Prewar Burma had an adequate supply of draft animals, including about 2,850,000 bullocks and 361,000 buffalo. In 1945, after the Japanese occupation, the shortage of draft power became acute due to the amount of meat required by the military. Agricultural operations were hampered, and the government had to pass legislation prohibiting the slaughter of cattle. The situation has now improved and there is a sufficient number of working bullocks available for agricultural operations and, also, for transport. However, it is regrettable to note that there is no proper breeding or rearing of cattle; they are merely left to nature. The maintenance of stud bulls is very seldom practiced, and artifical insemination is only a dream.

Agricultural education.—Although many useful results have been obtained from research laboratories and experimental stations, we are not in a position to reach all the farmers with these results of research because of the shortage of extension staff. Even if we can do so, the majority of farmers are still not receptive to scientific improvements, mainly because of inadequate education and the conservatism of the people. There is, however, a relatively high degree of literacy, amounting to about 56 per cent in 1941. An English commissioner reported soon after the annexation in 1885 that the proportion of people who could read and write was then far higher in Burma than in England. This was the fruit of the religious organization and the ancient culture. In every village there is at least one monastery, and the monks, by virtue of the veneration they commanded, succeeded in imparting to all the boys under ten years of age and also the girls the elements of

letters and practical morality. However, most of them obtained only a very elementary knowledge of reading and writing.

To give practical training to the sons of bona fide farmers who till the land, the Agricultural Department has opened eight farm schools, one in each agricultural division. Some 250 students are given practical training in the improved techniques of agriculture for nine months every year. After their training, most of these students are employed in the Agricultural Department as fieldmen or demonstrators, while some return to their respective villages to practice improved farming. In addition, a number of adult farmers are annually given short courses for seven days to one month on the Central Farms and are made acquainted with the improvements that have been achieved on these farms and in surrounding areas. These short courses serve as very good incentives, but their influence is not widespread or lasting. We need some youth organizations, such as the 4-H Clubs of America, to follow up these results. I wish that our Farmers Youth Leagues could devote more of their activities to improving the farming methods instead of exhausting their energies and time in politics, as they seem to do.

Extension service.—In almost every county in the United States there is at least one county agent and sometimes also an associate or an assistant, a home agent, and a Club agent, with additional specialists for particular projects as occasion arises. In Wisconsin, a state with 54,715 square miles and 186,735 farms covering 22,876,494 acres of farm land, there are 71 counties and a total of 72 county agents, 61 home agents, and 52 Club agents doing extension work with hundreds of local community leaders and 4-H Club members to assist in educating the farmers in their social and economic life. It is a unique arrangement.

In Burma, with an area of 621,000 square

miles and a cultivated area of 18 million acres, we have only about 120 district agricultural officers doing all the work of county agent, home agent, and Club agent, and sometimes also doing research and experimental work. The extension service is far too small to achieve any tangible results. Sir Bernard Binns has stated that the Agricultural Department, in spite of handicaps in the past, has put in a great deal of excellent work, and, given a larger staff and adequate funds, should in the near future be able to do much more.

Burma is also very backward in the availability of proper media for information. There is only one broadcasting station in Rangoon, and radios are rare luxuries of the urban people. Visual aids are still limited to a few movies in big cities. The government has now set up a mobile cinema unit, but the unsettled conditions in the country make it hardly possible to reach the rural population for whom it is meant. Newspapers, magazines, and journals are mainly confined to the urban areas and their suburbs, due to inadequate transport and communication facilities. A few bulletins and pamphlets distributed by the government departments sometimes reach the farmers, but they are seldom read with sufficient interest.

Land Tenure

The main problem of land tenure in Burma is the drift of agricultural land into the hands of nonagriculturists and, in particular, into the hands of foreign nonagriculturists. In 1941 nearly half the agricultural land in Lower Burma was in the hands of nonagriculturists, and in the principal rice-growing districts the proportion was much higher. In Upper Burma the drift had not proceeded so far, but the tendency was the same, and considerable areas, especially in the irrigated tracts, were in the hands of absentee owners. These nonagri-

culturist landlords are for the most part useless middlemen whose sole interest in the land is similiar to that of stockholders in a company and who fulfill no economic functions other than to provide short-term credit to their tenants. This service function is declining.

Before describing various forms of land tenure in Burma, it will be necessary to give a brief sketch of the agricultural systems in various parts of the country, because there is a striking correlation between the land holding systems and agrarian relationships and the agricultural practices followed. In brief, Burma may be divided into three significant parts: (1) The Humid Plains of Lower Burma, where the rainfall is as high as 80 to 250 inches, with paddy as a monoculture, (2) the Dry Plains of Central or Upper Burma, the seat of the old Burmese civilizations, where the rainfall drops to not more than 25 to 40 inches, and (3) the Humid Uplands, where shifting agriculture is carried on by primitive tribesmen in the horseshoe of the hills which encompass the Burmese plains. Tribal or communal tenures persist in the hills where the codes of primitive societies remain in force. In the Dry Plains of old Burma, peasant proprietorship is most strongly developed, and what tenancy exists is of the share or partnership type. On the other hand, fixed-rent tenancy and absentee-landlordism appear in extreme form in the main rice surplus areas of the Humid Plains of the Delta.

UPPER BURMA

The communal tenures in the hill tribes are not particularly relevant to this paper and hence will not be discussed. In Upper Burma, where the forms of land tenure have been modified by British legal concepts, although they are rooted in the historic antecedents of Burmese society, the type of agriculture is mainly on a subsistence scale for local consumption only. The growing of crops for sale and export has assumed importance during the last sixty years and has made farmers dependent on cash income. The influence of long-established customs which govern the mutual relations of agricultural and nonagricultural classes have tempered the effect of the market economy and the relative rise of land values. Thus the region of most unreliable rainfall and greatest variations in the yields of crops has the lowest amount of absentee-landlordism and rural indebtedness, as may be seen in Table 15.

TABLE 15

Ownership and Tenancy Patterns in Upper Burma*

	1928	1938	1948
PERCENTAGE OF CROP AREA HELD			
Agriculturists	90.2	85.8	90.0
Local nonagriculturists	4.1	5.9	5.0
Absentee nonagriculturists	5.7	8.3	5.0
PERCENTAGE OF CROP AREA RENTED			
Fixed rent	3.7	8.2	5.0
Share or partnership	16.3	21.5	16.0
Total area rented	20.0	29.7	21.0

*Source: *Report of the Land and Agriculture Committee, 1938*, Part I, Tenancy.

The figures for 1948 in Table 15 are estimated by the author. During the Japanese occupation in the years 1942–45, there was a tremendous amount of inflation and an influx of Japanese military currency. Most of the working people were able to redeem a good portion of the land mortgaged by their forefathers, and they became owner-cultivators themselves.

Before the annexation of Upper Burma in 1885, all land was classified as private, official, and royal.

Ownership rights to private agricultural land were acquired simply by clearing and using the land and paying the tax. These were generally the best lands available. The history of these tenure rights is an interesting parallel to the "squatters' rights" common during the early settlement of the United States. There was, however, the cherished tendency to abandon the land after a few years of cultivation and take new land. A landless man could settle on occupied but uncultivated land, provided the original owner made no objection at the time. The land would then become the private property of the settler.

Official land was quasi-feudal in that it originated as grants to the heads of the King's regiments, to be allocated among their retainers in return for their services. In practice, the official land tended to become private property.

Royal lands were considered the private property of the Kings, to be used for the maintenance of the courts. These lands were inherited from predecessors or acquired by marriage.

The British policy in Upper Burma was designed to get as much revenue as possible at once from the cultivators. Revenue officers recorded and assessed the persons who used the land as if they were the owners, regardless of the previous tenure relationships. All these became private properties and were classed as nonstate lands. The rest of the lands which were not occupied or cultivated at the time of the revenue survey were declared to be state lands, upon which rent in addition to taxes had to be paid if it were utilized by private persons. From the confusion caused by that policy, various new landholding rights arose.

In his booklet *Agriculture Economy in*

Burma (1948), B. O. Binns sums up the reasons for the much better agrarian position in Upper Burma as follows:

1. Dry Zone farming does not entail as large an initial cash investment as Wet Zone, most of the labor being supplied by the family. Communal harvesting and mutual aid traditions still are not extinct, thereby resulting in less need for seasonal loans. The farmers are consequently not forced into debt rapidly.

2. The tenancy arrangements are adjusted to soil and water conditions. The variations in rainfall and consequently in crop returns almost preclude a fixed rent basis. Share tenancy is most common and occupies almost half of the total rented area. Partnership tenancy, in which the landowner supplies seed and receives half the revenue, occupies one-third of the rented area, and fixed-rent tenancy only one-sixth.

3. The rental period ordinarily lasts for three or four years, according to the crop rotation. In some cases there are hereditary tenancies, usually among well-to-do people. Here the tenure is usually secure, and there is a friendly relationship between the lessee and the lessor.

4. According to the Buddhist inheritance laws, the property is divided equally among the heirs, and rapid fragmentation of holdings would have been expected. There is a tendency, however, to maintain the family estates as individual functioning units and to split only the net return.

5. The economic position of the peasantry is more secure because there is a variety of crops grown and there are opportunities for subsidiary income from handicraft production. Cottage industries, such as spinning, weaving, basket-making, etc., are better established in Upper Burma than elsewhere in the country.

LOWER BURMA

The conditions in Lower Burma are of quite a different order. Agriculture is not solely on a subsistence scale; it is on a commercial scale as well. Furnival in *An Introduction to the Political Economy* (1931) states that agriculture in Lower Burma is more akin to industry, having an almost unlimited supply of land and a dependable rainfall. The possibility of concentrating on a single crop has permitted a division of labor by alloting each process to a different group of skilled laborers, thus permitting production on a large scale. It is doubtful whether the same combination of circumstances has ever existed anywhere else, and for this reason the development of agriculture in Lower Burma presents economic features of great interest. The result has been production on a large scale, with a division of labor and financial arrangements that are typical of industry rather than of agriculture. The annexation of Lower Burma roughly coincided with the widespread introduction of steam navigation, the opening of the Suez Canal, and the era of great expansion in British overseas trade. The British connection thus drew the Burmese economy rather suddenly into intimate relationship with the world economy. The economic life of Burma prior to annexation had been chiefly feudal, based upon custom and the use of very little money in effecting exchanges. The modern economy of the type which now affected Lower Burma was individualistic, emphasizing freedom of contract and freedom of enterprise. This was something strange to the old Burmese way of life. In the competition with foreigners, in whom the new method and outlook were ingrained, the Burmans lost ground steadily and lost their former position. Where economic forces have free play, the weakest goes to the wall, and in the economic development of Burma, the Burmans, as stated above, have been in the unfortunate position of the weakest. Relatively, at least, we were poorer than before, when we were under the rule of our Burmese kings. We have now become a poor people in a rich country. In the divided society of Burma, with Europeans, Indians, and Chinese united only in the pursuit of individual gain, democratic machinery as it worked up to the winning of independence, produced a government no stronger or better able to control the economic forces of the nation than the older, colonial rule which it replaced. While the foreign element grew richer, the Burmans grew progressively poorer. Thailand, on the other hand, represents a good example of a fairly sound national economy under her own king.

Table 16 shows the rapid flow of land from the hands of the landed peasantry to the absentee landowners, mostly Indians, Chinese, and Burmese.

TABLE 16

OWNERSHIP AND TENANCY PATTERNS IN LOWER BURMA*

	1928	1938	1948
PERCENTAGE OF CROP AREA HELD			
Agriculturists	72.2	52.5	48.0
Local nonagriculturists	7.2	8.7	8.0
Absentee nonagriculturists	20.6	38.8	44.0
PERCENTAGE OF CROP AREA RENTED			
Fixed rent	40.6	57.2	58.0
Share or partnership	0.4	0.4	0.4
Total area rented	41.0	57.6	58.4

*Source: *Report of the Land and Agriculture Committee, 1938*, Part I, Tenancy.

The extent to which the crop land had passed into the control of nonagriculturists is not registered in the ownership statistics available. Many persons classified by the Land Records Department as agriculturists actually lived and worked in town, having no interest whatsoever in the land they acquired by mortgages and foreclosures except their share of the profit. The percentage of area rented is a more reliable index of the extent to which land is held by persons who do not work on it. J. R. Andrus (*Burmese Economic Life,* 1947) believes that it is doubtful whether more than 15 per cent of the land under crops in Lower Burma in 1941 was owned by genuine agriculturists free of mortgage.

All land in Lower Burma, with very few exceptions, was defined as belonging to the state; the cultivators were allowed to exercise private rights if they complied with certain requirements. There has never been a freehold in the English meaning of the word, or as it subsequently became known in Upper Burma. However, there has been little practical difference between "landholder's right" and the "bo-ba-baing," or nonstate land of Upper Burma. The landholder's right in Lower Burma is fully heritable and transferable after twelve years continuous occupation and payment of tax. A certificate is supposed to be issued to the landholder, but this is seldom, if ever, done. The government does not interfere with the status of the original occupier, his heir or successor as long as the tax assessments are paid regularly. If the land fell into disuse, it could still be claimed by the landholder within a ten- or twelve-year period; but a claim was not likely to be presented after two or three years of abandonment. Unused land reverts to the state, and temporary permits for its use are issued to other persons, although the latter cannot acquire landholder's rights as long as the original owner retains his lien. This last provision was of practical significance only during the period of rapidly expanding settlement when cultivators were shifting locations and conflicting claims to specific tracts were frequent.

About the years 1860–65, large areas were offered on easy terms to induce the capitalists to develop the country. The applicants proved to be petty speculators, nonagriculturists, who allowed the land to remain idle without any improvement and held it only to sell later at a profit. These grants were discontinued when it was found that they hindered instead of encouraged the extension of crops and the increase of land revenue. After 1870, the government policy was consistently designed to promote owner-operators. Small holdings, from fifteen to fifty acres, were granted to approved farmers tax-free for a certain number of years, during which the grantee was barred from mortgaging the land. Corruption in the administration of the regulation defeated its purpose, and by 1900 the scheme was given up. A lease system was introduced to facilitate the assessment of land revenue and to encourage people to remain in occupation of land they had taken up. Cultivators were offered a lease for a period of five or ten years during which they might extend their cultivation indefinitely without having to pay additional revenue. With the opening of the Suez Canal and the subsequent expansion of overseas trade, there was a scramble for land which did away with the need for special inducements to occupy the land. Thereafter land was rapidly acquired and brought under cultivation.

Agricultural Credit

The provision of adequate sources of agricultural credit is perhaps the next important single problem with which agriculture in Burma is faced. The provision of adequate, but not unduly easy, credit at a reasonable rate of interest was at all times a prerequisite to any important agricultural reform and in particular to any improvement in the status of the cultivator, whether owner or tenant. The credit needs of agriculture in Burma were provided entirely from private sources. Prior to the great slump of 1930, the principal private sources of credit were the big money-lenders, especially the Chettyars (a banking community from South India), who advanced funds to owner-cultivators and to tenants largely through the landlords. Gold, jewelry, and land were all acceptable as securities. The money-lenders were the principal source of both long-term and short-term credits. Tenant farmers usually took advances for short-term needs from their landlord, who in turn borrowed from the money-lenders.

After the slump, this source of credit was greatly restricted. The money-lenders, especially the Chettyars, continued to provide advances on a restricted scale to their own tenants. The Chettyars became less willing to advance money on the security of land, which came to be regarded with suspicion as an investment, with the result that this source of credit largely ceased to be available to both owner-cultivators and landlords. Deprived of their source of credit, many landlords found it impossible to make the customary advances to their tenants. As a result of these changes, all classes of cultivators had to seek alternative sources of credit. This they found in the practice of sabape on the advance sale of the crop. The sabape loan is a loan taken in cash or in kind and repayable in kind at harvest. It is similar to the crop mortgages that were common in the 1930's in the United States. This system and the similar system for credit retail sales had long been in vogue, but it became of much greater importance as a result of the slump. The lenders included all sorts of persons who had a little money to lend, but the principal class was perhaps that of the village shopkeepers, who were usually Indian or Chinese.

The objection to the system was the exorbitant rates of interest demanded and obtained. The rates, of course, varied according to the price of paddy, but except by accident, as in 1930, the rates seldom worked out at less than 250 per cent per annum. Such measures as the Usurious Loans Act were ineffective against these interest rates. Quite apart from the intrinsic defects of the Usurious Loans Act, recourse to a court simply meant the drying up of the source of credit, which the borrower could not afford to contemplate. The system was convenient to the borrower because no security was as a rule demanded. It was reasonably safe to the lender. Since he was on the spot and also very frequently the purveyor of the borrower's daily needs, he seldom failed to collect his dues.

Generally speaking, loans taken during the period of cultivation and repaid after the same harvest are not only a normal phenomenon to any form of agriculture but quite a harmless one, provided that the amounts paid out in interest on such loans are not so large as to impoverish the farmer and to force him to increase the amount of his loans from year to year. In Burma, unfortunately, this proviso has not applied. Even in the period prior to the slump of 1930, interest rates were unduly high. The first requisite to any improvement in the financial position of the agriculturist in Burma is the provision of an adequate supply of short-term credit at reasonable rates of interest. Unless agriculture in Burma is prosperous, it is useless to talk of great schemes for educational, social, or industrial development. It is primarily from agriculture that the funds for any such development must either directly or indirectly be derived.

The Banking Inquiry Committee of 1929–30 estimated that the total requirement of agriculture in the way of short-term loans was about Rs. 200 million annually. Of this requirement, the government had contributed only a meager portion of Rs. 2 million annually through the Agricultural Loans Act of 1883. The extension of the use of the Agricultural Loans Act will probably provide the readiest means of getting a government system of credit for short-term loans for the agriculturists.

Besides the direct loans to individual cultivators under the Agricultural Loans Act, the government of Burma has provided agricultural credit in the form of loans to agricultural co-operative credit societies. The co-operative movement was started early in the century as an answer to the extremely difficult problem of agricultural credit. It failed sadly after the world depression, due to mismanagement and inexperience. Steps are now being taken to reconstruct the whole co-operative structure on a more cautious and sound basis.

To provide long-term credit for the redemption of high interest rate mortgages on land, the purchase or extension of land, the construction of buildings or granaries, and the improvement of land the government had provided funds under the Land Improvement Loans Act of 1884. Here again the amount was inadequate. Suggestions have been made to provide such credit through a central bank which would not be a department of government nor an organization for the administration of which any minister would be directly responsible but a public utility corporation. This corporation would be, in its initial stages at any rate, largely financed by the government, which would retain an interest and certain powers of supervision. Establishment of land mortgage banks, a central land bank, and district land banks is under consideration.

Legislation

To protect the simple and unbusinesslike peasants from the results of their own lack of business acumen in dealing with Chettyars and other money lenders, a Land Alienation Act was first proposed in the years 1908–10. By the Act, the ultimate title to the land could not be pledged, and the creditor could at best hope to take it only for fifteen years, after which it must be returned to the original owner without further payment. Many arguments were marshalled against this Act and it was postponed until 1938. At that time, the Land and Agriculture Committee was appointed to make further inquiries, by which it was found that the horse had already disappeared before the stable could be locked. More than half the land had already gone into the hands of nonagriculturists, and by 1941 it was doubtful if more than 15 per cent of the land of Lower Burma was owned by genuine cultivators free of mortgage. However, this Act came into force in 1938 to prevent further drift.

A Tenancy Act, first proposed in 1896 and brought into force only in 1938, fixed fair rents and provided for secure tenancy. The unsatisfied tenants were required to submit their cases for review. Unfortunately, for political reasons the law was applied hastily and the applications for reduction of rent were judged by rule of thumb. The Act was invalidated by the fact that it was not upheld by the courts. In 1947, the Tenancy Standard Rent Act was passed; it fixed the rent at twice the land tax.

Under the Land Nationalization Act of 1948, land owned by absentee landlords, who have no interest whatsoever in agriculture, will be purchased by the payment of twelve times the land tax and will be redistributed to the landless agriculturists on easy terms. The effect of the passage of this Act cannot as yet be measured because of political unrest.

Summary

After independence, all the above acts and many others came into force with a view to raising the standard of living of the agrarian population. The improvement of agriculture alone may not, however, give the desired results. Together with the nationalization of agriculture and the improvement of its techniques, it might be necessary to promote suitable agricultural industries as well as other industries and, also, to expand the professions and services so that the national economy can be placed on a balanced and expanding basis.

I have attempted to outline some of the agrarian and land tenure problems of Burma with which I am familiar. The question of land tenure and its related problems is so multifarious and complicated that it calls for systematic research by academic institutions in consultation with the economic experts in the practical field in order that tangible results might accrue. The world land tenure conference and the subsequent seminars at the University of Wisconsin have given plenty of food for thought and future planning. For the first time the problems of land management and land relationships have been studied on a scientific and global basis, and the ground for future action cleared by mutual discussions and exchange of experiences from different parts of the world.

It would be most helpful to have some permanent organization which would make objective studies of situations as they develop in different areas and make the results of their studies available for action in the regions concerned. Regional meetings periodically arranged by the central organization would prove very helpful. More tangible results could be envisaged if a seminar on land tenure problems of Southeast Asia could be conducted in one of the centrally situated universities of Southeast Asia with a number of representatives from each country who would make an intensive study of particular problems pertinent to their countries.

As stated in the introduction, Burma has great potentialities and rich natural resources that can still be developed. The development will entail much financial and technical aid.

CO-OPERATION, CREDIT, AND CAPITAL IN
THE AGRICULTURE OF THAILAND

Theb Semthiti

YESTERDAY we heard about the land tenure problems in India and Pakistan from the honorable delegates from those two countries. India and Pakistan are big countries with large areas and large populations, and they are somewhat overpopulated. Today the scene is different. We come to Southeast Asia, and you will hear about the land tenure problems of the countries in this part of the world. There are some contrasts between the countries in this area and India and Pakistan in that the countries in Southeast Asia are comparatively small countries and are underpopulated. But it appears that every agricultural country, no matter how big or small, has quite similar problems and has a desire to eradicate them.

I come from a small country called Thailand which is situated in the central part of Southeast Asia, with Burma on the west and north, Laos and Cambodia on the east, and Malaya on the south. Thailand is unique in the sense that she has been able to maintain her independence through the past centuries when it was difficult at times for a country in Asia to exist as an independent country. It appears that at present Thailand is the only country in Southeast Asia which is able to maintain peace and order; her land tenure system may have contributed to this.

Since I work in the Department of Co-operatives, Ministry of Agriculture, this paper will be devoted to the programs carried out by this department in the promotion of improved economic and social conditions of the rural population of Thailand.

Thailand has a total area of about 500,000 square kilometers, or 200,000 square miles, with a population of about 18 millions. Of the total area only 10 per cent is cultivated or utilized. The largest area for cultivation is in the central part, where the population density is greatest. About 94 per cent of the crop area is cultivated in rice; the remaining 6 per cent of the crop area is used for the cultivation of tobacco, corn, rubber, cotton, pepper, and so on. It is estimated that from 83 per cent to 88 per cent of the total area devoted to crops is owner-operated.

Rice cultivation has been the main occupation of the people of Thailand from time immemorial, and due to the fact that there has never been a feudal system in land the majority of farmers who cultivate rice are small holders owning their own land. This has been the source of the people's contentment from the period of self-sufficiency to the era of commerce, when it became—and still is—the great source of the economic strength of the country. For the chief export and basis of foreign credit has been and still is Thai rice.

But commercialization inevitably created a demand for agricultural credit and was followed by farm indebtedness and the usurious rates of interest common to such a condition in nearly every country in the past. Besides, the practice of payment in kind is also common in this country, and Thai farmers have been exploited by this system in no less degree than in other agricultural countries. It is a stubborn fact that in localities where rice is cultivated for commercial purposes, the majority of the peasants are buried in the mire of debts, resulting sooner or later in their mortgaged lands being foreclosed and their title-deeds passed on to the creditors.

The government recognized the necessity of finding a means by which the farmers could provide a security good enough to commend itself to an organized credit institution; therefore, the introduction of co-operative credit societies proved to be a rational means of remedying this undesirable situation. It also proved to be of very great value in the expansion of the movement into other fields of co-operative enterprises. The co-operative movement was conceived to assist the indebted farmers, and the first co-operative credit societies were established in 1916 along Raiffeisen lines, after the preparatory work of organizing a a new department and training workers in the field.

At the beginning, expansion was necessarily slow, since farmers in Thailand, as in many other countries, are conservative and slow to take up new ideas. The idea of society members being responsible for each other's debts was entirely new to their conception, and it required a great deal of painstaking work by the field officials to get the idea accepted. Moreover, this period saw the commencement of the boom in rice following the end of World War I, when rice farmers became prosperous; but at the same time the seeds of distress were sown. High rice prices tempted farmers to increase their holding by acquiring land on borrowed capital, and the depression which followed caused even greater distress than when the co-operative movement was started ten years previously.

To relieve this distress a more rapid expansion in the number of societies was obviously called for, and it is to the great credit of every government since 1932 that the policy of steadily increasing the number of co-operative credit societies has consistently been followed. For a long period the co-operative societies were financed from a government fund and by loan from the Thai Commercial Bank under government guarantee. Credit from the above service was obtained at 6.5 per cent interest per annum. The societies in turn lent to their members at 9 per cent and 12 per cent for long-term and short-term loans respectively.

In January, 1947, the Bank for Cooperatives was sponsored by the government and commenced its operations with a capital of 10 million Baht, in which all the credit societies subscribe one share of 100 Baht each for every 5,000 Baht of loan granted to the societies. The rest of the stocks was temporarily held by the government. Funds of this bank are derived from the flotation of government Cooperative Bonds to the public at the rate of interest of 4.5 per cent within the period of thirty years, but the government reserves the right to redeem the bonds earlier, if it deems such a move expedient. Another source of funds is the government Savings Bank. These credits are obtainable by the co-operative societies at the rate of interest of 6 per cent. The societies in turn lend to their members at the rates of interest of 8 per cent and 10 per cent for long-term and short-term loans, respectively. The Department of Cooperatives, however, still serves as the link between this bank and the societies.

Since all the members of a credit society are responsible jointly and severally for the society's liabilities, they usually show great care in admitting members to their society. The qualifications imposed are that they must all live in the same village, must all know one another well, must be persons of good repute, and some at least must be able to read and write for the purpose of acting on the committee and keeping the society's accounts.

From what has already been said, it can be understood that the majority of societies were formed primarily to relieve farmers from their old debts and high rates of interest and to provide them with lower rates of interest. As mentioned elsewhere, farm indebtedness was generally heaviest in those parts of the country where production of rice was most commercialized; that is, within easy reach of Bangkok. So when credit societies were expanded into the northeast districts, their loans were used less for paying off old debts than for buying new land for cultivation.

The net profit of these credit societies is disposed of in the following manner: 90 per cent goes to the reserve fund for future services to the societies themselves, 5 per cent is allotted to the co-operative public welfare fund to be used for the promotion of public welfare in the community, and the remaining 5 per cent is carried to the central co-operative fund account at the Department of Cooperatives. This last-mentioned item is provided for in case any society should become insolvent when liquidated.

At the end of the year 1950, there were 7,631 credit societies with a total membership of 143,136, and the loans granted to these societies amounted to 103 million Baht.

Taken as a whole, co-operative credit societies in Thailand are found to be developing on a sound economic basis. From 1916 to the end of 1950, covering a period of over thirty-four years, only twenty-four credit societies were dissolved; among these, twenty-one were dissolved voluntarily and showed a credit balance. But during the last decade the Department of Cooperatives has also organized other types which have become important composites in the co-operative framework of the country.

One of these is the co-operative land-hire-purchase society, which serves to help land-less farmers to become landowners by enabling them to purchase farms on a hire-purchase plan. Members needing money to get started on their farms may also borrow from their society. A warehouse for the storage of paddy is built for each society so that the produce of members may be sold co-operatively, thus commanding a higher price for their products and saving the members the expense of having to build separate warehouses for themselves. A co-operative store is organized to render service in supplying members with everyday needs and agricultural implements. A number of old societies of this type have successfully achieved the task of helping farmers to become landowners with better prospect for the future. At present there are 23 co-operative land-hire-purchase societies organized with a total membership of 800 cultivating a total area of 7,200 acres. The negotiation for the purchase of farm land to the amount of 8,000 acres for the purpose of establishing land-hire-purchase co-operatives is also under way.

To help solve the problem of opening up new land for use, co-operative colonization societies have been organized. These appear in three types; namely, cotton growing, salt making, and general agricultural societies, the last two of which have been especially successful. Co-operative members of a number of old societies have acquired ownership of pieces of land complete with dwellings.

Members of societies originally formed to grow cotton have gradually turned their attention to other crops, especially sugar, which have very good returns owing to shortage during the war and after. Since rice also is high in price, increasing attention has been given to this staple, and an irrigation system is being put in so that growing the crop will be less hazardous than heretofore. At present there are altogether 55 co-operative colonization societies, with a membership of over 1,000, utilizing a total area of 10,640 acres. A scheme for the expansion of co-operatives of this type to cover a total area of 100,000 acres is also being started.

The government irrigation system at the present moment does not cover many parts of the central plain. To be assured of good water control, co-operative land improvement societies have been formed both with and without credit facilities. Their objects are similar, that is, to supplement rainfall with pumps when water is needed at certain times and to prevent too much flooding at others. For the latter, flood embankments have been constructed. One society has 320 hectares of land surrounded by embankments totalling 12 kilometers in length. At present there are 12 societies of this type.

To meet the common need of the people and avoid exorbitant charges, co-operative stores have been set up. Since its birth in 1938, this form of society has been rendering services both in rural and urban areas in supplying members with some of the everyday needs. There are at present 228 co-operative retail stores and a wholesale society in the north of Thailand to act as the central purchasing agent for co-operative stores in that district. There is also a central store section in the Department of Co-operatives which is being reorganized into the Cooperative Wholesale Society for the co-operative stores all over the country.

In addition to the various types of co-operative societies already described, there has been organized another type with the purpose of assisting farmers to market their produce with better prices and less dependence on the middlemen. This is the producers marketing society. This type of society includes paddy marketing, palm-sugar marketing, soya bean marketing, and salt marketing societies. The majority of them are quite successful. They have been organized since 1938 in those districts considered suitable for their existence.

In connection with the paddy marketing societies, mention should be made of the Thai Rice Company. This corporation, established in 1939, was formerly a semi-official company. The government held 73 per cent of the stocks, and the employees and public held the rest. It is one of the largest business organizations in the kingdom. It owns eleven mills of its own and rents more during the season. It has an elevator, and possesses steam and motor launches, boats to transport paddy, and warehouses to store the paddy and rice. The total volume of business it does in rice is about 25 per cent of a total of 1.5 million tons exported from the country. After World War II the government sold all its stocks in this company to the agricultural societies. The company therefore is now owned largely by co-operative societies.

For the rubber growers with small holdings in the south, five Cooperative Processing Societies have been organized for the processing of latex into sheet rubber for export.

Considered as a whole, the co-operative movement has been of great benefit financially and morally; collective responsibility for debts leads to a point of view opposed to improvidence and the careless use of money. It is therefore an indirect method of rural reconstruction; many types of co-operative societies have carried out programs for the amelioration of their communities. These programs result in the gradual abolition of the peasant's love of gambling, reduction in the prevalence of epidemic diseases among the livestock, and in the promotion of social gatherings, community welfare, rural hygiene, and security of life and property in general. In short, meritorious services are always being rendered in a community when a co-operative society comes into being.

Because of this aspect the government finds it beneficial to take part in encouraging the co-operative movement in every way and rendering aids in various forms, both technical and financial, to the co-operative movement; for peaceful agriculture means peaceful order in the community. The government of Thailand has great hopes in sponsoring the co-operative movement. It desires not only to help liquidate the farmers' debts and to finance agriculture but also to enable the tillers of the soil to get a fair share of the value of the crop from their productive efforts. The government also provides technical assistance that can be given in order to improve the condition of land tenure. With 143,138 farm families in the agricultural credit societies, the situation of the tenure of land seems somewhat secure. Lastly, the Thai government politically and economically aims at using these co-operatives as a weapon against communism, which is threatening Southeast Asia.

Since its initiation thirty-six years ago the co-operative movement in Thailand has proved successful to a certain extent. However, due to the fact that at present it can render service to only about 10 per cent of the total rural population, there is still a big task ahead before the movement will be in a position to serve agriculture as a whole.

It is generally agreed that the credit system of Thailand leaves a great deal to be desired and that the agricultural credit system is even more inadequate. The inadequacy in so far as agricultural credit is concerned stems from the total absence of specialized financing institutions except for the co-operative societies, the limitations on the maximum amount which the co-operatives can lend to members, and the reluctance of other financial institutions to place small loans. The net result is that often the farmers must borrow from relatives, friends, money-lenders, and merchants. In so far as loans made by relatives and friends are

concerned, apparently no great problem exists: in many instances, interest is neither expected nor paid, and payments of principal can often be postponed until more favorable times. Often, however, the same conditions which necessitate borrowing by a farmer will also prevent friends and relatives from being able to make the needed loans; the money-lender or the merchant then becomes the only resort. It is reported that these money-lenders or merchants charge rates of interest greatly in excess of the legal maximum of 15 per cent per annum, and in some instances go as high as 50 per cent and 60 per cent per annum. It is recognized, of course, that the actual interest, as well as repayment of principal, burden does not necessarily bear any relation to the nominal rate of interest at any given time or in any given country. In agricultural Thailand, however, where borrowing by farmers is intimately connected with the production of rice, and where rice (like other agricultural commodities) is subject to fluctuations in price, the actual cost of credit to the farmer is difficult if not impossible to ascertain. Since the borrowing is usually done at the beginning of the growing season—at the time when rice supplies are relatively low and rice prices relatively high—and repayment is usually made at harvest time—when the reverse is true—the amount repaid, expressed in terms of the product, is usually greater than the nominal rate. If rice is borrowed, say for seed, and rice is repaid, the actual rate of interest paid is again a function of fluctuation in the price of rice.

The need for agricultural credit, and, consequently, farmers' indebtedness, is greatest in the areas of commercialized agriculture, principally in the central plains and in the north. In the more self-sufficient areas in Thailand as elsewhere, very little credit is necessary except in cases of emergencies such as crop failures, illness, death, etc.; and even in these emergency circumstances, the community feeling is often strong enough for gifts and donations from neighbors to be sufficient to tide one over. It is estimated that only about one-half of the total rural indebtedness is considered as "harmful" because it is lent at exorbitant rates of interest by money-lenders who will claim the land if the interest is not paid.

As mentioned above, the co-operative credit society is the only financial institution for agriculture in existence in Thailand, and owing to the fact that the Bank for Cooperatives is not yet in a position to finance agriculture as a whole it has to limit the maximum loans granted to co-operative members. This shows that the co-operative credit societies are meant only to finance small farmers and small projects; yet financing is needed not only for small but also for large projects. At present the only external sources open to the bigger farmers are the commercial banks, the Savings Bank, and the insurance companies. These institutions are justly reluctant to lend on rural property. One of the great needs of the country is the provision of adequate credit facilities for the bigger farmers, either by bringing them within the orbit of the co-operative movement or by establishing special agricultural banks for them, such as a mortgage bank which will serve as a banker for agricultural banks in different agricultural centers. A mortgage bank is also one of the most effective means for mobilizing and properly channeling savings, since it provides opportunity for individuals to invest freely in land mortgage bonds sold in small denominations with sound guarantee.

The economy of Thailand is still underdeveloped and undiversified. National income is predominantly obtained from agriculture, though considerable income comes from forestry, mining, and fishing. There are scarcely any manufacturing industries of importance. Even in agriculture, rice holds such a dominant position that the whole economy of the country may be characterized as a rice economy. The surplus in rice and timber and the output of rubber and tin ore normally enable Thailand to import its requirements of industrial products.

At the present stage of the techniques of cultivation, the productive capacity is very small and results in small yield and low income per capita. Besides, only a small amount of savings have been canalized for development purposes, due not only to the deficiency in existing financial institutions and in their operations but also to the low rate of savings and to the fact that a considerable part of the meager savings are hoarded in precious metals and jewelry which remain unproductive and do not meet the needs of economic development or large-scale capital formation.

We have done all that we could to improve our agriculture with the meager funds available for this purpose. With the loans from the World Bank and the assistance from the ECA, both technical and financial, we shall be able to speed up the development programs for agriculture, such as irrigation, extension services, etc., in a much shorter time. I should like to take this opportunity on behalf of the government and the people of Thailand to thank the United States of America for the valuable help given to Thailand.

SOME ASPECTS OF LAND TENURE IN CAMBODIA

Tep Youth

BEFORE TAKING UP land tenure problems in Cambodia it would perhaps be interesting to know something of its geography, its topography, and its resources. These elements will be found indispensable for explaining the aforementioned problems in at least three-quarters of the cases.

General Background

GEOGRAPHY, TERRAIN, AND CLIMATE

Cambodia, one of the three Associated States of the French Union, is situated in the southwest of Indo-China. It is bounded on the north by Thailand and Laos, on the east and south by Viet-Nam, and on the west by the Gulf of Thailand and Thailand itself. Its area totals 175,500 square kilometers.

The Mekong River and its two tributaries, the Tonle Sap and the Bassac, pass through the central part of the country. These rivers play a role equivalent to that of the Nile for Egypt.

From the point of view of its terrain Cambodia may be divided into three quite different zones. In the north and east are found plateaus, the highest of which are found in the east on the Viet-Namese border. In the center there extends a plain which has a northwest-southeast orientation and which includes very fertile land. The southwest is covered by mountainous regions.

Because of its geographical location, Cambodia has a tropical climate, hot and humid. Being in the monsoon belt, Cambodia has only two seasons: the rainy season (from May to October) and the dry season (from November to April), and each has its corresponding agricultural season.

POPULATION

Cambodia has a population of about 3.5 millions. The density of population averages nineteen inhabitants per square kilometer. The population is concentrated in the plains area, especially in the five provinces of the center and south, for which the density of population averages from fifty to eighty inhabitants per square kilometer. The population is more scattered in the rest of the country, as, for example, in one of the northeast provinces—Stung Treng—where the density averages less than one inhabitant per square kilometer.

RESOURCES

Since there is almost no industry, most of the Cambodian population earns its living from the natural resources found in farming, forestry, fishing, and cattle raising. Thus, one can say that agriculture represents the very basis of the Cambodian economy. In terms of economic geography, the land of Cambodia may be divided as shown in Table 17. Thus, all the resources of the country have as their basis farming, forestry, fishing, and cattle raising. The rela-

TABLE 17

CLASSIFICATION OF LAND IN CAMBODIA

Type of Land	Area*
Improved land under cultivation	1,250
Land suitable for cultivation	8,000
Forests	8,000
Fishing preserves	300
Total	17,550

*In thousands of hectares.

tive importance of each will be indicated below.

AGRICULTURAL RESOURCES

Rice is the principal crop and occupies almost 80 per cent of the land under cultivation. The other crops, which are indeed the most profitable ones, are grown on the banks of the main streams and on the basaltic land. These include red corn, beans, soya beans, peanuts, sesame seeds, kapok, cotton, pepper, tobacco, hevea, sugar palms, fruit trees, and truck garden products. Table 18 gives the 1950 production figures. Reduced production of corn, cotton, pepper and hevea is due to the following factors: the low market price of corn, pepper plant diseases, and disturbed situation on the rubber plantations.

FORESTRY RESOURCES

As previously mentioned, forests cover almost half the total area of Cambodia (8 million hectares) on the plateaus and in the mountainous regions. These resources, which do not include state forest preserves of 3.8 million hectares, are carefully operated under the control of the Bureau of Forestry, Fishing, and Inland Waters. The 1941 production figures are as follows:

Timber	160,000 cubic meters
Fire wood	390,000 cubic meters
Charcoal	15,000 tons
Wood oil	50,000 hectoliters

FISHING

Most of the fishing is carried on in the inner lakes and streams. There is little fishing in the Gulf of Thailand. According to the economic bulletin for 1941, the annual production is approximately 100,000 tons of fresh fish and 14,000 tons of dried fish. This production not only satisfies local consumption needs but allows for some exportation to the Viet-Nam, Thailand, and Malaya.

TABLE 18
CROP PRODUCTION IN CAMBODIA, 1950

Products	Land Cultivated (in hectares)	Production (in tons)	Observations
Rice	1,100,000	1,356,000	
Red corn	26,000	35,000	160,000 tons in 1941
Beans	45,000	13,500	
Soya Beans	10,000	7,500	
Peanuts	4,000	5,000	
Sesame seeds	2,000	1,000	
Kapok	5,000	3,700	
Cotton	1,500	200	2,400 tons in 1941
Pepper	1,000	1,500	4,000 tons in 1941
Heavea (rubber)	75,000	18,000	20,000 hectares now
Sugar palms	3,000	32,000	350,000 feet produced
Raw silk	....	20	
Tobacco	8,000	4,800	
Total	1,280,500	1,478,220	

CATTLE RAISING

Cambodia has a relatively large number of cattle by comparison with the other Associated States of Indo-China. Cattle number approximately 1,000,000 head, including approximately 400,000 antelope. Cattle-raising furnishes both draft-cattle (buffaloes and oxen) and meat-cattle, a part of which is exported to the other capitals of the Associated States of Indo-China (approximately 42,000 oxen and 6,000 buffaloes yearly).

Land Tenure

According to facts already set forth, one can see that Cambodia possesses at the present time much land still to be put under cultivation (8 million hectares). However, on the lands at present under cultivation, 94 per cent of the farmers have holdings of less than five hectares, and 60 per cent of these own less than one hectare. This situation is due to the following factors: family farming, excessive parcelling of family lands under the inheritance law, disinclination of the farmers to leave their native villages, the lack of financial aid, and lack of manpower.

The farmers are either landowners or are considered as such. Those considered landowners, about 60 per cent of the farmers, are in this special situation because the lands which they cultivate have not yet been entered on the land registers. This failure to register these lands is due solely to the slowness of operations of the cadastral survey.

Sharecropping and farm tenancy exists only rarely and then on a few large estates.

Although they work farms of small area, the Cambodian peasants have a living standard which is not excessively low if one compares it with that found in Southeast Asia in general. For, in addition to farming, they spend their free time on other occupations

such as homecrafts (weaving, making of reed mats, etc.), refining of palm sugar, production of wood by-products, etc. Peasants who have no trade go to the cities where they are employed as coolies in various enterprises. Thus they can supplement their income and provide for their needs.

The living standard varies according to whether the peasant lives in the river bank zones or in the interior of the country.

In the river bank zones, since the land is made fertile by the annual overflow of the streams, farming is quite profitable. The peasants here are relatively well off. They are, indeed, better off than any other group in their class. They number one-third of the farming population of the land.

The interior of the country, which has poor soil, is given over chiefly to rice growing. Traditional methods are used. Only local needs are met, and relatively primitive working tools are put to use. The farmers seek neither to better their farming methods nor to make more fertile the soil with a view to higher production.

In addition to the poor quality of the land, one must take into consideration the poor climate and the very irregular rainfall. The rice farmers suffer in turn from either droughts or floods; thus the income that they receive from their farms is, for most of them, quite limited. It scarcely suffices for their subsistence and for paying their debts. These debts are generally acquired through advances either in kind or in cash at usurious rates of interest (60 to 100 per cent). As previously stated, it is the farmers' other occupations which save them in this lamentable state of affairs.

It should be pointed out that the Cambodian farmers have very modest needs which are not to be compared with those of American or European farmers, for the most favored standard of living in Cambodia can only compare with the average standard of these other lands.

One can conclude that the fate of Cambodian farmers, even the poor ones, is considerably less harsh than that of the underprivileged farmers in certain overpopulated lands of Asia. Food shortages are rare, since the local crops usually suffice. Their most pressing need is for certain creature-comforts.

Improving Standard of Living

With a view to improving the standard of living of the country in general, the Royal Cambodian government has taken strenuous steps to combat certain social evils, such as usury and speculation in agricultural products, and to increase agricultural production by extension of the land area under cultivation and by the improvement of farming methods.

A credit office for farmers has been set up. This institution grants loans up to one-third of the market value of the land and for a period not to exceed one year at an interest rate of 8 per cent. Because of the lack of sufficient funds this office at present is functioning in only a few provinces.

The struggle against speculation is still in an experimental stage. One small agricultural co-operative is now operating in one of the provinces, and if it is successful others will follow. It should be pointed out that the Cambodian peasants are not only great individualists but also are very distrustful of such undertakings.

In order to increase agricultural production, a program of agricultural hydraulic works (irrigation, drainage, and building of dikes) has been carried on since 1936. If the war had not intervened, progress would have been very great. Nevertheless, the following results have been obtained: 75,300 hectares have been put under irrigation; 3,500 hectares have been drained; and 17,000 hectares have been diked. The total amount of land improved in this way is, therefore, 95,800 hectares.

As the work advances, the land is being distributed to the inhabitants in lots of from three to five hectares. The recipients of these lots cultivate them under what is known as cultivation permits and have to pay only the land tax, at a slightly higher rate for the upkeep of improvements, and to fulfill certain conditions concerning the sale of the land whose ownership they will have acquired after five years' occupation.

To make up for the shortage of man power, the government and certain private enterprises have recently turned towards mechanized farming which, however, is unhappily still very uncommon. The great majority of the peasants continue to follow traditional methods of agriculture. Both the parcelling of the land and the farmers' individualism hinder the expansion of mechanized farming. Moreover, the high price of such equipment puts it beyond the reach of the farmers. To show the many advantages of such improvements for traditional Cambodian agriculture the government plans as an experiment to lend mechanical farm equipment to the farmers in one locality (Chhlong) for the working of four hundred hectares of land lying on the banks of rivers.

Conclusion

Much still remains to be done for the improvement of Cambodian agriculture. Lands still to be cultivated offer many possibilities. My personal suggestions in the way of remedial steps to be taken would be the following:

1. Education of the rural population in improved farming methods and in the formation and operation of co-operatives.

2. A stepping-up of the program of agricultural hydraulic works.

3. An extension of the credit office.

4. Extension of the road system into the zones which are still to be developed and put to agricultural uses.

5. Intensification of the fight against malaria.

6. Legislation to stop further parcelling of the land under the inheritance laws.

If these measures could be carried out in the near future, the problem of the standard agricultural production farm income would find a rapid solution; for, through increased agricultural production farm income would be increased and the standard of living would rise.

THE ATTITUDE OF THE MALAYAN PEASANT TOWARD THE TENURE PROBLEM OF MALAYA, WITH SPECIAL REFERENCE TO THE STATE OF KEDAH

Salim Akib

I CLAIM NO expert knowledge of the system of land tenure, but I have some practical experience as an agricultural officer in my country regarding the land tenure situation there. I will attempt to give you a very brief picture of this situation. My main interest in the conference, however, is to obtain some light on the land tenure problems so as to enable me to think out solutions which could be applied to meet the problem as it exists in my country.[1]

I may state that Malaya has an area of a little over 50,000 square miles, and a population of 5 millions. Only about one-third of the area is under cultivation. The main crops are rubber, rice, and coconuts, and a few minor crops used by the farmer in his household. As regards the land tenure system, 70 per cent of the total cultivated area is owned by landlords who do not cultivate it themselves but get it farmed by allotting small parcels of it to tenant families. The other 30 per cent is cultivated by small peasant owners. I may add that the area devoted to rubber is not included in these figures, because it is cultivated mainly under the plantation system.

The Malayan farmers are backward and illiterate, and they use primitive implements and traditional farming methods. In parts of the underdeveloped northern states the obsolescent and wasteful shifting form of crop cultivation, especially with dry-land rice interplanted with corn and truck crops, is still being practiced. The average farmer has little or no incentive to work hard and to better his living conditions. He is undernourished, poorly housed, and inadequately clothed. As is true in most parts of Southeast Asia, where four out of every five inhabitants have to till the good earth, agriculture is looked upon as an undignified and humble occupation. The farmer is enmeshed in dire poverty and misery, he is unprotected, and he is at the mercy of aggressive landlords. The rentals are very high, and there is usury and debt without end.

The Malayan peasant is a small farmer cultivating lands of uneconomic size varying from five to seven acres. The rice production at present is sufficient for only one-third of the consumption needs. The production of this staple crop may be stepped up considerably in view of the existence of adequate land resources suitable for rice farming. Improved land tenure systems will provide the necessary incentive for farmers to use improved cultural methods, fertilize their lands, and use selected seeds. In this way some contribution towards increased output per acre from existing farms will be made.

Apart from the small owner-cultivators

who own 30 per cent of the land, the rest of the landlords are absentee landlords. They spend back nothing on the land except payment of the annual land revenue to the government, which is about one dollar per acre for rice farms. The rents charged by landlords vary from 30 per cent to 40 per cent of the estimated average yield of the land concerned. Therefore, if the crop in any year is below normal the rent may form a much higher percentage of the crop.

Normally a written contract or agreement is entered into by the landlord and the tenant from year to year. This is a seasonal agreement. I wish to stress here that there is no long-term agreement of leases of the land to the tenant. This system is obviously not only detrimental to the interest of the tenant but it is also wasteful as a method of utilization of land resources. In other words, there is no such thing as security of tenure. Furthermore, the landlord seldom abides by the conditions and terms of such agreements. They are not legally recognized documents in most cases and are not worth the paper they are written on. Besides, the terms of the agreement are usually more in favor of the landlord than the tenant. This is due to the strong economic and social position of the landlord as against the tenant. For example, the landlord might stipulate that his rent in kind must be delivered from the main road to his door, mill, or other designated place. This involves extra handling and transportation cost, which cost falls on the tenant. The worst type of landlords insist on a security deposit in cash from the tenant varying from ten to twenty dollars per acre.

In the absence of farmers' co-operatives and easy credit at a low rate of interest, such as provided by the Farmers Home Administration in the United States, the farmer is forced to transact loans with professional money lenders, or usurers as they may appropriately be called, at exorbitant and extortionate rates of interest. Landlords will demand full rentals regardless of partial failure or reduced crops due to unavoidable circumstances, such as bad weather and heavy incidence of pests and disease. Non-compliance, of course, by the tenant under these extenuating and extraordinary circumstances may mean the eviction of the tenant from the land. There is no co-operation whatsoever among the farmers, but instead they work against each other competing for lands, thus playing right into the hands of the landlords.

The absence of farmers' co-operatives to handle the processing and marketing of produce and to supply the cultivator with household necessities and farm requirements, such as implements, fertilizers, seeds, and the like, or to provide him with loans to meet his legitimate cash needs, and the absence of farm tenancy laws to protect him against the landlord are some of the reasons responsible for the deplorable plight in which the average Malayan tenant farmer finds himself today. One evil practice to which desperate farmers in need of cash sometimes resort is to sell part of the rice crop in the ground, after planting, at about half its gross value at harvest. Such a practice is to be deprecated, since it not only involves the farmer in a loss but also results in the deterioration of the crop because of lack of proper attention by the purchaser, who usually is not an agriculturist.

About 95 per cent of the peasantry of Malaya are illiterate, and they have no leaders who could organize them for effective action or take their grievances to the proper authorities for redress. Owner-farmers live side by side in the "kampongs," or villages, with the tenant farmers. The former are usually better off economically and socially, and they live in good homes compared to the latter. It is natural that under such circumstances the tenant farmer should desire to have his own land and a standard of living comparable to his neighbor, the owner-farmer.

In trying to suggest measures to improve land tenure in Malaya I would like to quote Dr. Bennett's three essential principles underlying a just and equitable system of land tenure:

1. The farmer must be able to own land and to use the land he tills under fair conditions and terms of tenure.

2. The farmer must have access to credit on reasonable terms to enable him to farm efficiently whether as owner or tenant.

3. The farmer must have access to the knowledge and techniques that will make his efforts productive and profitable to him and society.

In the light of these principles, there seem to be two possible approaches with a view to improving land tenure in Malaya:

1. The short-term, temporary plan will be to introduce and enact farm tenancy legislation which will fix rent at fair and equitable levels and protect and provide security of tenure to tenants who fulfill their side of the bargain.

2. A long-term policy will be to enable farmers eventually to acquire farms of economic units of their own. This may be accomplished in two ways: (1) through the acquisition of holdings of absentee landlords by payment of just compensation and the redistribution of these lands among farmers in return for a payment which should be extended over a long period; and (2) through opening up new areas of land which have not yet been brought under cultivation. Such areas are available in large quantities, because in Malaya the cultivated area is only about one-third of the total of the country. This policy will lead to a reduction of the pressure of population on the cultivated areas and will also make the farms of an economic size. The organization of farm co-operatives and the provision of farm credit are of course necessary for both the plans outlined above.

When I left Malaya at the end of last year, a project under the Colombo Plan known as the Rural and Industrial Development Authority was constituted to attack and improve all the aspects of rural problems. I hope the discussion in this conference will throw some light on concrete ways and means of implementing the intentions of this project in respect to the land tenure situation in Malaya.

THE RICE ECONOMY OF SOUTHEAST ASIA: A COMMENT

𝕊𝕊𝕊𝕊   *Lauriston Sharp*

FROM THESE discussions we can see the contrast in conditions between Southeast Asia and other parts of Asia. We can say that the situation is relatively good, primarily because of the lack of population pressure and the availability of land which can be put into cultivation. The contrast between this area and some of the other areas of concern to this conference is considerable. It does not necessarily mean that we dare lie back and rest on our oars.

You should realize that rice culture in these areas is extremely stable. They do not get the extreme shortages of proper rain, and so forth, which will produce really serious production conditions in many parts of the mainland of Southeast Asia. They can count on a fairly stable production. The problem then is simply in these areas, where land comes under some pressure, to improve the actual product per land unit, and that is the problem that the Cambodian government is working on just as the Thai government is working on it.

With reference to the percentage of people engaged in rural occupations, one can say that generally throughout Southeast Asia, 80 per cent to 90 per cent of the population is in the country. Cambodia, I think, would have the largest percentage of farm people of all the areas of continental Southeast Asia.

One of the things that impressed me most in the year I spent in a Bangkok village is that the more the Southeast Asian farmer has, the more he wants. The old static peasant situation is gone where modern ideologies have made an impress at all. The village I am thinking about is some twenty miles from Bangkok, the capital of Thailand. It was subject to these waves of modern influence, both during the war and afterward. Here the days are completely over when the peasant will be satisfied with the kind of life had by his father or his grandfather.

There is a dynamic situation in this part of the world. This means that these problems of both land tenure and agricultural improvement, as well as reform in general, are of vital importance. They have to be answered whether or not the conditions are relatively good as they are in Southeast Asia or whether they are much more pressing as in other parts of the world.

THE HISTORICAL BACKGROUNDS OF THE TENURE PROBLEMS OF SOUTHEAST ASIA: A COMMENT

𝕊𝕊𝕊𝕊 *Karl Pelzer*

SOUTHEAST ASIA is a name for a region which includes some six countries—Burma, Thailand, Indochina on the mainland, and Malaya, Indonesia, and the Philippines in the south. Some of these are island countries, and Malaya, though physically located on the mainland, in many ways belongs with Indonesia and with the Philippines rather than with the mainland countries to the north. Now, Southeast Asia is a highly diverse region, especially when you look at such problems and topics as language distribution, race, or religion, political history, or even when you look at the economy or land tenure. Burma, Indochina, Thailand are the rice baskets of Southeast Asia. In normal times they export large quantities of rice. The bulk of this rice is produced of course by small farmers, many of whom are today deeply indebted—many of whom have lost their land as a result of over-indebtedness. In the Philippines and Indonesia we are dealing with rice-deficit areas because, as a result of economic history and political history, these countries have concentrated on the production of crops other than rice.

If you look at land tenure in Southeast Asia, especially, again, in the island regions, you come up very soon with the realization that land tenure cannot be understood in those areas unless you take into consideration the recent political history. Southeast Asia is a fascinating area in that we have here the possibility of comparing the effect of different colonial policy in a relatively small area. Here we have beside each other old Spanish, Portuguese, Dutch, French, British, and American colonial territory—for, as you know, all countries of Southeast Asia, with the exception of Thailand, have been at one time or another under a foreign rule. And it is hard to understand the difference between land tenure conditions in the Philippines and Indonesia without taking into consideration the colonial policy of the respective powers in the past. All of you are aware that an area like Indonesia is extremely important when it comes to plantation agriculture; but I wonder how many of you realize that almost without exception all of these plantations are operating on land that does not belong to the plantations—on land that was leased from the government under various terms. Most of these plantations are operating on seventy-five-year leases. Therefore, the Indonesian government of today is in a fortunate position to be able to continue the plantation leases if the government decides that this is of interest for the country from an economic and social point of view. The government can control the plantations; it can do away with them altogether and pursue a policy of strengthening small-scale farming —and I do not want to go into the question of whether that would be desirable or not; that is beside the point. The main point is that the government of today is in a position to change the structure of the country from the point of view of land tenure to a very considerable extent. And that is simply due to Dutch policy pursued in the past. There is a very important agrarian law of 1870 which explained a great many of these features. Compare that with the Philippines, where those plantations that are operating

are, with very few exceptions, all operating on privately owned land; and, as you will hear today, the government there is considering purchasing some of these large estates in order to subdivide them and distribute them among the small peasants.

Southeast Asia on the whole differs from India on the west and China and Japan on the north in that these countries still have possibility for expansion—for agricultural expansion—which means possibility of finding places for part of the population. However, one of the problems in Southeast Asia is the problem of maldistribution of people; that is, people are concentrated in certain favored regions.

In the Philippines, for example, this concentration is very marked. We have very high population densities in central Luzon, in the low coast provinces, the narrow strip of land along the northwest coast of the island of Luzon, with very high population densities in the islands of Cibu and a few other isolated areas. Similarly, there is a very serious problem of maldistribution in Indonesia. Most of you probably are familiar with the fact that the relatively small island of Java, an area of 50,000 square kilometers, has a population of over 50 million people and that long before the war the administrators of that area became concerned with the population problem and initiated some very interesting experiments in the field of redistribution of population by means of agricultural settlement.

FARM OWNERSHIP AND TENANCY IN THE PHILIPPINES

𝕊𝕊𝕊𝕊   *Jose E. Velmonte*

THE IMPORTANCE of agriculture in the economy of the Philippines is evident from the fact that of the total gross national product in 1949 of 4 billion 800 million pesos (U.S.

2 billion 400 million dollars), slightly over 50 per cent was derived from agriculture. In terms of Philippine exports, farm products in raw or semi-finished form represent

over 80 per cent of the value. And finally, the 1939 census reported that nearly 73 per cent of those in gainful occupations were connected with agriculture.

Land Utilization

The Philippine land area is nearly 30 million hectares. The soil cover as estimated by the Philippine Bureau of Forestry is shown in Table 19. The farm area repre-

TABLE 19
LAND UTILIZATION IN THE PHILIPPINES*

Kind	Area†
Commercial forests	13,200
Noncommercial forests	4,300
Open lands:	
Farm area	6,700
Grass lands	4,900
Swamps, etc.	600
Total	29,700

*Source: *Yearbook of Philippine Statistics*, 1946.
†In thousands of hectares.

sents about 22 per cent of the total. The forests and other areas, representing about 78 per cent, constitute the public domain. Estimates of the maximum cultivable area that may be brought under farms vary. The Bureau of Forestry estimates that as much as 10 million hectares more are alienable lands of the public domain, the greater portion of which may be converted into farm lands. The Economic Survey Mission to the Philippines in its report in 1950 placed additional land that is cultivable at 4 million hectares. Whatever is the correct figure, it is the belief that prospects for the expansion of agricultural production are very great indeed. If progressive and scientific methods can ultimately replace antiquated systems of production, food deficits may give way to

surpluses, and export crops which form the main support of Philippine overseas commerce may be expanded very substantially. Measures now under way for a comprehensive technical and economic aid program under ECA to raise levels of production envision a total outlay of 250 million dollars over a five-year period beginning with 1951.

Present production and acreage will show the degree of agricultural development. The area under cultivation to the principal crops is shown in Table 20.

TABLE 20
PRINCIPAL CROPS IN THE PHILIPPINES, 1949*

Crop	Area	Amount	Index 1941=100
FOOD CROPS			
Palay	2,164	2,491	105.4
Corn	866	534	93.4
Root crops	172	524	85.2
Fruits and nuts	203	.....	.....
Total	3,405	3,549	
EXPORT CROPS			
Abaca	283	62.4	27.0
Sugar	129	415.0	47.5
Tobacco	39	....	.....
Coconuts	965	....	.....
Desiccated coconut	.....	57.6	142.0
Copra	.....	528.7	222.0
Coconut oil	.....	61.3	38.1
Total	1,416	1,125.0	
Total all crops	4,821	4,674	

*In thousands of hectares and metric tons.

Population

By and large, the Philippines is not very densely populated, and, therefore, population pressure is not a serious problem. The 1939 census reported a population of 16 millions or a density of 54 inhabitants per square kilometer. In 1947 the mid-year estimate was 19.5 millions, or a population density of 66 persons per square kilometer. The problem, however, is not lack of land for an increasing population but rather a better distribution of the population. In well-settled areas such as the rice producing districts density is as high as 200 to 300 persons per square kilometer; in the new areas of Mindanao Island it is under 10 persons per square kilometer. The frequency distribution of density on the basis of the 1939 Census is shown in Table 21.

TABLE 21

POPULATION DENSITY IN THE
PHILIPPINES, 1939*

Density per sq. km.	Number of Provinces
1–50	17
51–100	11
101–150	12
151–200	4
201–250	3
251–300	2

*Source: *Economic Survey for Asia and the Far East,* 1947 (U.N. Economic Commission for Asia and the Far East).

Table 21 shows that the Philippines has at present a serious population problem which calls for a policy of moving population from points of high density to new regions in order to raise levels of production and planes of living.

Background of Tenure Problems

Land tenure is one of the most serious problems affecting agriculture. During the pre-Spanish period, or before the sixteenth century, private ownership of land was not well defined. Some kind of private property was recognized under the Barangays, which were tribal groups in part bound together by blood relationships. The Spanish conquest, which dates from the latter part of the sixteenth century to the end of the nineteenth century, brought about conditions favorable to the growth of farm tenancy. Ownership of all land except that held in private ownership by cabezas de barangay and others was claimed by the Crown. The encomienda system which was established soon after conquest was the Spanish colonial version of the feudal economy of medieval Europe. Favorites and those who had rendered valuable service to the Crown were given large grants of land from which the encomenderos might collect tributes from the people. Early in the seventeeth century after the abandonment of the encomienda system, which proved burdensome to the people because of exploitation and abuses, powerful religious corporations gained ascendancy and became owners of great landed estates. Towards the close of the Spanish rule, tenants of these large estates for several years refused to pay rents in protest against unjust exactions by their absentee landlords.

A Public Land Policy

Soon after the establishment of the American administration in the Philippines, the Philippine Bill, an organic act passed by the United States Congress in 1902, set forth the principle that the government is trustee of a great public domain which is to be developed to promote farm ownership for the greatest number. It established the principle of conveying to the inhabitants of the country agricultural lands of the public domain for homestead settlements not exceeding sixteen hectares to each individual. It set down limitations so that corporations may not acquire areas in excess of 1,024 hectares in order to prevent concentration of ownership. A public land law was passed by the civil administration in 1904, establishing the machinery to carry out the principles enunciated by congressional act.

Along with the above policy, there was launched a land-purchase program which aimed at the breaking up of large estates as a means of helping to bring about a stable government so necessary at the beginning of the American administration. The first step was the purchase by the government of about 160,000 hectares of friar lands (church lands) situated in some of the principal rice producing areas where tenancy conditions were at their worst. These negotiations were completed in 1904, and machinery was set up to reparcel them for sale, preferably to their holders, with payments spread over a twenty-year period. Since these were not public lands, their disposition did not come under the area limitations imposed by the public land law. After 1910, when there was fear that large blocks might fall into the hands of private corporations, such limitations were made applicable. Amendments in subsequent years to the original public land law tended to restrict grants of agricultural lands of the public domain to citizens of the Philippines and corporations controlled by them. Also, the homestead provisions were liberalized by enlarging the maximum area from sixteen to twenty-four hectares, and the cultivation and residence requirements were eased. The present Constitution of the Republic of the Philippines contains a provision which states that "Congress may authorize, upon payment of just compensation, the expropriation of lands to be sub-

divided into small lots and conveyed at cost to individuals" (Art. XIII, Sec. 4), and a provision which states that Congress "may determine by law the size of private agricultural land which individuals, corporations, or associations may acquire and hold" (Art. XIII, Sec. 3). Thus, the policy of promoting farm ownership as the ultimate land tenure policy for the Philippines has been firmly established.

Tenancy, a Serious Problem

Farm tenancy is usually associated with rice production. About 40 per cent of the total acreage devoted to the eight principal crops is planted to rice. As a result, the problems of sharecroppers in rice assume great importance. The tenure of 1,600,000 farm operators over the 6,690,000 hectares of land in the Philippines is shown in Table 22. If part owners are included, it will

TABLE 22
TENURE CLASSIFICATION OF FARM LANDS IN THE PHILIPPINES*

Tenure	Percentage of Farms	Percentage of Farm Area
Owners	49.2	55.0
Part owners	15.6	12.2
Share tenants	33.5	23.6
Other tenants	1.6	1.5
Farm managers	0.1	7.6

*Source: 1939 Census.

be seen that altogether farm tenancy represents 50.7 per cent of all farms and 37.4 per cent of the total farm area. This seems to be without justification considering that a wide public domain is being disposed of under increasingly liberal terms for homestead settlement.

The public land policy is based on the

belief that the ultimate land tenure policy in the Philippines should be a system that will lead finally to farm ownership by every one working the soil. Surveys show, however, that farm tenancy is not a usual rung of the agricultural ladder. With very low labor incomes and ruinous debts, tenants have no prospect of attaining ownership. This permanent condition of tenancy is a menace to progressive society, since it has intensified class struggle and is an indication of an unhealthy state of rural life. Before World War II, discontent in rural areas, especially in Central Luzon where rice tenancy is at its worst, culminated in the ascendancy of a socialist party which readily gained adherents under able leadership. This was the forerunner of a more serious Communist problem after World War II which now threatens the very stability of our free institutions. Many people believe that the present Huk movement in the country has its roots in the unsatisfactory tenure systems, for it may be no mere coincidence that the Communist movement in the country today is largely centered in those areas where the worst aspects of farm tenancy exist.

Factors Favoring Tenancy

It is of interest, therefore, to analyze briefly the economic and social factors which have favored the existence and permanency of tenancy in the Philippines despite forces tending to promote farm ownership as a large public domain and a liberal land policy. These factors are: the slow disposition of the public domain, the suitability of tenancy to rice farming, the low labor income of the tenant, the lease contract, and social factors.

The slow disposition of the public domain.—The public land policy of the Philippines is for the promotion of farm ownership by the greatest number. Concentration of land holdings is prevented by strict area limitations. Homestead settlement for the landless is encouraged by a steady liberalization of provisions on requirements of residence and cultivation. Yet during the first four decades of its operation (1904–1941) only about 850,000 hectares have been patented by about 69,000 homesteaders with an average holding of a little over 12 hectares. With about 10 million hectares more available for agricultural purposes, the area which has passed to freeholders is pitifully small. A basic cause for this situation is that individual initiative is relied upon in this difficult and expensive undertaking. The typical homesteader is a farmer of little capital trying to carve a farm out of the jungle, isolated from community life, and facing a number of problems far beyond his control. It had been found out that without organized land settlement under state aid and direction land disposition will prove slow.

The suitability of tenancy to rice farming.—Tenancy in the Philippines is usually associated with rice growing. This is not surprising, since the type of farming has a bearing on tenancy. It has been shown likewise in other countries that where methods of cultivation are simple, involving no complicated rotation systems, and when a crop can be grown by ignorant and unskilled labor using simple, inexpensive implements farm tenancy takes root easily.

Low labor income of the tenant.—Tenancy surveys made by the College of Agriculture of the University of the Philippines show that the labor income of the tenant in rice production before World War II was not more than 130 pesos '(U.S. $65) on a farm ranging in size from a little over one hectare to three hectares in area. With supplementary earnings, the farm income per tenant family was about 200 pesos (U.S. $100) annually. Making allowances for the rise in the indices of farm prices and wages after World War II, farm income may be conservatively placed at from 400 pesos to 450 pesos annually (U.S. $200 to $225). This is hardly sufficient to maintain even on bare subsistence a family of from five to six members.

The low labor income is traceable to three principal causes, namely, the small size of farm, the highly seasonal character of rice production, and the absence of opportunities for the tenant to use his idle months in profitable employment. The average size of farm land per farm is four hectares, of which the cultivated land per farm averages only less than two and one-half hectares.

TABLE 23

CLASSIFICATION OF FARMS BY SIZE
IN THE PHILIPPINES*

Size (hectares)	Percentage of Farms
0–1	22.5
1–2	30.0
2–5	34.5
5–10	9.0
10–	4.0
Total	100.0

*Source: 1939 Census.

Table 23 shows that over one-half of all farms are under two hectares, a size altogether too small to be economically profitable. This situation is further aggravated by the fact that the total labor time of the rice tenant is only about 112 days during the year. This is so because he raises only one crop of rice, since most farms are without irrigation facilities. Thus for about two-thirds of the year the land lies idle and the time of the tenant is frittered away in idleness.

The lease contract.—Studies of tenancy contracts show that much of the discontent of croppers is directly traceable to oppres-

sive exactions of many landlords despite seemingly fair contractual arrangements. The usual division of the crop is on a fifty-fifty basis with the tenant furnishing all labor, work animals, and a minimum of implements. Some cultivation expenses are shared equally. The landlord, however, finances the operations as well as the subsistence of the cropper by a system of advances at extortionate rates of interest. An appraisal of these contracts has shown that in so far as the conditions of farm operation and division of the crop are concerned, the terms are reasonably fair and equitable. What impairs the equity of the lease is the implied agreements on advances and loans on which are assessed ruinous rates of interest and which usually leave the cropper deprived of most of his share of the produce.

Social factors.—Social factors are interrelated with economic causes. The ignorance and illiteracy of the share tenant are also contributing causes in perpetuating his status. Socially, his position is low partly because of his lack of educational opportunities. With the landlord dominant socially, economically, and politically, the tenant becomes an unequal and voiceless partner in crop production. The tenant is proverbially shiftless and improvident. Earning a low income and carrying the weight of burdensome rates of interest assessed on his borrowings, the tenant finds himself in a vicious circle of drudgery, debt, and despair.

Land Reform

The goal of our agricultural policy is twofold. Measures are being exerted to promote all efforts to enable every farmer of ability, energy, and ambition to achieve ownership. Realizing that a certain amount of tenancy is unavoidable in any well ordered system of agriculture, a rational type of farm tenancy is being evolved that should protect the tenant's rights in line with a program of social justice.

ORGANIZED LAND SETTLEMENT

It has become evident that in the disposal of our large public domain for the promotion of farm ownership, only organized land settlement under state direction and aid can bring quick and effective results. The forerunner of organized land settlement was the establishment after 1910 of a number of agricultural colonies in selected areas of the public domain. Because there was scarcely any financial assistance to settlers other than expenses of transportation and because there was no organized technical guidance, the results were not fully effective. In 1939, a National Land Settlement Adminstration was created by legislative enactment, and organized land settlement under state direction and financial and technical assistance was vigorously prosecuted. Settlements on a large scale were started in the new region of Mindanao, particularly in Koronadal and Ala valleys, with an estimated area of over 100,000 hectares. World War II interrupted this work, but land settlement has become an accepted policy of the government, and during the last two years it has been prosecuted with greater vigor. A Land Settlement and Development Corporation has been organized which has taken over the functions of the defunct National Land Settlement Administration. The corporation has six extensive land reservations with an area of 450,000 hectares, of which 290,000 hectares are agricultural land. During the last eleven years, about 110,000 hectares of agricultural land have been allocated to settlers. Of these, only 30,000 hectares have been cultivated. The corporation also has 4,500 hectares under mechanized farming in Mindanao and Palawan islands. Under ECA sponsorship and financial assistance, land settlement will assume increasing proportions, and the settling of thousands of farmers seems nearer of accomplishment.

Along with this project, the armed forces of the Philippines have embarked on a modest land settlement project to provide homes and farms to surrendered Communists. The reservation covers 6,500 hectares, and the Army contemplates settling 500 families. Already 60 families have been established in the facilities for 100 already available.

In the administration of land settlement projects, tested principles that are essential to success are being applied, namely, selection of settlers, financial aid to settlers on a basis of long-term payments for land and improvements, provision for community life, highway improvement, and technical guidance and expert supervision in conducting the farm enterprise.

PURCHASE OF LARGE ESTATES

Following the purchase of friar lands in 1904 for resale to tenants thereof—referred to earlier in this paper—the government has pursued a policy of acquiring large estates as part of a comprehensive land purchase program under constitutional mandate. Hampered by inadequate funds and impaired by lack of vigorous leadership, its accomplishments have not been spectacular. In spite of these, however, by 1950 the Rural Progress Administration reported that 31 estates have been acquired for a total of almost 18 million pesos covering an area of over 40,000 hectares consisting of homesites and farm lands. The Economic Survey Mission of 1950 recommended a program of land redistribution, and as a result an Advisory Committee on Large Estates Problems[1] was created early in 1951. It has recommended a complete overhaul of the present administrative machinery, the conversion of small farms into prosperous family farms, and sustained technical guidance. It further recommended measures for better valuation procedures, more realistic terms for tenant purchasers, and a system of rural credit.

Alongside this advisory committee, a special committee was created by the Cabinet early in 1951 to study and advise ways and means of clearing land titles and to re-examine present laws and practices with respect to the use of the public domain. Its report[2] recommended certain changes in the public land laws tending to restrict further the area limitations imposed by existing laws. For example, it recommended sales to individuals of a maximum of 100 hectares as against 144 hectares, individual leases of 300 hectares instead of 1,024 hectares, and corporate leases of 500 as against 1,024 hectares. It also recommended various measures aimed at speeding issuance of patents and encouraging farm ownership.

Certain principles necessary to success of a land purchase program are now recognized, namely, selection of tenant purchasers and perhaps even a trial-lease period to determine their ultimate capacity; long-term financing with no down payment; annuities lower than rents; sustained help and guidance by the government during the period of payment; and limitations of the rights of purchasers to alienate their holdings to prevent speculation. It is our opinion, however, that a land purchase program for tenants should yield precedence to the far more fundamental problem of promoting farm ownership through the disposal of our large public domain. The development of our vacant lands by the creation of a great body of freeholders will confer greater social benefits upon the country and, what is more, will entail a much lower outlay financially, per farmer, than any land purchase program that may be adopted for tenants.

PROGRAM OF TENANCY IMPROVEMENT

Along with measures intended to pro-mote farm ownership, a program of rehabilitating tenants is being pursued. This is necessary because some farmers, even under most favorable conditions, may not be able to achieve ownership. Rehabilitation of tenants is both economic and social. Lease contracts are being readjusted, an operation made possible in part by legislation. The Philippine share tenancy acts provide three types of sharecropping in rice, namely, the fifty-fifty, fifty-five–forty-five, and seventy-thirty, the proportions varying according to financing, sharing of expenses of cultivation, and provision of capital for farm operations. A comprehensive and cheap credit system for farmers is sadly wanting in the Philippines. Outside of two government banks, the Philippine National Bank and the Rehabilitation Finance Corporation, which are not primarily designed to serve farmers, rural credit is deplorable. Co-operative credits were tried as early as 1915, but the failure of the system is the principal cause for the abhorrence and suspicion by farmers of all types of co-operation. Opportunities are gradually being created to enable the tenant to utilize his labor profitably throughout the year. Vegetable gardens, backyard poultry, secondary crops, and cottage industries are receiving more attention. Agricultural extension is being overhauled under competent American direction in order to make science serve the farmers effectively. The farm tenants are also being raised socially. Educational opportunities, health improvement measures, and other forms of social betterment which are now the object of government interest are solely needed to improve life in rural areas.

Summary

Agriculture is the premier industry in the Philippines and the principal support of its economy. Conditions of tenure, however, are not conducive to a healthy growth of the agricultural industries. In the present world-wide effort to raise levels of living in underdeveloped countries, such antiquated systems of tenure as the Philippines have will prove to be a deterrent factor. Farm tenancy is more and more becoming a serious problem that demands solution. It is usually associated with rice production in the Philippines, and it is in this area that some of the ugliest features of tenancy are found. Despite a liberal land policy in the promotion of farm ownership, the extent of tenancy is alarmingly great. What makes the problem even more serious is the fact that tenancy is a permanent condition and not a rung of the agricultural ladder. Eco-nomic and social factors have favored the growth of tenancy, namely, the slow disposition of the vast public domain, the suitability of rice farming to tenancy, the low labor income of the tenant, the tenancy contract, and, finally, the ignorance and thriftlessness of tenants. A vigorous program of land reform is underway which has for its main object the establishment of a great body of freeholders. Organized land settlement under state direction, a comprehensive program of land purchase aimed at breaking up of large estates, and a rational program of economic and social rehabilitation of tenants constitute the main features of this program.

LAND SETTLEMENT IN THE PHILIPPINES

 Luis Lichauco

ONE OF THE problems that confront the Philippine government today is the uneven distribution of land in the country. Large tracts of productive land are in the hands of a few, while the majority of the population who are engaged in farming are landless, in spite of the fact that the Philippines is primarily an agricultural country.

This problem is not of recent origin. It began more than three hundred years ago when the Islands came under Spanish rule. At that time, most of the lands were concentrated in the hands of religious corporations and Spaniards. The early laws governing lands in the Philippines were in the form of instructions issued by the Spanish Crown to its representatives to the effect that "it was his will that lands be settled and divided among those who conquered the inhabitants thereof, in order to encourage his soldiers in the colonization and settlement of the Islands, and in order also that they might be able to live with the comfort and convenience required." These land grants were referred to as encomiendas, which meant large parcels of land including its inhabitants and resources granted by the king to his subjects as rewards for service. This system of landholding began in 1571 upon instructions of Philip II of Spain, and was put to an end at the beginning of the nineteenth century as a result of the abuses perpetrated by the grantees. During the Spanish regime, it was also usual to grant titles to large tracts of land to religious corporations to enable them to support themselves.

In the case of religious corporations, the practice was to lease their lands to the occupants on a fixed rental basis. During the Philippine revolution in 1896, the Filipino tenants took advantage of the unsettled conditions, and as part of the revolutionary move refused to pay their rents. As soon as the government established by the Americans began to function after the Spanish-American War, these corporations filed ejectment proceedings against the tenants and succeeded in securing judgment in the corporations' favor. To prevent bloodshed in the enforcement of this judgment, and upon recommendation of the Schurman Commission, the Philippine Commission enacted a law appropriating funds for the purchase of these friar lands, as all the lands owned by the religious corporations came to be called. Through the efforts of Hon. William Howard Taft, the first American civil governor of the Philippines, the American Congress ratified this Act of the Philippine Commission on July 1, 1902. In December, 1905, the government purchased a portion of the friar lands for 14,474,000 pesos (approximately 7,155,946 dollars) out of the sale of Philippine government bonds authorized by the United States Congress, and disposed of them to tenants on an installment basis. This was not sufficient to solve the land problem, because only a small portion of the land held by the religious corporations could be purchased with the money appropriated. The Philippine government had to devise ways and means by which it could give land to the landless without the necessity of buying the land.

The Philippines had vast tracts of agricultural lands which could be subdivided and distributed to those who were willing to occupy and till them. To encourage the occupation of these lands, the Philippine legislature enacted several public land laws which defined the status of public lands and the different modes of their disposition and acquisition. These laws were later compiled into Commonwealth Act No. 141 and became known as the Public Land Act. The Act contained provisions for the disposition of agricultural lands of the public domain for homesteads, sale, lease, and confirmation of imperfect or incomplete titles by donation and by reservation.

The government found that the passage of laws, however liberal their provisions

may be for the acquisition of land, was not sufficient to induce people to migrate to underdeveloped regions. Following modern trends of solving population pressure in agricultural regions, the government established agricultural colonies in the provinces of Lanao and Cotabato in the island of Mindanao to be settled by Filipinos and Americans alike, especially retired American soldiers who had decided to make the Philippines their permanent domicile.

Mindanao is the second largest island in the Philippines. It includes 32 per cent of the country's territory but has today only about 11 per cent of the total population. At the beginning of the American regime in 1900 there were hardly any Christian Filipinos in Mindanao. The island's population consisted mainly of Moslem tribes known as "moros," a derivation from the the word "Moors," and pagan mountain tribes who occupied the interior of the island. It has rich natural resources and vast, fertile but undeveloped agricultural lands. This island is the equivalent in the Philippines of the great West in the United States, and today the pioneering and land settlement projects of the government are directed mostly, but not entirely, to this rich island. There are other areas that also offer opportunities for colonization work. Besides the seven agricultural colonies that were opened in Mindanao between 1913 and 1917, two others were added in the provinces of Bohol in the Visayan Islands and in the Cagayan Valley in the northeastern part of the island of Luzon. They were not well organized or pre-planned, nor were they subsidized. The whole scheme failed.

Subsidized migration started only in 1918, but the aid was limited to transport fare of the settlers. These landseekers were sent to public lands which had been previously located and in many instances subdivided. After their arrival in the place of settlement, however, the settlers were left to their own resources. No further assistance was given to them. Because of this procedure, many of the early pioneers suffered untold hardships and eventually died from malaria, starvation, and other hazards of the virgin country. Many of those who survived returned home discouraged, and the settlement plan failed. The experience of these early pioneers discouraged further migration to virgin territories under the government plan.

The first organized effort in land settlement was undertaken by the government through the National Land Settlement Administration, which was established June 3, 1939, during the administration of the late President Manuel Quezon. It was created as a government corporation and was to serve as an agency of the Commonwealth Government for the attainment of the following objectives: (1) to facilitate the acquisition, settlement and cultivation of lands whether acquired from the government or from private parties; (2) to afford opportunity to tenant farmers and small farmers from congested areas to own farms, and to extend this opportunity also to trainees who have completed the prescribed military training; (3) to encourage migration to sparsely populated regions and facilitate the amalgamation of the people in different sections of the Philippines; (4) to develop new money crops to take the place of export crops which stood to suffer from the loss of preferences which they enjoyed in the American market.

In order to enable the corporation to carry out the foregoing purposes, it was granted the following powers: (1) to hold areas of public agricultural lands for a period not exceeding twenty-five years, renewable by the President of the Philippines for another period of not exceeding twenty-five years; (2) to recommend to the President of the Philippines the reservation of public lands; (3) to open, develop, and dispose of the lands so reserved, held, surveyed, or subdivided to persons qualified under the Constitution and in accordance with the provisions of the Public Land Act; (4) to acquire from private parties those lands that are necessary to enable it to carry out the purpose for which it was created.

In addition to the foregoing, the National Land Settlement Administration, which hereafter I shall refer to by the abbreviation NLSA as it came to be popularly called, was further empowered to establish and operate power plants, water supply and irrigation systems, trading and co-operative stores, and to engage in the processing of agricultural products. It was given an advance capital of 5 million pesos, which was expended after thirty-three months of operation. The late President Quezon appointed as its first manager the late General Paulino Santos, who had had considerable experience in colonization work by virtue of his serving as Director of Prisons, which had under its administration a number of agricultural penal colonies.

For the first site of its settlement project, the NLSA chose the fertile Koronadal Valley in the Province of Cotabato, island of Mindanao. The project was opened on February 27, 1939, with an initial group of sixty-two settlers recruited from different parts of the country and accompanied personally by the manager. The area embraced by the project reservation was approximately 97,000 hectares (242,500 acres). This was subdivided, for administration purposes, into four settlement districts. The NLSA was able to open two settlement districts in two years. Each district was subdivided into a townsite, several barrios (villages), and the corresponding ten-hectare farm lots for the number of settlers that were to be settled in the district.

Each settler was allocated a farm lot and extended a credit line of 1,000 pesos in the form of a long-term loan to assist him in establishing himself. This amount was used by the settler to purchase his work animals and implements, to build his shelter, and to tide him over until he had raised his first subsistence crop. From February, 1939, to June, 1941, or a period of twenty-eight months, the NLSA had advanced a total of 1,585,000 pesos to the settlers. The rest of the initial capital was spent on the following phases of the project: surveying and subdivision work; construction of roads and bridges; opening and clearing of land; small irrigation systems; administration buildings and employees' quarters; bunkhouses for newly arrived settlers; malaria control, which rendered the area relatively safe from this hazard which had been fatal to many of the first pioneers in Mindanao; establishment and operation of hospitals (each district was provided with a hospital); establishment and operation of trading stores; financing of a settlers' marketing agency; schools, which were established later in each district and were extended to some of the barrios.

The policy of the NLSA was to foster diversified farming and to introduce the use of machinery. In a reasonably short time, the settlements started to produce rice, corn, cotton, peanuts, ramie, soybean, bananas, and vegetables. In the areas suitable for hemp and coffee, the settler planted them. They were encouraged to raise hogs and chickens in their backyards to increase the family income.

The two settlement projects were on their way to prosperity and some of the settlers were beginning to pay their first installments on the loans extended to them when the war broke out in December, 1941. Military operations and enemy occupation wiped out almost all the improvements in the settlements. Many of the settlers lost their homes, work animals, and farm equipment. Farms were abandoned as settlers evacuated

to other places in search of safety and relief from enemy occupation. When peace and a semblance of normalcy was restored to the islands, the settlers gradually began to return. However, the projects and the settlers both needed rehabilitation.

After the re-establishment of the government, the Philippine Congress appropriated the amount of 5 million pesos for the rehabilitation of the National Land Settlement Administration. This amount was further augmented by a bank loan of 1 million pesos. The destruction caused by the war, however, was so widespread and the NLSA was so burdened with administrative troubles that after a lapse of five years, very little material improvement was accomplished. The failure of the postwar administration of the NLSA to extend adequate financial assistance to the settlers delayed their rehabilitation, and a great many settlers were discouraged and lost their original interest and incentive in developing their farms. Discontent grew within the settlements to such proportions that it attracted government attention. It was finally decided to dissolve the NLSA and to create a new corporation in its place. The NLSA left a liability of nearly 2 million pesos.

In the reorganization of government corporations last year (1950), the problems of land settlement and land distribution were accorded top priority because of the prevailing social unrest in the country, particularly in the agricultural provinces of central Luzon, where the dissident movement originated. Most of those connected with the dissident outbreak were identified as small tenant-farmer peasants from the rice regions of Luzon. It was known that the dissident movement was Communist-led, and the government resolved that the wisest course it could take was to adopt a policy of attraction while being prepared to meet force with force in order to maintain peace and order. It was fully realized that the problem was a socio-economic one and that it had its roots in certain unfavorable conditions that had existed even in the remote past. Realizing the importance of the situation, President Quirino initiated a "land for the landless" policy. In pursuance of this policy, the governmental agencies concerned were mobilized to implement the program.

In the discussions that ensued, it was suggested that, as a means of effecting economy, the various phases of work involved in land settlement should be assigned to the instrumentalities concerned, with the administrative and supervisory powers vested in an entity similar to the NLSA. Dr. Salvador Araneta, Secretary of Economic Coordination, strenuously voiced his opposition to this proposal and took the position that the only way to carry out a program of land settlement to a successful conclusion was to creat an agency which should be vested with full powers of supervision, direction, co-ordination, and control over the work, from its inception to its final accomplishment. In this way, delays which are usual in governmental bureaucratic procedure would be avoided, economical operation would result, and fixed responsibility for the failure or success of the undertaking would be clearly determined.

The prewar experience of the NLSA in its settlement work in the wilderness of Mindanao recalled the fact that the success of its first two years of operation was the result of a properly financed and well-coordinated and controlled program. The prewar NLSA built a progressive rural community out of the wilderness. It placed its own personnel and funds on the various phases of settlement work, such as surveying and subdivision, land clearing, malaria control, construction of roads, bridges, and irrigation systems. Assistance extended by governmental bureaus or departments was merely in the form of technical advice.

As a result of these deliberations, the Land Settlement and Development Corporation, commonly known as LASEDECO, was created in late October of last year (1950). The LASEDECO was formed out of the merger of three government agencies, namely, the old National Land Settlement Administration, the Rice and Corn Production Administration, and the Machinery and Equipment Department of the National Development Company. With the establishment of LASEDECO, the Philippines has entered its third and most trying phase in land settlement work.

As I have endeavored to explain to you, the interest shown in land settlement work in the Philippines today is the result of the urgency of the Philippine social situation, which is menaced by a reaction from a segment of the population under the infiltration of Communism into the life-stream of the country. I say that this is our most trying phase because we are laboring under abnormal conditions caused by postwar maladjustments. It is not only the state of the government's finances that constitute our most vexing problem but also, and of even greater import, the state of mind of the people under the psychological stress and anxiety of our troubled times.

The LASEDECO has two main objectives. One is economic, and its purpose is to develop the vast agricultural resources of the country with a view to enriching the national economy and thus lay the foundation for the industrialization of the country. Its other objective is social, and the purpose is twofold: (1) to reduce population pressure in congested agricultural regions and (2) to afford opportunity for the landless to own farms and consequently bring about the growth of a strong class of independent and prosperous farmers.

For its capital the LASEDECO was granted the total net worth of the three dissolved entities, estimated to be 6 million pesos as of the end of the last fiscal period. Its cash fund on the date of its establishment was 1.8 million pesos. About one-eighth of this amount was diverted to the partial payment of gratuities to personnel separated from the service as a result of the reorganization and for purposes of economy.

The corporation has six land reservations acquired from the defunct National Land Settlement Administration and the Rice and Corn Production Administration, covering an aggregate area of 450,000 hectares. These lands are located in the islands of Mindanao and Palawan and in the province of Isabela in Luzon, with the greater portion concentrated in Mindanao. About 290,000 hectares of the total area are classified as agricultural land and 160,000 hectares as nonagricultural. During the last eleven years, about 110,000 hectares of agricultural lands have been allocated among 8,453 settlers, leaving 180,000 hectares still available for the opening of new settlement projects. It will require at least fourteen new land settlement projects to cover the remaining area that is still available within the reservations of the corporation for these purposes.

To acquaint you with the procedure which the LASEDECO follows in the establishment of settlement projects, I would like to describe the details of the program that we have prepared in connection with the proposed opening of LASEDECO settlement project No. 2 in the district of Lamian, Cotabato.

This district has an area of 14,000 hectares (35,000 acres), most of it flat land; and preliminary exploration of the region reveals it to be a fertile district adapted to the production of rice, corn, abaca (hemp), coffee, and cacao. About 60 per cent of the area is cogon land (grassland) and the rest is virgin and second-growth forest; the latter can be easily cleared with bulldozers.

The land settlement program for the district is a project to accommodate 1,200 settlers and their families, providing each settler with a home lot of 1950 square meters and a 10-hectare farm lot. These settlers will form a community of 20 barrios (villages), each comprising 60 families. The 14,000 hectares of land of the district will be allocated in the following manner: (1) 12,000 hectares for 1,200 farm lots, (2) 420 hectares for the 20 barrio sites, (3) 200 hectares for a townsite of 2,000 residential lots, (4) 600 hectares for the administration farm of LASEDECO, (5) 138 hectares for roads (a total of 75 kilometers of road), and (6) 642 hectares in communal forest, creeks, and streams.

The program for this district was conceived and prepared to set the general pattern for the subsequent settlement projects of the corporation.

Following the general procedure that the LASEDECO has adopted for all its new land settlement projects, the work will be divided into three parts, as follows: (1) soil survey of the area, general reconnaissance for malaria control to determine the program of malaria control work for the whole district, and boundary survey of the district; (2) road location survey and construction, boundary and subdivision survey of barrios, malaria control work for each barrio, land clearing of the barrio communal farms, and subdivision of ten-hectare farm lots; (3) allocation of home lots and farm lots to the settlers and land clearing of two hectares of land for each farm lot allocated.

In the preparation of the plan for this project, careful consideration was given to the time the work should be started and the period required for its completion. It is of vital importance that the pioneer settler begin his life in his new location in time to build his house and cultivate his home lot before the advent of the first agricultural planting season in the locality. The first year of the settler is the hardest and most critical in his new life in the settlement, and the allocation of his land to him should be timed in a manner that, upon receiving it, he will not spend idle months before he can begin raising his first subsistence crop which will tide him and his family over during their first lean year.

Soil survey.—The soil survey of the area will be undertaken by the Bureau of Soil Conservation. The LASEDECO, however, will defray the travelling expenses of the personnel. The agricultural program and soil management practices for the entire district will be based on the result of this survey.

Malaria control.—A general reconnaissance of the whole district will first be undertaken to determine the program of malaria control work for the whole district. Prior to admitting any settlers into the area, malaria control work will be instituted to minimize the hazards of malaria to them. As soon as the boundary survey and subdivision of home lots for each barrio is begun, malaria control for the barrio and vicinity will be undertaken so that by the time the settlers are admitted into the barrio, the place is rendered relatively safe for them. The malaria control work for the whole district will continue until the whole district becomes safe from this menace.

Surveying work.—All the surveying work will be undertaken by four survey parties. Each survey party will have a definite assignment, and each party will begin its work on the first day the project is started. With the exception of one survey party, which will begin the location survey of the main road that leads into the heart of the district, the rest will start with a boundary survey of the site of the project, and after this assignment each party will proceed with the location survey of the barrio road assigned to it and the boundary and subdivision survey of the barrios to be located

along the barrio road on which it had worked. All the surveying work will be coordinated in order to facilitate the synchronization of the other phases of the work—road construction, land clearing, and malaria control. The last three follow the survey parties.

Road construction.—The first road to be constructed will be the mail road that will connect the present base camp of LASEDECO at Banga with the new base camp of operations to be established in the new project. The construction of the main road will begin soon after the survey party has begun the location survey of this road. The road construction gang will follow the survey party.

The main road will have a thirty-meter right-of-way with a fifteen-meter travel way. The barrio roads will have a fifteen-meter right-of-way and a ten-meter travel way.

The communal farms and the land clearing plans.—Each barrio will have a 120-hectare communal farm designed to allow each settler of the said barrio to have two hectares to cultivate in his first planting season in the settlement. He will raise his first subsistence crop on the land. The communal farm will be located along the roadside, forming two strips on both sides of the road, each strip forming an area of 60 hectares. It was planned to locate the communal farm in this manner so that the land clearing of the farm can be started as soon as the location survey of the road has passed the area. Careful attention was given in working out the plan of operations so as to have this communal farm cleared before the advent of the first planting season of the settler in his new location.

The land clearing of these communal farms will be done almost simultaneously with the location survey of the road. The land clearing for the administration farm will also be started as soon as the boundary survey of this farm is in progress.

The base camp of operations.—The base camp of operations will be established in a section of the proposed townsite adjoining the six hundred-hectare administration farm of the Corporation. Building construction for the base camp will be started without waiting for the completion of the main road that will connect it with the present Banga Base Camp. The hauling of materials will be made via the old trails. The base camp will be provided with the following: one administration building, one store and property building, two staff cottages for two families, one machine shed and shop, four colony houses for eight families, one power plant shed, two bunkhouses for forty families, and a small hospital.

The bunkhouses are intended to provide temporary shelter to the settlers while they are in the process of building their houses in their respective home lots. As soon as each batch of settlers is able to move with their families to their respective home lots in the barrio, the other batch that will follow will make use of the bunkhouses.

Health and welfare.—A small hospital will be operated at the base camp under the charge of a physician and a registered nurse with the necessary attendants. It will be provided with essential equipment to handle emergency cases and will accommodate ten bed patients.

The barrios.—Each barrio will have 60 home lots of 1,950 square meters each and sites for a school, chapel, market, and plaza. Each barrio will also be provided with an artesian well.

The townsite.—The townsite plan will be prepared by the National Planning Commission in order to co-ordinate all land settlement projects with the plan of the government to establish modern communities in the country. The townsite will cover an area of two hundred hectares with the necessary sites for community and civic activities and two thousand residential lots. The townsite will be located adjoining the administration farm, which will provide ample space for its expansion in the future.

The administration farm.—The purpose of establishing an administration farm of the Corporation in the project is to provide the Corporation with a source of income to assist it in financing the local administration expenses of the settlement. Under the charter of the Corporation, the farm can be operated for five years only. After this time, the farm will be subdivided into ten-hectare farm lots for distribution to settlers, giving priority to those who have proved themselves worthy of acquiring additional land, provided they do not exceed the maximum of twenty-four hectares limited by the Public Land Act.

Allocation of land to settlers.—The distribution of land to the settlers will be made on the lottery system, and the first to be allocated will be each settler's home lot in the barrio. The Corporation will require the settler to build his house immediately and to put his home lot under cultivation by planting a vegetable garden and fruit trees and by starting a home piggery and poultry project. The ten-hectare farm lot will be the next to be distributed and each settler will be allocated a farm lot near his barrio. The planning of the barrio site and the subdivision of the farm lots were arranged to avoid settlers having to travel more than two kilometers to their farms.

The settler will have no time in the first year to do any clearing work in his farm lot and in order that he may not miss his first planting season, which might spell starvation to his family, he will be assigned to a portion comprising two hectares in the communal farm, which by the time he receives it will already be cleared by the Corporation and ready for land preparation and planting. This is where he will raise his first crop, which will be his subsistence crop for his first year in the settlement. After he has planted his land in the communal farm, he can start working on his farm lot.

The communal farms will be kept for only one year, and these areas will be absorbed by the ten-hectare farm lots which will be farmed individually by the settlers in the following agricultural year.

Under the plan evolved here, and provided that D-Day falls within the months of August and September, the first distribution of home lots and farm lots will begin on December 10 of this year, and by August of 1952 the distribution of all the home lots and farm lots to twelve hundred settlers will have been completed. By the end of twelve months from the time the project is started, each settler will have a ten-hectare farm lot and a home lot.

Schedule of operations.—A schedule of operations based on the operational procedure was prepared for the execution of the program for this project. It outlines in detail all the phases of the work and the time required to complete each one. This schedule co-ordinates and synchronizes all the different phases of the work and the time required to complete each phase. The initial day of the work is designated as D-Day, and the number of weeks required to complete each phase of the work is designated as D plus the number of weeks required to bring that work to completion.

D-Day must fall within the months of August and September in order that the land-clearing operations may be completed before the advent of the planting season to enable the settler to plant his first subsistence crop shortly after he has established himself in his new location.

Financial requirements.—The total financial requirement for the implementation of this program is 3,199,000 pesos. This amount will finance the opening and distribution of the land in Lamian District among 1,200 settlers. It completes the first phase of a land settlement project. The second phase is the extension of financial assistance to the settlers to enable them to develop their farms progressively.

In view of the unavailability of funds, no financial assistance can be extended to the settlers as was done by the prewar National Land Settlement Administration until the Philippine Congress can meet and appropriate funds during its session next year. If and when these funds are made available, each settler will be extended a credit line of two thousand pesos in the form of long-term loans at 4 per cent interest per annum and payable in ten annual installments. The settler, however, will not be required to start amortizing his loan until the end of his third agricultural year in the settlement, which would make the loan a thirteen-year loan.

Perhaps it is pertinent to point out at this juncture that settling down in a new and virgin territory is accompanied by many difficulties and hazards. We may recall the experience of the first settlers in America, many of whom died from the effects of the rough life in the colonies, or more recently of the opening of the Western frontier in the American continent. Our modern concept of organized and subsidized settlement, however, tries to minimize, if not entirely eliminate, the risks and hazards of pioneering life by providing the factors which will place the pioneers in a more advantageous position to conquer Nature. These common hazards, among others, are jungle diseases like malaria, lack of safe water supply for domestic use, lack of roads and bridges to make the area accessible, lack of medical facilities, food and equipment, and lack of established agencies for the enforcement of law and order in the community.

The Philippine government through its agency the Land Settlement and Development Corporation is determined in spite of existing limitations, to push through to a successful conclusion its postwar land settlement program.

The valuable aid which is expected from the United States through its Economic Cooperation Administration will come to us at a very opportune time in the social and economic development of our country. It will unfold to the Philippines and the Filipino people a new and promising era in its land settlement movement, which is an important phase in the government's plan to improve land tenure conditions in the country. The successful implementation of the Philippine land settlement program with the valuable aid of the American people through the ECA will be a lasting monument to the successful economic collaboration of the two nations in their experiment in the workability of international teamwork in the promotion of human welfare.

THE POPULATION OF SOUTHEAST ASIA

ᔑᔑᔑᔑ   *Irene B. Taeuber*

SOUTHEAST ASIA is the paradox of demographic and economic development. Here are crowded areas and empty spaces. Islands whose multiplying peoples would have made Malthus even more sorrowful than he was lie adjacent to historic islands of depopulation. Economic expansion and population redistribution can solve the immediate problems of the relation of people to resources. To those who have studied the demography of the area, however, optimism concerning the possibilities for economic development in the short run is tempered by the knowledge that economic development in the past has served primarily to increase the number of the people and so to render continally more difficult economic development whose goals are the increase in individual welfare rather than the increase in total product.

Analysis of the interrelations of economic development, population growth, and social change in Southeast Asia is a task as gigantic as it is critical. Such study is now under discussion by ECAFE[1] as a co-operative project of the countries concerned. For the outsider to attempt to guess at the conclusions of that study would be presumptuous. The alternative is to select type situations within the area and indicate the nature of the problems and the possible lines along which solutions may be sought. Three are selected here: (1) Java, classic prototype of the demographic consequences of economic development, lying adjacent to the vast and relatively empty Outer Islands of the Indies; (2) the Philippine Islands, cultural and demographic link between East and West, and great historic experiment in economic development and technical assistance; and (3) Ceylon, whose projects for agricultural expansion and public health have placed the potentialities of science for the alleviation and the intensification of the problems of population growth in stark outline.

Java[2]

In Java, civil disorder, ignorance of the principles of sanitation and nutrition, a fluctuating food supply, and epidemic and endemic diseases retarded population growth severely until the early nineteenth century. Then the colonial administration of the Dutch began to penetrate the life of the people, maintaining peace, introducing public health, spreading elementary hygiene, and improving agricultural techniques. The native people of Java and Madura increased from about 5 million in 1816 to 13 million in 1861, 30 million in 1905, 41 million in 1930. By the latter date Java was one of the most densely settled agricultural areas in the world, rivalled only by Egypt's Nile Valley, parts of India's Ganges, and some areas of China. Population per square mile of total area had reached 818 in all Java, 1274 in Jogjakarta. This was not the end of the process of growth. Continuing increase at the rate of 1.5 per cent per year, a rate less than that which had occurred in the past, would have produced a population of 116 million by the year 2000!

The rate of population increase in Java was not high in absolute terms. In fact, the rates of increase of the indigenous peoples of Java and of Europe between the Napoleonic wars and the present are roughly comparable. In both cases increase resulted from the limitation of the forces of death. In Europe the Industrial Revolution increased the productivity of human labor, fostered a new and radically different social and economic structure, and drew people into urban and industrial pursuits. The small family pattern became fact or ideal for increasing proportions of the people. In Java, on the contrary, numbers increased with few fundamental changes in social structure or mode of existence. People remained agricultural and subsisted primarily by what was grown locally. Limited education was given in the vernacular. Economic changes were implemented in ways that would minimize cultural shock. The attitudes, values, and habits of living of the people tended to remain those of immemorial time. Central in the ancient ways was the family, the wife whose role was work and babies, the youth whose childhood terminated abruptly with the labor of the fields and the home and whose maturity came early, with the creation of new families that were, in their turn, dedicated to human replacement.

Declining mortality and stable fertility could not co-exist permanently. Sooner or later the increasing pressure of people on subsistence would have led to increased mortality. The efficient activities of the colonial government of the Indies pushed the point of declining levels of living and increasing mortality farther and farther into the future through the development of the two aspects of the dual economy, the one, native agriculture itself, the other, employment opportunities outside that agriculture on the estates and in industries. The area under cultivation was expanded, and productivity increased through capital investment in irrigation works, agricultural research, and an extension service that took technologies directly to the people. The limits to expansion within Java and Madura were being approached, though, for in 1938 there were only .20 acre of irrigated rice land per capita, .27 acre of nonirrigated land. The half-acre available for each Indonesian might have been increased somewhat by the distribution of the land in estates, but this would have lessened the possibilities for wage labor at the same time that it jeopardized the commercial economy with which the income and welfare of Indonesians had become intertwined.

The Dutch remained in control of a situation they could neither manipulate nor liquidate. Enlightened administration and the preservation of the simple virtues of peasant life had created one of Asia's most acute population problems. Dutch policies were predicated on the myth of the "little people" who required supervision as children do. The myth became tragic approximation to truth as the increasing millions of people subsisted more and more precariously in an intricately balanced economy whose slightest deviation from the regular in functioning could lead to starvation and death for millions of the people for whom it had made life possible.

The demographic costs of the years of war and disorder are not measured in precise terms, for there are no statistics. In some areas the effects of the years of crisis appear to have been slight. In others there were great famines reminiscent of those of the Middle Ages; areas where the roads had reverted to the jungle, rice fields to the waving grass, while within the villages the dead, the dying, and the living were huddled together in a nightmare caricature of the potentialities of the twentieth century.

The establishment of the Republic of Indonesia may permit the re-establishment of the delicate balance of irrigation, malarial control, and supervision that maintained the peasants. In the long run economic development, improved health and expanded educational opportunities might lead to an altered position of the Indonesian woman and a lessened emphasis on numbers of children. This was the historic pattern of change in the West. In Indonesia, though, the pressure of numbers is so great that she cannot afford the long centuries that would be required to stabilize numbers without a direct approach to the problem. Three hundred and fifty years of colonialism with its heritage of perhaps 70 million people is fact. Repetition of Europe's history in the Indies as a whole would increase today's 70 million people to some 450 million by the twenty-third century. The only feasible alternative to demographic catastrophe would thus appear to be planned national action to introduce the small family pattern directly into the peasant villages.

The Philippine Islands[3]

The Philippine Islands are an extraordinary enclave in the rice lands of the Asian littoral. The immediate problems of population are those of economic development and internal redistribution rather than numbers or the increase in numbers. Man-resources

relationships and culture are alike intermediate between those of West and East. The palay rice fields are of the East; indeed in some areas agricultural pressure has created a vulnerability to malnutrition, disease, and death comparable to that in Indonesia. But the Philippines also include sugar centrals and other enterprises where tractors replace the man with the hoe or the digging stick. Economic factors are related to the cultural diversities of an island whose Malayan base absorbed elements from Mecca and Rome, Spain and the United States.

The demographic consequences of Spanish rule in the Philippines were similiar to those of Dutch rule in Indonesia, for the forces of death were lessened at the same time that the family institution was left intact or even strengthened. Peace replaced strife, the food situation improved, and beginnings were made in education and medical care. American policies were likewise comparable to those that produced the classic dual economies of the South East. Emphasis was placed on the development of the agricultural export crops, generally produced on highly capitalized plantations, while the majority of the people subsisted on the meager products of their own land. In general, their holdings were small, their capital scanty, and their incomes low.

The Philippine Islands constitute an experiment that permits analysis of the demographic consequences of assisted economic development. Their experience is somewhat comparable to that now under discussion by the various nations and the international organizations for underdeveloped areas. The lesson of the Philippines, superficially viewed, would seem to be ominous. In the thirty-six years between the first American census of 1903 and the last of 1939 the population more than doubled. In the period of less than a decade that separated the last American census from the first

Philippine census, the population increased almost 20 per cent. And the potential for future growth is impaired only slightly. Death rates, while reduced far below the primitive level, remain high by Western standards. Birth rates may have declined somewhat in the more favored areas, but the balance of the evidence indicates that the high fertility of Asia's rice lands still characterizes the majority of the peasants of the Philippines.

Ceylon[4]

In both Java and the Philippines the critical factor would appear to be the relationship between the rate of economic development and the rate of population increase. The centuries available to the Europe of the sixteenth and seventeenth centuries are not available to the ex-colonial peoples whose numbers have already increased from four- to six-fold or more during the centuries of imposed order and development. Moreover, the accelerated pace of economic development must be balanced against the rapidity of declines in mortality made possible by modern technology. The classic illustration of the reality of this new factor in the population problem is Ceylon.

The economy that developed in Ceylon as a result of the interpenetration of Western and native economies was viable in the sense that exports balanced the necessary imports. The relation between peoples and subsistence was precarious, though, for an internal agricultural production that yielded only one-third of the food requirements coexisted with an estate economy whose value product fluctuated with production quotas and prices determined on world or Empire markets. Confidence in the health of the economy was shaken by the failure of the Southwest monsoon in 1934 and a severe malaria epidemic in the years 1934–1935. Emergency food and medical relief curbed mortality before it reached the levels char-

acteristic of such dual catastrophes in the past, but the Ceylonese accepted this limited tragedy as grim warning of the human hazards of their economic structure.

During the prewar and war years comprehensive plans were made for economic development, the movement of settlers into the relatively empty and mosquito-infested areas of the North and East, and the extension of health facilities. With war's end and independence, development plans passed from blueprint to project. Irrigation and land reclamation were to provide land for an additional ten thousand families each year for five years. The utilization of DDT for mosquito control was precondition to settlement in the infested areas, however, and there was a comprehensive island-wide project. The general death rate which had been over twenty per thousand population from 1940 to 1946 dropped to twelve or thirteen. Natural increase which had been less than 2 per cent per year shot upward to approach or reach 3 per cent per year.

Projection of a rate of population increase of 3 per cent per year far into the future would lead to estimates of numbers so fantastic as to be inconceivable in a world tied to technologies similar to those that now exist. The ultimate consequence of the continued existence of relatively uncontrolled fertility and drastically limited mortality would have to be an increase in the death rate, whether through a rise in the general level of mortality within an altered causal matrix or through the recurrence of the cataclysms that have decimated Asia's people so often in the past. Spectacular declines in mortality make fertility control an acute problem of the present rather than a remote and rather academic problem of some future period.

Reflections

Let us now assess the problems of population growth in term of facts rather than taking refuge in specious optimism, the theories of Malthus, or the bemoanings that the Soviets call "the neo-Malthusianism of the American imperialists." Land reform is not a solution to all the population problems of densely settled agrarian areas. It is conceivable that solutions to population problems could be achieved without land reform. Nonetheless, the two are intimately related as continuing cause and effect. Land reforms taken in disregard of the population situation may involve no solutions to that problem but only a continuing race to move slowly or to stay in the same place. Land reforms taken in full realization of the problems of population growth and as part of a comprehensive national attack on the problem may act as catalyst to stimulate the altered cultural values and the changing individual motivations that lead to family limitation. If land reform helps to establish this altered physical and cultural environment, the problem for the society, and particularly for the public health people, becomes that of the discovery and the diffusion of the means of control that are acceptable to the people of the society and consistent with their historic values.

In this field in which the family, religion, and the deepest values and aspirations of peoples are involved solutions must be indigenous. We who became the chance possessors of two great and almost empty continents in the fifteenth century are humbled by the magnitude of the problems that you face in the world of the twentieth century. We believe that they are soluble with today's social, biological, and physical sciences, and that the sciences of tomorrow will contribute further to the possibilities of solutions. Personally I should like to add that co-operation in the search for a feasible and acceptable means for the limitation of fertility would seem to approach a moral responsibility for a West that has offered freely of its technical know-how in the fields of economic development and public health. We have co-operated with you in the creation of the population problem; we hope that through more democratic procedures than in the past we shall be allowed to co-operate with you in the search for solutions.

ᏜᏜᏜᏜ   DISCUSSION

ALBERTO ARCA-PARRÓ—I am not going to raise any specific question, but I would like to emphasize the interesting remarks that have been brought to this conference by Mrs. Taeuber regarding the significance of population increase or population policy for land tenure policy and economic development of any country. The picture she has given us of the increase of population in Southeast Asia is in many ways the same as is happening in some of the Latin American countries. Because of the improvement of health techniques the death rate has been cut down in some cases, as she has mentioned, to twelve per thousand or even eleven per thousand. I was rather surprised myself, in looking over the death rates in Venezuela during the last ten years or so, to find that they have come down in some cases to eleven and even ten per thousand. Such a rate was reached in Europe only after a very, very long time of effort. We have to admit that the use of modern techniques has really improved health conditions. On the other hand, the birth rate is very difficult to shorten or to cut down. We still have in Venezuela, Peru, Colombia, and many other countries, a birth rate of forty per thousand, sometimes even forty-five. These will mean an enormous difference in population, with a low death rate. Since our population in most of the Latin Americas is mainly a rural population, where such rates are prevailing the speed of our population growth is enormous. Really this is the main problem, I would say, the number one problem that we have to look for in any plan for land tenure reform. Otherwise, if you don't have in mind what the complications or repercussions are on the size of population growth, within a few years the same problem will arise. In consequence we would have to revise our plans every five or ten years. Any plan, I think, has to be done with a far-reaching view. That's why Mrs. Taeuber wisely made not a recommendation but a reference to a small-size family. But what does it mean in our country? A small family is a product of industrialization, in many ways. How could a selected society get the idea of a small-size family? Mrs. Taeuber was right, too, in saying that the solutions have to be indigenous within each country. Although the means to the answer, no doubt, will be the use of various techniques of biology or medical science, I believe there are social elements that may have to be taken into consideration as well. The beliefs of the people, the religious faith; even more than these, cultural developments. We have seen what is happening in our own countries. If you compare the rate of population increase or the rate of fertility between the rural zones and the urban zones, it is lower in the latter places. If you take any of the capitals of the Latin American countries and compare those local rates with the rural rates you will see the difference. This means that the social factors, the way of life, are important in the changing of birth rates.

Development requires not only the idea of giving land to the peon but also of seeing how they are going to live. It is not just a matter of making each peon a good unit of production like a machine or a tool.

It is essential to give him a better standard of living. With the better standard of living, a change of attitude and ideas will come. Otherwise, although we might increase production, of course, we are going to keep the agrarian problem on the same level unless the standard of living is changed.

Very few things have been said in this conference about the problem of housing in the rural areas. We have been talking so much about land, but land just to produce on. But what about land to live on? Regarding the rural housing unit, what efforts have we made? People have to live within some kind of shelter. We have been talking so much about farms, about trying to get the most out of the soil, but we have said very little about how the people should live. I should think the answer to Mrs. Taeuber's paper really comes to: How should the people on the farm live in the future?

JOSE E. VELTMONTE—I would like to ask, what are the prospects for a diminishing birth rate and diminished growth rate in the Philippines?

MRS. TAEUBER—One of my great desires is to have a really careful study of fertility in the Philippines. We tried in the Philippines' census of 1938 to find the differences of fertility among the various parts of the Philippine Islands through using ratios of children to women. The evidence then was that in the more prosperous areas, particularly in the areas which were adjacent to major communication routes, the ratios were lower. There was also the very definitely Western pattern of social and economic differences in fertility within the city of Manila. Impressionistically, the Philippines appears to be, so far as its population is concerned, both Eastern and Western, or intermediate between the two, and I would suspect that a beginning to the answer as to problems of family size might be secured through this very careful analysis for the Philippines, which does give you all kinds of conditions. I don't know the answer to that, and I hope that a study is being made in the Philippines.

Mr. Veltmonte—I do not have any pretensions about knowledge of demographic conditions, Dr. Taeuber, but I can say this, though, as a matter of observation, that the birth rate in the Philippines has definitely come down. About thirty or forty years ago the size of family was about ten or twelve; the present generation now has a size of family of four, five, or six. But what is disturbing, of course, is the fact, I think, that religion has a great deal to do in this differential birth rate. We have prospects, I believe, of finally going through the cycle, in the sense that the rate of population increase tends to slow down a bit as education and standards of living rise.

Mrs. Taeuber—The Philippines gives more evidence of this Western type transition than any other area in the East. Can you trace any relationship between that and the extent of education?

Mr. Veltmonte—I am sorry, but I don't think I am capable of doing that. One thing more I would like to say before I finish. The Rockefeller Foundation late last year sent out a number of technical men who wanted to interest us in demographic studies, but there are no very reliable statistics on population or birth rates in the Philippines.

Alfred Bonné—This stimulating paper Dr. Taeuber has presented us fits well into the many contributions of population research from Princeton on the very important subject of population development in Southeastern Asia and Asia in general. But I wonder sometimes whether the projections which are usually connected with these present ratios are justified to the extent they are made. We have just entered a phase which is of the greatest significance for the economic and social fate of underdeveloped countries. I think that the very process of economic development implies a change in the population development and trades. The process of economic development means a very different attitude and outlook on the part of the individual and society. We have the opportunity to observe the impact of an intensive process of economic development in techniques in the industrialized areas in Asia. In a recent publication about India, Kingsley Davis' *The Population of India and Pakistan,* we find quite a number of revealing conclusions as to the effect of industrialization in the big towns of India —in the eastern towns. It is not only the stabilization of the death rate but the reduction of the birth rate which can be noted, and I wonder whether it is justified to conceive a development for the coming twenty-five years as is now done.

Mrs. Taeuber—I would like to give two answers to that. One, I was one of the group in the office at Princeton that projected the future population of Europe and the Soviet Union, and since that lamented effort I have made no further projections. So far as I know, no one thinks that India fifty or one hundreds years from now will be in process of becoming an England, and there is little evidence of substantial reduction in rural fertility in India. I would like to make two points. First, the problems of raising levels of living would be so much simpler if population growth were lighter. It is not a problem of whether people can be fed at subsistence level, if you are taking a nutritional improvement approach. The question is, how can you do it most efficiently? Second, I think that in this situation we simply are not being scientific if we say that all elements except one can be changed, that this one cannot be touched. A scientific approach to the problem of population increase in the Far East would involve local studies on the attitudes and values of the people, and then social experiments to determine how the desired social changes might be stimulated in rural society. One of the major reasons we cannot project populations accurately is because we have to assume that the future will involve an ordered development of the past. Perhaps this will not be true in the Far East. I would repeat that even in the problem of realistic projections of future populations the major thing that we can do is to offer whatever help we can; and that help can be made available only in terms of specific requests for help by specific countries.

MR. BONNÉ—I have spent quite some time in various settlement areas of Indonesia before the war and in the Philippines both before and after the war. I have observed that in communities that have gone through the initial period of great difficulties, provided there is medical service in the community, the family will increase faster than the same family would have increased in Java or in the area from which they came in Sabu or other parts of the Philippines. There is more food available, and most likely there is more attention paid to health conditions than in the original village. There was not as much medical care available in the old colonization area as in the new; as a result more children survive and will grow up to adulthood in some of these colonization areas than would have survived had the family not migrated. Actually colonization activities of this or that country may, at least locally, and in the initial stages certainly, lead to an increase in the growth rate.

MRS. TAEUBER—One should never consider a topic such as I did this morning without presenting a monograph on the subject. If the best social scientists in the United States had been sent to Indonesia in 1930, at the request of the Dutch government to evaluate Dutch policies from the standpoint of social science, I am quite certain that we would have given the

Dutch an extraordinary commendation. Here were policies that maintained the indigenous peoples in their native cultures. I heard discussions of assistance of the fishing area in a particular group of little villages, and the problem of how the fleet would go out, when they would come back, how long the men would be gone, who would go. All of this was in great detail, and it was always assumed that the new economic developments must proceed without disturbance to local life. Socially this may have been very desirable. The difficulty is that this type of policy will tend to maximize the rate of population increase. Dutch policies involved intelligent economic development; they involved technical assistance and management; they did take into account local cultures. And I suspect that the acuteness of the population problem of Java is due very directly to the intelligence, the social consciousness, and the efficiency of the Dutch administration. Now, this is a very disturbing thing. The fundamental problem is one of colonial administration, whether it be Dutch, British, or American. Whatever the leadership under colonialism the technical and managerial positions were filled by people extraneous to the culture, so that there was blockage of the growth and mobility of a broad group of people capable of administering their own affairs.

JAN M. VAN ROSSEM—I would like to make one comment and ask one question. The comment: Someone remarked a little while ago on the extremely high reproduction rate in colonized areas. Now in the Netherlands, we have found the same thing happening in the reclaimed areas in our country, a film of which you will see tonight. The settlement policy has been aimed at getting young farmers who work very well, who meet the necessary requirements. The result of this in the population field is that the reproduction rate in this area is higher than anyone ever imagined that it ever could be in Western Europe. This itself brings up a problem. We have made new lands and there we put the best people we have, and the result is that we get more people.

The question I have is to Dr. Taeuber. I have always thought that the solution to the population pressure problem would lie in the industrialization of a country. What I gathered from you was that you don't think that this will work for the Eastern and Far Eastern countries and that you think that the direct action by educational work on the population—reproduction of population—would be a solution to it. Am I right in this?

Mrs. Taeuber—I am feeling very humble here. I would not claim to be an expert on even such a limited field of population as the Far East or Southeast Asia, or even the islands of Southeast Asia. I suspect that there are substantial possibilities for industrial development in Indonesia and the Philippines. The resources and the aspects of theoretical solutions to industrial development are simpler than in an India or a China. I suspect, however, that the economic solutions would be much simpler if the growing cities would not have to assume responsibilities for absorbing an increasing population which has to be drained off from the rural areas. I would like to digress one minute. The one country in the Far East which has undergone very comprehensive urbanization and industrial develop-

ment is Japan; and Japan from the Meiji restoration to 1945 kept its rural population from any appreciable growth. The entire natural increase was absorbed in urban areas, the birth rate on the whole following the same trend that it had followed in the West with urbanization and industrialization. I know of no single Japanese economist, no single Japanese sociologist, no single Japanese population expert who does not believe that the political past of Japan would have been different and the economic present would be simpler if Japan had cut her rate of population increase more rapidly than she did. Japan began following the Western pattern with the Restoration; she had 30 million people in the middle of the nineteenth century, 73 million by 1940. In the census of 1950 she had 83 million; at the end of 1952 she had 86.0 million. Now, Japan has supported her increasing population, and on the whole she has done it at increasing levels of living. But, it seems to me, the problem is not whether people can live or die. If you look at this as a problem in the increase of human welfare, then the goal is the most efficient way to secure the maximum increases in welfare over the long run. Thus whatever the possibilities for industrialization, the decline of rural birth rates would make a substantial contribution to the achievement of increasing levels of living within the rural areas and in the nations as wholes.

POPULATION AND THE LAND TENURE PROBLEM

Report of the Working Party

Chairmen, *Conrad Taeuber and Irene B. Taeuber*

The level of living of two-thirds of the world's population is directly dependent on agriculture. Generally this level is far below the levels of living of other groups of the population.

In areas with a high density of rural population, we find the lowest levels of living and the world's most pressing tenure problem. Some governments have relied on land reform as one element in their population policy, for a well-established and prosperous agricultural population is often assumed to make major contributions to a country's population growth. Therefore, three questions arise: (1) Does land reform, altering the adjustment of the land resources to population, affect the population trends of the country? (2) Do population trends, altering the adjustment of the population to land resources, affect the land tenure situation? (3) To what extent can land reform improve the level of living in the countryside?

The countries in which land tenure problems are especially acute are predominantly agricultural. Typically, their birth rates are high. Recent developments that have reduced death rates have brought about or made possible a situation in which population increases rapidly, for birth rates have tended to remain at levels which were in line with the former high levels of mortality.

Where large numbers of people are competing for limited land resources, the result is an inefficient agriculture having a large number of holdings that are both small in size and excessively fragmented. The main inefficiencies of excessive fragmentation of individual holdings are: (1) inefficient use of the soil, which results in considerable losses of cultivable land used for roadways and fences, great difficulties in water supply, and use of submarginal lands; (2) inefficient use of capital, which prevents the use of farm machinery and mechanized transport and which results in the frequent use of storage units which are large in number and of inefficient size; and (3) inefficient use of labor, by which much time is wasted in going to and from scattered parcels and the use of many kinds of labor-saving equipment is prevented.

The main inefficiencies of holdings that are too small are those listed above under excessive fragmentation and, most important of all, considerable underemployment of the farm labor supply.

The inefficiencies of agriculture in these regions are not the only forces that are lowering the level of living of the tillers of the soil. The high prices or rents of land which they have to pay also play an important role.

By altering the adjustment of the population to land resources, population growth has a bad effect upon the land tenure situation.

It is perfectly clear that improvement of the land tenure situation in these regions will considerably improve the efficiency of the units of production. Will the net income of the farmer and his level of living improve, too?

After an improvement of the land tenure situation, the number of farm people being the same they will compete as furiously as before for the equally limited land resources. Receiving higher gross returns, they will only pay higher prices and rents for land. The standard of living does not rise; there is no effect on population trends.

Land reform, although altering the adjustment of the land resources to population, is no guarantee against a further population growth.

Land Tenure Opportunities

There are areas and countries that need to have more population on their good land, both through migration from other countries and through migration from their overcrowded or inferior areas.

But the most common situation is the one in which land reform requires a reduction in the number of persons attempting to wrest a living from the soil, with concurrent expansion of employment in industrial and other nonfarm jobs.

In some cases, the forms of land-holding may tend to reserve large areas of land for uses other than cultivation and settlement.

In other instances, the form of land-holding calls for so large a superstructure of intermediaries between the worker on the land and the ultimate owner that there is no possibility of providing an adequate return to any of the persons entitled to a share of the product.

Inheritance laws and practices are an integral part of the family structure of a country, for it is by inheritance that the family passes on to the next generation its property, rights, and status.

Where large families are the rule, the need to provide for all of the members often has led to excessive fragmentation of holdings. On the other hand, there are a number of cases in which large agricultural groups have accepted family limitation as a means of preventing future reduction in size of holding.

Dealing with Population Problems

It must be kept in mind that the basic population facts of birth, death, and emigration are so intimately related to all aspects of a nation's life that every major effort to improve the nation's levels of living will have significant demographic effects. Conversely, the trends of population growth and emigration are the setting in which programs of land reform must be worked out; these forces condition the scope of the programs and the speed with which they can be developed.

1. A land reform program is an important element in any program for adjusting population to the land resources. By contributing to increased production and enabling the operator to retain a larger share of the product, it contributes to improved levels of living of the agricultural population. It is recognized, however, that one of the first consequences of an improvement in levels of living may be a stimulation of population growth. Land reform in conjunction with immigration, reclamation, and other measures to increase production can make a significant contribution to the expansion of the national economy.

2. Land reform which involves essentially only a transfer of proprietorship or a consolidation of fragmented holdings is not likely to have direct demographic effects.

3. Effective measures for the reduction of population pressure on the land requires not only agricultural measures but at the same time an expansion of industrial and other employment. The transfer of population from agriculture to industry, however, may be slow, especially when necessary capital is limited or must be secured from foreign sources. While the long-run contribution of industrialization to the relief of population pressure on the land is clear, the short-run effects may not be so apparent. In fact, in at least one country the first reaction of an artisan group which had been displaced by industrialization was to seek employment in an already overcrowded agriculture.

4. Emigration of population to other countries is under active consideration in a number of countries. While it undoubtedly can alleviate some acute situations, its scope in the present-day world is likely to be most limited. Emigration, as one of a group of related measures, can be of assistance in a land reform program; it was not considered by the working party to be a major measure.

5. It was felt that in some areas the density of population on the land is so great that individual owner-operated holdings of an adequate size are not possible and that some other form of organization, such as co-operative farming, may provide a means for the more efficient combination of land and labor.

6. If fertility levels should be reduced, a new balance might be achieved. There are areas of the world which have already achieved a balance between fertility and the new low levels of mortality. If this is

not achieved, the increases in the total population of a country during the next decades might be so large as to negate any expected improvements that might result from land reform and associated measures.

7. Control of fertility involves the most fundamental attitudes that people hold. Consideration of this problem leads far beyond the scope of this working party.

LAND REFORM AND ITS DEVELOPMENT IN CHINA SINCE 1927

Tseng Hsiao

CHINA IS essentially an agricultural country of long history. As far back as 1122 B.C., China began to develop her agriculture, and in approximately 200 B.C. the system of private landownership was established. Over the centuries, farming has remained the economic foundation of the country, and landowning has been regarded by the people not only as a sound investment but also as a means of indicating individual or, more correctly, family social status. Historically, inheritance has been the chief method of securing landownership. Based on the concept of kinship and family continuity, the inheritance system emphasizes equal division of land among the sons, and this process of division may go on from generation to generation. However, much of China's vast territory is not cultivable because of mountains, insufficient rainfall, extreme cold, or poor soil, and not all cultivable land has been put under the plow. Thus a great demand for land, coupled with the minute division of land resulting from inheritance, created in the country a large number of landowners with small holdings. These landowners were generally engaged in other walks of life and generally leased their land to farmers for cultivation and collected the rents. Conversely, the bona fide farmers who owned no land or owned too little had to cultivate other people's land for a living. These were the peculiar circumstances under which the wide practice of the tenancy system in China developed.

The following are the basic facts regarding the land problem in China.

1. The total area of China proper is estimated at 9,814,247 square kilometers. The percentage of cultivated land is 13.2 per cent.

2. Of the total population in China approximately 470 million persons—about 80 per cent—represent the farming population.

3. The average cultivated area is estimated at about twenty-five mow per farm household and five mow per individual farmer. (Six mow equal one acre; fifteen mow equal one hectare.)

4. Of the farming population, 33 per cent are tenant farmers who depend for their living solely on cultivating the land of one or more owners; 25 per cent are the part-owner farmers who own too little; and 42 per cent are owner farmers. (Source: *China Handbook,* 1950.)

5. Because of the large percentage of the farming population and the difficulty of acquiring land, the rent is very high; the average rental rate is 50 per cent of the annual main crop yield, but in some extreme cases it runs up to 80 per cent.

From the foregoing it can be seen that 58 per cent of the farming population comprise the tenant farmers and part-owner farmers who either do not own land or own too little and who are subjected to paying high rents. Added to the high rents is the lack of security of tenure; the tenant's right of lease is by and large at the mercy of landowners. The other 42 per cent of the small owner farmers generally cultivate not more than fifteen mow (about two and one-half acres) of their own land and have to pay heavy taxes amounting to approximately 20 per cent of the annual produce. Both classes lead a precarious existence; whenever any natural calamity or political upheaval befalls them their livelihood at once becomes totally insecure. Indeed, they constitute the principal cause of the long period of civil and economic instability in China.

Dr. Sun Yat-sen, father of the Chinese Republic, realized that the seriousness of the land tenure problem was at the root of all our troubles and thus held the key to the very existence of the nation. He called the attention of his country to the principle that unless and until a satisfactory solution was found to improve the livelihood of the peasant class there could be no real national stability and security and that only when the tillers owned the land they cultivated could his revolution be regarded as a genuine one. He therefore attached great importance to land reform in his revolutionary theories and advocated principles such as the "equalization of land rights," "land to the tiller" and "full utilization of land." What was meant by these slogans?

Dr. Sun held that land should be owned under a system in which the owner would set his own land value assessment and report it to the government; the government would levy a land tax on the basis of the owner's report; the government could buy back the land if the assessment made by the owner was deemed too low; after the land value had been fixed, all increase in land value had to revert to the community, as the increases would be considered due to the improvements made by society and to the development of industry and commerce.

Dr. Sun suggested that the government should adopt measures to enable those who till the land to become its owners. Such measures could consist of the limitation of the profits of landowners, better protection of tenants and independent farmers, and the reduction of rent.

Under the slogan "full utilization of land" Dr. Sun included the cultivation of wasteland which would help to adjust the area of cultivation of each farmer or farm household to the standard of the economic family size. The farmer as a result would be in a better financial position and given greater incentives to improve his land, thus bringing about an increase in production. Dr. Sun also suggested as a means of reducing the farm population, a nation-wide construction project which would provide employment in a great many fields other than agricultural for surplus people.

Measures toward Land Reform

The Chinese revolution of 1926–27, which was guided entirely by Dr. Sun's principles, witnessed the rise of Peasant Associations in many parts of the country. The slogans then used were protection of the peasants' interests, reduction of rent and taxes, and allocation of land to farmers. Thus, a general consciousness on the part of the peasants of their own problems manifested itself in a desire for improvement. With the successful conclusion of the revolution and the establishment of the National government at Nanking in 1927, measures were taken to translate Dr. Sun's ideas into action. The first step toward land reform was to order a rent reduction of 25 per cent, so that the then prevailing rent—50 per cent of the annual main crop yield—would be reduced to 37.5 per cent of the annual main crop yield. The reduction was carried out with considerable success throughout the province of Chekiang, while plans for carrying out a similar program in other provinces were retarded by the breakup of the revolutionary coalition and the withdrawal of the Chinese Communists in 1927.

The next step taken by the government was the promulgation of the Land Law of 1930 which was drawn up largely on the basis of Dr. Sun's principles. Some of the important provisions of the Land Law were as follows:

1. The government should conduct a nation-wide cadastral survey and registration of land to provide the basis for assessing land values.

2. The land tax should be levied according to the statutory land value on a progressive basis; at the most the rate should not exceed 5 per cent of the total statutory land value.

3. Farm ownership should be gradually transferred to the tenants through peaceful methods, such as purchase.

4. Prior to acquiring ownership of the land, tenants (while renting land) should be given security of tenure by preventing landowners from practicing evictions at will.

5. The rent should not exceed 37.5 per cent of the annual main crop yield.

With these legislative provisions in force, the land reform program in China would have been gradually implemented had there been a unified government that could have devoted itself to peaceful pursuits. Unfortunately, since the promulgation of the Land Law the National government had been faced with the military rebellion of the Chinese Communists, who in 1928 established the Chinese Soviet regime in the greater part of Kiangsi Province, and subsequently with the Japanese aggression in Manchuria in 1931. Henceforth, the government was busily engaged in military operations in the face of national emergency and could spare little attention to matters concerning land reform. However, between the years 1932 and 1936 considerable progress was made in Kiangsu, Chekiang, and Kiangsi provinces where extensive cadastral survey and land registration were conducted as the preliminary steps for the application of the new land tax as provided for in the Land Law. Particularly in Kiangsu Province the land value tax was successfully carried out. In Kiangsi Province, after the recovery of the occupied areas from the Chinese Soviet regime, land confiscated previously by the Communists was re-allotted to the people, and farm co-operatives were introduced to restore agricultural production. In the meantime the Chinese Farmer's Bank was organized and charged with the administration of the extension of agricultural loans for the increase of agricultural production, the development of irrigation, agricultural extension, the increase of agricultural by-products, and other agricultural improvements. The loans were to be repaid in installments at a low interest rate.

Despite the eight long years of war against Japan, during which farmers were overburdened with the military expenditure, two noteworthy facts emerged: (1) the increase of agricultural loans and (2) the experiment in fostering independent farmers. The agricultural loans granted by the Farmer's Bank were steadily increased from $1,527,474,000 (Chinese currency) in 1943 to $3,638,185,000 in 1945, and a certain portion of this was used in helping farmers purchase land. Of particular significance was the land purchase program accomplished in Lungyen and Peipei.

Lungyen is a rural county in Fukien Province, South China. The program, begun in 1942, was completed in 1947. It called for the purchase of all tenant-operated land in Lungyen by the local government for its resale to bona fide farmers. The purchase price was paid partly in cash and partly in land bonds issued by the Farmer's Bank. The land bonds were to be amortized in ten annual installments. The local government bought a total of 262,458 mow of land (45,580 acres) and transferred the land to a total of 32,242 farmers under the program. As a result the farmers of the whole county of Lungyen became owner-operators. Subsequent investigation in 1947 showed that compared with the pre-reform years, farm production in the county was greatly increased and the farmers' living conditions improved. The food production was increased 22 per cent; hogs raised by farmers increased 30 per cent and the number of children in schools doubled.

Peipei is a rural district in Chungking where over 64 per cent of the land had been tilled by tenants and the rental in many cases had been as high as 80 per cent. In 1943 the government selected an area in Peipei and expropriated all holdings of the absentee owners and redistributed them among the tillers. The entire district organized itself into co-operative farms, which led to a 30 per cent increase in production. In 1942, before the reform, 1,287 piculs (one *picul* equals .0551 short tons) of the 1,839 piculs of farm produce were turned over to owners as rent. After the reform in 1945, the yield was 2,400 piculs, of which less than 300 piculs were paid out as taxes and yearly installments to repay the loan for buying the land. These were the two successful and significant accomplishments which gave the government great encouragement to extend the program of fostering independent farmers.

In the postwar period, land reform became a popular cry. The new constitution of China adopted at the National People's Assembly in 1947 contained a special provision which defined the land reform policy. Again, when the first popularly-elected legislature convened in the same year, a draft plan of land reform formulated by the Chinese Land Reform Association was submitted by me in my capacity as one of the legislators. The plan envisaged the enactment of a law whereby all land currently cultivated by tenants should immediately be owned by them, with the proviso that they

pay to the original owner the value of the land equivalent to seven times the annual rent (which must not exceed 37.5 per cent of the annual yield) in fourteen yearly installments. Though the bill did not become a law, its essential points won the approval of a number of provincial governments whose provincial regulations were drawn up in conformity with its spirit. No province, however, was able to put it into actual operation because the entire Chinese mainland was soon overrun by the Communists.

Mention should be made of the 25 per cent rent reduction program in Szechuan Province. It was carried out by the Provincial government with the technical and financial assistance of the JCRR for a period of four months from July to November, 1949. The program extended to an area of 303,000 square kilometers including 138 counties, and farmers benefited by it were estimated at 17,500,000 persons. The achievement would have been made more extensive had it not been for the subsequent Communist occupation of the province.

Proposed Solutions

In view of the foregoing it must be admitted that land reform in China over the last two decades, though based on definite and sound policies, was not carried out as extensively and speedily as expected; a large percentage of farmers were not able to acquire landownership within a reasonably short period, and, what is of more fundamental importance, they were not able to improve their livelihood. In consequence, it was possible for the Communists to take full advantage of the situation for their political propaganda carried on under the disguise of "land reform."

A separate report concerning the situation on China's mainland will be circulated to you. I should like to add here that the policy adopted by the Chinese Communists is both ruthless and unrealistic. It is ruthless because it has restored to such measures as "class struggle," "liquidation," and "confiscation" instead of a peaceful method of promoting landownership. It is unrealistic because it has divided the small-size farmland of China into even smaller units, resulting in the uneconomic use of land resources. This, plus the exorbitant rate of land taxes, which is as high as 60 per cent of the annual produce currently imposed upon the farmers by the Communists, has made land-sharing a burden rather than a blessing to the people and has worsened the already shattered rural economy of China.

The question may now be asked: What would be a more desirable solution to the land reform problem in China? My concrete proposals for land reform in China, which are the result of study over a period of years by the Land Reform Association and which meet with popular approval, may be summarized as follows:

1. Agricultural land should belong to those who till it. Tenant farmers should obtain ownership of the land which they are currently tilling and the present tenant system should be wiped out.

2. To compensate the landowner whose land the tenant bought, the tenant should be required to pay the original owner the value of the land at a price equivalent to seven times the annual rent currently fixed at 37.5 per cent of the annual main crop yield, payable in fourteen annual installments. (In Formosa it is proposed for the tenant to pay in advance 30 per cent cash of the total value of the land, and for the poor tenant this payment shall be financed by the government in the form of credit through the Land Bank.)

3. The amount of land newly purchased by the tenant should be gradually increased to the economic family size. For this purpose, the existing fragmented farms and small holdings should be regrouped and consolidated. The state should initiate a nation-wide program of rural reconstruction to include irrigation, village roads, peasant dwellings, public works, and the reclamation of wastelands in order that a great portion of the agricultural workers may be absorbed by other employment, thus reducing in proportion the number of farming population and expanding the size of farming area.

4. The present inheritance system should be revised to the extent that the family-size farmland should not be permitted further division due to inheritance. In cases where farmland is transferred to the hands of those who do not cultivate the land, the government should have the priority of buying back the land and re-allotting it to the genuine farmer.

5. The land tax should be levied on the basis of the land value on a progressive scale and the rate should not exceed 8 per cent of the current value of the land.

6. The family-size farm should be given technical and financial assistance. It would also be necessary to organize various types of agricultural co-operatives to provide public storage, machine stations, and other facilities. All this would help the farmers to develop a sound and modern agricultural economy.

The above points, I believe, should form the basis of China's land reform with a view to helping the peasants to be economically independent; such type of reform will ultimately lead to a more rational land utilization and to the nation's economic development as a whole.

Before concluding, I would like to invite the attention of the conference to a subject which may merit serious consideration, and that is the creation of an International Fund with a specific function of providing financial assistance for land reform to the underdeveloped countries. While recognizing that land reform in underdeveloped countries—agricultural countries in particular—must be accomplished through peaceful methods of acquiring landownership by farmers, we all will agree, I am sure, that legislative measures alone would be slow and insufficient to carry out the objective and that financial assistance is more urgently needed. In view of the financial inability of the majority of the farmers and in view of the stringent national budget of the countries concerned, it is suggested that an international financial agency be established to meet this difficulty. With the international aid the farmers' banks or land banks in the countries concerned would be assisted in

carrying out a well-planned credit extension to the farmers for their acquiring landownership. It should be pointed out that such an international fund as suggested above is not intended to be charity in any sense; it will be operated in the form of credit extension to be paid up in annual installments with the farm produce as security. I believe this would be the feasible solution to the land tenure problem now facing many of the countries. I shall be grateful indeed for any consideration this memorable world gathering may give to this suggestion.

THE RENT REDUCTION AND LAND PURCHASE PROGRAM IN FORMOSA

Hui-sun Tang

FORMOSA has a total area of 35,960 square kilometers. High mountains stretch from the north to the south covering all the eastern and a large part of the central regions of the island. Over 60 per cent of the total land area is mountainous and of little value for agricultural uses. Only the western part is plain land with fertile soil. Of this plain land, 838,190 hectares, or 24 per cent of the total land area, are cultivated. Among this cultivated land 518,710 hectares, or 62 per cent, are paddy field, 319,480 hectares, or 38 per cent, dry land.

The most important farm crop in Formosa is rice, for which more than 48 per cent of the total cultivated land is being used. In 1950, 1,420,000 metric tons of rice were produced. This was more than enough to feed the whole population of the island. Next to rice is sugar cane, which is cultivated in southern Formosa. More than 12 per cent of the cultivated land is devoted to this crop. About 650,000 metric tons of refined sugar were produced in 1950. Sugar is the most important export commodity and

plays an indispensable role in the Formosan economy. Other important farm crops are sweet potatoes, bananas, tea, pineapples, jute, peanuts, and citrus fruits.

The population of Formosa has been increasing rapidly. In 1900 the total population was only 2,750,000 while at the present time it is 7,686,000. It has increased nearly threefold within half a century. Of the 7,686,000 inhabitants the farm population constitutes 60 per cent. The percentage distribution of farm tenancy is as follows: owner-operators 35 per cent, part-owners 26 per cent, and tenants 39 per cent. About 56 per cent of the total farmland is under tenant operation. The average holding of each farm family is 1.3 hectares; and over 70 per cent of the farms are under 2 hectares. As a result intensive cultivation has been pushed to a very great extent. Even so, the small farms can hardly provide an acceptable standard of living for a family of six.

The tenant condition in Formosa before rent reduction was very bad. Rents were at least 50 per cent of the crop. In addition, the tenants had to furnish their own fertilizers, farm equipment, and farm buildings. They had no security of tenure. It depended very much upon the good will of the landlord. Coupled with the small acreage they cultivated, it was extremely difficult for them to make both ends meet. The net result was discontent and unrest. Determined to correct this situation, General Chen Cheng, now Premier of the Chinese National government in Formosa, instituted a rent reduction program in early 1949. He did this with the active co-operation and assistance of the Chinese-American Joint Commission on Rural Reconstruction.

Under the rent reduction program a maximum rent payment is fixed at 37.5 per cent of the annual main crop yield on the farm. However, I must make it clear that our scheme has nothing to do with actual harvest. We fixed a standard yield for each grade of land in advance. In Formosa we have a complete set of land cadastral records which classify all farmlands into twenty-six grades according to soil fertility and productivity. (See tables 24 and 25.) This enables the land commission in each locality to figure out their standard yields. With the standard yields clearly fixed, it is a simple matter to find out how much rent a tract of land should pay according to the new rate. Let me give you an illustration. Suppose there is a tenant who rented one hectare of a fifth-grade paddy field. Its standard yield is fixed at 10,000 catties of rice. Formerly

TABLE 24

GRADES OF PADDY LAND WITH STANDARD YIELDS OF RICE FOR THREE
SELECTED LOCALITIES OF FORMOSA*

| GRADE OF PADDY FIELD | YIELD (in catties per chia†) | | | GRADE OF PADDY FIELD | YIELD (in catties per chia†) | | |
	Kaoh-siung County	Taitung County	Taichung City		Kaoh-siung County	Taitung County	Taichung City
1	12,000	11,000	14,110	14	4,400	3,700	4,500
2	11,500	10,500	13,700	15	3,500	3,400	4,900
3	11,000	10,000	12,870	16	3,200	3,000	4,150
4	10,500	9,600	12,040	17	2,800	2,700	3,900
5	10,000	8,800	10,960	18	2,500	2,400	3,150
6	9,500	8,300	10,210	19	2,200	2,100	2,740
7	8,800	7,800	9,550	20	2,000	1,800	2,320
8	8,200	7,000	8,800	21	1,800	1,600	2,080
9	7,600	6,000	8,050	22	1,600	1,300	1,910
10	7,000	5,500	7,470	23	1,400	1,100	1,660
11	6,300	5,000	6,810	24	1,200	900	1,390
12	5,700	4,500	6,140	25	1,000	850	.....
13	5,000	4,000	5,430	26	800	800	.....

*Source: Bureau of Land Administration, Formosa.
†One catty equals .5968 kilogram; 1 chia equals .9699 hectare.

TABLE 25

GRADES OF DRY LAND WITH STANDARD YIELDS OF SWEET POTATOES FOR THREE
SELECTED LOCALITIES OF FORMOSA*

GRADE OF DRY LAND	YIELD (in catties per chia†)			GRADE OF DRY LAND	YIELD (in catties per chia†)		
	Kaoh-siung County	Taitung County	Taichung City		Kaoh-siung County	Taitung County	Taichung City
1	49,000	44,000	63,720	14	16,000	14,500	18,740
2	46,000	40,000	58,000	15	14,000	12,500	17,150
3	42,000	35,000	53,600	16	13,000	11,000	15,650
4	39,000	30,500	48,720	17	12,000	9,500	14,060
5	35,000	29,000	44,980	18	10,000	8,000	12,460
6	33,000	28,000	41,420	19	9,000	7,000	10,960
7	32,000	27,500	38,230	20	8,000	6,000	9,370
8	30,000	26,500	37,480	21	7,000	5,000	7,810
9	29,000	25,000	32,050	22	6,000	4,000	7,030
10	25,000	21,000	28,860	23	5,000	3,000	6,260
11	23,000	20,000	25,770	24	4,000	2,500	6,090
12	21,000	18,000	22,660	25	......	2,000	6,150
13	18,000	16,500	20,330	26	......	1,500	4,690

*Source: Bureau of Land Administration, Formosa.

†One catty equals .5968 kilogram; 1 chia equals .9699 hectare.

the tenant had to pay 50 per cent, or 5,000 catties, of his rice crop to his landlord. Under the rent reduction program he pays no more than 37.5 per cent, or 3,750 catties, regardless of the amount he actually harvested.

The results of Formosa's rent reduction program can be explained in several ways. In the first place, the tenants' income has been increased. Previously, few tenants in Formosa could fill up their daily rice bowls. After rent reduction, they not only had enough rice to eat but also surplus to sell in exchange for other necessities. Our field inspectors frequently overheard the people joking about "37.5 per cent houses," "37.5 per cent buffaloes," and "37.5 per cent weddings," etc. To us these are compliments.

Furthermore, the rent reduction program has also encouraged farm production. Since farm rent has been regulated, tenants could now enjoy the full portion of any increased production over their maximum rent payments. As a result, the rice production increased each year. For example, the rice production before rent reduction was only 1,068,000 metric tons. In 1949, one year after the reform, the production was increased to 1,214,500 metric tons. In 1950, it went up to 1,420,000 meric tons. This year, 1951, an estimate of 1,500,000 metric tons is expected. Other factors might have contributed to the increase, but rent reduction certainly is an important one.

Finally, the rent reduction program has made the tenant farmers more secure. For under the present program there is a provision that fixes the lease tenure at six years. This is an improvement and is all for the tenants' benefit.

However, the program we carried out in Formosa was not entirely free from difficulties. When the program was well under way there came complaints from the landlords. They protested that the land classification upon which the standard yields are based is inaccurate. They asked the government to revise it. This demand, if fully accepted, would have required the government to undertake an over-all land reclassification, and the rent reduction program which had been carried out would have been done away with. The landlords' complaints were exaggerated, as was revealed by a careful re-examination of the problem.

Another problem was the effort of the landlords to evade the reform. The major form of evasion was that the landlord forced the tenant to terminate the lease before its expiration but termed the act of termination as voluntary. One year after the program was initiated, there arose a total of about 10,000 cases of such lease termination. Besides, there were also other types of evasions. For instance, some landlords made an agreement with the tenants that the latter pretended to be the hired laborer of the former. In so doing, the landlords were freed from the restrictions of the rent reduction program. Or in some cases, the tenant agreed to buy the rented land and sell it to other persons at a higher price for the landlord. The two parties would subsequently share the difference of the price oversold. Also, there were cases where the landlord simply refused to reduce the rent.

To deal with the situation, the government instituted a rigid supervision program on a regional basis and employed regular rent inspectors to investigate and settle the matters according to the following principles.

First, forced termination of lease must not be allowed and land must be returned to the original tenant. Secondly, refusal to reduce rent must be prohibited. Thirdly, evasions of other nature must be settled either by mediation or by arbitration on the principle that land should be tilled by actual tillers. Fortunately, all the attempts of evasions as mentioned above were stopped in time and the program has been successfully carried out.

With the rent reduction work still being carried on in Formosa, the Chinese National government on the island inaugurated this year a program to sell the public land to tenant farmers. In Formosa, there are about 180,000 hectares of public land which comprise about one-fifth of the total cultivated area of the island. Of the vast public holdings, two-thirds—about 120,000 hectares—are operated by the Formosa Sugar Corporation. The rest is administered by the Formosa Salt Corporation, Provincial Department of Agriculture and Forestry, Provincial Bureau of Social Affairs, and Formosa Land Bank. Besides, there is also a part of the public land rented out directly to the tenant farmers by the local government. Of the land operated by the Formosa Sugar Corporation, 59,000 hectares are under direct operation of the Corporation and the rest is under tenant operation. The rental rate on these tenant-operated lands is 25 per cent of the annual main crop yield.

In planning further land reforms, the Provincial government in Formosa has decided to sell part of the lands to the tenant farmers, retaining the part which is necessary for the operation of the government enterprises, including sugar cane production by the Sugar Corporation. The Provincial government has promulgated a set of rules governing the sale procedure of public land, which was approved by the National government in May, 1951. The rules consist of the following features: (1) the present tenant farmer shall have the priority to pur-chase the land he tills, (2) each tenant family may purchase one-half to two hec-tares of paddy field or one to four hectares of dry land, (3) the purchase price is 2.5 times the total annual main crop yield of the land purchased and shall be paid in ten annual installments, and (4) each annual installment payment, including land tax, shall not exceeed 37.5 per cent of the annual main crop yield.

This public land sale program has been in operation since July of this year. The total acreage for sale, for the time being, is 86,000 hectares, of which 36,000 hectares are allocated for first sale and 50,000 hec-tares for second sale. This total acreage of 86,000 hectares represents 18.4 per cent of the total tenanted land on the island. A total of about 100,000 tenant families will be benefited under the program. This figure represents 16 per cent of the total farm families on the island. This program, once completed, will greatly aid the government in speeding up steps for requiring the land-lords to sell their surplus land.

After the completion of the public land purchase program, there will be a law to limit the private land holdings. The govern-ment anticipates purchasing the excessive private land holdings and selling them to the tenant farmers as a means of enabling them to become owners of the land they till. The Chinese government in Formosa is now preparing a preliminary draft of the program. The main points in this program are roughly as follows:

1. The government will undertake an island-wide survey of the present land hold-ings in order to ascertain the actual condi-tions of land distribution at the present time to serve as the basis for making a landownership and land use inventory of the whole island.

2. Landlords shall be permitted to retain one hectare of paddy field or two hectares of dry land as the maximum retention acreage of a landlord's family. Excessive acreage over this maximum retention acre-age shall be purchased by the government and resold to the tenant farmers.

3. Purchase price shall be fixed at 2.5 times the annual main crop yield on the land.

4. The compensation for the land shall be made partly in cash, partly in bonds which are redeemable in kind within ten years, and partly in stocks of government enterprises; and the ratio shall be fixed according to the acreage of land sold.

5. The annual installment payment of land price, including land tax, by the ten-ant purchaser shall not exceed 37.5 per cent of the annual main crop yield.

This program shall be initiated as soon as it becomes a national law. The land-holding survey program which provides the technical basis in implementing this pro-gram is already under way with the finan-cial and technical aid from the Joint Com-mission on Rural Reconstruction. It will be completed within a period of six months. As for the land purchase program as a whole, we are very hopeful because the rent reduction program has created certain favor-able conditions for it. Right now, we have already witnessed the drop of land prices and the weakening of the landlord's desire for landownership.

The above statement represents a brief presentation of the steps of land reform as exemplified by the rent reduction already carried out and the land purchase program now undertaken. All these measures have been designed after careful study and im-plemented with a systematic procedure with the aid and encouragement of the Joint Commission on Rural Reconstruction. In general, they represent a continual procedure of reform, which was started with rent reduction, which was followed by land hold-ings limitation, and which is to be concluded with tenant's land purchase. The final goal is to build up a family farm system as the mainstay of an improved agriculture, a stronghold against communism and a nursery of democracy.

LAND REFORM IN JAPAN

Keiki Owada

BEFORE I deal with land reform in Japan, I shall give you a short sketch of Japanese agriculture, because I am afraid that very few people can appreciate what land reform is or is not without some knowledge of Japanese agriculture.

Japan consists of four main islands. The total area is only 369,842 square kilometers, or an area a little smaller than the state of California. On this small land we have about 83 million people.

The land of Japan is very mountainous. The total area of cultivated land is only 5.04 million hectares, or 12.5 million acres, which is only about 14 per cent of the total area of the country. This land is worked by 6.2 million farm families. There is roughly 2 acres per family.

Most of the land is under food crops such as rice, wheat, barley, potatoes, etc. We have very little pasture land, and animal husbandry plays a very insignificant role in Japanese agriculture. Climatic conditions are generally favorable, and precipitation is ample. For this reason, in certain parts of Japan the farmer can harvest more than one crop from the same piece of land. Because of this factor the harvested acreage is 40 per cent larger than the arable acreage.

According to the 1950 World Agricultural Census, the number of farm households is 6,176,419, comprising 37,810,936 people, which is about 46 per cent of the total population.

While agriculture is the basis of the country's economy, it does not rate high as a source of income. It accounts for only 21 per cent of the total national income, including the income from forestry. I must point out that this figure is much better than the prewar level, because of the land reform and the good prices for agricultural products after the war.

While the average farm holding is 2 acres, in reality many farmers cultivate less than 2 acres. Farmers who cultivate less than 1 acre represent 41 per cent of the total number of farmers, and 73 per cent of all the farmers cultivate less than 2.5 acres. The number of farmers who cultivate more than 50 acres is only 392 throughout Japan. With the exception of sericulture, agricultural production has almost recovered to the prewar levels. The annual production of rice after the war averages 63 million koku of brown rice, or 320 million bushels; this is 45 bushels of brown rice per acre. Livestock has also recovered. The number of cattle is 2.5 million, including 200,000 milk cows. These figures exceed the prewar level.

Cultivation is almost entirely by hand. There are a few exceptions. Plowing work before seeding is done mostly by horses or cattle. And in most cases hulling and polishing of rice and barley and wheat milling are done by simple hand-operated machines.

Although Japanese agriculture is one of the most intensive, and although the productivity per land unit is very high, it takes much labor and much fertilizer. For instance, it takes 734 hours of labor and as much as 84 pounds of nitrogen, 67 pounds of phosphate, and 84 pounds of potash (including manure) per acre of rice cultivation. Productivity per man cannot be very high. We are now trying to find efficient measures to improve the productivity both per land unit and per man. The so-called Japanese type small tractors are being used more and more. They were only 569 in number in 1942, and 11,131 in 1950. They have 3 to 5 horsepower and can plow one acre a day.

There are some bright sides to our rural life. About 97 per cent of all farmers have electricity. More than 95 per cent of them can read and write. More than 50 per cent of them have radios. Such cultural conditions helped to carry out the land reform.

There are naturally many dark sides, too. Farmers' wives work too hard not only at home but also in the fields. The farmers' diet is poor. They take only 66.2 grams (2.3 ounces) of protein, including only 13.8 grams (0.5 ounces) of animal and fish protein a day.

Conditions Before Land Reform

Some 47 per cent of our total cultivated land was tenanted land in 1944, just before land reform. Farmers who were full owners represented 32 per cent, part-owner farmers 40 per cent, and tenants 28 per cent of the total number of farmers. In the 1870's the tenanted land was estimated at about 30 per cent, but it increased year by year through indebtedness and foreclosures as a result of inability to repay the debts to the usurers and merchants.

Our land tenure conditions had two characteristics: high rent in kind and lack of security of tenure.

On paddy land rent was approximately 50 per cent of the crop. It should be noted that while the landlord paid the land tax, the tenant had to pay for the expensive fertilizers, provide his own equipment, seed, house and farm buildings. The rent, in effect, was more than 50 per cent.

Basically the tenant could remain on the land only when the landlord wished him to. The land reform instituted a basic change in this respect. Before the land reform, the landlords behaved as if it were a privilege to cultivate their land. The tenants had to go to the landlord hat-in-hand begging for a loan, reduction of rent in case of crop failures, etc. The severe conditions of tenancy resulted in much discontent, unrest, and in out-and-out uprisings against the landlords. This was particularly true during the 1920's and 1930's.

The explanation for these unsatisfactory tenancy conditions is twofold: unequal bargaining relations between landowners and tenants and surplus of farm population. The landowners were in the privileged position because they enjoyed economic and political power. We have been troubled by surplus population, especially in the villages. Despite the tremendous industrial expansion and shift of farm population to urban and industrial centers, the number of farm households in 1950 is larger than it was sixty or seventy years ago. It was this continued pressure on a rather limited areable area that gave rise to the extremely difficult landlord-tenant relations. Land rents could not but be high under these conditions.

Improving Tenure Conditions

For many years before land reform was brought about tenants recognized their unreasonable and intolerable position. The tenant unions came into existence as a result. They demanded a permanent reduction of rent and security of tenure. The repressive measures of the government during World War II put an end to these organizations. After the war the unions re-emerged and actively participated in carrying out land reform.

The Ministry of Agriculture and Forestry understood the evils of the land tenure system and attempted to correct the situation. The following steps were taken both before and during the second world war.

1. The government promulgated the Tenancy Disputes Mediation Law and in 1924 appointed land tenure specialists to settle tenancy disputes. These specialists later on contributed greatly to the enforcement of the reform.

2. The government in 1922 undertook a program to promote the establishment of owner-operated farms; the program was further strengthened in 1926. It gave financial aid to tenants who wished to buy land. Under this system 383,000 tenants bought 690,000 acres of land between 1926 and 1940.

3. Beginning with the Sino-Japanese War in 1937 and culminating in the Pacific War, the government found itself compelled to improve land tenure conditions. Failure would have resulted in a decline in the volume of the badly needed food collections. The government therefore instituted the Agricultural Land Adjustment Law in 1938 for the purpose of giving the tenants greater security of tenure.

4. The government froze rentals and the price of land at the 1939 level. The government also instituted in 1941 a rice price policy which clearly discriminated against the landlord and in favor of the tenant.

The Start of Land Reform

Japan surrendered to the Allied Forces in August, 1945, and its militaristic government was done away with. The Ministry of Agriculture and Forestry believed that land reform was an indispensable measure to stabilize rural Japan. It therefore prepared a draft of a law which, after discussion with SCAP officials, was finally enacted in October, 1946. The legislation is known under the following titles: Owner-Farmer Establishment, Special Measures Law, and the Agricultural Land Adjustment Law. General MacArthur had much to do with the enactment of these laws. It was he who issued the famous directive of December 9, 1945, in which he stated that "the Japanese Imperial Government is directed to take measures to insure that those who till the soil of Japan shall have more equal opportunity to enjoy the fruits of their labor."

Contents of Legislation

The main provisions of the land reform law are as follows:

1. The government purchased all absentee-owned land.

2. Resident landlords were permitted to retain an average of two and one-half acres of tenant-cultivated land; in Hokkaido, where land is more plentiful, they were allowed an average of ten acres; everything above these limits had to be sold to the government.

3. Owner-cultivators were restricted to the ownership of an average of seven and one-half acres in the islands of Honshu, Shikoku, and Kyushu, and to an average of thirty acres in Hokkaido. However, they may be permitted to cultivate more if the productivity of the land is lowered by subdivision or if the holding is cultivated by family labor.

4. The land purchased by the government was to be resold to the tenants.

5. The government purchased the land at an average price of 3,000 yen per acre for paddy (rice) land and 1,800 yen per acre for dry land. In addition, landlords received a subsidy of 880 yen per acre of paddy land and 520 yen per acre of upland within the limit of the area mentioned in (3), above.

The price to the new purchasers was calculated by capitalizing an annual rent figure. In calculating this rent figure an effort was made to determine a fair rent that would permit the farmer buying the land to reap a fair profit, taking into consideration the fact that all rice was compulsorily collected by the government at a low official price, excluding only the rice used by the farmer for his home consumption. The fair price of the land to the landlords was differently calculated. It was determined by capitalizing the net income from the lands, or, in other words, rent minus land taxes. This value average 3,880 yen per acre of paddy land and 2,320 yen per acre of upland. The government paid the above-mentioned subsidy to the landlords to compensate for these differences between the prices charged the new purchasers and the so-called fair prices for the landlords.

It was the postwar inflation that made the price of the land very cheap. Before land reform began, the postwar inflation had already grown serious. When the draft of the Land Reform Law was under discussion in the Diet, the price of brown rice per koku (roughly 5 bushels) was 300 yen. When the purchase of land began this price had risen to 550 yen. It rose to 1,700 yen by the end of 1947 and to 3,595 yen by the end of 1948.

Under such conditions some people insisted that the price of land under the land reform law was extremely low and that it should be changed to a higher level. The government did not agree. It well understood that if the price was changed to a higher one the landlords would surely defer their sale of land to the government, in anticipation of still higher prices later on. The government had decided to accomplish land reform by the end of 1948. If land reform was delayed, it would become more and more difficult to accomplish it, if not impossible. The government concluded that it preferred to accomplish land reform as quickly as possible at the original price level rather than to satisfy the landlords' demands for higher land prices.

6. The government paid the landlords in twenty-four-year annuity bonds bearing an interest rate of 3.65 per cent per annum. The bonds, originally nonredeemable, are now redeemable, and the government has paid up 80 per cent of the bond value.

7. Tenants can pay for the land in one payment or in several, not to exceed thirty annual installments, at an annual interest rate of 3.2 per cent.

8. To administer the land transfer, the legislation created local, prefectural, and national land commissions. A local commission consists of five tenants, two owner-farmers, and three landlords. The local commissions are the most important agencies of the reform, since they determine the purchase and sale of the land and who is to purchase the land. The prefectural commissions are the agencies through which the over-all policies of the Central Land Commission came down to the eleven thousand villages of Japan.

9. Since the Reform did not aim to abolish tenancy as an institution, the legislation provided for measures to ease tenant burdens. The provisions are as follows. Rents in kind are abolished. They must be paid in cash at a stated amount not exceeding 25 per cent of the value of the rice crop and 15 per cent of the value of the other crops. Verbal rental agreements are abolished. Written contracts specifying all the pertinent points are obligatory. A landlord cannot take back the rented land, either for the purpose of re-renting it or for his own use, unless he has good cause and has secured the approval of the local land commission.

Difficulties in Carrying Out Reform

The land transfer involved some 30 or 40 million pieces of land. This alone indicates how difficult the task was. Even more difficult was the fact that the program called for dealing with thousands upon thousands of landlords, most of whom held a small acreage. Moreover, the landlords as a class were naturally opposed to the reform, particularly the smaller landlords. They realized that not only their land was at stake but their political and social position in the communities as well. But in the main, they accepted the reform—even though grudgingly. They knew that the reform was bound to come sooner or later. The fact that the Occupation was supporting it helped to overcome the opposition. But above all, what helped matters most was the fact that the farmers wanted the reform, that the land commissions worked with great devotion, and that the government, through the Ministry of Agriculture, did its part. Altogether, the Ministry officials, the members of the commissions, and their staffs accounted for nearly four hundred thousand people. These people fulfilled their responsibilities so well that within a period of three years the purchase and sale program was a reality.

Accomplishments of Land Reform

1. According to the latest statistics of 31 March, 1951, the government purchased 4,369,000 acres of cultivated land. In addition, the government got 455,000 acres of cultivated land chiefly under the provisions of the Property Tax Law. The government resold 4,751,000 acres of cultivated land to 4,204,000 farmers. In addition, the government purchased 40,000 tenant houses and 900,000 acres of pasture land. Furthermore, one should add 1.5 million acres of land for reclamation, also resold to the tenants.

The farmers have already paid 76 per cent of the price of the land in cash, and the landowners have received payments amounting to 80 per cent of the value of the bonds. Thus, rented land is now only 11 per cent of the total cultivated land. According to the 1950 census the composition of rural dwellers has completely changed. The owner farmers now comprise 67 per cent, owner farmers who also rent land represent 26 per cent, tenant farmers who

also own some land 7 per cent, and pure tenant farmers represent only 5 per cent of all farm households in Japan. In the words of General MacArthur, Japanese farmers do now enjoy the fruits of their labor. This is an indispensable element towards the development of a more democratic rural society.

2. The rent in cash has been fairly controlled.

3. Written contracts are widespread. The latest survey shows that 61 per cent of the contracts are in writing in accordance with the model contract issued by the government. This provides the tenants with very fair land tenure conditions.

4. Land reform was just what Japanese tenants had been looking for. If they did not wish it we could not have enforced the program, no matter how hard we tried. They made sure that their best people were on the commissions, watched the work of the commissions, followed the literature dealing with the reforms, and generally tried to make certain of their gains.

Agricultural Problems after Reform

What land reform accomplished in Japan has been mentioned above. What land reform could not accomplish is also clear.

1. The number of farmers has increased from 5,536,608 in 1944 to 6,176,419 in 1950, owing to the wartime industrial destruction and consequent unemployment and to repatriation from abroad. The average size of cultivated unit has accordingly decreased from 2.4 acres in 1944 to 2 acres in 1950.

2. We must increase farm income through higher productivity. Our ten thousand farm improvement agents and seven hundred home improvement agents are expected to make their contribution to that end.

3. We must encourage still further the farmers' co-operative movement. We have now about 30,000 agricultural co-ops. There is no farmer who does not belong to some

co-op. Our agricultural co-ops had very hard times in 1949 when a temporary deflation overtook Japan, but they are now in fairly good shape. The latest data show that the farmers sell 98 per cent of their rice, barley, and wheat to the government through their co-ops; they purchase 80 per cent of their fertilizer through their co-ops; their deposits with the co-ops are estimated at 71 per cent of all their deposits.

4. We must provide the farmers with a good credit system. Short-term credit is given now to the farmers by their co-ops and by the Bank of Japan through the co-ops. Long-term credit is also given by the government. The farmers of Japan have been troubled especially by the shortage of long-term credit. Under the land reform they could not easily mortgage the land as loan security.

5. The present farm taxation system in Japan is rather reasonable, but we must be sure that it will stay that way.

6. We must take urgent measures to prevent the ill-effects of the inheritance provision of the new constitution. If the provision is left unchanged, the land of Japan will be even more fragmented than it is now.

7. Land reclamation is one of our major problems. We have been encouraging reclamation for two purposes: to give employment to repatriates and to enlarge the acreage under cultivation. In five years after World War II, Japan reclaimed 961,000 acres, established 130,000 new farm households, and enabled 500,000 farmers to enlarge their holdings.

8. The problem we are most concerned with is to decrease the farm population through industrialization and emigration, if possible. The birth rate in the villages is high—higher than in the urban centers. The villages are badly in need of a source of alternative occupations. Birth control is absolutely necessary to prevent further population increase, but this cannot decrease the already existing huge farm population.

In conclusion, let me say that without underestimating the great importance of the land reforms, much more must be done in the field of agricultural economy in order to insure for the farmer a good measure of economic stability.

LAND REFORM IN JAPAN: A COMMENT

Wolf I. Ladejinsky

I wish to devote the next twenty minutes or so to an elaboration of some of the points made by the previous speaker, Mr. Owada. He has sketched for you the agricultural conditions prevailing in Japan before the war, the cause underlying the need for a land reform, the main provisions of the reform program, and some of its consequences. For my part, I should like to begin by telling you why so profound an agrarian revolution was carried out peacefully, without bloodshed or damage to property. There are a number of reasons why

the shift of ownership of land from the "haves" to the "have nots," within a period of not quite three years, was not accompanied by any revolutionary upheaval. This is particularly significant, considering the fact that the great majority of the landlords were staunchly opposed to a program which compelled them to sell the land at very low prices. How, then, was this opposition overcome?

The doctrine of absolute obedience to authority is accepted unquestioningly by Japanese society—and the landlords were no exception. The American Occupation has been the main source of authority; the spokesman of that authority was General Douglas MacArthur, and the strong support of a land reform insured its acceptance.

General MacArthur was unstinting in his efforts to bring about a condition as a result of which "those who cultivate the soil of Japan shall enjoy the fruits of their labor." He understood that bringing even a semblance of democracy to Japan, and cutting the political ground from under the feet of the Communists, depended upon the improvement of the lot of those who worked the land. He knew that there was no point preaching democracy on an empty stomach.

It would be difficult to overestimate the position taken by the Occupation, but I must point out that even General MacArthur's authority could not have altered the traditional land structure if conditions had not been ripe for the move. More specifically, the land reform idea was a Japanese idea, rather than one imposed by the conqueror upon the conquered. As Mr. Owada pointed out, throughout the 1920's and the 1930's the Japanese had made numerous efforts, albeit unsuccessful, to carry out some kind of a reform that would enable the tenants to acquire the landlords' land. The seething unrest and discontent among the poverty-stricken Japanese farmers caused the various governments to give the problem some thought. You may be surprised to learn that some of the most blatant militarists of Japan were anxious to set the country's agricultural house in order. Thus, the Minister of War, General Araki, stated in 1938 that inasmuch as Japan's army is a peasant army, and inasmuch as a strong army must be a contented army, peasant ownership of land is the prime prerequisite. Of course, the forces opposing any change in the status quo were too strong, and nothing much was done about a land redistribution program or any other program that

might have eased the lot of the working farmer of Japan. But the conditions demanding a change were there, and the Occupation was the midwife, as it were, to a reform which was long overdue.

The tenant-union movement in Japan was very strong and it contributed greatly to the implementation of the program.

The Japanese landlords followed carefully the deliberations of the Four Power Allied Council in Japan. The Soviet representatives demanded an agrarian reform in the usual Soviet style. The landlords, therefore, accepted more readily a program shaped without the benefit of Russian guidance, even though such a program would not have been acceptable to them under normal conditions. In short, the attitude of the Russians was yet another factor that helped to overcome the opposition.

Surprising though it may seem to a Westerner, there were a few landlords in Japan who did understand that reform was overdue and supported it by deed. This attitude was well expressed by a landlord who told me that "it is high time that we landlords step one down and the tenants step one up, so that the two may meet for the first time." This is the type of uneconomic man in Japan who accepted a program which certainly did not benefit him on economic, political and social grounds.

Another factor worth mentioning is that during the war the Japanese government was most anxious about securing as ample a food supply as possible. In order to achieve that it sought to improve the economic conditions of the tenants who cultivated half of the land of Japan. The net result was a price system for agricultural products which discriminated in favor of the tenant as against the landlord. The freezing of rents prior to the end of the war was yet another element which made landlord ownership of land less profitable than in the past.

Finally, I must call your attention to the fact that 95 per cent of the Japanese people read and write. This applies to the farmers as well. This factor of literacy goes a long way to explain the remarkable technical progress of Japanese agriculture despite the seemingly meager means of production; it explains also why the tenants of Japan were able to grasp the main provisions of the reform legislation. Those who are familiar with the latter know that only clever lawyers can find their way through the maze of laws, ordinances, and amendments to the amendments. Yet the excellent work of popularization done by the Japanese Ministry of Agriculture, coupled with the literacy of the farmers, played a great role in the successful application of the program.

Such, in the main, are the elements, which, taken together, made possible the realization of the reform. But how relevant are these same elements to a consideration of land reform programs in Southeast Asia, the Middle East, and in Latin America? The answer, I am afraid, is in the negative. With but few exceptions, such as India, for example, I do not know of any powerful leaders in those parts of the world deeply concerned with the land and the farmer on the land, of tenant unions lending their support to the cause, of uneconomic men rising above their personal interest, of a literate peasantry, etc. Above all, the zeal to deal with the problem with the seriousness it deserves is the exception rather than the rule. Yet, I submit that if and when the talking stage of land reform will give way to that of action, then some of the Japanese experience is worth the most careful consideration, particularly on the part of those countries where the population pressure on the land is great and alternative sources of occupation are lacking. The experience I have in mind relates to the purchase of the land by the government, to price, and to the method of administering the program.

Mr. Owada has stated that it was the government that bought the land from the landlords and in turn resold it to the tenants. In these all-important matters there was no direct contact between the landlords and the tenants. This procedure rests on past experience, which shows that where land is at premium and the economic and political power of the landlords is strong the bargaining position of the tenant vis-a-vis the landlord is so weak that an agreement can be reached only on the landlords' terms. The two decades of Japanese paper reforms prior to World War II amply demonstrates this point. The same results will obtain in many other countries of Asia if the purchase transactions are to be left in the hands of the landlord and tenant.

Another point which has relevance to many another country is that unless the landlord is compelled by law to sell the land and at a fixed price no land reform that would really benefit the farmer can be carried out. The reason why all Japanese tenancy measures were frustrated in the past was that the price of land was left to negotiations between landlord and tenant and that when the former was willing to sell land the transaction was on his own terms only. In the long run this meant prohibitive prices—and no sales. I am not at all suggesting that the Japanese price formula, operating as it did under highly inflationary conditions, is worth emulating. Each country will have to devise its own yardstick, but in doing that it is well to keep in mind the following points.

(1) No tenant of Asia is in a position to pay for the land the prevailing market price, especially where the pressure on the land is great; if he were, there would be no need for a land reform. The price must be fixed with the view of enabling the tenants to acquire the land, just as a given program should be drafted with an eye to benefit those who actually till the soil.

(2) The land reform program should provide for the compulsory sale of land in a volume sufficient to satisfy the basic land needs of the tenantry. It is my belief that these principles which are part and parcel of the Japanese land reform legislation can very well apply in other parts of Asia.

Mr. Owada has mentioned the great role played by the land commissions in carrying out the reform. I would like to underscore the fact that but for this truly grass roots activity on the part of the local land commissions only a minor part of the program would have been carried out. The duties performed by the commissions have given rise to a form of adult education and new leadership, the significance of which would be hard to overestimate. Farm tenant members of the land commissions who were obviously ill at ease and insecure in their new posts in early 1947 were seasoned performers in 1949. The very creation of the commissions afforded all the adult farm population, tenants as well as owners, an opportunity to vote on a matter of utmost concern to all elements of the village. At the same time, the composition of the commissions proclaimed the fact that the tenants' interests were to be protected by the tenants themselves, rather than by someone acting on their behalf within the traditional pattern of rural Japan. Approximately 150,-000 or more people received new leadership training, and probably a good half of them were from the farm tenant group. The pre-reform arguments that only the landlords could exercise leadership, make the decisions, and administer proved baseless. This may prove equally baseless in other countries once the farmers themselves are called upon to administer the program at the level that really matters, namely the village level.

Mr. Owada has touched upon some of the consequences of the reform in Japan. I wish to add a few words on this very important subject of economic, social, and political benefits derived from this shift in ownership. It will take a good deal more time before the economic consequences can be measured statistically. All one can say in the meantime is that because the average holding of new owners is not more than two acres, and in most cases only half of that, the reform cannot solve all their problems. On the other hand, it will surely alleviate the burdensome conditions of the past, as well as forestall the inequities that feed on them. The important thing is that they acquired the one thing the farmers the world over want most: a piece of land of their own. I don't know what economic value one attaches to this factor, to this newly-gained incentive to improve the land in every way possible. If the famous English agriculturist Arthur Young was right in saying that "the magic of property [ownership of land] turns sand into gold" —and I believe he was—then the new owners of land in Japan stand in a good way of bettering their economic status within, of course, the great limitation imposed by one- or two-acre holdings.

On the social side, the reform has narrowed down the traditional differences between classes in the village. One doesn't have to be an economic determinist to appreciate the fact that when the Japanese landlords lost much of their affluence they also lost much of their influence. It would be a mistake, however, to assume that their place in rural Japan has been completely undermined. Fortunately, the Japanese land reform didn't displace one class and put in its place another. What is taking place now is the sharing of power between the old and the new leadership. Both are meeting now on the agricultural committees, co-operative and school boards, and in village offices. They rub elbows, dealing with common problems. Here lies the hope of new leadership and the idea of citizenship rights—

both foreign to pre-reform Japan. I should also add this: along with the ownership of land spread among the multitude of farmers is the foundation of a more satisfying rural life and the beginning of political and social democracy.

I would like to call the attention of the delegates to the political consequences of the land reform in Japan. Much thought was given to this matter, since the drafters of the legislation were cognizant of the need to insure political stability in the countryside and to prevent the Communists from getting a foothold there. I am happy to say that the results justified the most optimistic expectations. The Communists of Japan tried hard to exploit the agrarian difficulties of the country and to use them as a base from which they would infiltrate the entire Japanese economy. However, in opposing the program on the ground that it was just another capitalistic device to enslave the farmers, they lost all popular support in the rural districts. By strengthening the principle of private property where it was weakest, i.e., at the base of the social pyramid, the reform has created a huge class of staunch opponents of the Communist ideology. Even the landlords who carried the financial burdens of the reform frankly admit that. By multiplying the number of independent land-owning peasants, there came into being a middle-of-the-road, stable rural society and a barrier against political extremism. Recent elections to the agricultural commissions throughout Japan show that the Communist vote is only .3 per cent of all the votes cast. It is fair to conclude that the agrarian reform has taken the wind out of the political sails of the Communists. In judging the results of the reform and the sacrifices the reform imposed upon the landlords, particularly under the impact of the inflationary period of 1947/48, it is well to keep the over-all purposes of the reform in mind.

Before I conclude my comments on Mr. Owada's paper, I wish to touch once again upon the political issues as they relate to a land reform program. From the papers and talks with the delegates I gathered the impression that an inordinate amount of emphasis is placed on the technical difficulties which accompany the formulation and the implementation of a land reform program. The existence of such problems is undeniable, but they are not insurmountable. A careful study of the experience in Japan, Formosa, and India should help to minimize the technical difficulties. But in the long run, there is no ready-made formula equally applicable to the Middle East and Latin America, for example, or even to individual countries within a given region. Each country must approach the problem of reform in its own way and learn from experience, buttressed of course by the knowledge of the successes and failures of those already engaged in such enterprises. My own experience in Asia leads me to the conclusion that the real agrarian reform difficulties are political or ideological, if you will, rather than technical. More concretely, in many a country land reform is overdue not because of lack of knowledge as to how to go about it but because the powers that be have no interest in programs of that kind and are wedded to the status quo. This is certainly true of many parts of Asia, including the Middle East—areas with which I am familiar. The tendency there is to wait until it is too late, and it is against this state of affairs that we must speak out.

In agrarian countries the cultivator of the soil must be placed "in the center of the peace." No government can count on popular support without the peasant support; it is that or no support at all. The Communists are aware of it, and have therefore placed the land question with the slogan of "land for the landless," in the center of Asian politics. The Communists are masters at exploiting agrarian discontent for their own political ends. This was their main weapon of seizing power in Russia, and this is the manner in which the Chinese Communists defeated the Nationalist government in China. The lessons of this strategy should be all too clear to the non-Communist regimes. This is not the case, unfortunately. The tendency to maintain the status quo in the face of the Communist exploitation of the peasants' hunger for landownership is still overwhelming. In effect this means that the anti-reform landlords and governments play into the hands of the Communists, they become their unwilling allies and the creators of a revolutionary situation from which only the Communists stand to benefit. I wish to conclude, therefore, by saying that whatever else we do at this conference, the delegates might very profitably carry home the message that if land reforms to improve the welfare of the peasants are not initiated before it is too late and from above, i.e., by those who have the land and the political power, then they, the Communists, will do it for them. In that event, much more will be lost than the landlords' land.

Part VIII   AFRICAN LAND TENURES

OPENING REMARKS BY THE CHAIRMAN

Daniel A. Chapman

WE HAVE MET here this morning to consider African land tenure problems in relation to the social and economic development of African peoples. In other words, what can be done about the systems of land holding and land use in Africa in order to build up healthy, happy, and prosperous communities in that continent? This is indeed an appropriate subject for study in a world conference such as this. The happiness and prosperity of African communities should be a matter of interest to the rest of the world. Africa supplies the rest of the world with valuable raw materials from her farms, forests, and mines; Africa furnishes markets for foreign imports; and people from other parts of the world come to make permanent homes in Africa or to stay only for a while. In war no less than in peace, the world has demanded much of Africa. Africa, indeed, is a dark continent only to those who shut their eyes when they turn to the continent. Professor Herskovits is here to present to you a general background of the subject before you.

I have been thinking about Professor Herskovits for several days. What shall I say about him? In a sense, I hold him and one other person in special esteem. That other person is Professor Westermann of the University of Berlin, the author of the book *The African Today and Tomorrow.* Now, there are several reasons why I am very happy to introduce Professor Herskovits. First, he is a man who is keenly interested in the study of African communities, so to speak, of the anatomy and physiology of African societies. But, as I was telling him this morning, he refuses to go a step further and to act as a doctor to prescribe a cure for our social ills. He will tell you how African societies operate, but he prefers to leave you to decide on what to do if you find any diseases therein. Apart from his own interest in Africa and in Africans in Africa, he has taken a keen interest in the peoples of African descent found in the new world and in the Caribbean region. Professor Herskovits has also built up a great school of anthropology at Northwestern University, and from there he has sent out students not only to Africa but also to other parts of the world. We have among us today one of his students who has just come back from the Gold Coast, where he has worked in my wife's home area; we will probably ask him to say a few words during our discussion. To me, however, it is a matter of regret that there are not enough Africans here at this conference; because we do have in Africa today a number of well educated and competent Africans who are able to present our land tenure problems before you, to exchange views with you, and to see what we can learn from the experience of other countries, especially from the experience of this country, the United States. Here in this country, you have all the climates of the world except the equatorial. You have a great variety of problems some of which we have in common with you. Besides, you have 15 million of our own people living among you here.

Well, Dr. Herskovits has not only studied African problems himself and also sent his students from here to Africa to engage in research; he has also brought Africans here or assisted them to come here to study and to widen their horizon. For all these things I am very happy indeed to introduce him to you.

SOME PROBLEMS OF LAND TENURE IN CONTEMPORARY AFRICA[1]

𝕊𝕊𝕊𝕊 *Melville J. Herskovits*

THE TOPIC that has been assigned to me is a formidable one. The immensity of the region involved, the size of its populations, the degree of variation in the customs of its peoples, the differences to be discerned in the types of contact with other societies that has marked its historic experience, and the varied responses to that contact—all these make up a body of materials as vast as it is complex.

This holds true even when we limit our area to Africa south of the Sahara, as we must do if we are to have even a minimal measure of unity in our subject matter. For North Africa, important though it may be, is ethnically, historically, linguistically, and culturally far more related to the Near and Middle East and to Southern Europe than it is to the bulk of the African continent. To the scientist who must phrase his problems in terms of functional relationships, Africa south of the Sahara is thus less heterogeneous, and permits of the analysis of particular problems in terms of the unities that underlie the differences.

At the outset, I should like to consider as background for our discussion some of the basic assumptions that will mark this treatment. I shall next try to describe the background of pre-contract land use before indicating, very briefly, the different experiences of the Africans in various parts of the sub-Saharan continent under contact with foreign modes of life. I shall then move on to sketch some problems in the control and use of the land that press for solution at the present time and, finally, touch on the troubled question of changing land use as this relates to problems of the morale of the indigenous population.

My basic assumptions may be phrased as two propositions with which you may already be familiar but which, in approaching any problem of moment where human life is involved and where modes of human living, particularly changing modes of human living, are concerned, cannot too often be made explicit.

In the first place, it is impossible to grasp the full significance of any situation without some understanding of the pre-existing historical matrix out of which it has developed. In the face of present-day pressures, and because of the urgency of the problems we face, we too often tend to forget that the questions we are attempting to solve have roots that go deep into the past. It follows, then, that any approach to a practical problem which ignores its historical setting will to that extent be unsatisfactory, while any solution proposed in such circumstances will of necessity fail to have valid perspective.

In the second place, the force of preexisting custom must always be recognized and, especially where external pressure for new modes of life is being exerted on a people, must be given full accounting. If this is not done, not only will we run the risk of proposing remedies that are unrealistic and unworkable but we may also institute programs that are dangerous or demoralizing. In the case of Africa, it is patricularly important to keep this constantly in mind. It is ironic that the Africans, not politically free agents in most of the continent, are presumed by many persons to be passive in the situations that affect them. This is exemplified by the fact that proposals for change have perhaps nowhere else been drawn so unilaterally and with so little consultation of the people most concerned.

It seems to have made little difference in this regard whether plans drawn with the utmost care by the most competent technicians and with the best of good will by Colonial governments, United Nations agencies, or by a neutral country such as the United States are considered. In all these instances, only what was to be done *for* or *to* the African has been set forth, while the reactions of the Africans or the degree to which a proposed solution might or might not be in line with their pre-established ways of life have been ignored. It is true that this latter factor is beginning to be taken into account, probably because of the failure of various plans that were drawn up without taking the force of pre-existing custom into account. It is to be hoped that these indications are correct, that we are learning, even if we are learning the hard way, the fact that the ways of life of a people present a body of imponderables that must be continuously taken into account by those who would bring about change in any phase of their life. Certainly the lesson has by no means been learned as well as it must be. And this is why it must continuously be stressed that where the force of these imponderables is not a major factor in planning, solutions will be unrealistic, at best unworkable, where they are not positively harmful.

We may, then, in the light of the propositions that have been advanced, proceed to examine the background of indigenous African civilization against which any attempt to introduce changes in the area of our interest here—land-use—must be projected. Yet the nature of the problem of land-use dictates that we must take the ecological as well as the cultural factor into account. Hence, even though I will in this discussion stress the human factor and take it for granted that specialists, such as yourselves, are informed as to the ecological component in the situation, I may be permitted to recall to you something of the natural setting of Africa.

Looking at a relief map of the continent, it becomes apparent that Africa is something like an inverted dinner plate. With two exceptions, in Italian Somaliland and on the west coast, the continent is ringed by a coastal plain, behind which a series of elevations rise abruptly. Sometimes, as in the west, these are reduced to hills, but elsewhere, as in the Cameroons and in East Africa, they take the form of great mountain masses. Whether accentuated or not, they must be negotiated before the interior plateau is reached. This is why the rivers descend to the sea in a series of cataracts or waterfalls, a fact that has made entry into the continent by water routes so difficult and that constitutes the reason so often given for the supposedly long isolation of Africa from the rest of the world.

In truth, however, Africa has not been isolated from the rest of the world, for the idea is no more than a reflection of the fact that European contact with Africa, which was by sea, was relatively late and that the penetration of Africa by Europeans from the seacoast proved to be so difficult an undertaking. The fact of the matter is that the contacts of Africa south of the Sahara with Northern Africa and the Near East have been continuous and close, while communication with the rest of the Old World has not been lacking. It is interesting to realize that what is called Morocco leather in Europe is named not for its source of origin but for its point of introduction into Europe—Morocco! It was brought to Morocco, however, across the Sahara from the south where, in northern Nigeria, it is still made for export to the north. Nor should we forget that coastal Africans have for centuries been in contact with the seafarers of Europe, since the earliest period of European expansion in the fifteenth century.

The amount of high bush, or what is called jungle, is relatively slight in Africa. We do not know its exact extent, but it is certainly not as extensive as thought by those who are not acquainted with the geography of the continent. In eastern Africa, in much of the Congo basin, away from the rivers, and in other regions, open land predominates. East Africa is one of the great grazing areas of the world. The Congo basin was not grazed because of the presence of the tsetse fly; rather its open country was used for agriculture, and has for untold years supported a considerable population. Western Africa also is predominantly agricultural; the size of its aboriginal population has from earliest days of European contact impressed those who visited it. There were cities in western Africa, predating European control, with populations of 250,000 to 300,000 and many communities comprising twenty, thirty, forty thousand persons or more.

One of the major problems of Africa derives from the character of the soil, much of which is of poor quality and thus difficult to work. The heavy tropical rains tend to leach out much of its valuable chemical contents if the land is exposed to them, this being one of the principal reasons why many of the projects for large-scale farming operations in Africa have not been as successful as those who laid them

out without testing the qualities and capacities of the soil had hoped they would be. The shifting cultivation of the natives permits the forest to protect the soil, preserving its ability to yield crops and inhibiting the kind of erosion we know to be so great a danger to world food resources. Here, indeed, we have an example of the importance in introducing new forms of cultivation into Africa or any other region of the world of giving the most careful consideration to any pre-existing ecological balance that has been achieved between the population and the land on which it lives. One will have to think many times before disturbing that balance if one is not to waste much of the potential productivity of Africa or other areas, if one is to develop those potentialities in terms that will utilize rather than destroy the capacities of the land.

Figure 1, Cultural Areas of Africa, is a map which is not ordinarily seen except by anthropologists but which gives a basis for considering the human, or cultural, factor when seeking to understand the problems of the continent. It is what we call technically a culture-area map; it indicates the manner in which the indigenous cultures of the continent may be classified in terms of the characteristic modes of life of their inhabitants, ways that must be reckoned with in any over-all planning. In a sense, these regional divisions may be taken as broadly representing different responses to the background of the natural environment. The divisions with which we here will be most concerned are the East African cattle area, the Congo basin, the Guinea Coast, and the Western Sudan.

The regions which are marked Hottentot and Bushman represent areas in terms of cultures as they existed in the days before European control. The Hottentot and Bushman peoples do still exist, but the experiences that they have had at the hands of an expanding frontier in South Africa

FIG. 1—CULTURE AREAS OF
          AFRICA

have not been hospitable to the continuation of their ways of life. Most of those who survived the shock of contact with Europeans have been driven back into the less desirable parts of their aboriginal territory —in the case of the Bushmen, into the least livable portions of the Kalahari Desert, a desert that in some places puts the Sahara to shame.

What a culture-area map really represents is an expression of the broad differences found in the modes of life of the people in different parts of a major world area. Thus in East Africa, for example, if we take

land-use as our point of departure, agriculture provides subsistence. Yet from the viewpoint of its subsistence economy, East Africa has a very simple system. The various local groups are self-supporting; none of the great markets found in other parts of the continent are present; there was no money in the sense of the cowrie shell or the bars of salt or the other least common denominators of value found in other parts of the continent. The groups were small in size and economically self-sufficient. The agricultural work was carried on in terms of patterns that are found over most of

Africa, whereby the hard labor of clearing the land is done by men, the women thereafter preparing the soil, planting, cultivating, and reaping. The men were occupied with other matters, particularly with their cattle, and it is from this fact that we come upon an apt illustration of the difficulties inherent in trying to apply new criteria of value and usage to an area where these values and usages have been re-established.

You may notice that, on our culture-area map of Africa, the region we are discussing is named the East African Cattle Area. This is not because cattle are or were the most important factor in the subsistence economy of these people. In most of the area there would be as much reluctance to slaughter a cow for food as a European would have to light a cigarette with a bill of high denomination. Cattle were not money, but without them a person could have no position in society and his prestige would be nil. Cattle, as a matter of fact, though outstandingly important in the economy, functioned in what I like to think of as the prestige economy, as against the subsistence economy. It is scarcely necessary to point to the relevance of this position of cattle in the culture of the East Africans for plans to make of their country a great world food reservoir by exploiting the potentialities of the grazing land. The land will support the cattle, but the people will not raise them for slaughter.

If we contrast this picture with that of the Congo basin, the Guinea Coast, and the Western Sudan the difference is striking. Populations are larger, with settled communities, highly integrated political systems, and a considerable specialization of labor. It is from the Congo, West Africa, and the Sudan that the great works of wood carving, brass casting, and ivory carving which have taken so important a place in the world of art have been derived. It is in this area that one finds the weavers, the iron workers, the traders, all of whom are specialists in the European sense of the word. If, indeed, I were to compare the cultures of these areas with something in the historical background of Europe, I should say that they could best be thought of in terms of the feudal scene. The functioning of these specialists is and has been furthered by the presence of a money economy, which means that the exchanges of goods and payment of services necessitated by a complex culture and a dense population were facilitated.

It must be understood that underlying these differences in the cultures of Africa are certain basic unities and that it would throw our discussion out of perspective if we stressed the differences to the neglect of these similarities. Thus in all Africa, so far as it is possible to determine, one finds group control and discipline at a very high level. Even among the peoples where one would not expect this, as where herding makes for a nomadic way of life, the controls are nevertheless present, based on well-established principles that arise out of the relationship between the people and the political institutions that they have set up in their historic experience for their own governing. There is one point I should like to make here as pertinent in this connection. Too often in discussing the ways of life of non-European peoples who do not have written languages the word "custom" tends to be used to denote these regulatory devices rather than the term "law." As far as I can see, this is not a helpful usage. It is true that where there is no writing, custom is law; but custom is also law where there is writing, if those of us who live in literate societies consider some of the most effective controls over our own behavior, while it is notorious that to the degree, among ourselves, that where a law is not in accord with custom its effectiveness tends to be nullified.

A second unity that, though in a measure

present in all human society, marks Africa particularly is the degree to which there are units that effectively function in terms of the co-operative principles. The degree of co-operation in African life is outstanding. It varies from the age-groups of young men who came together under a leader to herd cattle in East Africa to the co-operative agricultural work-associations found in West Africa and the Congo. These co-operative groups, furthermore, are marked by their institutional status. They are not casual, not just a group of persons who come together to do something. They are the members of a community who work at specific tasks under the direction of a responsible leader, this factor of responsible leadership going back to the point of group control and discipline I have already stated to be so characteristic of the civilizations of Africa.

Another factor of importance in all the continent that must be taken into account in dealing with Africans, and which certainly must enter into the discussion of the tenure problems and land-use in other parts of the world, is the role of the supernatural. It may seem curious to inject this note here, but I submit that in any civilization where a cult of the ancestors, for example, dictates the reasons why people are devoted to their land, this element in their belief-system is crucial if proposals to introduce changes in the holding or use of the land go beyond narrow technical considerations and are to achieve any measure of co-operation. Certainly, in Africa, the relationship between a given group and the deities believed to control the land plus the ancestors who are attached to the particular plots where they lived is absolutely critical. As a matter of fact, religion is so close to the daily life of the African that it is unrealistic to move into any aspect of his existence without taking this into account.

Though difficult to describe, a fourth

point that marks the African is agreed on by students of African societies and by Africans themselves who have trained themselves to look objectively at their own culture as a very real factor in African life. This is what I have come to call psychological resilience and adaptability, something that, though intangible, must be taken into account in any kind of planning, on any level. What do I mean by this intangible factor? There are certain people who, when presented with the need to change in their way of life, find adaptation of the greatest difficulty. They become demoralized, lost in a situation that is too much for them. That, for example, partially explains why contact in the United States with Europeans resulted in the extinction of many American Indian tribes and the demoralization of most others. The American Indian tends to be less resilient, less adaptable, when presented with a new situation than the African who, on the contrary, everywhere tends to adjust to new orientations. One of the reasons he is able to do this is because of the nature of the contacts, both friendly and hostile, between peoples over the vast African continent that continuously occurred before the Europeans arrived. Today, one of the reasons why the changes in the mode of life of Africans have such a dynamic quality is that the interest of the Africans themselves in taking over what seems to them beneficial in Euro-American cultures. They are convinced that, in this way, they can achieve ends that will gain for them the advantages other people have gained through technical development and a command of the intellectual resources that have enriched the material life of those from whom they are learning.

The contact of Africans with Europeans has differed considerably from area to area. The case of South Africa is a special one. Here the contact that has existed since the seventeenth century has been of a dual nature. The initial settlement, known today as Cape Town, was dominated by the English; later, people of Netherlands extraction moved in. These were the Boers, or, as they prefer to be called today, the Afrikaaners. Thus a particular kind of control was superimposed upon the various cultural groups, including the Hottentot and Bushmen, in addition to the Bantu to the east. It is scarcely necessary to repeat the tale of how the Boers refused to accept English sovereignty; how they embarked on their great trek, moving northward to found their own state; how this eventually resulted in the formation of the present Dominion. What concerns us here is the fact that this historical sequence of events has resulted in the present-day situation in South Africa which, as far as problems of human adjustment are concerned, makes that country one of the most difficult spots on earth.

It is well for us to remember, however, that in South Africa this development is not entirely unlike certain aspects of the history of the Americas. In South Africa the results, as far as the indigenous population is concerned, are different from what happened to the Indian peoples of the United States. This arises primarily from the fact that whereas aboriginally the part of North America which became the United States was sparsely settled, the native population of South Africa has always been appreciable in number. Today there are about 8 million native Africans there, as against 3 million persons of European origin, plus a considerable number of Indians. Certainly the fact is significant for an understanding of the problems of land use that in South Africa the large numbers of Europeans who settled there, taking over the best land for their own use, forced still larger bodies of Africans, who aboriginally had pastoral or nomadic economies, to exist on small tracts,

thus creating the difficult problems of the reserve that now are so pressing in the Union.

In Eastern Africa—that is, along the east coast—and in the coastal region of much of West Africa, particularly in Nigeria, the Gold Coast, and the Gambia, contacts which were primarily with England in the early days took the form of trade. Rule by the English frequently resulted from treaties made with chiefs, which established protectorates that in most cases actually or in effect became colonies. However, in British Africa alone the situation varies from one marked by the tensions that have arisen from the contact with white settlers in the East to that in the Gold Coast and Nigeria, colonies which have moved far along the road to effective self-government.

In those parts of west and equatorial Africa where France is the ruling power a different pattern of development has prevailed. Here policy has been dictated by the desire to make French citizens of the leaders of the areas, resulting in a situation quite different from that in British Africa. The enormous area of the Belgian Congo with its great mineral resources similarly represents a development and policy peculiar to it. We cannot here go into the story of the Congo Free State and how the controls of earlier days have since been changed in the interest of more effective utilization of its human and natural potentialities. Nor can we do more than point to the special problems of the great Portuguese territories of Angola and of Mozambique (Portuguese East Africa). Here the pattern is again different, both in the way in which controls were introduced and in the nature of their present form, especially as this affects land tenure and the use of land and manpower.

The significance of an understanding of native cultures and the contacts they have had with European powers for those concerned with land use becomes apparent when we realize that about three-fourths of the population of Africa is dependent upon agriculture. The problems regarding the control and use of land at the present time are thus particularly pressing. These problems take various forms. One has to do with attempts to resolve the question of the pressure of population on the land by the development of irrigation projects and through land allotments. Two of these which have achieved some measure of success may be mentioned—the Gezira project on the upper Nile and that of the French in the Middle Niger. Both aim at making it possible for the natives to have a more stable internal economy while producing cash crops for the world market. In the Anglo-Egyptian Sudan, where many of the farmers have come in from other areas, the problem of land allotment is, however, far less difficult than where a people are living on ancestral land, in terms of their existing culture, especially where that land is traditionally under the control of the chief who allots it as representative of the people.

One of the growing problems of modern Africa is that of mechanized agriculture and the rural wage worker since, with the development of industry, various plantation schemes are coming more and more into competition in the labor market with those newer enterprises. This is not only the case where the wage workers in the mines of South Africa, the Katanga region of the Belgian Congo, Northern Rhodesia, Nigeria, or the Gold Coast are involved. In Liberia, for example, the Firestone plantations are now competing with the mining operations of the Republic Steel Corporation for available workers. Or, again, in Portuguese territory and in the Belgian Congo the sisal, cotton, and coffee plantations are drawing labor into a different kind of competition where large-scale agriculture competes with the traditional family garden. Population pressure where native peoples

in East and South Africa, as already mentioned, have been segregated on reserves presents another problem. On these reserves, the increase in population has caused the land to be intensively utilized for growing food and raising herds, which in turn leads to ever-increasing demands on soil that result in serious erosion. Thus here we see in some areas the beginning and in others the completion of the dreary cycle of land destruction that we are coming to know so well over the world.

This brings us to another problem that Africa presents in common with all colonial areas—that of the cash crops versus subsistence cultivation. It is already of moment in such territories as Uganda, where great emphasis has been laid on the production of cotton and other cash crops; here the growing of both cash and subsistence crops is being encouraged by government action. In the Gold Coast, the problem of the cocoa trees that have been attacked by the swollen shoot disease has raised many economic, social, and, through repercussions, political questions that would not have presented themselves if there had been a greater degree of crop diversification. One of the ways in which a more adequate utilization of land can be achieved, however, is through co-operative efforts, which permit the transfer of a deep-seated pattern of African cultures to the present-day scene. No better example of this is to be had than can be found precisely in the Gold Coast, where the co-operatives of native cocoa growers have long functioned effectively. Similar co-operatives are also found elsewhere, and, on the basis of traditional usage, can be further expanded in terms of modern developments.

Actually in Africa many populations are moving at present from group ownership of land, whereby portions of tribal holdings are alloted for individual or family use by the recognized authority, usually the chief or king, to individual ownership. There is a corresponding movement, as regards land tenure, toward a modification of sanctions that are wholly supernatural, so that secular as well as religious sanctions come into play, or in which secular factors bulk large. In terms of the nascent nationalities in Africa, furthermore, the fact that an individual of Nigeria thinks of himself as a Nigerian as well as a Yoruba or that an inhabitant of the Gold Coast will speak of himself as a citizen of the Gold Coast as well as indicate that he is a Fanti or an Ashanti is also indicative of the growing pressures consequent on the movement from internal tribal to external multi-tribal or foreign political controls.

We are faced, then, in Africa as elsewhere, with the problem of the relationship of changing patterns of land tenure to social disorganization. For when the accepted modes of holding land are broken, all existing institutions of society are to some degree affected. The family, the clan, the local grouping cannot function as it did under the old system. Too often, moreover, this kind of disintegration of social institutions is followed by psychological demoralization. Thus one of the greatest problems in Africa today is how to encourage the African, how to have Africans encourage other Africans to utilize their resources to the best advantage in ways that will not be at conflict with pre-existing beliefs and sanctions but that will at the same time make available to the world the resources of Africa and to Africa the resources of the world.

SOME PROBLEMS OF LAND TENURE IN CONTEMPORARY AFRICA: A COMMENT

William Bascom

I WOULD LIKE to go back to one of the early points made by Professor Herskovits, one which I think is a basic one. This is that in planning with regard to Africa, the European powers tend to approach it almost as an area in vacuum and to think that the decisions can be made by themselves. Africa is, of course, one of the great so-called underdeveloped areas of the world, and when anyone starts to think of its possibilities for development he may become over-enthusiastic. Here is a great continent, a great region for agriculture, with a large population that can serve as laborers. I have seen this frequently, even among people in our own government who have been thinking of what America could do in the way of developing Africa with the consent of the present colonial powers and with assumed consent of the Africans. If they are reminded that there are great deserts and that tropical jungles present difficulties for modern mechanization, their enthusiasm is not dampened. Let us take the richest part of the land, use the Africans as laborers, and develop modern farms using modern techniques.

This whole approach forgets completely that the Africans who are already there have rights and interests in their land. These are not only economic in nature but have their sanctions in religion, and have been the custom for untold centuries. The general pattern is that the land is held by communal groups of a political or a family type, with the land allocated to these groups on the basis of use. If any foreign government or any foreign power were to come in and take the land for modern development, even for the benefit of the Africans, it would mean that the people would be pushed off of it. For the success of any of these projects one thinks of taking the best land, which means that the Africans would be pushed to less desirable land or would be employed as wage laborers on these new projects. This type of thinking has a very long history, and both Africans and some Europeans who have been working in Africa have spoken out against it. For example, one French anthropologist working in French West Africa emphasized in his writings that there was no acre of land in Africa which was not owned by someone, no palm tree which was not the private property of some person. Africa is not a vacuum which can be occupied and developed. One has to think of the present rights of Africans and the patterns of land tenure as they have developed in the past in making any plans for development.

Actually several patterns have been followed in different parts of Africa in introducing new types of land tenure and the retention of the old types. In South Africa, as we have already seen, there was a true colonization on a large scale, with the result that the African peoples were pushed onto smaller and smaller reserves, paralleling in many ways our own reservation system for the American Indians. Here again, the new European settlers were obviously anxious to obtain the most fertile lands in South Africa, and its results have been most distressing for the Africans. This reserve pattern is not universal in Africa, however. It is found in the Union of South Africa, particularly in certain portions of it, but was not even universal throughout the whole Dominion.

In the early days there was another pattern which has by now largely disappeared, although there are still many important vestiges of it, and that is the concession system. It was developed by the Belgians in the Congo, by the French in Equatorial Africa, and by the Germans in the Cameroons in the last part of the last century shortly after the partitioning of Africa. Actually it came between the Berlin conference and the turn of the century, and I believe the idea for it probably goes back to the Belgian Free State and to the peculiar problems that it faced in financing the colony under the terms of the Berlin agreement. The general pattern was to give monopoly rights in huge tracts of land to private companies. These did not always involve an ownership of the land, but in any case the companies were given exclusive rights to buy and sell in the areas concerned. This technique was used primarily in the development of trade in rubber and ivory, and led to abuses which brought about later reforms. A company could set its own prices for rubber, and it could set its own prices for the goods that were being sold to the Africans. It had administrative power over the Africans, and physical violence was sometimes used to force the people to produce quotas of rubber or ivory which the company had set for them. At the end of the last century, the abuses of this system received international publicity and steps were made to change them, with Belgium taking over the Congo from King Leopold. Reform was also initiated in the German Cameroons and in Equatorial Africa, and during the course of years the size of the concessions has been reduced. On the other hand, it is still important in some areas where large areas are owned by private companies or jointly by the company and the government.

Another pattern which has been followed resulted in the alienation of land from African peoples is the plantation system, even though this is on a smaller scale than the concession system. A European farmer, for example, is given land to establish a banana or coffee plantation or a sisal plantation. He is either given freehold to the land by the government or a lease for a long enough period to give him security to justify investing in its development. This of course is the familiar pattern in East Africa, where it is particularly important. The European is the manager of the plantation, the entrepreneur, the employer of African labor, and the one who sets the policies and plans the whole working of the plantation. The African is simply hired wage labor, working for someone else on land that for centuries belonged to his ancestors.

A third pattern has been followed throughout most of West Africa, both British and French. Although plantations do exist, more so in the French colonies, they have been kept at a minimum. In the vast area of French West Africa alienation for freeholds to whites amounts to less than six hundred square miles; in the British West Africa colonies it is even less. In West Africa the pattern has been the development of production for export in the hands of African farmers. You find that all of the cocoa of the Gold Coast and Nigeria and almost all of the coconuts, palm oil and palm kernels, and groundnuts that are produced in this area are grown by African farmers who own their own land and who raise and sell their products to the European trading firms. Here the European acts as a middleman buying from the African and selling to Europe, while the African is the entrepreneur in agriculture. The pattern is of course different in the case of mining, where the management is European controlled and where Africans are used as wage laborers.

The differences between these patterns are important for the African and for his economic status. In West Africa there are really three alternatives between which the African has the free right of choice. If he wishes, he can stay on his land and support himself by subsistence farming. His African traditions provide him ways of building houses, of weavng cloth, and of supplying all the necessities of life. Even though these are regarded as inadequate by the educated African today, they made possible survival for thousands of years and they can still keep people alive at the present time. Secondly, he can go to work for wages in the mines, on the railroads, in government, or in private business. Thirdly, he has the alternative of producing export crops for sale. The latter two courses of action, wage labor and production of cash crops, provide him with money income with which to pay taxes and to buy European goods that he desires. As long as the African controls the land and has land on which he has the right to farm, he has a free choice between these three alternatives. Once the land is taken away from him, he loses the possibility of subsistence farming, and he loses the possibility of raising cash crops on his own. He is reduced to the one alternative of wage labor. He can work for Europeans or he can starve.

It is for this reason I think that the policies that have been adopted by different European powers are important for the whole problem of African economy, especially their policies with regard to land tenure and land alienation. One finds that these policies have not been consistent along national lines. The British in East and West Africa have followed quite different patterns. The French have followed different patterns in the Cameroons and French West Africa. But whatever the policy that has been followed, it has a fundamental influence upon the economic future and the very independence of the African. The introduction of the sale of land, which in many African societies was unknown before white contact, has also resulted in the alienation of land. Although it was done voluntarily the end result is the same, and again we can see parallels in the cases where

American Indians sold their land and then had no way to support themselves.

This is the one thing that I wish to bring out here. We must never lose sight of the fact that the land of Africa is owned by Africans and that it is idle and dangerous speculation for Americans to ask, "What shall *we* do to develop the continent of Africa?"

AGRARIAN REFORM AND ECONOMIC DEVELOPMENT

Edmundo Flores

WHEN THE strategy of the economic progress of underdeveloped areas is discussed, one of the first subjects considered is agrarian reform. The reasons for this are fairly evident. A program of social reform in a developed country may be achieved by resorting to such measures as new taxation systems, rationing, price control, nationalization of certain industries, subsidies to special activities, or similar measures which, in effect, imply a redistribution of income according to a given ideal of social justice. In the case of underdeveloped areas, agriculture is often the main, if not the sole, source of wealth, and ownership of land is the basis for the prevailing standard of income distribution; thus there is the inevitability of introducing changes in the land tenure pattern when contemplating any program of economic reorganization. However, land reform is nothing but the first step in an effective program of economic development; and the solution to an agrarian problem, even granting the accomplishment of an ideal land tenure pattern, ultimately has to be sought outside the field of agricultural economics.

Two sets of factors are responsible for this outcome. The first lies in the dynamics of agriculture, the second in the dependent role which agriculture has in modern production. The emergence of a problem concerning economic development or reform in an underdeveloped area implies both a defective resource utilization pattern and a markedly uneven standard of income distribution. Under these circumstances, population pressure tends to lower consumption to subsistence levels, while extreme differences in wealth prevent investment and the possibility of introducing improvements in productive techniques. A program of economic expansion can be initiated only through the structuration of a different resource utilization pattern in which activities other than agriculture need to be established in order to absorb population growth and to produce necessary capital and consumption goods. Only if alternative sources of employment are made available will it be possible to increase efficiency in agriculture, to accumulate food and raw materials for the nonagricultural population and for industrial needs, and to increase the standard of living and the purchasing power of the farmer.

As agricultural productivity increases, the need for industrial requisites—transports, farm machinery, chemical products, etc.—grows, and the strategic factor of expansion shifts from spatial limitations and lack of incentives due to institutional obstacles to scarcity of capital and lack of enterprise and technical know-how.

The experience of Mexico, first in agrarian reform and later in an all-around policy of economic development, illustrates the case. During the last four decades, Mexico has experienced the most extraordinary change in its social, political, and economic structure. The student of contemporary Mexico—whether sociologist, economist, artist, or political scientist—finds such an overwhelming display of new facts, trends, and institutions in such a rapid process of change as to almost defy analysis. The catalyst which set in motion this process of economic development was land reform.

Formerly an area of conspicuous political instability and social and economic inequality, contemporary Mexico devotes its energy to the consolidation and progress of its economy, to the welfare of its people, and to the development of a culture which reveals strong characteristics of its own.

Until a few years ago the main concern of economists and planners, either in research or on policy-making levels, centered around the application of the agrarian laws —readjustments in the land tenure pattern through the breaking up of large estates, opening of new lands, and resettlement of population. This stage reached its climax during the administration of President Lazaro Cardenas, 1935–40. At the same time a new approach to the solution of Mexico's economic development began to take shape, and the policy of land reform was followed by expropriation of the oil, nationalization of the railroads, and new legislation for the development of electrical industry, all of which meant a new economic policy which sought the development of the country's economy in a more integrated way.

The economic consequences of land redistribution need at least brief analysis. The one outstanding accomplishment of the agrarian reform was the destruction of the latifundio and with it the obstacles which acted against economic development. Although this was a substantial accomplishment, in essence it was a negative one. The problem still remained of building up a new agricultural economy which would substitute advantageously for the latifundia. Land redistribution as carried on in Mexico had to be followed immediately by the participation of the state as a managerial agent with financing, planning, and administrative responsibilities.

The initial aim of the agrarian reform was limited to the granting of a parcel of land to every adult Mexican. Besides that, there was not much else. An analysis in retrospect shows that this policy suffered from serious pitfalls in the form of static assumptions: neither population growth or changes in land use nor technical improvements or the possibility of new fields of economic activity were anticipated. To the well-known slogan of "land and freedom," one could add a motto implicit—"once a peasant, always a peasant." But there were dynamic forces which soon changed economic conditions to such an extent that economic policy had to widen its scope.

For purposes of analysis, these forces are classified into two groups. The first deals with population growth, the second with the induced effects of government expenditures and the effect of innovations over the general economy.

Before the agrarian revolution, population growth was checked by high mortality rates, malnutrition, an exceedingly low level of real income, and, in general, by adverse living conditions for the majority. Extreme differences in income distribution were a serious obstacle to investment. One of the immediate effects of land redistribution was the diversion of agricultural production (even granting a serious decrease in its volume) from the usual market channels to self-consumption. This factor, aided by some psychological elements, foremost among which was a feeling of security and freedom, had the immediate effect of a considerable increase in population. In order to counteract this increasing pressure of population against the traditionally available land resources, the government, thinking in terms of an agrarian economy, resorted to measures which were calculated to increase the land area with the aim of providing new land. The opening of new lands, mostly through communications and irrigation, brought with it a further increase in the rate of population growth due to accompanying measures of sanitation and to the increase in employment which was made possible by the construction of highways and dams.

Government expenditures on irrigation works and highways represented an effort at a high technical level which was accompanied by measures such as sanitation, supply of drinking water, medical services, widespread use of DDT, and other measures which decreased still further the mortality rate and thus accentuated population growth. In turn, the effect of government expenditures on public works increased employment and stimulated general economic activity.

When the land reform was initiated there was a flight of capital in search of security from agriculture to the cities. At first, most of this capital was invested in speculative ventures in urban real estate, but soon it was attracted to the construction industry and from there it gradually spread to other industrial branches. Thus a few years after land reform had diverted capital away from agriculture, the assistance of this capital was secured and utilized through the establishment of industries new to the country. The expansion of cities as well as the program of irrigation and communications stimulated the construction industries, while increased world demand for agricultural goods and strategic minerals gave an added impetus to production.

During the last fifteen years Mexico has witnessed important shifts of population in both the geographical and occupational sense. Urban growth has been spectacular, and the traditional seat of agriculture in the central area of the country has suffered a gradual displacement towards the north-ern areas, where irrigation has made possible high yields per unit of land and where productivity has increased considerably. Estimates concerning the percentage of active population engaged in agriculture show that while in 1940 65 per cent of the active population was engaged in agriculture in 1950 this percentage diminished to approximately 55 per cent. At the same time agricultural income increased from 17 per cent of the total national income in 1938 to 20 per cent in 1948. While national income increased 4.8 times in a decade, agricultural income increased 5.7 times. The average annual increase in agricultural production 1945–49 was 5.4, while the average annual increase in population amounted to 2.8. (Data from the *Dirección general de Estadistica;* estimate from the Bank of Mexico.)

This indicates that Mexican agriculture has entered a stage of development which, in the last analysis, represents the success of the policy pursued by the state during the last four decades. The latifundio has disappeared, land hunger has been satisfied, and a start has been made towards the creation of favorable conditions for efficient production and distribution of agricultural goods. The development of industry and services has opened alternative sources of employment which to some extent absorb population being displaced from agriculture and, at the same time, has led to the production of essential capital and consumption goods.

Four decades ago land reform was a vital issue to 95 per cent of the total population and the only way out from poverty and social inequality. At that time any attempt at social reform had to be formulated in terms of land. Today agricultural policy still constitutes an important tool for economic progress, but it has lost its overwhelming predominance. Ownership of land may be regarded still as a desirable goal, but the general well-being of the population and its economic and political freedom no longer have to be associated with this ideal and perhaps could be more aptly described if referred to real wages or to income levels.

This does not mean that the agricultural economy has ceased to present problems. On the contrary, as agriculture has entered this new stage, its complexity has increased considerably and its dependence on outside influences has been accentuated. Besides the familiar aspects of tenure, financing, and education, there are new and pressing problems of distribution, marketing, prices, and employment, as well as managerial and technical aspects which require study and solutions that cannot be improvised.

Mexico made its agrarian reform through a costly process of trial and error; many detours were necessary for lack of previous experience, and perhaps the results attained were meager when compared with the effort required. There is, however, one positive feature of the Mexican agrarian revolution which should not be forgotten. As other Indo-American countries enter the path of economic expansion, they will be faced by problems similar to those encountered in Mexico. At this juncture the Mexican experience will undoubtedly serve to keep them in the right course and will save them from some of the errors which we did not know how to avoid.

LAND TENURE PROBLEMS IN CHILE

José Ramón Astorga

HERE ARE some notes on the economic and social situation of agriculture in the Republic of Chile. There are also some references to her industrial problems. I am not going to read all of the paper, since you will have individual copies to consult.

This material has been gathered by national organizations of my country and by the Economic Committee for Latin America —CEDAL—of the United Nations. Many national and foreign technicians have collaborated. They have provided a documented and complete report of matters concerning the national economy in its population, agrarian, and industrial aspects. Chile with her natural resources of hydraulic power, copper, coal, nitrate, iron, and oil is aiming at a progressive industrialization.

I shall simply limit myself to reporting on certain problems derived from land tenure, summing up some studies or focusing on general aspects that are not specifically considered here.

It must be said that Chile is a country more than 4,000 kilometers long and, on the average, 190 kilometers wide and is located on the immense Cordillera of the Andes and bordered by the Pacific Ocean. It has varied climate ranging from the subtropical in the north to the antarctic in the south. That is why it presents a varied ecology, adequate for diversified agriculture but complicated because of its dissimilarities.

In the northern desert zone, agriculture is precarious because of the lack of water; there is no rainfall and irrigation is scarce. In the central zone, with good irrigated land, agriculture is bountiful. In the south-central zone, cereals and grasses are produced—a region of forests, lakes, and plains. In the Magellan zone there are grassy steppes where millions of sheep are raised.

Along the thousands of kilometers of coast, the country has abundant resources for food supply in a vast maritime flora and fauna. Complementing this picture we can only give a very brief idea of the grandeur of the landscape of that country. Many people will ask: "Where are the problems in that country?" You will see that there are some, and although some may be less acute than others which have been discussed here, they still constitute factors for economic deficiencies, for social unrest, and for serious worry for the government of our democratic republic.

The population of Chile is about 5.8 millions, engaged in the following occupations: agriculture, 34 per cent; industry, 17 per cent; government service, 15 per cent; and commerce, 8 per cent.

Although these figures and others that I shall give correspond to true statistical data, I shall ask you to keep them as reference, since I shall use them in round numbers to avoid giving too many insignificant details.

As we see from these figures, a majority of the population of Chile is engaged in agriculture. Of the 550,000 active farmers, who with their families form the total of 2 million people, 25 per cent are owners or renters; the rest work for wages or are sharecroppers or laborers who, through a salary or a share in the crops, or both, work directly and personally on the land for other people. The social legislation which has been in force since 1925 is not enough to cover the food needs, housing, unemployment, and education of those who work for wages and their families, but it does protect them to some extent from economic losses due to illness, disability, and old age.

The existence of this mass of people working the land, living in inferior housing (a farmer earns approximately one-third of the wages of an industrial worker) and hoping for the right to happiness in this life retards the industrialization of the country because the mass has no purchasing power for manufactured articles; makes an inadequate use of natural resources; and, eventually, it is a powerful factor for social instability propitious for a revolutionary infiltration of any type, especially of the communist type.

The system of big landholdings (Latifundio) has given rise to radical movements with the motto "land belongs to the one who works it." Well, who is against this, and who insists that the land does not belong to the one who works it? In this slogan the salaried farmers see the interpretation of the most intimate desires, but who can convince the large landowner that that position is just and that he should make the solution of the problem easier? The Bible alreadys says that it would be easier for a camel to go through the eye of a needle.

The situation can best be understood if we take into consideration the fact that Chile has 31 million hectares adaptable for agriculture, classified as shown in Table 26.

TABLE 26

CLASSIFICATION OF AGRICULTURAL
LAND IN CHILE

Type of Land	Area*	Percentage of total
Arable	5.5	21
Mountains and forests	19.0	56
Natural prairies	6.5	23

*In millions of hectares.

In this regard, I should like to point out that 64 per cent of the total number of land owners have plots of less than 20 hectares. These occupy 2 per cent of the agricultural area. By contrast there are 1,400 land owners with more than 2,000 hectares each. Although these units are only 1 per cent of the total number of holdings they contain 60 per cent of the agricultural land of the country.

These figures represent the coexistence of two problems, both equally acute: on the

one hand, the large landholdings, or latifundios, and on the other hand, small landholdings, or minifundios. It is obvious to
conclude that the majority of the wage earners work on the large estates and that even
many of the small land owners hire themselves out as laborers on those lands to supplement their income.

These two problems bring about the following situations: (1) A large part of the
big landholdings, made up of excellent land,
either is not cultivated or is cultivated extensively. Their owners need to put forth
no greater effort in order to live comfort-
ably. (2) The extremely small holdings,
made up generally of good lands, are not
used for agricultural and livestock production because of their small size.

We have pointed out the two pillars on
which the fundamental problems of land
tenure in Chile are based and which, in
general, are common to all Latin American
countries. This is due to the origin of the
system of agricultural ownership created
during Spanish and Portuguese colonial
times, based on large grants, or "encomiendas," made by the Crown.

The book *Chile, Its Land and Its People*
by George MacBride, University of California professor, published in 1935, which
is an excellent study of our social problems
of agriculture, ends with the following
words: "The elimination of the system of
the supremacy of the hacienda, although it
may bring about tumult and difficulties,
will mean an advancement toward a greater
and united Chile; it will mean the more
profitable use of natural resources, a higher
standard of living for the masses of the
people, greater education for the whole nation, more genuine freedom and more complete harmony among the different elements
of the population."

I shall summarize the measures which
have been adopted to solve those problems.

Administrative measures.—These measures include the formation and endow-
ment of public services to stimulate the rationalization of agriculture based on scientific research, the corresponding planning
and divulging of information, and the study
and application of laws tending to rectify
the agricultural structure of the country.
This has been done to the Ministries of
Agriculture and Land and Settlement.

Social and political measures.—These include the distribution of state lands. Unfortunately, the reserves of agricultural lands
to be distributed are few. The majority of
public lands were sold in the middle of the
last century and are incorporated into a
system of large landholdings. An institute
has been created for settlement to acquire
large landholdings and to subdivide them
in a technical and rational way; the plots
are sold to selected applicants on credit at
low interest rates and for long terms. The
settlers are organized into co-operatives. On
this I can point out the following remarkable facts. First, from the year 1930 to the
present more than 350,000 hectares have
been subdivided among 3,200 settlers. Second, comparative surveys of the production
of the land subdivided show net qualitative
and quantitative increases in production
with relation to the time when these same
lands were not subdivided. There are two
negative points. First, co-operatives in general function inefficiently. Second, in view
of the acute inflation which the country is
undergoing, the fact that the plots are sold
on a long-term basis has made the recovery
of capital impossible. Another observation
which might be made is that in this way
the problem could be solved 200 years from
now, according to what has occurred up to
the present period.

Education.—The state stimulates agricultural education and disseminates information through the College of Agriculture
and Veterinary Science of the University
of Chile and through various other agri-

cultural schools which train technicians in several specialties. There is another College of Agriculture which is a branch of the Catholic University in the capital city.

Political and economic solutions.—These include low interest credits, special credits, and rental of mechanized equipment. The low interest credits of 5 per cent per year (the current interest rate in Chile is 12 per cent) are granted under certain controls for the purpose of fulfilling plans of agricultural and livestock rationalization and development. Nevertheless, the amount of these credits is very limited, and for the most part the credits serve the large landholders and their renters. They do not benefit substantially either the small landholders or the wage earners. Besides, to protect them from the inflationary process, these credits are granted for very short terms—six months to three years. The special credits for acquiring machinery, purebred stock, for irrigation, etc. are more liberal in their terms—from two to five years. They have brought about a slight increase in irrigation, in production of milk, and in mechanization of our agriculture. I should point out in this respect that 25 per cent of Chilean agriculture is mechanized. Rental of mechanized equipment is designed to bring about a more intensive working of the land under cultivation as well as the extension of areas of cultivation. Mechanized equipment is located in several stations in different regions of the country. The use of this equipment has been satisfactory. In the period 1950/51, 75,000 hectares of land were made ready for planting, 82,000 hectares were harvested, and 1,200 hectares were cleared.

All these activities take place through state institutions or institutions depending upon the state. The magnitude of the problems makes any other course impossible. This is not at odds with the spirit of free enterprise because through state services there are many people who serve enthusiastically the cause of public welfare and human solidarity; their spirit of free enterprise consists in service to others. On the other hand, the state is not an end but a means toward collective welfare; it does not coerce; it helps; it orients; it stimulates; it plans; and it tries to build the foundations for the future with rational and foresighted criteria. In Chile through the abuse of land cultivation and of free enterprise, we have suffered the loss of thousands of hectares through erosion. All this is being attacked, and we are trying to recover worn-out soils through a vigorous policy of reforestation. Here we have received valuable aid from the FAO.

We are undertaking the study of extending our agricultural area through irrigation. Perhaps we could rehabilitate no less than 1 million hectares, but this requires considerable investment. In reality, our land is potentially rich, but it is hard and elusive.

We are studying ways of making agriculture productive, since in spite of the efforts made so far, as described above, it does not give a satisfactory yield. Thus the index of population increase lately has surpassed the index of agricultural production. One of the means of rapid development—one that has the advantage of being converted into a solution of the problem of large landholding—is conventional immigration. Thus, for example, a Chilean-Italian company has been formed with capital from both countries. The company intends to acquire lands, to subdivide them, to build improvements (buildings, canals, roads, drainage, etc.), and to endow them with agricultural implements. It will bring settlers from Italy. Some property has already been acquired—the San Manuel hacienda with some 1,000 irrigated hectares and about 35,000 hectares in other types of land. This property was acquired for 12 million Chilean pesos (about $130,000). Here 140 settlers will be installed. In order to prepare the settlement, as far as work and implements are concerned, an investment of 54 million Chilean pesos is extended. It is evident that no former owner had ever made an investment of this type, which undoubtedly will raise the production level of that settlement.

On the same pattern, other surveys are practically finished to settle other areas, and there is a possibility of installing immediately some five thousand families or more. Capital is lacking, however, to carry on this work. It is estimated that the establishment of each family made up of four members costs some five thousand dollars to insure their subsistence until the land becomes productive.

We come to the end of this sketchy presentation of our topic. However, I would not like to end without making mention of a problem which is related to land tenure

regarding productivity and collective welfare, which is what we are studying. I would like to point out how convenient it would be if we could co-ordinate the production of the countries to end the self-sufficient and self-supplying spirit, wherever it may exist, which creates customs barriers and stimulates artificial agricultural production. Because of the increasing interrelationship that the economic processes of nations have reached, there is no doubt that we should strive for a kind of world planning of agriculture according to regional ecology and better distribution of agricultural crops. We don't know whether it would be possible to talk about this and discuss it or even approve it among technical and scientific people, but heaven help us if some politician or some diplomat gets a hand in it. Then a wave of resounding words would drown the idea and the end of time would come amidst the foam. Thank you.

AGRICULTURAL PRODUCTION AND SOME LAND TENURE PROBLEMS IN URUGUAY

Eduardo Llovet

I wish to thank the government of this great country for the opportunity it has offered me of attending this conference in which topics of the greatest interest for the future of our civilization are discussed. We have come to discuss our problems of land tenure, be they great or small. Through the exchange of information will come a better knowledge of the world situation and a better understanding among the delegates of the countries represented here.

I am going to present a brief outline of a small country of South America. The figures I give will not convey an idea of its size. What may be of value is a statement of the purposes that have inspired my country's

legislators and its government to pass the beneficial laws whose benefits can be seen in the application of the laws.

Uruguay has an area of 186,926 square kilometers, or 72,153 square miles. It is located between 30 degrees and 35 degrees south latitude. It has a population of 2,400,000 persons. Its monetary unit is the peso, which is equal to about 40 cents in United States money (free rate). The annual average temperature of Uruguay is 16.8° C.

The largest difference in rainfall in Uruguay exists between the north zone, where the annual average is 1,193 millimeters, and the River Plate zone, where 949 millimeters is usually recorded. The differences in rainfall in the various parts of the country are compensated for by differences in temperature, which causes higher or lower evaporation rates. The climatic characteristics of Uruguay are shown in Table 27.

TABLE 27

CLIMATIC CHARACTERISTICS OF URUGUAY

Zone	Summer (Dec.– Feb.)	Autumn (Mar.– May)	Winter (June– Aug.)	Spring (Sept.– Nov.)
AVERAGE SEASONAL TEMPERATURE (CENTIGRADE)				
North	24.7	18.6	12.4	18.3
North-east	23.8	18.1	11.7	17.4
Central	23.7	17.4	11.4	17.2
River				
Plate	22.5	17.2	10.7	15.7
Ocean	22.5	17.3	11.2	16.2
AVERAGE SEASONAL RAINFALL (MILLIMETERS)				
North	295	366	258	274
Northeast	251	310	302	247
Central	240	303	245	246
River				
Plate	215	274	234	226
Ocean	228	283	265	226

In general, it can be stated with reference to temperature and evaporation that during summer the amount of precipitation is usually somewhat deficient. However, rainfall is considered satisfactory during the rest of the year for range grasses, cereals, and forage crops. Orchard growers and commercial vegetable gardeners and a few commercial crop growers need irrigation facilities.

Agronomy

Uruguayan soils are generally thin with reference to the humus layer. This is due not only to geological formations but to other factors which have exercised an influence during the time of man. Such negative factors include the characteristics of precipitation and the gradient of slopes, which are usually 3 per cent to 8 per cent but sometimes as steep as 15 to 20 per cent.

The depletion of soils was caused in the past by man and farms. Man destroyed the natural forests. Native grasses grazed by livestock during the past two centuries have deteriorated.

In spite of those factors, Uruguay still possesses great soil reserves on which is based the nation's economy. Cattle and sheep raising occupy 85 per cent and farming 10 per cent of the national area, or 16 million and 1.5 million hectares, respectively. The conversion of natural pastures to meat, hides, and bones without returning natural elements to the soil has caused a serious soil depletion. At present, maintenance and improvement of soils is carried out by the use of fertilizers, conservation practices to avoid erosion, and a more rational use of pasture land.

Social Features

Since the nation's population is concentrated in Montevideo—a city with nearly 1 million people—and in certain interior cities, such concentration of city dwellers does not favor a bigger and better production. Only about 15 per cent of the total population consists of farmers, including their families, who live and work on the farms. The evident scarcity of farm labor hinders more intensive cultivation, rational farming methods, and forestation on a greater scale, all of which are urgently needed.

The concentration of the population in

the cities and villages is due to the more comfortable life in these centers, increasing industrialization without adequate planning, inadequate subdivision of land, and the lack of modern rural laws. Rural laws would mold a new way of life for farmers, stimulate their love for rural work, and improve rural welfare and social conditions.

This summary description of the main features of Uruguay and the population with reference to the economic features—essentially of an agricultural character—shows completely the importance of the problems which will be discussed at this conference. The writer wishes primarily to state what has been done with reference to resettlement and hopes to profit from the experience of other countries. I do not wish to tire the listeners with statistics which can be found in the bulletins that I have brought with me and which were handed over to the secretary of the conference.

Uruguayan Resettlement Laws

The government's activities with reference to settlement though dating back to the end of the past century began with the Law of January 22, 1913, through which a loan of 500,000 pesos was authorized. This money was to be used to buy and to subdivide land for farming and livestock raising. The farms were sold for cash or by installments for as long as a thirty-year period. No land tax was paid for ten years if at least half of the acreage was cultivated. A decree of August 9, 1913, created a Consulting Resettlement Committee, which decided how to apply the above-mentioned law.

The Law of June 20, 1921, commenced the system of giving credits to buyers of land up to 85 per cent of the value of each unit, without necessarily following the strict regulations of the organic law of the official mortgage bank, Banco Hipotecario. Loan contracts required farmers to work the land themselves or with the help of their family

and permitted hired labor only in exceptional circumstances. The settlers were not allowed to mortgage or to sell their farms during the first five years. No settler or family could occupy more than seventy-five hectares. All tax exemptions accorded by the Law of 1913 were maintained.

What was the work done by the Consulting Committee of Resettlement under these two laws? Eight colonies were founded with a total area of 23,845 hectares. All of them were located in the Departments of Paysandú and Río Negro, except one in San José consisting of 4,810 hectares and another in Canelones of 872 hectares. No expropriation took place. All the land was bought directly from the owners. The main feature of the distribution of these areas was the excessive subdivision. The majority of the units had an area of 40 hectares; the few larger units did not exceed 75 hectares, the maximum size permitted by the Law of October 21, 1921, which amended Article 6 of the Law of June 20 of the same year.

As a consequence the settlers dedicated their efforts to one crop only, which consisted of cereals in most cases. Even under these unfavorable conditions good work was done. The settlements in the proximity of Paysandú became the essential basis for the industrial growth of this town. These settlements supplied wheat for the big flour mills of Fraschini, Estefanel, Pons, Cassaretto, and others. Later on the settlers sent their farm produce to the growing town of Paysandú, thus starting a new development.

Rural Development and Resettlement

The Department of Rural Development and Resettlement was founded by the Law of September 10, 1923, under the direction of the Banco Hipotecario. This Department was to be administered by the board of directors and two government delegates. At first, the Supervisor of Agriculture and Livestock and the Inspector of Settlement (who is now Director of the Immigration Office) were appointed as delegates.

This new department received a capital of 3 million pesos in rural development and settlement bonds. This capital was administered independently of the other economic and financial banking transactions. The Law of 1923 gave to the settlers the same exemptions from taxes as the previous laws but called for a minimum down payment of 15 per cent. The rest was given by the bank as a mortgage loan, according to the Law of June 20, 1921. When the appraised value was less than the price actually paid, the Office of Rural Development gave an additional loan covering the difference. Also the loss caused by the sale of the bonds at less than their nominal value was covered by the additional loan.

Unfortunately the maximum area of the farm units was not changed by the new law. Most farmers continued their cereal growing, and only in a few cases was farm production diversified. Moreover, it was required for loan purposes that 50 per cent of the land was to be suitable for farming.

Then the capital of the department was increased by an additional 2 million pesos bond issue, according to the Law of May 10, 1929. By this Law the bank was allowed to grant loans, first up to 75 per cent of the first mortgage and in addition 25 per cent by a second mortgage. This kind of transaction was only possible when the bank sold a farm from the settlement after three years of occupation by the tenant, provided that he had proved his capabilities as a good farmer. Mortgage loans for single farms (outside the settlements) by contract between seller and farmer continued under the rule of the Law of September 10, 1923.

Finally, after nine years, a new law called Loan Law for Medium Size Farms was ratified. This law was proposed first by the writer of this report, who was at that time in charge of the Department of Rural

Welfare and Resettlement. The Board of Directors received this proposition with great interest and a bill was sent to Congress. This legislative body passed the bill with a few amendments. Under this law the farm unit was increased up to three hundred hectares, at which point mixed farming or ranching enterprises were to be undertaken. Moreover, the farmers who benefited from this law were required to plant forage crops amounting to 20 per cent of the unit areas; only in exceptional cases could this requirement be overlooked, i.e., if bank technicians declared that rotational practices were not necessary for unusually good range lands.

This was the first important step towards cattle production. It is specially noteworthy that while in all previous loans under existing laws a great number of mortgage failures were recorded no failure was reported under the newer law. This may be due to the greater solvency of the farmers who operated under the new law and, also, to the fact that in all cases 25 per cent of the appraised value had to be paid in cash as a down payment.

New Resettlement Laws

On June 20, 1933, a new law was ratified. It authorized the government to float a new 5 million peso issue of bonds, credited to the Rural Development and Settlement Department, in order to expand the resettlement. This issue did not take place. The law required that the price of the land bought with these bonds should not exceed its tax appraisal value. This disposition made it impossible to buy land. Nevertheless, interesting legal changes were made by this law. From then on it was allowed to extend credit up to 20 per cent of the value of the property for buying cattle and for providing permanent improvements essential for production.

Later on three other laws were ratified.

These laws referred mainly to the so-called "desalojados" (landless tenants), and they contributed a great deal to the resettlement legislation. The Law of September 20, 1939, provides for the Banco Hipotecario to acquire land for those tenants who were forced to abandon their farms before April 30 of the next year. The Law of September 19, 1941, declared that all land suited for mixed crop and livestock farming is considered essential to public welfare. This law authorizes also the expropriation of this land according to the dispositions of the Law of March 28, 1912 (Expropriation Law).

Farm units, which had been limited in size by the Law of January 30, 1932, could now be increased, even up to 500 and 1,000 hectares, if four of the members of the board of directors voted in favor of the allotment and if the land was suited for crop and livestock production.

Finally, the Law of December 31, 1945, authorized a new issue of rural development bonds for the purpose of settling the problem of landless tenants. Paragraph 4 of this law contained interesting dispositions regarding expropriation proceedings. The exact wording of this paragraph was included in Law No. 11.029 by which the National Institute of Resettlement was founded. By this Law the Institute took over the expropriation functions formerly handled by the Department of Rural Development and Resettlement of the Banco Hipotecario.

According to Paragraph 5, the price of the alloted units would be determined by the productive capacity of the land. The settlers were allowed to pay during the first three years only two-thirds of the mortgage liabilities. The settler had to conform to technical advice laid down by the Department of Rural Development and Resettlement. The capital destined to production credits was increased to 1 million pesos, up to which amount the Banco de la República

had to open a special credit account at 4 per cent interest through which the Rural Development Department could grant credits for the establishment of individual settlers, establishment of co-operatives, etc. There is no doubt that this law contained many long-needed, just, and socially far-reaching dispositions. Congress, which studied the related problems and passed the bill, had shown great understanding of the problems involved.

After this short survey of the legal aspect, the accomplishments during twenty-five years of activity (September, 1923, to June, 1948) by the Department of Rural Development and Resettlement will be outlined. The capital of the Department amounted to 8 million pesos in bonds authorized by the laws of 1923, 1929, and 1945. Lack of capital and some of the above-mentioned dispositions—mitigated by the laws of 1932 and 1941—prevented the Department from more complete action until 1945. Nevertheless, this Department performed an important job. Its accomplishments may be summed up as follows: 139,464 hectares of settlements and other lands were acquired in units up to December 31, 1947, and loans were granted to buyers of 49,717 hectares of independent farm units. The total amount of land transferred was 189,181 hectares.

To the above figures can be added the settlements founded by the Consulting Settlements Commission (23,845 hectares), bringing the total of settlements to 163,309 hectares. Together with mortgage loans with respect to independent units (49,717 hectares) the total area amounts to 213,026 hectares; 2,843 farms were acquired, the majority of which are today occupied by farmers and their families.

After this first period of thirty-five years, the National Institute of Resettlement was founded by Law No. 11.029 (January 12, 1948). The Institute started its activities in June, 1948.

National Institute of Resettlement

The first board of directors was appointed on July 18, 1948, and started its work on the premises of the Department of Rural Development and Resettlement of the Banco Hipotecario, in accordance with Paragraph 2 of the Law. The board of directors commenced its activities by planning the technical and administrative organization of the Institute and preparing the first budget.

In September, the Institute moved to its temporary offices with the staff taken over from the Department of Rural Development and Resettlement. The Institute had to overcome many difficulties characteristic of those faced by all new institutions. Its task consists in the solution of economic and social problems which are of fundamental importance to the nation.

Important factors such as the rapidly increasing land, the flaws of antiquated laws, and the great difficulty of selling bonds, as well as the very small capital, retarded all ideas and plans. However, in general it can be said that the Institute's work has been satisfactory.

The capital of the Institute according to the dispositions of Paragraph 108 of Law No. 11.029 was formed on June 18, 1948. It consists of 25,187,494 pesos in bonds and cash in the following amounts: 3,806,500 pesos in loan bonds and 20 million pesos in bonds of rural development and resettlement, and 1,380,994 pesos in cash.

The 20 million in bonds were handed over to the Institute by the government on November 12, 1948. On February 4, 1950, a part of the newly printed resettlement bonds could be deposited as security with different official institutions for 1,875,000 pesos in cash. Later the bonds could be sold, and, in consequence, the expropriations could be initiated with the capital obtained through this sale.

On August 31, 1951 the Institute possessed 12,225,400 pesos in bonds and 8,036,712 pesos in cash.

Land surveys made by the Institute for resettlement purposes not only accomplished the principal objective of the law but in addition served as basis for an agronomic map. Up to now the surveyed area amounts to 1,653,952 hectares.

A land survey is made whenever Institute technicians are called to inspect the property. The above-mentioned figure of surveyed land corresponds to 10 per cent of the usable national territory. This work has been done with increasing celerity and effectiveness in the last three years. In a very few years a rough survey of all the Uruguayan territory will have been made and the quality and value of the land deduced.

On the other hand, the Minister of Agriculture plans the setting up of a thorough agronomic national map. For such a work special financial means, which can be granted only by Congress, will be needed.

The Institute has granted 550 loans for the acquisition of farms according to Paragraph 23 of Law No. 11.029, by which the settlers must live on the land and do their own work. The loans amounted to 80 per cent of the appraisal value of the farms. The Banco Hipotecario spent in these operations 4,324,881 pesos in bonds, and the Institute paid 628,657 pesos in cash. These loans correspond to an area of 25,064 hectares. In addition, 43 loans were granted by the Institute for permanent improvements amounting to 100,000 pesos. These loans amount to 25 per cent of the appraised value of each unit.

The Institute allotted 238 units with a total area of 36,392 hectares, an average of 154 hectares per farmer. The average might appear high, but the units include different types of production, such as livestock, crop, and truck farms.

The area of land acquired according to

dispositions of Law No. 11.029 amounts to 31,222 hectares at a cost of 4,922,776 pesos.

The Institute took over the settlements of the Department of Rural Development and Resettlement consisting of 175,784 hectares (2,000 units), the actual value of which amounts to approximately 25 million pesos.

Expropriation proceedings commenced by the Banco Hipotecario but not yet finished correspond to a total area of 37,279 hectares. Expropriations started by the Institute correspond to a total area of 81,510 hectares. Expropriations decided by the Institute but not carried out because of the land owners' agreement to arrange among themselves for the subdivision and settlement according to the dispositions of the Law amount to 21,205 hectares. The total value of these three land groups expropriated by the Institute, according to the appraisal of the Institute's technicians, amounts to 27,867,880 pesos.

It can be seen from the above-mentioned figures that the Institute's work has only started and that time is needed to increase its activities. However, positive results can be expected in the near future.

Summary

The economy of Uruguay is based on agriculture and livestock production, cattle and sheep production being the most important. Approximately 90 per cent of the total area devoted to agriculture is dedicated to the production of forage crops. Industrial enterprises in Uruguay are devoted primarily to the manufacture of livestock products. A fertile soil and a favorable climate permit the wide variety of crops such as wheat, linseed, corn, sunflower seed, oats, barley, rice, and peanuts. The area devoted to the production of wheat is the largest. Almost any crop adapted to a subtropical or temperate climate can prosper in this country. Oranges, lemons, tangerines, tomatoes, asparagus, beans, and other vegetables are produced. The production of grapes is of great importance, since there is a growing wine industry. In spite of the diversity and importance of the agricultural production, its income hardly represents 10 to 15 per cent of the total income of national production based primarily on livestock. A large part of the production of wheat is for export. Practically all the linseed is exported.

Uruguay has more cattle and sheep per unit area than any other Latin American country. Although the area of the country is relatively small, Uruguay occupies second place in sheep production. A large percentage of the land is under cultivation, and livestock raising operates on an extensive scale. The herds are fed almost exclusively with forage obtained from natural pastures. The sheep industry is operated almost exclusively for the production of wool, since meat production is of a secondary importance. Only a small amount of mutton is exported. Uruguay occupies one of the most prominent places in the world as exporter both of wool and of frozen meat.

Cattle and sheep production in Uruguay makes use of the most modern technique. Only animals of the best quality are used for the improvement of the herd. The quality of livestock products is excellent, and the butchering of animals and the processing of the products is done in modern packing plants. Cattle raising is general all over the country. Beef is one of the main articles consumed by the people. The principal products sent to world markets are wool, meat, hides, and furs, but on a smaller scale other products are exported, such as cattle, meat extracts, fats, beef broth, bones, and horns. Cattle products constitute 85 to 90 per cent of the total exports. The economic prosperity of the country depends primarily on the prevailing world prices of wool, meat, and hides. Approximately 75 per cent of the total production is exported, a relatively high per capita export value.

The dairy industry in Uruguay has developed principally around the large cities, especially for the supply of fresh milk. The country produces enough hogs and poultry for domestic consumption. The forestry resources of Uruguay are not very extensive, especially if they are compared with those of other countries in Latin America. Forestry products are of relatively minor importance in the internal economy of the country.

REVIEW OF THE TENURE SITUATION IN PARAGUAY
AND AN INTEGRATED LAND REFORM PROGRAM

Claudio Romero

PARAGUAY is a small country, with few inhabitants, located in the center of South America. It is bordered by Argentina on the south, southwest, and southeast, by Brazil on the north and northeast, and by Bolivia on the north and northwest. It enjoys an exuberant vegetation, it is irrigated by numerous rivers and streams, and it has a delightful and peaceful climate, beautiful mountains, large forests, rolling hills, and valleys. These natural conditions have caused scientists and others to consider the country as a "garden, an earthly paradise, placed in the heart of South America." It has an area of 40.7 million hectares and a population of 1.5 million inhabitants. Its economic structure is predominantly agricultural. Some 70 per cent of the total population is devoted to farming.

For some twenty years in the history of Paraguay under the governments of the two Lopez, father and son, from 1844 to 1865 (when the Triple Alliance War broke out), the country progressed to such an extent that it set an example as a model of an almost perfect economic and social structure.

An outstanding fact of this period was the almost complete absence of taxes on the people. The country was rich; the coffers of the state because of an honest administration were full of gold. Roads were being constructed, factories being established, schools being opened everywhere, and unceasing public works were being realized. Customs were simple; there was full harmony in social living; there was frankness and joy of living in all the Paraguayan people; and there was a hospitality which has become proverbial, coming straight from the heart.

Every Paraguayan family had some land, a home, and all Paraguayan families were like one big happy family in which they all considered themselves brothers, having in their hearts love for their land and in their conscience love and respect for God and their fellow men.

In short, the people lived happily with the complete fulfillment of the necessities of life and were healthy, strong, peaceful, and hard-working.

The Triple Alliance War and later successive civil wars ended all that work of a whole peace-loving nation, all that constructive work, all that education, and destroyed the fraternal feeling of Paraguayans toward their fellow men. Because of this circumstance and the adulteration of all the values that make up the complex life of a nation, we arrived at a continuous lack of equilibrium in economic matters and in all of those factors that constitute agricultural exploitation which are, as is well known, climate, land, capital, labor, and intelligent guidance.

In Paraguay, as we have said, the climate

is excellent and mild. The average yearly mean temperature is 20°–24° C., or 68°– 75.2° F., with a relative humidity of 70–80 per cent. There is abundant rainfall with an annual mean of 1,600 millimeters, or 64 inches, uniformly distributed, with periods of drought which extend from July to the end of August.

Storms are almost unknown; there is a clear blue sky most of the year. The country is well irrigated; it is covered with damp and thick forests; and there is a splendid sun. In the Chaco region during the war with Bolivia no cases of tetanus were recorded, and it was concluded that that region did not have any tetanus germs. Land and work, two of the factors already mentioned, are fine in themselves. But the first factor, land, is poorly distributed, because there are large land holdings (*latifundios*) concentrated in the hands of a few who either do not exploit them or, if they do so, they do it from the point of view of an excessive personal interest, causing those lands to be out of tune with the national economy. There are also *minifundios* (small land holdings), which, grouped together, congest certain zones and cause inhabitants to lead a precarious life because of the lack of land, means of production, and education.

The land is poorly distributed because of the arbitrary fashion in which the system of laissez-faire has worked. This system has ruled over the ruins of that powerful economic and social organization, of which we spoke before, for over half a century. During this time, instead of working toward the economic welfare of the nation, the system has corrupted everything: the essential values of national life, the economy, the good government, social life, and culture. As to work (human elements), under that system of lack of ability, of apathy, of corruption, and uncontrolled ambition, the people of Paraguay were governed like slaves or pariahs with only apparent free-

dom. They were kept apart through a policy of base passions which created a continuous, abnormal state of war between brothers and made them unstable and disunited.

With regard to capital, this continued instability of the almost chronic armed struggles, of tremendous personal ambition in the past brought about a constant distrust abroad and prevented the influx of capital into the country. The opposite happened with the flight of capital, which has been invested abroad since that time, preventing its circulation within the national territory either in the form of credit or in the form of new productive investments. This resulted in a static economic structure whose servants, the producers, the Paraguayan people, if not employed to kill each other were made to work for a mere pittance (because they could not even have enough for clothing, for land, and homes of their own), and for the exclusive benefit of outside interests, whose representatives, heartless Paraguayans, were in power.

The last factor of agricultural exploitation—intelligent guidance—up to the present has not become very tangible, not because of lack of capability but as a consequence of the considerations and reasons already stated. This is also due to a systematic persecution of national values, whether these values be past, present, or future, carried out by the so-called liberal regime (which actually curtailed liberty), which is an enemy of our environment and progress and of the welfare of the Paraguayan people.

Before going on, let us examine the statistics which, with their mute eloquence, are proof of what has been stated. The figures are taken from the agricultural census made by STICA—the Servicio Tecnico Interamericana de Cooperacion Agricola (Interamerican Technical Service for Agricultural Cooperation). They are for the years 1942/43 and 1943/44.

In 1943, 94,498 farms had an area of 1,549,785 hectares, 3.7 per cent of the total area of the country, with an average of 16.4 hectares per farm. The cultivated area included 333,979 hectares, or less than 1 per cent of the total area. General crops were planted on 297,256 hectares, fruit and forestry products on 36,053 hectares—3.1 and .4 hectares per farm, respectively, or a total of 3.5 hectares per farm. Of a total of 82,069 farms reported, there were 32,881 farms on fiscal, or national, land. A total of 94,498 farms reported were distributed in the following fashion:

15,079 farms of individual owners
6,130 farms of individual renters
59,706 farms of individual occupants
2,100 farms of renting owners
3,449 farms of occupying owners
7,497 farms of occupying renters
537 farms of occupying renting owners

As for agricultural implements available in 1943, it was reported that there were in that year 31,372 steel plows, 33,256 wooden plows, 27,062 carts, 32,520 different implements such as reaping machines, planting machines, pulverizers, grinding machines, tractors, etc. From these figures it was discovered that 71.8 per cent of the farms lacked steel plows, 54.7 lacked plows of any kind, and 45.3 per cent had no implements of any kind.

Of a total of 94,498 farms reported, there were 10,266 stone or brick houses, 83,466 frame houses, 80,469 miscellaneous types of houses, and 63,343 structures of other types.

A total of 93,892 farms had cash income of 34,426,070 guaranies (approximately 11,105,850 dollars) distributed as shown in Table 28.

The extension of credit was as follows: Out of 94,495 farms, 26,728, or 28.3 per cent, received credit. The total amount of credit was 2,443,360 guaranies, or an average of 26 guaranies for the total number of

farms and an average of 91 guaranies for the farms actually receiving credit.

On 44,090 out of a total of 94,401 farms the farmers were working outside of their farms—36 per cent of the total farms. The total income from this work outside of the farm was 5,386,640 guaranies, an average of 57 guaranies per farm. This work outside the farm is in farm labor and industrial labor. The wages for those two general types of work can differ greatly. Likewise, the farm wages vary within themselves considerably; they are less when lunch is paid for by the owner, but even this custom varies according to the locality. The work

TABLE 28

SOURCES OF INCOME FOR 93,892 PARAGUAYAN FARMS, 1953

Source	Amount (guaranies)	Percentage of total
General crops	14,641,505	42.5
Fruit and forest products	2,410,129	7.0
Seeds	62,086	.2
Work outside the farm	5,386,640	15.6
Sale of animals	5,288,388	15.4
Sale of animal products	2,701,039	7.8
Miscellaneous products	3,736,886	10.9
Other income	199,397	.6
Total	34,426,070	100.0

contract usually includes, besides the manual labor, the use of oxen, carts, or farm implements.

The farm population increased, on a total of 94,498 farms, to 540,873 persons, distributed as follows: 235,755 males, 225,180 females, and 79,938 relatives who lived with the family. The family was defined by the census as a group of people who live under the same roof. The children who had left the home were omitted; on the other hand, the relatives who lived with the family were included. This made an average of 5.7 persons per family. In regard to laborers, the number living on these farms was 9,285. The distribution of 94,434 farmers by sex and nationality is shown in Table 29. No

TABLE 29

DISTRIBUTION OF FARM LABORERS IN PARAGUAY BY NATIONALITY AND SEX

Nationality	Male	Female	Total
Paraguayan	79,102	9,379	88,481
Argentinian	1,191	78	1,269
Brazilian	483	30	513
Other South American	75	.....	75
German	1,027	47	1,074
Northwest European	59	3	62
Southeast European	2,393	65	2,458
Oriental	133	2	135
Other	358	9	367
Total	84,821	9,613	94,434

census was taken on farms of less than one hectare. However, incidental information allows for a fairly reliable calculation of the total number of such farms. This is calculated to have been 25,633 at the time of the census. The census did not include farms of less than one hectare. It is estimated, however, that these farms numbered approximately 25,600 and that, based on an average of about six persons per family, approximately 153,800 people lived on them.

Other recent studies which have been published in magazines give the total distribution of the land of the country.

First, it should be said that Paraguay is divided into two large regions: the Western region, or Chaco, with some 24.7 million hectares and the Eastern region with some 16 million hectares. In the Western region, 14 owners own 7,567,387 hectares. In the Eastern region, 11 owners own 5,548,444 hectares. The total of 25 large landowners own 13,115,831 hectares, or more than one-fourth of the total area of the country. A total of 1526 medium-large landowners own 15,549,844 hectares, or more than a third of the total area of the country. Several small landholders own 2 million hectares, or 4.9 per cent of the total area of the country.

The total amount of private property is therefore 30,665,675 hectares, which, subtracted from 40,673,200 hectares, the total area of Paraguay, leaves 10,007,525 hectares in the fiscal reserve.

Private property comprises 75.4 per cent of the total area of the country, fiscal reserve, 24.6 per cent. There are 1 million hectares as fiscal reserve in the Eastern region and 9 million hectares in the Western, or Chaco, region. Up to 1950, 700,000 hectares in the Eastern region had been expropriated. Therefore, there are 1,700,000 hectares disposable. Some 600,000 hectares of fiscal land in the Eastern region and some 6 million hectares in the Western region have been rented.

In a study made by STICA, one may see the distribution of land from the point of view of forest, country, and crop life. The land is distributed among the different uses as follows: 33 per cent virgin forest, 11 per cent exploited forest, 52 per cent fields, 2 per cent lakes, and 2 per cent crops.

Because the time is short, I shall summarize.

According to the data gathered by the Paraguayan Meat Corporation and mentioned by Dr. Carlos A. Pedretti in his article "Aspects of Paraguayan Production" in the *Review of the Center of Students of*

Economics for May, 1950 (Vol. XII, No. 102) there were 43,027 cattlemen in the Republic in 1946. The number of livestock was as follows: cattle, 3,431,935 head; sheep, 224,000 head; horses, 367,000 head; hogs, 428,000 head.

According to the report of the Bank of Paraguay made in 1947, we have the following data on consumption. There were 34,957 head of cattle packed by the meat packing houses, of which 30,075 head were for export and 4,882 head for internal consumption. COPACAR packed 399,849 head of cattle, of which 84,666 head were for consumption in the Capital, 265,928 head were for consumption in the interior, and 14,298 head were for miscellaneous consumption. If large movements of cattle escaped control, these figures do not represent the total production of cattle.

The total value of exported cattle products was 25,038,000 guaranies. The meat packed was valued at 11,781,000 guaranies, the refrigerated products at 4,773,000 guaranies, and the hides at 8,484,000 guaranies. From this total one must deduct the value of imported cattle to get a net export value.

According to the article by Pedretti noted above, in 1944 forest products amounted to 1,364,000 tons, of which firewood amounted to 1,102,000 tons and beams and logs to 106,000 tons. The total value of forest products was 28,742,000 guaranies, of which firewood amounted to 6,821,000 guaranies, beams and logs to 4,586,000 guaranies, tannin to 6,411,000 guaranies, and sawed lumber to 3,270,000 guaranies.

The net worth of agricultural products amounted to 85,650,000 guaranies and that of cattle products to 64,250,000 guaranies.

According to a study made in 1946 by Dr. Carlos Soler and Professor Milan Cirovic, published under the title of "Essay on National Rent" and mentioned by Dr. Pedretti, the value of industrial production is 138,000,000 guaranies.

Returning to the farmers, we shall say that some 30 per cent of them are illiterate. The Ministry of Education has begun a great movement against illiteracy in the whole country.

In 1943, according to the census of STICA, in a total of 18,890 farms, there were 3,246 farms with groves, or 17 per cent of the total farms.

Conclusions

Certain conclusions can be drawn. (1) There is bad distribution of land in Paraguay. (2) The population of the country is concentrated in certain areas. (3) There is only routine farm, cattle, and forest exploitation because of the lack of sufficient credit. This, in effect, means that there are few implements and machines and that there is a lack of education of the farmer. (4) The economic statistics are inadequate. (5) There is a slow increase in population, whose density is 3.7 inhabitants per square kilometer. (6) There are few immigrants. (7) The standard of living of the farmer is very low. (8) Approximately 50 per cent of the farmers work outside their farms. (9) In Paraguay, 59,072 farmers are landless.

From these conclusions, it seems necessary that there be an integral agrarian reform, a new structure for the national economy. This reconstruction is a laborious, arduous task; it implies a total revolution, a new order of things; and it demands a maximum of devotion and an unbreakable will. The educated sectors of society ought to support this task and pay attention to the country which was the most maligned, since it suffered the wrong as a result of the poor government of which we have spoken.

And in this crucial moment in history in which the people and the government are so closely identified there falls to the Institute for Agrarian Reform, as its name implies, this specific mission: the organization of an agriculture which is progressing toward the balance of all those factors (climate, land, capital, labor, and intelligent direction) which we have already mentioned. It will be possible to realize this by means of an organic plan that would facilitate the means of arriving at a rational economic-social structure whose center would be man surrounded by all the attributes which are inherent in him: dignity, liberty, education, decency, personality, and well-being. The program or plan (I shall speak in general terms) intended to set in motion the economic potential of the country is divided into two major parts.

First, there are works of wide scope, with modern organization in technique, social and professional education, and with adequate financing for a special purpose.

Second, there are routine projects which would continue to be modernized by means of the possibilities of the normal budget which also would continue to strengthen and make dynamic its many ramifications.

The Institute of Agrarian Reform under the direction of a very capable man who is very dynamic and has clear vision for the future of the country, Dr. Roberto L. Petit, has begun its work. It has initiated the founding of consumption and production co-operatives among the small farmers in various settlements. We may note here that there exist some 147 settlements, of which 30 are private; the rest belong to the nation. Teaching of writing and reading and the education and supervision of the farmers have been accomplished. Up to the present many thousands of provisory titles have been given to the farmers. There exists in this respect an agrarian statute which fixes the norms and proceedings for the acquisition of properties, just as for expropriation for public use of private properties.

The Institute for Agrarian Reform is an autonomous institution. It has prepared a forestry statute providing for studies and fixing norms in regard to rational exploitation of forest, forestation, and reforestation. Credit is given in effect (by the department corresponding to the Bank of Paraguay and the Agricultural Rehabilitation Credit), and farm implements within economic possibilities are provided.

In summary, they are not reaching the farmer with words but with deeds. And they are instructing him, orientating him in order to create an atmosphere of cordiality, harmony, and co-operation. They are causing the farmer to identify himself with his land and enjoy and exercise the right of individual ownership with a social function to which we Paraguayans are naturally inclined by tradition and history.

The Institute of Agrarian Reform seeks the joining together of all the technical, economic, and cultural forces for this project of the redemption of the farmer. It places itself in contact with the international organizations, with the technical organs and missions in order to find a solution to the problems of selective immigration, to give technical aid, to translate credit and monetary aid into farm implements and other productive improvements. The institute seeks to aid the farmer in achieving the knowledge and orientation which will enable him to attain comfortable working conditions, which will enable him to be a worthy exponent of the political-economic-social balance, and which will enable him to form his personality conscientiously, proud of himself and fully enjoying the joys of life.

And, to close, in the name of Dr. Roberto L. Petit, President of the Institute of Agrarian Reform of Paraguay, and in my own name I wish to thank Dr. Parsons, the members of the commission which organized this conference, and the teachers and students of the University of Wisconsin, where study and work are so intimately related. I wish to thank them for having facilitated this meeting of the representatives of so many people who are seeking eagerly the disappearance of misery and the increase in the dignity of man and social well-being and happiness on earth.

THE PROBLEM OF LAND OWNERSHIP IN PERU

Francisco Ponce de León

I WISH, first, to express my very sincere gratitude to President Fred of the University of Wisconsin and to those who, together with him, have organized this conference for the honor extended to me by their invitation to participate as a member of it. At the same time, I congratulate those who decided upon such an event or have patronized it in any way.

The problems connected with land, because of their nature and consequence, are preoccupying the scholars and the governments of all countries in the world! It could not be otherwise since the land is the main source of wealth—that is, of all the products man needs to meet his most important demands for food, clothing, and lodging.

The welfare of a nation depends everywhere on the way the resources of the land are distributed and used. It is for this reason that the study and knowledge of any problem concerning property, the possession and the use of land in its manifold aspects—juridical, economical, industrial, political, and social—presents such special interest and importance. Each one of these aspects has its own ways and peculiarities in the various countries and even in the different areas of any one country. It is necessary, therefore, to know, as fully and deeply as possible, any characteristics and peculiarities assumed by the problems connected with land in different countries in order to make comparisons and establish their similarities and differences, to see whatever they may have in common, and, what is the most important thing, to find any possible solutions. This

conference has, no doubt, such a purpose. And I wish to state, in this regard, my agreement with the ideas of the President of the University of Wisconsin, expressed in his invitation, that the deliberations and decisions of this conference can be of great significance for the future of mankind.

I finish this foreword by expressing my deepest wishes that our work will have the fullest success.

Brief Geographical References

Peru is a democratic republic. The power of the state emanates from the people and is exercised by public officials with the restrictions established by law and by constitution.

Peru is situated in the west central part of South America. It covers an approximate area of 1,249,000 square kilometers from parallel 020'20" northern latitude to 18° 20'02" southern latitude and from meridians 68°20'20" to 81°40' western longitude. Peru joins on the north with the Republic of Ecuador, on the northwest with Colombia, on the east with Brazil, on the southeast with Bolivia, on the south with Chile, and on the west with the Pacific Ocean.

The country is crossed from north to south by the chain of the Andes, which causes its division into three large zones; namely, the coast, the mountains, and the forest or jungle.

The coast zone, extending 130,000 square kilometers, is a narrow strip of land with an average width of 60 kilometers along the seaboard. This strip of land, mostly a sandy desert, becomes fertile and highly productive in the valleys watered by the rivers from the western range of mountains. These rivers are of very scant and variable flow. Therefore, the first problem in the coast zone is the need for irrigation. According to official information I have at hand, the lands under cultivation scarcely amount to 530,170 hectares. This represents 32.9 per cent of the total arable lands in the whole Republic. It is in this region, however, that farming has reached its greatest development; farming has become intensive in some valleys, with investments of substantial capital in sugar cane, cotton, rice, and connected industries. Another feature of this region is the scarcity of labor, a fact causing, in colonial times, the importation of many Negro and Chinese workers. Since then, they have become elements of Peruvian society together with the indigenous race and the white race from Spain and other European countries. Intermarriage has produced a great variety of crossbreeds—"zambos" (Indian and Negro half-breed), mulattoes, "chinos cholos" (Chinese-Indian half-breed) —among the lower classes. At the present time, the scarcity of labor has caused the rise of wages and the use of mechanical implements and machinery. It can be said that mechanized farming has started in this area and is now relatively well established.

The mountain region, or "Sierra," is all the area between the ranges of the Andes from its western slopes to its branches and foothills on the eastern side, where the third region, or "forest," begins. The terrain in this area is very steep—from high summits over 7,000 meters above sea level, covered with perpetual snow, to deep valleys at only 600 or 700 meters above sea level. Large plateaus, like those of Puno, valleys and canyons, with slopes more or less steep, are the main features of this area and at the same time a serious obstacle for communication and, in general, for the proper utilization of land. The main resources of this region are mining and natural pastures. Farming and stock raising are extensive. Labor is cheap due to the indigenous population. Climate and crops vary with the altitude. In very high areas, or "puna," the main crops are potatoes, "quinua," "canihua," and barley. In the ravines or canyons of temperate climate corn, wheat, beans, other grains and fruits are cultivated. In the lowest valleys, with a hot climate, sugar cane, coffee, cocoa, coca, etc. are produced.

The area of the Sierra is 520,000 square kilometers; there are, however, only 924,700 hectares. This represents 57.5 per cent of the total area of 1,609,620 hectares cultivated in the Republic.

The region of the forest, or jungle, extends eastward from the eastern slope of the Andes. This area is covered by forests in its totality; hence the name of "jungle." Its altitude above sea level ranges from 1,000 meters in the accessible valleys, or "cejas do montaña," to about 200 or 300 meters on the plains. It is crossed by the rivers forming the Amazon River basin running generally from southwest to northeast. All these rivers have their origin in the Andean chain, and after a long and very sinuous course through ravines and valleys they join together in the north and form the Amazon River, the biggest in the world. These rivers are, up to the present time, the principal means of communication in that Peruvian area. In the last few years some roads have been constructed in the north, the center, and the south of the Republic. The present government has begun the construction of a railroad which, starting from Tambo del Sol on kilometer 92 of the Oroya-Cerro de Pasco railway and going across Oxapampa will end in Pucallpa, near the Ucayali River, which is navigable at that point at any time of the year. Also, an airline service has been established, with very good results and a good future. The zone has an area of 500,000 square kilometers, of which only 154,750 hectares are under cultivation—only 9.6 per cent of the total lands under cultivation in the Republic.

Since colonial times, when its exploration was started in search for the famous region of "El Dorado," and at the present time, the Peruvian jungle has been considered the richest area in Peru in all kinds of resources. And it really is. Oil in its subsoil, gold in its stream placers, and wood in its forest are riches that nature offers prodigally and generously to human effort for exploitation. Adding to all this anything that may be obtainable by means of industry through cultivation of its extensive plains, it may be easily understood why this region may be considered one of the richest and most promising on the continent.

Historical Background

PRE-COLONIAL PERIOD

It is well known that before the arrival of the Spaniards, Peru was a vast Empire ruled by the Incas from their great capital, the city of Cuzco. Peru covered all the Ecuadorian territory, the coast and the mountain regions of present-day Peru, the Peruvian-Bolivian plateau of Lake Titicaca, and the regions in northern Chile and Argentina. This immense territory was divided into four great regions called Colla-Suyo, Anti-Suyo, Conti-Suyo, and Chincha-Suyo, from which the name of Tahuantisuyo is derived (the four "suyos"). This empire, with its original political and social organization, was the last stage of a long process, the origin of which goes back several centuries before the discovery of America.

Of all that is known at present about the social and political organization of the Tahuantisuyo, only the agrarian regime and the institution of the ayllu are of particular interest to us. The "ayllu" is a family group having a real or fictitious relationship established in a particular region or "marca."

Primitive people who lived in the valleys of the coast and mountains before they were subjected by the Incas were organized into "ayllu" groups. Leaving to historians the study of the origin and evolution of the "ayllu," we shall refer to facts generally admitted as being characteristic. "Ayllu" literally means a kin or group of kins, or, in other terms, a family and groups of a family. The ayllu's members were linked by a blood or affinity relationship, common origin, uses, customs, and interests. It is perhaps interesting to mention that there was a common usage of the "marca," or region, in which the ayllu was established and co-operation in work by means of the *ayni* and the *minka*.

The renowned Peruvian writer Jorge Basadre in his work *History of Peruvian Law* has made a recapitulation of everything that chroniclers, historians, and sociologists have written, within and outside of Peru, about the "ayllu." I consider such a work a very valuable recapitulation, especially because of the moderation and objectivity used by the writer in his judgment about the information and opinions compiled by him, and therefore, I deem it convenient to include a short summary thereof.

"Marca."—This is an Aymará word, existing also in Quechuan zones. To the great surprise of people not expert in the matter, it exists also in the German language with the same meaning; that is, it expresses the zone where a community is established and also the sum total of the inhabitants of a region. "Marca" is, therefore, the region owned by the "ayllu."

The lands of the "ayllu" were divided as follows: (a) lands under immediate cultivation ("llacta-pacha") or lands belonging to the village, at the side of which the scattered houses of the small town ("llacta") were erected; (b) pasture lands, where livestock was maintained, these lands not being distributed; and (c) fallow lands ("marca-pacha").

Rights of "ayllu" members.—These rights and duties included the right: (1) to receive enough land for themselves and their families, (2) to have a house constructed with the support of all the useful members of the "ayllu" ("minka-ayni"), (3) to cut fire-wood in the woods, to hunt, to fish, to share in the livestock returns, to use the water and roads, (4) to be supported in case of disability or illness.

The existence of the agrarian community and the state, as an original note of the Peruvian case.—The "ayllu" was the foundation in Incaic times not only of work and of the indigenous population but also of villages and towns, of the endogamic marriage, the worship of the "huacas," or Indian tombs (the worship of the sun was only a form of "huaca" worship), of administrative organization, and of the military, judicial, and legal organization.

When the Incas destroyed the power of the local chiefs ("caciques") they consolidated the local "ayllus." They atomized the empire territory in order to make it as homogeneous as possible and to favor the development of the lords' culture. The "ayllu" no longer served the "ayllu" itself but the state in its administrative and expansion aims; the "ayllus" were the weft of the tributary and administrative network.

The consequences of conquest by the Incas.—Those "ayllus" were not the same as before the Incaic expansion. The new sovereign imposed his religion and language upon them, without prescribing, however, the local worships and languages.

After the conquest of new territories by the Inca armies, the situation in the empire was more or less as follows:

Public officials recorded, by means of *quipus,* the number of men, children, women, ages, animals, dwellings, woods, mines, fountains, etc., and thereafter the tributes demanded by the Inca were imposed (a) in produce or species, (b) in work or labor contribution, divided into duties with no change of domicile and duties with a temporary change of domicile. People were required to change radically their social situation ("mitmaes," "yanacuanas," "acllas").

In the same way that public officials catalogued people, others measured land, or perhaps made a relief map, or increased the area under cultivation by means of the construction of new canals and terraces. Teachers arrived also to teach the use of certain materials and seeds. A fundamental separation of the "ayllu" lands was also made. Traditionally it has been said that a part remained in service of the Inca, that is to say, at the service of the state, another part at the service of sun, or religion, and the third part for the community, for the purpose of being distributed amongst the heads of the families.

The statement is well known about each householder in the community being assigned a "tupa" (tract of land), one for each son and a half for each daughter. It can be thus ascertained that everything necessary was separated for each member of the "ayllu." The "ayllu" was, therefore, disposed of first.

Some persons have fixed the "tupa" at 2,700 square meters, but no doubt it varied according to the locality. Cunow has stated that the custom was to allot the lands so that each one received sufficient soil to meet his requirements. We suppose that in sandy or waste regions an area three or four times larger than in regions with good clay lands was allotted.

The lands delivered to the members of the community could not be sold, bestowed, leased, or transferred. Their farmers had a mere right of use. Annually the distribution was made by apportioning lands to as many persons as there were in the community.

What happened if the population increased? According to Garcilazo, some lands were taken from the Inca, cultivation was improved, and a better use of the land was made by means of terraces, irrigation, etc.

If some province was barren, according to Cobo, the Inca assigned to it some lands in warm regions, in the coast or Sierra valleys. The lands of the Inca, or Emperor, and the sun were those in excess of the lands allotted to the "ayllu." Besides, the Inca was allotted mines of precious metals and coca plantations. When possible, Garcilazo says, the Inca appropriated those lands which had been tillable by imperial colonization.

Summing up, one can say that when authority of the Inca was established in a region, state property appears, together with community property. A characteristic of the Inca state is that the upper class maintained the collective property for the tributary class.

Characteristics of Inca rights.—Cultivation of rural lands was made according to a predetermined sequence. Garcilazo says that such sequence was as follows: worship lands, Inca lands, community lands. Castro Pozo states that cultivation started with Inca lands and finished with lower class lands. Perhaps there were differences according to the regions.

Other characteristics were: the regulation of seeding and harvest time, subject to ceremonies according to the calendar and the church, the fertilization of lands by means of the "guano" of coastal islands, llama manure, and dead fishes, and a general bond of endeavor, between entertainments and feasts or festivals.

The poor and the rich.—Within the regulation of land and labor already outlined, any possibilities of social differences were diminished. It has been said that equality in poverty made the Indians rich. There was, however, a begining of differences between the poor and the rich. "A lover of poor men," the Inca was called, according to Garcilazo.

The property rights of the "ayllu" and the state.—The historical prolongation of the collective property rule gave a special meaning to the Peruvian juridical reality. The right to property according to the juridical system imported by the Spaniards, which has lasted up to the present time, originated in Rome. It implies that a thing is subject to its owner in every condition and that any intervention of others is rejected. Among Peruvians such a conception did not prevail. Indians identified property with ownership. Inca community put usage in the first juridical plane. Property did not mean mere authority, but was impregnated with family duties towards neighbors, the community, and, later on, the state.

THE COLONY

The Spanish conquest was the starting point of a radical change in the agrarian system of Peru. Colonial laws had, as a juridical base, the principle that the lands of America were a patrimony of the Spanish Royal Crown, from whom any titles of individual property must emanate.

In order to encourage colonization, the "Ordinance of Populations" of Philip II established liberal rules for grants of lands to Spaniards, called "Capitulations," under the promise of pacifying the natives and preaching the Faith to them. The "pacifiers" should choose territories suitable to the health and support of the inhabitants, to the encouragement of trade, propagation of the faith, and good government. If they found villages or towns, a piece of land should be set aside for pastures, common to all the inhabitants, and to provide revenue for the municipality ("Propios"). Out of the remaining, the "pacifier" took a fourth for himself, and the three remaining parts were allotted to the inhabitants.

The allotments of houses and ground-lots,

as well as farm lands, were made by means of contracts called "asientos" (establishments), their extent being determined by the social status and merits of the applicant. The above-mentioned ordinance determined the extent of each of the two principal types of "repartimiento" (allotments of territories): the "peonia" (quality of land given to soldiers in a conquered country) and the "caballeria." The latter was the most important since it comprised a ground-lot of 100 by 200 ancient yards, 500 "fanegas" (about 1.59 acre each) for wheat or barley growing, 50 for corn, 40 for trees, and pastures for 50 swine, 100 cattle, 20 mares, 500 sheep, and 100 goats. The unreasonable liberalism of the first Colonial agrarian laws, aggravated by abuse, gave rise to the formation of great territorial properties which soon absorbed the indigenous property. The Spanish kings very soon realized that the settlers evaded both their ordinances intended to protect the Indian property and those destined to restrict the extent of territorial properties. Realizing then the danger of abandoning the fate of the Colonial lands to the liberality and whims of the governors, they reduced the power granted to them to make allotments of lands. The new system established was chiefly inspired by the necessity of obtaining resources for the exhausted treasury of the Crown. According to this new system, the Colonial government could not adjudicate any vacant lands requested by individuals except by sale at public auction and under the condition of submitting the contract to Royal approval. As a previous measure for the adoption of a new system, a period for litigation of all property titles not directly granted by the King was fixed. Illegal concessions could be admitted to "compromise" by means of payment of certain sums of money, provided they were protected by a period of possession of ten years or more, as the case might be.

Colonial laws recognized the right of Indians to keep their properties, and a number of decrees were promulgated to protect them. In practice, however, such measures were ineffective, and some of them contrary to their purpose. Viceroy Toledo, in his report to Philip II, said in 1652 that if it was true that upon making the allotment of lands the commissioners had instructions intended to prevent any injustices being done to the natives, he found in his visit that such prohibition was not respected, since the Indians reported to him and cried: "We desire land because we have none to sow."

Unfortunately, neither the foresighted measures of Toledo nor those put into practice on different occasions prevented a large part of the indigenous property from going, legally or illegally, to the hands of the Spaniards or creoles. One of the institutions that facilitated such legalized plunder was that of the "encomiendas." According to the legal concept of such institution, the "encomendero" was a protector entrusted with the collection of tribute and the education and christianization of the taxpayers; but in reality he was a feudal lord, master of lives and property.

In short, the Colonial agrarian system replaced a great many of the indigenous agrarian communities with private property cultivated by the Indians under a feudal organization. Such large estates, far from becoming divided, as time went on, were concentrated and consolidated in a few hands because the immovable property was subject to a number of obstacles and perpetual burdens which immobolized them, such as entailed estates, chaplaincies, foundations, patronages, and other related types of property.

Farming and livestock breeding.—The Spaniards brought products from Asia and Europe not produced in America, such as wheat, sugar cane, rice, barley, grape-vines, olive trees, rye, hemp, oranges, etc. They brought also iron implements much better than the rough tools used by the natives, as well as breeding and farming animals unknown to the natives, such as oxen and horses. However, in spite of these benefits, the comparison of results between those obtained by Colonial farming and those of Inca farming is completely unfavorable to the Colony in spite of the technical superiority. Spaniards and creoles destroyed or abandoned, in their avidity for gold or easy riches, the wonderful aqueducts, roads, terraces, and other works for irrigation, cultivations, and trade constructed by ancient Peruvians. This was the first cause of agricultural backwardness. Another cause was the lack of aptitude and fondness for farming by the new inhabitants. Agricultural work was then mercenary, only practiced by slaves and Indians. The work performed by slaves on the coast, who performed their tasks only through fear of the whip, and the work of the Indians subjected to servitude was fully inefficient.

THE REPUBLIC

Once the independence of Peru was proclaimed, the first rulers and congresses, inspired by the ideas of the French Revolution, endeavored to declare in their constitutions, laws and decrees, individual liberties, guarantees for property, and suppression of economic burdens prevailing in Colonial feudalism. One of the first constitutional declarations stated that any property was alienable even if it belonged to "manos muertas" (unalienable estates), and any concept of supremacy was abolished. Tributes and personal service of various kinds ("pongos," "mitas," "encomiendas," "yanaconazgos") were also abolished.

The first rulers of the Republic, San Martin and Bolivar, issued a series of decrees inspired by the purest feeling for justice, understanding, and sympathy towards the Indian population and dedicated to the purpose of redeeming the Republic from the situation of prostration and servitude suffered by the natives during Colonial times. This is the meaning of the decree promulgated by San Martin on August 29, 1821, in which tributes are abolished, providing that in the future the natives will no longer be called "Indians" but "Peruvians," and the decree of August 28 of the same year, in which the services of "mitas," "pongos," and "encomiendas" were abolished as well as any kind of personal servitude. The decree issued by Simon Bolivar on April 8 has the same meaning, which, among other things, provided for the sale at public auction of national lands, excepting the lands owned by the Indians, which were declared under their ownership and could be sold or alienated in any manner. This decree provided for the allotment of the "lands of the community" among all the natives "not enjoying any other kind of land," allotting to married men a larger area than to single men. Hence, no Indian would remain without his piece of land.

PRESENT SITUATION

By virtue of the above resolutions and others that it is not necessary to quote, the lands of towns, villages, and communities, as well as those of the Indian families or "ayllus" were an easy prey for those who greedily began to take possession of them, using any means, legal or otherwise—in my opinion, more through fraud or violence than by legal means. It is in this way that, since 1821, when the Peruvian independence was proclaimed, until the promulgation of the Constitution in 1920, the lands formerly belonging to many natives and to their communities went to the hands of individuals, and thus great estates or farms were formed. And the former owners, that is, the natives living on said estates, have become the "yanacones," lessees or partners of the new owners.

How many farms there are of such great areas that they could be considered as being "latifundios" (large landholdings), their total extent in hectares, the area cultivated or exploited by their owners and, also the proportion of the lands not under cultivation, the declared value of these properties for the purposes of real estate taxes, their actual value, the average revenue or productivity of same—all these are questions and information that should be carefully collected in order to know fully the problems inherent in excessive ownership of lands.

The actual and ostensible fact is that there are very large estates in the three regions of Peru: the coast, the Sierra, and the forest or jungle. It is also a well-known fact that in such properties there is a great population of Indians who are "yanacones," lessees or sharecroppers. Thus the serious social, economic, and political problem arises with its two elements or factors, i.e., on the one side, large tracts of land in the hands of a few owners and, on the other side, a great number of Indian farmers with very little, if any, land to cultivate. This is, I repeat, one of the most serious problems to be faced with a realistic criterion in my country and in those other countries where equal or similar conditions prevail.

Considering the importance and transcendency, in my opinion, of the problem, I wish to refer, even though very superficially, to some of the most outstanding aspects. From an economic point of view, large landholdings (latifundisms) determine, on the one side, a great difference between a rich owner possessing vast and very productive lands and, on the other side, those lacking any amount of land and not having any other means of livelihood than their personal, physical, or material work, as mere farmhands or laborers, with remunerations much lower than a living wage. This situation of poverty is the cause of deficient nutrition, crowded and unhealthy dwellings, susceptibility to disease, ignorance, submission and dependency on the owner, with perhaps a repressed feeling of rebelliousness—in short, all the unrest to be expected of those who can not satisfy their primary needs because their financial situation does not allow it. This is the situation of the Indian and mixed blood masses, the cultural broth for the propagation of dissolving ideas and doctrines. He who has nothing, the indigent harassed by necessity, easily becomes an extremist renegade, a dangerous element. The complete ignorance of most Indians and mixed bloods makes them impervious to extremist doctrines at the present time, up to a certain point; however, the campaign against illiteracy, the diffusion of elementary, or primary, education not accompanied by a civic, moral, and religious education perhaps will prepare and make them more receptive to heed those who, by conviction or by following instructions they may have received, in a frank or in a clandestine way, may spread the doctrines of international communism. If we think of the means followed by extremist sectarianism, we have to recognize how easy the minds of such semi-civilized or uncultivated people can be carried away by passion to violent ways. Happily enough, this danger has been recognized, and, therefore, adequate action and work have been started already to prevent and to avoid it. But before going into this policy of social foresight, I must show still other aspects of the problem.

On the opposite side of "latifundism" there is also the problem inherent in a highly fragmentary land ownership, which is generally called "minifund." It is the natural and logical consequence of the fact that there is but a little land in the hands of many people or, in other words, that there are many people owning small plots of land, the product of which is not enough to cover their needs. Such minute division of property in some regions of my country has reached inconceivable proportions. The small holdings under cultivation, owned by numerous Indian families, have been divided and subdivided by virtue of inheritance rights through several generations, thus, I daresay, becoming almost infinitesimal. Personally, in the exercise of my profession as a lawyer in a genuinely indigenous community, the province of Canchis, in Cuzco Department, I have seen and witnessed the unyielding struggle of members of the same family to divide by furrows the very small plots of land they possessed. I know that similar things happen in other departments, such as those of Puno and Apurimac.

The excessive subdivision of property under cultivation and pasture lands is a cause of endless law suits between the joint-owners and adjacent owners, thus causing expenses which are entirely out of proportion to the value of the disputed plots, besides the loss of time in judicial or administrative formalities before the proper authorities. Such claims about ownership and possession of land are more numerous and prejudicial when the location and quality is more desirable. The ancestral attachment of the Indian to the land he owns induces him to defend and dispute the use of the soil, not taking into consideration the expensive legal proceedings and all the harm they create. It is not an overstatement to say that such expenses and damages often represent eight or ten times the value of the disputed land. Frequently, also, these disputes become real fights with subsequent personal injury, more or less serious, and sometimes death. The Indians who live on the lands of the large estates also have their difficulties with the landlords when their conditions of work or remuneration are intolerable to them. In former years, such revolts were more and more frequent. They assumed the character of true violence and resulted in turmoils owing to the action of some agents interested in promoting such conflicts. In many cases the police or the armed forces had to intervene in order to re-establish order and to guarantee the rights, safety, and lives of the landlords. While I am writing these lines, there comes to my mind more than one case in which such revolts had a tragic character and originated many lawsuits against large numbers of rebellious Indians.

Indians are generally peaceful, and they usually fulfill willingly all their duties in the tasks imposed on them since time immemorial for the use of the lands and pastures of the estates. When the landlord maintains good relations with them and is understanding and kind, inspired by an elementary feeling of justice, then there are no conflicts; the landlord or employer is considered as a protector and usually is respected and faithfully served. Happily enough, there are many of these cases in which the landlords have earned the confidence and co-operation of their laborers or sharecroppers without violence. But the fact that there were bloody revolts shows that some had abused their rights and exercised their rights despotically with personal punishments and exactions. This situation has notably changed in the last few years because of the guarantees given by political, police, and judicial authorities. This has been made possible by recently constructed means of communication and chiefly, perhaps, by a better cultural level that has been attained by the upper classes, to which the landlords generally belong. The new ideas about property as a social function and a feeling of sympathy towards those who, with their personal labor, make the land productive have brought the landlords closer to their sharecroppers or lessees, thus bettering their relations with a feeling of equity. Many other factors have had their bearing on this change, among them the policy of protection of the natives started many years ago, to which I will refer later on.

The opinions above expressed regarding the existence of large estates or latifundios and the excessively small properties are based on my personal knowledge and professional experience. I would like to express in definite figures the total extent or even an approximate estimate of such properties, but at the moment I am writing this report I lack the necessary data. One official source from which to obtain this information is the Registry of Real Estate, in effect since 1888, with offices in Lima, the capital of the Republic, and in the capitals of the departments or provinces. The registration of immovable property is made by virtue of titles stated in a public deed, specifying location, boundaries, extent, and value. Information from the Registry of Real Estate can furnish the total number of the recorded immovable properties and approximately their respective areas and value. Except for the number of properties recorded, the other data may be only of very relative value for different reasons. The registrations have been made on the basis of very old titles in which no boundaries or areas are specified. Many properties have not even been surveyed. Their extension has been only calculated into "fanegadas" or "topos." In other cases, when some measures have been effected, they were empirical and defective. The old land surveyors did not use any compass or chain; they measured the boundaries by means of armfuls or steps, or with ropes, and other times merely by sight. Therefore, the extensions allotted to rural properties appearing in the Registry of Real Estate do not always correspond to real areas. A similiar thing happens with prices or value. There are many properties appearing with much lower values because they were recorded in older times, and since then no reason has arisen to record new

values. Other properties also have very low values because their owners did not declare a true value, thus avoiding the payment of large taxes. It can be added to the foregoing that a great many properties are not recorded because of some fault in their titles, and therefore, the information in the Registry of Real Estate can include only a part of the rural properties, the ones already recorded; but properties not recorded are in the majority. However, in order to have an idea about the extent of rural real estate, no doubt the information of the Registry of the Real Estate could be very valuable, considering the fact that large estates, with some exceptions, have legal deeds and, therefore, have been recorded. The opposite is true for small holdings; they are registered only in a small proportion; most of them are not recorded at all because of deficient titles or because of ignorance or neglect of their owners considering the difficulties of the formalities and expenses to be incurred. For these reasons, any information from the Registry of Real Estate, which is valuable in many respects, is not complete and accurate.

Another source of information is the Census of Rural Land Taxes. Collection of the land taxes is entrusted to the Department of Collections of the Bureau of Deposits and Consignments. This department has branches all over the Republic, in the capitals of the provinces, where the registry of rural properties is made, subject to payment of land taxes. Periodically, the Inspectors of the Collection Department travel over the whole Republic to rectify the roll of taxpayers and to ascertain in person the true conditions of the estates of rural properties—the total area, cultivated, tillable, and nontillable sections, pastures, status of crops, dwellings, offices, plantations, implements, livestock, etc. The whole information is used to calculate the productivity of land and its value, and, on the basis of them, to appraise the rate of the land tax. Owing to this work that the Collection Department is effecting in a systematic way, the yearly revenue from rural land and from industrial and profit taxes has increased, as indicated by the reports issued by the Manager of the Bureau of Deposits and Consignments and by the General Budget Bureau of the Republic.

Besides the great properties and those which are excessively small, there are also properties of medium size, with a productivity sufficient for the maintenance of one family. Of course, these medium-size properties are ideal for the welfare of the people. No practical estimate can be made, however, about the area of land sufficient for the maintenance of a family, since it would be necessary to take into consideration several factors. Regarding the land, its location or situation with respect to consumer centers, means of communication, and cost of transportation all affect the sale price of products which are to compete in the market with equal products of other landowners. Concerning the owners, the size of a family is to be considered, as well as its social position. From a merely doctrinary point of view, according to a democratic criterion, the latter circumstances should not be taken into consideration. In principle, I agree; however, in countries like Peru in which social composition and organization imply the existence and juxtaposition of elements of different races, with economic and cultural standings deeply different, a realistic and pragmatic feeling induces us to accept, even unwillingly, such differences and to act accordingly. There are, in fact, rural lower classes whose needs and living standards are very low, though not really hopelessly indigent. I refer to those numerous classes which everywhere integrate the great mass of the population and which are beneath what we normally call the middle class. I refer to the classes of workers and manual laborers and, especially, to the small farmers. Such classes should be assured a type of rural property which allows them to support their families in relative comfort without privations.

Referring again to reality, I can assure you that there are many people and families of lower and middle classes owning sufficient lands to live on from their income. That is to say, there is the middle land property, the extent of which can not be accurately stated. The revenue of this land is more or less adequate to the needs of the owner.

Of course, it would be desirable to promote the increase of this type of property. To this end, two inverse procedures should be employed: on the one hand, there should be a redistribution of land holdings starting with the state lands and ending with the expropriation of surplus lands, not exploited, of large estates; on the other hand, there should be an endeavor, by legal means, to effect the consolidation of small properties. In the present Civil Code there are provisions in that direction. Article 1450 states that the following are entitled to the right of redemption: (1) "comuneros," or jointholders, in the sale of undivided lots or a piece of property; (2) the owner of adjacent land when there is a debt against rural property, the extent of which does not exceed three hectares, or when the former and the latter together do not exceed ten hectares. Similar provisions could be adopted for the division of rural properties in cases of legal succession or testamentary execution and in general for any divisions or allotments, when necessary, whatever the title of jointownership might be. It is preferable that one or two joint-owners should keep the rural property of sufficient size in order to use it with satisfactory results. Subdividing the property too much invariably results in difficult and uneconomical exploitation.

Lease, Sharecropping, "Yanaconaje"

The concentration of property in a few hands, to which I referred in the above paragraphs, and the fact that many owners are not exploiting their properties have given rise to extensive leasing of land. A lease of any real estate property is made, generally, "ad corpus" and not by hectares, some valleys of the coast excepted. The law determines all forms, conditions, requirements, and formalities of the contracts, as well as the rights and duties of the contracting parties.

Any lessee by working and obtaining products from lands which the owner does not want or is unable to work fulfills a useful function; however, at times the lessee is only an intermediary who subleases the whole, or part, of the land. In these cases, it is apparent that he acts as a mere speculator and adds to the cost of production.

Large properties in order to be exploited, either by the owners or by the lessees, require labor. Some properties have their own laborers, that is to say, numerous families of Indians and mixed bloods who, since time immemorial, live on the property and work on the best lands of the farm for the landlord. As compensation, they have the use of small surplus lands, and they maintain their livestock in the pastures of the estate.

On farms lacking laborers, the landlords have to obtain them by allotting the land to "yanacones" and "aparceros." "Yanacon" is the laborer and lessee of a plot who pays the lease with his labor on the farm for a certain number of days per week. "Aparcero" is the lessee who pays his lease with part of the products of the land under cultivation. Their share varies according to regions and can be up to 50 per cent of the harvest.

Since the owners of the farms or their lessees never work personally, all agricultural work is done by colonists or servants, or by "yanacones" or "aparceros," who are Indians or mixed bloods. Therefore, we can see the important economic function fulfilled by this part of the population, the largest, in the productive activities of the country. It is easily seen also that there is the need for bettering their economic and social situation. This we are endeavoring to do, for we know their situation very well. When I was a student at the College of Law of Cuzco University, I wrote a paper entitled "Systems of Leases for Lands Under Cultivation in the Cuzco Department and the Problem of Allotments." This paper was included in a booklet published by the above-mentioned University in 1946 on the occasion of the 250th anniversary of its founding, entitled *At the Service of the Peruvian Aborigines.*

Indigenous Communities

In this summary, however short it may be, I have to refer to the so-called indigenous communities. In fact, in all the above paragraphs I have made frequent allusions and references to these groups; therefore, I shall only enlarge and point out some ideas about such communities.

Indigenous communities, really, are a leftover of the pre-Colonial "ayllus." The name *comunidad* is Spanish and comes from Colonial times. As we have seen in the first part of this report, the Spaniards, when they founded villages or towns according to royal ordinances, at the moment of effecting the allotment and distribution of lands reserved a part of them for the common use or exploitation by the inhabitants of the village or hamlet and left also a part of the lands for the "ayllus" or families of the aborigines. The Indians, according to their ancient customs, used to cultivate communally the lands left to them in the same way as in pre-colonial times, that is to say, by annual allotments, and limited themselves to enjoying the use of the land, but did not dispose of properties or their appurtenances. It can be thus explained that the communities are lands owned by groups of indigenous families. By extension, a family group is also called community.

We have already seen that, when independence was proclaimed, in the first years of the Republic the aborigines of communities were declared the owners of their allotments and were allowed to dispose of them freely. Since then, legally, the communities disappeared, due to the fact that the lands remained in the exclusive ownership of those who had them in their possession. However, in fact, doubtless because of their ancestral customs, the "ayllus" have survived through all vicissitudes and at the present time there are still some who are keeping the communal property of the lands under cultivation, the annual allotments, and the community of pastures and woods.

The survival of the "ayllu" and the collective system of work give a peculiar character to the agrarian problem in Peru. It has been the object of numerous studies and an abundance of literature. There are some who believe that communal property is the cause of the backwardness observed in the Indian classes, and they advise that its dissolution should be encouraged. Others, on the contrary, think that communal property is one more link of solidarity among the "comuneros," because it gives them unity and power in their struggles with other social classes for the defense of their properties and interests. This question has been solved in a practical way with the provisions of the Constitution of 1920, which recognized a legal status to communities and declared, at the same time, their right of property inalienable and imprescriptible. Also the present Constitution of 1933 contains equal provisions. By virtue of all such constitutional provisions, the indigenous

communities now enjoy a legal existence or status.

We shall see now what is the real situation of indigenous communities regarding ownership of lands. There are but few who still keep a common ownership of lands under cultivation and annual distribution. Most of them have divided such lands into lots, especially irrigation lands; and they only maintain the community of pasture lands and woods. Finally, there are many communities, as I said before, that have lost the ownership of their lands, these lands having passed to private ownership—that is, to those who have purchased them by a purchase contract or by other legal means.

In all these communities there is still the co-operation of work. Each "comunero" cultivates his plot of land with the help of the other members of the community, and he is also under obligation to give equal collaboration to the others. This system of collaboration in agricultural work is called "ayni."

For many years, Congress and the government of Peru have understood the necessity of promoting the improvement of the economic, social, and cultural conditions of the aboriginal population, and for such purpose they have promulgated laws and resolutions to protect their persons and properties. Of all the laws in effect I will only mention the most important.

Clause XI of the present constitution states that the indigenous communities have a legal status and legal capacity; that the state guarantees the property of the communities; that such properties are imprescriptible and inalienable, except in the case of expropriation for public benefit, with compensation; that the state will endeavor, preferably, to allot lands to indigenous communities not possessing them in a sufficient amount to cover their population requirements and that private properties can be expropriated, for such purpose, with compensation.

The above provisions show that Peru realizes fully the real situation of the communities of aborigines and has a clear understanding of the policy to be followed. However, achievement of these aims is still to be accomplished.

The present Civil Code of 1936 contains the following provisions: Communities are subject to pertinent provisions contained in the constitution, and legislation is to be enacted according to such provisions. It is compulsory to keep the registration of each community in its special registry. Also required is the formation of tax lists of communities. Communities are represented by their delegates elected by their members. Communities shall not lease or assign the use of their lands to the owners of communal properties.

By a Supreme Decree dated July 24, 1925, it was prescribed that surveys were to be made of lands owned by indigenous communities. By Supreme Resolution of August 28 of the same year the Official Registry of Indigenous Communities was created in a section of the Ministry of Development.

By Law No. 8547 of June 11, 1937, the Bureau of Indigenous Affairs was created within the Ministry of Public Health and Social Welfare with the purpose of orienting and developing the government action in favor of the Indian population, to insure their incorporation into national activities, and to assure their economic welfare. The functions of this Bureau are as follows: to study all the aspects of the Indian problem and to propose any legislation and administrative measures tending to assure the economic and cultural welfare of the Indian population; to organize arbitration courts to hear any suits arising between the natives and between them and other persons; to solve administratively any claims and complaints of the Indians; to pass judgment on documents concerning the survey and official registration of communities; to organize the tax list of lands of the communities and their respective statistics; to suggest the adoption of provisions ruling contractual relations between the indigenous population and the owners of rural lands; and other related functions.

The Bureau has the free services of an Attorney's Office for Indians, created by Supreme Decree of November 14, 1941, the purpose of which is to sponsor the Indians in all their requests and claims.

By Resolution 9812 of January 19, 1943, the Peruvian Congress approved the Convention on the Inter-American Indian Institute, as decided in the First Inter-American Congress held in Patzcuaro.

By Ministerial Resolution of May 15, 1946, the Peruvian Indian Institute was organized.

Any review of all laws and resolutions in effect, according to which the Peruvian government is developing its policy of protection to the aboriginal population and, in general, its agrarian policy, would demand a longer time than I have available; therefore, I refer you to the publication *Legislacion Indigenista del Peru* (Indian Legislation in Peru) issued by the Bureau of Indigenous Affairs in 1948 and to other publications.

Recapitulation

In comparison with the total area of Peru, lands under cultivation are but a small part.

In the region of the coast, the principal necessity is that of irrigating new lands. The scarcity of laborers has brought about the use of mechanized equipment.

In the Sierra, farming and livestock breeding are extensive. This being rough country, the costs of transportation and of marketing products, as well as the costs of fertilizers and better systems of cultivation, are increasingly large.

The jungle is presently under a plan of colonization, with the construction of roads and a railroad. Here, too, there is a scarcity of labor.

The most important phenomenon recorded by the economic history of Peru is the concentration of rural property, which started in colonial times and continued under the Republic. This is why many native peasants possess no land or very small holdings inconveniently subdivided.

The decentralization of rural property is a national need in order to improve the social and economic condition of a large part of the population. The constitution of the country contains provisions allowing the powers of the state to act in such direction.

The "communities" of natives are the survival of the pre-Colonial "ayllu." The constitution and laws have recognized them by giving them a legal status, and the national policy is aimed at promoting their material and moral welfare.

LAND TENURE PROBLEMS ROOTED IN THE
ETHNIC HISTORY OF LATIN AMERICA

𝒮𝒮𝒮𝒮   *Alberto Arca-Parró*

FOR THE Latin American nations, whose autochthonous population had reached a high degree of civilization before the discovery of the continent, the land problem has a different connotation and meaning than for those nations where the native population had a lesser degree of demographic and cultural development or, in fact, was virtually destroyed. Consequently, the countries whose most important demographic foundation is precisely the autochthonous group, in their desire to seek a solution to their multiple problems, among which the agrarian problem is of capital importance, have fallen into the error of designating the indigenous problem the one which, in reality, is a complex group of social and economic problems.

Columbus' ignorance, and that of his contemporaries, attributed to the inhabitants of the New World the name of "Indios" (Indians) which eventually became a derogatory term. Following this way of thinking, in some of our countries there are people who think that the greatest harm that nature can have caused is to have allowed a numerous autochthonous population. For those people, the indigenous population has undoubtedly the significance of a negative factor in the formation of their respective nationalities. On the other hand, for those who appreciate in their true worth their contributions to the demographic and economic process of those same countries, the so-called "Indian problem" has a very different connotation and meaning: it is a struggle of population sectors culturally affected during the course of several centuries by the clash of cultures. Under the protection of a fortunate lack of racial discrimination, the biological "mestizaje" (intermarriage of the Indian and white races) has developed more rapidly than the cultural mestizaje. Because of this fact, in several Latin American countries the predominant national phenomenon continues to be the process of transculturation, rather than amalgamation of economies and cultural values.

In using the term "Indian" or "indigenous" in the course of this brief exposition, I do it without attributing to it any racial or political connotation, simply because, up to the present, no other term is known which makes it possible to differentiate or distinguish the population sectors which in some Latin American countries are suffering the consequences of living patterns imposed upon them by the Conquistadores. In effect, for the latter, in Mexico, Peru, and Bolivia as well as in other countries, more than the farm lands and the mines, the real loot consisted of arms to exploit them, especially the mines. That is why the famous Colombian writer German Arciniegas points out, and justly so, in one of his books: "All the wealth of the Latin American colonies consists of human wealth. The vassal is the only one who produces in these West Indies. Spain has been established in America for two and a half centuries and she has not even worried seriously about the scientific exploitation of the mines. The mine is the Indian, not gold. When the Conquistadores won these lands for the crown, they found mountains of gold, of clean pure metal, worked by the pre-Colombian gold miners for many centuries."

It becomes difficult, almost impossible, to analyze and understand the structure of property and land tenure in some Latin American countries without referring to the colonial institutions which originated it. In effect, for the Spanish Conquistador, the land was worth more not so much because of its own natural resources as because of the number of Indians who, while inhabiting it, not only had to exploit it but had to work outside of it for the benefit of their master. There fell to Philip II the sad privilege of creating one of the most perfect instruments for the exploitation of the indigenous population of America. In comparison with that population the Conquistadores were so few that in order to satisfy their greed for riches they had to utilize it to the fullest. Like many others, a Royal Charter of 1576 came to legalize an ignominious undertaking cleverly disguised as apparent preoccupations of a spiritual nature. The "encomienda" was established. It was defined as "the right granted by royal grace to the servants of America in order to receive and to gather for them the tribute of the Indians who are entrusted (encomendado) as a whole for one whole lifetime and of the life of one descendant with the charge of providing for the spiritual and material welfare of the Indians."

As the Bolivian sociologist Rafael A. Reyeros affirms, the "encomendero" (person in charge of an encomienda) as a feudal lord had duties towards the king who had granted the privilege. "He was sovereign by delegation, he administered justice, he collected taxes, profits and charges of any kind which were owed to the Crown, respecting the established legal situation, and the privileges acquired by the different social classes." In order to fulfill his obligation of paying tribute to his kind, the encomendero had to collect it from the encomendados (men entrusted to his care) appealing thus to all the imaginable means of coercion, with the efficient collaboration of the authorities who were usually appointed by him to serve his interests best. Historians state that aside from the doctrinarian priest, the teacher was never found who could teach reading and writing at least to the children of the encomienda, as royal ordinances prescribed.

In order to complete the picture of the exploitation of the aboriginal population, adapting the encomienda to the increasing necessities of compulsory labor, the repartimentos and the mitas were created. Through the repartimento thousands of Indians were assigned to certain people for the exploitation of the mines, the cultivation of coca, and the work in the textile mills. The mita, the complement of the repartimento, was the compulsory recruiting for periods up to three and four years, between the ages of eighteen and fifty, for working in the mines.

In famous mines, such as those of Huancavelica and Potosi, in territory which today belongs to Peru and Bolivia, respectively, it has been affirmed that the native workers who, together with their families, were taken by force to exploit mercury, silver, and other minerals were in the thousands.

There is incontrovertible proof that the impact of the conquest had disastrous repercussions on the demography of a large geoeconomic region, dominated by the Incas, known as Tahuantinsuyo, which today constitutes Peru, Bolivia, part of Ecuador, with an influence on the northern part of Argentina and Chile. The accelerated increment of mining inevitably determined the abandonment of agriculture, whose development had given prestige and power to the Incas. The method of forced labor, undernourishment, and diseases of European origin undoubtedly determined a serious process of depopulation, the effects of which are probably being overcome in this century in the three countries mentioned first, whose total population, under different circumstances, might have exceeded 20 million at the present time.

The economic effects of the process of depopulation were not ignored by the Spanish rulers of Peru. The clearest example is, without a doubt, illustrated by the attitude of Viceroy Francisco de Toledo, who between 1540 and 1575 traveled through a large part of the extensive territory entrusted to his care with the object of finding out personally about the conditions in which the people lived and dictating measures conducive to their good government.

One of the greatest projects of Toledo was to promote the concentration of population. To this end he founded the so-called reducciones, a remote paternal and protective relationship toward the aboriginal population and, at the same time, an antecedent of the concentration camps of the times of Hitler in Germany, because of the

suffering to which, in reality, that population was subjected by the authorities in spite of the regulations to the contrary.

Whatever the motives may have been which induced Toledo to establish, as has been stated, several hundred reducciones during his long trip through the Viceroyalty of Peru, it is necessary to recognize in him the deep intuition of a statesman upon realizing that the exaggerated geographical dispersion of population constituted a serious problem for his administration.

The reducciones were established near the mines and other enterprises controlled by the Spaniards. That is the economic meaning of their establishment. They should have become real reservoirs of labor. In order to justify the measure and the rigidity of the regulations, civilizing purposes were attributed to them. The natives should learn to live as civilized people, according to the saying of the conquistadores. The truth is that they gained nothing which contributed effectively to their individual and collective betterment. The most serious part is that such a deplorable situation has not developed noticeably in some of the regions of the former Tahuantinsuyo. Thus, Rafael Reyeros in his thought-provoking study on the "Pongueaje" in Bolivia in 1949 points out with disillusionment: "Five centuries after the conquest and after more than a century of republican life the Indians are in the same condition as they were in the days of Toledo. They live scattered next to their farms and pasture lands, as ignorant and subjected as they were in Colonial times. And the worst part of it is that they are bound, as then, to the tribute of personal servitude with all its inhuman magnitude."

Fortunately, the desolate picture which Reyeros paints is not reproduced with the same characteristics in all regions occupied by the indigenous population. There are, on the contrary, examples which justifiably open the way of hope and of optimism about the possibilities and capabilities of that population. One of those examples is the persevering work of the Mexican Agrarian Reform; another, on a smaller scale, is the results obtained in Peru through isolated legislative efforts. This does not exclude, in the case of Peru as well as Bolivia, Ecuador, and other countries, the urgent necessity of studying with much more effective criteria than previously the real causes of the agrarian problem and of seeking the corresponding solutions. An exposition, necessarily brief such as this one, does not offer the opportunity to point out several of those causes, much less to analyze them. Nevertheless, I should like to refer briefly to two of them which, in my opinion, are common to some of the countries mentioned and, apparently, have not been studied too much or up to the present time have been given little importance, namely, geographical dispersion of the population and unnoticed demographic pressure.

Geographic population dispersion.—As we have pointed out before, although this phenomenon already constituted a fundamental problem of one of the rulers of Peru, Bolivia, and Ecuador nearly four hundred years ago, the truth is that in these countries, at least in Peru, it seems to survive with similar characteristics. The formation and growth of towns and cities, although it has concentrated important groups of population, has not been, to be sure, a determining factor for radical change in the social structure of the farm population, except in one of its regions, the coast. The rural population continues to live in several thousand small centers of population, whose number increases probably from year to year without being reached by the benefits of the social and political organization of the country. Thus the population census of 1940 made evident that nearly one-third of the population of school age, between the ages of six and fourteen, was not receiving any education, principally because it lived distributed in thousands of small centers of population with an average of less than fifty inhabitants. Under such circumstances it is virtually impossible for the state to be able to establish schools and other services for the community, such as sanitation, for example.

We must agree that the same phenomenon of dispersion of population has a negative repercussion on the development and improvement of agriculture. In effect, we must admit that even if we had adequate economic resources available it is very difficult, if not impossible, to take the new technical concepts or modern means of farming to thousands of farmers who cultivate a few hectares of land almost always in family groups living three thousand to thirty-five hundred meters above sea level, in places where even the smallest and most powerful jeeps cannot reach, and at times not even horses.

If such people have established their homes and fields on the slopes of the mountains, frequently taking advantage of the terraces which their ancestors, more patient and more numerous than they, built, this is due to causes which it has not been possible for them to overcome. Among those causes the one that acts with most intensity is the lack of other lands which will offer better conditions for living and farming. This is, to be sure, one of the cases in which with eloquent clarity the laws stated by the economist about the sequence of occupation and use of the land by man are fulfilled.

Unnoticed demographic pressure.—This is another phenomenon which still has not been carefully studied in our countries. Generally it is based on the supposition, unfounded to be sure, that as long as a country has only four, five, or ten inhabitants per square kilometer it is almost inconceivable that demographic pressure can exist, that, on the contrary, those are countries generously endowed by nature, and that without greater difficulty they could support a population two and even three times greater than the present one.

Nevertheless, in many cases, particularly in the Andean countries of the Americas, the problem should be formulated in its true aspects and, consequently, analyzed from other angles. In effect, several of the countries that show such low coefficients of density as the ones mentioned are acting, in reality, under the influence of a fallacy. If in a country whose territory is a million square kilometers the exact area of land under cultivation and land which could be put under cultivation will be determined by discarding those which under no circumstances could be utilized even with the help of modern technology, said coefficients, in some cases, could be multiplied by ten, twenty, and, perhaps, thirty.

It has frequently been stated that certain regions are not exploited agriculturally because the population of the country that owns them is small in comparison to their territory. Such is the case of the South American countries which have extensive areas virtually uninhabited in the great Amazon and Orinoco basins. However, the corresponding surveys would make evident that as long as the national and even the international economies are not modified substantially, those regions will continue being mere geo-economic reserves for a more or less remote future. An aggregate of economic facts and phenomena as well as facts and phenomena of a different nature make almost impossible, for the time being, the extensive utilization of the natural resources of those regions. Therefore, in some of those countries, in spite of the fact that there exist enormous unproductive areas, we might even say uninhabited, the population is struggling to transfer from one place to another in search of farm lands; and, finally, on not finding them, it goes to the cities, where it increases to a pathological degree.

Under such circumstances, when the farmer either through his own means or through state participation, has taken possession of all or the largest part of the land usable for immediate cultivation without succeeding in producing all the food that the population requires, it is evident that there exists a serious problem of readjustment between the factors Man and Land. This is a problem which, in fact, responds to the phenomenon of demographic pressure, whose effects go somewhat unnoticed in the Latin American countries partly because of the deficient nutrition of their populations. However, in some of them the resulting problems are acquiring alarming proportions. Without wishing to exaggerate I believe that through an aggregation of factors of a demographic, economic, social, and cultural nature in the countries of dense indigenous population such as Peru, Bolivia, and Ecuador those problems are becoming more acute each day. That is why it is indispensable and urgent to study them with scientific criteria and to seek the wisest and most equitable solutions as quickly as possible.

Unfortunately, in none of the three countries mentioned is there statistical information regarding their respective agricultural and livestock processes which could permit the development of studies such as we have indicated. They have census statistics on population but not on agriculture, at least not brought up to date. Peru took a population census in 1940; probably next year it will take another one again, together with the agricultural and livestock census. As part of the program of the census of the Americas, Bolivia and Ecuador, as I understand it, have taken only their population census during the course of 1950. Under such circumstances, it is evidently very difficult to determine the technical foundations of an agrarian policy for any of these countries. However, those who in our respective countries have imposed upon ourselves the vocational obligation to study their great social and economic problems have not resigned ourselves to postponing them indefinitely. We have analyzed them in the light of available information, appealing to supplementary references to avoid premature or subjective generalizations as much as possible. That is why there are many studies on such problems which, in spite of the above-mentioned difficulties, have succeeded in being the objective expression of collective needs long and deeply felt.

It was under these unfavorable circumstances, incidentally, that a few years ago I set out to study the disturbing problem of the land tenure system of the Indian communities of Peru and the supplying of more land to them. I had previously participated in the incorporation of Article 211 into the present Constitution, which provides for the granting of lands by the state to the Indian communities which do not have them in sufficient size to satisfy the needs of the population.

The legal personnel of the Indian communities is recognized and guaranteed by express regulations of the Peruvian Constitution of 1933. It is under the protection of these regulations that, in the last few years, they have intensified the revision of their titles on the lands which they exploit. This has given rise to the clarification of the legal value of the respective titles, in opposition to the corresponding titles to lands which are part of individual land holdings. In spite of the fact that frequently individual owners can offer titles which, according to law, will justify their possession, the fact is that almost invariably there results a conflict of a social rather than a judicial nature between the communities and the individual owners.

As a consequence of the above-mentioned study, I became convinced that a law was indispensable which would permit the application of the already mentioned Article 211 of the Constitution. In spite of the time that has elapsed, the problem still maintains its timeliness. Because of that, and because it is directly related to the theme that I have tried to develop in this exposition, I consider it opportune to point out the following conclusions.

1. The conflicts arising from the claims of the Indian Communities in Peru on the best right of ownership of cultivated and pasture lands, constitute one of the most acute manifestations of the so-called Indian problem, whose causes rather than being of a racial nature assume a demographic, economic, social, and cultural aspect.

2. The analysis of the economic and social causes of the problem reveals a marked tendency towards its acuteness, especially because of the high specific density of population in relation to the tillable or economically adequate land, which determines the phenomenon of demographic pressure, with ostensible manifestation in important areas of the region of the Sierra.

3. While the mortality rate has declined slightly, the birth rate has remained appreciably high, particularly in the rural areas, resulting in an annual increase of at least 140,000 inhabitants, without the areas of food production increasing in a corresponding proportion.

4. Under such circumstances it is necessary to provide adequate means for the effective application of Article 211 of the Constitution, and the state should proceed to the expropriation with adequate compensation of the lands of individual ownership bordering on the communities which, according to special investigations, lack sufficient land to satisfy their needs.

5. Upon adjudicating said lands to the interested communities they will be provided, through a special institute of rural credit, with credit, farming implements, and technical guidance necessary to increase their production, to improve their standard of living, and to contribute in a fair proportion to the amortization of the price of the land in a time limit no shorter than fifteen years.

There is no doubt that measures suggested only tend to give a transitory solution to one of the various aspects of the agrarian problem. Nevertheless, their adoption would relieve to an appreciable degree the situation of an important sector of the agrarian population which, together with the Yanaconas (Indians bound to personal service), sharecroppers, and renters make up the continuing victims of the notable agricultural practices established by the Incas. They constitute today the largest group of the working force of Peru which has not been fully reached by the advancement of social legislation. As long as integral solutions are not furnished for the Peruvian agrarian problem, incorrectly called the Indian problem, they will continue to live in a very inferior situation to that of the industrial worker, whose occupational diversification has allowed him a greater educational development, the starting point for his economic and social betterment.

SOME ASPECTS OF LAND TENURE IN BRAZIL

𝄞𝄞𝄞𝄞   João Gonçalves deSouza

IT IS MY privilege and responsibility to talk before this conference on a subject which is new to most Latin American nations, especially Brazil, i.e., social security for landless workers. In spite of this being a new area of study, I could not resist the opportunity to say what I think will be possible and necessary in this field either to consolidate or enlarge initiatives where they are. Before doing this, I will try to give you an idea of the main relationships between men and land in Brazil so that we can understand this problem better from the angle of the so-called underdeveloped nations.

The basic problem with which the majority of our nations of Latin America are now confronted is the improvement of the level of living of the landless worker in order to create a rural middle class economically strong and socially healthy. Such a problem is a permanent menace to the peace of America and a constant problem to our leaders and men of responsibility.

In many cases the social distance between the large holdings on the one hand and the workers on the other is so large that something should be done to achieve four main objectives: (1) to increase food production, (2) to avoid abrupt and violent destruction of the agrarian economic structure of these nations, (3) to create economic and social security for the farm people in communities in which they live, and (4) to create or enlarge a rural middle class of rural families tilling their own soil, raising their own cows, as a fundamental base of a democracy of free and independent men.

Tradition and Rural Traits

To start with, I want to call your attention to the rural tradition and the main characteristics of the nation of farmers that Brazil is today, notwithstanding a strong tendency to accelerate her industrialization in some areas according to conditions observed in the last twenty years.

Since the beginning of her history Brazil

has been a nation typically rural. The structure of her economy, based on coffee, cattle raising, cotton, rubber, wood industry, and the functional character of her social institutions show that Brazil is today still an agrarian nation. The houses, customs, the way of life, the arrangement between people and the land, size of families, natural increase in population, and the basic social values in the country are evidences of a nation typically rural.

Now, let us go into some specific details which I think are essential to the understanding of the subject with which I am going to deal.

The Land and Its Utilization

Brazil, larger than the United States, has roughly 8.5 million square kilometers of territory. Of the total amount of 846,400,000 hectares of land, only 200 million comprised the properties counted in the 1940 census. In other words, only 23.36 per cent of the total area of Brazil in farming was tabulated in the 1940 census. The percentage for the United States in 1940 was 55.7 per cent; for France in 1939 it was 96.6 per cent. The small number of people per occupied area together with the low capacity of production per unit of area show the extensive character of our agriculture when taken into consideration in the national picture.

While the average area of farms in the United States in 1940 was 70.4 hectares and in France 9.5 hectares in 1939, in Brazil the average area per farm was 103.8 hectares, which gives an average of 19 hectares per person.

"The low rent of the land and a larger number of people per farm are extensive characteristics of Brazilian agriculture."[1]

In regard to the types of farming, the census considered four main groups: agriculture, mixed exploitation (agriculture and cattle raising), cattle raising, all other types together. The most important group was that of mixed exploitation, which embraced

TABLE 30

BRAZILIAN FARMS ACCORDING TO TYPES OF EXPLOITATION, 1940*

Type of Farming	Number of Farms	Farm Area	1939 Value (cruzeiros)	Permanent Workers
Agriculture	30 99	11.19	21.52	24.50
Large-scale	0.41	1.35	7.01	3.37
Small-scale	30.58	9.84	14.51	21.13
Mixed agriculture	59.53	47.25	63.93	63.43
Large-scale	0.22	2.97	8.49	4.48
Small-scale	59.31	44.28	55.44	58.95
Cattle raising	6.06	37.79	14.03	10.09
Large-scale	3.04	33.73	12.97	8.00
Small-scale	3.02	4.06	1.06	2.09
Other	3.42	3.77	0.52	1.98
Total	100.00	100.00	100.00	100.00

*In percentages of totals.

59.53 per cent of the number of all properties, 47.25 per cent of the total area, 63.43 per cent of the people permanently occupied, and 55.63 per cent of the total value of the farms in cruzeiros. This group contributes 63.93 per cent of the value of the total production of the country.[2]

In other words, in 1940 there were in Brazil 1,904,589 farms with a total area of 197,720,247 hectares, with a production of 8 billion cruzeiros, and with 10,532,847 people permanently engaged in agriculture. These numbers are better presented in percentage form, as shown in Table 30.

Table 30 shows a series of facts which should be analyzed if we want to understand the nature and relationships between people and the land in Brazil and the natural difficulties we will have to face when we try to enact social legislation for landless workers. The table shows the following conclusions. (1) Of the total number of farms in Brazil 60 per cent are engaged in mixed agriculture, 31 per cent in agriculture as such, and 6 per cent in cattle raising. (2) While in the case of agriculture we have 31 per cent of the number of farms with 11 per cent of the total area, in the case of cattle raising we have 6 per cent of the farms comprising 37.79 per cent of the total area. (3) The mixed activity contributes 64 per cent of the total value of production, agriculture 21.5 per cent, and cattle raising 14 per cent.

Exploitation on a larger scale (plantation system) is characterized by the extension of the medium area of farms (342 hectares in agriculture, 1,394 in mixed activities, and 1,152 in cattle raising), and by the large number of occupied people per unit (45 in agriculture, 112 in mixed activities, and 15 in cattle raising).

Utilization of Land

How has the land been utilized? Without mentioning the losses from erosion and in-

adequate farming methods, let's see the way the land has been used according to types of farming.

TABLE 31

MAJOR CLASSES OF LAND UTILIZATION IN BRAZIL, 1940

Type of Use	Hectares	Percentage of total
Agriculture	18,835,430	9.53
Pasture	88,141,733	44.58
Forests	49,085,464	24.82
Noncultivated lands	29,296,493	14.82
Nonproductive lands	12,361,127	6.25
Total	197,720,247	100.00

Table 31 shows that the area in agriculture is less than 10 per cent of the land utilized and that pastures cover 44.58 per cent of the total. Less than one-fourth of the total area of the farms was forest land and one-sixth was land not taken into utilization. Summarizing this table according to the character of exploitation on a large and on a small scale, we have the figures shown in Table 32. From Table 32 we can see that agriculture in Brazil is an activity on a small scale and that cattle raising is an activity on a large scale.

Size of Farms in Brazil

If we group all the properties in Brazil into five classes we have the figures shown in Table 33, which shows small, medium, large, very large farms, and exceptionally large classes of farms according to area.[8] The small farms, with a maximum of 10 hectares, comprise 34 per cent of the total number of farms and only one-fourth of the farm area but absorb one-fifth of the total number of people farming. The medium-

TABLE 32

DISTRIBUTION OF LAND AMONG LARGE- AND SMALL-SCALE UNITS OF OPERATION
IN BRAZIL, 1940*

Size of Operation	Agriculture	Pasture	Forest and Unproductive Lands	All Types
Large-scale	20.97	52.04	28.00	38.05
Small-scale	78.00	46.52	65.39	58.18
Nonfarming utilization or waste land	1.03	1.44	6.61	3.77
Total	100.00	100.00	100.00	100.00

*In percentages of totals.

size farms—from 10 to 100 hectares—and the large farms—from 100 to 1,000 hectares—together constitute the most important group. They embrace 64 per cent of the number of farms, 51 per cent of the farm area, 72 per cent of the value of the farms, 78 per cent of total farm production, and 73 per cent of the people farming. The very large farms—from 1,000 to 10,000 hectares—and the exceptionally large farms—10,000 hectares and over—together comprise only 1.45 per cent of the number of all farms in Brazil. However, they comprise almost one-half of the area of all farms (48.31 per cent) and produce one-tenth of the total production with just 6.5 per cent of the people farming.

Thus, if you take latifundium in its spatial meaning, Brazil is still a land of latifundia. In fact, less than 2 per cent of the farms in 1940 had almost one-half of the area of the total farms. However, we should underline the tendency shown by the last three censuses—the natural breaking down

TABLE 33

RELATIVE IMPORTANCE OF FARMS IN BRAZIL ACCORDING TO SCALE OF OPERATIONS,
1940*

Classes	Number of Farms	Farm Area	Value of Farms	Value of Production	Number of Farmers
Small	34.43	1.46	6.48	11.32	20.01
Medium	51.30	16.75	33.61	43.88	45.61
Large	12.82	33.48	38.45	34.32	27.80
Very large	1.39	31.37	18.67	9.55	5.94
Exceptionally large	0.06	16.94	2.79	0.93	0.64
Total	100.00	100.00	100.00	100.00	100.00

*In percentages of totals.

of the large holdings, especially because of the heritage system. By the way, this process is going too far in the opposite direction; in fact, the federal district and the state of Maranhao had, respectively, 70 and 80 per cent of the farms with less than five hectares.

Tenure of Land

In regard to tenure, almost all of the farms (93.16 per cent) are owned by private individuals, with only 5.25 per cent owned by state and federal governments.[4] Who owns the land in Brazil? How is it operated?

The large majority of the properties in Brazil are owned and cultivated by the owners (72.28 per cent). As many as 9.3 per cent are operated by administrators, 11.63 per cent by renters, 5.72 per cent by occupants. The administrator is more frequent in monoculture, in the latifundia exploitation as in the case of coffee, sugar cane, cocoa, rubber, etc. We see that 9 per cent of the administrators handle 22 per cent of the area of all farms. Table 34 gives the complete idea of this problem.

Now a word in regard to the tendency to break down the large farms and the forms by which they are operated. Comparative data of the 1850, 1920, 1940, and 1950 censuses show two clear tendencies: (1) The number of small farms is increasing to a great extent; the medium-size farms are relatively stationary; and the large or latifundia are breaking down. This tendency, which is socially good, is checked by the following tendency, which is not so good. (2) Between the 1920 and 1940 censuses the number of owners in Brazil increased 240 per cent, while the number of administrators increased 367 per cent and the renters 960 per cent. In other words, comparing the administrators with proprietors, the increase was 2 to 1; the proportion of renters to owners was 4 to 1. This means that the large holders are still moving to cities and transferring their lands to administrators and renters.[5]

To be sure, the meaning behind these data led social scientists to formulate conclusions which are true for some areas of the country but not true for Brazil as a whole. The first conclusion is: "The Brazilians are divided into a small handful of proprietors and an overwhelming majority of pauperized laborers who are bound in one way or another to a pastoral regime."[6] The second remark is more recent and reads as follows: "The shift from coffee to cotton production apparently has been responsible for an expression of farm tenancy observed by some experts during recent decades."[7]

These facts, numbers, and tendencies

TABLE 34

Number and Percentage of Farms in Brazil According to Tenure

Tenure	Number of Farms	Area (in hectares)	Number of Farmers	Per Cent of Farms	Per Cent of Area	Per Cent of Farmers
Proprietors	1,376,602	127,276,879	7,628,840	72.28	69.48	72.43
Administrators	178,376	44,832,481	1,579,012	9.37	20.53	14.99
Renters	221,505	19,117,981	894,723	11.63	8.46	8.50
Occupants	109,016	5,278,125	375,457	5.72	1.31	3.56
Others	19,090	1,214,781	54,815	1.00	0.22	0.52
Total	1,904,589	197,720,247	10,532,847	100.00	100.00	100.00

stressed before lead us naturally to consider the problem from a new angle, that is to say, from the viewpoint of the increase of the population of Brazil. Some figures will help to understand not only the man-land relationships but also the social implications.

According to the 1950 census the population of Brazil was 52,645,479.[8] Between 1940 and 1950 there was a net increase of 11,409,-164 people, or a relative increase of 27.67 per cent in the period. Brazil is today the most populated of the Latin nations, including France and Italy. Such a rate of increase, one of the largest in the world and one which characterizes agrarian nations less industrialized, varies very much from farm to city and from area to area. The ten largest cities in 1940 had 10 per cent of the total population of the country, a percentage which increased to 13 per cent in 1950. On the other hand, while the relative increase of people in a period of ten years for the nation was, as we saw before, 27.67 per cent, this figure rose to 50 per cent and 70 per cent in the pioneer states of Goias and Parana. In the western part of Goias the demographic increase was 141.5 per cent.[9] This happened not because of international migration but mainly because of internal migratory influx of landless workers, renters, and small farmers looking for new homes in new areas of the country. The main areas from which the migrants came are the northeastern states and the central and eastern states (Minas and Estado do Rio).[10]

Tenure Types

Now it is time to give some attention to the social rural structure of Brazil, through which we can see the main obstacles to carrying out a program of social legislation and social security for landless workers.

In Brazil we have enormous variation in numbers of social classes tilling the land.

The proprietors (large, medium, and small), the administrators, renters, share croppers, hired labor, colono, agregado, vaquero, empreiteiro, are the main human types of rural Brazil representing different tenure classes and social processes.

The proprietor is the owner of the land. In the diversified agriculture in the southern states where foreign migrants (Italians, Germans, Japanese) have been established, the proprietor is the one who tills the soil with his own family without outside help. This constitutes an overwhelming majority of the rural middle class, economically well established and socially progressive. In the case of commercialized agriculture, as for example in the coffee area (S. Paulo, Parana) and cattle raising area (central western states and R. G. do Sul), in the sugar cane zone (Northeast and E. do Rio), in cocoa exploitation (south of Bahia), in rubber and Brazil nuts (Amazon Valley), the proprietor is the absentee owner. The absentee is a cultural trait of the Spanish and Portuguese way of farming in Latin America. The administrator is the one who takes care of the farm in place of the owner; he generally receives cash per month. The renter works in place of the owner, to whom he pays rent in cash or kind, or both. When he pays in kind he is called parceiro because parceiro (sharecropper) is a form of land use in many parts of the country.[11]

The vaqueiro is the man who takes care of the cattle on the farm in the absence of the owner. On those farms the number of cattle runs into the thousands; this is not on the scale of the small family enterprise. If the stock is of superior quality, the vaqueiro receives a fixed monthly payment in cash, which varies from area to area of the country. If the stock is of inferior quality, the vaqueiro takes the "sorte," that is, in every four calves he can take one. That is quite common in the states of Piaui and Marahao. In the San Francisco Valley, where in 1940 there were 9,604,000 cows,[12] about 90 per cent of the cattle raisers fall in that category. The vaqueiro receives for his work calves instead of cash. According to a recent field study done in the San Francisco area, the same tendency was found there.[13] Just to mention the San Francisco Basin, where at this time a large economic and social recovery program has been patterned after that of TVA, the author found six different types of renters. In the coffee plantation area we find three types: (1) the contratista (man who clears the land, plants the seeds for coffee or food production; the owner receives the coffee production, and the food production goes to the contratista), (2) the meeiro (a fifty-fifty arrangement), and (3) the hired workers as such, who receive cash, education, and health services from the owners.

In the case of commercialized production, the population pyramid of Brazil shows at the top the richer class of owners, at the middle, renters, share croppers, administra-

tors, small farmers, and at the bottom a large mass of laborers. The first class has a very high level and standard of living; the second class has a medium standard of living; and the lowest class in some cases live well, but the majority of them, when taken as a whole, compose a mass of unstable, illiterate, and poor population.

This is the human picture of rural life in Brazil in its fundamental aspects. We still have to consider that in spite of having 52,600,000 people in 1950, the demographic density for the country as a whole was only 6.2 people per square kilometer. This demographic density dropped to 1 person per square kilometer and lower in the central western states and in the extreme north. Since the means of transportation by land are still so difficult in the above areas and the social structure so strong, these figures will give you an idea of how great are the difficulties in carrying out a program of social education and social security for people so spread out and geographically separated.

LAND TENURE PROBLEMS OF COLOMBIA

𝄐𝄐𝄐𝄐   *Pedro Bernal*

Two BASIC facts are deduced from the interesting talks that we have heard here these last few days and which have brought us up to date on the land tenure situation in a good number of countries.

First, most nations consider the problem from two points of view: one, that vast tracts of land in the control of a few prevent many men who desire to own and work land from access to it; the opposite point of view is that excessively small plots cause a general state of poverty due to the very tiny area which each head of a family can cultivate for the support of himself and his family.

The second fact which stands out in these

papers is that all countries have made or are making reforms they believe are suited to their environment, their legal systems, their historical, geographical, and topographical conditions and which are designed to remedy the situation to the extent considered just and equitable and that to this end each one is applying the economic resources at its disposal, which, being very small, limit the action of each government. For this reason, the process is slow and the results long overdue.

I don't believe it is necessary to go into any great detail in this paper, since the case of Colombia is essentially the same as that of other countries, especially in Latin America. Briefly, it is the following. (1) About 70 per cent of the population of Colombia is composed of campesinos (agricultural workers) who live on the land. (2) The people have a strong desire to possess land and to work it, and they are slowly improving their systems and procedures of cultivation insofar as topographical conditions permit the use of modern working tools. (3) Colombia is not overpopulated, and there are vast lands that we have not occupied; all of us Colombians could be landowners of tracts that in other countries might be called latifundia, although it seems to me that this word has only relative value for each country and even within each country for each environment of uniform conditions. (4) Although, ignoring this term, I should admit that there are some zones in Colombia in which the tracts of land are excessively large even for the Colombian environment and that there are other sections where the land is divided into such small parcels that they are inadequate for the decent support of a family, given the methods of cultivation used there and the poor training of the campesino.

These conditions will be better understood after a short explanation of the topography of Colombia. In the southern part of the country the Andes form a knot from which three cordilleras branch out towards the north and the Caribbean. They are high chains with steep slopes, lofty peaks, some of them snow-capped, and plateaus which are not over-large. Between these cordilleras there are valleys at altitudes varying from sea level up to more than two thousand meters, with all the characteristics of the tropical zone: high temperatures, alternate periods of drought and heavy rainfall, and malaria and other endemic diseases no less serious. Along the center of these valleys are great rivers which collect the waters from these mountains and flow towards the north: Magdalena, Cauca, and Atrato.

The eastern cordillera slopes off on its eastern side to the vast interior plains (llanos) with poor vegetation, thin layer of topsoil, with natural pastures of low nutritive value—plains which extend to our frontiers with Venezuela and continue beyond them to the south. This cordillera ends in the timeless tropical forests crossed by rapid rivers which empty into the Amazon at our frontier with Brazil and Peru.

It is entirely understandable why the Spanish immigrants who followed the discovery of America preferred to settle upon the mountain lands of medium or high altitudes, where, besides searching for gold, they found climate and living conditions which contrasted less sharply than the valleys with the environment they had left in their native country. With the exception of some few places having all the tropical characteristics, such as Cartagena, the Spaniards settled in altitudes of one thousand or more meters, where the temperatures were milder and where the tropical plagues are less strong or less likely to occur, according to the altitudes. Gonzalo Jimenes de Quesada, the conqueror from Spain who gave New Granada its name, crossed these dense jungles with his men from the Caribbean coasts and battled these rivers until they found, not the El Dorado (golden land) which they sought, but the sabana (plateau), where they founded the city of Santa Fe, today Bogota, the capital of the country, at 2,300 meters (8,400 feet) above sea level and 1,200 kilometers (750 miles) from the Atlantic coast. This sabana is the largest plain at that altitude in Colombia.

Doubtless this first colonization of the country started the movement which has continued along the cordilleras, the population scattering over them as they multiplied. This force is so marked that the population from one group, the Antioquians, wanderers and pioneers, in general do not descend to the valleys, but spread throughout the country following the mountain chains which, although somewhat inhospitable, are preferred by them for their agricultural and livestock enterprises, especially for the cultivation of coffee. It might be interesting to note here that about two years ago a book by an observant and studious person was published, called *Antioquian Colonization in Western Colombia.*

The result of this process of colonization that I have briefly described is that the majority of the population of Colombia is located on the sloping, irregular lands of the mountains and suffers all the consequences of such a location: difficult and costly means of communication, expensive transportation, costly agricultural production by the sweat of the brow, not mechanized labor, underproduction, and, most serious of all, terrible erosion. What can be produced in the future—and not the very distant future—on these slopes plowed two or three times a year and then swept of their topsoil by the intense tropical rains?

Colombia represents the most abnormal of situations: intensive agriculture on the steep slopes and forests and cattle ranges on the fertile, level plains.

Naturally, the distribution of population has been the factor determining the laying out and construction of communication routes, and these in turn determine the location of markets for the produce of each zone. The high cost of transportation and difficult living conditions at any distance away from the village and from the roads and railways cause considerable pressure on the prices of lands which are better located with respect to transportation and markets.

On the other hand, those investors are never absent who acquire lands as the most secure outlet for the investment of their capital or who merely await the capitalization of these lands with no further interest in their development—all of which is a

very natural consequence of the turbulent political situation of the country during the past century and of the instability of the currency. A few months ago, the Currie Mission made an over-all study of the conditions in Colombia and suggested new taxes for lands over a certain size which did not produce a determined annual minimum of product as a means of forcing the landowners either to cultivate the lands adequately or to sell them to those who could and would cultivate them intensively. The idea was not very well received because, we believe, man responds better to the stimulant than the sanction, because there are many ways of creating interest in remunerative cultivation, and because the state can control speculation by opening new opportunities for labor in the vast tracts of public lands which it still possesses.

From the above it is found that there are two very clear solutions to our land tenure problem. One solution is a just redistribution of those lands located in the zones having the greatest population densities, which are, incidentally, quite extensive. The other solution is (to use the English verb although it does not have exactly the same meaning in Spanish) to "reclaim" our valleys, the public lands, and place them at the disposal of man. Of all of us the state is the greatest latifundista.

In order to facilitate the acquisition of land by the peasants we have in Colombia two institutions. One of them, called the Institute of Land Distribution and Colonization (Instituto de Parcelación y Colonización), founded only in 1948, is designed to solve our land tenancy problems in the two ways just mentioned: by the purchase from private owners of lands, which are sold in plots of adequate size to poor farmers on long-term mortgages at low interest rates and by colonization, which requires a great deal of investment. The first is enjoying some success, although it leaves much to be desired due to very limited financial resources. Very little or nothing has been done with respect to colonization for the same reason—insufficient capital.

The other institution which gives aid to the farmers is the Agricultural Credit Bank (Caja de Crédito Agrario), founded in 1931, which step by step has built up its present capital reserves of 55 million Colombian pesos (something over 19 million dollars), which provides valuable service to agriculture and which holds the esteem not only of the farmers but the Colombian people as a whole. The capital of this bank belongs in large part to the state, but among its stockholders are also found some associations and a few private individuals. The principal function of the Bank is to provide the farmers with credit for crops, for installations of various kinds, and for machinery and equipment. The Bank also carries on credit operations for the acquisition of small properties, although this activity will have to be reduced so as not to constitute an excessive drain on the production credit resources of the Bank, since the country has suffered a serious deficit in food products during the last few years. During the fiscal year ending June 30, 1951, the Credit Bank completed 144,365 credit operations at a total value of 146,126,206 Colombian pesos. The average loan made was 1,059 pesos, and it is interesting to note that 97.71 per cent of the loans were for amounts under 5,000 pesos.

This is what we are doing now and what we will continue to do. We believe we have found the proper way, and we will follow it. Our government is making a special effort every day to provide these institutions with new sources of capital. But in spite of this we are not going along at the speed which we desire and which is necessary.

Land redistribution requires capital investments of some size. The poor farmer

has to be given long terms in which to redeem his lands; probably he will be able to do nothing more than meet the interest payments during the first few years until he has his little enterprise well under way. He must also be given the means for constructing his home, and he must be provided with working tools.

Colonization requires even greater investments. In some of the valleys, such as the Cauca, the population has increased considerably during the last thirty years, and mechanized agriculture has developed on these lands of excellent quality, which lands formerly were used for grazing in the most primitive way. But we still have very extensive valleys with good soil for agriculture, low population density, and immense zones of virgin forest, largely the property of the state.

We feel the strong necessity of occupying these valleys, not only to make a greater number of Colombians landholders but also to increase production and lower prices, of mechanizing agriculture wherever possible, and of reducing the agriculture carried on on the mountainous slopes in order to reduce erosion. We cannot do this without opening communication routes, building schools, improving sanitation, without, in many cases, engaging in irrigation, and without being able to fall back on even the most elementary amenities of life. The tropics is an unbridled enemy of man, and the fight for a living in the tropics is a hard one. The struggle, however, is not by any means hopeless.

I believe that the programs of all the countries represented at this very opportune conference at the University of Wisconsin can be implemented to solve their land tenancy problem; each one requires capital investments, very much as we do, in greater or lesser quantities according to the delay in development.

I also believe that all of them—or almost

all—find themselves in the same financial difficulties as we do for the carrying out of these programs in the short time desired. Governments which do not have large national budgets, governments of poor countries, are constantly pressed by necessities, attention to which cannot be delayed. When distributing their limited funds they do not know whether to use them for the shirt or the pants because it is not enough for both. So they postpone from year to year these other needs and problems which seem to them less pressing.

Let us hope that out of this conference will come clear ideas on the financing of the programs which might be prepared to solve the problems of each country with respect to land tenure. I find the proposal of the Delegate from Lebanon very opportune; that is, that this conference be continued in the form of a permanent committee, which with the aid of the information gathered by the conference will study and make recommendations concerning the financial aspects. It is certain that without resolving this question little of permanent value can be derived from this most interesting meeting. Once this problem is solved, all of us will be able to see that the problems of land tenure are solved along the road of peace and democracy, that free men continue being free, and that human justice be a reflection, even though a pale reflection, of the infinite justice of God.

SOCIAL WELFARE AND TENURE PROBLEMS IN THE AGRARIAN REFORM PROGRAM OF VENEZUELA

𝄢𝄢𝄢𝄢   *George W. Hill, Gregorio Beltrán, and Cristina Mariño*

"ONE OF THE great hopes of the country has been to be able to develop a program that will lead to the gradual improvement in the way of life for its rural people, and to the establishment of the rural economy upon a solid foundation."

Thus reads the first paragraph of the preamble in the decree by which, on June 28, 1949, the Military Junta of the government of Venezuela created the National Agrarian Institute. The preamble together with the discussion (proyecto) which preceded it suggest the historical origins of the contemporary agrarian problems and, equally as clearly, imply the social remedies if the agrarian reform is to accomplish its purpose.

Venezuela's large impoverished rural population and the low productive output of its agricultural and livestock industries, which had reached an unprecedented low point at the outbreak of World War II, are the inevitable result of the chaotic history of its land tenure system. To overcome the handicaps which present-day rural Venezuela has inherited calls for a deep-ploughing agrarian reform, and because the land problems are so inextricably tied into complex human problems the execution of the agrarian reform calls for the utmost social skill in its long-range planning and year-to-year functioning. There follows a historical analysis of the problem and the social and economic forms which some of the remedial measures may assume.

Evolution of the Tenure System

In order to evaluate a complex economic, sociological, or historical problem, one cannot be satisfied with examining isolated facts, but should attempt to analyze and interpret the accumulation of social, historical, and economic circumstances that have determined it. Therefore, when speaking of land tenure and of the different ways in which agricultural property has been acquired in Venezuela it is necessary to start with colonial times and consider the social customs and economic systems which Spain contributed with the discovery of the New World.

TRANSPLANTING OLD WORLD PATTERNS

It is well known that the discovery of the New World was unexpected, even to the Spaniards. Columbus and his men sailed for the Far East looking for the spices which Europe could not then obtain because of the Islamic control of the Middle East. The result was that upon reaching the lands of the New World they did nothing but marvel at their exuberance and take possession of everything in sight. A few years were enough to convince Spain that she had acquired a new and unexplored continent, and it was then that Columbus, the great Admiral, returned in 1497 with authority to distribute the new land among the discoverers. But the fertility of the land, although apparent, was not enough; it did not attract new settlers. Therefore, Columbus, seeking a way of obtaining greater profits for himself and his companions, began to impose on the Indians a tribute, which at the beginning consisted of gold, cotton, and staples, but soon was to be converted into forced labor.

In this fashion, the first repartimientos, which were nothing more than a transfer of Spanish customs according to which peninsular lands were distributed among the settlers, came to constitute the encomiendas which combined the factors of land and labor. The encomienda was an institution designed to protect the Indians and to indoctrinate them in the Catholic faith, but in reality it served only to enslave them. The repartimiento was, then, the initial form of land tenure in America. Parallel to it, individual ownership acquired by purchase either from the conquistadores already established or from the crown, and more

likely through occupation, was to grow and develop. The land acquired through the repartimientos in a few years was to become a personal inheritance of the conquistador, and it, together with that acquired in any other manner, purchase or occupation, would constitute the ownership that in time attained truly amazing characteristics. This was the system which created in Venezuela a class of territorial nobility, a veritable aristocracy, based on the ownership of large tracts of land, which day by day gained a stronger hold on the land and on the economic power it assumed, until by the nineteenth century they considered themselves to be lords and masters of the national destiny. This new class could also be expected to fight the Spanish Crown until national independence was secured.

However, many years passed before the Spaniards realized the economic value of the land. The first Spaniards who came to America did not have any ideas of permanent settlement and much less of cultivating the land. The conquistadores, for the most part, were men of the common people, lacking in resources, or they were the younger brothers of noblemen, but both types had a common purpose and objective: to become rich and to return to Europe as soon as possible. Spain itself did not seem to have any more interest in agriculture than her colonial adventurers. This was a time of mercantilism; the accumulation of the greatest amount possible of gold and precious metals was the aim. Spain demanded nothing more of her envoys. Money and gold were to be brought back at all costs.

Unfortunately, Venezuela was not in the same situation as the mineral-bearing countries, Peru and Mexico. The search for El Dorado was fruitless, and only a few unproductive veins of gold were exploited. Because of this the migration to this country was small. It should also be kept in mind that the climate was not hospitable, that

Spain was placing many restrictions on immigration to the continent, and that many other factors, direct or indirect, influenced the development of Venezuela's rural economy.

EARLY COLONIAL LAND PATTERNS

Venezuelan history begins with the conquistadores having to resign themselves to settlement on the lands that they had acquired. Farmers were few. In 1520, Father Bartolome de las Casas attempted to bring peninsular farmers to Venezuela. He formed an expedition which unfortunately did not succeed because the members got only as far as Puerto Rico and chose to remain there. On the other hand, the majority of the Indians had been exterminated, and the few who remained were not willing to work in the fields, and they fled before the possibility of being caught in the harsh conditions which the Spaniards had created, which amounted to virtual enslavement, although, in theory, they were to be incorporated in the encomienda system. Under a plea of protecting the Indians, Father Bartolome obtained permission from the Crown to import Negroes. This move gave no protection for the Indians, and it benefited only the landowners. It was in this period that land ownership began to be strengthened, when the descendants of the Spaniards began accumulating large tracts of land because they could not count on the necessary imported Negro labor for its exploitation. An indication of the importance that was being given to agricultural land ownership during the middle of the sixteenth century is the discussion by the town councils of the right of assignment of lands. Because of this attempted usurpation of power by the local councils it became necessary for the home government to issue a royal decree in 1573 reserving that right for the Crown. However, the difficulty of communications with the mother country

made it necessary the following year to grant the audiencias, or courts, the right to assign lands and to solve problems relating to them. Thus, in this manner legal control of land transactions first passed into colonial hands.

Aside from individual ownership, we find two other types of ownership: the ejidos, or common property, of the city government, intangible and respected, and the ejidos assigned to the Indians according to law. The latter land rights of the Indians were never respected and served the conquistadores and their descendants as a source of land increase to this group.

What happened in the northern part of the hemisphere, where the immigrants came with their families, settled, and worked the land themselves, or at least had men of their own race doing the labor, did not happen in South America. Here, on the contrary, a few men enjoyed large territories which they might supervise regularly but whose labor and cultivation was in the hands of classes devoid of all rights, sunken into slavery, servitude, and ignorance—classes which, not having any freedom, could hardly react against the system. It is evident, then, that instead of becoming weaker, the latifundio continued increasing day by day and that at the end of one or two centuries the aspiration of those who came to South and Central America was not only to find rich mines but also to acquire large plantations of cacao, indigo, cotton, etc., which would yield the desired profits.

Such a situation remained unchanged in its foundations. There was nothing capable of changing it. On the contrary, all the regulations, all the circumstances worked in favor of the status quo. The Crown did not allow free trade, and reserved for itself an absolute and complete monopoly of the colonies through the House of Trade of Seville. It made no monetary investments in favor of colonization; on the contrary, taxes increased in order to enrich the mother country. Immigration, as we have already stated, was subjected to many restrictions and hindrances. Communications with the peninsula were sporadic. In 1728, Philip V drew up a contract with a group of Basques who formed the Compania Guipuzcoana, and granted them a monopoly of commerce and exchange with the province of Caracas and authority to combat smuggling. The contributions of this monopolistic company to Venezuela, whether beneficial or not for the colony, have been and still are being discussed. What can be stated without a doubt is that, because of the company, traffic and commerce were regularized between Venezuela and the mother country, assuring a market for the producers and resulting in a stabilized economic situation. In 1776, the creation of private commercial companies—both Spanish and foreign—was authorized, provided they presented to the consulate of Cadiz an authentic copy of their charter and thus, in fact, ended the monopoly of the Basque trading company. The landowners, who had looked upon the company with disapproval, found their aspirations for trade, free and with greater profits, finally realized.

The landowners, now masters of economic and social power and believing logically that these lands which their ancestors had conquered and owned for three centuries belonged to them by right, were not willing to have the government of the colony in the hands of representatives of the Crown and to have the peninsular Spaniards occupy the best political positions. Moreover, the ideas of the European encyclopedists began to have their effects. The surge for independence was nearing a reality.

WAR FOR INDEPENDENCE

The situation created in Spain by the Napoleonic conquests gave the awaited signal, and thus on April 19, 1810, was constituted the supreme assembly, "Preserver of the rights of Ferdinand VII," nominally, but at the same time the Capitan General of Caracas was sent back to Spain. We find ourselves, thus, before the first step of independence. Who had brought it to a head? The mantuanos,[1] or white men born in America, were the only ones who had the right to take part in civic government and who, under an apparent submission to the Spanish Crown, could hide their separatist feelings. Thus, they were able to initiate with success the movement of independence, a movement which the lower classes could not have initiated. Any possible move in that direction on their part would have been interpreted as rebellion. Besides, their attempts would not have had—nor did they have—the support of the economically-dominating classes, classes who looked with fear on any movement which might endanger their properties and privileges. In fact, the reaction of the landowners to the first attempts at independence by the lower classes was to offer help to the Crown's representative. It is possible that the mantuanos did not consider the lower-class movement opportune. It is difficult otherwise to understand the motives of this upper class which had defended its racial purity by surrounding it with all social prerogatives, by building an impregnable class wall around itself.[2] Likewise, it would be difficult to understand how this class could be the initiators of a movement of independence; they, the same who were going to offer political and social equality to all citizens and who, like equals, were going to fight at the side of all half-breeds, the mulatto, and the Negroes—all fighting for one idea: a free republic, sovereign and independent.

A few years more had to pass, however, before achieving the union desired by the liberators and repudiated at first and distrusted by the common people. The fact that the leaders of the movement were the same who supported the economic and social power of the province, the same who—as we said before—opposed any attempt at equality of classes, caused the distrust and at other times the indifference with which the popular masses answered the call to arms. Furthermore, the lower classes preferred to defend the Spanish sovereignty rather than join a movement which seemed of doubtful benefit to them and have to fight by the side of these same landowners at whose hands they had suffered generations of racial and class discrimination. In fact, General Tomas Boves, the Spanish leader in the llanos, exploited this class feeling when he pronounced the death penalty among his troops on all the white criollos[3] who persisted in racial persecutions, and he offered land, a real stimulus, to the commoner who would join his royal band. In fact, he decreed that all the property of the mantuanos killed at his order or that of his lieutenants should pass as property to the soldiers. This policy of Boves—a policy which General Paez, the rebel leader, was to follow later in the plains—worked against the success of the independence movement because of the mistrust between the popular masses, who formed the bulk of the royalist forces, and the mantuanos. Gradually, the popular masses realized the true road that they should follow. They saw that independence was not "another link in the royalist chain"; they realized that the actions of the liberators were founded on good intentions, that they fulfilled their offers, and that to continue fighting on the side of Spain was against their real purpose.

A further factor which drew the masses away from the royal army was the joining of the rebellion by General Paez, who was a recognized leader of the llanos. Furthermore, Paez acted with foresight that others had not had when he found himself isolated in the plains of Arauca and, alone in a hostile region, understood that the way of obtaining the support of the plainsmen was to offer them lands seized from the Spaniards. This offer was first limited to the lands of the state of Apure but later became broader, extending to all lands taken over by the rebellion. When Paez joined the army of the Liberator, he felt that his offer still continued to be the best way to win the support of the people; he presented this plan to General Simon Bolivar, who approved it and with slight modifications made it applicable to the whole army. The Liberator even proposed in 1817 the so-called "Law of Division," but it was never put into effect. As a token of recognition of the lands that would later be given them the men were given a bonus.

STRUGGLE FOR LAND REFORM

Struggle after struggle, defeats, and victories led to the final victory and the consolidation of the independence. But in the meantime what had become of the territorial riches of the colonies? Dwindled! What real changes had the land tenure system undergone? None!

This can be explained in various ways. One, there was the state of war itself, the insecurity, the constant ravages of the regions which passed from one group to the other. No one could identify himself in any satisfactory way with the land or its exploitation under these conditions. Two, the leaders of the movement of liberation were for the most part precisely those who owned all the territorial property. Three, there was uncertainty about the ideas and purposes of the revolution, since the landholding leaders had no other purpose than to obtain independence; they were fighting for a greater voice in the rule of their own destinies. Four, except for the incentive of the plainsmen who followed Paez, there was no economic motive in the battle for independence. Five, there existed no organized industrial or bourgeois class capable of effective self-expression. Even though the mass of the people had the desire to own land, to enjoy its benefits, and to reach the level of the landowners, they lacked the strength, the preparation, the capacity, and education necessary to work toward their objectives. This is evident if we appreciate that the education of the Negroes, mulattoes, etc. did not go beyond a rudimentary knowledge of language and Christian doctrine. They were permitted to carry on commerce only on a minor scale and to engage in trades considered dishonorable for the noblemen. Six, although the differences in class and racial privileges had been ostensibly abolished, slavery, a system preventing thousands of men from being free and from owning land, continued unchanged because the emancipation laws that were passed were not effective enough to abolish the practice.

The system of land tenure of the colonial period passed over to the new republic without undergoing any change in its foundations. True, many of the rich families were ruined, but their lands fell only into the hands of other large holders. The system remained the same: large expanses of land in the hands of a few and a large population that was landless. Only a few of the mixed bloods were fortunate enough to acquire property.

Nevertheless, the masses who made independence possible demanded the fulfillment of the promises made to them. They had their war bonuses, but they wanted to cash them for the lands promised them. Dissatisfaction was general when they could not obtain what they desired, and the situation grew more desperate—so much so that the Liberator recommended the matter to Congress. The majority of the army decided to sell their bonuses, which were offered for as little as 10 per cent of their value, a circumstance which was advantageous to

Paez and other leaders, as well as to general speculators. Through this change of events, new powerful landholders were created. In August of 1830, Congress voided the confiscatory laws of October 16, 1821, and July 30, 1824, which had been passed against the subjects of the Spanish government. The new laws assisted the legitimate successors of property to perfect titles. It added also that from then on there would be a stop to the adjudication which was decreed through the law of September 28, 1821, and through the decrees of March 7 and June 19, 1827, to the principal creditors and holders of military bonuses, and that the property rights and actions which were confiscated and not assigned either completely or in part were to be submitted to public auction for their worth or whatever was offered for them in terms of credit documents of a military nature. Through these decrees many lands returned to their former owners, but the sale of military bonuses also offered a large number of speculators the opportunity to obtain large tracts of land at low prices.

A historical opportunity to end the system of latifundia, or at least to grant lands to the dispossessed classes, was lost. The process of land concentration became more and more acute. The Secretary of the Treasury, in his report for the fiscal year 1856/57 complained of the small revenue that the government enjoyed from the sale of land at very low prices under the system and that with the land acquired, varying from ten to sixty square leagues, the concentration of land wealth in the hands of a few had been made easier. He stated, and justly so, that this situation, aggravating the already serious conditions of the masses of landless settlers, in exchange for a small number of opulent landowners, would bring about many calamities and that the resulting economic inequality would have a direct and unavoidable influence on the political and economic progress of the country.

The freedom of the slaves, decreed in 1854, did not change the land situation. Those who previously had been slaves came to be free citizens politically but not economically, since the majority were compelled to continue working on the haciendas and plantations of their former masters in exchange for unsatisfactory working conditions and a pittance in salaries.

When the Federal Revolution broke out, the popular masses joined with the hope of changing the political, social, and economic outlook of the nation. But once again history repeated itself, because when the struggle was finished and the Peace of Coche was signed in 1863, the landless were in the same situation as before with respect to land. Only in some of the social inequalities did they succeed in changing the old aristocratic molds of the upper classes to open the way toward equality by the abolishment of class restrictions.

LATIFUNDISM INCREASES

The concentration of the land continued unabated through the nineteenth century, and its effects were felt throughout the whole national economy with a serious decrease in foreign commerce. Civil wars continued, revolution was waged, constitution succeeded constitution, new laws nullifying others only weeks or months old were continually passed. In the meantime, large areas of land remained abandoned, and small areas received only haphazard cultivation. With the military occupation of a region came poverty, the destruction of plantations, and the extermination of livestock. The landowner seldom lived on the ranch; he hardly visited it. From Caracas, and even from Europe, he was satisfied with receiving the small or large profits that the lands produced. He invested nothing on the upkeep of his farms, which naturally were subjected to the most primitive form of exploitation and constantly diminished in fertility. Mortgages were increased by the absentee owners; plantations were exchanged at low prices; but little of the property was passed on to the landless. On the contrary, it was concentrated more and more in the hands of a few. The landless farmer, squatter, or occupant was compelled to live in insecurity, poverty, ill with malaria and other diseases. Naturally, he could not be very much interested in improving his crops, since he knew that whatever he did to improve the farm would not be acknowledged by the owners and that whether the crop be good or bad he would have to pay exorbitant rent or hand over the greater part of the product he had attained with his work and his primitive methods.

During the regime of General Juan Vicente Gomez (1908–1936) the concentration of land reached its maximum; from the very first he coveted the richest lands which systematically became his. The fact that Gomez did not have to pay his laborers, since most of them were army recruits and many were political enemies, increased his reputedly fabulous profits, and the poverty of the small farmer continued to increase under this unequal competition.

With the discovery and exploitation of Venezuela's immense oil riches, the aspirations of the rulers, of the politicians friendly to the Gomez regime, and of the classes possessing economic power were changed. It was no longer only agricultural land which would produce wealth. Industry began to develop, and capital was accumulated in the cities. Subsistence farmers and laborers abandoned the land in search of better wages. The profits obtained by the landowners with oil revenues were not reinvested in the land, and the concentration of land with the advent of oil became more extensive with its natural consequences. Agriculture was abandoned, and the production of crops decreased while the poverty of the mass of small farmers increased.

The results of the 1950 agricultural and livestock census are not yet available. Therefore, we can only use data compiled from the census of 1936. At that time no census was taken of public and communal land (ejidos and baldios), giving statistics only of private property which numbered 69,777, with a total of 218,496 farms or explotaciones. That census also shows that 90 per cent of the land was in the hands of very few landowners, 5 per cent of them to be exact, and that the property of these landowners for the most part exceeded a thousand hectares, proving thus that there existed in the country a large concentration of land holdings, much larger than that which exists in other countries suffering from the same problem.

All of the several governments since 1936 have stressed the need for an agricultural reform, but only with the passage of the Agrarian Law of June 28, 1949, has appreciable progress been made in the program. The historical processes of the last four and a half centuries, described in detail above, have left their mark on present-day land tenure relations in Venezuela. Venezuela is in the grip of the economic and cultural patterns forged in the preceding centuries of its colonial and national existence. In a true sense, only now has there been ushered in a genuine social and economic revolution, bloodless to be sure, marking the beginning of efforts toward bringing economic prosperity and social equality for the rural Venezuelan.[4]

Social Welfare and Agrarian Reform

GENESIS OF SOCIAL WELFARE

Welfare, as a general term, refers to the conditions of society in terms of its well-being. In a specific sense it refers to those acts and procedures which are adopted to assist in the correction of social and economic problems, the alleviation of poverty

and unemployment, the care of the sick and the blind, the care of children and the aged. In short, social welfare is concerned with the eradication of conditions which make for personal and social disorganization.

Throughout the world the intervention of government in the field of social welfare is a relatively recent innovation. The Scandinavian countries have one of the longest histories of modern state-supervised social welfare programs; the so-called Bevan Welfare Plan in England was preceded in comprehensiveness by the social welfare programs of some of the British Dominions, especially New Zealand. Only after the great depression of the thirties, heralded by the stock market crash of 1929, did the government of the United States for the first time in its history take part in the granting of public assistance and relief to its citizens, which undifferentiated emergency program has now evolved into a comprehensive social welfare policy. Symptomatic of the growth of public awareness and responsibility of the federal government in the United States in social welfare were the recent attempts made by some of the Truman administration to create a new Cabinet post, that of Secretary of Social or Public Welfare.

Social welfare has its roots in human needs, and, as a consequence, the institutions which lie closest to the individual have also been the agencies of social welfare since the dawn of history. The family was the primitive man's welfare organization, and later the great family or the clan helped minister to the needs of its members. In backward areas of the world the family or the clan are still the only source of help when an individual suffers need.

Charity, or alms-giving, is a practice found in all the pre-Christian literature of the world. The Christian church was not reticent to engage in organized welfare work. St.

Gregory, it is recorded, divided Rome into districts and parishes in A.D. 590 and placed a Deacon in charge of each district to distribute alms among the poor and the widows and to assume charge of orphans and even old people. The history of the monasteries down through the Middle Ages is replete with accounts of their relief and welfare activities.

THE WELFARE STATE

The responsibility of the modern state for the welfare of the individual dates from the passage of the English Poor Law, enacted in 1601 during the reign of Queen Elizabeth. This law authorized each parish to raise funds by taxation or by gift to provide means for the care of the needy. The national government and the public treasury were part of the program, but responsibility of administration was placed squarely upon the local governing bodies. The Elizabethan Poor Law, as it became known, spread over the English-speaking world, and even today many rural areas in North America have their "poor laws" and "poor house commissioners."

With the advent of the Industrial Revolution and the rise of our great cities, which resulted in large concentrations of population, responsibility for social welfare had to be assumed by the new industrial class of employers. Mass unemployment was common. Malnutrition resulting from inadequate earnings and ineffective distribution of the available food supply, diseases and epidemics brought on by overcrowded living in urban slums lacking even the rudiments of sanitary and hygienic facilities, industrial accidents, drunkenness and crime, and the other corollary forces of social disorganization compelled industrial leaders to create welfare agencies. A system of community welfare agencies and private philanthropic organizations grew out of the industrial revolution. This was especially true of the later mass production years of this epoch.

It has been only in the last few decades of the present century that the broad aspects of social welfare were assumed to be the responsibility of national governments. By then, life had become too complex and the problems of society too large to allow the family, the church, the rural poor relief commissioners, the urban Community Chest, or private philanthropy to cope successfully with the problems. The reality of the "welfare state" is now an accepted fact in most advanced countries, and, notwithstanding the emotion with which some attack the concept, it simply means that the most-inclusive organization of society now admits and accepts the responsibility for the welfare of its individual members. In this sense, the state does not in any way assume more responsibility—more complex, to be sure—than did primitive man's earliest welfare organization, the family. For the primitive man, his family was his most inclusive social organization, his clan was absolute. The state has now assumed the role for which the family previously functioned.

In by-gone years alms-giving was synonymous with social welfare and, by and large, alms-giving was adequate to meet welfare needs in simple societies. Today, social welfare is a combination of many factors: it includes the relief of poverty and unemployment; it assumes the right of all to better health, better diet, and better housing, and proceeds accordingly; it embodies the abolition of illiteracy, the improvement of means of communication, more efficient production, more consumers' goods; it assumes the public solution of problems over which the individual has little or no control. Each year sees governments all over the world not only increasing their activities in social welfare, but each year sees the means becoming more and more specialized to meet the needs which the ever-increasingly complex urban society creates.

Social welfare in the rural areas, even in the more advanced countries economically, is not as segmentalized or differentiated as among urban people: the difference is due to the basic structure and social organization of rural society. Rural society is a closely knit organization with the family as the basic unit around which the organization revolves. Around the family grow its corollary kinship groups, its neighborhoods and villages.

Social welfare programs in the cities are built around the needs of the individuals who make up the highly-structured society of urban areas; thus, for urbanites, there are special programs for the unemployed adult worker, the mother, the child, the old person, the cripple, the mentally handicapped, the drunkard, the criminal, etc. Social welfare activities in the rural community are more concerned with the environmental aspects of group living than they are with the individual; hence, rural programs tend to be concentrated upon problems of sanitation, water supply, housing, adult education, communications, soil erosion, etc. It has been assumed that, once the defective environmental factors are corrected in which rural families, rural neighborhoods, and rural communities are found, the cohesive force of rural social organization will be able to assume the welfare of its individual members. By and large, programs based upon this assumption have been found effective.

Economic activity assumes different forms in urban and rural societies. In rural society it is integrated around the family, whereas it revolves around the individual in urban society. In the rural community there is only one enterprise, the farm, and the way this enterprise is managed makes of the farm, the home, and the family one integrated unit. The industry is sheltered in the same house in which the family lives; a single group of buildings shelters the livestock as well as the family.

Inadequate living facilities and a low level of living are both a cause and effect of poor production on the farm, but little can be done to improve either without increasing the family's productive income. Hence in the rural community social welfare is closely associated with economic development programs which will increase the productivity of the family's economic base, or its farm.

In rural Venezuela, which has been retarded for so many generations, the welfare and production programs become almost one. Only a true agrarian reform program can be an inclusive rural welfare program. Only an agrarian reform program has the authority, the resources, and facilities to create and to administer a comprehensive rural development program, including parcelling and distribution of land, restoration of soil fertility, building of farm-to-market roads, reforestation and drainage, eradication of disease, redistribution of the population, improving the educational and farm-family managerial capacity, and other factors which are involved in the man-land ratio.

INCLUSIVENESS OF AGRARIAN REFORM

A frontal attack all along the line, as above outlined, is long overdue in Venezuela's underdeveloped rural areas which have suffered from so many centuries of neglect and unequal opportunity. To a great extent the current problems of rural Venezuela resemble in their origin and pervasiveness those which have obtained in the old South and the Appalachian highland of the United States. It was a combination of historical processes which created the antisocial land tenure system and which, in turn, led to the family poverty, disease, and ignorance, the land erosion, single-cropping practices, low farm productivity, and the resulting socio-cultural isolation of the victims in this problem area of the United States. Low interest farm loans were not enough to rehabilitate this people; neither could they continue to be carried on the emergency relief or public assistance rolls. They needed a program that could dig deeply into the subsoil to get at the roots of their social and economic maladjustment. It had to be a program that could change basic attitudes and habits of living to make for this people a new way of life. It was for this people that the unprecedented rural social welfare programs of the Farm Security Administration and the Tennessee Valley Authority were specifically designed in the middle 1930's.

Venezuela's agrarian reform likewise has to be more than alms-giving or public relief; yes, it has to be more than a land program—it is an all-inclusive rural welfare program designed to give each rural Venezuelan an opportunity to share a way of life which the events of history have heretofore not permitted.

That population considerations are basic to any agrarian policy in any and all countries should be axiomatic. Population numbers are in a constant state of flux, and demographic phenomena affect land use, especially on the demand side. But there are other considerations in addition to mere numbers of people. There are rural-urban migrations which have in recent years altered Venezuela's population landscape in drastic fashion. There are qualitative considerations as well, such as disease, malnutrition, and illiteracy—all of these influence the productive capacity of the farm family and are factors of primary concern in an agrarian program, and all require frontal attacks for their solution.

Education likewise is the foundation upon which an agrarian reform program must rest. Educational activities in the agrarian program assume many forms, not the least of which is the attempt to change adult behavior patterns so that antiquated farm and home methods of the rural Venezuelan will be replaced with modern farm and home-management technique. There is no royal road to shortcuts in education; on the contrary, the transition from a machete-and-oxen economy to one of mechanized farming, if successful, must be an evolutionary one.

Opening up new lands through land clearing, drainage, and irrigation, clarification of titles, and parcelling of currently idle lands provide the physical base of the agrarian program. Through a careful family selection process, immigrants and nationals find their way to new lands. Credit for housing, the purchase of machinery, seeds, fertilizers, and insecticides signal the start of actual farming operations, and supervision in the preparation of first annual farm plans and guidance in homemaking help to assure a successful start in farming and living. Construction of farm-to-market roads and storage facilities and modernization of marketing processes complete the agrarian cycle from the farmer and his land to the urban consumer. Medical services and hospital facilities, a community school, a recreation center, and a church make for full community living. For many rural Venezuelans this is their first opportunity to enjoy community facilities which urbanites have long taken for granted; and for many European refugees it means the beginning of life as free people in a new country.

Because the problems are complex and because their solution impinges on all of the social, economic, and political beliefs and institutions of the people, the program must needs be drafted on a long-time prospectus. Fortunately, Venezuela is able to proceed on a long-range basis, whereas most countries with similar problems lack the land and the natural resources to effectuate a healthy balance between the people and the resources. Venezuela's known and foreseeable resources in land, petroleum, minerals, and water power provide economic opportunity for its existing population and for a fair share of people who are now surplus in other less fortunate regions of the world. While a large share of the existing population does not enjoy a standard of living which the nation's resources can provide, the country does not need to fear a scarcity of the potential to bring about the necessary adjustments, and its agrarian reform program is evidence of its concern to raise standards of living.

Obviously there is no quick way to develop an agrarian policy that will assure maximum production and an optimum standard of living for all of the rural population. The faulty land tenure system, archaic production methods and marketing systems, and the poverty and ignorance of the large landless population are too deeply entrenched in tradition to hope for overnight cures. However, the goals can be achieved with greater alacrity and with more positive results if the Agrarian Institute functions under a co-ordinated and well-planned policy.

Planning, in a democracy, does not mean regimentation. It is the orderly marshalling of scientific evidence to enable a program— a major societal undertaking in this instance —to be guided toward a recognizable and socially desirable goal. In its long-range aspects the agrarian reform will aim at certain general goals of food production, population distribution, and land development in the major demographic regions of the country.[5] The Agrarian Institute will also have short-range targets or, more correctly, it will develop a series of short-range goals which can be achieved from year to year and which can be expanded or contracted as the social welfare and food-production needs dictate. Experience, as it is gained from year to year, will temper immediate activities. Annual achievements will permit the long-range plans to be under constant scrutiny, so that at all times the general goals of the agrarian reform will be consonant with the basic needs of the people of Venezuela. With planning and execution of its activities on a high level the National Agrarian Institute has promise of giving Venezuela "a program that will lead to the gradual improvement in the way of life for its rural people."

THE NATIONAL AGRARIAN INSTITUTE AND
LAND TENURE RELATIONS IN VENEZUELA

 Armando Tamayo

THE principal problem that Venezuela must face before considering industrialization is the land problem, since all the present forms of land tenure are the legacy of colonial times whose defects merit and demand a quick and adequate solution.

The only real innovation of modern times in land tenure with progressive aims has been the creation of the system of agricultural colonies, which operates according to present laws to prevent the monopoly of an excessive amount of land on the part of one person, because the succession or transfer of land tenure takes place under official control.

Another innovation in Venezuela, as far as land tenure is concerned, was the creation of agrarian co-operative communities according to administrative patterns imported from other countries, which tried to assimilate Venezuelan environment with little knowledge of their real processes. The co-operative communities failed because no one understood their function, although in principle the program had considerable merit.

The most general land tenure forms inherited from colonial times involved the Crown lands, which were acquired through usual commercial means and which were within the reach of Spaniards and criollos (native whites) only and through military procedure once independence took place.

Today public lands can be acquired through the law of the same name, though such acquisition requires a costly survey of the land desired, which is a long and tedious process only available to those who know the law is in existence and who have the means to cover the expenses required by the processing of the petition. These obstacles have been overcome by the present agrarian law, so that petitioners of public lands can contact the National Agrarian Institute which fulfills the legal requirements and requests the transfer. Once the legal transfer is made, the granting is made to a community group or to individuals, national or foreign.

Another disadvantage for the small farmer is the lack of knowledge of the forestry and water law, without which the lands cannot be cleared; but if the settler works lands belonging to the Agrarian Institute, the latter acting as owner, he secures operating permission from the Ministry of Agriculture, who then gives the farmer the corresponding authority.

In communal lands (ejidos) private ownership of the land has been abolished. That is, it cannot be granted, nor purchased, nor mortgaged, nor alienated in any way; in other words, the lands are inalienable. The municipalities, through authority of the National Agrarian Institute, can lease these contracts for a fixed time. The leases are renewable, and the clauses stipulate the profitable use of the land.

Sharecropping

Because of the difficulty of ownership in the country, the land tenure system most frequent is occupancy through payment of rent in kind, which, at times, reaches a high of 50 per cent of production on some annual crops. The system varies a little as far as permanent crops are concerned, especially cacao and coffee. The variation consists of an obligation on the part of the occupant to seed the area agreed upon with the owner and a promise to sell the owner half of the planting when commercial production begins, since the other half, according to agreement, represents the value of the contribution of land made by the landowner.

These two systems are known by the name of medianeria (sharecropping). They have originated the founding of large agricultural enterprises. The enterprises are of general types—livestock combined with both annual and perennial crops, with annual crops being replaced by pasture.

The Conuco

Conuco is the cultivation of an area of land equal to the capacity of a single family using nothing but hand tools.

In the conuco system, the land does not belong to the one who cultivates it, because of which tenure is unstable, transitory, encouraging no efforts or investments of a permanent nature such as improved housing, planting of fruit trees, and soil conservation. It is the cause of the annual migration of farmers in search of new lands, resulting in social disorganization when educational, health, and social programs cannot reach the migrating people for whom they are intended.

Land Leases

Leasing of land between private individuals.—The leasing of land between private individuals may be considered the usual division of the rent which the land produces. Individual agreements are common when owners who are not interested in the direct management of their farms prefer to function as typical absentee landlords.

When differences occur between the parties, they may request the intervention of the Agrarian Institute, which has authority to regulate leases. The statute stipulates that rental may not exceed 5 per cent of the value of the land and that rental payments cannot be demanded in advance or in kind.

Land holdings leased by the government to be sublet.—When the relationship between the owner and the renters or occupants develops into a dispute, the government has authority to take over the property by leasing, and then it can sublet the property to interested parties with whom an agreement can be reached.

This system has serious defects, one of which is that the solution is temporary. Another is that at times the renters do not fulfill their financial obligations; this results in a loss to the government. There are other cases in which an owner of land which yields no financial benefits because he has not been sufficiently interested in its rational exploitation or because he may find that it is partially or completely occupied creates an imaginary dispute in order to try to sell or rent the land to the government.

Land belonging to the nation.—Land belonging to the nation, if it is productive, interests private individuals and can be had through purchase or lease.

Latifundia

It is frequently said that the problem of large land holdings, or latifundia, cannot be serious in Venezuela because the nation has a large amount of land called national property, public lands, and communal lands (ejidos), with which the situation of the conuco farmer could be improved without affecting the present situation of private large land holdings. But the situation is different. The government-owned property, for the most part, is made up of forests, mountainous terrain and frequently is usable only for pasture, so that only through a great sacrifice of energy and financial expenditures could they produce a minimum of yields for the social group among whom it could be distributed.

Agricultural Settlements

The national government, aiming at the solution of the agrarian problem, has been creating agricultural settlements or colonies which operate under the direction and supervision of the National Agrarian Institute. To this end the National Agrarian Institute can lease communal land or obtain national lands; it can use lands bought from private individuals or accepted as donations or received through inheritance, and when the circumstances warrant, it has authority to expropriate private lands. In all these cases and for the same purposes, the National Agrarian Institute has priority on the lands adjacent to the settlements under its direction.

For the founding of an agricultural settlement or colony, or a livestock settlement, the following factors stipulated in the agrarian law must be fulfilled: (1) flat topography, (2) good soil, (3) irrigation possibilities or sufficient rainfall to insure the success of the crops, (4) climate and health conditions, and (5) means of communication.

After these requirements are fulfilled, the Agrarian Institute works out the subdivision plan with the estimated cost of needed improvements and determines fair cost value to colonists who are to be settled on the lands.

The assignment of parcels, which may be made to nationals or foreigners, is subjected to the regulations determined by the National Agrarian Institute, which fixes the maximum and minimum amount of land which may be assigned to each member or to each family. The Institute is charged with parcelling lands in such a manner that they will be economic units and that they will increase national production.

When the National Agrarian Institute distributes its own lands, the parcels are placed on sale on a long-term basis; but when it deals with ejidos, it can only offer them for rent on a low rent and long-term basis.

Each plot is provided with housing, water, electric power installations, and agricultural implements which will insure the successful establishment of the family in the country.

Agrarian Organizations

In order to fulfill the regulations of the Agrarian Institute and to interpret the aims of the present government of Venezuela, the Institute has reorganized technically in the short period of twenty-six months since its creation agricultural settlements existing since 1936. It has created new organizations with programs and working plans scientifically designed to contribute effectively to the production of necessary foodstuffs and to the improvement of living conditions in the country through a fair distribution of land. It has a technical and administrative staff to supervise the colonists, and the economic aid of the government assures the farmer hygienic housing and the organization of its agricultural enterprise on a remunerative basis. In this manner the government is centralizing and solving the urgent sanitation and educational problems of rural people and giving the protection needed by rural families, which are the principal source of the national demographic increase.

A total of twenty-five centers, units, and agricultural settlements are at present under the direction and control of the National Agrarian Institute. Among these organiza-

tions I shall make reference to one which, because of its magnitude and its clear and definite economic and social projections, stands out in a very special manner. It is the agricultural unit of Turen. Turen is in the western section of Venezuela. It is part of an extensive and uniform plain which gently slopes from the north to the south. In this zone, fed by two rivers, the Agrarian Institute is carrying out the most extensive project of agricultural organization undertaken until now in favor of the restoration of the agriculture of Venezuela.

In its initial stages, it has 20,600 hectares, with the possibility of increasing to 55,000 hectares, which, it is estimated, constitutes the total usable soil of the region. It has an altitude of 160 meters above sea level, a mean temperature of 26 degrees, and 2,000 millimeters of yearly rainfall.

The soil of this agricultural unit is adaptable for the majority of tropical crops: rice, corn, bananas, cotton, tobacco, sugar cane, beans, sesame, sorghum, as well as all vegetables, citrus fruits, and legumes.

Development of the Agricultural Unit

The work of the organization includes soil surveys, land surveys, land clearing, construction of an administrative center, cultivation, irrigation and drainage, parcelling of land, and extension of credit to underwrite development expenses and living needs.

Construction of the administrative center includes the construction of the following units: administration building, electric plant, deep wells for irrigation, machine shop, tanks, police station, experimental station laboratory building, rural social center, guest house, hospital, church, machinery shed, dining room for workers, manager's house, technical director's house, employee's houses, houses for workers, supply house, carpentry shop, and drying sheds.

Cultivation includes planning, acquisition

of machinery, training of tractor workers, preparation of the soil, sowing, cultivation, harvesting, and marketing.

Irrigation includes planning and construction, and parcelling of land includes planning, division of the land, construction of housing units, construction of roads, selection of families, and transporting the families to the plots.

The development of the original unit, in its initial 20,600 hectares, will be finished by the end of 1952, two years ahead of schedule. Each family, carefully chosen among nationals and immigrants in a proportion of 60 to 40 per cent, respectively, has a plot of 35 to 40 hectares, a housing unit, sanitary facilities, credit, and agricultural machinery. The land and buildings have been contracted to them in ownership, to be paid for within 25 years. The average cost of a hectare, including all installations, is 1,600 bolivares. Each farm family in addition to a house has a barn for cattle, a chicken coop, pig sty, a rabbit hutch, a machinery shed, and fruit storage space.

The agricultural unit of Turen is the synthesis of the agrarian policy of the government and shows in a clear and objective fashion the contrast between the systems of feudal exploitation of the land and the modern technical processes. From a yoke of oxen to the tractor, from the planting stick to the planter, from the unsanitary farmhouse to the comfortable home—that is the itinerary in the reversal of the way of living which is being improved. It is the agrarian reform on the march. It is the revolution of our economy.

The agricultural unit of Turen is of particular importance because it furnishes an experiment for focusing attention on and solving the fundamental aspects of the national land problem; it concentrates on the social question, which consists of guiding the conuco farmers towards a modern system of farming assisted by supervised credit; it concentrates on economic phases of mechanization and diversification of crops to incorporate the farmer into large scale national production and on the spiritual phase of life by creating bonds of solidarity among the rural population. We seek their successful establishment on the land; we are giving them cultural advantages and instilling in them sanitary habits for the improvement of their standard of living.

Among the different colonies, the National Agrarian Institute has installed centers of rural improvement, in which the following activities are undertaken: manual training courses, home economics courses, educational and cultural discussions, sports, movies, recreational activities, courses in reading and writing, and medical and social assistance.

The government of Venezuela has endowed the National Agrarian Institute with the necessary funds to establish progressively over the country the agricultural centers and units for settlements which are necessary for the solution of our land problems and of the problems of the men who work the land.

AGRICULTURAL CO-OPERATION IN MEXICO
IN RELATION TO SMALL LANDHOLDINGS

 Marco Antonio Durán

ONE OF THE most severe agricultural problems which Mexico has had to face in the last decades has been the influence of land tenure; the land tenure policy as stated in the Constitution of 1917 has raised questions regarding the possibility of agricultural intensification through the incorporation in each unit of the necessary technical resources to elevate its productivity to the highest levels which modern resources make possible. We are speaking, in short, of the influence that can be found in the development of agriculture attributable to the size of the agricultural undertaking. Mexican law sanctions a size of plots whose area is no greater than one hundred irrigated hectares, two hundred hectares of nonirrigated land, or its equivalent in other types of land such as pasture, uncultivated lands, forests, etc. It is necessary to go back in history to explain in a qualitative and quantitative fashion the present situation, which had its origin in the revolution initiated in 1910 and which gave rise, beginning in 1915, to an agrarian reform which completely upset the land tenure system of Mexico.

Historic Problems of Tenure

Throughout a historical process initiated from the beginning of the Spanish Conquest and ending at the beginning of this century, a phenomenon took place which consisted in the creation of large agricultural holdings (latifundios) which increased to the detriment of the small property or the communal property which Mexican villages had had since the beginning of the conquest. These were similar, in the majority of the cases, to the institutions which existed at that time in Spain, called ejidos, a name which was used also in Mexico. The ejido is an institution in which the lands belong to a village whose exploitation, individual or collective, is distributed among the inhabitants of that village. This institution came to be a condition for the formation of new centers of population in such a way that a great majority of those villages had been endowed in colonial times with this benefit; however, there was also a tendency for the land that was being settled to be concentrated in a few hands.

THE EJIDO

Diverse circumstances influenced the land tenure systems, both during colonial times and after independence was achieved. During the latter period, more than once, the danger implicit in large landholdings (latifundismo) was seen; and more than once it was realized that the latifundio system was slowly absorbing the communal lands of the villages. When the 1857 Constitution was enforced, the basic document of the so-called Laws of Reform, all civil and religious corporations were denied the right to own land, and among the civil corporations were included the villages which possessed communal lands. Although there were rectifications later on, the fact is that these laws brought about the disappearance of a good part of the ejidos; they were absorbed by the large landholdings. Later, those administering the colonization policy realized, upon demanding the titles of ownership of village lands, that titles did not exist or that they were very defective. This deficiency facilitated the despoiling of communal lands, which up to then had been the traditional property of each population nucleus.

This exposition is very brief, but it is enough to give an idea of the evolution of this economic phenomenon which resulted, during the first decade of this century, in the existence of a class of large landholders economically powerful and unyielding, owning the immense majority of Mexican lands divided into enormous properties. As an example the Terrazas holdings in the state of Chihuahua can be mentioned which had an area of more than 2.5 million hectares.

THE LATIFUNDIO

The latifundio was not a progressive agricultural exploitation. On the contrary, it maintained agriculture in a deplorably backward state in relation to the existing technical resources of the times, and it based its prosperity more on the meager yieldings of the poorly worked land and on the very low wages of an unprotected farmer than on an attitude towards increasing productivity of the land. A good part of the large landholdings were subjected to a system of indirect exploitation, principally through sharecropping (aparceria). This is a contract in which the owner furnishes the land and some working implements and the aparcero (sharecropper) furnishes his labor and care; the crops are divided almost always into two equal parts. This system means that with the minimum investment the owner obtains a high rent from a deficiently cultivated land, to the disadvantage of the real worker who made it produce.

This situation of agricultural backwardness created, among other things, a rural proletariat subjected to starvation wages and in very poor condition as far as their personal standing was concerned. There was an almost complete absence of liberties, since the large landholder, like the feudal lord of old, exercised his political and economic influence in order that the farmers located on his property should live as medieval serfs subjected to his iron rule and with a very remote possibility of evading his authority. Pseudolegal processes were put into practice to insure the stay of cheap labor, as well as other economic processes of coercion such as the debt system and the company stores. The farmer could never repay these debts, and this bound him cruelly to the master in such a way that the debts became hereditary, affecting not only the one who contracted them but also his descendants.

The Revolution and Land Problems

Under these conditions, the revolution of 1910 broke out, initiated under political premises. The revolutionists assumed power and created new governments up to the year 1915, in which they began to face economic powers. The preconstitutional law of January 6 was passed, which, taking into account the lack of economic resources of the farmer and the plundering of lands which had belonged to the villagers, had the generous ambition of correcting the monopoly of land. Thus it dictated the restitution of despoiled lands, taking them away from the large estates which owned them illegally. These ideas became a constitutional precept in 1917, and in Article 27 of the Political Constitution of February 5 of that year, the regulations for land tenure in Mexico were established. The general provisions were: the restitution of communal lands taken away from the villages that had owned them, the granting of lands to the villages which did not have them, and the subdividing of large estates to convert them into small holdings. From this comes the total overthrowing of the land tenure system in Mexico. The political constitution orders the destruction of the old latifundios and the creation of only two land tenure systems, namely, the communal lands of the villages, called ejidos, and the small private landholdings whose area can be no greater than one hundred hectares of irrigated land, two hundred hectares of nonirrigated land, or the equivalent decreed by law in some other type of land.

EJIDOS REACTIVATED

As far as the ejido is concerned, throughout the thirty-four years of its creation according to the above-mentioned constitutional processes, some modifications have taken place in such a way that the final realization implies the existence of ejido parcels from four to twenty hectares. The smaller plots are more frequently found.

The concept of the ejido needs an explanation. The ejido is made up of several parts: cultivated land, pasture lands, mountains, uncultivated lands, etc., and the so-called "fundo legal," or the site where the town owning those lands is located.

Cultivated lands are destined to be subdivided among the inhabitants of the village in order that each parcel will form an unalienable family patrimony. The pasture, mountain, and other lands are under a communal utilization plan for the grazing of cattle or for fulfilling the needs of the village in the case of mountain land. The fundo legal is divided up into lots for the building of the houses of the farmers. One of the indices of the ejido is the parcel of cultivated lands which each farmer has received and which, as I said before, varies from four up to twenty hectares.

The ejido lands have the peculiar characteristic that they do not constitute an absolute, but rather a limited property right, since they are subject to the legal conditions of being unalienable, imprescriptible, and unseizable. That is to say, they are not subject to acts of commerce. The perpetual nature of this ownership is guaranteed and cannot be altered in any way.

SMALL HOLDINGS CREATED

On the other hand, based on Article 27, a large number of small landholdings have been created, whose area runs from plots smaller than one hectare up to several thousands of hectares, depending on the type of land that constitutes them. These have been created by different proceedings derived from the above mentioned fundamental law; namely, subdivisions freely made by former large landholders; the enforcement of laws passed by local state governments for the partition of large landholding, showing different provisions, according to the state in which they have been passed, especially, with regard to area, which varies from 10 hectares of irrigated land up to 40,000 of pasture lands; the remains of former haciendas (large landholdings) which were not expropriated for the formation of ejidos (the laws respected the so-called zone of protection in every former hacienda); the readjustment of property in the Irrigation Districts, which have been formed through the construction of hydraulic works by the federal government where the area distribution of land has been modified, in order to form agricultural units which will fill better than the previous ones the demands of a correct organization of irrigation and a better economic performance; lands belonging to the nation settled according to the Settlement Laws which have been passed and emanating also from Article 27 of the Constitution.

One can easily see that this diversity of origin of the small landholdings (pequeña propiedad) necessarily must result in a variety as far as the area of the existing plots is concerned in such a way that, next to numerous minifundios (smallest property), there has been formed also many landholdings typified by the maximum area of one hundred hectares of irrigated land established by law.

CURRENT TENURE SITUATION

To give an idea of the land tenure situation in Mexico, I quote some figures on existing ejidos from the Ejido Census of 1940. According to this census there were 14,681 ejidos, 1,601,680 ejido farmers, a total of 28,921,259 hectares of ejido lands, and a total area of cultivated lands of 7,045,217 hectares. The ejido lands were distributed as follows: irrigated lands, 994,235 hectares; humid lands, 342,893 hectares; nonirrigated lands, 5,358,877 hectares; lands occupied by crops with a vegetative cycle greater than one year, 349,212 hectares; pasture land area, 10,658,916 hectares; forest area, 6,872,424 hectares; area of productive fallow lands, 1,696,477 hectares; area of unproductive lands, 2,648,225 hectares.

The figures given next are for the lands not under the ejido system and are from

TABLE 35

Classification of Non-Ejido Lands in Mexico by Size of Plots*

Size (hectares)	No. of Plots	Total Area
5 or less	928,593	1,157,285
5.1–25	156,200	1,960,507
25.1–50	46,466	1,742,528
50.1–100	31,763	2,374,910
100.1–200	22,695	3,346,732
200.1–500	17,428	5,695,120
500.1–1,000	6,087	4,455,366
1,000.1–5,000	6,883	15,547,956
5,000.1–10,000	1,342	9,751,944
10,000.1–	1,472	54,456,469
Total	1,218,929	100,488,817

*Source: Agricultural and Livestock Census, 1940.

the Agricultural and Livestock Census of 1940. Table 35 shows the classification of non-ejido lands by area. The lands included in the 1940 census are classified as follows: total area, 100,497,817 hectares; total area of cultivated lands, 7,825,858 hectares. These lands were distributed as follows: irrigated lands, 738,124 hectares; humid lands, 422,-643 hectares; nonirrigated lands, 6,164,570 hectares; lands occupied by crops with a vegetative cycle greater than one year, 500,-521 hectares; pasture land area, 45,603,356 hectares; forest area, 31,782,795 hectares; area of productive fallow lands, 7,111,979 hectares; area of unproductive lands, 8,164,-829 hectares.

It must be made clear that the irrigated areas recorded to date have increased by approximately 1 million hectares.

It can easily be seen that in the matter of cultivated lands, the average which each individual or head of a family has as an ejido parcel or plot is 4.4 hectares. This

gives an idea of the extent of these agricultural enterprises.

Upon examining the figures on the properties not under the ejido system, we see with regard to very small properties the very important fact that there are more than 900,000 plots that are less than five hectares which, because of their size, are in an analogous or inferior situation with respect to the ejido parcel.

PROBLEMS OF AGRARIAN REFORM

This distribution of land in an environment constantly in evolution as is the case in Mexico has surely been somewhat modified by this time, but it still can serve as an example of how land holdings are distributed, and it is appropriate enough to illustrate the great problems that our agrarian reform has brought out in the established land tenure systems.

We must state that our agrarian reform has been, above all, a generous act of social justice which tries to place in the hands of all Mexican farmers a piece of land to which they can apply their effort and their labor for a better life and a greater agricultural production. We in Mexico have called this act of distribution of territorial property "democratization of the land," but I think that this expression is too cold to express the high patriotic sense which has inspired our agrarian reform. We must also state here that although it is true that this situation has created great problems of an economic nature subsequent to that land redistribution, such problems, no matter how great, we think have a solution. Even so, it is our duty to maintain and stimulate that small property called the ejido, which, as I said before, represents the practical realization of a supreme aspiration for social justice. In the struggle to solve the great problems which this enormous division of land implies and to achieve for the farmer an authentic improvement of the lands that our agrarian reform has granted to him, it is natural that we should discover many defects, many flaws. But each day there is a better consolidation of the exact knowledge of those adverse realities, so that, without violating the fundamental principle that inspired this very important part of our agrarian reform, the defects can be corrected. Processes of correction will be crystallized, and we will succeed in this undertaking which has now become a tradition in my country.

Problems in Agricultural Development

CLIMATE AND RAINFALL

Before mentioning the problems that this division of Mexican lands implies, it is necessary to report on a fact that affects in a very important way the development of agriculture and that in Mexico presents very pronounced adverse characteristics on over 50 per cent of the national territory. This factor is climate, and rainfall is part of it. In more than 50 per cent of Mexican territory rains are scarce, frequently insufficient for a stable agriculture without the help of irrigation. Rainfall occurs in the summer with an absolute drought from October to May, with the result that on more than half our territory only precarious cultivation is possible each year when rainfall is the only available water. It is very important to take this into account. Even the mere mention gives an idea of the unfavorable conditions under which the farmers who are living in these areas of scarce rainfall have to work and produce. It is difficult under these circumstances to introduce modern techniques into agriculture because of the risks that would be taken. That is why, in the last quarter of a century, one of the efforts of Mexico to improve her agriculture has been the construction of many irrigation projects taking advantage of surface streams, with which more than 1.5 million hectares have come under irrigation in places where, be-fore, agriculture either was very mediocre or almost impossible. On the other hand, through different means, among which agricultural credits have played an important part, the drilling of artesian wells has been promoted on a large scale. These wells make use of subterraneous waters and make possible the irrigation of desert regions whose economic life is barely beginning. Thus, we have succeeded in bringing under irrigation in those regions an area which I judge to be not less than 300,000 hectares. It has not been possible for me to compile exact data on this matter, although official surveys indicate nearly 200,000 hectares irrigated. To this I have added my estimate, backed by my personal observations that, thanks to government encouragement, there have been farmers who with personal resources and without outside help have irrigated with water from wells an area no less than 100,000 additional hectares.

INSUFFICIENT CAPITAL

After having described in a very summary fashion the essence of the Mexican agrarian reform which took place during the past thirty-four years and which affected deeply the structure of land tenure, as well as noting the results that I have expressed in the figures already mentioned, it is necessary to examine the new panorama of land distribution in order to point out the economic problems that such results have brought out. These are problems which for the most part lie in the extent of the farming unit of land resulting from that action.

I do not wish to go deeper into the complicated concept of the magnitude of agricultural exploitation whose analysis corresponds more to a course in rural economics than to a paper like this which is trying to bring out in a concrete form the fundamental problems which, in my opinion, affect all the agricultural land of my country. To measure the magnitude of the agricultural unit, taking into account all aspects that have a bearing on it—area, adequate availability of water, sufficient and adequate investment of capital, type of cultivation and crops, distance from the centers of supply and consumption, the intensity of cultivation, means of communication, climate, etc.—is a task corresponding more to the judgment on isolated agricultural units than an examination as a whole of the agrarian situation of a country. Although these factors must be taken into account, it is also certain that they cannot be evaluated in the simple way in which one can examine an isolated agricultural unit. Because of that, it is necessary to take into account some general basis for judging and to look there for the fundamental pivots around which move diverse economic and technical factors which influence the intensification of agriculture.

The purposes of every agrarian reform are, undoubtedly, the increase of agricultural production in the national interest of providing for the consumption of the inhabitants, the formation of a prosperous and efficient farming class which is rooted to the soil, and the production of industrial articles whether for domestic consumption or for export. Agricultural intensification and the resulting increase of the production of the soil are achieved through the adoption of modern technical scientific resources, gradually better known to the farmer, and through acts designed to counteract the effects of factors inhibiting agricultural development—such as the scarcity of water for a vigorous life of the crops under cultivation, as well as other accidents of a climatic nature; the isolation of the agricultural units through lack of means of communication; price fluctuations in agricultural markets, and so forth. In addition there are other depressive factors of a sociological nature, such as the cultural backwardness of certain groups of population and their tra-

ditional clinging to obsolete technical systems. In my judgment, all those technical, economic, and sociological aspects are subjected to a central pivot which, in the last analysis, is the possibility of sufficient capital investments without which those technical resources would always be beyond the reach of the farmer. Without these resources he cannot struggle successfully against the adversities of the physical environment, nor will he be able to develop adequately into superior levels of culture because poverty and hunger are the worst enemies of cultural development.

I have wished to place greater emphasis on the premise that one of the factors in the intensification of agriculture is adequate investment of capital in the agricultural undertaking because in my country the agrarian reform, which has created the structure of a new system of rural life, has brought about a panorama in which that investment of capital finds serious difficulties. These derive exclusively from the physical size of the new agricultural units created in the last few years, whose area varies between less than one hectare and a hundred hectares of cultivated land of the best quality. The most casual observer will easily discover that in this picture there are serious difficulties for the realization of agricultural intensification in each and every one of the agricultural enterprises located on each of the existing plots. In short, the great number of minifundios is a condition limiting necessary capital investments. Let us take one of the clearest examples—agricultural machinery. It is practically impossible to have the cultivators of isolated plots of an area less than five hectares owning a tractor of even the smallest type, since their productive capacity and the profits obtained by the farmer do not allow either the necessary investment or an adequate amortization of that investment. This is especially true if we take into account another factor of enormous importance, the climate. These three—climate, capital investments, and size of plots—form the fundamental trilogy around which rotate all the other problems of the agricultural unit.

The climatic problems already described in regard to agriculture can be condensed in very few words, leaving aside a detailed description of the characteristics of each of the prevailing climates in the Republic of Mexico. The greater part of the Mexican territory is subjected to rainfall which comes only a few months of the year—from May to September—rainfall which in over 50 per cent of that territory may be insufficient for an adequate crop development. This insufficiency may be due to scarcity, inadequate distribution, or to great abnormalities throughout the years. In the lands subjected to this deficient rainfall, agriculture is mediocre, fortuitous, and full of risks, in such a way that its economy does not accept the necessary investment of capital for the absorption of technical resources of intensification.

CLIMATIC DIFFERENCES AND IRRIGATION

Speaking in very general terms, Mexico can be divided into three large climatic zones: the northern zone, the central plateau, and the coast region south of the Tropic of Cancer.

The northern zone is made up of large desert areas, where precipitation is deficient all the year round and where agriculture is possible only through irrigation; extensive cattle raising prevails in nonirrigated places.

The central plateau is of a mild climate at a great altitude above sea level where rainfall is less deficient than in the north, but which has great fluctuations in rainfall and in the weather throughout its territory. In this zone temperate climate crops are grown with the limitation that wintry weather establishes a relatively short period for growing.

The coast south of the Tropic of Cancer, where the regions of greatest rainfall are located, is without a well-defined winter but with high temperatures. Here the actions of man are threatened by endemic tropical diseases, such as malaria.

The crucial problem for Mexican agriculture is the lack of water, and the remedy of this evil has been the construction of irrigation works to make use of large surface drains and small brooks, a task which was begun under government auspices almost simultaneously with the redistribution of land and which continues with greater intensity each day. In the last few years the development of subterraneous waters has been intensified for the same purposes. In addition to the lands formerly irrigated, in the last twenty-five years more than 1.5 million hectares have received the benefit of irrigation. The construction of irrigation projects, indispensable to the reclamation of a good part of the lands of Mexico from their semi-desert condition, has been one of the problems of the investment of large capital for agricultural intensification. In the larger projects, this investment has been made directly by the government, which has been the only agency capable of promoting them. In the smaller projects, mainly in the drilling of wells, the investment has been made by the farmers themselves, whether with official or private credit or with their own resources. This is but a consequence of a geographical condition adverse to agriculture which has a decisive influence on agricultural development. Clearly this constitutes a problem which will not be solved except after many more years of effort and after making use of the available water for the benefits of agriculture through the production of electric power for industry.

After this digression about irrigation, we must point out the relationships that exist among the main factors that we have been analyzing. Agricultural intensification needs great investment of capital, and many obstacles are found to this investment, independent of the financial availability of that capital in necessary amounts. The minifundio system by its very nature rejects those investments. Finally, the climatic deficiencies which result in a lack of water for crops make agriculture the victim of those adverse climates and devoid of modern technical resources, and not until the initial investment for irrigation works its progress can agriculture be promoted by a steady and prolonged effort. At present this effort has gone beyond government intervention to the active participation of the farmers concerned.

Capital and Co-operative Credit

Simultaneously with the initiation of great irrigation works, some twenty-five years ago, the need was seen to insure to the many small agricultural holdings created by the agrarian reform the necessary credit for their improvement and exploitation. When the problem of organization of agricultural credit was discussed, we had to face the difficult reality of the existence of a large number of small landowners with plots of varied areas, with very diverse economic capabilities, spread throughout wide expanses of land, growing very different crops. Ways had to be found for credit institutions to give the necessary credit to hundreds of thousands of small users of that credit. This constituted a very complex administrative problem which could not be solved through ordinary banking systems. Furthermore, the guarantees offered by isolated small landholders were weak, especially since the varied administrative problem itself prevented watching over the investments and the guarantees. Finally there was a need to overcome great difficulties in order that isolated small landholders could gain any benefit from their agricultural units, which, because of their size and their isolation, constituted weak and unprotected units, economically speaking. If credit presented great difficulty, other necessary measures for the correct direction of these units presented even greater difficulties. Because of this, and in order to solve the problem of credit, the formula of co-operation was adopted. This was amplified in all aspects necessary to organize the farmers into societies which not only function as intermediaries between the sources of credit and their members but also present a stronger united guarantee than the sum of the small guarantees of each small isolated landholder. These associations are also capable of taking part in other diverse co-operative aspects of a higher type adequate to the interests of the community and to each one of the farmers.

AGRICULTURAL CREDIT

Thus in 1926 the National Bank of Agritural Credit was born and the so-called National System of Agricultural Credit was founded, made up of co-operative units which at present have the name of Local Association of Agricultural Credit, with the role of auxiliary credit institutions. Such associations, of an indisputable democratic nature, gather in their midst farmers of one locality who are brought together by co-operative responsibility and are handled through an Administrative Council and a Committee of Vigilance which takes charge of enforcing the decisions made by the General Assembly of Members. The Assembly is the supreme authority of the company or association and always acts within the regulations prescribed by the Agricultural Credit Law. By law, the National Bank of Agritural Credit watches over the associations.

The local Associations of Agricultural Credit, I repeat, are of a co-operative nature. This can be proved by mentioning the purposes for which they were created as specified below.

The legislator in agricultural credit matters, in setting up the National System of Agricultural Credit, was inspired by results achieved in Europe in the matter of co-operative credit, of which the clearest and best known examples are the Raiffeisen and Schulze-Delitzsch Societies. The success of these societies has been commented upon on many occasions and in abundant literature on the matter. These comments show how co-operation is capable of solving the problems of the small users of credit which here, as everywhere else in the world, present serious difficulties in reaching the primary sources of capital.

But the Mexican legislator went farther. He had before him the picture of rural reality of a Mexico which was being transformed through the agrarian reform which established as a final goal two institutions of land tenure, namely, the ejido and the small landholding. He was inspired by his ambition to the point of trying to solve, through Local Associations of Agricultural Credit, many other aspects of the economy of the rural environment entrusted now to ejido and small farmers. Account was taken of the possibility of a great abundance of small-size agricultural units. It was noted also that their small size often leads to an uneconomical minifundio system with economic obstacles to agricultural development which become more acute as the smallness is accentuated. The legislator thought, as legislators of the majority of the countries of the world have thought, that where agrarian reforms, peaceful or violent, have given rise to a great number of small landholdings, the co-operative association was necessary for the many aspects of the organization of the agricultural enterprise based on these factors in order to overcome the disadvantages of its own smallness.

LOCAL CREDIT SOCIETIES

Thus the Agricultural Credit Law authorized the local Societies of Agricultural Credit to obtain for their members the necessary credit for their agricultural units by creating a moral entity with sufficient solvency and credit capacity through the addition of the small solvencies and the small abilities to pay of each one of its members. It also pointed out the very important functions of encouraging and organizing the agricultural livestock or forestry unit of the locality. The law also authorized the acquiring for sale or rent for its associates or for their common use seeds, animals for breeding purposes, work animals, implements, fertilizers, agricultural machinery, or the industrialization of agricultural or forestry products. Likewise it made possible for the societies the performance of very important work of a definite co-operative nature for the construction, acquisition, or management of warehouses, granaries, dams, canals, and other works of a permanent nature for land improvement, as well as the processing of livestock and agricultural products or the co-operative packing and sale of these products. For this last purpose the society has been authorized to act always as an agent for the concentration, classification, packing, transformation, and sale of the products of its members. Besides, as a very important function and related to the others mentioned, the association was authorized to exploit the goods that its members may offer because of economic reasons for their cultivation and use by the same association.

Intimately linked to the financial operations of the association, as far as the possibility of obtaining money from outside sources and making loans to its members goes, is the legal authority to issue bonds with a guarantee of real estate of the members and with the guarantee of the National Bank of Agricultural Credit. Although this has not been realized in practice up to now, I think that in the historic moments in which agricultural organization is ripening, the time is coming when the issue of bonds as a resort for financing the operations of credit associations will become a reality.

From the social point of view, the law grants the association the authority to act as savings banks and entrusts them with the care of the best economic organization possible of their members and the care of their intellectual, moral, and social advancement. At the same time, the association is by law a representative of its members for the settlement of administrative and fiscal matters that may come up with the federal government, with state governments, or with municipalities.

The co-operative organization of the small farmers responds, and always has responded, to the situation created by the Mexican agrarian reform, since the combination of the small farmers permits an action similar to that which can be exercised by the large agricultural unit. The exercise of the actions, described in the previous paragraph, would be impossible for the isolated farmer, owner of an intensely subdivided land. However, in subdividing the land full consideration has been given to the right of every Mexican peasant to a piece of land to work, to the fact that the ownership of that land is a stimulus for agricultural work, for increased production, for the assurance of the social peace which did not exist in other times, and for the harmonious integration of a strong and coherent nationality in order that the farming group of Mexico will have foundations that will insure it the enjoyment of democratic freedoms to which it has indisputable right. On these spiritual, patriotic, and economic bases rests our agrarian reform and the co-operative organization of the land units which are its result.

But what has been said would be absolutely rhetorical if everything that has been done were not submitted to a very severe criticism in order to discover all the problems that sooner or later must be solved so that the supreme aspirations can become a reality in practice. Up to this time I have spoken in very general terms. The time has come to subdivide and classify partial problems which, although they will still be treated in general terms, will permit a clear notion of the principal problem that the new land tenure system brings and of how far the co-operative organization already described has been able to solve the problems of the minifundio system.

It is convenient, before going on, to give some historical background of great interest and to analyze it. Ten years after the National Bank of Agricultural Credit was founded, this institution was divided into two other institutions, or rather, it gave rise to another institution of agricultural credit —the National Bank of Ejidal Credit.

In 1926, when the National Bank of Agricultural Credit was founded, it was entrusted with the organization and financing of small ejido units and of non-ejido landholders. Ten years later experience showed that the existing legal differences between the ejido farmers and the small landholders demanded a different treatment. The small landholder has no more limitations on the possession of his land than those which are derived from government action to improve agricultural exploitations. His land can be the object of free trade; it can be mortgaged, rented; or he can carry out any other commercial contract with regard to it. That property can be affected only in the public interest.

CO-OPERATIVE ORGANIZATIONS

The ejido farmer possesses cultivated lands divided into small plots with different characteristics, since that land is, in reality, the property of each town or village, for the use of its inhabitants who can be perpetual owners provided they work the land. Each plot constitutes a family unit, which is not subjected to acts of commerce. No one can affect the perpetual nature of ownership by the township that has received its benefit. Agricultural credit cannot be based on the mortgaging guarantee of the land. The smallness of the ejido plot demands co-operative organization more than in any other case. The Bank of Ejidal Credit was authorized to act in the ejidos where the same limitations about the possession of the land and the smallness of that property demand special treatment and care to see that the laws which created the ejidos were not violated. We must add to this the fact that in the majority of the cases the ejido farmers are the farm group less favored as far as cultural aspects are concerned and, therefore, the least capable of understanding the advantages of the co-operative credit system and credit itself. The effort, therefore, has been and will continue to be greater than in the small landholding in all aspects of agricultural intensification. It has even become necessary to be tolerant in a way not required with the small landholders, with the exception of the very small landholders who are in equal or worse conditions than the ejido farmers as far as the area of land they own is concerned. The very small landholders form a subgroup of people without cohesion and with few possibilities of association because of the geographical dispersion; this has caused in previous years the passage of a regrouping law for the small landholdings, which had the intention of making the uneconomical minifundio system disappear through absorption into larger plots. Such a law did not have, nor will it have, any practical results, since only a slow economic evolution can bring those results—an evolution which will be impossible in the regions with scarce tillable land as densely populated as is the case, for example, of the Valley of Oaxaca, where property is measured by tenths of hectares. At any rate, it is

possible to say that a good part of this very small non-ejido property, which amounts to nearly a million plots, is incapable of being included into a co-operative form and which does not receive the benefits of agricultural credit. As a consequence the economic conditions are inferior to those of the ejido, where, no matter how bad the situation may be in some cases, the members may at least resort to association and can secure credit for their crops and for the intensification of those crops. This problem is a complicated matter, which is probably being solved in part by organizing all possible local Societies of Agricultural Credit. On the other hand, perhaps it could be solved through individual credit, very difficult to operate; but I presume that there will be a good part of them that will not be helped and which little by little, through an economic process of consolidation, will form larger and better constituted landholdings. In this regrouping of the small landholdings only economic influences will play a part, since it is to be doubted that government action would be very successful. This problem includes 1.15 per cent of the total area of the plots recorded in the 1940 census.

LIMITATIONS ON CREDIT CO-OPERATIVES

Probably in accordance with the ideas expressed up to this point, one might believe the thesis that co-operative credit and organization includes absolutely all the small landholders created upon the application of the Mexican agrarian reform. To affirm this would be unacceptable, since even though it is true that co-operation in agriculture helps solve the problems that the isolated small farmer could not solve it is also true that as the size of the agricultural unit becomes larger the need for co-operative association becomes smaller—as seems to be proved in the case of the non-ejido holdings of Mexico. In the case of the relatively uniform ejidos because of their peculiar characteristics, co-operative organization becomes imperative.

After having advanced with great impulse in the formation of the ejidos we have come close to the point of equilibrium after satisfying the greater part of the need for land on the part of the villages through the granting or returning of ejidos. This advance in previous times accounted for the restlessness and uneasiness of landowners who feared for their land and was a factor that inhibited the farmer himself in the investment of capital and inhibited that capital in its investment on the land. The former small landholder now feels secure in the possession of his land, as well as the newly established small landholder who settles a desert or the tropical forest or who farms and improves former units in the central plateau. Once the former obstacles to agricultural development have disappeared, the small landholder surges forth to the task of working the land and intensifying production. That small landholder, who has been increasing for a little over five years in a vigorous and definitive fashion, aspires to own the maximum land that the law allows and to form a landholding class which, because of its economic capabilities, can lead an independent life without the need of association. In other words, the small owner with one hundred irrigated hectares has enough guarantees to get the necessary credit for the working of his land and the intensification of agriculture and to make the necessary land improvements for that intensification. He is capable of entering the markets, and he is capable of solving his own problems without the need of resorting to association with a local society of agricultural credit. This points to a limitation of the possibilities of co-operative organization.

As I said before, as the size of the property increases, the economic capabilities of the farmer probably increase, thus creating an individual capable of being acceptable for credit on his own and of solving his own problems without outside intervention. There are exceptions, naturally, in the unfortunate case of a decrease in prices or meterological accidents, to which his fellow cultivators who own less land and are less capable are likewise subjected. To determine what area is necessary for this individual action of agricultural improvement is a very difficult task, since, although it is true that the extent of the land has a bearing on it, it is also true that there are other factors very worthy of being taken into account, such as the effects of the weather of which I have already spoken. There are owners of one hundred or two hundred hectares of land with deficient rainfall whose economic conditions are perhaps worse than those of many owners of twenty hectares of irrigated land. On the other hand, the diversity of crops, conditioned principally by the region in which the plot is located or by the high prices of some products, establishes a great diversification of conditions, such as, for example, the productivity of wheat, corn, coconuts, bananas, and hemp. The mere mention of these crops suggests, beside the diverse technical problems, economic conditions which are also variable. Each crop determines a special condition of the farmer as far as his economic capacity is concerned. It is impossible to make a severe and detailed analysis of the economy of these crops when one wishes to encourage them, but it can be affirmed, in general terms, that it is almost certain that beginning with thirty hectares of irrigated land and with sixty hectares of nonirrigated land, the landholder has decreasing need of co-operative association, until we get to the cases of an area greater than those mentioned in which that co-operative association is almost unnecessary. This is especially likely if we take into account the fact that in spite of the benefits of co-operative organization the farmer, just as he dreams of being the absolute owner of his land, also dreams about being the absolute master of his acts and refuses that association whenever he can.

This would not have been understood during the first years of credit and co-operative organization, during which such organization was considered to be worthy of being set up without exception. The farmer was forced to join, even though he was fully conscious of the fact that because of his economic capabilities and his guarantees he had no need of associating in order to exploit his property effectively. But experience showed that this was an unacceptable hypothesis, that co-operation is efficient and indisputable up to a certain point, and that after that we must take into account the individual himself and treat him as such to stimulate agriculture. This caused in the last few years a large increase in credit operations with farmers, without disregarding the co-operative organization wherever it was necessary, and account has been taken of the existence of individuals who do not need to associate, as well as the individual customers of the National Bank of Agricultural and Livestock Credit,[1] whose numbers have increased a great deal. In 1945 there were 1,014 local Associations of Agricultural Credit with 36,147 members; the individual clients numbered 158. In 1950 the number of associations and members was, respectively, 1,396 and 42,673; on the other hand, the number of individual borrowers had gone up to 4,254. While the number of associations hardly had a 37 per cent increase, the number of individual clients had become 30 times greater, which proves the previous remarks about the attention being given to the non-associated farmer. This does not mean that the farmer who does not participate in the co-operative movement will not have the possibility of associating to defend his interests in some other way; but those associations have nothing to do with co-operative organization, since that farmer of a high economic position and culture, in many cases higher than the average farmer, forms agricultural associations, agricultural chambers, and other organizations on a national or local scale designed to protect his interests.

Perhaps everything that has been said up to here is only a description of what is being done in Mexico. But through that description we are trying to uphold and demonstrate the fundamental thesis that knowing as we do the economic defects of the minifundio system and its incapability to absorb by itself all modern technical resources co-operative organization is the only means we have to overcome those deficiencies. Finally, I wish to report that, mainly through the local Associations of Agricultural Credit in Mexico, credit has been granted in the last five years for 512,941,312 pesos. This constituted, on one hand, the financing of yearly expenses of exploitation for about 50,000 agricultural units, and, on the other hand, the incorporation into them of capital which spells the application of technical resources, in addition to the opening up of new lands for cultivation which have increased the national agricultural patrimony. To quote some figures, 160,000 hectares have been cleared; 2,105 wells have been drilled capable of irrigating 150,000 hectares; 3,519 tractors, equipped in different ways according to the crops and the purposes for which they are destined, have been bought to improve the working of the land in approximately 160,000 hectares. This action has been distributed throughout the deserts of the north, the tropical forests, and the central plateau in an effort to bring about uniformity of purpose throughout the whole country.

NEED FOR PRIVATE CAPITAL

But the needs of Mexican agriculture are much greater than the figures previously quoted, and these figures are the product of government action only. Private banking has also granted agricultural credit on a small scale. One of the goals which is being pursued at present, and which is expected to be reached mostly through the co-operative organization which I have described, is to have private capital diverted to agriculture in order to complement government action and to make the improvement of Mexican agriculture more energetic and firm—an agriculture which has shown a constant increase for the last twenty-five years, the increase becoming more pronounced in the last few years. Undoubtedly with the present economic situation that increase will continue growing until it solves the problems of investment of capital, once the difficulties that the new land tenure systems present have been overcome. This is a remark and nothing more, since the analysis of the financial importance of guiding private capital towards agriculture would require another chapter of long and complicated exposition. It is enough to state that it will be the next step in the agricultural development of Mexico, a step which like the previous ones presents great difficulties but which will likewise be made possible thanks to the unquestionable tenacity which has been shown in each one of these undertakings.

FUNCTIONS OF CO-OPERATIVES

All that has been stated implies a constant effort applied for twenty-five years to the development of co-operative organizations among the farmers of the nation. To the figures already mentioned we should add, to complete the information, those which correspond to the local associations for ejidal credit, organized by the National Bank of Ejidal Credit, which amount to 6,539 with 501,788 members, all of them with the characteristics of the minifundio system already mentioned. Both banks—Agricultural

and Ejidal Credit—have sponsored this effort, which has not been simple. Co-operation is not easy to implant nor is it easy to develop, since the farmer refuses in a large number of cases to associate with others, and his refusal only disappears when he is convinced of the benefits of the co-operative system. On the other hand, this co-operative system progresses with a certain speed among farmers of higher culture. However, it advances very slowly among farmers of an inferior culture. Co-operation implies the mutual and satisfactory knowledge of the members and perhaps, without exaggeration, also their mutual friendship. Likewise, it implies a similarity of economic capabilities. The administration of a society of this type turns out to be complicated for most of the organized groups. There is a need in the greater majority of cases for steady and prolonged work to convince them and educate them into the co-operative system. The implanting of the co-operative organization takes a very long time, and many failures, partial or total, may occur, since, in the last analysis, it implies the formation of a new spirit of mutual aid among the farmers. This may be possible in places where the tradition of the small landholdings and the exact knowledge of the needs of the same are factors available to overcome those obstacles through co-operation; but in a country like Mexico, which performed its agrarian reform yesterday and today is trying to organize its economy, those conditions do not exist, and they must be created after a great deal of work.

In addition, we must take into account the fact that co-operative organization is a strictly democratic process. That is to say, co-operative organization cannot be imposed by law or by government order, but it must be an attitude accepted fully by each farmer. Without this requisite co-operation is impossible, since one cannot conceive that through any means of coercion an individual, whatever his cultural or economic level may be, will accept in good faith the responsibility for solidarity and the obligations that are implied in co-operative association. If this acceptance is achieved by coercion, surely back in the conscience of every man there will be rebelliousness against this association, and that rebelliousness will always be a factor for failure. Our experience proves all this. The results which have been pointed out have been achieved through an effort of a quarter of a century; and, nevertheless, we think that there is still much to be done and much to be improved. The steps along the path of co-operative relations have been slow and painful, but we believe, also, that after this problem is attacked, each step, no matter how small it may be, means real advancement in the intensification of our agriculture in Mexico.

This means, in the last analysis, that the co-operative formula for the organization of the small farmers will be nothing more than a brilliant theory with few practical realizations if, in order to make it come true, these experiences are not taken into account which indicate the amount and quality of effort that must necessarily be applied to achieve the desired goal. It is frequently stated that for every agrarian reform which creates many small landholdings there should be a co-operative organization of small landholders along economic lines. This is undoubtedly true, but in order to achieve that a greater and more prolonged effort is needed than is necessary to bring about the agrarian reform itself.

LAND TENURE AND LAND DISTRIBUTION IN CUBA

 Manuel Rodríguez-Cabrera

UPON RETURNING to my country, it will be a great honor to relate that I lived at the University of Wisconsin and that I was treated very cordially by its faculty and by my fellow delegates from nations near and far.

We experienced great joy in Cuba when we found out that the University of Wisconsin is interested in problems of land tenure. We knew that this university was not only a state institution but also a University of the World because so many students from many different countries have visited its hospitable classrooms. At present, because it concerns itself with such vital problems as the problem of land tenure, I believe that this institution well deserves the title of University of Humanity.

I should be extremely happy if the material that I shall report on could be of some use; but I am sure that we shall owe more to this university than what we can contribute to it.

From attending meetings of this conference and from materials I gathered beforehand, I know positively that Cuba is better off as far as agrarian problems go than other countries. This feeling instead of comforting and consoling us produces in us intense concern which makes us dissatisfied with our present situation. We want to improve.

We know that great social problems have very deep roots in the land problem. Each day it becomes more evident in all nations, and especially among the most advanced democracies, that although the right of ownership is considered one of the most important individual rights of man, which serves as a stimulus for progress both individual and collective, it is also true that in order to preserve this right it is indispensable to place limitations on its social functions, since, in special cases, an individual may try to benefit too much, to the detriment of the society in which he lives or at least to the detriment of part of that society.

When the property to which he has a right is represented by land, the need to recognize its social function becomes more evident, especially when he is the owner of large tracts of land which he cannot exploit in a reasonable way either through cultivation or through livestock raising.

Although the concentration of land in the hands of a few is regrettable, the minifundios, or very small landholdings, are disastrous.

The solution which I consider to be correct lies in turning landless farmers who are the victims of usury into owners, with an adequate area for the support of their family, through the sale of land to be paid for on long terms, with a co-operative organization and the necessary aid to make the land productive. He who has the ownership of land will have a patrimony to defend and will become a real citizen because he will have no inferiority complex. The partial sums of the defense of those properties will yield a grand total—the defense of the nation.

We wish wholeheartedly to have no nation suffering in poverty. The purchasing power which is increasing in these nations opens the doors to strong and future markets. The big problem, then, is an economic problem.

Statistics of Cuba

I should like to give you complete information on statistics in Cuba as reported by the 1946 Agricultural Census, but I know that it would be a tedious task and that so many figures would overwhelm you. I shall limit myself, then, to touch upon, in a very superficial manner, those points which justify our participation in this conference, leaving the bulk of my material in the hands of the university, if it deems it useful. I am ready to furnish information within my knowledge to anybody who is interested in the matter. I consider that after stating this I can begin in earnest.

Cuba is an island with a population of about 5 million inhabitants, with an average mean temperature of 25° C. and an approximate rainfall of 54 inches per year. According to the above-mentioned census, Cuba has 159,958 farms with a total area of 9,077,068 hectares, or 22,692,715 acres. This area represents 79.3 per cent of the total area of the nation. There are 1,970,404 cultivated hectares, which represent 17.2 per cent of the national area. The pasture lands include 3,897,217 hectares, or 42.9 per cent of the total area in farms. The area of forestry lands is 1,265,697 hectares, or 11.05 per cent of the nation. The "marabu" area (Dychrostachys nutans, Benth., a plant of the mimosa family) is 268,151 hectares, or 3 per cent of the total area in farms. The area assigned to other uses, which includes roads, buildings, and unproductive lands, is 1,650,405 hectares, or 18.2 per cent of the total area in farms.

The distribution of land in Cuba by tenure is shown in Table 36.

TABLE 36

DISTRIBUTION OF LAND IN CUBA BY TENURE*

Tenure	Per Cent
Owners	32.4
Managers or administrators	25.6
Renters	30.0
Sub-renters	2.4
Sharecroppers (Pertidarios)	6.1
Squatters (Precaristas)	0.8
Total	100.0

*In percentage of total farm area.

The average rent paid by renters and sub-renters is $3.28 per hectare.

The rural population constitutes 50.4 per cent of the population. Only 30 per cent of the total number of farms are operated by their owners. Of our exports 90 per cent are made up of sugar, tobacco, minerals, rum, alcohol, fibers, fruit, and vegetables.

Of the existing farms in Cuba 84.6 per cent are less than 50 hectares, or 19.9 per cent of the total area in farms. Farms of more than 1,000 hectares represent 0.56 per cent of the total number of farms and occupy 36.1 per cent of the total area of farms in the nation.

In order to compare the degree of agricultural usability, we can state that the farms of less than 50 hectares devote 40 per cent of their area to crops, and farms of more than 50 hectares, 10 per cent.

Renters and sharecroppers represent 54 per cent of the total of the nation. The average area of all farms is 56.7 hectares. The number of agricultural workers in 1945 was 829,668. At present, we have 3,000 tractors, or one tractor for every 657 hectares.

The total area of irrigated land in Cuba is 59,809 hectares. This total represents 4 per cent of the total number of farms, 0.7 per cent of the total farm area, and 3 per cent of the total cultivated area.

The total value of agricultural production, as reported by the 1946 Agricultural Census, was 331,885,242 pesos—an average of 36.56 pesos per farmed hectare.

The fertilized area was 144,983 hectares, or 7.4 per cent of the total cultivated area.

According to the bovine cattle survey, there were 4,115,733 head of cattle.

Milk production amounted to 408,159,413 liters, cheese production to 2,229,414 kilograms, cream production to 328,169 kilograms, sugar cane production to 29,256,983 metric tons, and honey to 2,564,524 kilograms.

Tobacco production was valued at 33,-844,244 pesos, coffee at 10,472,608 pesos, livestock products at 69,476,465 pesos, cereals and vegetables at 31,159,678 pesos, foodstuffs at 22,094,997 pesos, truck garden products at 2,870,707 pesos, forestry products at 2,028,943 pesos, fruit products at 6,570,726 pesos, other vegetable products at 16,683,089 pesos, and honey at 518,338 pesos.

Distribution of Land

I shall refer now to an attempt to distribute land among farmers which turned out to be a colossal failure. The Law of December 17, 1937, decreed a distribution of land to be given free to farmers out of the few lands belonging to the state, lands, incidentally, not of the best quality. The best lands long ago went into the hands of powerful large landholders who were influential with previous governments. This free distribution with no economic aid created an apathetic type of farmer, and very soon the farmers began to sell their plots, which quickly passed on to other hands.

From this experiment we deduced that no free lands should be granted. Probably the majority of those who obtain royalties of five hundred dollars make no effort except to invite their friends to spend it with them; but if the five hundred dollars are the product of honest work, then it is a different matter.

The Development Bank

Now I shall give you some details of Law No. 5 of December 20, 1950, which created the Agricultural and Industrial Development Bank of Cuba (Banco de Fomento Agricola e Industrial), to which I have the honor of belonging. This is an autonomous organization, free from politics, with funds of its own, with a legal personality, of an indefinite duration, and with full authority to acquire rights and obligations. Its object is to create, encourage, and maintain financial facilities for agricultural development and diversification in order to raise the standard of living of the people. To fulfill this aim, it grants loans to farmers. The terms granted may be for eighteen months, five years, and even up to twenty-five years, depending on the purpose and the security offered. Loans may be granted to agricultural, livestock, or fishing enterprises. In purpose they may be acquisitive, for improvements and refinancing. As to security, this may be personal or involve a financial backer, a mortgage or a pignoration. As to its economic aspect, the maximum amount to be borrowed is regulated by the security offered.

The ratios of loans to types of security are as follows: in mortgage loans, 50 per cent of the guarantee; in loans requiring a financial backer or small rural credit, 60 per cent; in pignorative loans, 70 per cent; in movable goods, 75 per cent; and in bonds issued by the bank itself or in state securities, 90 per cent of the guarantee.

The interest rate has been fixed at 8 per cent yearly, always on the remaining balance.

The Agricultural and Industrial Development Bank of Cuba at the present time is organizing Credit Associations and Organizations for Rural Credit in order to extend the benefits of credit to the whole of the Republic. These associations will use their capital to grant loans, and they will be able to discount their contracts with the Bank in order to widen their activities. The Development Bank will make new discounts on the Banco Nacional of Cuba.

The patronatos (rural credit institutions) are real agents of the Bank, but here the farmers themselves lend their collaboration to make the function of the Bank more rapid and more effective.

After an application for credit has been studied and approved, there is an investigation by experts who evaluate the securities given. After the loan has been approved, the contracts are drawn up.

The Bank maintains strict vigilance over the investment of the loans and the date of their recovery.

Fund for Agrarian Development

The Special Fund for Agrarian Development was created by Law No. 2 of May 22, 1951, and is regulated by Presidential Decree No. 2969 of July 18 of the same year, with an active capital of 5 million pesos. With this fund, lands are acquired and distributed with a maximum area of 26.8 hectares for each beneficiary. In this way the eviction of renting farmers is avoided by those who may have started such proceedings. Lands are acquired through purchase or expropriation in order to settle squatters or salaried farmers there. It encourages agriculture through loans for the acquisition of implements and for the development of projects tending to improve agriculture. This Special Fund is financed through amounts resulting from a 4 per cent tax on the excess profits not distributed of corporations when they amount to more than 30 per cent of the capital paid for them.

The estimates and appraisal of those lands are to be made by experts appointed by the Agricultural and Industrial Development Bank of Cuba; the division of that land into parcels which are to constitute private holdings and with the required recording in the Office of Records of Property will be made through the Ministerio de Hacienda (Ministry of the Treasury). Finally, the Ministry of Agriculture will determine the selection of the lands that are to be acquired, distributed, or developed, the areas, quality, location, and crops to which they must be devoted. The terms given for their payment are set at twenty-five years. Farmers are required to make annual payments with a rate of interest set at 2 per cent yearly. They are required to carry out their plans for exploitation of the farm, to follow the methods of cultivation, and to adhere to soil conservation measures set by the Ministry of Agriculture. They have to make their permanent residence on the farm and work it without being able to devote that farm totally or partially to sugar cane. The farm, mortgaged to the state to guarantee future annual payments, cannot be sold by the owner, even if he should settle his debt before the contracted time, except after ten years from the time when it was acquired. If after those ten years have elasped, he wishes to sell it, he will necessarily have to grant an option to the state, who will be able to purchase it for the same price paid originally by the farmer.

Up to the end of the twenty-five years prescribed by law, the owner cannot sell his farm freely if he has acquired it through this plan. During that time, the farmer will be unable to rent the farm, to make a sharecropping agreement, or any type of arrangement implying the working of the land by third parties. From this regulation are exempted the widow of the farmer, the minor children of the same who are unable to work the farm, or those persons whose disability has occurred a year after the death of the farmer. They cannot rent or cultivate additional land nor work for wages on other farms without permission granted by the Ministry of Agriculture.

Settlement of Precarista

One of the vital problems affecting Cuban farmers is eviction because of failure to pay stipulated rent. The hard-working and honest farmer who because of bad weather, such as drought, rains, cyclones, or any other happenings beyond his control, and who was, therefore, unable to pay the owner the rent for the land he occupies will find the state willing to lend him needed help, thanks to the provisions of this plan. The farmer will have ten years in which to reimburse the state for that rent paid by the latter, plus 2 per cent interest on the money invested, if the unpaid rent reaches two yearly payments as a maximum and is not higher than 250 pesos.

Whenever the eviction of farmer families takes place, if those farmers have been occupying the lands that they work with or without the consent of the owner but with no legal title to them, and if the Ministry of Justice becomes aware of this fact because the interested parties have requested the benefits granted by the present Agrarian Development Plan, that Ministry shall inform the Ministry of Agriculture. If the latter decides to settle the farmer on the land which he has occupied until then as a squatter, proceedings will be started to effect the purchase of the farm in question through the same processes and requirements established for the purchase of divisible lands which we have already mentioned. If the owner of the land refuses to sell, then compulsory expropriation proceedings will be started. Once the land is adjudicated to the state, it will be turned over to the farmer through the same prerequisities and conditions already mentioned.

This measure is of a high social significance and of wide amplitude in a new agrarian policy destined to curb the latifundio system and to distribute among those who need it most lands which otherwise would remain unproductive or idle or under absentee ownership.

Agricultural Development

Through the plan of agricultural development, every farmer who owns the land which he works will have the right to obtain through sums designated for this purpose aid which will amount to one-fourth the true value of the land.

The sums thus acquired will have to be invested by the farmer in accordance with plans approved beforehand by the Ministry of Agriculture for the development, repair, and improvement of the farm, including adequate as well as comfortable and sanitary housing, so that the family can develop in a civilized social environment which will be morally satisfactory and to which they are entitled.

The solutions to the agrarian problem of Cuba therefore seem to be the following:

1. To provide land for renting farmers and sharecroppers, since they represent 54 per cent of the number of those included in the different tenure systems.

2. To increase mechanized agriculture, since we have at present only one tractor for every 657 hectares of cultivated land.

3. To increase irrigation, since we only irrigate 3 per cent of the total cultivated area.

4. To increase the means of communication, since out of the 159,958 farms only 50,958 have the service of motor vehicles during the year.

5. Rural electrification must be intensified, since the greater part of this service reaches only the cities and towns.

6. A policy of protection and regulation of rural prices that will guarantee sufficient remunerative income for farmers.

7. Improvement of our livestock, especially dairy cattle.

8. Sanitation and nutrition measures for the rural population.

TENURE INNOVATIONS AND AGRICULTURAL PRODUCTION IN PUERTO RICO

Luis Rivera Santos

MANY OF US might have asked ourselves why the University of Wisconsin and the other sponsors of this conference invited the Department of Agriculture of Puerto Rico to participate in the discussion of the world land tenure problems. From the physical standpoint you have to examine a world atlas with a searching eye if you want to spot Puerto Rico. Of course, you can always find that it is at a point 18 degrees north latitude and 66 degrees west longitude. By air the island is 1,065 miles from Miami, 1,400 miles from New York, and 500 miles from the northern coast of Venezuela in South America.

If you examine a map of the Caribbean basin, again, you can locate the island as a dot between the Atlantic and the Caribbean. Physically, Puerto Rico is a small place indeed! But there are other significant reasons for the decision to invite Puerto Rico to this gathering and for our decision to accept readily such an honor. Our experience in land reform may make a contribution to the attainment of the objectives of this conference.

In the first place, our country, which is only 100 miles long by 36 miles wide, or 3,600 square miles in area, is nursing over 2,200,000 inhabitants, all of them citizens of the United States. If we were to count heads, Puerto Rico has as many people as, or more people than, such important states as Florida, New Mexico, South Dakota, North Dakota, Utah, South Carolina, and some others of the smaller states.

Compared with the Latin American countries, Puerto Rico has a population larger than Costa Rica, the Dominican Republic, Honduras, Nicaragua, Panama, and El Salvador.

I must not delay saying that we are mentioning population just to give an idea of relationships. We do not brag of our population. In fact, the problem caused by a density of 645 persons per square mile is one of Puerto Rico's great problems. Population and resources are out of balance in the Island.

Variety of Tenure Reform Schemes

As stated before, there are other reasons much more meaningful in terms of the struggle of man to improve his lot on earth. We will see those reasons as we probe into the problem of land tenure in Puerto Rico, into the effects of different programs on productivity, and into the impact of such programs on social organization and attitudes. In the area of land reform, Puerto Rico has tried programs varying from the small plot of land, more of an urban than of a rural nature, to the thought-provoking scheme of proportional-profit farms. Between those two extremes there is much of interest for both the practitioner and the student of land tenure reform, productivity, and social interaction.

Though land tenure reforms of accountable consequences started exactly thirty years ago, those of the last ten years have been the most meaningful. Developments during the past four years and plans being made at the present time are particularly significant.

The Problem

In order to understand land tenure innovations in Puerto Rico, we have to distinguish between those directed at the particular problems we are trying to solve in the island and those which are meaningful as a solution to specific problems in Puerto Rico but which are of universal and permanent value as an approach to tenure problems in other areas of the world having a similar socio-economic setting.

In considering the Island's problems we have to think of over 2,200,000 persons living and depending for their subsistence on a land area somewhat less than 2,100,000

acres, of which approximately 70 per cent is hilly and mountainous. Puerto Rico has only 1,900,000 acres of land in farms, of which 1,350,000 acres are tillable. The net result is an average of just about one-half of one acre of tillable land per person.

Puerto Rico lives up to the rule that in regions where agriculture is the socio-economic determinant of living standards, the system of land tenure emerges as a subject of paramount importance. Centuries of an agrarian economy have developed an agrarian scale of values. Puerto Ricans are basically agrarian in feeling, though a shift from agrarianism to urbanism is taking place. If we add to this agrarian tradition the fact that the Island must, at this time, nurse 645 persons per square mile and that, during the stage of rapid agricultural economic development, both latifundia and absentee ownership were at their height, it is very easy to see why land tenure is loaded with a semi-religious emotional intensity.

The land tenure system in Puerto Rico up to 1900 was typical of a country in process of colonization and incipient exploitation. Large estates of the best land were controlled by a few land owners, whether through purchase or grant. Four-fifths of the population was landless. However, even a population density as high as 278 persons per square mile in 1899 had not created any noticeable demand for a revision of land tenure policy.

The advent of the American government in Puerto Rico witnessed the development of high-powered absentee ownership based mainly on the exploitation of sugar cane—a crop protected by a high tariff. Capital from the United States took control of the highly productive sugar cane lands, which were to become the backbone of the Island's economy. Because of the nature of the industry and other economic forces, large-scale operations characterized sugar cane growing and manufacturing. "Land concentration probably reached its peak around 1930. In 1934/35, sugar companies and allied interests controlled 400,000 acres of land, of which 280,000 were owned and 120,000 were leased."[1] "Lands controlled by sugar mills and related interests constituted over 50 per cent of all the land in farms growing sugar cane. Gayer and Homan estimated that four big companies and allied interests owned about 107,000 acres and leased approximately 78,000 acres, operating a total of 185,000 acres or 46 per cent of all the land operated by sugar interests."[2] In 1940, the 1,900,000 acres of land in farms comprised 55,000 farm units. Nearly three-fourths of the total number of farm units were less than twenty acres in size. In contrast, farms with over five hundred acres comprised only 0.6 per cent of all farms but represented 31 per cent of the land. Most of these large farms were sugar cane holdings established in the most productive soils.

Certainly, a greater efficiency, both technological and administrative, and greater income were secured from these large units. But they existed at a social cost involving masses of hoe-agriculture laborers with very little opportunity for improving their skills, a great inequality in the distribution of income, a strangling absentee ownership, and above all a disintegrated and frustrated community withering incentives for group action and for self-improvement. A logical by-product of this situation was a general clamor for reform in land tenure arrangements in the sugar cane industry. The programs instituted and their effects will be discussed later on in this paper.

Next to the sugar cane areas, the coffee and tobacco highland areas have generated the greatest unrest. But unlike the case in sugar cane, where the laborers themselves were leading, in the case of the highlands, social scientists had to lead the inquiry into the suitability of existing tenure patterns.

The mountain area has been considered for many years a depressed region. Low yields, high costs of production, poor land utilization, lack of marketing facilities, inadequate land tenure, lack of services and facilities, isolation from the flow of social development, and difficult setting for organized group action and self-help have been pointed out as the most important of the problems to be solved if the mountain area is to make its full contribution to the welfare of the Island.

In particular, the problems of the coffee region have commanded careful study and extensive discussion. During the ten years preceding the United States occupation of Puerto Rico, coffee was the leading economic enterprise. The loss of the protection enjoyed under the Spanish government and the consequent loss of the European market, followed by the hurricane of 1899, reduced its economic importance considerably.

Land tenure in the tobacco area resembles the pattern prevailing in the coffee area. There is a large number of owner-operated farms, and there are some large farms in the hands of local absentee owners. The tobacco area is characterized by a system of sharecropping without any form of written contract. Tenure is not secure beyond the tobacco crop, but it may be prolonged until the later harvest of some short-season crops which usually follow tobacco. Poor land utilization, lack of cover, and erosion are commonplace in the tobacco area.

By way of summary we can say that latifundia and manager-operated farms are characteristic of large-scale sugar cane enterprises. The coffee, tobacco, fruit, and general crops regions are characterized by a high proportion of ownership. Tenants are more or less evenly distributed throughout the different agricultural regions, and most farm laborers live scattered in the rural areas in poor houses built on sites provided by the landlord. This is the general background for Puerto Rico's land tenure reform.

Homestead Program of 1921

Institutionalized land reform in Puerto Rico starts with the Homestead Commission Act of 1921. It was the traditional approach, namely, that land distribution was, of itself, a good thing. So we had a program of unplanned land distribution among farm workers. Basic requirements for successful land reform and increased productivity, such as machinery, equipment, farm buildings, credit, supervision, community services and facilities, development of community life, co-operation, and all the other things that contribute to a better and more productive farm life, were completely overlooked.

In addition, the low productivity of the soils, the ruggedness of the topography of the land distributed, and the isolation and inaccessibility of most of the homesteads greatly hindered the success of this program. However, from the point of view of a social philosophy it was a very significant start in land tenure reform, and it did improve the living standards of the farm laborers who had the privilege of getting a farm of average productivity.

From 1921 to 1942 a total of 2,455 subsistence homesteads with a total of approximately 38,157 acres were established. The average size of the farms was 15 acres. In this case the number of acres is not a good measure of size because of the nature of the soil and other physical characteristics of the farms. In fact, most of the farms proved to be too poor to operate as economic farm units.

In spite of the fact that lands distributed were completely inadequate, the plots under this program are yielding more than they were when the program was started. But yields are not enough. In terms of human rehabilitation the program has fallen piteously short of its objective.

Reconstruction Administration

The New Deal programs which had such a tremendous impact upon American life during the thirties had their influence on Puerto Rico. In 1935, the Puerto Rico Reconstruction Administration, a federal agency, which was to execute a rural reconstruction plan, started a program of land reform which was to affect land tenure in Puerto Rico. Among other things, this rural rehabilitation plan provided for the establishment of 10,339 one- to three-acre subsistence plots, mostly in the coffee, fruits, and tobacco areas. In addition to providing small plots the Puerto Rico Reconstruction Administration built dwellings for a large number of the families covered by their program. As of June 30, 1950, 7,093 dwellings had been provided at a total cost of about 7 million dollars.

The families pay a small rental for the house and the land. Many of them have already signed purchase agreements to pay for the house and land on a monthly installment basis over a period of ten to twenty-five years.

The Puerto Rico Reconstruction Administration made the first attempt to solve the problem of latifundia and absentee ownership of sugar cane lands by acquiring in 1936 the sugar mill "Central Lafayette." The property acquired comprised 10,000 acres of land in a very productive region owned by an absentee French family. The best lands of this estate were divided into twelve units, supposedly organized as a co-operative. After a poor performance which lasted three years, the lands were sold to individual farmers in plots ranging from 11 to 140 acres. Another sugar mill, "Central Los Caños" controlling 5,466 acres, was bought by a group of nineteen farmers, organized as a co-operative and financed by the Puerto Rico Reconstruction Administration. This project has been very successful in terms of increase in production. The purchase of these two sugar mills started an aggressive land tenure reform in the sugar cane area, which is at present being successfully carried out by the Land Authority of Puerto Rico.

The activities of the Puerto Rico Reconstruction Administration represent some improvement over the Homestead Program, particularly in the efforts made to improve citizenship through community participation and group activities. It brought into more intensive cultivation some submarginal lands and increased the productivity of such lands.

A socio-economic study made in 1947 of one of the projects established by the Puerto Rico Reconstruction Administration indicates that the total gross receipts from the plots for that year amounted to $225, of which farm privileges averaged $156 per family. Total income during the year of the study averaged $733 per family. After making the necessary correction for increases in cost of living, this figure constitutes a great improvement over the $279 average income of the families before they were resettled. Housing conditions in this project have improved greatly. Before the families were resettled, 84 per cent of their homes were shacks. At present 64 per cent of the homes are built of concrete, 28 per cent of bricks, 6 per cent of lumber, and 2 per cent of adobe. The study shows also that the families have more food and a more varied choice in their diet. They are making a better and wider use of community services and institutions.

From the vantage viewpoint of 1951 we can say that the program lacked integration. It was not preceded by the necessary planning and was not followed by the necessary education. But we must give credit to the program for a variety of experiences which later saved the government of Puerto Rico much trial-and-error work.

Farmers Home Administration

The program of the Farmers Home Administration, formerly Farm Security Administration, represents the most consistent attempt of the federal government to affect land tenure in Puerto Rico. It is rooted in the time-honored glorification by the United States of country life and family farms. In Puerto Rico it fits basic socio-economic needs as well as ideological concepts. Its Farm Ownership Program was initiated in Puerto Rico in March, 1938. Up to June 30, 1950, the Farmers Home Administration had made loans amounting to approximately 4 million dollars to finance the purchase of 31,405 acres by 775 farmers. The program has been carried out mostly through the subdivision of 175 large farms into family-type farms.

The standards of the Farmers Home Administration are higher than those of any other agency in regard to the size of the family-type farm. The average farm is forty acres in size. Because of prevailing conditions and scarcity of land, so high a standard has been questioned. Puerto Rico must develop her own standards based on existing social and economic realities.

"A distinguishing feature of this agency's programs is its objective to strengthen the farm people with whom it works to enable them to cope better with their own problems to help themselves, and eventually to become independent so that they will require no special aid from the government. This strengthening process operates in the field of agriculture and homemaking science through the building of confidence and morale in the minds and hearts of the people."[3]

In the Farmers Home Administration program we can see the first signs of a broad and comprehensive approach to the farm problem. The agency has relied mainly on traditional farm enterprises and has not been interested in pioneering in new forms of land utilization which might prove to be of greater benefit to the country and to the families themselves. In spite of these short-comings the impact of the program on production has been significant. This may be attributed in part to its well-organized supervised credit activities.

An economic study of four of the larger projects established by the Farmers Home Administration was made during the years 1944/45 and 1946/47, respectively. They show that the effects of the change in tenure upon production are very significant. For the four projects the area in sugar cane was maintained at about 4,000 acres. However, great progress was made towards a balanced type of farming. Food crops increased from 119 acres to over 1,700 acres. Since the lands purchased belonged to large sugar cane farm operators no livestock was raised in them. At the time of the study there were over 2,724 animal units in these farms. In addition, the pasture lands had been greatly improved in their carrying capacity.

Land Law of Puerto Rico

The Land Law of Puerto Rico, Act. No. 26, approved by the Legislature of Puerto Rico in 1941, created the Land Authority of Puerto Rico and other tenure innovation programs under the Department of Agriculture and Commerce. The Authority is a government instrumentality for the purpose of carrying out the provision of the Land Law. The statement of motives, which outlines the social and economic philosophy of the Law, reads as follows:

The Legislature of Puerto Rico, by the present declaration and through the instrumentality of this Act, states that the land in Puerto Rico is to be considered as a source of life, dignity and economic freedom for the men and women who till it, and it is declared that it is the policy of the People of Puerto

Rico that finally each person who tills the land shall be the owner of the land which supports him. . . .

This fundamental public policy would not be complete if it were not accompanied by, as a corollary germane to its nature and scope, the purpose of providing that in the case of land where, for natural or economic reasons, the division of the land is not advisable from a standpoint of efficiency, the greatest diffusion possible of the economic benefits of the land may still be effected, thereby contributing to raise substantially the standard of living of the greatest possible number of families. It is with a view to this phase of the legislative purpose that it is considered indispensable to make provision for the creation of the proportional-profit farms through which the diffusion of the wealth may be effected, to the point efficiency makes advisable, without parceling of the land.

The Land Law has been most important in remodelling traditional land tenure in accordance with government policy and in harmony with Puerto Rican needs. An integrated over-all approach to human revival and land reform is embodied in its four programs: (1) the proportional-profit farm, (2) the family farm, (3) the resettlement of squatters ("agregados") in organized rural communities, (4) an education program to develop group action and improve community living.

The proportional-profit farm is the latest and most promising Puerto Rican approach to increased production and to improved distribution of profits in agriculture. The concept of the proportional-profit farm is Puerto Rico's contribution in the field of land tenure. As stated by Mr. Ramón Colón Torres, Commissioner of Agriculture and Commerce: "Recognizing that land is our principal resource and that it is too scarce for the needs of our population, an attempt was made to formulate a system which would guarantee the greatest income from the land and at the same time a better distribution of that income. To that end, under Title IV of the Law, the proportional-profit farms were created. This is a new and interesting scheme of tenure through which the advantages of large scale operation are maintained without sacrificing a better distribution of its economic income."

The program helps develop in the laborers a sense of responsibility and efficiency since they are sharing the profits. In a broader sense they are partners in the farm enterprise. The laborers share in the net profit of the farms in proportion to the days each has worked and to the wages or salaries received as an advance on his labor on the farm. The laborers are free to decide to sell their work, and they can work on the farm or not. From 1944 to 1951 proportional-profit farms, which cover about 100,-000 acres, have distributed over 3 million dollars as profits among 37,000 laborers and have kept in reserve about 1,400,000 dollars.

In general, the proportional-profit farm has increased production and improved land use. A study of four projects shows that sugar cane production on these proportional-profit farms increased from 339,000 tons to 605,000 tons, or 78 per cent. This compares favorably with 19.2 per cent increase in production for the Island.

Though it may be too early to pass judgment on the proportional-profit farm program of the Land Authority, it is time to start evaluating its accomplishments. Any such appraisal has to take into consideration the nature of the experiment and the socio-economic setting which serves as background. Problems of a general nature, such as education and health, which in the traditional farm management approach are scarcely taken into consideration, become the core in a program like the one under discussion. From this vantage point, the human values and attitudes, for once, are seen to stand by the side of such items as cost of production and capital investment. This may be shocking to some agricultural economists. It should not be so shocking to rural sociologists and social anthropologists. It is in the light of all these factors that evaluation of the program becomes really meaningful.

Through the Rural Community Program entrusted to the Social Programs Administration of the Department of Agriculture, plots of one-fourth of one acre to three acres are provided in usufruct for rural landless farm laborers. This land ownership represents the realization of the dream of every farm laborer: a plot where he can build his home, plant some subsistence crops, raise some domestic animals, rear a family, and above all provide for the freedom to exercise his democratic rights and to sell his labor in the open market without the limitation of dependency which characterized his life as a squatter (agregado). This feeling of freedom is a psychological restoration of man for his struggles. There is a rebirth of the powers and potentialities of a real citizen. A man who does not share the discussion of his problems and those of his community, who is not a participant in the solution of those problems, who does not exercise his rights and perform his duties is a human being—but he is not a citizen of democracy.

Over 25,000[4] families have already been resettled in 181 rural communities, thereby reforming the scattered pattern of rural settlement existing in Puerto Rico. The rural communities or villages so organized run from 100 to 500 families. They are designed following the most progressive principles in rural community planning. The design provides for the establishment of such services and facilities as schools, health centers, parks, consumers' co-operatives, churches, community pastures, and others. The subdivision contemplates the most economic means for providing streets, water supply, and electric facilities. To this end the physical setting is of crucial importance. Furthermore, it helps to provide the proper climate for rural community life which, in turn, facilitates co-operatives, education, and direct group action. The "Community Action Plan," sponsored by the Social Programs Administration of the Department of Agriculture, has shown that mutual aid and self-help thrive best where an integrated community life exists.

These small plots are making a substantial contribution to the economy of the Island. For the year ending June 30, 1950, over 7,000 acres of food crops[5] were harvested. In addition, about 9,000 acres were planted but not yet harvested. As of the same date, livestock sales amounted to about 7 million dollars.[6] Since the land selected for a Rural Community site is not usually under intensive cultivation, these figures largely represent additional production.

The family-type farm program developed by the Social Programs Administration is the Puerto Rican government counterpart to the Farmers Home Administration Program (Federal). It is conceived on the principle that, in addition to the agrarian ideology and high esteem of rural life, the family farm is an answer to a better land utilization, especially in the highlands.

Up to June 30, 1950, 420 family farms with a total of 6,000 acres had been established throughout the Island, mostly in the highlands. The cost of the land improvements amounted to $284,202.

During the fiscal year ending June 30, 1950, these farms produced crops and livestock whose estimated value was over $330,-000. Again, these figures represent, to a large extent, added production. This is due to the fact that the program is being developed primarily on lands which were not previously under cultivation.

These farms are sold to tenants, sharecroppers, and agregados on a forty-year installment plan. Candidates are selected on the basis of, among other things, the capacity of the family to manage and improve a farm. Co-operative action is stimulated among these small farmers.

Other Programs of Land Reform

The struggle which will lead to higher standards of production and consumption has different lines of attack, of which land tenure reform is an important one. However, important as land tenure is, it must be brought into its proper relationship in the over-all problem of agriculture. Land tenure by itself is not a cure-all. It must be supported by other measures such as education and services which provide the many other things that make up the good life. They are essential to any acceptable system of land tenure if it is to work and afford opportunities for decent living to the people on the land. May I say at this point that it is not enough to dream and hope. It is not sufficient to have a good law; it is necessary to see that there is not a lag between statutory provisions and actual economic development. Such lags are not unusual in practice.

We have to look at land reform in the context of the broader agricultural situation and the always significant social implications. When we look into land reform throughout the world, with few exceptions, it seems as if we, as citizens of the world, have not made much use of centuries of experience. What have we done? What are we doing? What do we plan to do?

Look at the man whom we resettled in a fairly good tract of land and asked to be a good farmer. We forgot that the good life includes things that are not found on a tract of land and that to be a good farmer you need other things in addition to land and in addition to the machinery, equipment, and livestock needed to run a farm. We forgot all about education, health, recreation, and many other necessary services and facilities. We might as well wrap him up in a legal fee simple title, shoot him to the moon, and ask him to raise a family and be a good farmer.

Land reform is no longer a matter of subdividing a large plot and giving it in fee simple or in usufruct or in any other conventional way to a distressed rural family.

Land reform, if it is to be of value in terms of providing the population with a richer life, requires broader ideological and practical concepts. We need to look into the farmer and his family and into the other farmers and the other families. We need to look into social organization.

In the light of the results of our different land tenure approaches, in terms of their contribution to the satisfaction of human needs, policies and programs are always in the process of remaking. It is fitting and proper to mention some of the latest developments intended to provide the best setting for the success of what Governor Muñoz Marín has so colorfully called the "bootstrap operation" in the "Battle of Production."

We have, of course, the traditional Vocational Education and Extension Service Program. In addition, we have of recent inception the following programs:

1. A credit program for co-operatives—the Puerto Rico Bank Cooperatives.

2. A credit in kind program—the Food Production and Distribution Program.

3. The Land Use Survey, which is intended to provide a basis for land use planning in accordance with Puerto Rican needs.

4. The Soil Conservation Districts. The law creating the Soil Conservation Districts in Puerto Rico will adequately serve as a rural zoning law to enforce land use plans.

5. The Integrated Agricultural Programs. This is an over-all integrated agricultural plan which will be completed in the next few months. It is intended to provide a general guide for agricultural development in Puerto Rico. It is being worked out with close co-operation between all federal and insular agricultural agencies. This activity is sponsored by the Department of Agriculture of Puerto Rico.

6. An artificial insemination program, which is intended to improve our dairy breeds of cattle on a short-term plan. This program is closely co-ordinated with pasture improvement activities.

7. A soil liming program. Puerto Rico's soils are generally acid. The soil liming program will greatly increase productivity at a low cost.

8. The Marketing Administration, which is in charge of organizing the efficient distribution of the agricultural produce.

Impressive as all this may be, and in spite of the achievements, there is a lot more to be done.

At the present time, as mentioned before, a joint effort is being made by the Insular and Federal governments for the development of a comprehensive agricultural program for the island. This program, for the first time, will bring together all the segments of the problem and will pave the way for a concerted action by both Insular and Federal agencies in Puerto Rico. In all our efforts to cope with agricultural problems the Island has had, and continues to have, the sympathetic understanding and the full co-operation of the Federal government and its various agencies.

Rural Community Organization

We have recognized this need for over-all integrated approach in Puerto Rico and it will be convenient, at this time, to outline briefly this over-all improvement effort from the standpoint of social action.

Pervading the whole agricultural structure and underlying the efforts to improve rural life is Puerto Rico's policy of creating the right climate based on the proposition that if rural life is to be effectively improved, especially in underdeveloped areas, it will depend, to a large extent, on the rural families themselves. After some successful experience in low-cost rural housing, organizing consumers' co-operatives, providing drinking water at low costs, and general physical improvement of rural settlements, we are wondering if in this present program we are not on the track of answering many of the social and economic problems with which humanity has coped for generations without any visible sign of success. Isolated, unplanned examples of mutual aid and self-help could be cited in every country. But it is the planned, the purposeful organization of the community for direct group action that gives special significance to what we have called the "Community Action Plan." Allow me to mention that through organized self-help and co-operative action we have been able to build a reinforced concrete house of 18 feet by 18 feet for the unbelievable cost to the government of $300.

May I finish these remarks by saying that Puerto Rico, as an integral part of the United States, is definitely committed to a democratic way of life politically, socially, and economically. In our country there is in the making one of the most capable citizenries of the world to live and practice one of the purest democracies of the world. There you will find unfailing faith in the success of the undertaking to shape our future through self-help, in harmony with our needs and in harmony with the broader objective of man on earth. Man, the family, that common denominator of the toils of humanity, is the center of gravity of present-day Puerto Rican agricultural policy. Science is being recruited to serve man, not as one of his tools for selfish ends. Technology is being harnessed to serve man. Man will not become the slave of his technological feats in Puerto Rico.

What is going on in Puerto Rico is the story of man boldly decided to become master of his own destiny, in spite of the great handicaps of overpopulation and definitely limited land and other natural resources. There you can see in action the will-power and the firm determination to solve our problems and to improve standards of living. Puerto Rico is a beehive; the murmuring of the swarm is being heard across the Caribbean and over the Atlantic. You are all invited to visit Puerto Rico. You will be most welcome to see what is going on in our "pilot plant" of social action.

SOCIAL SECURITY FOR LANDLESS WORKERS: THE EXPERIENCE OF BRAZIL

   João Gonçalves deSouza

IN SPITE of the difficulty of applying a program of social security for landless workers in many nations of Latin America and Asia, we think this should and can be done. What do I mean by social security? Which are the areas that should be covered by some scheme of social security and what types of persons should be covered? The International Labor Organization of the United Nations recently issued a book on the subject which I think has up-to-date material on this point.[1] What I want to ask are the following three questions: (1) How are landless workers included in present schemes of social security in certain groups of nations? (2) What are the solutions these

schemes are offering to cover landless people? (3) What is the Brazilian experience,
if any, in this field?

Before World War II and especially after
it, social security made great improvement
all over the world. I am speaking about
laws which apply equally to all kinds of
workers regardless of status, whether city
worker or farmer. I don't say that the situation in agriculture has improved in the
same space of time and at the same speed
that it has with the city worker. Farm people in comparison with city people are
always handicapped, and in some cases the
difference in progress can be measured by
centuries even in the same country. According to social security schemes for landless workers, we can consider the nations of
the world in six different groups according
to the interest they have in these schemes.
First, there are those whose laws are advanced and seek to cover a major number
of risks. This is the case of Australia, Chile,
Czechoslovakia, Italy, New Zealand, Sweden, and the United Kingdom. Second,
there are those nations where social legislation covers landless workers in one or
more risks. This is the case in Belgium,
Bulgaria, Canada, Costa Rica, Cuba, Ecuador, Finland, Guatemala, Ireland, Netherlands, Norway, Mexico, Peru, Switzerland,
Uruguay, and the United States. Third,
there are those whose social security for city
people is very progressive but for agricultural workers is limited to just one field of
application, as, for instance, accident compensation. This is the case of Argentina and
Brazil and a few other nations. Fourth,
some states of Asia, especially China, India,
Burma, Ceylon, Malaya, and Thailand, are
working hard to offer social services to poor
land workers in farm areas. But they are
handicapped by lack of both doctors and
hospitals. Fifth, there is a group of nations
which has good and progressive legislation
for city people and has tried to extend the

plan for farm people, but for some reason
or another the plan did not work out. This
is the case of the majority of Latin American
states, especially Colombia, Dominican Republic, Ecuador, Guatemala, and Mexico.
Sixth, more than 50 per cent of the total
number of nations did not have time to
think seriously about a plan of social
security for farm people.

Why are social security schemes today
more advanced for urban workers than for
rural people? The explanation follows.
Rural people do not constitute a homogeneous group as do city people. Some
work all year around; others only a part
of the year. Some receive salaries in cash,
others in kind, or both, as in the case of
Brazil and other nations which were mentioned here by other delegates of this conference. In the United States it is not so
common to have hired workers outside the
family, but in countries like my own, particularly in commercialized agriculture or
the plantation system, we frequently have
a dozen or more hired workers in the same
economic unit. There is the question of
rent. Agriculture does not give the same
percentage of rents in the majority of nations as compared with industry. This does
not permit rural employers to offer better
salaries to employees. Thus the reason why
the quota reserved for social security for
rural workers is small. From nothing we can
deduct nothing. A new impediment to social security for farm people is the lack of
good organization for agricultural countries
today. The so-called professional risks have
not the same degree of frequency and intensity they used to have in urban areas
except where agriculture is highly mechanized. The prevalence of social classes
and a lack of clear distinction between them
makes it difficult to establish a program as
could easily be done for city workers. The
dispersion of rural workers in comparison
with the concentration of city workers

makes a great difference. In Brazil 70 per cent of the industrial proletariat are located in a fringe area of one hundred kilometers from the border of the Atlantic Ocean, while the farm workers are spread all over the country. This creates many difficulties, including that of collecting money to be used for social security.

Those are the difficulties; they actually exist. But some of them have been used as an excuse for not trying to do anything for farm people. This situation is aggravated by the fact that many of our leaders, administrators and politicians, are so urban-minded that they just do not think seriously about farm problems. However, the landless worker should have better social status and more security on the land and in his job. A major part of his work is hard and calls for physical strength. It is carried out in the open, sunshine or rain, in hot or cold weather. His capacity to earn money depends exclusively on his ability and his health. Occupational illness, invalidity, old age, unemployment, and maternity effect not only those living and working in cities but also those in rural areas. On the other hand, mechanized agriculture, a trait of developed nations of the western hemisphere, has been creating possibilities for occupational accidents. Thus there is real need for doing something to face these situations. I think it is possible to do something and that we should start in at least one or two experimental areas of risks. As a matter of fact, those difficulties can be met "by means of special adjustments if necessary, thereby enabling general schemes of social security to be extended to include wage earners in agriculture as well. The countries in which this has been done afford proof that it is possible."[2]

The Example of Brazil

In Brazil, social legislation and social security are advanced, but little has been done in favor of the farm landless workers. And we are a nation of farmers. In 1941 a law[3] established a scheme for family allowance in rural areas for families with eight or more children. This law has been fully applied, even in the most geographically isolated areas of the country. On the other hand, in Brazil, like Argentina, Australia, Belgium, Bulgaria, Chile, Cuba, Czechoslovakia, Denmark, Finland, Hungary, Ireland, Mexico, New Zealand, Portugal, Sweden, United Kingdom, and Uruguay, the landless workers are covered by a general social legislation regarding employment injury. When we speak of labor legislation as such, some articles (Articles 505 and 506 of Consolidacao das leis do Trabalho) are fully extended to farm workers. But for one reason or another they could not be applied. A former Minister of Labor in Brazil declared that such things could not be done because he thought some basic study should be made by the government regarding the rural social problems in order to know the exact conditions of the social classes in agriculture.[4] And now, eight years later, we are still waiting for this basic study.

However, in spite of all this, in many communities of the country rural employers anticipated the lack of governmental social assistance and set out on a program to give their workers social, medical, and educational assistance. Since 1907 the coffee planters in the south and later the sugar cane planters in the northeast put into action a program of free medical care and educational assistance to farm laborers and their families. In order to achieve this, almost every large farm or sugar cane Usina has one doctor and one dentist to attend to the health needs of this community. When there is a scarcity of doctors, some farmers get together and raise money to pay one doctor and one dentist to serve the whole community once a week or once a month.

Even hospitalization of landless workers is paid through such an arrangement.

At this time a law is being projected for which I was personally responsible in large measure. It is in Congress now and I think at this time has already been passed.[5] By means of this law we institute a foundation to offer social services for rural communities and rural people, especially in the field of food, health, clothes, education, and sanitation. Also, it aims to introduce a combined program of agricultural education, home economics, co-operatives, and small rural industries. This foundation is a private organization which will be maintained with money raised in a compulsory manner from rural industries, agricultural employers, and commerce, when localized in rural areas, in addition to gifts and donations, and budgetary monies from federal, state, and local governments. National, state, and county councils to plan and direct this foundation are to be composed of equal numbers of employers, employees, and leaders of the community. This foundation, Servico Social Rural, is the first national measure aiming to bring about through adequate social laws a little more economic security for landless workers without which the insecurity of the life of the people is a permanent menace to the stability of our social institutions.

SOCIAL SECURITY PROBLEMS OF SHARECROPPERS AND FARM LABORERS

Report of the Working Party

  Chairman, *Lowry Nelson*

THE PRELIMINARY discussion centered about the meaning and scope of the phrase "social security" as regards types of risks to be covered and agricultural groups needing protection and assistance. It was the opinion of the group that social security should be broadly conceived to include general social legislation such as minimum wages, conditions of work, and public services of a general character, especially health services and education, as well as the conventional types of protection and benefits. These latter include old age and survivors' benefits, medical care, maternity benefits, family allowances, accident and disability insurance, unemployment benefits, etc.

With few exceptions, reports given by members of the working party on conditions in their respective countries revealed an almost universal lack of legislation to provide social security for the groups under consideration. A number of the countries, however, have some protective legislation for various types of industrial workers. Of all countries represented, Chile probably has the only comprehensive social security program in operation for rural workers, on which the group had a report from the delegate from Chile. The member of the working party from Trinidad reported that most of the governments of the British West Indies have minimum wage legislation, rural health centers, and welfare centers.

The discussion emphasized that many of the problems of sharecroppers and laborers are often shared by other classes in the rural population, such as small proprietors and tenants, although it was recognized that special problems exist among the landless workers. More than the usual measures of land reform will be necessary to meet the needs of landless workers.

While recognizing the great difficulty in most of the countries in obtaining social security legislation for farm people, the committee felt that a number of general measures should be adopted which would enhance the welfare of all tenure groups. Among these measures are the extension of public health services to rural areas, which should emphasize the control of infectious diseases, the elimination of parasites, and the general improvement in sanitation. Such action by government might well be given the highest priority.

Among measures for the improvement of rural life in general, the working party laid much stress on the extension of opportunities for education. Along with formal schooling for children, programs of adult education should be carried on at the same time. It was felt that a combined attack on debilitating diseases and illiteracy would contribute greatly to improving productivity and would lay the foundation for later legislation to provide protection against the various hazards of rural workers.

Along with these measures for the improvement of rural life in general, farm people can participate in social security programs supported by general public funds and open to all citizens on the basis of specific needs. Typical of such programs are old age assistance, family allowances, aids to the blind and to other disabled persons. In such cases the test for eligibility is the need of the applicant. The inclusion of the resident rural population presents no special problems, and in the programs in existence they have usually been included. Rather, the question is whether a country can afford the program. Migratory farm families, however, do present a special problem. They are one of the most disadvantaged groups, and it is difficult to reach them even with general programs of health and education.

Special problems exist in the extension of social security programs, based on contributions, to sharecroppers and agricultural laborers. These include old age, survivors', and unemployment insurance. Usually such programs have covered persons working for wages, and, in particular, unemployment is a hazard facing only those who are employed under a wage contract. Also, it is difficult to extend an insurance program to people with very low incomes. Administration of such programs for rural people would be difficult in some cases because of the magnitude of the population involved, in others because of difficulty of supervision and collection from a scattered rural population. It would be even more difficult to administer an insurance program for migratory farm laborers.

In its survey of landless workers and other needy tenure classes, and in its search for means of meeting their security requirements, the group made use of the pioneer, and very valuable, work of the International Labor Organization—*International Survey of Social Security* (Geneva, 1950). We are also indebted to the International Labor Office, Washington branch, for the bibliography used in the workshop.

This working party regards land tenure adjustments and social security legislation as complementary techniques for achieving the common purpose of attaining greater security for all people. It hopes that the conference will accept this viewpoint and include both among the measures that it emphasizes.

Part X LAND TENURE AND THE
INTRODUCTION OF NEW TECHNOLOGIES

OPENING REMARKS BY THE CHAIRMAN

§§§§   *Eduardo Neale-Silva*

THE MEETING is called to order. I shall now explain the order of events. First we shall have a presentation by Dr. James G. Maddox, to be followed by a discussion, and then there will be another presentation by Professor Henry S. Sterling, followed again by a discussion period. Later on, there will be an interchange of questions and answers among all the speakers. The public is also invited to ask questions.

The first speaker this afternoon, Dr. James G. Maddox, is a member of the American International Association—a non-profit Rockefeller project for social and economic development in Latin America. Dr.

Maddox spent two years at Harvard as visiting lecturer. In addition, he has worked in various capacities in the Farm Security Administration in the Division of Rural Rehabilitation. The subject of Dr. Maddox's discussion will be "Transferring Agricultural Technology from Developed to Underdeveloped Areas." Because of the special significance of Dr. Maddox's work in connection with various phases of land tenure, I have requested him to be kind enough to give us some information on the organization with which he is connected.

Ladies and gentlemen, it is a great pleasure indeed to present to you Dr. Maddox.

TRANSFERRING AGRICULTURAL TECHNOLOGY
FROM DEVELOPED TO UNDERDEVELOPED AREAS

§§§§   *James G. Maddox*

ONE OF THE big problems facing the world today is the extent to which agricultural technology can be transferred from the well-developed areas of the world to the more underdeveloped areas. The belief that many technologies can be transferred from country to country is one of the foundation stones of all international technical assistance programs, including our Point Four activities. I want to center my discussion this afternoon around this problem.

Before I do that, and in line with the suggestion that the chairman has made, let me

mention very briefly the organization that I am connected with and the type of work which we do. The American International Association is a nonprofit organization which was formed by Nelson Rockefeller and his brothers in 1946. It is engaged in a technical assistance program privately financed by donations from business companies and by members of the Rockefeller family. It is a separate and distinct organization from the International Basic Economy Corporation, which is often called IBEC. The latter is a profit-making corporation which has invested in several business companies that operate in Venezuela, Brazil, and Ecuador. The American International Association has programs, at the present time, only in Venezuela and Brazil. In these countries it is focusing attention on improving agricultural production and nutrition. It operates action-type programs in partnership with agencies of the co-operating governments. Its methods are similar to those of some of the publicly supported agencies, such as the Institute of Inter-American Affairs.

I will come back later, as time permits, to an explanation of the methods we use, and, if the audience is interested, to a detailed description of our present projects.

I would like, however, at this time, to turn to the more general subject of the possibilities and problems of transferring agricultural technology from a country such as the United States to any one of the many underdeveloped countries of the world. As a first step, I would like to call your attention to a simplified classification of agricultural technologies.

One group of agricultural technologies springs from the biological sciences. Illustrations are the high-producing, scientifically-bred varieties of plants and animals, including, of course, various types of hybrids. Also, there is a group of vaccines for the prevention or cure of livestock and poultry diseases which are basically biological in nature.

A second group is what I call the chemical type of agricultural technology, because it springs largely from the work of the chemist. Examples of it are the ordinary commercial fertilizers so commonly used in many countries, a large and important list of insecticides and fungicides, and also weed killers. Still another example is some of the modern supplements to livestock rations.

A third group of agricultural technologies springs from the work of the physicists and the engineers. Examples are tractors, the many complicated farm machines and equipment that go with power farming, and also a long list of other things such as farm buildings, silos, and storage facilities, and even farm-to-market roads and marketing facilities. All these are basically engineering structures or designs.

Now, why make this kind of a classification of agricultural technologies? There are several reasons. I want to mention only two or three. First of all, I want you to recognize the breadth and the complexity of the term "technology." It is not simply machinery and equipment. It includes many other things, as we use the word in the United States. Secondly, I want you to realize that advances in one field of technology are often dependent upon advances in another field. If we had not had the development of vaccines, for instance, to prevent hog cholera, we would not have been able to develop high-producing breeds of hogs. The even-growing characteristics of hybrid corn, a less obvious illustration, has been an important factor in encouraging tractor farming and the mechanical harvesting of corn. The fact that many countries do not have an even-growing variety of corn puts tremendous burdens on the engineer to develop a machine which will mechanically harvest corn.

The major point is that underdeveloped countries need to move ahead more or less simultaneously with a series of interrelated technological advances, some of which are biological, some of which are chemical, some of which are engineering in their origin. We are concerned, then, with the advancing front of science and with how applied forms of science intertwine in complex interrelationships so that progress in one area must often await the solution of a problem in a totally different area.

A third reason for classifying technologies into three groups is the different effects which these different types of technologies have on local institutions when they are adopted by farmers. This, I hope, we will have time to discuss later. For the time being, let me give you an example of what I mean.

A very small farmer, without any substantial change in the size of his holdings or in his tenure relationships, can start using fungicides or pesticides to increase the yields of his crops. Likewise, he can usually start using fertilizer without necessitating a change in the size of his holding. If, on the other hand, he is to adopt power farming and use tractors, it is almost inevitable that he will have to increase the size of his farm. To do this usually requires a change in his tenure relationships, and this usually runs into political and economic traditions of long standing which present real delays to progress.

Now let me mention another classification which I think will be helpful in understanding the problem. There is a minimum of three stages through which each agricultural technology must pass before it results in increased productivity and higher standards of living on the farm.

The first of these stages I call the "pure science or research stage." It usually takes place in the laboratory or on the experiment station farm. In connection with such a simple thing, for instance, as hybrid seed corn, there had to be a great deal of pure research on the part of geneticists before they understood well enough the principles of plant breeding to develop a productive hybrid. Likewise, before there could be a farm tractor, there had to be a great deal of research by physicists and engineers in developing the internal combustion engine. This "pure science" stage often appears to have little direct or immediate reference to the problems of farmers.

A second stage is one of "experimentation and application." The problem here is to take an idea, or set of ideas and principles, and apply them in an experimental manner to the practical problems of farm people. Closely connected with this pattern of applied experimentation is the work of the businessman, who must often develop the techniques for producing and distributing some kind of product which embodies the new technology. Many ideas or working models of the scientists never reach the stage of being applied on the farm because they are unprofitable to manufacture or market or for some reason meet technical difficulties which take years to solve in adapting them to farm conditions.

For example, after productive corn hybrids were developed, it still took a very great deal of work and time to organize businesses which would produce hybrid seed in volume, dry it, store it, package it, and transport it to farmers. A more complicated example, of course, is the cotton picking machine. The basic principles of that machine were developed years ago, and a few crude models actually picked cotton almost a generation before there were machines that could be put to use on as many as one hundred farms.

A third stage in the development of a technology is the adoption of it by large numbers of farmers. After the pure scientist has done his work, after the applied scientist and businessman have done their work and have something which can be offered to farmers in large volume, there is still the problem of getting farmers to accept the new technology. In any given instance, it may be a new type of fertilizer, a new seed, a new machine, or simply a new plowing or planting practice. Whatever it is, a big and important step before it produces results in the way of increased productivity and higher standards of living is to obtain its widespread adoption by farmers. Sometimes, this stage in the process is visualized as the main problem, or even the only problem, in getting a more widespread use of new agricultural technologies. Such a view overlooks the significance of the scientist and the businessman in the total process of creating something which the farmer can put to use on the farm.

We can bring together the classifications of (1) types of agricultural technologies and (2) the stages of development which each passes through by a form such as shown in Figure 2.

A form of the type shown in Figure 2 can be useful in answering the question: What are the impediments to the introduction of agricultural technologies into X country? The question can be answered in terms of all or any one of the three types of agricultural technologies with respect to each stage in its developmental process. Each of the vacant blocks in the form would then become a list of impediments and would focus attention on the type of action that is needed.

This is obviously a simple analytical de-

vice which can guide our thinking and which can be expanded to any desired degree of specificness. I have introduced it here because I thought it might be a helpful gadget to some of you who want to analyze the situation within your own countries.

With this general framework let us raise the questions: To what extent can the modern technologies now being used by farmers in the United States be transferred to other countries without having to go through a long process of pure science research and of experimentation and adaptation to the new setting? Can the first two of the three stages in the development process be short-cut, so that underdeveloped countries will not have to retrace all the steps in the long road over which agricultural technology has traveled in this country?

Generally speaking, I think that you can transfer from a developed to an underdeveloped country the engineering types of technologies without great adaptation. A

Types of Agricultural Technologies	Stages of Development		
	Pure Science Research	Experimentation and Application	Adoption by Farmers
Biological			
Chemical			
Engineering			

Fig. 2—Form Showing Stages of Development of Agricultural Technologies

tractor, for instance, with perhaps some small adjustments in its carburetor and its cooling system, will do essentially the same work in Mexico or in Venezuela or in India or in any other country as it does in Iowa, providing, of course, that it is driven and serviced by a man who is equally as proficient as the Iowa man. To a very great extent, this type of technology can be transferred from one country to another without having to go through the first two stages within the underdeveloped country.

At the other extreme is the biological type of technology. A hybrid corn which will produce well in southern Wisconsin or Iowa when transferred to Venezuela, Mexico, Guatemala, or other tropical countries may be nothing but a weed. It may even be true that some of the vaccines and fungicides developed in a given environment cannot be transferred to totally different environments and produce results. The upshot of this fact, if it is true, as I believe it to be, is that the underdeveloped countries will have to have a relatively large staff of scientists, particularly in the biological and chemical fields, to take the pure science ideas from the developed countries and adapt them to their particular environment.

That which can be transferred or transported from one country to another is the scientific method—the method by which you produce a vaccine, the method by which you produce hybrid corn, or the method by which you produce antibiotics—but not necessarily the materials, the germ plasm, the substance itself. If it is primarily the method of adaptation that can be transferred, this imposes upon the underdeveloped countries the necessity of having a group of scientists and of giving administrative and financial support to those scientists so that they can make the necessary adaptations. This difficulty of transporting technologies from one country to another has nothing to do with international politics,

with methods of financing, attitudes of individuals or groups, or with restrictive powers held by some monopolies. I am speaking of physical limitations on the transfer of technologies. I am saying that, in general, they are greatest in the biological field; they are second greatest in the chemical field; and they are of relatively small consequence with respect to the engineering type of technology. The latter can be transported from one country to another without great difficulty.

If the problems of financing could be worked out, the developed countries could virtually flood the underdeveloped ones with tractors, plows, silos, and a score of other engineering technologies. Of course, the problem of financing cannot be ignored, and for many countries it is paramount. However, I am trying to focus attention on a different problem, namely, that an underdeveloped country can have its coffers filled with dollars and still not be able to buy its needed biological technologies and many of its chemical technologies. It may be able to buy or receive through various kinds of technical assistance programs the services of men who know how to employ the tools of science and develop, within its own environment, the biological and chemical technologies that will get results. This, however, takes time, and it necessitates a setting in which scientists can fruitfully work. Because of basic differences in agricultural technologies, and because there is great need for haste, both the developed and underdeveloped countries can easily fall into the trap of trying to substitute tractors, plows, and mowing machines for geneticists, pathologists, soil scientists, and a dozen other types of specialists.

If it is true that most underdeveloped countries must have a relatively large number of scientists to breed new varieties of crops and new strains of livestock to produce new vaccines that fit the needs of their environment, to analyze their soils and carry on fertilization experiments, and to conduct research in dozens of other lines there are certain types of difficulties involved that should be frankly recognized.

For instance, there is a shortage of agricultural scientists in most underdeveloped countries. Moreover, the cultures of many of these countries are without a scientific tradition and do not give a high social status to the scientist. Positions of prestige in their social organization are usually held by military men, by politicians, by poets or literary men, and to a lesser extent by administrators. This is quite different from the situation in this country.

In many undeveloped countries the scientist is handicapped by poor working conditions, lack of job security, and unwillingness on the part of public institutions to provide continuing financial support for research work which does not show quick results. Since the very nature of much research work, particularly in the agricultural sciences, necessitates many years of study and experimentation, it is not a popular field in which unstable or politically insecure governments invest public funds. They are more likely to put their support behind activities that will directly strengthen their power or will get quick, even if temporary, popular acclaim.

Most of what I have just been saying pertains to the "research" and "applied science" stages through which technologies must pass on the long road they travel from being just an "idea" to being something tangible and specific that a farmer can use, apply, or put into practice on his farm. In the great task of getting thousands, or even millions, of impoverished, tradition-minded farmers to accept the new technologies and put them to use on their farms, there are still other difficulties and problems to which groups like this should give calm and objective attention.

For instance, the lack of rudimentary education—the ability to read and write and understand the radio and newspaper—on the part of millions of farm people in the underdeveloped countries is a big and important impediment to the adoption of new agricultural technologies. Moreover, a high proportion of the farmers in many of these countries does not make sufficient income to have the savings with which to buy even such small items as good seed, fertilizer, insecticides, and improved hand tools. The lack of such savings is too commonly not offset by a decent agricultural credit system which makes small loans available on reasonable terms and conditions. Along with little education, low incomes, and inadequate credit facilities, there are often insecure and inequitable tenure arrangements and farms that are too small for anything like efficient operations.

These are the types of problems that must be faced and solved country by country, community by community, and family by family before really great strides can be made in getting the farmers of backward countries to adopt new and improved technologies. To overcome them is a task that will tax the ingenuity, the patience, and the mutual understanding of the leadership in both developed and underdeveloped countries. With these problems of farm adoption of new ideas and practices, perhaps the most important assistance that the developed countries can offer is demonstrations of the methods by which farmers can be educated, by which farm credit institutions can be organized and operated efficiently, by which tenure arrangements can be improved in an orderly and evolutionary manner, and by which the work of this nature can be tied in with the research and experimentation which I mentioned a few minutes ago. If such demonstrations could be carried out in all the underdeveloped countries of the world, where each of them would have to be designed and moulded to fit the existing cultural, political, and physical environment, they would have tremendous influence in shaping the future destiny of the world.

I am irrevocably convinced that the millions of under-privileged rural people in this world are anxious to make progress along the general lines that have been traveled by the more fortunate peoples of the developed countries. Many complicated problems have to be overcome before their desires will be fulfilled. The most impor-

tant barriers, however, are in the field of political relationships. The transfer of technology from one environment to another is no simple problem, as I hope my remarks have made clear, but enough of the accumulated knowledge of science can be transferred from country to country, so that progress in the underdeveloped areas of the world can go forward more rapidly than would be the case if they did not have the experience of the developed countries on which to draw.

DISCUSSION

EDMUNDO FLORES—I would like to make an additional comment on the introduction of new techniques to backward areas, not from the viewpoint of the technological obstacles that this introduction may present but rather from the standpoint of the economic difficulties which such introduction may imply. For this I wish to establish a classification between what economists call labor-saving devices and capital-saving devices. I believe that any careful attempt to introduce advanced technological methods to backward areas has to take into consideration how these innovations will adapt themselves into the general economic setting of the area. Maddox has talked about three types of technological adjustments—biological, chemical, and engineering. It is rather unfortunate that the engineering type, represented by tractors, bulldozers, and several other mechanical innovations, is the type of innovation which has attracted the most attention, which carries a certain magic. This type of innovation is essentially a labor-saving device. To adapt tractors to the agriculture of an area which has surplus manpower and at the same time suffers from scarcity of savings, capital, which has troubles in the balance of

payments and, of course, which doesn't produce tractors, will sooner or later create serious problems for the economy of an area. Thus, I believe that, with exceptions, of course, the emphasis has to be put on the adoption of biological innovations. The work of the Rockefeller commission done in Mexico in the development of hybrid corn seeds is a clear example of this procedure. It, however, should be added that although the Rockefeller Foundation has worked very intensively in the last few years, according to recent estimates by the Foundation and a Mexican organization which is in charge of exploiting the use of the new seeds developed by the commission, the innovations made have affected only about 5 per cent of the total corn produced in the country. This example illustrates the difficulties which this type of innovation carries. Just to finish, I would like to insist on the inconvenience of introducing innovations which will make more acute some of the problems of national development.

MR. MADDOX—I agree completely with what Mr. Flores has said. There is a whole area of discussion—which I hoped someone would stir up—on the ways and means of encouraging farmers to adopt these new biological technologies. For example, why is it that you do not get more than 5 per cent of the farmers in Mexico to use the new seed which the scientist has produced to fit the particular conditions of Mexico?

ANTONIO POSADA—I am not in complete agreement with Dr. Flores' remarks. He says that we should give more emphasis to the development of one type of technological procedure, that is, a particular type of technology, and that we should give more emphasis to the biological type of technology than to engineering. I believe that advances in one field of technology are related to the advances in other fields and that, if we concentrate on the biological type of technology, the results obtained might not be worthwhile because we don't implement them with other types. I think that we should try to have an integrated program and not particularize in any one field.

MR. FLORES—A country that is in the process of development has to depend heavily on imports. Equipment is a large part of importations. You have to import a number of things that are indispensable, but there is also an area where you may have an alternative. This alternative is the possibility of using a tractor or a bulldozer for land clearing or the possibility of using labor.

Labor is right there too, and the importation of an additional tractor will create additional problems. So when possible the problem is whether or not it is advisable to substitute the use of the machinery which is used in advanced countries for native labor. There are, of course, areas where this problem is real. I think definitely that preference should be given to domestic labor.

MR. POSADA—I am in agreement with Dr. Flores on the fact that the introduction of some types of machinery would be very costly, and surely now we have to be careful to avoid the flight of capital from our own countries because we have very small amounts of foreign exchange, but I think I understood him to say that we should not shift from manual labor to highly mechanized agriculture because it would create labor problems. In that case I would be in complete agreement with him. I agree that we should introduce this change in a relatively slow way, but I would not disturb agricultural development of any country just because we would create a labor problem. It is true that we would have some people who would not have immediate employment, but in the long run they will find employment in normal activities. We should try to get employment for these people and develop all areas of the national economy.

HENRY S. STERLING—I agree with everything that Dr. Maddox has said, but for purposes of perspective it seems to me that two points should be made. First of all, as most of us realize, a large proportion of all of the farmed area and of the farm population of Latin America is in a pre-scientific stage in which none of these new advances in scientific agriculture which he analyzed for us have as yet been adopted, or even dreamed of, and in which they are not likely to be adopted for an indeterminate period. This is because the people are isolated by distance, or by completely different cultural levels, or by cultural inertia—defined as the reluctance of a conservative rural society to adopt new ideas. In my experience, for example, in parts of central eastern Mexico, I found that only a very small proportion of the farmers have access to scientific agriculture or scientific methods. Characteristically, they farm their land as they and their ancestors have farmed it for thousands of years. It may be true that a given field has grown corn (and I don't mean hybrid corn) for a thousand years without rotations of crops—except for some intercultivation of beans or squash with the corn—and without rest except for periods of fallow. Fallowing is the only means they have of resting or improving the soil. Many farmers haven't even heard of fertilization, much less practice it. Many others are not able to practice it because of the lack of animals to provide manures or of economic means to procure artificial fertilizers.

The other point I would like to make is that there are certain segments of the Latin American farm population which according to field investigators have been descending in the technological scale rather than ascending. They are going the wrong way. Observers such as Waibel and Lynn Smith, who have studied the relatively recent European colonization in south Brazil, for example, tell us that these colonists, who came (or whose ancestors came) from countries like Germany and Italy with relatively advanced techniques, have lost many of these techniques. This is true even of such fairly simple practices as the use of the plow and crop rotation and the inclusion of livestock and forage crops in the farm economy for the maintenance of soil fertility. The colonists have become poor whites.

In short, the greatest obstacles to the introduction of technological improvement in underdeveloped areas may prove to be the cultural inertia and poverty of much of the rural population. And in some areas of declining technological levels considerable effort may be needed if we are even to "stay in the same place."

CHAIRMAN—I take this opportunity to add a few words about our second speaker, Professor Henry S. Sterling. He has been connected with the University of Wisconsin for many years as a professor in the Department of Geography. Aside from his interest in the general field of Latin American geography, Professor Sterling has been particularly interested in the changing Mexican rural economy, a subject to which he has devoted his attention, both as a field investigator and as a research worker. I take great pleasure in introducing to you Professor Henry S. Sterling.

AN EVALUATION OF MEXICO'S PRINCIPAL TYPES OF FARM OPERATION AND OF THEIR SIGNIFICANCE TO OTHER LATIN AMERICAN COUNTRIES

〽〽〽〽　　*Henry S. Sterling*

IT APPEARS from the foregoing discussion that the ease of introducing technological improvements in Latin America depends in part on the assimilative capacity, economic and cultural, of the individual farm operator. It may therefore be useful to examine the experience of one Latin American country, Mexico, in its attempts to broaden land ownership at several levels and facilitate the introduction of improved techniques and living standards.

It seems to me that much of the literature on land tenure and land reform tends to oversimplify the problem of raising such standards in underdeveloped areas of the world. Not only is land reform usually not sufficient in itself, but in some of the world's problem areas it may be of relatively minor importance. The factors involved in improving the status of an agrarian society are manifold and complexly interrelated. In addition to land tenure itself, they may include the density of rural population, kinds and quality of agricultural land, the actual and potential productivity of the latter under various types of farm management, the technological level of farm operators and their receptivity to new ideas, the size and accessibility of markets, and the amount of government and private aid available in the form of credit facilities, agricultural extension, health and education services, etc.

It follows that we find an almost infinite variety of problem situations in various parts of Latin America, resulting from different combinations of these and other factors. Obviously, any remedial program should not only be tailored to fit the particular problems of a specific region, after careful investigation of the facts, but should be carefully balanced so as to make due provision for all of the important, interrelated factors in the situation and the effects that change in any one of them may have upon the others. Nowhere has this truism been more clearly demonstrated than in Mexico, where land reform was carried out at so disproportionate a rate, compared to that of other remedial programs that should have been synchronized with it, that the Mexican revolution has not only fallen far short of its goals but has created new problems as serious as those it sought to solve.

Three main classes of farm operation stand out in the present rural economy of Mexico. They are a sub-subsistence lower class, a lower middle-class of "family" farms, and an upper middle-class of smaller landed gentry. Each existed before the agrarian revolution which began in 1910, and each has been more or less enlarged in the process of agrarian reform. I will first define each briefly and then discuss them and their significance, both in Mexico and in certain other parts of Latin America.

The "dwarf" farm or sub-subsistence holding, usually termed minifundio in Spanish, is best defined as a holding which is too small, under prevailing land use methods and crops, to support the family that occupies it or to keep it busy all of the time. In Mexico the dwarf-farmer class combines two large groups—small private landowners and ejidatarios. The former live for the most part in village communities, working pieces of formerly communal arable land which was subdivided among their ancestors during the nineteenth century. Most ejidatarios enjoy the usufruct of small parcels in the many new ejidos, expropriated from former haciendas and granted to village communities, new and old, to be subdivided among those with no land or too little land for their needs. The two groups are appropriately discussed together, because very often the private owner and ejidatario are one and the same person. Legally, it was perfectly possible for an existing small dwarf-farm owner to receive an ejidal allotment or parcel and thereby increase his holding up to the maximum permitted under the ejidal program. Ejidatarios in some cases also bought land to supplement oversmall holdings. Thus many dwarf farms are now partly private, partly ejidal.

The second category, the family farm, has in general been the one most widely praised in the literature on Latin American land tenure, for it is theoretically good. In Mexico, it has been defined as being large enough to support the family that occupies it and keep its members busy. It may even permit them to produce a surplus for sale, if they want to.

The third class is uncommon in the United States, but is found in most Latin American countries under various names. In English, its members might be called "gentleman farmers," or "smaller landed gentry." The important distinction between their medium-size and larger holdings and the other two classes is that the former are worked not by the owners and their families but usually by hired workers, who may be either landless laborers or dwarf farmers who piece out their income by part-time work on larger farms.

It becomes obvious from the foregoing that Mexico has followed a dual approach, or double standard, in land reform. In practice, the program has been very much like the situation in big city hospitals, where most people who need medical aid are likely to be in the low income group. Depending on how low their income is, they receive essential help either without charge or at very low cost. There are, however, better accommodations and service for the relatively few who can pay for them. Here one can have a private room with a view and flowers by his bedside, instead of sleeping in a ward and sharing facilities with a lot of other people. So in Mexico, the splitting up of hacienda land into a vast number of small parcels, both ejidal and private, has greatly extended land ownership at the dwarf farm or minifundio level. At the same time, it was possible for existing property-owners, or those with influence or capital, to remain or become landowners on a larger scale. And this was not only perfectly legal, but was in many districts even encouraged.

The Dwarf Holding

Of these three distinct types of Mexican farm operation, the minifundio is by far the most important, both numerically and in its share of Mexico's total arable land. The more than 15,000 ejidos created during the last forty years now include over a quarter of all the farm land and over half of all the cultivated land in Mexico. They have been split up, for the most part, into more than a million and one-half individual parcels, averaging less than 5 hectares (12.5 acres) of crop land apiece.[1] In addition, there is another considerable segment of the rural population owning very small private holdings, most of which have been occupied by village farmers for generations. There are more than 1 million such holdings, ranging in size from less than one hectare to ten hectares (of total land area).[2] Together, then, Mexico's ejidal and very small private holdings total more than 2.5

million parcels, most of which are too small or unproductive, except where they are combined into larger units, to support adequately the families which occupy them.

Although Mexican observers display varying degrees of optimism about the future prospects of this greatly enlarged minifundial class, most concede that it has for the most part been economically unsuccessful so far. The agrarian program, to be sure, is still in a relatively early stage, and Mexicans look forward to another half-century or more of trying to make it work. So far, however, it has "frozen" between 1 and 2 million rural families into a straight jacket, so to speak, of uneconomically small holdings. It would be politically almost impossible to reverse the process and "put Humpty Dumpty together again" into larger pieces. Most of the individual minifundios are worked individually rather than co-operatively, which of course increases the mechanical difficulties and inefficiency of the system. Most of them are operated on a low technological level, without even the simpler modern techniques which could be available to them without much economic outlay or scientific research, such as seed selection, crop rotation, mixed-crop-and-livestock farming, and the like. Most of them have insufficient credit facilities. Less than one-fourth of all ejidatarios have been receiving credit from the Ejidal Credit Bank set up for the purpose, and that fourth is the one which needs credit least.[3] That is, it comprises the best risks, in a banker's sense —those who have the best land and highest output and hence the greatest ability to repay the loans. Many members of this submerged class are isolated, physically or culturally, from the economic life of the nation. That is, they remain in a "closed" or subsistence economy, due either to lack of access to markets or mere force of habit and tradition. In short, the standard of living of this vast minifundio class has on the whole been raised little, if at all, during the last several decades. Ejidal and other new small-scale farms have multiplied at a rate far faster than that at which the new farmers could be educated or financed to take full advantage of their new status.

Mexico's experience with the minifundio can be helpful to other Latin American countries which share the same system. In some countries dwarf farms have come into being spontaneously, in others, as the result of deliberate planning. They may have evolved spontaneously for a number of reasons. Rural population is so dense in some areas that there is not enough land to go round unless it is sliced very thin, so to speak. Elsewhere, over-fragmentation has resulted from inheritance laws or from the simple fact that a large proportion of all farmers in some countries are on so low a technological level that they cannot work more than small areas of land because of the mere manual labor involved.

Certain minifundial systems, on the other hand, have been created deliberately as parts of integrated, planned regional economies. For example, the Venezuelan colonization program of the Instituto Agrario Nacional provides not only for family farms of twenty to forty hectares to be operated by machinery, but also for microparcelas of six to ten hectares each. The latter are given to former Venezuelan squatters or tenants who are considered incapable at first of working larger units because of their primitive technological level. It is hoped that the younger of these, at least, may be taught to practice modern farming techniques and hence graduate to the larger, family-sized holdings. It is feared that the older or more conservative ones may never graduate out of the minifundio class. Puerto Rico has established a number of large "proportional-profit" farms, especially on government-owned sugar plantations. The workers on such farms benefit in two ways. They are given little pieces of land on which to grow subsistence crops and build their houses, and are also paid wages varying with the kind of work they do on the plantation itself. A similar practice is followed in some collective ejidos in Mexico, such as certain sugar plantations in the states of Puebla and Veracruz. In all three of these cases, it should be noted that opportunities for supplementary employment, technological education, and other aids are included in the plan, so that the minifundial families have some assurance of achieving an adequate level of living. The individual members of the Mexican collectives, for example, do quite well wherever administration is reasonably efficient and the profits need not be divided among too many of them.[4]

Elsewhere, the occasional success of the Mexican dwarf farm seems to have resulted from a favorable combination of several interrelated, variable factors. These include land, technological level, degree of commercialization and access to markets, and availability of credit. "Land" must be evaluated in terms not only of area but also of quality and the number of months during the year that it can be cropped, as determined by temperature, rainfall, and the availability of irrigation water. Thus it would be more realistic to speak of a farmer as having so many "acre-months" of land of a given quality, rather than so many acres. At least as important as land are the farming techniques used. Whereas four or five acres of fertile irrigated land with a twelve-months' growing season might support a family if reasonably efficient, intensive methods are used, several times as much land may be required with primitive methods. Almost as important may be the degree to which the farmer includes cash crops in his farm economy. It has been demonstrated that in districts having adequate access to market, farmers may earn enough money by growing and selling suitable cash crops not only to buy the corn and other subsistence crops that they could have grown on the same land but also to provide a comfortable cash surplus. They may thus achieve a higher standard of living without any change in farming techniques. Finally, it has been found that such improvements as these in minifundial productivity depend in many cases on adequate agricultural credit. Where handled through well-administered credit co-operatives, this can provide the vital incentive or lever whereby to persuade the dwarf farmer to make optimum use of his land.

The Family-Size Farm

The family farm, comprising the second broad category, has seemed to many students of Latin America to be the great hope of the future. Its operator is an independent farmer in that he doesn't need to work part-time for anybody. He represents a sort of lower middle-class instead of the lower class to which the dwarf farmer belongs. Different students have claimed for him all the following advantages over other types of farm operation: (a) relative stability, because he has a stake in his farm and would lose by instability; (b) more intensive and careful use of his land, because he is improving his own property; (c) a firmer anchorage to the soil, with less tendency to move on to new areas; and (d) a generally higher level of living.

In Mexico there may be as many as 100,000 to 150,000 of these family farms, both new and old.[5] They range in size from as little as five to ten hectares of the best land to fifty or even one hundred hectares of poor land, depending on type of land use and technological level. Many of them have existed for a long time, either scattered about the countryside or clustered loosely in rancherías, or comprising the more substantial holdings of village communities. Their number has been greatly

increased during the revolution in several ways. Many of the new "family" farm owners were formerly tenants who have been able to buy their tenant holdings. Others are former dwarf farmers who have come up in the world by adding to their land.

Strangely, there is much difference of opinion in Mexico as to the viability and utility of this type. Many extol it, on more or less theoretical grounds, on the principle that the man who works the land should own it, or for the reasons outlined above. Some frown upon the family farm as being in general too small or inefficient to serve as an effective medium for commercial production of agricultural products for the urban and export markets. It is true that the Mexican family-size farm tends to suffer from certain technical or economic disadvantages. Not only is it small, but it tends to be only slightly mechanized and to have relatively little of the scientific approach to farming. Many family-size farms are still largely on the subsistence level. Yet there is no reason why the family farm cannot modernize and adopt scientific methods. It is in a better position to do so than the dwarf farm, and it needs less economic and technical assistance from outside agencies. There are already enough examples of enterprising, modern family farms in Mexico to indicate that under reasonably favorable conditions the family farm should be able eventually to realize most of its theoretical advantages.

The best evidence of the potentialities of the family-size farm is to be found in several other parts of Latin America. At first glance, there seems to be a confusing variety of such farms, as to size, technological level, degree of participation in the commercial life of the countries concerned, and resultant levels of living. Many differ little from the poorer Mexican family farm in their adherence to traditional techniques. Although much may depend on the cultural background of the farmers concerned, even European immigrants have in several parts of Latin America retrograded to a more primitive technological level, due to isolation or other adverse factors.

It is highly significant, however, that where reasonably favored as to amount and quality of land, access to market, and sustained group settlement by farmers of moderately advanced agricultural techniques, certain farm districts composed predominantly of family-size farms have achieved a high level of prosperity. These include favored parts of south middle Chile, south Brazil, the Santa Fe district of the Argentine Pampa, the Antioquia region of Colombia, and the Costa Rican Meseta. Particularly promising are certain districts of planned colonization in which much technical advice and assistance from government or private agencies have helped to ensure the success of carefully selected settlers. Notable examples are colonies established by the Instituto Agrario Nacional in Venezuela,[6] the North Parana Land Company in South Brazil, and the Instituto de Colonización of Buenos Aires Province, Argentina. In the latter, farms as large as three hundred to seven hundred acres can be operated by single families, thanks to a high degree of mechanization, the relatively small labor requirements of the prevailing alfalfa-livestock economy, and scientific methods.[7]

Still more interesting in some ways, if less assured of success, is an experiment going on in the remote interior sertão of the Brazilian Planalto. Here the government is establishing family-type farms for poor, landless Brazilians and is attempting to train them to operate such farms on a modern scale, with the simplest of machinery and such methods as crop rotation, the use of livestock or fertilizers to maintain soil fertility, and the production of cash crops.[8] Here the government must cope with three difficult problems. In the first place, it must reconvert the colonists from the only agricultural system they know, that of primitive shifting cultivation, which is widespread in the more sparsely populated woodlands of the American low-latitudes. Instead of maintaining the fertility of his fields year after year, as the more advanced Latin American and North American farmers have learned to do, the primitive shifting cultivator clears a new field every year or so and abandons the old one to the encroaching forest. Even if the directors of the colony can wean the colonists from this "cream-skimming" type of agriculture, they must still solve the difficult problem of producing and marketing cash products, in the face of high freight rates to a distant domestic market and competition from other producers much closer to that market.

Smaller Landed Gentry

The third type of farm operation which is conspicuous in Mexico is that of the smaller landed gentry, or upper middle-class landowners, who do not participate in the manual work of their farms. The latter are worked by peones, or perhaps by tenant farmers who squat upon the owner's land and provide part of his labor supply in lieu of rent. This third type may vary in Mexico from as little as twenty hectares of high grade, irrigated land to the generous legal maximum of one hundred hectares of irrigated land, two hundred hectares of seasonal crop land, or larger areas of pasture or woodland. It is considered by many Mexicans to be the most effective medium for commercial production of surplus commodities for the urban and foreign markets, because it seems to have preserved or revived some of the advantages enjoyed by more progressive haciendas before the agrarian reform. Among these advantages are the relatively large size of the upper middle-class farm and its better command of capital and of scientific methods of agriculture and farm management. Being smaller than the former hacienda, it has been forced to become more intensive and specialized wherever the quality of land made this possible. It now accounts, for example, for much of Mexico's commercial output of dairy products, tropical fruits, and other specialties. On the other hand, it is better able than are the smaller family and dwarf farms to make effective use of dry or unproductive land which must be used extensively. The larger farm also has an obvious advantage for the production of commodities requiring costly or complex processing (such as sugar cane), or long "waiting" costs (such as perennial tree crops, maguey, henequen, and the like).

By North American standards, this most successful of Mexico's types of farm operation is something of an anomaly. The majority of farmers in the United States enjoy all or most of these same advantages; yet they operate their own farms with a minimum of hired help. The same is true of those partly mechanized family farms of the Argentine Pampa previously referred to. The peon-operated farm of the smaller landed gentry in Latin America seems to have evolved from a combination of abundant native labor and the Iberian convention that it was socially demeaning to do manual labor. It has survived and even multiplied in a number of areas where labor has ceased to be either abundant or cheap. Although such survival is undoubtedly due in part to the prestige factor, it would be unwise to assume that the Mexican upper middle-class farm is an anachronism which will eventually disappear. As long as it can maintain its relative advantage over other types of farm operation in over-all efficiency and productiveness, there will continue to be strong arguments for its preservation.

DISCUSSION

M. H. SUFI—I would like to add that there is a lack of the proper education. This is certainly true of my country, Pakistan, and is, to a great extent, true of India as well. The point I would like to make is that the lack of agricultural leadership is connected with the system of education which a country develops. In the case of India, of which my country was a part four years ago, the system of education was not developed by the people themselves; it was given to us by England. In this country, America, your educational leaders have insisted from the very beginning that education should be practical. They have been putting a great value on technological methods. Our universities turn out a large number of graduates who know a lot about Shakespeare, Keats, Shelley, but we don't have many agriculturists, we don't have engineers, whom we need. It would perhaps be of interest for you to know that we have four agricultural colleges in Pakistan and the enrollment in these colleges is just five hundred—in a country where 85 per cent of the people depend upon agriculture for a living. I took my M.A. degree in English literature, and I am very fond of poetry.

JAMES G. MADDOX—Perhaps the one comment which I should make is that in characterizing the societies of underdeveloped countries as being short on scientists and not giving a very high social status to scientists, I certainly had no desire to cast reflections on those societies. I view these problems in as objective a sense as possible. It is perfectly all right with me for any of the people from the underdeveloped countries to feel strongly about this characterization of mine, if it is essentially correct; so if they want to go back and do something about it, that is the real thing that we want to accomplish. If, of course, I am essentially wrong, then I want to apologize and say let us turn our attention to some other problem. But whether it is caused by the British system of schooling or by the commerical and vested interest as has been the case in many instances, I think the point is that those of us who are engaged in this effort, which certainly must be a co-operative and mutual effort as between the developed and underdeveloped countries, should take cognizance of such facts, if they are facts, and then design and progress, and do something about the situation. I for one would certainly like to indicate that I, personally, and the organization which I represent are concerned about these problems from that point of view. What can we do about them? We have no desire to cast reflections on those countries.

FRANCISCO PONCE DE LEÓN—I want to express my agreement with the idea expressed by the first speaker [Dr. Maddox]. When he said that one of the impediments for technical aid is the lack of culture among some of the farmers in the countries of Latin America, we are not offended because it happens to be true. I should like to mention also some other impediments for this kind of technical aid. I think the greatest of them all is an economic one. In fact, if I refer to the mechanization of agriculture, we realize that these agricultural implements have really prohibitive prices. Added to this is the fact that the agriculturists do not really enjoy a very good economic position, due, among many other reasons, to the many barriers to the free exportation of their products. We know that the best way to stimulate production in any industry is by creating new markets within and without the country, so that all the economic barriers that stand in the way may not asphyxiate industry or agriculture. Another impediment of

physical nature militating against the technical aid described by Dr. Maddox is the topography of the Pacific countries where machinery cannot be used so freely. And finally, I should like to add two more ideas regarding the concept expressed by the last speaker [Professor Sterling]. I believe that the terms employed when we talk about land tenure must have a precise meaning since, generally speaking, one term may mean different things to different people. What the gentleman said in connection with Mexico— that the revolution aided them toward the creation of the small farm—I should like him to clarify. I believe the term minifundio or dwarf farm is used to refer to those land properties that are underneath the economic level, that is to say, those that are excessively subdivided.

CHAIRMAN—Professor Sterling, is there any comment you would like to add?

MR. STERLING—I think that Dr. Ponce de León and I are in agreement as to the meaning of the terms. By minifundio I mean a holding uneconomically small, that is, too small to support the family which occupies it. Whereas, what he calls a farm of economic size, I have called a "family farm," or one large enough to support the family that operates it. This, like the minifundio, has greatly multiplied as a result of Mexico's agrarian reforms.

JOSÉ RAMON ASTORGA—In relation to technology in agriculture, it is necessary to bear in mind that the human element in a country, generally backward educationally and culturally, must be trained for the handling of the implements of mechanization, sometimes very complex, and which require special care. I should like to mention here the experiment being conducted in Chile with very good results to train those working with agricultural machinery. It consists in giving mechanical instruction in the army during compulsory military service. The young farmers that come to military service are trained for a short time in military affairs and afterwards they are moved to a farm owned by the army where, for a year and a half or two, they receive special instruction on how to handle machinery. They are also given general ideas on the cultivation of the main products of the country. In that manner, every year, we are preparing about 700 to 1,000 men who know how to handle tractors and machines and who are experienced for our agricultural enterprises.

MR. MADDOX—That is the best use that has been made of a Latin American army since 1824.

I should also like to comment on the question regarding the American International Association. There is some material which I could send you. I do not have any here that would be very elucidating.

Let me describe first the work of the American International Association, which is the organization with which I am connected. This is a nonprofit organization. We are now operating in two countries—Venezuela and Brazil. Our major activity, although not our exclusive activity, is to develop in each of those countries a good extension service and farm credit system. We enter into agreements with the ministry of agriculture or other appropriate agencies in these countries. By the terms of the agreement we then establish what is commonly called a servicio, a jointly financed and jointly managed organization. The American International Association supplies a part of the money and the co-operating agency of the government, either of Venezuela or Brazil, supplies another part. There is a board of directors of the organization made up equally of representatives of the American International Association and of the participating government or government agencies. This board meets ordinarily once or twice a month, and the people who serve as board members have other full-time positions. There is, however, a full-time execu-

tive director of the organization—a director of the servicio or of the consejo. We commonly use the name consejo in Venezuela, which, roughly translated, is a council. The CBR, or Rural Welfare Council, in Venezuela uses its money solely for the purpose of hiring technicians, both from North America and from Venezuela, and for providing those technicians with the necessary jeeps, automobiles, office fixtures, so that they can work in direct contact with farm families. Local offices are often similar to the offices of a county agricultural agent in this country, if the county agriculture agent in this country were also a representative of the Farm Credit Administration and, therefore, had a line of credit which he could extend to farmers. The combination of credit and education is of crucial importance to the programs which we are carrying out in both Brazil and Venezuela. We feel that two of the greatest impediments to advancing technology are the lack of education and the lack of capital on the part of the farmers. We try, therefore, in one organization to combine those two things, education and credit. These organizations have local offices staffed ordinarily by some three to five, sometimes eight or nine, technicians. In Brazil all local office technicians are Brazilians. There are only three North Americans in the organization, and they are primarily for the purpose of training Brazilians who work directly in touch with families at the local office level. In Venezuela there is a much larger proportion of North American technicians, but in all instances there is at least one, and usually more than one, Venezuelan trainee who works side by side with the North American technician to learn how to carry on an agricultural extension program with supervised credit as one of the important techniques. The aim of our organization is to develop a group of trained technicians in these countries who are trained, not in the sense of being agriculturists or plant pathologists or soil scientists but in the methods of teaching farmers and of making agricultural credit loans to farmers. We hope, therefore, to work out of the picture and leave behind in each country an established, going organization of their own technicians trained in extension and farm credit methods.

CHAIRMAN—There will be time for just one more question.

EDMUNDO FLORES—I should like to refer to the technological aspects that were analyzed by Dr. Maddox and especially the difficulties in the implantation of some technological improvements which seem to me were omitted in this discussion. The difficulties to which I will allude are due exclusively to the lack of rain in certain places where it is not possible to have irrigation or where it has not been possible to have it as yet. It seems to me that the lack of enough humidity for cultivation is a limitation of a very serious nature for the application of any techniques. This was alluded to in the description of technological aid to hybrid corn and to artificial insemination. I should like to analyze what would be the results if these two techniques were brought to a land where rain should be either insufficient or poorly distributed during the vegetative cycle of plants. Of course, fertilizers, to be utilized by plants, need to be dissolved in water from the soil. If that water is missing, it is impossible for the plants to profit by these fertilizers. In my own country we have developed some hybrids among which there are some that have been adapted to certain lands of medium precipitation. These hybrids, when farmed under comparable conditions ordinarily give 15 per cent more than the seed that has not been improved. However, if

these hybrids are artificially fertilized, the crop is increased three times and sometimes four times. If, unfortunately, due to the climate, there is not enough rain, neither the hybrid seed nor the fertilizer will make any results possible.

I should like to emphasize these statements because I think that in places like the ones I have described one must promote a very intense new policy towards the good use of water, both on top or underneath the surface, before you use any other means or any different type of technique. In lands where there is little rain the agriculturist cannot invest any more capital than what he has invested traditionally for centuries. I think it is almost impossible at any time to risk any larger capital on whatever hopes he may have for the technical application of new ideas.

MANUEL RODRÍGUEZ-CABRERA—It seems to me that the delegate from Peru and I have had exactly the same thought. As to the first part I would like to make an addition. Many Latin Americans have come to this country to study in American universities, and for this reason there are some men who are prepared in the agricultural field. Some, for example, first took their classes in Cuba and then came to this country to amplify their knowledge, but when they go back home some political movement may displace them, and men who worked for ten years may be replaced to make room for others who are just beginners. Thus, the work of ten years is completely lost.

CHAIRMAN—May I take this opportunity to thank all the members of the round table, Dr. Maddox, Professor Sterling, Dr. Flores, and Señor Posada for having been present here today. The meeting is closed.

PRINCIPLES OF TENURE IN ENGLAND AND WALES

James J. MacGregor

IN ENGLAND it might reasonably be held that for at least a thousand years there have been no sudden or violent changes in the disposition of land. By contrast, the revolt of the French peasantry, which culminated in the storming of the Bastille in 1789, inevitably had a very direct and sweeping effect on the systems of land holding in that country.

Even before the Norman Conquest of 1066 the manor was a key feature of the English system of land holding and working. The chief influence of the conquest was the emphasis which it gave to the feudal systems of tenure. The system was based on the theory that all land was derived by grant from the King, who was the only absolute owner. The grant was made in exchange for services—nearly always military—of the tenant. The relationship of the King to his tenants was called tenure. The process of subletting the land by the tenants in chief was known as subinfeudation, and while theoretically the process could go on through many degrees of letting, in practice the steps were not numerous.

The process of subinfeudation was unpopular and was prohibited in the *Statute Quia Empiores,* in 1289. By this measure the right of every freeman to dispose of his land was confirmed, and after any transfer the grantee was to hold, not of the grantor, but of the grantor's lord and perform the same services as the grantor. One result of this statute, which was never repealed, was that no new relation of lord and tenant has been possible on a grant of a fee simple estate in land since 1289.

The main distinctions between the various kinds of tenure depended on the form of the services performed by the tenant. There were two main classifications: lay tenure—by far the more important—and spiritual tenure. The lay tenure took two forms: tenure in chivalry, where military services were required, and tenure in socage, in which the services were nonmilitary. By the Statute of Tenures in 1660, retrospectively effective to 1645, the distinctives of freehold tenures were abolished by making them all take the form of common socage. Most of the special services and occasional incidents were also abolished. The incidents which existed between 1660 and 1925, although many of them had become obsolete by the end of the period, were fealty, suit of court, chief rent, relief, heriot, and escheat.

While tenure indicated the relation between lord and tenant the concept of estate indicated the interest of the tenant in land. Estates were classified as estates of freehold and those less than freehold. The former were further divided into estates of inheritance and estates not of inheritance; that is, estates of mere freehold, with length usually dependent on a life or an event. The estates which were less than freehold were either certain, as for "a term of years," or uncertain, as when "at will" or "at sufrance."

Estates of freehold took four forms: fee simple, estate tail, estate for life, and *estate pour autre vie.* For all practical purposes fee simple is synonymous with absolute ownership.

Estate tail was one form of estate of inheritance. For nearly six centuries, between 1285 and 1834, the Statute of Westminster II, 1286, governed how the intention of a donor as expressed in the gift of land should in future be observed. The receiver of the gift of land could not alienate it to the exclusion of his issue. In default of any issue the gift would revert to the donor or his heirs. In this way the estate was prevented from ever being a fee simple absolute. The word tail derives from *talliatum,* meaning to cut down, or, in this context, to restrict, to the line of heirs specified. In the fifteenth century it was established that the tenant-in-tail might bar the entail by the procedure of a common "recovery" or a fine, which were collusive actions, the former dependent on the judgment of the court. The Fines and Recoveries Act of 1883 abolished these methods of barring entails and substituted the smallest of any assurance—except a will—by which a fee simple could have been disposed of, provided the assurance was enrolled until 1875 in the Court of Chancery and thereafter in the Central Office of the Supreme Court within six months of its execution. Since 1925 an entail, by the Law of Property Act of that year, no longer exists as a legal estate but only as "an equitable interest," i.e., an "entailed interest." The relevant legal fee simple of the entailed interest must be vested in a trustee or trustees. It had been stated that possibly two-thirds of the agricultural land in England and Wales was subject to entails, which were not necessarily accompanied by a charge on the land for the maintenance of persons other than the life-tenant.[1] Such problems do, however, exist and serve to show how complex legal arrangements may be directly detrimental to the standard of equipment on the land.

An estate for life was one of mere freehold, and, since the 1925 Law of Property Act, cannot be a legal estate but only an equitable interest called a life interest.

The *estate pour autre vie* is a type of life interest, not on the tenant's life but for that of another individual known as the *cestui que vie.* This interest also now can exist only as an equitable interest.

Copyhold was an important feature of the English system of land tenure, but had been completely abolished or enfranchised by the end of 1935 by the Law of Property Act of 1922 of which certain provisions became operative from January, 1926.

Copyholds were lands forming part of a manor, and were originally granted by the lord to his tenants in a limited sense, i.e., as tenants at will. For a very long time, however, they became more or less independent of the will of the lord except in a nominal way. The name of this form of tenure arose because the tenant's title consisted of copies of the court roll of the manor. Copyhold land was thus divided into two estates: the freehold estate of the lord and the customary estate of the tenant. The former estate was almost purely nominal although it claimed a number of dues and fines which were often very valuable. The tenant had other restrictions on leasing and alienating his interest without the lord's permission, and the minerals and timber were reserved to the lord.

Before the year 1926, copyhold land could be converted into freehold by various ways, such as agreement, and during the nineteenth century various statutes—the last was the Copyhold Act of 1894—assisted this process, known as enfranchisement. After 1926, all copyholds were enfranchised, but provision was made for compensation to the lord and his steward for the loss of certain of their rights, known as manorial incidents. These incidents were divided at this time into three groups: (1) those automatically extinguished, i.e., the more obsolete rights; (2) those temporally preserved before extinguishment by the end of 1935; and these could have been extinguished by a compensation agreement, or compulsorily when one party served a notice on the others to determine the amount of the compensation; and (3) those permanently preserved unless the parties agreed to their extinguishment. This last group included: (1) the tenant's rights of common; (2) the right of either lord or tenant to mines, minerals, gravel pits, and quarries; (3) lord's rights over fairs, markets, and sporting; and (4) the liability of either lord or tenant for the construction, repair, and maintenance of the dikes, ditches, sea walls, bridges, etc.

By the passing of this historical system of land tenure, and with the other influences of the series of property acts in the 1920's, it could be said that the landlord and tenant legislation and the general rights in land were greatly simplified and the tenure of land made relatively homogeneous for England and Wales as a whole.

The net effect of the Law of Property Act of 1925 (Section 1) was to reduce the number of legal estates and interests which could exist in land as follows:

(1) The only estates in land which are capable of subsisting or of being conveyed or created at law are: (a) an estate in fee simple absolute in possession; (b) a term of years absolute.

(2) The only interests or charges in or over land which are capable of subsisting or of being conveyed or created at law are: (a) an easement, right or privilege in or over land for an interest equivalent to an estate in fee simple absolute in possession or a term of years absolute; (b) a rent charge in possession issuing out of or charge on land being either perpetual or for a term of years absolute; (c) a charge by way of legal mortgage; (d) land tax and any other similar charge on land which is not created

by an instrument; (e) rights of entry exercisable over or in respect of a legal term of years absolute, or annexed, for any purpose, to a legal rent charge.

(3) All other estates, interests and charges in or over land take effect as equitable interests.

The Pattern of Land Holding

In spite of the fundamental importance of land there is no comprehensive record of the manner in which the land of England is held in individual properties. A serious attempt had been made in the early seventies of last century to arrive at an accurate estimate of the area and rental value of the separate estates. In 1874 this inquiry produced a Parliamentary Paper popularly known as the New Domesday Book.[2] Considering only land held by persons owning ten acres or more, 58 per cent of this land was owned by the 7 per cent of the people owning five hundred acres or more; conversely, the 70 per cent owning from ten to one hundred acres each owned 11 per cent of the total area in tracts larger than ten acres.

Since the publication of the 1874 report there has been no comprehensive or official account to indicate the changes in ownership distribution.[3] The changes can, however, be inferred from other sources. The Agricultural Statistics show, for certain years, the proportion of farming land and number of holdings mainly occupied by tenants. These statistics, by themselves, do not offer much clue to the changing size distribution of separate ownerships, but they do indicate changing type of ownership. The over-all trend from 1890 up to World War I appeared to be slightly towards tenancy rather than owner-occupation. From contemporary evidence, such as that supplied by A. H. Johnson,[4] it would appear that this movement was associated with the development of the larger estates—a development which had been in operation for some time previous to 1870.

The outstanding feature of the annual agricultural statistics is the very marked growth of owner-occupation recorded in the early twenties of this century. This growth was a definite reflection of changing ownership, as it is well known that many estates were broken up in the years following World War I and bought, very often, by tenants.[5] In terms of total farm land, by 1927 the proportion of owner-occupation had trebled from the prewar years to over 36 per cent. During this period *The Times* noted this trend with a column appropriately entitled "England Changing Hands."[6]

However, before discussing some of the reasons for this change in private land ownership during the 1920's, trends in public land ownership will be noted. The trend has been one of increasing public ownership of land. Complete figures are not available, but it was stated in the House of Commons in November, 1936, that nearly 1,900,000 acres were owned by central and local government authorities out of a total of 37.3 million acres for England and Wales. More than a half was owned by the Forestry Commission, which had been set up under the Forestry Act of 1919, when, according to the Sixteenth Report of the Commission, the government recognized that private landlords had neither the desire nor the capital to provide woodlands which did not give an immediate return. A more leisurely development of public ownership, fostered by the state, has been that of the County Council Small Holdings estates, which in aggregate exceeded 467,000 acres in England and Wales in 1947. In addition to the above area, there is a considerable acreage held by other semi-public bodies including schools, colleges, charities, and the National Trust. The Ecclesiastical Commissioners and the Universities own about 240,000 acres each, although it is probable that some of these

older institutions have a smaller area than formerly. An unknown area is subject to common rights, while town and country planning schemes have jurisdiction over a further large area. Within the last thirty years or so there has been a movement to acquire land for parks and open spaces in or near towns. London has developed its own green belt. Usually more than 50,000 acres were annually withdrawn from agricultural uses in the course of public development for building roads and other amenities in the years 1928–1934.[7]

The Landlord in English Tenure

The stage had been set for the striking fall in the proportion of tenant farms in England during the 1920's by a series of fundamental changes in the economic and social position of the landlord after 1880. The latter year approximately marked the culmination of a period lasting some forty years, which is often referred to historically as "the golden age of British agriculture." From this time forward agriculture in Britain began to feel the loss of the Corn Laws, which had been repealed in 1846. Yet the country remained firmly behind a policy of free trade in the interests of growing industrial classes. Not until 1931 did Britain return to a very moderate and selective protection for a few horticultural products. In the meantime, agriculture entered a serious depression, reaching its bottom in about 1894. Thereafter, with considerable reorganization in favor of livestock farming it maintained fairly general stability until the first world war. The war and immediate postwar years temporarily restored prosperous conditions to agriculture.

Concurrently with these trends in the general economic position of British agriculture, land as a source of income was acquiring a lesser significance. One of the traditional functions claimed of the landlord in the landlord-tenant system was to act as a buffer against economic depression through rent adjustment. Whatever the motivating forces, the end result was that in fact agricultural rents did follow a fairly general downward trend after 1870. On the other hand, public tax on land tended to increase. In Britain the Property Tax (Schedule A of Income Tax) forms the major part of this first call and principal burden on land. Under Schedule A, the income from the ownership of land is directly taxed on the basis of a defined annual valuation, which in practice corresponds closely to the rent worth. Owing to various specific legislative provisions relating to tax deduction on land, it is only possible to arrive at a rough measure of the burden on landowners. It is clear, however, from movements in the Standard Rate of Income Tax in Great Britain (see Table 37) that the burden was a gradually increasing one up to the first world war and that thereafter the increase was exceedingly rapid.

There are other lesser public burdens on land in Britain.

1. Land tax is an insignificant proportion of national revenue.

2. Local taxes (rates) are paid by the owner only insofar as he is the occupier. However, the incidence of this tax is often claimed to be shifted in part or in whole to the landlord through inclusion in rent charge. The actual proportionate incidence, no doubt, varies according to a number of different circumstances.

3. Although falling with very unequal weight on individual properties of unfavorable value tithe ranks closest to general property tax as a burden on landowners. The Tithe Commutation Act of 1836 linked the annual rent charge to the septennial average of corn prices, and this basis was retained until 1918. Until 1915 a close correspondence existed between value of tithe and fluctuation of rents. From 1878 to 1901 the trend was downward. Thereafter there was a slight rise in tithe until the war when the rise in corn prices sent its value up out of all proportion to rent and instigated agitation culminating in the Tithe Acts of 1918 and 1925, which pegged the upward rise. In 1936 statutory arrangements were made for the redemption of tithe over the subsequent sixty years. In summary, tithe charges increased somewhat between 1901 and 1917 but still remained a relatively small burden on land. It was between 1917 and 1936 that it became most important as a charge to the landowner; this was in spite of the fact that the legislation of 1918 and 1925 released him from what would otherwise have been a heavier burden. The proportionate burden had increased due to the decline of rents against which tithe would need be charged. The smaller proportion

TABLE 37

STANDARD RATES OF INCOME TAX
PER £ FOR GREAT BRITAIN

Year	Rate
1870/71	/4
1874/75	/2
1880/81	/6
1884/85	/6
1888/89	/6
1900/01	1/–
1903/04	11/–
1909/10	1/2
1914/15	1/8
1915/16	3/–
1916/17	5/–
1918/19	6/–
1930/31	4/6
1936/37	4/9
1938/39	5/6
1939/40	7/–
1940/41	8/6
1941/42	10/–
1946/47	9/–

of landowners who were receivers of tithe had benefited more or less conversely as the payers of tithe.

4. The final public charge on landowners that should be noted is the death duty. This form of imperial taxation applies to all forms of property whether realty or personalty so that its incidence is not peculiar to landowners. However, in actual fact it often appears as a direct charge, as many landowners have all or most of their capital invested in their agricultural estates. Hence, due to its uncertain threat and its high proportionate rate to total capital invested, death duty has appeared as an important factor in the breakup of rural estates. In this way death duties or the threat of death duties ranks high among the public burdens on private land in Britain. Like tithe, the incidence of death duty falls with very unequal weight on individual properties. The rate of death duties has gradually been scaled upwards on a sliding scale varying with the total value of property. Agriculture, until 1949, had the important concession of being at the 1919 rate, whereas nonagricultural property had had several increases in that thirty year period. After 1949 agricultural property continued to have a very substantial concession, as the agricultural rate was then fixed at 55 per cent of the nonagricultural rate.

The general conclusion to be drawn is that by the first world war the economic position of the landlord had considerably deteriorated. At least with fallen rents and rising public charges against land his net return for maintenance and improvement and personal income had unquestionably decreased. It is not a surprising fact that maintenance was sacrificed, thus sowing the seeds of chronic under-investment in agriculture. Nor is it surprising that during the prosperous time around the first world war, with which was associated increasing land values, many landowners sought to take advantage of the only real opportunity they had had in years to cut down on their land investment without considerable capital loss. An additional factor was the decline in the social prestige and political power of land ownership which had been going on for several years.

The position is well illustrated by the conclusion of a Departmental Inquiry in 1912; namely, "the evidence we have heard makes it quite clear that tenants do not desire to purchase their farms except as an alternative to leaving altogether." The landlord was one interested party that had not gained in the preceding decades, and with no social stigma attached to tenancy, it is not surprising that the tenant farmers of England claimed that "a bad landlord was better than none." However, during those few years, in many cases, tenants did face a choice between purchasing their farms or leaving. For at this time the landlord still retained the right to sell farms with vacant possession.

This trend toward an increasing number of owner-operators and the consequent reduction in the average size of ownership unit was, however, short-lived. Following the Corn Production Act (Repeal) Act 1921, which removed the price guarantees for agricultural products, the market for farms declined, and in 1941 the proportion of farm land held by owner-occupiers was still only 33 per cent.[8] Thus, most of the land of Britain is still farmed under the landlord and tenant system. There would be fairly general agreement in England with Orwin's statement that "capitalist farming under a tenancy system is inevitable in a country so highly and so universally industrialized as England, for although other countries, with an agriculture mainly of the small owner-occupier type are also industrialized, in them the segregation of urban and rural industry is very marked, and the anachronism of a peasant class diffused through an organized and industrial community is impossible."[9] But, in addition, there is also little ideological opposition to a maintenance or even extension of the tenant-farmer principle in Britain. It has been shown that a generally acceptable system of tenants' rights can be established with statutory backing. There has, however, been a serious questioning of the capacity of the private landowner to fulfill the roles of long-term investment and efficient land management. On these grounds powerful arguments have been put forward for nationalization of land. The general line of argument is that nationalization should preserve the essential features of the landlord and tenant system, which has proved itself suitable for British requirements and conditions. The land, however, would be administered from the estate management point of view in large blocks and with an efficient administrative and maintenance staff. At the same time the state would be in the position to supply the permanent equipment for its tenant farms more effectively than the private landlord has done since 1880. By holding all the land it is also argued that it would be relatively easy to reallocate and lay out the land in more economic farming units. Nationalization of land has in the past had support in both the Liberal and Labor parties. However, the former is now a minority party, and the latter, while in power, has shown little signs of considering practical implementation of land nationalization. Rather, it would appear that the labor government was content to control land use and development value through the wide and indirect powers of the 1947 Town and Country Planning Act —although the Conservative government which followed it has already modified and reduced the tight control affecting changes in land uses—and to influence land management and investment through the powers of the Agriculture Act of 1947 and where necessary to assist with desired maintenance

and improvement of farms by indirect state grants and assistance. The latter was a feature of the Agriculture Act of 1947, as it had also been of the Agriculture Miscellaneous Provisions Acts of 1940, 1941, and 1944 and the Finance Act of 1945.

The problem of adequate investment in agriculture for long-term national security and in the light of changing conditions in the commercial world is today perhaps the crucial issue in British farming. The way to efficient land management is also open to vigorous debate. But, in general, it may be stated again that there is a general acceptance of the tenant basis to farming and general satisfaction in the system of tenancy which has been established under progressive legislation entitled or associated with the Agricultural Holdings Acts. This legislation will now be discussed briefly.

Agricultural Holdings Acts

The development of legislation under the Agricultural Holdings Acts had the net effect on the owner of reducing considerably the original very wide powers which he might exercise over his landed property. The other statutes referred to in this section sanctioned the claims of tenants and public authorities in ways which—without questioning the social or ethical justice—were further to interfere with the comparative freedom of private ownership which existed before the end of the nineteenth century.

Starting with the first of the Agricultural Holdings Acts in 1875 a very comprehensive body of law guarding and defending more precisely the rights of the tenant has been built up through the acts of 1906 and 1923 to the final legislation embodied in the Agricultural Act of 1947 and the Agricultural Holdings Act of 1948. While the principal aim of the acts has been to remedy a one-time common injustice of failure to pay for tenants' improvements, they deal with many other points including the procedure for ascertaining and recovering compensation and claims for disturbance, the length of notice to quit, the right of the tenant to fixtures and buildings, the law of procedure under a distress, etc.

The position at common law was that a tenant had no right to compensation for unexhausted improvement or acts of husbandry. At the same time he was under an obligation to cultivate his holdings in a husbandlike manner, and failing this his landlord could recover damages. Yet the landlord was not obliged to compensate the tenant for doing more than was necessary or even to pay for seeds or labor expended in the last year of the tenancy. The common law attitude to fixtures followed the general maxim of *quidquid plantatur solo solo cedit* —whatever is planted in or affixed to the soil goes with the soil. This extreme and rather rigid doctrine was relaxed at an early date insofar as the fixtures were erected for trade and domestic convenience, but in 1803 (*Elwes* v. *Mawe*) it was decided that the relaxation did not extend to agricultural fixtures. Fixtures on the farm thus became the absolute property of the landlord, but in the Landlord and Tenant Act of 1857, fixtures could be removed by the tenant if they had been erected with the landlord's written consent.

Although, as will be stated shortly, the first attempt to give statutory recognition to tenant's compensation for improvement was ineffective, there grew out of the hardships and inadequacies of the common law system privileges which were misnamed "customs of the country." Strictly speaking, these privileges were "customs of the district" as they varied very greatly in many localities. Under these the tenant was recompensed in most counties for the seed and labor of the final year and for the preparatory cultivations for a future crop to be harvested by the incoming occupier. To a more limited extent part payments were made for artificial ma-

nures and purchased feeding stuffs. In eighteen counties in England and in certain parts of South Wales allowances were made for more permanent improvements by the tenant. Warwickshire, Leicestershire, Yorkshire, and Glamorganshire are mentioned particularly because their systems of compensation were fairly definite. The case of *Moosley* v. *Ludlam* in 1851 decided that in Derbyshire the custom to pay compensation for drainage although done without the landlord's knowledge or consent was a reasonable custom. The establishment of a sound basis for compensation for tenant improvements has been a fundamental part of the Agricultural Holdings Act. The principle of legal recognition of tenant right was first introduced (in a comprehensive form) in the 1875 act. Although landlords contracted out of this act through an escape clause, the principle involved became the basis of the several Agricultural Holdings Acts which followed it.

Under the 1875 act three classes of improvement were recognized for compensation after a maximum period of twenty, seven, and two years respectively: (1) the first class included thirteen of the more permanent improvements and required the landlord's consent; (2) six improvements which although not permanent, were durable and the tenant was required to give notice of these; (3) temporary improvements of which the landlord did not receive any notice. Although the number and type of improvement included in each class has been changed in some of the later holdings acts, this initial classification remains very similar to the present day. An important feature of this act was that it recognized the freedom of the tenants and the landlords to make their own bargains; it also had a useful provision that the agreements could adopt any part of the act in writing. This was of great benefit to the landlord, as one of the provisions in the act recognized his title to meet the tenant's claim with a counter-claim for waste or breach of covenant, as up until then any enforcement of such counter-claims by action at law was difficult and costly, while the act provided a simple method. Another important feature was that which enabled limited owners —who held the bulk of the land in the United Kingdom—to charge the holding with any compensation due to tenants.

Because of its reception and criticism and the depression years which followed shortly after the first Agricultural Holdings Act, it became necessary to amend it. The Agricultural Holdings Act of 1883 was the result. J. H. Clapham[10] described the new act as cumbrous and stated that it was to require much interpretation and amendment, although "it marked an important turning point in the history of the Land Laws."

This act which developed naturally out of the experience of the earlier act laid down scales of compensation to tenants for ordinary improvements such as chalking, fertilizing, and feeding of cattle with produce not produced on the farm. Landlords could not contract out of the provisions affecting these improvements unless to make more favorable arrangement. It could also override all customs of the country unless they were more favorable to the tenant. Thus, the measure made a revolutionary step by interfering with the freedom of contract between landlord and tenant. Compensation could not be paid to the outgoing tenant for the more permanent improvement unless the landlord had previously given his written consent to the improvement. With drainage, it was laid down that the tenant would have to notify the landlord before commencing on it and the landlord could do the work and charge interest on it or come to terms with the tenant. Only in the event of no terms being arranged or the landlord refusing to execute the work was compensation to be paid. A scheme of

arbitration for fixing compensation was also laid down. In respect to yearly tenancies, the notice to quit was extended from six months to twelve months except where the parties should specifically agree otherwise. The law of fixtures was amended to the advantage of the tenant and the distraining for rent was limited to one year's rent.

The object of the act was to encourage the tenant in good cultivation through ordinary improvements, while reserving to the landlord the general direction to which the land and permanent equipment should be put. According to Shaw Lefevre[11] there were widespread complaints about the inadequacy of the compensation awarded to outgoing tenants by arbitrators. But, as he pointed out, it was also desirable that incoming tenants should not be hampered by large payments for that which did them no real benefit.

As a good deal of freedom was left to the interpretation of certain parts of the act, particularly on the amount of compensation, this appears to have created a certain amount of difficulty. A contributory difficulty was the clause preventing the tenant claiming as part of his improvement what was "justly due to the inherent capabilities of the soil."

The principles of these two early statutes were extended or modified in later acts, and the 1908 Agricultural Holdings Act consolidated the Agricultural Holdings Acts of 1883, 1900, and 1906, the Tenant's Compensation Act of 1890, and the Market Gardeners' Compensation Act of 1895, which were then repealed. This act, therefore, embodied the outstanding advances made in the 1906 act whereby the landlord's control was shed on two important points: first, the tenant was enabled to have freedom of cropping, it being recognized that the restrictive covenants while being based often on proved and traditional methods had lagged somewhat behind the proved discoveries of more modern times, and, second, the agricultural landlord lost the right to repossess his property after due notice, without compensation for disturbance to the tenant unless the landlord could show "good and sufficient cause." This was a definite step in the direction of the dual ownership of the land. This act also provided compensation for game damage.

Part II of the 1920 Agricultural Act was an amendment of the 1908 act and still further restricted the power of the landlord. It defined more precisely the conditions under which a tenant could obtain disturbance compensation and the amounts to which he was entitled. Experience has shown that the relevant clause in the 1906 act was inoperative in practice,[12] and this measure made it almost impossible to remove a tenant except for bad farming. The 1920 act also gave the tenant the right to demand arbitration which, if refused, made the landlord liable to pay for disturbance. The act also provided for the administration of an estate by a receiver and manager appointed by the Minister of Agriculture, if such a step were deemed necessary in the national interest; that is, if any part of an estate was grossly mismanaged "to such an extent as to prejudice materially the production of food thereon and the welfare of those who are engaged in the cultivation of the estate." Although this clause was repealed in the Corn Production Acts (Repeal) Act, 1921, before an occasion had arisen for its use, it was significant as indicating the trend of modern legislation towards still further reduction of the landowner's powers. This latter power reappeared in the 1947 legislation.

The act of 1921 amended the act of 1920, and finally all these enactments were consolidated into the 1923 act, which was followed shortly after its passing by the Agriculture (Amendment) Act, 1923, which was incorporated in Section 57 of the consolidat-

ing act. Thus, the tenant was left with all reasonable security, as he had compensation for improvements, freedom of cropping and sale of crops, and compensation for disturbance. However, freedom of cropping was not quite complete; permanent pasture could not be broken up freely, and often the land had to be left as it was taken by the tenant. For operation in the last year of the tenancy the tenant had to rely upon the customs of the country to satisfy his claims. Some writers regarded the provisions for disturbance claims as the most important feature of the history of landlord and tenant law in Britain up to 1923. It has also been remarked that the British system of tenancy, as a result of this development of the Holdings Acts, seemed to provide everything necessary to agricultural and social stability, and, when the economic environment is congenial, no one is likely to quarrel with the assertion.

The Agriculture Act of 1947 was to make the relationship between landlord and tenant still more precise, and introduced some further safeguarding provisions for both parties. The main purpose of the 1947 act was to give legislative effect to the government's agricultural policy which was announced at the end of 1945. "The objective of this policy is to promote a stable and efficient agricultural industry capable of producing such part of the nation's food as in the national interest it was desirable to produce in the United Kingdom, and of producing it at minimum prices consistent with proper remuneration and living conditions for farmers and workers in agriculture and an adequate return on capital invested."

The first part of the 1947 act was, therefore, concerned with the arrangements for stability through guaranteed prices and assured markets. Stability, however, was only regarded as a partial policy, and it was the government's view that the state had both the right and the duty to see that the agricultural industry attained the highest possible degree of efficiency. The advantages of technical education and advice as a means to this end were emphasized. The setting up of the National Agricultural Advisory Service in 1946 to help farmers and the proposed strengthening of the Ministry's Land Service to help owners of land on estate management problems are moves of considerable importance. The government felt that there would be a minority of farmers and landowners who might not take advantage of these services. Accordingly, as a corollary to the provisions for stability, power must be taken to ensure that all agricultural land will be managed efficiently. This aspect of the agricultural policy is covered in the second part of the act which sets out general standards of good estate management and of good husbandry. Where landowners and farmers are not attaining these standards the Minister of Agriculture has power to place them under supervision, to issue specific directions to them, and, if necessary, to dispossess them.

These standards are drawn up in very general terms for estate management. The minimum standard "is such as to be reasonably adequate, having regard to the character and situation of the land and other relevant circumstances, to enable an occupier of the land reasonably skilled in husbandry to maintain efficient production as respects both the kind of produce and the quality and quantity thereof." Attention will thus be paid to the extent to which the landowner is providing or maintaining and repairing the fixed equipment so that the land is capable of being farmed efficiently.

The rules of good husbandry imply that a farm holding must be farmed in such a way that, having regard to the character and situation of the holding and the standard of its management, the occupier is maintaining a reasonable standard of efficient production, while keeping the unit in a condition to enable that standard to be maintained in the future.

In order to decide whether a farmer is fulfilling his responsibilities under the rules attention will be paid to the extent to which he keeps the arable and grassland "in a good state of cultivation and fertility and in good condition," to the proper stocking of the unit with livestock and their efficient management, to the "necessary" steps taken to deal with pests and diseases, to the "necessary" steps taken to deal with harvesting, and to the "necessary" work of maintenance and repair.

Where an owner or an occupier has failed in his responsibilities, before a supervision order is made or a direction served on him the persons concerned must be given an opportunity to make representations to County Agricultural Executive Committees. Where an owner has received a direction he can appeal to the Agricultural Land Tribunal if the estimated cost of the work, together with the cost on other fixed equipment in the previous two years exceeds the annual value of the relevant value of the land. Failure to comply with the direction creates a liability to a fine not exceeding one hundred pounds, and the CAEC can do the work and recover the reasonable cost.

Supervision orders have to be reviewed at least once a year, and where an owner or occupier, after a period of not less than one year, fails to show satisfactory improvement he may be dispossessed. He may be dispossessed in a shorter time if he fails to comply with a direction. On the occasion of an annual review of a supervision order where the land is let, a landlord or tenant may make representations that the tenant or the landlord under supervision, as the case may be, should be dispossessed for failing to show satisfactory improvement. If his request is refused by the CAEC he may appeal to the Agricultural Land Tribunal. Before the CAEC decides on dispossession it must give both owner and occupier an opportunity to make representations and even after it decides to proceed there is still the right of appeal to the Agricultural Land Tribunal.

Dispossession for an owner will be by compulsory purchase and for an occupier by a request to vacate the farm. An owner-occupier will be required to let the land to a tenant approved by the CAEC. Where the occupier is a tenant, the owner will be required either to farm the land himself or to let it to an approved tenant. At least three months will be allowed to vacate the land, and the dispossessed occupier will be entitled to compensation for improvements and tenant right but not to compensation for disturbance.

Part III of the Agriculture Act of 1947 deals with the general relationship of landlord and tenant under agricultural tenancies so as to bring the law into line with the aims of the new agricultural policy. Substantial parts of the Agricultural Holdings Act of 1923 have been amended and some new provisions added.

A comprehensive code is set out for compensation from a landlord to a tenant for improvements and tenant right and for compensation from a tenant to a landlord for dilapidations and other deterioration of the holding during the period of tenancy.

The items for which a tenant can claim compensation are broadly divided into three classes, which are set out in schedules. Long-term improvements carried out by the tenant give him the right to compensation on the basis of the increased value of the holding attributable to the improvement. In order to limit the landlords' payments to reasonable amounts, these are limited to the increased value having regard to the character of the holding and the average requirements of tenants reasonably skilled

in husbandry. This is a different basis from that in the 1923 act which laid down that compensation should be determined on the value of the incoming tenant. This right requires the previous consent of the landlord for the improvements, although for certain long-term improvements, such as those not likely to alter the character of the holding, if the landlord unreasonably refuses consent and the Ministry of Agriculture gives consent, then the right to compensation is upheld.

Medium term improvements such as liming and mole drainage are compensated for on the basis of the value to an incoming tenant. Like the 1923 act provisions, previous consent of the landlord is not required. Compensation for items included in "tenant right," which before the act was based either upon the "customs of the country" or on the contract of tenancy, is now based upon the value of such improvements to an incoming tenant. The method of calculating the value is laid down by regulations. The landlord and tenant, however, in a written tenancy agreement may substitute an alternative measure of compensation and method of calculation. The aim of this change is to get greater uniformity and certainty into the methods of paying tenant right compensation.

A landlord is also entitled to compensation against an outgoing tenant neglecting his responsibilities under the rules of good husbandry in specific directions. The basis is the cost of making good the damage, but a written agreement basis may be substituted. The landlord is also entitled to additional compensation for the general deterioration of the holding.

Although many persons thought that there was substantial security of tenure in the provisions of the 1923 Agricultural Holdings Act which gave compensation for disturbance, this was not regarded as adequate security. The 1947 act provides that where a notice to quit is given to a tenant, he shall be entitled to object to the notice, which then shall only become effective if the landlord has received the Minister's consent. Apart from one or two minor considerations the Minister's decision will be guided by the effect on farm efficiency. The tenant's right to object is excluded in certain obvious or reasonable circumstances, such as where the landlord has had a certificate of bad husbandry, where the tenant has gone bankrupt, or where the tenant has materially prejudiced the landlord's interest by a breach of his tenancy agreement which cannot be remedied.

Some provisions about contracts of tenancy in the 1947 act affect the relations of landlord and tenants in new ways. In order that rents can be adjusted in accordance with the economic circumstances of the industry, the tenant can claim rent adjustment by arbitration, but it must remain at such level for three years. Leases are not affected by this arrangement. A landlord is enabled to obtain an increased rent where he has carried out an improvement which has increased the value of the holding. This new statutory right has been introduced to encourage the modernization and improvement of the equipment on the land. Freedom of cropping, which was almost complete in the 1923 act, has been slightly extended. In order to fix the liability for the repair, maintenance, and insurance of all fixed equipment either on the landlord or the tenant, the Minister is empowered to make by regulations a model clause dealing with this liability. This clause will be read into all tenancy agreements unless a written agreement on this point already existed.

Certain disputes arising at the termination of a tenancy were in the 1923 act to be settled by arbitration, and now all claims, of whatever nature, have to be settled by this procedure, which is also speeded up.

Small holding policy is the subject of Part IV of the 1947 act. No discussion, however brief, of land tenure in Britain can omit reference to aspects of the conscious policy of settling men on the land. Land settlement has been tried in Britain many times in the past, but the existing small holdings, which have been encouraged by the state through the county or local authorities, started with the Small Holdings Act of 1892. This act was followed by others in 1908, 1926, and 1931, and the fruit of this legislation was 28,700 holdings spread over 467,000 acres, or an average of 17 acres per holding. The holdings varied, however, from just over 1 acre of bare land to 50 acres equipped with house and buildings. A large proportion were not equipped and were too small for full-time occupation.

In the past, the function expected of the small holdings policy has taken three main forms: before World War I they were to satisfy a hunger for land; after the war they were used to settle ex-servicemen who desired farm life; and in the years of economic depression to settle unemployed people on the land.

The government which passed the 1947 Agriculture Act, however, felt that none of these objectives were sound for a land settlement policy and also that without previous agricultural experience it was difficult to ensure success. Accordingly, the main idea behind the Smallholding Policy, contained in Part IV of the Act, was to use small holdings as a step in the agricultural "ladder" for those with experience but with limited capital resources. While the administration of the small holdings is left to the local authorities the Minister's powers of supervision and control have been extended to ensure that the new policy is duly executed. This implies that consideration will be given to such things as the use of good land, the balance between large and small holdings and adequate equipment and layout of individual holdings to provide a reasonable livelihood where schemes are developed.

In the selection of tenants due weight will be given to agricultural experience, and preference will be given to agricultural workers and to others such as sons of small farmers. It is not intended that lack of capital alone will debar a suitable applicant from improving his position on the agricultural ladder or that he will have to wait until middle age before taking a small holding. Thus powers are given to the Minister to grant loans at reasonable rates of interest, up to 75 per cent of the total amount of working capital, which is regarded as necessary for efficient working of the holding.

Various forms of co-operation are to be encouraged. Powers are granted to the local small holding authorities to encourage co-operative schemes for the benefit of their tenants, and with the Minister's approval arrangements may be made to a group of people who wish to farm the holdings on a co-operative basis. The past experience of the Land Settlement Association and of the Welsh Land Settlement Society is regarded as extremely valuable in assessing the application of co-operative methods to small holdings, especially where market gardening has been practiced. These two bodies are to make further experiments with our systems of farming.

Where small holding authorities expect to suffer a loss through the provision of small holdings they are enabled to obtain through the Minister a contribution not exceeding 75 per cent of the estimated loss—an arrangement which is practically the same as that of the 1926 Small Holdings and Allotments Act. The latest act permits of larger sizes of holding to be included in these schemes and "smallholdings" may in future not exceed 75 acres or 150 pounds per annum in rental, compared with the previous limits of 50 acres and 100 pounds.

Part V of the act deals with the administrative machinery necessary to operate the new agricultural policies as well as with certain general and miscellaneous aspects such as agricultural statistics, acquisition and management of land, special directions to secure production, money grants, pest and weed control, provision of goods and services, and supplementary provisions. The administrative bodies constituted under the act include the Agricultural Land Commission, County Agricultural Executive Committees, and the Agricultural Land Tribunal. The function of the first of these bodies is to manage land vested in the Minister and placed by him at their disposal and also to act in an advisory capacity on management. The act provides for the constitution of the County Agricultural Executive Committees which will act as the Minister's agents. They will carry out the agricultural policy under the general direction of the Minister and are the direct successors of the War Agricultural Executive Committees, which helped so greatly to increase food production during the war. The work of the Agricultural Land Tribunal will be mainly concerned with dispossession of owners and tenants offending against the rules of good estate management and good husbandry respectively, directions on owners for the provision of fixed equipment, retention or purchase of land in possesion, control of the splitting up of farm units, consents to notices to quit, and certificates of bad husbandry. The decisions of the Tribunal will in all cases be final.

Much more could be said about the Agriculture Act of 1947, for it is lengthy and contains many detailed clauses covering a great variety of problems. However, some of the more significant aspects have been selected. It is important, finally, to stress the fact that this legislation merely represents the culmination of a series of statutes defining more precisely the rights and obligations of those who own and occupy the farm land of England and Wales. It is, perhaps, like the development of the law of Property, typical of the slow evolution which has marked the legislation of England. In many ways it perpetuates the best features of the landlord and tenant system which has proved its appropriateness for English conditions. At the same time along with other legislation it sets limits to the control which the landowner has over his own property. Just as in the past, under pressure of chang-

ing economic pressures and under changing technological applications, farming methods have shown some considerable adaptability, so here there is recognition of the need to have an appropriate legal framework for the changed circumstances. The keynote of the 1947 act is an efficiency of farm and of estate management, and accordingly it covers many aspects of agricultural policy which were absent from the more limited Agricultural Holdings Acts which preceded it.

LAND TENURE ISSUES IN WESTERN EUROPE SINCE THE FRENCH REVOLUTION

Constantin C. von Dietze

I HAVE THE privilege and the responsibility to deal before this conference on world land tenure problems with the land tenure issues in Western Europe since the French Revolution. I shall not be too particular as to the literal meaning of the words defining the topic. I shall have to refer to some ideas and measures which preceded the French Revolution. Moreover, I shall not confine myself to Western Europe on this side of the Iron Curtain. Finally, we shall take in mind the decisive influences of economic situations and of the general economic and political order on the real value of land tenure systems. Thus extending the topic, I have to be all the more aware of not going into details. It will be my task to point out some major issues, which, I hope, will be of interest and which may be helpful to approach present-day problems in other parts of the world. To Northern Europe, on whose land tenure issues we are going to have another paper immediately, I shall have to point only in a few broad lines, showing the all-European bearing of some of our problems.

Already in 1776, Adam Smith, in his

famous book *Wealth of Nations* explained ideas on land tenure, some of which are of really actual and long-lasting importance. He dealt with the regulations that, so far, had discouraged agriculture and business, and he pointed out that his country's favorable laws and customs concerning land tenure had contributed more to her wealth than all the highly praised regulations and measures concerning the commercial life. We have to lay stress upon the fact that Adam Smith regarded good land tenure as a most valuable and indispensable condition for increasing the wealth of a nation, for developing a country.

So, in the emancipation of the peasants, as it was brought about in the French Revolution and in the legislations of other continental European states before and after this revolution, the purpose of economic progress was important, but it was not the only important point. Besides, we see an object of a political and constitutional nature: a modern state was to be built up; consequently, feudal authorities hampering or even cutting the relations between a government and its citizens were to be abolished. Moreover, we have to pay attention to the social point of view; social justice and human rights were to be realized.

In the days of the French Revolution, Europe was badly in need of technical and economic progress. The pressure of a population growing as never before was to be felt. Those were the days of Malthus. His apprehensions were not evil dreams of a pessimist; they were based on the facts as he could see them. For Europe they were not realized because technical advances were effected which surpassed all expectations. Reforms in land tenure were one of the means—and a very important one indeed—to open the way to technical progress. Albrecht Thaer, who at the beginning of the nineteenth century advocated the model of English farming and particularly the Norfolk rotation as the reasonable method of farm management in German agriculture, was one of the men who took part in the compilation of the laws determining the emancipation of the peasants in Prussia. As Doreen Warriner, in her most interesting book on the economics of peasant farming, has pointed out, the emancipation of the peasants in continental Europe had two objectives: (1) to end the open-field systems —which, by the way, had been quite adequate to the needs of earlier centuries with a much smaller population; (2) to abolish serfdom.

The absolute monarchy which, in France, was destroyed by the Revolution of 1789 had the same purpose of emancipating the peasants. Absolute monarchs had started this emancipation in many European countries some decades before that date. It was their desire and their interest to do away with the feudal rights which stood in the way of a modern administration and taxation. In a good many cases they protected and supported the peasants against their landlords. On the other hand, in countries where the political power was vested in a parliament dominated by landlords, the peasants had to disappear. That happened in England, in Mecklenburg, and in Western Pomerania, then under the King of Sweden, who was far away and consequently could not exercise his power in that part of his kingdom vigorously. In these countries, we see a most efficient land consolidation, but at the expense of the peasant class. In the eastern provinces of Prussia, however, only the smaller peasants not capable of keeping draught horses were excluded from getting ownership of the land.

As to the problems of ownership, we find two different conceptions, two different ways of approaching the problems of social justice and human rights. In most of the European countries, the numerous old forms of divided ownership were abolished, and the institution of superior and subordinate ownerships disappeared. Henceforth there was to be only one full ownership. But who should be the full owner, the former manorial lord or the peasant? If the landlord received full ownership, the peasant, as a rule, remained on the farm he was operating as a tenant or a metayer. The percentage of land held by tenants in various European countries shows us which kind of policy was followed in the emancipation of the peasants. While in France, Belgium, and the Netherlands about 50 per cent of the agricultural land is operated by tenants, the percentage is about 30 per cent or more in Italy and Spain, only 12 per cent in Germany, and 5 per cent in Denmark. In both cases the old liberal conception of economic and social order, as advocated by the adherents of Adam Smith, determined the issue.

They believed that the individual realizing his own advantage and profit, as long as he kept to orderly, noncriminal ways and means, would under competition make for the best wealth of nations. They did not adopt a laissez faire policy in the strict sense of the term. Otherwise, they would have let the old systems of land tenure die gradually, and they would have stood aside while peasants were turned from their subordinate ownership and serfdom into tenants or into laborers under more or less hard and insecure conditions. They were out to create a situation in which each individual would have the full freedom to dispose of his abilities, of his land, and of his implements. For this purpose, they started land consolidation which was destined to dispense with compulsory rotations, and they distributed the common pastures and forests to individual owners or gave them to villages, counties, and states which would operate the forests and rent the pastures to individual operators. Only after having accomplished what they considered to be the conditions for the benefits of free competition, they, immediately or gradually, gave freedom of contract and free disposal of the land.

This type of land policy, sooner or later, notwithstanding some modifications, became uniform all over Europe. From the beginning and up to our times it has been enthusiastically praised or ardently attacked and criticized. By the end of the nineteenth century its brilliant successes as well as its shortcomings could be judged.

So, it could be seen that the very best land tenure by itself does not guarantee a satisfactory living, particularly not to small landowners. When the peasants got full ownership, but on a piece of land which was not sufficient for the subsistence of their families, their situation was changed only legally. As a matter of fact, they had to offer their services at low wages or to pay excessive rents for additional land to the neighboring landowners. They were even worse off than those who had lost their land altogether and had become mere wage-earning workers. For by owning a bit of land many people stuck to it and would not

make use of the freedom of emigration. On the other hand the organization of a wage-earning laboring class on large holdings brought new social problems, even if these laborers or their children could find independent and paying occupations by going into the cities or overseas. The afflux of migratory laborers of different nationalities and of a lower standard of living was one of the new problems.

Moreover, during the agricultural depression which began in the seventies and lasted until the end of the nineteenth century, there were instances where tenants were doing better than highly indebted owners. Their rents were lowered while debts in cash and interests, even when keeping the same level nominally, became more and more burdensome. It was to be learned that the most perfect land tenure becomes worthless or even dangerous in an agricultural depression and particularly in times of deflation.

At the same time, it could be seen that the hope expressed in the slogan "the soil goes to the best cultivator" was not always justified. Sometimes the soil went to the most wealthy man, who would not cultivate the land at all but who desired it as a way of giving himself a higher social air, or as a hunting ground, or as a capital investment.

The men who determined land policies in Europe in the eighties and nineties and up to World War I were fully aware of the great results the old liberal land policy had brought about in economic and technical development. But they stood for avoiding its shortcomings and for overcoming the social dangers it had brought about. In our country they named themselves Agrarian Reformers. They were closely connected with the movement for social policy. One of their leading men was Max Sering.

In England, in those days, freedom of contract was abandoned in the field of tenancy in order to give a better security to tenants, and the small holdings movement sprang up, showing that people no longer believed that the best distribution of land would come automatically. On the continent, the agrarian reformers tried to do justice to the peasant nature of farming. Unfortunately, the use of this word is misleading. We cannot translate the terms "paysan," "Bauer," or "Krestjanin" into English without the danger of misconception. People in England and in America are inclined to look at a peasant as a miserable and poor farmer, hardly better than a serf. In Europe, no doubt, there were and are peasants of a backward type, in very miserable conditions. But there were and are also peasants as free, as efficient, and as prosperous as a good many American farmers. What do we mean by calling them Bauern, paysans, or peasants? We mean their attitude to the land. They regard their farms not as a capitalistic asset that you will give away if you can find better returns anywhere else but as the home of their ancestors as well as of their children and grandchildren. They may operate it quite businesslike and most efficiently, but they would not sell it except under hard necessity. A peasant selling a family farm for mere profit would disgrace himself in the eyes of his family and of his neighbors. By the way, this attitude is not restricted to operating owners; you will find it with a good many tenants whose families are connected with the same place for generations, though they have—or at any rate had during the nineteenth century—no security. A landlord expelling such a tenant without very urgent reasons would have been condemned severely by public opinion.

The agrarian reformers were aiming at legislation which would be in harmony with the feelings and traditions of the peasant population and which would help to keep the farms in the families. They were against a total recognition of capitalistic principles.

They would not let them rule in contradiction to the attitudes of peasants. But they were not altogether anticapitalistic. They stood for preserving the incentives of private initiative and of competition, and they disliked coercion. They were well aware that a legal improvement in land tenure can do harm; for instance, security given to the tenant may easily cut down the supply of land for renting; laws protecting indebted farmers may easily have a deterring effect on creditors. So their proposals and programs were very carefully balanced; generally speaking, they were conservative. They strongly advocated the co-operative movement, as initiated by Raiffeisen in the sixties.

The practical results were important in the small holdings movement. It spread all over Europe. In many cases a new legal status was given to new holdings which were laid out on reclaimed land and, to a much higher degree, on broken-up estates. While a revival of divided ownership was deliberately avoided, mainly for political reasons, the usefulness a divided ownership shows clearly for creating new holdings was practically achieved by granting ownership on conditions. For sale, except within the family, and for splitting, the consent of a government controlled agency or of a county council was required, and for a period of some decades the land could not be mortgaged without consent. Moreover, it could be repurchased if the owner did not observe good husbandry practices. These new holdings, at the same time, were put under special inheritance laws favoring the succession of one child without intolerable encumbrance. But just as these inheritance laws were not coercive, they regulated intestate succession, and the civil law granted the freedom of making wills. These special inheritance laws were in accordance with the practices of the peasant population in great parts of Central and Northern Europe. They had developed for centuries. In many cases the laws adapted to these traditions had become invalid. Now a general tendency grew up to have them revived or shaped afresh not only for new holdings but wherever the feelings of the rural population would be in their favor.

In France, in Italy, and in some other countries—e.g., in southwestern Germany— the equal subdivision of land amongst all children has been the rule for many centuries. The French Code Civil has even to a certain degree enforced equal subdivision of land and in so far restricted the freedom of wills that were acknowledged in Roman law. In these parts of Europe, tendencies similar to those of the described agrarian reformers were to be felt. They eventually led even to a loosening of the rules of the Code Civil.

On the other hand, France had led the way in creating a new legal institution named "bien de famille" in 1909. Switzerland, Germany, and Italy followed. In Germany this type of land tenure was called "Heimstatte." But this term, though philologically the same as homestead, meant something quite different from the U.S. homestead law of 1862. It was shaped according to the demands of the "land reformers," i.e., of the single-tax movement influenced by Henry George. Such holdings could not be alienated, mortgaged, or distrained. There have not been very many applicants for these holdings—most of them for dwelling purposes, only a few for agricultural use—because such a homesteader was practically excluded from credit facilities.

Now, for a short while, I have to draw your attention to Russia. The so-called Stolypin land reform, initiated in 1906, may be called the climax of the legislation bringing about the emancipation of peasants in Europe. As a matter of fact, the Russian Tsar had emancipated the peasants in the

sixties. But much remained to be done. By his land policy, Stolypin tried to prevent the uprise of communism. In "wagering on the strong" and in giving to the Russian peasants the incentives of occupying ownership and of free disposal of their land, he adhered to liberalism as Adam Smith had advocated it. But at the same time, he made use of the experiences gained during the nineteenth century and of some ideas of the agrarian reformers. The major points of the Stolypin land reform were:

1. The old family ownership in peasant land was replaced by the individual ownership of the head of a family. If this step violated the feelings of parts of the peasant population it merely anticipated what was going on already, namely the dying out of family ownership. It was to be observed also in Serbia and Bulgaria with the "Zadruga." The family communities lost their background with the abandonment of mere subsistence farming.

2. The dissolution of the village commune, the "Mir," was encouraged or even enforced. Not in all Russia, but in many parts, mainly in central and northern Russia, the village commune had been exercising the periodical repartition of the land.

3. Land consolidation was initiated on a large scale.

4. Large estates owned by the Tsar or by the nobility were broken up into peasant holdings. At the same time thousands of peasants got a chance to claim new land in Siberia.

While old village communities of a co-operative nature were dissolved, encouragement was given to a modern co-operative movement offering credit facilities and better marketing. It was in an ownership on condition granted to the newly established peasants and in the fostering of co-operatives that the Russian land policy of those days made use of the experiences and of the ideas prevailing in Central and Western Europe. As to the problems connected with co-operative systems, what they are able to achieve and what is beyond their reach, we shall face them later on, after having traced some issues which came up between the wars.

Practicing a war economy, many governments made encroachments on agricultural marketing and even on agricultural production which would have been unimaginable before. In European countries shut off by blockade from overseas resources their encroachments were of the most rigid nature. While in England agricultural production was encouraged by minimum prices, in Germany the farmers had to deliver their products to public agencies on maximum prices fixed far below the amount that could be obtained in the market. Their situation compared with prewar conditions was radically changed, although the law determining land tenure remained what it was. This kind of war economy proved unbearable, and it disappeared soon after 1918. But there were some permanent consequences of methods introduced during or immediately following the war.

In many countries all transfers of agricultural land except those within the nearest family became subject to the consent of local authorities. This rule had been introduced primarily in order to prevent those who had gained from war conditions from acquiring land. However, it was kept or even strengthened for general purposes. In some countries, a general obligation of farmers to follow the rules of good husbandry was proclaimed legally. Violators could be dispossessed by the government. Though such laws have had practical consequences only under certain conditions, they reveal a far-reaching change in the general conception of land ownership, putting it under a kind of state supervision in some regards. Planned zoning, preventing, for instance, high prices of land sold from farms

for housing purposes, or prescribing reforestation in other areas, comes into the same picture. There were even programs of establishing a permanent planned economy as to the agricultural production, commanding the farmer what he should grow on his land, which and how many animals he should raise. Though during the depression after 1929 compulsory methods of this kind were adopted in not a few countries, there is no inclination to maintain or to revive them without need. Thus, also, the far-reaching rules which had been imposed on indebted farmers who had been included in a relief action, for the purpose of insuring financial stability, may be regarded as merely temporary. Socialists in Europe decidedly opposed to communism have made it clear in their programs that family peasant farms should remain in free ownership and that they should be influenced in the use of their land primarily by regulating the prices of agricultural products.

Immediately after the war greater energies were devoted to the small holdings movement. For this purpose expropriation, which before 1914 was applied merely in exceptional cases, was provided for on a much larger scale. Moreover, tenants were given rights to renew their leases after the expiration of contracts and to claim fair rents in special courts. As distinct from England, continental legislation, for good reasons, was somewhat shy in granting security to tenants where land was rented only to a small percentage. Here, it was providing a valuable flexible factor, either by establishing a consolidation of operation when ownership was equally subdivided or by giving a chance of adapting the operated land to the size of the family when farm ownership remained stable. Moreover, would-be tenants, particularly part-time farmers, can easily be shut off from the chance of getting land when security and low rents are granted to tenants who are already using the land. In England, however, an act of 1923 gave a better security to tenants, and further important steps in the same direction were made. The model of Ireland, where the tenants acquired full ownership, was followed in Finland.

In Finland, Austria, Germany, and Hungary whenever land was taken by expropriation and given to small holders the former owner had to get a fair compensation. The other countries of Eastern Europe, extending from Estonia in the north to Bulgaria in the south, adopted more revolutionary methods. Their land policy was directed by various motives. One of them was essentially nationalistic. Let me deal with this first. Most of these countries had just gained their political independence. Resentments of the past, national pride, and a desire to strengthen the country's unity lead them to expropriate the estates, not merely or even not primarily because they were large estates but because they were in the hands of a minority of different nationality. Generally, only a low compensation was given —in some cases even none at all. Anyhow, the nationalistic or racial motive was not yet proclaimed openly, and family farms were not subject to expropriation. Public opinion and even international minority legislation condemned the expulsion of men from the land they and their ancestors had owned and cultivated merely because of their nationality or race. Where it took place, shrewd means or tricks were to be applied.

But between Bulgaria, Greece, and Turkey an exchange of populations was performed. I need not describe all the horrible facts of exchange and expulsion or even extirpation of millions of men after the outbreak of World War II, at first by Hitler, then by those who had suffered under him, who fought and ultimately defeated him. It is one of the greatest tragedies in history, brought about by detestable criminal acts and by retaliations which did not follow

the rule of the Old Testament "an eye for an eye and a tooth for a tooth," but which retaliated with ten teeth for one tooth or with ten human lives for one eye. It shows in a terrifying way to what devilish consequences an exaggerated, self-adoring nationalism leads. To our conference it is essential to see how the security of land tenure is fading away under the menaces of such a nationalistic ardor. No system of land tenure will stand and help as long as the nations and their leaders will not find ways to overcome the vicious circles of crime and retaliation and to heal the wounds and the scars of the past by acknowledging that they are under God and under his commandments.

But let us look back once more to the time between the wars. In Eastern Europe another motive of land reform was to meet the bolshevist propaganda. Indeed, in all those countries, the whole social and political life was based on a family-sized peasantry owning its land under conditions opposed to collectivization. The population was growing rapidly and there was bitter need for better economic conditions. Co-operatives were organized to bring relief. And they did a great amount of helpful work indeed. But they could not solve all the problems, even before the depression of the early thirties condemned them to many failures. The land tenure system of Europe, which even now is to a high degree based on individualistic principles, no doubt needs to be supplemented by co-operative organization and action. Well-conceived legislation as to the nature, the foundation, and operation of co-operative societies should not be forgotten in considering the issues of land tenure.

But we had to learn that there are definite limits to the objectives a co-operative system can obtain. No doubt the co-operatives have had great successes in providing the farmers with good credit facilities, in breaking the monopolies of usurers, middle-men, or landlords exacting excessive rents. They have also done well in marketing. In these fields, they are giving assistance to individual producers without abolishing their independence. Co-operative use of machinery, co-operative tillage or stock raising involve much more difficult problems and even conflicts. Only where an exceptionally strong religious feeling rules a community, may individual production be replaced by group production on a voluntary basis. And even such group production will not by its mere existence offer sufficient technical advantages to give subsistence means to a growing population and at the same time to raise the standard of living.

Most of the large-scale joint-stock farming systems are brought about by coercion. If in such a system co-operatives exist, they have changed their nature though perhaps retaining their name. In a totalitarian economy, co-operatives as well as trade unions are bound to become the agencies of an all-planning political authority. In the same way, systems of land tenure, though keeping the terms we are accustomed to in a free and open society, get quite a different meaning under a totalitarian rule.

After the Nazis had come to power one of the many good stories about them told of the following incident. "A farmer owning twenty cows asked a friend: 'What is the difference between the Communists, the Socialists, and the National Socialists?' The friend answered: 'If the Communists come to power, they will take all your cows. The Socialists will take ten and let you keep ten. The National Socialists will tell you: You are and you remain the full owner of these cows, you and your offspring for at least one thousand years. We protect you in your ownership by all sorts of laws. But we are going to milk these cows.'"

From what I said before, you will see that this story is not quite fair to our So-cialist friends. But it shows what the whole political and economic order means as to a system of land tenure.

Without paying attention to the totalitarian economy of the "Reichsnahrstand" we shall not understand the full meaning of the "Reichserbhofgesetz." Moreover, there are misleading representations and misunderstandings of the inheritance rules enforced by this law. Sometimes they are dealt with in quite a sympathetic way, perhaps even more in other countries than in Germany herself. So you may have read in the paper on the evolution of land tenure by V. Liversage.[1]

"In some parts, such as Denmark, the farmers adopt any possible expedient to maintain family farms as intact units, and in Nazi Germany the pre-existing custom was crystallized into a legal creation of impartible holdings." As a matter of fact, it is not only for its disgraceful racial provisions that Max Sering and others have attacked the Reichserbhof law, but because it was absolutely contrary to the traditions and feelings of our rural population, though proclaiming to realize the old Teutonic principles of peasant inheritance. It was absolutely compulsory, while all the previous laws aimed at maintaining the family farm as an intact unit gave freedom of will and of disposal intervivos. It excluded the wives and daughters from succession, something that had not been heard of in our peasant families for more than one thousand years. And it gave the whole farm to one heir, refusing the other children a share in the value of the farm, while for many centuries equal shares of all children were recognized. Merely the application of this principle, in most parts of our country, was modified so that the farm remained undivided and one child could run it without intolerable encumbrance. Those who are sympathetic with the former Reichserbhof law are so because they think of the farm as an economic unit and, perhaps, of the splendor of a family. But we should approach land tenure problems not only from an economical and technical point of view; neither should we be guided by romantic ideas. The fact is that children who will not see any chance of getting a share in the value of their parent's farm will lose the feeling that "this is *our* farm, those are *our* cows, and these are *our* potatoes," and they will not have any interest in maintaining or increasing the value of this farm by working with the parents. The roots of family life may be touched by an intellectualist regulation of land tenure problems, and while the unity of the farm may be maintained, the family will be split.

Now, coming to a conclusion, I should like to give a summary of some major issues, which, however, will be far from covering the whole field of land tenure issues in Europe.

1. Gustav Schweller, whose picture I was very glad to see in Madison's library, has given us a general aspect. About fifty years ago he said: "There are two tendencies to be met again and again in land policies: (a) increase of free individual ownership in the interest of technical progress, (b) the subordination of all private ownership, its size, its alienability, the extent to which it can be indebted, and its inheritability to the common interest of the nation."

2. No particular form or system of land tenure can give the only right and definite answer. In that regard, I am very glad indeed to be in full agreement with Mr. Liversage. In the last paragraph of his paper he says: "The system of land tenure is not the most important thing. The results depend on how the system, whatever it may be, is worked, upon the general outlook and traditions of the farming and landowning population."

3. A variety of land tenure systems is, so-to-say, natural, particularly to Europe. We have tenant farmers on comparatively large holdings in Great Britain. Large holdings involving important problems of agricultural labor have survived also in some regions of the continent, while peasant owners on family-size holdings have prevailed in a good many parts of Continental Europe, peasants in the situation of tenants or metayers in other parts. There is no clear difference as to the economic consequences of these systems as such. The standard of farming and of living is practically the same in Denmark with 5 per cent rented land and in the Netherlands with 50 per cent.

4. Some common features of land tenure and land policies can be traced out in the part of Europe that is not under Soviet rule. Incentives of individual initiative are maintained and encouraged. Individual farming is supplemented by co-operative action. The state has a right of supervision in certain fields. On the other hand, farming is not subjected to continual and changing demands from above. It is fitted into a general economic order based on the principles of co-ordination, not of subordination.

5. Land consolidation is a major problem in a good many regions of continental Europe. It is generally recognized that land tenure and particularly inheritance laws and customs should not prevent the consolidation of strip parcels nor lead to a new splitting of consolidated blocks. But the exigencies of economic and technical efficiency to maintain farms as current units are to be balanced with the human point of view, with the customs and feelings determining rural family life.

6. In some parts of Europe, as in Italy, in Spain, and, owing to the influx of refugees, also in Western Germany, circumstances require the breaking up or cutting down of large estates. From the economic point of view, it must be watched that the land should be given to efficient cultivators.

After this summary, let me add only one more word. In 1912, the Russian Minister of Agriculture, then in charge of the land reforms, said to a German economist, "What Russia wants is a peace time of at least thirty years." With the outbreak of war in 1914, the land reform work in Russia was stopped. War led to the triumph of bolshevism. May Europe and the whole world graciously be saved from another war that would easily frustrate all hopes we may set in land tenure and reasonable land reform.

TENURE ISSUES IN THE SCANDINAVIAN COUNTRIES

G. R. Ytterborn

THE HISTORY of land tenure—that is, the history of the division of land into holdings and the various forms of land grants, etc.— is long and varying in Scandinavia as well as in the other West European countries. Joint ownership and common use of big areas has been followed by the division of land into separate holdings. The tendency has mostly been to parcel out the land into smaller farm units, although the opposite tendency, that of combining pieces of land into larger farm units, has been of occasional prevalence. During the shifting ages, the chief landowners have been the state, the church, the nobility, and the peasants. In some periods, and most frequently, the land has been tilled by the owners themselves; but in others, a land grant in some form of tenancy has been widely applied. I shall deal quite briefly with the earliest period. The greater part of my material will be restricted to the systems prevalent in more recent history, systems which have especially affected the development and the present state of agriculture. My statements will chiefly be based on facts taken from Swedish conditions; but in many respects, Norway and Denmark present a parallel course of development. Sometimes, however, these countries have had a different development, and in the course of my lecture I shall point out their specific differences.

Division of Land into Holdings

We do not know anything certain about the procedure of land division at the time when cultivation of the soil started. However, from the twelfth and thirteenth centuries we learn that big areas of land were the common property of a village community. In some cases land of that nature was owned and used by the patriarchal family, consisting of the paterfamilias with wife, children, grandchildren, their wives, husbands, and so forth—perhaps thirty to fifty members in all. Such examples are well known from Norway, where that kind of co-operative farming remained longer in existence than in the other Scandinavian countries. However, gradually the land was divided among the members of the village community into holdings, which ordinarily would consist of a number of strips of land located in different places. Due to land division because of inheritance and to the reclaiming of new land for further cultivation, holdings of various size arose in the course of the Middle Ages. In the fifteenth century taxation was made a personal affair. Accordingly, the government became interested in seeing to it that the holdings were neither too small for the farmers' abilities to pay their taxes nor too big, in which case the number of tax-paying farmers became less. For that reason, it was decided that a "tax homestead" should not be divided without special permission. In case of inheritance, the heir of primogeniture right should release the shares of his co-heirs. In the latter part of the seventeenth century, however, consent was given that a "tax home-stead" could be divided down to one-fourth, and about the middle of the eighteenth century a further step was taken allowing the division of the property into even smaller holdings.

Up to that time the ability of tax-paying had formed the basis of land division into holdings. In the beginning of the nineteenth century, a new principle to that effect was launched. It stated that each holding into which the property could be divided should be sufficient to make it possible for at least three adults to draw their subsistence from it. This meant in reality a sort of family farm. The right of release in cases of inheritance was still existing as a principle, but was ineffective if the person in question did not assert his right. The practical result was that land was further divided. This was also a period of increasing population—in the fifty years from 1860 to 1910 about 952,000 Swedes emigrated, most of them to America. The increasing population also led to a growing demand for land and a demand for extended right of land division. The liberalistic currents in politics in the latter part of the nineteenth century strengthened the demand for free division of land. It was alleged that nobody could better judge how the land ought to be divided than those who were to use it, and in 1896 Sweden passed a law providing practically unrestricted division of land. This law did not, however, remain in force for more than thirty years. It soon became clear that the farmers could not have sufficient income from many of the too-small holdings. Even more inconceivable was their possibility of increasing their standard of living like other groups of the people. In 1926 a new law was passed prohibiting free division of land and providing that land could not be divided unless the new holdings, with regard to size and quality, were permanently suitable for their purpose. From

that time the development has proceeded on these lines, to which I shall revert later on.

In Norway a kind of primogeniture or allodial right (*Odelsrett* and *Åsaetesrett*) has been the basic principle during the whole of this period, and still is. This has probably led to a restraint on the land division. In Denmark also the development has in some respects been different from that in Sweden. Whereas Sweden in the late eighties levied duties on agricultural products, Denmark retained its free trade. Especially farmers of small holdings would then extend the animal production, based on the import of concentrated cattle food, and this has in turn affected the development of the land division.

Measures to Consolidate Holdings

I have mentioned previously that when the land of the village community was divided into holdings, each of these holdings consisted of a number of small strips of land located in different places. Because of the division which sometimes took place on account of inheritance, these strips became even smaller. Through marriage it might happen that both husband and wife owned inherited holdings which would then make up a mutual holding of double the number of strips. One holding might consist of up to fifty such strips, frequently not broader than, say, six or seven yards. This division impeded the development of a rational form of agriculture. It led among other things to a big waste of work and obstructed efficient cultivation of the soil. In order to remove these inconveniences, Sweden passed a law in 1757, according to which a landowner had the right of claiming consolidation to the effect that each holding should consist of not more than two, three, or at most four allotments. On the other hand, the houses of the village community were still to be located in the village, which among other things meant a comparatively long distance to the fields. Laws of similar kind were passed in Denmark in 1781 and in Norway in 1821. In the beginning of the nineteenth century and in 1827 new laws of consolidation were passed. These laws made possible a further improvement in the consolidation of holdings. Often all cultivated land could be placed in one or two allotments. The houses were mostly moved out from the community and placed more conveniently in relation to the fields of the holding. The consolidation of fragmented holdings that has taken place later on and that has spread over the whole of Sweden has led to an unprecedented development of agriculture in several respects. There are, however, those who are of the opinion that one has gone too far in the matter of moving out the farmsteads. In many districts the farmsteads are now remotely situated and cannot avail themselves of the many social and economic advantages of a more urban inhabitation. It is now generally assumed that the best solution of this problem would be to locate the farmsteads in smaller villages, each consisting of maybe four to six farms.

Rationalizing the Holdings

The division of land into holdings in the three Scandinavian countries will be seen from the figures in Table 38. The material is taken from the latest agricultural statistics. As will be seen from the figures in Table 38 small holdings are dominant in number. This is especially the case in Norway and, although to a lesser degree, in Sweden. In Denmark the medium-size holdings are somewhat more common. However, to these areas of cultivated land should be added a smaller or larger area of woodland, especially in Norway and Sweden, and this means a quite valuable complement, both with regard to employment and concerning income from the farm. Most holdings in the smallest group are so-called part-time farms, where the farmer has his chief income from

other kinds of work. In Denmark, many small holdings are normally industralized in such a way that they carry on an extensive animal production, based partly on

TABLE 38

LANDHOLDINGS IN DENMARK, NORWAY, AND SWEDEN

Number of Hectares	Number of Holdings	Percentage of Total
DENMARK		
0.55–3	23,250	11.3
3–5	22,524	10.9
5–10	55,677	26.9
10–15	31,343	15.2
15–30	50,422	24.4
30–60	19,574	9.5
60–120	2,942	1.4
120–240	649	1.3
240–	254	0.1
NORWAY		
0.2–2	98,241	40.48
2–5	80,122	33.02
5–10	43,526	17.93
10–20	15,597	6.43
20–50	4,809	1.98
50–100	342	0.14
100–	37	0.02
SWEDEN		
0.26–2	118,214	28.5
2–5	107,776	26.0
5–10	94,844	22.9
10–20	58,477	14.1
20–30	17,030	4.1
30–50	10,710	2.6
50–100	5,065	1.2
100–	2,325	0.6

the import of feed concentrates for the cattle.

In a great many holdings of two to ten hectares of cultivated land, the agriculture is practically the owner's only way of employment and support. In the beginning of this century these holdings might, especially if some woodland was part of them, be considered to furnish fairly sufficient employment and support. This is still the case in places where they can be used for the cultivation of fruit and vegetables. However, where the production must primarily be directed toward cattle food and animal products, which is generally the case, these holdings will, with the present possibilities of mechanized farming and the demands for a higher standard of living, be extremely unsatisfactory. During the last fifteen years this question has been a matter of close attention. In 1939, Sweden set up a new program for its "homestead" promotion. The new goal of this activity, which had previously been directed toward the establishment of new farms, was especially to acquire additional land for holdings too small to be economic farm units. (By economic farm unit is meant a family farm—a farm which can fully employ and support a family.) After the matter had undergone comprehensive consideration in a government committee, a further step was taken in 1948. An agricultural long-term program was agreed upon, which can be expressed in the following three paragraphs.

1. The farmers shall, if the agriculture is carried on in a rational way, be ensured the same real income as that of comparable groups.

2. The size of the total agricultural production shall principally be adapted to domestic consumption requirements.

3. The noneconomic farm unit shall be enlarged with additional land and when necessary consolidated. At the same time the holdings shall be well equipped with roads, ditches, and houses.

No general rule can be set up for the holding being an economic farm unit. That question must be settled in each case. Roughly speaking, it is assumed that a holding with little access to woodland should be brought up to ten to twenty hectares of cultivated land. This assumption is based on rather extensive economic researches.

Land for the enlarging of noneconomic farm units is obtained through purchases of land in the open market, through making use of the law providing priority right of purchase, and, as the last means, through expropriation. The law providing priority right of purchase states that in the case of sale of holdings, the government may, in order to enlarge noneconomic farm units, buy such holdings at the price fixed in the contract between the seller and the buyer. Exception is made if the sale is made to wife and husband, children, grandchildren, brothers, or sisters. Limited use of this law has been made up till now. Generally, enlargement takes place through purchases of land in the open market, mostly without any activity on the part of the government. Usually, holdings which are noneconomic farm units are the ones purchased. This activity is made possible and facilitated by the population development, or, perhaps more precisely expressed, by the fact that industry employs an ever-increasing part of the population. Since 1880 the farm population has decreased in number, not only relatively but even absolutely. From 1940 the decrease has been up to 1.5 per cent or 2 per cent per year. Young people from the farms join other industries and leave the holdings that cannot ensure them full employment and reasonable income. Thus around fifteen hundred independent holdings yearly are at present available as additional land to supplement others and are utilized for that purpose. This number corresponds to 0.7 per cent of the number of the holdings of two to ten hectares of arable cultivated land.

The activity of enlarging and consolidating holdings is supposed to be performed according to set plans, partly plans covering the whole administrative county districts, partly more local plans comprising a greater or smaller number of holdings. The activity is also supported by the government granting of a guarantee for loans and of granting subsidies, on liberal terms, for the purchase of additional land, consolidations through redistribution of land or exchange of fields, building and repair of roads, barns and drainage, clearing away of stones, reclamation of new land, planting of hedges and woods to protect the soil—all in accordance with plans made or approved by the government agency responsible for the fulfillment of the agricultural program. Even for building of dwelling houses, special loans and subsidies are granted by the government.

In Denmark similar steps have been taken, but they have been adapted to the conditions ruling there. The development of the agricultural population presents another pattern there. The farming population is not decreasing in Denmark as it is in Sweden. The size of the production is not adapted to the Danish requirement of articles of food. On the contrary, the agricultural products are the chief articles of export. A very large animal production is characteristic of the Danish agriculture, the production of feed for the cattle being completed with imported concentrated feed. The object of the Danish agricultural policy has been rather an increase than a decrease in the number of holdings, but at the same time it has been an enlargement of the holdings of noneconomic farm units. According to the Danish law of 1948 on enlarging small holdings and noneconomical farm units, the farmer who has less than eight hectares of arable land might claim additional land. Such land is procured through purchase in the open market or through the taking over of sold holdings, this being supported by the government priority right of purchase provided by the law mentioned. Different from the Swedish law, which in principle concerns all holdings that are sold, the Danish one is directly applicable only in the case of holdings of a certain minimum value. A holding must not unrestrictedly be used as additional land, only the part of it that can be separated without too great inconvenience for the holding in question.

Norway is at present preparing a law on priority right of purchase similar to the Swedish one. The background, however, is quite different. Norway is not yet self-supporting with regard to articles of food. The population trend is somewhat different from that of Sweden. Reclamation of land and establishment of new holdings is still taking place. The natural qualifications, topography, etc., are obstacles to the enlarging of farms to make them economic units. Therefore it is not to be expected that the activity of enlarging Norwegian holdings of noneconomic farm units will take place in exactly the same way as in Sweden.

The effects of the farming policy carried on in the Scandinavian countries will probably lead in Denmark to a slight increase in the number of holdings and, with regard to the distribution of holdings according to size, to a decrease in the three to ten hectare holdings and those bigger than thirty hectares but to an increase in the intermediate holdings of ten to thirty hectares. In Norway it will probably lead to an unaltered or a slightly decreased number of holdings and, with regard to distribution, to a decrease in the two to five hectare holdings, and a slight increase in the five to twenty hectare holdings. In Sweden, also, it will probably lead to a definite decrease in the number of holdings and, with regard to distribution, to a decrease in the two to ten hectare holdings and an increase in the holdings of ten to thirty hectares.

Land Owners and Tenants

In all the three Scandinavian countries the land in most of the holdings is tilled by the owners themselves. There are, however, many great differences, as will be seen from the figures in Table 39 taken from the latest agricultural statistics.

TABLE 39

LAND TILLAGE IN DENMARK, NORWAY, AND SWEDEN BY SIZE OF HOLDING AND TENURE

Size of Holdings (hectares)	Total Number of Hectares	Tilled by Owners (hectares)	Tilled by Tenants (hectares)	Percentage Tilled by Tenants
		DENMARK		
3–10	78,201	76,491	1,710	2.2
10–60	101,339	97,274	4,065	4.0
60–	22,843	22,417	426	1.4
Total	202,383	196,182	6,201	3.1
		NORWAY		
0.5–	213,441	198,408	15,033	7.0
		SWEDEN		
2–10	202,620	172,502	30,118	17.6
10–50	86,217	63,350	22,867	26.5
50–	7,390	4,483	2,907	39.0
Total	296,227	240,335	55,892	18.8

As will appear from the figures in Table 39, in Denmark and Norway the land is for the most part tilled by the owner, the number of tenants being extremely small. In Sweden, the leasing of land is considerably more common, although it does not play as large a part as in some other coun-

tries. The difference in the three Scandinavian countries in this respect is partly the result of historical causes, partly a result of the different views with regard to the leasing system. In Denmark more than in the other Scandinavian countries they have for a long time aimed at a system of farming to the effect that the owner of the land shall also be the tiller of it. This has been carried through by means of legislation and financial help to tenants for the buying of the land they use.

The relations between owners and tenants are ultimately regulated by legislation. The extent of legislation seems to be related to that of the leaseholding practiced. In Sweden there exists a very detailed legislation chiefly for the protection of leaseholders. This is especially the case with regard to the so-called social leaseholdings, certain important categories of holdings of fifty hectares of cultivated land at the highest. For them a series of the rules are compulsory; that is, they are valid even though the parties have agreed on another arrangement. Among other things, it is provided that the contract of leaseholding has to be written. The lease has to be either restricted in time (not under five years) or for a lifetime. The leaseholder and his descendants have the right of option. The lease is to be stated in money only. The landlord is subject to considerable obligations concerning buildings and their maintenance. Denmark also has a very extensive lease legislation. In all the three Scandinavian countries the leaseholder has a priority right of purchase if the holding he leases is sold. Even if the lease has its drawbacks, it has also its advantages. Among other things, persons with limited means at their disposal can start as independent farmers.

Restricted Right of Acquiring Land

From periods back in history there have been various restrictions with regard to the acquiring of land in the Scandinavian countries. The chief restrictions of this kind in present-day Sweden are found in a law of 1925 prohibiting in certain cases the right of corporations to acquire landed property. The law of 1945 restricts still further the right of acquiring landed property. The latter, which is the most important one, has been passed to prevent acquiring of land for speculative purposes and also to prevent the land from becoming the property of nonfarmers who would then become absentee landlords. Similar legislation is found in Denmark and Norway, but in those countries the restriction is valid upon the amount of land a person may own. Thus in Denmark, according to a law of 1951, a man with his wife and children cannot own more than two holdings, and in Norway the right of acquiring land is restricted to certain areas, which are different in the different parts of the country.

Preventing Neglect of Land

I shall just make passing mention of the fact that in all the three Scandinavian countries laws have been passed to prevent neglect of land. In principle, this means that the holding may not be neglected to the extent that its potential power of production is jeopardized, that indispensable buildings may not be removed, and that cultivated land may not be used for the planting of forest without special permission being obtained from the government agency that possesses the power of giving dispensation from the statutes. In Denmark, the law sets down additional provisions to the effect that two holdings cannot be tilled as a unit; they both must be individually provided with houses and farm inventory.

Related Agricultural Problems

In this paper I have used the phrase land tenure in the restricted sense, as I think we in Europe usually interpret it: man's relation to land. Therefore, I have omitted such important subjects, and subjects so closely related with land tenure, as the farmers' credit system, farmers' co-operatives, and farm labor problems. In order to complete the picture, however, I would like to say a few words about these subjects as related to Sweden.

The credit problem seems, for the present, to be well solved. The farmer can borrow money in any commercial bank, savings bank, or credit co-operative in order to buy a farm, to improve the farmhouses, draining systems, roads, etc., or to buy implements for the farm. If the farmer's property is not a satisfactory security, the government under certain conditions guarantees payment of the loan if the farmer should fail to pay. The period within which the loan shall be repaid is determined by the use of the money borrowed. Since the security, which is either farm property or government guarantee, must be considered good, the interest is the same whether it is a first mortgage loan or a loan for buying implements. At present, the interest is 3.5 per cent to 4 per cent.

Farmers' co-operatives in all lines—marketing and purchasing, as well as credit co-operatives—are well developed throughout the country, and they are considered to be in a strong position. Co-operative concerns handle more than 95 per cent of the milk delivered to dairies, 70 per cent of the slaughtered animals, and 65 per cent of the cereals and eggs marketed, as well as of the feed and fertilizers purchased.

The farm laborers have reached a good status. They are well organized, and their terms of employment are strictly defined in a collective agreement. Since 1938, a law was passed according to which every worker is entitled to a vacation. According to a decision of the Parliament this year, the vacation shall amount to three weeks yearly. Since 1916, every worker is legally insured against accidents. In this connection, the laws concerning the right to organize, the court of labor, and the protection of labor may also be mentioned.

Present Position of Agriculture

I shall conclude with a few words as to the development of Swedish agriculture and its present position. From 1870 to 1950 the total population has increased from 4.2 to 7.1 millions. Up to the end of 1870 agriculture had a dominant position in the economic life of the country. Nearly 75 per cent of the total population was engaged in agriculture, forestry, and fishing. Industry and commerce occupied 20 per cent. Since then, the country has become highly industrialized. At present, agriculture, forestry, and fishing will probably not occupy more than 26 per cent, and industry and commerce 64 per cent of the total population.

This does not mean that the importance of agriculture has decreased or that its production has gone down. On the contrary, agricultural production has, during this period, increased more than ever before. The amount of vegetable products has more than doubled, and animal production has more than trebled since 1870. This increased production has led to a higher degree of self-sufficiency and a better food standard for the people.

During the last ten to fifteen years, agriculture has become highly mechanized. The number of tractors has increased from 18,000 before World War II to about 65,000 at present. This means that there are, on the average, fifty-seven hectares of cultivated land per tractor. Since the end of 1930 the farmers have obtained 5,000 combines. As to other agricultural machines and tools, the development has been about the same.

An improved tenure system, improved techniques, and increased mechanization are the main reasons for the increasing production at the same time as the population engaged in agriculture has been decreasing. The pronounced increase of the nonagricultural population has been taken care of, thanks to the industralization of the country. The increase in agricultural production in relation to the number of people engaged in agriculture can in a somewhat simplified manner be expressed as follows: At the end of 1870, three persons were needed to produce food for four persons, while at present only one person is needed to produce the same amount of food.

The long-term agricultural program which was adopted in 1948 and on which I have commented was the result of a comprehensive and thorough investigation concerning the weaknesses and the needs of agriculture. There is hardly any doubt that as the program is carried through it will mean a further and rather strong development of agriculture.

THE ITALIAN AGRARIAN REFORM

 Manlio Rossi-Doria

THE QUESTION about which many persons are probably puzzled in thinking of Italy is how it is possible to speak of a land reform in a country whose land is intensively cultivated and whose land ownership is mainly too much split up instead of being too much concentrated.

That the question is genuine may be seen by the fact that it corresponds to the common Italian opinion and that nobody worried about it until recent years. You will probably be interested to note that, after the first world war when many European countries accomplished their land reform, in my country the problem was neither solved nor even really discussed. Nevertheless, if you accurately analyze the situation, you can see that Italy is one of the countries in which owners who are the actual cultivators hold the smaller portion of the land and in which the greater part of the productive surface is owned by social classes who do not cultivate the soil directly.

A few figures, gathered from the volumes of the national surveys on the distribution of land ownership and that of holding types published by our Institute of Agricultural Economics[1] are sufficient to support what I just said.

Land Ownership in Italy

The total productive surface in Italy is nearly 28 million hectares or 69.2 million acres. Of these, the private owners, including institutions of a private character (welfare and church institutions or companies), own nearly 24 million hectares; and 4 million hectares are owned by the state or the communes. Since the land owned by the latter is in the mountains, it is mainly forest and pasture. Of the privately owned land,

8 million hectares are in forest and pasture and 16 million hectares are under cultivation. Six million hectares, or 37.5 per cent of this cultivated area, belong to small cultivating owners. The remaining 62.5 per cent, or 10 million hectares, belongs to landowners who do not cultivate it directly and hold it in different forms: in tenancy, in "mezzadria" (metayage), or in owner-operated farms with wage earners or sharecroppers. (See Table 40.)

On the other hand, if we consider the distribution of productive surface, not in relation to holding systems but according to the size of the property, the picture is equally significant. Let us consider, for the sake of simplicity, only the privately owned land (excluding also the ownership of the institutions considered before, whose total property amounts to 2.2 million hectares.) (See Table 41.[2])

TABLE 40

DISTRIBUTION OF PRIVATELY OWNED CULTIVATED LAND IN ITALY BY TYPE OF TENURE

Kind of Holding	Area (in hectares)	Percentage of Total
Cultivator-owners	6,000,000	37.5
Noncultivating owners:		
Cultivating tenants	3,000,000	18.8
Mezzadri (metayers)	5,000,000	31.2
Wage-earners or		
sharecroppers	2,000,000	12.5
Total	16,000,000	100.0

TABLE 41

DISTRIBUTION OF PRIVATELY OWNED LAND IN ITALY ACCORDING TO SIZE OF HOLDING

Holding (hectares)	Area (in hectares)	Percentage of Total
5 or less	6,700,000	32
5–50	7,400,000	35
50–200	3,200,000	15
200–	3,800,000	18
Total	21,100,000	100

If we suppose—as it is possible—that all the land owned by small cultivator-owners belongs to the first two size classes, it results that the land owned by the noncultivating owners—or bourgeois owners as they are named in Italy to contrast them with the peasants—is subdivided approximately as shown in Table 42.[3]

In summary, the Italian situation relating

TABLE 42

NONCULTIVATING OWNERSHIP OF LAND
IN ITALY BY SIZE OF HOLDING

Holding (hectares)	Area (in hectares)	Percentage of Total
50 or less	6,000,000	46.2
50–200	3,200,000	24.6
200–	3,800,000	29.2
Total	13,000,000	100.0

to land tenure is characterized by: (1) the existence of a numerous class of small and very small peasant cultivating owners, whose land is so split up and limited as to be insufficient in most cases for the subsistence of owning families; (2) the fact that the large part of cultivated land is owned by noncultivating owners; and (3) the fact that these noncultivating owners are a very numerous class—more than 300,000—composed mainly of small or medium owners, not of big ones.

These facts are sufficient to indicate the peculiar difficulties of a land reform in Italy. If the predominance of noncultivating ownership really shows the advisability of a land reform with the purpose of increasing the surface owned by peasant cultivators, the fact that the noncultivating owners are mainly small and medium and, therefore, a very important and numerous social class of the country signifies that the land reform is difficult, not to say impossible.

This purely statistical introduction to the problem is, nevertheless, inadequate to understand the real situation.

Although the land distribution is nearly the same in all the Italian provinces, the real situation is yet very different among them, the tenure problems varying greatly in the different provinces. In the provinces of north and central Italy and in some coastal areas of the south and in Sicily, the concentration of landownership in the hands of noncultivating owners did not hinder but, on the contrary, favored the improvement of agriculture, capital investment, and the building up of very intensively managed farms. Such results were produced in some cases by the contract of mezzadria,[4] in others by the direct farming of owners or of big tenants with the aid of wage-earners, or by special long-term contracts used in the south for the planting of citrus and olive trees or of vineyards. By contrast, in other internal or coastal areas of the south and the islands and in some provinces of central Italy (Roman Campagna and Roman and Tuscan Maremma) the noncultivating owners, possessing the largest part of the land, did not improve it or invest capital in it. Rather they held it, doing nothing except renting it either directly to the peasants or to medium-size tenants, whose farms managed with the aid of wage-earners were quite primitive and technically and socially unsatisfactory.

It would be very interesting to illustrate the reasons for this different evolution of land tenure in my country which brought some of the Italian provinces to the height of the most progressive and intensive agriculture and left others at the low level of the most poor and primitive. Time not permitting this, it is now sufficient to stress that this distinction between intensive agricultural areas and extensive ones had been much more important in deciding on land reform than the distribution of landownership itself.

From what we have said so far, it should be evident that Italy is facing not one but two land reform problems. Primarily, Italy must emancipate the provinces of the south from the intolerable conditions under which agriculture and social life are struggling there. These circumstances keep these populations down at the lowest level of civilization, comparable only to some of the poorest Asiatic, Near-Eastern, or South European countries, and leaving land utilization in a condition which is sharply in contrast with the needs of modern agriculture. From a second point of view, in Italy we are considering the desirability of stabilizing our rural social structure, promoting everywhere the increase of surface owned by cultivating peasants, reducing thereby the number of wage-earners and of other agricultural workers, and giving greater stability to the tenants and mezzadri.

The problem of land reform was really faced and discussed in Italy in recent years with the aim of solving the two problems, but I must immediately repeat that we have not yet a definite policy, and there are doubts and discussions, and will be for a long time.

In the second part of this paper I will speak exclusively of the land reform as it is conceived and applied in the special districts of south and central Italy to which the approved laws refer. In order to cover the topic I must speak briefly on the proposals made to solve the problem of land reform, with the aim of changing everywhere the land tenure structure and social relations.

Land Reform Legislation

After many discussions and hesitations, last year our government's policy seemed to be attempting to move at the same time along three different ways.

First, they presented to Parliament the draft of a general land reform law, according to which all the properties whose taxable revenue was larger than a determinate value (30,000 lire in the main cases and 100,000 lire for the lands whose unit value per hectare was larger) would be obliged to give up a portion of the owned land (calculated according to the percentual values fixed in a special table and varying with the revenue) and would so contribute to the build-

ing up of a new cultivating ownership.

Secondly, they had maintained in effect a law approved in 1946, according to which the building up of cultivating-ownership was aided by financing the free purchases of land to the peasants.

Thirdly, they presented to the Parliament a bill intended to regulate all the contracts between landowners and tenants or mezzadri or other working rural groups. According to this bill, either the rents or the share-quotas would be established by law with the aid of special commissions; and—what is more important—the interruption of contracts was prohibited in all cases save the few for which a "right cause" could be shown, and the tenant or mezzadro obtained the fixed right to be preferred in the eventual purchasing of the holding.

Now, after a year of continuous debate, the tendency seems to be a little different, although it is not yet possible to say how deeply it has changed and what exactly is the thought of the new Minister of Agriculture, who took office only a few months ago. It is probable, indeed, that new proposals should be framed to meet the strong arguments put forward on many sides and not only by the landowners.

To the first of the bills which relates to the expropriation of all properties exceeding a certain limit, it was objected that the law would be contrary at the same time to justice and to convenience, since it extended the same treatment to the absentee landlords, who had given nothing to the land, as to the good ones who had improved it and who had invested in it considerable capital and had assured a good and modern management of the farms. These objectors have stressed, also, that the expropriation of an improved holding with its implements and livestock would be very expensive and would, therefore, encounter large difficulties of payment either by the peasants or by the state.

To the second bill, which relates to the regulation of contracts between landowners and tenants or mezzadri, and which has been discussed and approved by the House of Representatives but has not yet been discussed by the Senate, it was objected, first, that it would be very difficult to apply such a general regulation to a country as variable as Italy and to very different and complicated contracts. Secondly, it was claimed that the adoption of the rigid principle of stabilization of tenants and mezzadri on the holdings could have as a consequence a crystallization of social relations. This would be very dangerous in an overcrowded country like Italy, because it would prevent the spontaneous adjustments which confer flexibility on the agricultural social structure; and it would have killed the incentives to competition and to selection of the farm families, upon which in the past and in the future depends the success and the progress of production.

We have reason to believe that such arguments will be seriously considered by the legislators so that the proposals will be deeply changed, and it will be necessary to wait a little longer until the new policy in this field has been decided. In studying the problems, economists and politicians have more and more understood that the success of land reform in Italy, as probably in other countries, depends upon the respect of all the spontaneous positive processes of adjustment and progress, when change is not absolutely necessary.

If the above-mentioned considerations have delayed the approval of the general land reform laws in Italy, the laws relating to land reform in the underdeveloped areas of south and central Italy have been very rapidly approved and applied.

The first land reform law, the so-called Sila Law, was approved on May 10, 1950, to be applied to a large territory in Calabria, including the Sila highland plateau and the Ionian coastal areas, which are below it. The law was immediately carried into effect, and during the last year it has attained many of its goals.

The second land reform law—the "extract" law, so called because it was "extracted" from the bill relating to general land reform and approved without waiting the approval of the general bill—was approved on October 20, 1950, and went into effect in the first months of the present year, when the districts of its application were determined.

The two laws are practically the same, differing only in some details of expropriation criteria. According to the Sila Law, subject to expropriation are all the properties whose size is larger than three hundred hectares. The expropriation refers only to the portion of the land which exceeds such a limit, but it is not carried out if the land is intensively cultivated or if it cannot be utilized as cultivable land. According to the "extract" law, the expropriation is performed starting from a taxable revenue limit, assessed in 30,000 lire, instead of from a surface limit. The expropriation takes place above such limits by a progressive scale, whose percentages grow with the growing of the taxable revenue—that is with the increase of property. Practically, however, the two laws do operate without large differences.

The Sila and "Extract" Laws

The other articles are the same in the two laws. They fix equally the following principles.

1. The expropriation plans must be prepared with a particular procedure intended to avoid mistakes or discriminations.

2. The compensation to the expropriated owners is equal to the value of expropriated land, calculated two years before for the general property tax.

3. This compensation will normally be

paid three-quarters in bonds and a quarter in cash, but may be paid all in cash if the expropriated owner shows the will to invest the compensation value in the improvement of this remaining land.

4. The expropriation, redistribution, and main reclamation of land, as well as the administration of technical and financial assistance to the cultivators, are entrusted to special regional agencies with their own independent direction although co-ordinated by the Ministry of Agriculture.

5. The expropriation, redistribution, settlement, reclamation, and credit are financed by special and adequate funds.

6. The land must be allocated either directly to cultivating peasants who are totally deprived of property or own very little or to other agricultural workers; the allocations must have a temporary character for three years until the assignees have demonstrated their will and capacity for good management.

7. The new owners will repay the expropriation value and either two-thirds of anticipated capital costs or of building and land improvement costs (preliminarily reduced by normal state contributions) in thirty years at an interest rate of 3.5 per cent.

8. They must be members of co-operatives built up for marketing or processing purposes or with the aim of a common utilization of farm machinery.

According to the two approved laws, land reform will be applied in the districts indicated in Table 43, in which total surface, the expropriated surface, and the total compensation value of expropriated lands are shown approximately.[5]

Proposed Expropriation

As may be noted, land reform will be carried out on a total surface of 8.5 million hectares, equal to 30 per cent of the national total surface, and the total amount of ex-propriated land will be approximately 739,-000 hectares. The total compensation to the expropriated owners will probably amount to 73 billion lire (equal to 112 million dollars). This is equivalent to 100,000 lire an hectare, or $62.30 an acre.

Let us relate the expropriation data with the data mentioned at the beginning of my report, and we will see that the expropriated land will be equal to 7.4 per cent of the land owned by noncultivating owners and that it will increase the surface of the land owned by the cultivators by 13 per cent.

Considering land reform from this point of view, it appears a rather modest event. It is very important certainly as a step towards a gradual increase of cultivating ownership but not more important than the increase of the same ownership at the end of the first world war—when more than 1 million hectares were spontaneously bought by the peasants, who had been enriched by devaluation of money, increase of prices, and a blocking of leases.

If you consider, on the contrary, land reform in the framework of the areas in which it will be applied, it appears as a very important event because it will change their situation radically and will allow a general reordering and improving of agriculture and social life. In these districts land reform will really abolish large estates, make cultivators' ownership predominant, and develop a complete transformation of land tenure systems.

The figures given in Table 43 are those of the plans and programs. Considering the fact that the laws have been in effect only a few months, a small part of these programs has been carried out. In Calabria, where we started first, expropriations have been carried out for the two-thirds of the estimate[6] (50,000 hectares) and redistribution of land has been carried on for three-fifths of the expropriated surface (30,000

TABLE 43

Land Reform in Italy by Districts*

District	Total Area	Expro-priated Area	Compen-sation
Po Delta	317	40	9,200
Maremma	982	196	20,600
Fucino	14	14	2,000
Campania	125	9	1,500
Puglia-Basilicata	1,450	165	18,200
Calabria	580	80	5,600
Sardegna	2,400	85	3,600
Sicilia (provisory)	2,570	150	12,000
Total	8,438	739	72,700

*In thousands of hectares and millions of lire.

hectares). For the other districts the data on October 1 were the following: Maremma and Fucino expropriated land, 33,000 hectares, or 16 per cent of estimate; Apulia and Basilicata expropriated land, 29,000 hectares, or 17.5 per cent of estimate; but the expropriation decrees are following very rapidly in these months. On October 1 the total expropriated surface was 109,000 hectares, but further plans were announced for 178,000 hectares.

Land Reform by Regions

In the indicated districts land reform presents very different aspects and problems. The land reform will be mainly concentrated in the south of Italy and in the islands, where its features and problems are very similar to those for Calabria. The problems in the districts of central and north Italy are, on the contrary, quite different.

Maremma is a large flat coastal area, abandoned for many centuries because of the terrible dominating malaria. During the last fifty or more years, when it was finally possible to fight malaria, the district was reclaimed, put into cultivation little by little, and improved by the big landlords, who owned the larger part of it. Despite the progress of reclamation and intensification of farming, the land tenure system remained characterized by the predominance either of large farms operated with the aid of wage-earners or of large "mezzadria" holdings, so that the situation did not correspond to the requirements of a denser population, which is both desirable and possible in this district.

The aim of the land reform in Maremma is actually not only the change of local workers or mezzadri to cultivator-owners, but also the immigration and settlement of a considerable number of outside families.

The situation in Fucino and the Delta of the Po is quite different. The Fucino as described in Silone's famous novel, *Fontamara,* was until the last century a lake in the midst of the Abruzzi mountains. Its surface of more than 14,000 hectares was drained by Prince Torlonia, who owned it until the recent expropriation and rented it in small plots to small tenants of the surrounding villages. Thanks to land reform, Prince Torlonia was entirely expropriated, and the small peasant tenants, who cultivate each a little more than one hectare will be changed into small owners—aided by technical and financial assistance, organized in the new marketing, processing, and machinery co-operative.

The Delta of the Po, or Low Po Valley, is in a different position. What is now the most fertile soil of Italy was made up of marshes and fish lakes seventy years ago. Land reclamations were carried out here principally by big companies who maintained the ownership of reclaimed land and who now hold it in large and modern capitalistic farms, with the aid of wage-earners and share-croppers. The district, which was previously unpopulated, was in recent years populated by families of wage-earners attracted here by the carrying out of reclamation works; these workers are now in excess of the needs of the intensively cultivated and highly mechanized farms. In spite of the tremendous increase of production, therefore, land reclamation has created a severe social problem of a large class of wage earners without any stability on the land, without employment during several months in the year (it has been calculated that a wage-earner works no more than 150 days in a year), and strongly organized in militant unions. It is hoped that land reform, expropriating the land of the companies, will stabilize the situation of the wage-earners and change them into small cultivating owners. However, it is a widely held opinion that this is not the way to solve the exceptional economic and social problems of the district and that probably workers' stabilization can be achieved without expropriating such well-managed farms as those of the companies. The problem of land reform in this district, therefore, is still under discussion.

Land Reform in the South

The brief comments above on land reform districts of north and central Italy will show how various and complicated is our land reform problem. We must now see which are the problems and features of land reform in the south, where the largest and most important areas are concentrated. To show concretely these features and problems, instead of describing separately the situation of each one of the southern districts, it will be better to consider the situation and development in Calabria, where land reform first started, and where it has progressed farther than elsewhere.

The Sila law applies to a territory of 530,000 hectares including within its boundaries more than 350,000 inhabitants mostly occupied in agriculture. More than one-third of this vast territory consists of a large mountain plateau, with an altitude of approximately 1,200 meters above sea level, which, up to the present day, was commonly used for the summer pasturage of animals coming from the lower-lying coastal districts and only secondarily for seasonal crops of potatoes and rye by the local population. The other two-thirds of the territory is made up of very rugged coastal districts subject to erosion, which were terribly infested by malaria up to a few years ago. The dense agricultural population in this vast zone, while presenting notable differences in the conditions of each village and of each zone, is one of the poorest of all southern Italy. This population is concentrated in large villages, where families of five to eight people live in a single room with the cattle, and cultivate, usually as tenants, small pieces of land—sometimes five or ten or fifteen in number, very distant from each other. From this land they get a bare subsistence, with an average income of 150,000 lire (230 dollars) per year. Their consumption is very small: even though they turn over 90 per cent of their income to food, this does not provide any sugar, very little milk (five liters a year per person), very little meat (five or six times during the year), and even very few vegetables, fats, or cheese. Their diet is limited, therefore, to bread and to pasta with a little greens. It is not surprising that under these conditions the health situation is very poor, and so is education. The number of illiterates is very high, and even greater is the number of those whose knowledge barely extends beyond that of the alphabet.

The Need for Emigration

I do not have the time to go into detail, but I would like to make clear to you that here we face one of the most tragic conditions of rural poverty in overpopulated areas.

Certainly, bad distribution of property and absentee landownership are partly responsible for the situation, but because of the extreme natural poverty of the territory it would be well to restrict land use to forest and pasturage only, if the dense population did not prevent it. This district, together with the similar neighboring districts of the Basilicata, is that which has contributed most to emigration from the end of the last century to 1920; for later years also, emigration has been the only salvation for these people. Through emigration, population diminished, and some improvement was effected in living conditions, together with a certain increase in cultivating ownership. But these advantages had been almost cancelled by the increase of population since 1920, which has exceeded 50 per cent. This increase has forced people to live in groups of three where formerly two people could ill afford to live, without any increase of sources of income and without the rise of any new activity, erosion having decreased production even further.

The land reform and the reclamation program are here aiming at the increase of production, the stabilization of the majority of the agricultural population, and the increase of income and of living conditions. These are certainly goals which we must attain, and we can attain them in part. But it would be very dishonest and dangerous to foster the illusion that one can solve the economic and social problems of this and the other southern regions in this manner or even by means of the limited contemporary industrialization which is possible. Even with all this, the southern populations cannot help taking again the road of emigration.

Let us return to the problems of reform.

In Calabria, in the territory in question, which extends to more than 530,000 hectares, the properties larger than 300 hectares totaled more than 100,000 hectares, of which

over one-third was in the hands of only three owners. The law will expropriate 75,-000 hectares, i.e., three-fourths of the area; almost 50,000 hectares of this land is already in the hands of the agency that carries out the land reform, known as the Opera Valorizzazione Sila.

The problem of the redistribution and transformation of the expropriated territory differs from district to district of the vast area and calls for different solutions and different regulations—thus involving a long and difficult study of conditions and planning of measures.

Nearly 16,000 hectares of this territory is on the plateau of the Sila, at an altitude of 100 meters, without inhabited centers, without housing, with few roads, and with a cold and snowy winter. In such territory the peasants will be able to live and to prosper only after land reclamation and other improvements, including irrigation, have been introduced.

Another section, which includes 32,000 hectares, lies in a vast arid zone which is infested by malaria, without roads, with only two large inhabited centers, without houses in the countryside, without drinking water, without trees, lashed by strong winds, with many clay soils, strongly subject to erosion, and with some of the best lands still occupied by bush and kept in that condition as a hunting preserve. Here the peasants live a miserable life, using the primitive aid of donkeys and mules and raising wheat and horsebeans in pieces of land which are often very distant (up to twenty kilometers) from the inhabited centers. The land reform agency, in order to stabilize peasant family holdings here as much as possible, must do everything, from building roads, houses, and aqueducts, to planting trees, leveling the land, introducing machinery, guiding the peasants step by step in the difficult construction of a new world.

A third section of 7,000 hectares includes

expropriated land which is excellent alluvial soil and which possesses abundant water for irrigation, thanks to the construction of two large reservoirs for hydroelectric usage on the Sila Plateau. Five thousand hectares of this area lie in the low valley of the river Neto and 2,000 hectares in the Sibari Plain. The prospects in this case are excellent because the good soil and irrigation will multiply production tenfold and thus will provide a good settlement to more than 3,000 families, with holdings of two or three hectares; but also in this case everything must be built up, beginning with the completion of the greater irrigation and land reclamation works, which are now being realized with the aid of the Economic Cooperation Administration, and including the breaking of the sod, tree planting, housing, and much more.

Finally, the last 20,000 hectares are scattered in the rugged hilly districts between the mountains and the coast. This is very poor land, which in many ways would be better abandoned or reforested but which instead will have to be the first to be distributed and improved; the population is so dense that there is little possibility of its partial transfer to the above-mentioned less populated areas. One must, therefore, distribute land at once to the peasants and then help them to settle and to improve gradually. One hopes here to see repeated the miracle of industrious effort which has happened in many other poor, rugged, and eroded areas of our country, by which the population lives a life which, if not prosperous, is at least less miserable than that of the present peasants. This is what is being done today at Santa Severina and Melissa. These are the first communes in which the land has been distributed, and the hard work of soil erosion control and conquest of the land presents the dramatic and even foolhardy aspects that you will see in many scenes of the motion picture.[7]

Some Interpretations

I have tried to illustrate in some detail the situation and the problems which we are facing in Calabria in order to show you their complexities. Here are brought together in a relatively small territory technical problems which are to be found usually in very distant and different countries. But I have done it mainly to make you understand how our land reform involves much more than the expropriation and redistribution of areas, including as it does the very building up of the land; therefore, it involves an impressive technical and financial effort. This is the reason why today, after many negative past experiences, our land reform is not carried out by spontaneous initiative of the peasants, to be left alone with the land assigned to each, but instead through the administration of special agencies, whose task is not only that of regulating redistribution especially difficult and delicate in an overpopulated country like ours but also and especially that of aiding technically and financially the peasants in their hard period of the essential transformation of the land and the agriculture.

My speech is already too long and I must conclude. This is just the point at which I would have liked to go into the difficulties, the details, what is still doubtful and debatable in what we are doing—that is, the selection of the peasants and the distribution of the land, size and type of the holdings to be established, participation of the peasants in the work of transformation, cost and financing of the reform, participation of the state, methods of credit and reimbursement for land and works, introduction and co-operative management of machines and their problems, constitution of the co-operatives and their working, and the transition from the introductory phase to the final one.

This could be the subject of another report, if I did not realize that my country is

too small to deserve such prolonged attention by a conference which covers all the
world. However, I shall be happy to speak
with anyone who wishes to, because I think
that our experience, however modest, can be
useful to all. After all, the problems of this
conference are mainly those of the economics of poverty, and it is therefore natural that the experience of the poorer may
also provide instruction to all, including the
rich.

Part XII THE COMMUNIST APPROACH TO THE LAND PROBLEM IN EASTERN EUROPE

SOME OF THE PROBLEMS OF LAND TENURE IN EASTERN EUROPE

Michael B. Petrovich

BETWEEN the Germans and Italians in the West and the Russians to the East there live some 80 million Poles, Czechs, Slovaks, Magyars, Rumanians, Bulgars, Yugoslavs, Albanians, and Greeks. They occupy a vast area which defies generalization. Probably the most useful over-all geographic designation devised for this part of the European continent is the German expression "Zwischenland," or "in-between-land." In present official terminology the countries of Eastern Europe are styled "people's democracies" —a term which establishes them as a political and economic in-between land as well since they are considered to be, in a transitional phase, "on the road to socialism." The even more descriptive designation, "the iron curtain countries," testifies to the fact that all of these peoples are now committed to a single broad political, social, and economic way of life.

Neither geography nor history points to the unity of this highly complex region. Geographically Eastern Europe is divided into three distinct areas: the Baltic, the Danubian, and the Balkan. Each of these areas is in turn subdivided into physical zones which cut across political boundaries and often dissect a single small country into many parts. Marked differences in climate, soil, and topography impose upon the inhabitants of Eastern Europe correspondingly different means of sustaining life from the good earth and the bad.

The historical differences which rend this region are even more profound. The whole area is a maelstrom of languages, and religions and ethnic strains among which the Slavs, the Magyars, and the Rumanians predominate. The soil of these peoples is rich with the blood which their Russian, German, and Turkish imperial masters have shed there in centuries of conflict. The minds of these peoples are scarred battlefields on which the conflicting cultures of West and East have fought bitterly for a millenium. And whether the dominant rule was that of West or East, the East Europeans generally suffered from the same institutions: political authoritarianism, rule by the bureaucracy and army, and the economic oppression of the peasant masses.

Despite these geographic and historical differences, Eastern Europe is bound by a predominantly agrarian way of life. With the exception of certain industrial areas in Bohemia, Silesia, southern Poland, and the oil fields of Rumania, Eastern Europe is overwhelmingly peasant Europe. It is inescapable, therefore, that the land problem in its broadest conception is the central question which besets this region. It is on its ultimate solution that the entire political and social structure largely rests.

In our time the forces of communism have undertaken the gigantic task of solving the agrarian questions in Eastern Europe. Like their predecessors, the present Communist leaders are beset by the same basic problem: there are more humans in Eastern Europe than the soil can presently support. Sometimes this problem is called "over-population" and sometimes "low productivity of the soil," but both amount to the same quandary.

It would be grossly unfair to accuse the post-World War I succession states of indifference to the plight of the peasantry or even failure to alleviate their lot. With varying degrees of success, all of the East European governments which came to power in 1918 carried out land reforms which brought some relief to the population. Yet in almost every case and for a variety of reasons, the reforms were inadequate. Where land was actually distributed the reforms grew out of political and national considerations rather than social and economic policy. In most cases the land distributed belonged to the dispossessed foreign landlords—largely Germans and Hungarians. Newly acquired frontier provinces were usually colonized by the new dominant nationality at the expense of local minority groups. For example, Poles were given preference over White Russians in Eastern Poland, Serbs over Albanians in Macedonia, and Rumanians over Bulgars in Dobrudja. In the two countries where the existence of large estates demanded the most drastic reforms—Poland and Hungary—despite ambitious programs the Esterhazy, Festetics, Radziwill, Potocki, and other families as well as the Roman Catholic church were still permitted to own huge estates. What distribution was carried out was actually not rational from a purely economic point of view. Large land units farmed with modern methods on mass production lines would have certainly yielded a higher return than parcelling the land. Nevertheless, social and political factors made it desirable in most cases to attempt to satisfy the land hunger of the individual peasant families.

Where distribution was not carried out in sufficient measure, emigration of the peasants to foreign lands such as the United States continued to provide some outlet, though emigration can hardly be called a solution in any social sense. A much better method would have been the absorption of the peasant population by industrialization, but absence of capital, competition from more advanced countries, and other reasons usually militated against the establishment of local industries. Other measures had to be considered: technical education, intensive cultivation of noncereals, development of transportation, public works program, agrarian co-operatives, subsidies and credits, cheaper farm machinery. It was through such means that the Danish farmer was able to produce three times as much on the same acreage as the Yugoslav. But Yugoslavia, Bulgaria, or Rumania was not Denmark. Other considerations took precedence over the welfare of the peasant.

Despite the gains made between the two world wars, the reasons for failure were many. In the political arena, those peasant parties which were most interested in improving the peasant's lot and most representative of the peasant's wishes were suppressed or out-maneuvered by the new ruling groups. Peasant party leaders such as Stamboliskii in Bulgaria, Maniu in Rumania, Radic in Yugoslavia, all suffered violent death or persecution in their time just as they or their successors are suffering under the present Communist regimes. Led by other ambitions and fears, most governments of Eastern Europe were more interested in garrisons than agricultural schools. Too little of the state budget went for rural agricultural stations, health service, farm implements, or farm credits. What co-operatives the peasant parties sponsored were discouraged by the government. The peasantry was burdened with taxes to pay for building cities, for theaters the inside of which they rarely saw, and for the salaries of bureaucrats who did little for them and frequently made life more miserable. Government subsidies often went to infant industries whose products were too expensive for the moneyless peasant.

Had local political and social conditions been more favorable to the peasant, the East European land problem might have been alleviated. It is doubtful, however, whether it could have been solved with the best of intentions on the part of the local governments. Just as the peasant was discriminated against by other classes in his own country, so the peasant countries of Eastern Europe were discriminated against by a capitalist world. One must remember that in Eastern Europe an industrial Bohemia is an exception while agrarian Hungary and Yugoslavia are the rule. Imperialist ambitions combined with an inexorable economic law to make the countries of Eastern Europe the virtual colonies of Germany and Italy years before Hitler and Mussolini physically invaded their eastern neighbors. The agrarian problem in Eastern Europe, then, is not only a local problem but an international one. It poses a basic question which is far from peculiar to Eastern Europe: What is an agrarian country to do in order to exist as an independent, democratic nation and to enjoy a decent standard of living in the face of the economic supremacy of industrial countries?

That the largely agrarian countries of Eastern Europe fell before the onslaught of their neighbors from 1938 through 1941 is but the ultimate physical manifestation of a hard economic fact. With the German, Italian, and Russian invasions one government after another fell or was made impotent. What these governments might have accomplished had they been given more years of peace became an academic question. The second world war devastated whole countries in Eastern Europe. No-

where did the four horsemen of the Apocalypse reap a greater harvest than in Poland and Yugoslavia. In their wake came a troubled peace which brought with it all of the miseries and hardships that have always attended political and social revolution. The end of the war put in power a whole constellation of Communist-dominated governments in Eastern Europe.

Even their very existence in this part of the world presented an anomaly. Small native Communist parties set themselves up with Soviet backing in countries where they had little tradition or influence. As contemporary witnesses of this revolution we are naturally more aroused or impressed by its undoubtedly violent nature. More impartial future historians may well conclude, however, that the East European revolution followed an already established pattern: the Communist regimes moved into a kind of political and moral vacuum in which old leaders, old issues, old parties, old institutions no longer exerted their customary force.

Even more anomalous was the fact that the new leaders of these countries owed allegiance to an ideology—Marxism—that had been specifically designed to apply not to backward agrarian countries but to highly developed capitalist countries. The peasantry had long suffered at the hands of a feudal aristocratic minority and infant bourgeois minority. It was now faced by the regime of another minority which claimed to rule in the name of an infant working class. It is little wonder that communism in Eastern Europe is developing one paradoxical situation after another.

A most noteworthy paradox which took place in 1945/46 in each of the newly-styled people's democracies was the carrying out of another land reform program—this time by the Communist leaders. Laws were passed which made it illegal for anyone to possess more than 50 hectares, or about 125 acres, of land in Czechoslovakia, Poland, Hungary and Rumania. In Yugoslavia the limit set was 35 hectares (86 acres) and in Bulgaria 20 hectares (50 acres). The result of this land reform program is that there are now in Eastern Europe about 12 million farms most of which are under 10 acres. Some 48 million acres (including forest land) were appropriated by the East European governments, of which 30 million acres (an area the size of England and Wales) were distributed to some 3 million peasant families. The paradox involved is this: with these land reforms socialist governments carried out a basically capitalist policy. For reasons of immediate strategy Communist leaders, who were sworn to do battle with the incipient capitalist tendencies of the class enemy in the countryside, were actually abetting those capitalist tendencies by feeding the peasantry with more land.

There are several theoretical and real factors which can be raised to explain this apparent contradiction. First, the new Communist-dominated governments were not averse to winning the temporary support or at least neutralization of the peasant masses so as to be left free to liquidate the middle class. Second, by granting land especially to the poor peasants the Communists were hoping to gain their support for the next stage—the liquidation of the rich peasants as a class. Besides, the devastation of war forced the new governments to depend on the good will of the peasant, the real economic backbone of the region, for several badly needed good harvests. Thus a previous pattern was repeated: land reform was again carried out on the basis of political and social necessity rather than economic rationalism.

What have been the general results of the land distribution carried out thus far by the Communist leaders? Especially in countries which had already experienced fairly effective land reforms before the war and which were traditionally small landholding countries such as Bulgaria, Yugoslavia, and Rumania there was actually little land to distribute. Again a previous pattern was followed with the distribution of land which once belonged to the expelled German and Hungarian minority. In no East European country can it be said that the Communists have yet instituted a basic revolution in the outward forms of land tenure even as far-reaching, let us say, as the reforms carried out in Japan under American occupation. Those East European peasants who did receive land obtained very little, usually about seven acres per beneficiary, which does not comprise a land unit even in the Balkans. This means that statistically the average landholding in Eastern Europe is even smaller today and—from the standpoint of agrarian economics, at least—less rational than before. Redistribution did not increase cultivation. That was not its primary purpose.

It is clear that the land distribution carried out thus far by the Communist leaders of Eastern Europe must be regarded primarily as a temporary political and social measure preparatory to a more serious revolution on the land. The reforms have undoubtedly served to help those who needed help most. New class divisions between the rich and poor peasants are being encouraged. That eventual collectivization is the goal of the present regimes is evident both from theory and practice. Government control over agriculture through a variety of agencies has reduced the independence of the peasant land owners to a minimum. Price control, monopoly of large farm machinery, crop quotas, and other means already familiar to observers of the Soviet scene have been added to the more traditional inducements of subsidization and government contracts. Meanwhile the establishment of model collective state farms and the pressure exerted on peasants to join co-operative ventures of various kinds point to a future in which only the timing seems as yet uncertain.

Why is reorganization of farming needed in Eastern Europe? First, the farms are too small. In the more densely populated areas not only are the farms small in themselves, but they are divided into many parcels or strips which are reminiscent of medieval times. In Yugoslavia, for example, a thirty-acre farm may be fragmented into twenty-five parcels. The peasants themselves have realized that such a system is senseless and wasteful. Second, many regions in Eastern Europe grow the wrong crops and in the wrong way. They grow grain crops through extensive farming and a primitive rotation system in which year after year wheat follows corn and corn follows wheat. Instead of practicing intensive farming suitable to a densely populated area, the East European peasant is trying to farm like the Kansas farmer. Instead of using farm animals for meat and dairy products, the East European peasant uses them for locomotion and power. Miss Doreen Warriner, a shrewd, though politically unreliable, analyst of agrarian economics in Eastern Europe, writes that the poorer peasant eats his corn and sells his wheat whereas what he ought to do is to feed his corn to the pigs, sell the pigs, and eat his wheat. Lack of machines, ignorance of modern techniques, absence of capital for self-improvement are but some of the factors which impede agriculture in Eastern Europe. It is no wonder that an average East European farm produces about one-third less than a comparable West European farm even though each East European acre has to feed twice as many people.

Although the right of private property is constitutionally guaranteed by the present governments in Eastern Europe, the trend is definitely toward collectivization by degrees. The agency of this process is the producer's labor co-operative. In theory, at least, the members join voluntarily and pool their land for the purpose of machine cultivation. Farm animals are likewise pooled, though each family may keep a cow or pig for its own needs. At the end of the year, the income is divided among the members according to units, known as work-days, and to the land area contributed by each member. It is this latter feature that distinguishes the East European co-operative from the Soviet "kolkhoz," where distribution is only according to work done. In the East European co-operative as now constituted, the wealthier farmer gets a higher return than the poor farmer because of the greater area of land he has pooled. On the other hand, certain restrictive laws limiting the proportion of the income distributed to the members prevents the co-operative from being turned into a joint stock venture. It is too early to express any final opinions with respect to the ultimate success of these co-operatives.

The results of the co-ops have thus far been disappointing to the governments which have established them. Even where the co-ops have shown higher yields, the statistics do not reveal that it is often because they received special privileges and grants from the government in machinery, subsidies, and the like. Furthermore, articles in the Communist press written in the spirit of self-criticism reveal flagrant malpractices: the forcing of peasants into co-ops, the illegal requisitioning of pastures, the forced purchase by co-ops at unduly low fixed prices for farm animals from independent farmers, and other violations. Recent reports indicate that even in Yugoslavia, where Tito's policy is supposedly more considerate of the peasant, the opposition of the countryside to the government's tactics is obvious. If the example of the Soviet Union may be taken as a guide, peasant opposition may delay or make more difficult the transition from private to collective farming in Eastern Europe, but it will not be permitted to hinder the process.

The unmistakable trend toward agrarian collectivization in Eastern Europe, already an accomplished fact in the Soviet Union, presents in sharp contrast a dilemma which is currently faced by much of the world. The Western tradition of laissez-faire economics coupled with democracy accepts as a basic tenet that the independent concept of the private farmer is alone compatible with political freedom and economic well-being. It is not our purpose here to challenge this belief on theoretical grounds but rather to point out that the theory itself has had and now has even less application to East European reality.

Whatever political or social programs one may espouse or desire for Eastern Europe, the hard fact is that (1) the land holds a larger population than it can decently support; (2) the small size of most landholdings in the area makes rational economic exploitation impossible without some form of co-operative effort; and (3) no agency except government exists in this area which could carry out such needed measures as industrialization, resettlement, mechanization of agriculture where necessary, the encouragement of intensive rather than extensive farming, and so on.

Acceptance of the above propositions by no means entails acceptance of the present governments of Eastern Europe or even of their program. The term "collectivization" is indeed a broad concept which lends itself to various interpretation. There is no need to accept the Soviet definition. The idea is certainly not new in Eastern Europe. Peasants in this region have known some form of mutual co-operation for centuries. Planning is not synonymous with a centralized dictatorship. Real land reform need not be based on class hatred.

To most American observers it will appear evident that the agrarian program of the present Communist-led regimes in Eastern Europe would not be politically and socially desirable even if it were economically feasible. Unmistakable signs of peasant resistance to increasing government pressure in the Eastern European countries may be taken as evidence that the peasantry there will not be reconciled to that program. On the other hand, it would be unfortunate if our evaluation of the present regimes in Eastern Europe would blind Americans to the fact that problems exist in Eastern Europe which cannot be solved on the basis of a farm economy such as ours. While our techniques will undoubtedly serve as an example to the world, the basic institutions and premises of our way of life are not only incomprehensible to others but out of physical reach. Only by recognizing this can we make the wisest application of our co-operation with other nations. What more can we wish for any people than what it wants for itself? Political circumstances have placed an obstacle between our world and that of Eastern Europe. What the future may bring is uncertain. Yet Eastern Europe offers both a challenge and an object lesson which may be applied to large areas with similar problems throughout that part of the globe which is accessible to us. The challenge lies in the attempt to solve land tenure problems without sacrificing political and social democracy or local traditions to the solution. The object lesson offered by Eastern Europe is that neither in practice nor even theory does the Communist program meet that challenge.

COLLECTIVIZATION OF AGRICULTURE IN SOVIET RUSSIA

$𝄞𝄞𝄞𝄞$ *Lazar Volin*

AGRARIAN democracy is confronted today with a double challenge: the challenge of the survival of feudal or semifeudal forms of land tenure which provoke agrarian unrest that is cleverly exploited by those twin enemies of democracy, communism and fascism, and the challenge of Soviet collectivism.

That agrarian collectivism is part and parcel of world communism in action is not open to doubt. It is no longer confined to the Soviet official frontiers, which themselves have greatly expanded. Since the war, it has been apparent that wherever the Soviet fiat reaches, the kolkhoz, as the Russians call the collective farm, eventually follows as a symbol of the Soviet way of life. Thus, the Russian collectivization experiment is today of more than merely academic or theoretical interest to the free world. It is appropriate, therefore, that a conference such as this should address itself to so serious a challenge.

That collectivization of agriculture has always been the ultimate objective of the Bolsheviks is made abundantly clear by Lenin's writings and by official party literature. The Bolshevik position rests squarely on the Marxist dogma, which has been swallowed by Russian Marxists lock, stock, and barrel ever since the Marxists split off from the older agrarian-minded Russian socialism of the Narodniki or Populists in the 1880's. Central to this dogma is the predilection for bigness arising from the Marx-Engels doctrine of superiority of large-scale production in agriculture as in the manufacturing industry. Both agriculture and industry are envisaged as subject to the same evolutionary law of concentration, uninhibited

by the economic law of diminishing returns or the biological factors peculiar to agriculture. Only large-scale farming is capable, according to this view, of applying effectively the results of modern science and technology. And a corollary of all this is the thesis of the eventual disappearance of the small peasant producer.[1]

However, the writings of Marx, and especially of Engels and Lenin, tend to support the view that the Marxist-Leninist ideology does not preclude a gradualist approach to agricultural collectivization. Lenin, himself, as is well known, was a great master of compromise in the agrarian sphere. In 1917, he even took over the program of his opponents, the agrarian-minded Socialist Revolutionaries, and championed the rebellious small peasant farmers against the landlords. It was, undoubtedly, this policy of appeasement of the peasants by giving them a green light to divide the estate land which helped the Bolsheviks to consolidate power after they seized it. And herein lies a lesson of crucial importance for other countries in which the issue of land reform is ripe or over-ripe. For if the democratic Kerensky government had realized in 1917 that speed was of the essence in the matter of land reform to which they were committed, the Bolsheviks would have been deprived of an important advantage in their bid for power—of posing as defenders of peasants' interests and aspirations for land. The Russian peasants, however, apparently had an early premonition of evil things to come from the Bolshevist regime. This was seen on the only occasion when the peasants were able to vote as they pleased; that is, in the relatively free elections to the Constituent Assembly, held soon after the Bolsheviks seized power in November, 1917. In that election the peasants voted overwhelmingly against Lenin's party and gave a large majority to his opponents, the Socialist Revolutionaries. Needless to say, the Assembly was speedily dispersed by the Bolsheviks, who clamored for its convocation when they were in opposition.

In fact, conflict of the Soviet government with the peasantry began early. Despite this, the gradualist approach to collectivization prevailed, with Stalin's approval, until the late twenties. The reasons for the abandonment of gradualism and for the radical shift of the Soviet agrarian policy towards speedy collectivization were partly ideological and partly grounded in the economic and political situation of Soviet Russia. For one thing, the Soviet regime was more strongly entrenched after a decade of existence and could, therefore, follow a bolder policy than during the earlier years. Nevertheless, the ever-present suspicion of peasant agriculture as a breeding ground of capitalism, which might encircle and defeat socialism, or, as I would prefer to call it, Sovietism in the USSR, persisted. This suspicion was theoretically inspired by the Marxist dogma and was reflected in Lenin's often-quoted proposition that "small-scale production gives birth to capitalism and the bourgeoisie constantly, daily, hourly, with elemental force and in vast proportion." Not only small individual farming but even a peasant in a collective farm cultivating his kitchen garden of an acre or two is suspect.

Even more important was the ambitious and lopsided industrialization program of the five-year plans. This involved, in the first instance, the development of heavy industry, which again was dictated by a combination of ideological and politico-military considerations. Such an industrial expansion required, of course, capital. And where was the requisite capital to be drawn from when foreign sources were unavailable, if not largely from agriculture? In an agrarian country like Russia, it was, as Stalin admitted, something of a tribute paid by agriculture on the altar of socialist industrialization in the form of high taxes and the famous "scissors"—the opening of the scissors representing the disparity between the low prices paid by the state for farm products and high prices charged for manufactured goods of the nationalized monopolistic industry.

The peasants naturally resisted such squeezing tactics by refusing to sell their produce to the government, especially when the harvest was poor. On occasion, they even went so far as to curtail production. The net effect was that the propensity of small peasant farming towards self-sufficiency was greatly enhanced by the industrialization policy of the Soviet government—the very policy which urgently required increased production for the market but did not offer sufficient incentives to stimulate the peasants to produce. Let us not forget in this connection that the division of the estates in 1917 also dealt a serious blow to commercial production.

The Soviet leadership, therefore, was confronted, in the late twenties, with a crucial dilemma: either to slow down the tempo and alter the character of industrialization by shifting the emphasis from heavy to light industry producing consumer goods, or to acquire thoroughgoing control of agriculture, which was the last citadel of individualism in the USSR, since all the other important branches of economy were already nationalized. Stalin was bent on "building socialism in one country" and wanted now to out-Trotsky the exiled Trotsky, who advocated a more rapid industrialization and a tougher policy against the peasants. Stalin also became resolved upon rapid industrialization and maximum development of heavy industry. Any deviation from this course he rejected as a "suicide, a blow to our whole industry . . . a retreat from the objective of industrialization of our country and, on the contrary, its transformation into an appendix to the capitalistic economy." However, he conceded that the situation would have been different if Russia was an industrial country like Germany or was not the only country with a "proletariat dictatorship."

With such a firm commitment to "socialist" industrialization, the die was cast for a collectivist solution of the agrarian problem. The collectivization policy was also encouraged by three theoretically attractive ideas which certainly are not inherent in or, with the exception of the machine-tractor stations, peculiar to a collectivist system: (1) The advantage of rapidly consolidating into larger fields the numerous, scattered, non-contiguous strips into which small peasant holdings were usually divided and which were a source of much inefficiency. In this connection it must also be pointed out that as a result of the division and redivision of holdings during the Revolution and post-revolutionary period many uneconomic farm units, lacking draft power and implements, were created. (2) The enthusiasm for the tractor, which, as I mentioned in my paper on machine-tractor stations in this volume, fascinated Soviet leaders from Lenin down. The tractor reinforced the Marxist faith in the efficacy of large-scale farming and was to be the spearhead of technical revolution in agriculture. (3) The possibility of maximizing the use of tractors, combines, and other farm machinery by pooling them in state-owned central machine-tractor stations.

I shall not linger here on the gruesome aspects of the forced collectivization and liquidation of the so-called kulaki, or fists. The horrible ordeal of Russian peasants during the frightful thirties, driven into collectives or off the land, must be only too well known to you. Doubtless, Marx and Engels, who so eloquently portrayed the hardships of the British factory worker during the industrial

revolution, and, maybe, even Lenin, would turn in their graves if they could see the up-rooted, starving, suffering humanity in the Russian countryside as the practical consequence of the doctrines they preached. Stalin, it is true, nonchalantly declared, in 1929, in regard to the liquidation of the kulaki that, in accordance with the Russian proverb, "once you cut off the head there is no use crying about the hair." But Stalin, too, confessed to Winston Churchill, during his wartime visit to Moscow, that the terrible strain of the collectivization struggle with the peasantry exceeded even that of the war.

By the middle 1930's, collectivization became an accomplished fact. Thus, the trend towards small peasant farming, which set in with the emancipation of the Russian peasantry from serfdom in the 1860's and which was confirmed by the peasant revolution of 1917/18, was reversed. At a staggering cost, both economic and human, the land and capital of some 20 million small independent peasant farmers were pooled together, with certain exceptions, into some 240,000 collective farms, or kolkhozy. Side by side with these, there were set up about 4,000 relatively large state farms (sovkhozy), owned and operated outright by the government with the aid of hired wage labor. In addition, there were more than 6,000 state machine-tractor stations servicing the collectives and acting as an important mechanism for extraction of farm products from the collective agriculture. In 1938, 86 per cent of the crop area was cultivated by collectives, 9 per cent by state farms, and only 5 per cent was farmed individually, mainly as kitchen garden holdings of members of collectives.

Just a few words about the salient features of the new collective farms.[2] They are essentially institutions of socialized production, though not all production was socialized. The peasant family also does a little farming of its own. Consumption has remained primarily on an individual or family basis. The peasant families continue to live in their own dwellings in the villages as they did, for the most part, before collectivization. Tractors, combines, and other complicated machinery are owned as a rule not by the collectives but by the state MTS. Thus collectives are divorced from their power-machine base, which is controlled and operated by the state, though they still own the greatly decreased number of horses.

Full-fledged communistic farms, as well as the more simple types of producers' co-operatives for joint cultivation of land organized during earlier stages of collectivization, were banned in favor of what is known as the present artel type of collective. Economic equality in collective farms was tabooed by the levellers of the Kremlin in the interest of productive efficiency. A complicated system of payment by results, resembling a piece-work wage, was introduced. There is a steep differentiation of the income of collective farmers according to amount of work and skill required. The growth of a new aristocracy of skilled labor and farm supervisors and managers has been encouraged. No payment is permitted for land or capital contributed by members in present-day collective farms. The collective farmer is a residual claimant to the income of the collective after the obligations to the state for the delivery of farm products, including payments to machine-tractor stations, are met. These deliveries have the first priority, or, as Stalin significantly put it, they constitute the first commandment of the collective farmers. Capital and current production expenses must also be defrayed before any distribution is made to members, except for small advances. Thus, the collective farmer bears practically all the risks that the independent farmer does, but, unlike the latter, he has actually no share in the control of the collective enterprise.

It is true that in theory the collective farm is a democratic, self-governing organization, electing its own officers. In practice, however, the collective farms' self-government is largely a fiction. The Bolshevik authorities appoint and remove the officers of collectives at will. In turn, the latter boss the rank and file farmers and often manage the finances of the collectives as they please. This situation has not changed, despite incessant fulminations in the Soviet press against the expensive and inefficient collective farm bureaucracy. And, in any event, the collective farms are supposed to function within the orbit of Soviet planned economy. The collectives must fulfill the goals and regulations of the Kremlin planners, which their local agents must enforce at any cost. These goals and regulations, with regard to which the peasants, in practice, have nothing to say, touch nearly every aspect of farm production and distribution. The collective farmer, therefore, lost the degree of independence possessed by the small peasant farmer, but he has not gained the advantages of a regular wage possessed by the Soviet factory worker; nor has he the joy that comes from participation in a genuinely democratic co-operative undertaking, like the co-operative farms in Israel.

By contrast, the Soviet government, which has full power of control over collective farming and is a partner with a first priority to its portion of the output, does not share, or shares little, in the risks. Thus, Soviet agrarian collectivism is like a double-faced Janus, looking with one face towards the Communist party state and with the other towards the peasant.

I will pass over quickly the crisis into which collectivization had plunged Russian agriculture in the early thirties. The poorly worked, weedy fields, with consequent low yields per acre and small production of crops, the mounting exactions of the Soviet state, which kept the city worker alive but brought famine to the Russian countryside in which several million people perished, the disastrous decline in livestock numbers, including draft animals, the consequent shortage of draft animal power, which could not be rapidly replaced by tractors, and the detrimental effect on the standard of living of the people of Russia—on their diet, clothing, and footwear—these are the manifestations of the crisis which are probably familiar to all of you.

Confronted with this crisis, the Soviet government proceeded, in the middle thirties, to what was known in Soviet terminology as the "organizational-economic" strengthening of collective farming. Without giving up its grip over Russian agriculture, the government introduced concessions to peasant individualism. These concessions were on a much more limited scale than in 1921, when Lenin introduced the celebrated New Economic Policy, or NEP. Unlimited requisitions of farm products were replaced by a stiff but none-the-less certain tax in kind. Peasants were encouraged to operate on their own an acre or so of land and a few animals in addition to their work on the collective farms. It was a sort of "an acre and a cow" type of farming. With it went also restricted, but by no means unimportant, opportunities to sell part of their produce in the free market at much higher prices than were paid by the government. This "acre and a cow" policy was especially emphasized with the promulgation, in 1935, of the new "model charter," or constitution, of the collective farm. The charter, moreover, aimed to end the instability of collective land holding. It provides that the tenure of the collectives in the land they occupy is to be permanent, and a title deed is to be issued to each collective farm after proper surveying operations.

Turning now to the question of the size of the farm unit, it is evident that at first no limit was set. The maxim "the larger the better" guided early Soviet collectivization practice. This gigantomania, as later it began to be disparagingly called, is much better recognized in the case of the huge state farms. The average sown area per state grain farm for the 1932 harvest exceeded 11,000 acres, and the total land area per farm at the beginning of that year was more than 37,000 acres. Similar tendencies towards gigantomania, though on a smaller scale, prevailed also in the collectivization of peasant farming.

However, by the mid 1930's, it seemed as if the costly lesson was learned—that hugeness is not synonymous with optimum size or good farm management. At any rate, many of the large state farms were subdivided and some of their land was turned over to collectives.

In the case of collective farms, also, inefficiencies resulting from early unlimited growth began to be recognized. In the first place, the subdivision of collectives into so-called brigades or sections, headed by a brigadier or foreman, was officially emphasized. Each brigade was to include from forty to sixty workers and was to be assigned a separate plot of land for a period of several years, covering a crop rotation cycle, as well as the necessary animal draft power and farm implements. In the late thirties, a smaller operational unit in the collectives, the so-called zveno (literally "link"), or squad, of about a dozen workers came much to the fore. The squads were especially favored by the Soviet authorities for growing of intensive crops requiring a great deal of labor, such as sugar beets and cotton. But their use in grain farming was also encouraged. These squads were particularly effective in combatting the frequently slip-shod work of the MTS. The small squads appeared to have enlisted to a greater extent the interest of the collective farmers in their work than the larger brigades.

Subdivisions of large collectives also was

not uncommon in the 1930's. For example, four large collectives in the Spassk district of Ryazan Province in central Russian were each divided into two. On the other hand, the very small collective farms in the northern and north-central regions were long considered inefficient, and "voluntary" merger of such collectives was officially "recommended." But, it should be noted that the character of the terrain itself in the northern and north-central regions, criss-crossed by forests, lakes, marshes, etc., militated against large farms, just as the level, more uniform terrain favored large farms in the southern and eastern steppes. Be that as it may, in the north the average size of the collective farm was increasing in the middle thirties, while in the south and east it was decreasing. In general, however, such subdivision and merger of collective farms as took place before the war were proceeding in a quiet, orderly manner, without the usual fanfare of a drive or campaign so characteristic of the Soviet organizational methods.

The restricted concessions to peasants and the end of gigantomania contributed greatly to such recovery as took place in Soviet agricultural production after the severe underproduction crisis. Increased mechanical equipment and improved farm practices and attention to yields per acre also helped. However, this recovery was too limited in the face of the rapidly growing population to make the early Bolshevik promises of a more abundant life for the masses a reality. But the Soviet government was able to acquire cheaply increasing supplies of farm products, and this greatly facilitated its super-industrialization program with all its waste and inefficiency. The flow of surplus manpower from collectivized agriculture to industry also contributed to its development.

The phase of limited concessions to appease the peasants ended in the late 1930's. The pendulum of Soviet agrarian policy

again took a sharp swing towards intensified collectivism. The tax in kind was increased by changing the basis of assessment from the crop area, specified by the government plan, to the total or arable land of a collective. Measures were also taken for the building up of communal or collectivized livestock which, as could be expected, proved to be the Achilles' heel of collective farming. But the government's effort principally centered on the curbing of personal farming by the collective farmers on their small plots, who, incidentally, owned most of the livestock except horses.

In theory, of course, the personal farming of the collectivized peasants is supposed to have a strictly supplementary character, subsidiary to the basic economy of the collective farm. In practice, however, personal farming has played a much more important role in the economic welfare of the peasants in collective farms. It has also proved a thorn in the side of the Kremlin. Such personal farming creates an economic dualism in the collective that may and does result in competition and conflict between the collectivist and the individualist elements, which the present artel organization of collective farming is supposed to reconcile.

Frequent complaints were made by Soviet spokesmen that the peasants, particularly women, cultivate these little plots most intensively to the neglect of collective fields. This is especially true when the returns from collective farms are small—and they often have been very small. But it is a sort of a vicious circle. For the very preoccupation of the peasant with personal farming frequently tended to keep the collective farm returns small.

It is, of course, not the addition of a few hundred thousand acres to the several hundred million acres of collective land that is coveted by the Kremlin. It is, rather, the peasant labor employed on the personal plots and the example it may set of poor collective discipline. With smaller personal plots, more of the peasant's time should be available for work on the collective farm. He is likely to become a more compliant worker, more akin to the factory proletariat. Likewise the development of collectivized (communal) animal husbandry at the expense of individually owned livestock, an objective relentlessly pursued by the Soviet government, helps the process of conversion of the peasant farmer into an agricultural laborer.

The wartime decline in collective agricultural production and the existence of considerable untilled land provided an opportunity for extending again personal farming of collective farmers, which was tolerated by the government. But since 1946, the government called for a halt of this temporary leniency and reverted to the stringent collectivist policy pursued before the war. Until 1950, however, there were no significant departures from the prewar pattern of Soviet agrarian collectivism. But during that year a new phenomenon leading to what may be, perhaps, best designated as super-collectivism came to the foreground.[3]

The first bombshell was an unsigned article in *Pravda* of February 19, 1950. It severely criticized the member of the Politburo and Chairman of the Council for Kolkhoz Affairs, Andreev, who was long the Kremlin's authoritative spokesman on agricultural policy. Andreev was accused of championing the widespread use of the zveno (the squad) in preference to the large unit, the brigade. The article entirely overlooks the numerous claims made in Soviet publications that the crops received much better care under the zveno system, with favorable effects on yields. Immediately following the publication of the article, a campaign was started in the Soviet press, extolling the brigade and condemning the formerly much favored zveno. Incidentally, Andreev characteristically "confessed" publicly to his errors a few days after the

critical *Pravda* article. More, however, was to come in the way of gigantomania.

Sporadic reports of collective farm mergers, which had a suspicious ring, began to appear in the Soviet press late in 1949. But on March 7, 1950, another member of the Politburo and the new Moscow party boss, Khrushchev, made an "election" speech which was the opening gun in a far-reaching collective farm merger campaign.

The merger campaign apparently began in the Moscow province, which served as a sort of a geographic spearhead. However, it was not confined to any particular locality but spread far and wide over the whole Soviet Union from the Baltic to the Pacific and from the Arctic to the Black Sea. Regions where farms were large were affected equally with those where they were small.

It was stated by the Minister of Agriculture, Benediktov, in March, 1951, that the number of collective farms during 1950 decreased from 252,000 to 123,000. More than two-thirds of all collectives were merged into 60,000 large super-collective farms. The number of collectives merged in the new consolidated farms varied from two to fourteen. Mergers involving seven to nine collectives were not uncommon. However, as Khrushchev pointed out, many of the mergers were affected only "legally," i.e., administratively, and actual unification was still to be carried out.

The phase of the merger campaign which created, perhaps, the most furor, was the prospective large-scale resettlement of the rural population. A strong impression was given by official speeches and press reports that the merger of collectives was also to be accompanied by the integration of numerous villages into a smaller number of larger settlements, sometimes called agro-towns (agro-gorod). This, however, became very soon a dead issue.

In speeches and articles dealing with the theme of farm consolidation, Khrushchev and other Soviet spokesmen painted an attractive picture of supposed advantages and benefits of large collective farms as compared with smaller units. It is doubtful, however, whether technical advantages of large-scale farming really weighed so heavily in the merger campaign. For, as was pointed out earlier, this campaign has not confined itself to the consolidation of only small collectives. Farms which everywhere outside of the USSR would be considered as large were affected as well.

Much was made, for instance, of the consolidation of the relatively small fields to facilitate tractor operations. But this will be difficult to carry out precisely in the small collectives of the northern and central regions where it would be most advantageous. Here, as was pointed out before, small tracts of tillable land are dotted with forests, lakes, marshes, etc. In general, the rapid indiscriminate farm mergers, without regard to the wide regional variations in topographical, soil, and climatic conditions, or types of farming in so large a country as Soviet Russia suggest strongly that the central objective of this policy is not primarily to secure greater efficiency in the combination and use of various factors of production. Of course, there are probably some instances in which mergers of two or more collectives may be conducive to more efficient operation. But it is a far cry from this to the reviving of the gigantomania of the early 1930's, which was officially repeatedly condemned as detrimental to efficiency.

What, then, was the rationale of the merger drive? It is symptomatic that Khrushcev stressed the key role of managers in the consolidated farms and the necessity of paying them higher salaries. After the merger campaign was underway, much was made in the Soviet press of the consolidated Communist party organizations in the merged collectives. In this manner the relative importance of the Communists

and the Communist control mechanism is enhanced in the new super-collectives.

It can be gathered from these and many other clues that an ironclad government control of collectives has been a powerful motive behind the merger drive. The smaller the number of collectives, the easier it is to find managers who are not only efficient but also politically reliable from the Soviet point of view and will zealously deliver the prescribed quotas of farm products. Furthermore, while the elective character of the management in the collectives had been largely a formality before the merger campaign, it is likely to become even more so. The gap between the new management of the large consolidated collective farms and the rank and file is likely to grow. Such a depersonalization of management is very important from the Soviet standpoint since it tends to increase the driving power of the managers and, *ipso facto,* to tighten the labor discipline in collectives.

Thus, the merger of farms into super-collectives should enable the government to exercise stricter controls. This conforms to the generally more collectivist trend of the Soviet agrarian policy since the late thirties, which was only temporarily relaxed during the war. What is more important, the tightening of control is closely linked with the central objective of Soviet agrarian policy, namely, the maximizing of agricultural production and especially of government procurements of farm products. For the Kremlin has been confronted with rather slow post-war recovery of agriculture. This, in the face of growing numbers of mouths to feed and the intensive preparation for war, in which food plays so signal a role. In order to increase production, it was natural for the Bolsheviks to resort to ruthless driving of farm labor in the consolidated collectives, rather than to rely on increased economic incentives to farmers. Such incentives would have to be in terms of consumer goods, which are in short supply, due largely to the emphasis on armament. The shortages of manpower and draft power since the war, which require increased exertion of the available labor force on the farms, probably also contributed to the decision to buttress the collective farm management.

The merger of collectives also provided new opportunities for limitation of personal farming of collective farmers, which should make more labor available for collective work. There are indications that when several collective farms were merged, the size of each member's personal plot was often scaled down to the level of the collective with the smallest plots. Statements in the Soviet press in 1951 criticized the reduction of the plots, but it may well be a case of locking the barn after the horse is stolen.

Much, no doubt, remains to be done to implement consolidation, even from an administrative standpoint, let alone the more technical aspects. The selection of new managers for the super-collective farms has not proven an easy task. Even more time will be required for such matters as the consolidation of collective fields, building of new farm centers, etc.

As a matter of fact, the super-collective farm may well prove, as did its predecessors in the early thirties, too unwieldy to manage. Should the Kremlin become convinced of this, it would probably not hesitate to jetison the super-collectives, to redivide them. At least, this is the lesson of past Soviet experience. Furthermore, the whole scheme of super-collective farming is predicated on the continued submission of the Russian peasant to the increasing stringency of Soviet regimentation.

That there is a reservoir of smouldering peasant unrest in Russia is hardly doubted by anyone at all familiar with Russian history and contemporary agrarian conditions. Every tightening of the collectivist screw is bound to increase agrarian discontent. The farm merger is certainly in this class. The Kremlin, however, has usually exhibited sufficient elasticity in opening the safety valve of peasant appeasement just enough to prevent an explosion; but as soon as the danger passes, the collectivist offensive is resumed. This has occurred on the Soviet scene in every decade.

Should the new agrarian offensive appear to affect the peasant morale too adversely, it is probable that the Kremlin will make another of its famous zigzags and the gigantomania trend represented by the super-collectives may be reversed. After all, strategic retreats are no novelty to the Bolsheviks who were taught by Lenin that the road to their goals is often not a straight road, but more like a mountain path with many twists and turns.

On the other hand, there has been some speculation that the merger movement may be brought to its logical conclusion, in a complete integration of collective peasant agriculture with state farming into a single "socialist" type, patterned essentially on the state farm. It is argued that the trend towards growing operational control of the collectives by the government and the increase in their size, as a result of the mergers, as well as ideological considerations, dictate their eventual assimilation in such a unified system. Perhaps such an amalgamation may occur eventually.

During the next few years, however, it is doubtful whether the Kermlin would be willing to substitute the regular wage payment for labor prevailing in the state farms for the method under which members of the collectives are merely residual claimants to its income. The collective farm method of payment is much more profitable to the Soviet government. And so long as this is the case, it is probable that the fiction of self-government and separate existence of collective and state farms will be maintained.

The famous historical economist Gustav Schmoller stated that, "from 1500 to 1850 the great social question of the day in Europe was the peasant question."[4] But in Western Europe, the peasant question as a social problem was largely settled by the great French Revolution and the agrarian reforms which were inspired by it, in harmony with the historic aspirations of the people who till the soil. In Russia, however, the peasant question cannot be considered solved as yet by collectivization, which was not spontaneous but imposed on the peasantry by force from above. The compulsory collectivization certainly is not in accord with the Russian peasant's age-long yearning for land and independence. Nor has collectivization brought the peasant masses an improved standard of living; often it has brought the contrary. And this strengthens the belief that the challenge of Soviet collectivism to agrarian democracy is really less formidable than it may appear on the surface.

THE SIGNIFICANCE OF LAND TENURE IN THE DEVELOPMENT OF EVENTS IN RUSSIA: A COMMENT

Dimitri Pronin

IN RUSSIA agriculture plays a decisive role in the development of political events. The social composition of Russia, where 80 per cent of the population before the Revolution and about 65 per cent now in the Soviet Union are engaged in farm work, makes this influence understandable. It is typical of Russian history of recent centuries that all political movements have their roots in the question of land tenure and agriculture.

The uprising of Pugachov in the eighteenth century and the revolutionary movements of Narodovolcy in the nineteenth century had their basic motivation in the question of land tenure. Typical was the slogan of the revolutionary movements: "Soil and Freedom," or "Zemlja i Wolja." And you can see that soil is mentioned before freedom.

Often the rebellions were carried out not as a political struggle against the Czar but under promises of revolutionaries to receive sufficient farm land for the peasantry.

The intellectuals engaged in revolutionary movements in return for the support of the peasantry used sometimes falsifications of so-called "Golden Charters," or "Zolotaja Gramota," which were distributed among peasants as accepted by the Czar himself.

In the beginning of the last century, after peasant tumults of 1905/6, the Emperor's Free Economical Society in Petersburg made a survey in 1907 of the grounds of these rebellions and published the results in *Works of the Emperor's Free Economical Society: Agrarian Movement in Russia 1905–1906.* This survey gives as the main reason for the uprisings the insufficient acreage of peasant farm land.

The most capable statesman of prerevolutionary Russia, Prime Minister P. A. Stolypin, started the program for improving the agrarian conditions under the Czarist regime. The goal was to make these conditions healthier and to improve the agricultural practices of peasant farmers. Great success accompanied his activity during the first years of the program. In the period 1906–10, the acreage of small farmers' holdings (peasantry) was increased 14.4 million acres—mostly arable land and meadows.

This area was bought by small farmers from big estates with the help (credit) of government bank institutions. A resettlement program was developed, and the entire number of new settlers in Central Asia, Siberia, and the Far East during the same period (1906–10) reached 2.5 million people.

But the most important part of the program was connected with the consolidation of scattered parcels and the shaping up of independent, healthy, middle-size farms. Great efforts were made also for the improvement of agricultural practices (an activity of Zemstwo-regional self-government).

The revolutionary groups, whose aim was to destroy the old regime, made the agrarian question a main part of their programs. They requested an immediate confiscation of big farms and estates.

Stolypin, opposed from the right by the reactionary conservative groups and attacked from the left wing, was killed in Kiev (1911) by the anarchist Bagrov; and his program, calculated for a twenty-year period, was left uncompleted.

The Communist party (Bolsheviks) came into power in 1917 by taking over the popular agrarian program and slogans of their adversaries (Socialist-Revolutionists) and hiding temporarily their own (Marxist) program in the agrarian question. It was thus that V. Lenin acquired the support of the peasantry. His successor, I. Stalin, thanked the peasantry for help by a collectivization drive in 1928/29. But this drive was the greatest and most harmful shock that came from the Communist regime during these first thirty-four years of existence on Russian territory.

One of the results of the second world war was the weakening of the control of the collective farms by the government and the party. This happened because all the energies of the Soviet authorities were absorbed in things directly connected with the military efforts. Promises of a more liberal policy in agriculture were given to hold the support of the majority of the population (rural part) during the war. This weakening of collective pincers could be seen in the enlarging of garden parcels of families, the taking of some part of the collective land by farmers themselves, and in the increasing of the number of livestock farmers were permitted to have in their own possession (only one cow and one hog per family is allowed collective farmers).

The first period after the war (1945–47) was used by the party government to stop these developments, to return the situation to the status which existed before World War II. To raise the effectiveness of the work on collective farms the Soviet authorities introduced some changes in the internal structure of organization of work in the collectives. (Decision of the CKVKP and of the Council of Ministers of USSR from September 19, 1946.) The man who introduced these ideas was a member of Politburo, Andreev. He was appointed in September, 1946, as Chief of Special Council for Affairs of Collective Farms in the Council of Ministers of USSR.

He disagreed with the tendency of shaping large (gigantic) collective farms and believed that a greater effectiveness in the work of a collective farmer could be achieved by shaping small working groups of five to ten men (so-called "zveno"). The people in such small units would know one another, sometimes be relatives, could work each year on the same area of collective soil. They would be more interested in the results of their work than the big working units composed of 100 to 150 workers (so-called "brigades"). The latter are not connected with a definite area of a collective farm and do not have a special interest in the production of the farm, but rather in the credit for the number of hours (working days) which they have earned.

The February, 1947, meeting of the Central Committee of the Communist Party

(Bolsheviks) agreed with the policy of Andreev. The reward received by the members of small units ("zveno") was also in "working days," but it made these people more interested in the results of their work and in care of the soil. During the years 1947–49 this was the official policy of the government and party. (Decision of Council of Ministers, USSR, April 19, 1948.)

But the natural tendency of this procedure to drift toward a return to ownership made that kind of organization dangerous in the eyes of the higher leadership of USSR. Small groups tried to work year after year on the same part of the collective farm, and in this way the main idea of the Soviet leaders to uproot the rural population and to shape the peasant-farmer into a proletarian worker was failing.

On February 19, 1950, an article appeared in *Pravda* under the title "About the Perversion in Organization of Work in Collective Farms." An article with such a decisive ideological meaning can appear in *Pravda* only after action by the plenum of Politburo. Consequently, Andreev must, as it is a custom in the Soviet Union, confess and regret his mistake. He did.

After this time a new drive on the part of the party and government against the collective farms was begun with the aim of removing the shadow of independent work on the farms. The aim was that the peasant farmer should disappear completely. In his place on the land there had to be a proletarized worker who was not tied to the soil and who had to execute only such a portion of the work as he was ordered. This psychological approach plays the most prominent role in the new program. The other important matter at the moment is the easier control over a rural population thus concentrated in big collective farms.

The experience of the last war showed that the peasant-farmers, a majority of the population, are "potential enemies" of the Soviet system. The abolition and division of collective farms without the help, and sometimes against the will, of German occupants was the best proof of the correctness of this concept.

So the beginning of 1950 saw the beginning of a policy of "enlargement" of collective farms. This means that the smaller collective farms were being combined into bigger "kolkhoz." An average of from three to five collective farms were shaped into one new "enlarged" collective farm. In the meantime, the organization of work into small working groups, "zveno," was declared to be a heresy; and a brigade (100 to 150 workers) is now accepted as the basic unit for organization of labor in the collective farm.

The official explanation is that the using of machinery and modern agricultural methods is much easier on big collective farms than on small collectives. A big propaganda drive through Soviet literature has been started (i.e., Babaevski, *The Cavalier of Golden Star,* Kostyshev, *Under Sky of Native Country,* both published in 1950) where the idea of gigantic collective farms is praised. Andreev has been replaced by Nikita Krushchev, who is known as the adversary of Andreev in the question of organization of work on collective farms and who is the man who suggested certain ideas about the "enlarged kolkhoz."

While Andreev's program appears to have been a policy in the direction of appeasement of the peasantry, the new program is an open war on the peasantry, as such. It is a program of completely uprooting and enslaving the farmer-peasant. He must become completely detached from the soil he tills. He must be changed into a part of a great machine dominated by party and government. The economy of the country again— as it was in the 1928–33 collectivization drive—must be sacrificed to the stubborn line of politicians. Notwithstanding the loud propaganda efforts, which present the "en-larged collectives" as "agro-towns" (where the houses of collective workers will be nice cottages with electrification and all other facilities) the real picture is that by such action the peasants are forced to leave their primitive but separate houses in their vil-lages and to settle in hurriedly-erected bar-racks or in over-crowded houses in a village which was chosen as the center of a new "enlarged" collective farm. It shows clearly that if the policy of Andreev was going in the direction of a compromise with the rural population, the new policy is treating the peasant farmers quite openly as an ele-ment or a group who are not only under sus-picion but must be put in a situation where they can be carefully watched and controlled.

The most recent reports from the Soviet Union (in 1951) concerning the discontinu-ing of this activity do not change the over-all picture. Primarily, the greatest part of the resettlement program is completed; and secondarily, the passive resistance against these measures and the discontent of collec-tive farm peasants have not changed the pol-icy itself, but have resulted only in requests for adjustment to local conditions and that the action be accomplished over a longer period of time.

Part XIII   ROLE OF LAND TENURE IN SHAPING THE
             TYPE OF FARMING IN THE UNITED STATES

TENURE PROBLEMS OF THE AMERICAN INDIAN

🌀🌀🌀   *John Provinse*

FOR MANY of you this paper will be an old story—a rehash of material that has been rehashed countless times by many competent and some incompetent people during the past 150 years, with most of the interpretations slanted to achieve a political, economic, or, occasionally, a social, end. I bring little, if anything, new, either in basic material or in interpretation. I can say to those of you who know the problem that the problem is still with us.

To those of you who have not heard the story before I suggest one note of warning: reserve your judgment beyond this paper, for no one person, even more expert than I, in thirty to forty minutes is capable of presenting the complex tangle of legal, equitable, political, and economic considerations that for many years have characterized Indian land tenure in this country and which characterize it still.

Given two circumstances of the European expansion into America after 1600, a tangled pattern of land tenure for the American Indian holdings was almost inevitable. Those two circumstances were:

First, an ill-defined aboriginal pattern of land ownership in a vast, rich, under-developed and sparsely inhabited continent. Students of politics speak often these days of power vacuums—areas of such rudimentary or unorganized political control that they tend to attract, even to suck in, stronger outside political control. In aboriginal America for some three centuries after 1600 such a vacuum existed in terms of native ownership and tenure of land as such concepts were accepted generally in England and most of Europe.

Secondly, in North America at least, where England became predominant, there is little question but that England, after stabilizing its sovereignty in America as far as France, Spain, and the rest of Europe were concerned, could have extinguished all Indian tenure by right of conquest and could have started from scratch with the English system. It chose otherwise. While retaining ultimate sovereignty over the entire land mass, it split off a large splinter from the bundle of rights which go to make up complete ownership and recognized and protected native rights of use and occupancy wherever it found them. Whether it did this, because against the constant threat of Indian reprisal it was necessary to compromise, just as an outside political power moving into a power vacuum is often forced to compromise with such leadership as it finds there, or whether it was a natural result of the operation of the equity side of English law, is not material here. The fact is, all title was not extinguished in the Crown's original dealings with the Indians, and the United States, when it took over from England, continued the recognition of a beneficial title or interest in the Indian tribes.

These two circumstances, the existence of an ownership vacuum and the recognition of a beneficial interest in the Indians, are the bases from which our complex Indian land tenure problem has arisen.

At the time of the European invasion of America—in my early history books it was the settlement rather than the invasion of America—there was plenty of land for everyone. The incoming settlers did not need to dispossess the Indians of all their land—only such portions as the settlers needed from time to time—and the British Crown was insistent that any land taken from the Indians had to be purchased at a going fair price and concurred in by the tribal representatives. The recognition of Indian possession and use was inherent in this British policy of purchase, and such continued as the practice after the United States became independent of Britain. The United States, since 1789, has paid out hundreds of millions of dollars to Indian tribes for their holdings or in settlement of land claims. The 15 million dollars which Jefferson paid to Napoleon for the Louisiana Purchase and the total of 80-odd million dollars which the United States paid to procure title to all European holdings in the United States territory amount in fact to just a good annual interest payment on the capital payments made to the Indian groups. Actually, little more was obtained from the European purchases than the right to negotiate with the affected Indian groups who occupied the territory to which the European countries relinquished their claim.

For many years the United States federal government made little, if any, effort to interfere with the actual tenure arrangements of the various Indian tribes as far as their own tribal lands were concerned. The government was content to maintain its overall sovereignty and control but to recognize and respect the Indian right to possession and use of lands retained by the Indians. For any lands left to the Indians there was some curiosity but little real concern about how the tribes applied their own tenure patterns. It is of interest, therefore, to note the aboriginal pattern of land holding. Exceptions to any generalization can be found, and almost all known forms or concepts of land holding can be described somewhere in aboriginal America; but without too much distortion, the Indian tenure pattern can be characterized briefly as (1) a right of beneficial use and occupancy, rather than exclusive fee ownership; (2) a group right rather than an individual one. There was a concept of private property among the American Indians of an exclusive nature, with ownership solely in the individual, but it was not often found attaching to land. It was extremely difficult for Indians to think of land as private property or as a commodity that could be bought, or sold, or permanently alienated.

Against this aboriginal pattern of beneficial use by actual occupants, based on group rather than individual possession (a pattern of course to be found with little variation throughout the preliterate world), the Europeans brought a concept of private individual ownership, reinforced by the whole gamut of English common law. Coupled with this legal concept of land tenure was a hunger—a land hunger which for most of the settlers could not be appeased in England or on the continent of Europe. The vast, underdeveloped areas of the eastern seaboard of America did not satiate this hunger; they acted rather to whet the appetites of those already here and to attract with magnetic force those still across the Atlantic. As the westward push for land went on, the Indians were either surrounded and insulated or were kept ahead of the movement by force, treaties, or arranged migration. America was like the repeal of some great land prohibition act, and our forefathers went on a big real estate binge, a land-owning and land-exploiting binge that comes as close probably to the Golden Age of human freedom as any era the world has so far known.

This binge of individualism, ruthless, exploitative, speculative, and often personally dangerous, was encouraged by the national law-makers in the national Capitol and protected by the military forces in the field. It left in its wake some 375 treaties, some 4,000 federal statutes, and countless executive orders and court decisions dealing with Indian affairs, the great bulk of them concerning Indian lands. And the law-making process still goes on: Nearly 5 per cent of the bills introduced into the recent Eightieth Congress (439 out of 10,108) were Indian bills; 6 per cent of the acts passed by that Congress (78 out of 1,363) were Indian acts; 10 per cent of the acts of that Congress vetoed by the President (7 out of 70) were Indian acts. Most of this Indian legislation in 1950 also dealt with land or interest in land.

Had all the 4,000 laws on Indian lands been passed at the same time, or had they all followed the same pattern over 150 years, it is likely we would have avoided a few of the complexities of Indian tenure. But American expansion, though spectacularly rapid, was not always at an even rate or with consistent values and policies. The policies toward Indians and their lands over the years were subject to the developing national morality and to the vagaries of our democratic system with its periodic changes in party control. Indian affairs even to this day have not been so removed from the political whirlpool that stability of program can be assured either to the bureau which administers Indian affairs or the Indians who are trying to plan their future lives.

The Indian land holdings in the United States at present are approximately 56 million acres, somewhat larger than the area of the state of Minnesota. These holdings, with minor exceptions, are in the states west of the Mississippi River, and within that area every state, excluding possibly Missouri and Arkansas, has some Indian land, with major concentrations in the southwest and the northern Great Plains. The largest single block is in the 15 million-acre Navajo Reservation in Arizona, New Mexico, and Utah.

Of this 56 million acres, the bulk is relatively poor land. Eighty per cent of it has less than twenty inches of rainfall annually, and a fourth of the total is in areas with less than ten inches of rainfall. Sixty per cent of the land is utilizable only as open grazing land, 30 per cent is combined grazing and forest land, about 5 per cent is in farm land, principally nonirrigable, and 5 per cent is waste land. Less than 1 per cent is irrigated. Twenty-five per cent of the land is critically damaged by soil erosion. These over-all figures of course obscure some favorable situations for those tribes whose aboriginal occupancy or final treaty arrangements eventually left them in parmanent possession of good land.

The tenure pattern of this 56 million acres at present is as follows: 66 per cent is in tribal ownership; 30 per cent is in individual allotments; and 4 per cent is reserved by the government for various administrative purposes—school land, demontration areas, and such.

Practically all of these lands—both tribal and those allotted in severalty—have two common characteristics: (1) They are held in trust by the federal government and hence are subject to alienation by the Indians or tribes only with the consent of the government, either by order of the Secretary of the Interior or by Act of Congress. (2) With a few exception, they are exempt from local taxation just as are other lands under the control of the federal government, a fact which gives rise constantly to state complaint about loss of revenue from real estate taxes and which also gives rise to an impression that such nontaxed Indian lands are public lands, which they, of course, are not, being the property of the individual Indian or tribe.

The tribally owned lands (two-thirds of the total Indian holdings) are a less acute administrative problem so far as tenure is concerned than are the allotted lands. Title resides in the tribe, and the use of the land is determined by tribal custom or the tribal authorities, subject to some supervisory responsibilities reposed by law in the Secretary of the Interior. The largest areas of tribal lands are in our southwest, as reference to the map will show, but there are some other sizeable reservations in other parts of the country, such as the Menominee Reservation in Wisconsin, the Wind River Reservation in Wyoming, the Red Lake Reservation in Minnesota.

In many tribal areas, particularly in the southwest, the pattern of use in these reservations follows the customary use patterns that characterized the pre-European tenure practices. There is no absolute fee which an individual can dispose of at will. It is his or his family's to use and occupy as long as beneficial use is made of it, but it cannot be transferred by a user to someone outside the tribe. The historical patterns of use have resulted in some inequities in size of holdings, since rights of use can often have become vested in individuals and in families to the exclusion of new generations. In several tribally controlled reservations aggressive individuals or families have more than their proportionate share of the usable land, and, of course, it is extremely difficult for any tribal governing body to penalize these enterprising members of the tribe by any program of expropriation, with or without payment. The individual or family interest is, however, almost universally regarded as a use interest, and upon the expiration of the use the land reverts to the tribe for reassignment to some other member. In keeping with the fact that a livelihood based on agriculture generally results in more continuously settled occupancy than does a livestock or grazing economy, use

and occupancy tenure in agricultural areas is generally more permanent—that is, of longer duration in farming areas than in grazing areas. For example, among the agricultural Pueblo Indians of the Rio Grande many families have lived on and farmed the same lands for a dozen generations. This generalization cannot be stretched too far, however, since there are also to be found on the Navajo Reservation, in a predominantly grazing economy, many families who have lived on and used the same grazing areas for several generations.

One aspect of tribally owned reservations is of particular significance. That is the fact that on these reservations the land, that is the surface area of the land, is used almost exclusively by the Indians themselves, rather than by outsiders. They often may not use it as efficiently or as productively as could some of their better equipped non-Indian neighbors, but such use as is made of it is generally by the Indians and for their subsistence. This is in contrast to the experience on the individually allotted lands, where use of the land by Indians is constantly decreasing, for reasons which I will remark on later in the discussion of the allotted lands.

It is important to point out before leaving the discussion of tribal lands that in addition to the surface rights on the tribally controlled reservations which are devoted largely to grazing and agriculture, most tribes also have sub-surface rights to oil and minerals underlying their lands, and many have timber resources of considerable value. With some noteworthy exceptions where tribal enterprises have been established to harvest and sell tribal timber, such as Menominee and Navajo, these resources are exploited through lease, sales, and royalty contracts to outsiders, rather than through individual or tribal effort. The proceeds of such contracts are deposited in a tribal account and can be used for tribal expenses, the development of additional tribal enterprises, or paid out per capita to the members of the tribe. This source of income is becoming of increasing importance as sub-surface surveys of the reservations are intensified and as our industrial and scientific research discloses new properties and new uses for our national mineral resources.

The other principal type of Indian-owned land is the allotted or individually controlled acreages. This one-third of the Indian holding (some 17 million acres) has become the most vexing problem of Indian resource management due primarily to the peculiar status in which it is held.

Allotment in severalty is not a recent development in Indian land policy. It was suggested as early as the Jefferson administration (1800–1808), was strongly advocated by Andrew Jackson (President 1828–36), and during the entire nineteenth century was regarded as the only successful solution for the Indian problem. As one reads back through the early reports of the Indian Commissioners and the Secretaries of Interior there is scarcely a dissenting expression to the judgment that Indians could never be brought into American society until their tribally held lands were divided among them on an individual basis. Civilization was equated with individual private ownership—without it the Indian would remain primitive, illiterate, and shiftless.

The pressure was not alone from those anxious to gain possession of the Indian lands, which was easier to do after it was allotted in severalty; it was also advocated by many good friends of the Indian. Many allotments had been made prior to the 1880's to various individual Indians for services rendered or for other reasons, and even some whole tribes were allotted, but it was not until 1887, with the passage of the General Allotment Act, that a comprehensive scheme was enacted into law by Congress. That scheme, taking at least part of a page out of the 1863 Homestead Act, provided for allotment in severalty to tribal members in homestead-sized tracts. After allotment to the individuals of a tribe, any surplus lands on a reservation were to be opened to non-Indian settlement, the proceeds of sale of such surplus, or "ceded" lands, as they were called, to go to the Indian tribe.

The allotment process began in the Plains areas and proceeded as rapidly as surveys could be completed and boundaries established. By the late 1920's more than two-thirds of the Indians on 118 reservations had received allotments and most of the so-called "surplus" lands, after allotment, were opened for entry and sold. Between 1887 and 1934 the land in Indian control was reduced from 138 million to 52 million acres. Out of 40 million acres allotted to individuals 23 million acres (nearly 60 per cent) on which fee patents were issued and the trust removed were disposed of by the Indians by sale to non-Indians. By 1934 individual Indians had some 17 million acres still in trust status.

The mere fact of individual ownership did not bring about that automatic change in the cultural habits of the Indian that the supporters of the Allotment Act had anticipated. Indians did not become thrifty farmers over night or even over the years. They showed little interest in the sedentary and often arduous existence of their non-Indian neighbors, and even those who might aspire to settle down as farmers had neither the experience to compete successfully nor access to credit facilities that might have tided them over the first hard years. The result was non-use of much of the land by the Indian allottees and increasing pressure by non-Indians to put it to use. The solution was leasing to non-Indians first authorized by Congress for the lands of over-age and disabled allottees who could not themselves operate their lands and soon extended to cover any unused lands. Much of the remaining allotted land still held in trust for the Indians—that is, the lands which were not alienated completely—fell into non-Indian use through the lease practices. And once non-Indian leaseholds were established on reservations it became extremely difficult to dislodge the non-Indian lessees.

A further factor that encouraged leasing was the matter of inheritance of the individualized trust land which began to create a problem soon after the Allottment Act was passed. Since the land was held in trust by the government, the allotment on the death of the original allottee was inherited by several heirs, no one of which usually was in a position to make use of an individual portion of the original 160-acre tract. The answer was more leasing and a division among the heirs of the rents. With each succeeding generation the heirs increased, resulting in countless current situations where hundreds of heirs participate in the rents of an original allotment and receive a few cents annually, resulting also in many situations in which present living heirs have minute fractional interest in a score or more of allotments widely scattered and incapable of any beneficial use by the owner except through sale or by sharing in lease rentals. The heirship problem is currently the most baffling problem of the Bureau and the already burdensome administrative difficulties of probate, of surveys, of bookkeeping, of proper land use by the Indians themselves are being compounded each year.

The disastrous effects of the Allotment Act on the Indian land base were so obvious that by the 1920's the allotment program was slowed down considerably, and by 1933 the country was prepared to adopt protective legislation for the remaining Indian lands. The Indian Reorganization Act (the Wheeler-Howard Act) of 1934 specifically abandoned the policy of individual allotments. Alienation of land through sales and fee patents was summarily stopped and reversal of policy in favor of land acquisition was adopted. Under such policy 4 million acres of land have been added to the Indian estate since 1934, bringing the total acreage to its present figure of 56 million acres.

With regard to the heirship problem, some, but not much, progress is being made. For every forward step in retrieving land from heirship status and consolidating it in usable blocks, the inevitable passage of time with its death-toll of original allottees and their heirs, and now the heirs of heirs, relentlessly puts more and more land, in ever smaller and smaller amounts, in an ever increasing number of heirs. The Land Planning Committee of the National Resources Planning Board, in its excellent report on this whole problem of Indian land in 1935 enumerated several possible courses of action, not necessarily mutually exclusive, which can contribute to alleviating if not completely solving the heirship problem: (1) purchase of the heirship interests by the tribe for reassignment in usable blocks; (2) surrender by the allottee of his scattered interests in return for grazing rights, for a pension or subsistence grant, for assignment of other land, for a proportionate interest in the tribal land enterprises. Any one of these requires, of course, not only full co-operation of the tribal governing body but assumes also that the tribe has a working capital either of money or of land to make the necessary exchanges or purchases. Many tribes do not have such working capital. In many cases also the breakdown of tribal organization under the allotment system and the intermingling of non-Indian holdings on the reservation handicaps tribal operations. Individualization, after several generations, has in many areas taken hold to such an extent as to interfere seriously with relinquishment of individual title in fee or trust and accepting in lieu thereof an assignment, with restrictions on alienation, from a tribal authority.

In some cases, however, tribal programs are moving ahead. In one instance land exchanges between the individual heirs and the tribe are being made, and an individual who has undivided interests in several parcels of land deeds these over to the tribe in exchange for an individual assignment on a usable tribal acreage of equal value (Cheyenne River). Under this arrangement the assignee is empowered to devise by will or otherwise any improvements he may place on the land, or may designate a beneficiary to succeed him. In general this is working out successfully, and about a third of a million acres have passed into tribal ownership; but it is a slow-moving operation, and it is also under constant attack from some members of the tribe who prefer a fee or trust patent title rather than a mere assigned interest from the tribe.

In another reservation a land enterprise inaugurated by the tribe provides for the issuance of shares or certificates of interest for lands turned in and for the negotiability among tribal members of these certificates. In this situation, of course, it is much more possible for aggressive individuals by purchases and exchanges to obtain possession of undue numbers of shares and thereby control a disproportionate part of the available acreage on the reservation. On this reservation there has been some collusive effort on the part of non-Indians, working through friendly tribal members, to obtain control of grazing areas for non-Indian stock. About one-fifth of the million one-dollar shares in this enterprise are now held by the tribe itself.

Numerous cattle and livestock associations have also been organized which are having considerable success through co-operative opperation on both allotted and tribal lands without interfering with the present trust titles.

The Bureau at present is preparing for the Congress legislation which would pro-

vide a large revolving fund for the purchase of the heirship and fractionated lands under a plan which would place the purchased interests in tribal ownership but would require a rental charge on the use of land so purchased until such time as the federal government is reimbursed for the purchase money advanced. Such a fund will provide a working capital for many tribes not now able to finance out of their own funds a blocking up of the divided heirship interests. Since this plan requires repayment to the federal government it can not be regarded either as a federal dole or as a second payment for land already bought and paid for once by the government. This approach, if the Congress agrees and will appropriate funds from year to year to keep it going, is probably the most constructive over-all attack on the heirship problem so far devised. It will require, however, in addition to congressional action, the full co-operation of the tribal groups themselves, and since the fractionation and heirship problem is greatest among those groups where because of individual allotment the tribal co-operative machinery is weakest, it will necessitate much educational effort on the part of government workers and tribal leaders who undertake to put such a program into effect.

Some Indian groups, due to their historic practices, can easily continue a tribal ownership pattern and accept as quite natural an assignment arrangement; but others will not. Among the community-minded Pueblo Indians in the southwest, for example, title to land is in the Pueblo or village but an individual family has undisputed right to possession and use so long as it occupies and uses the land. The family can even exchange its holdings with other members of the Pueblo. This is an old and well stabilized tenure pattern and though it can result, and sometimes does, in undue control by some enterprising individual it seldom results in non-use of available land or exploitation by non-Indian users. The Cherokee Indians of North Carolina many years ago pooled their lands and are successfully operating as a tribal corporation, tribal members holding their small farms on use assignment rather than in fee simple title. And, of course, the huge Navajo Reservation is completely on a use and occupancy basis with extended families or larger kinship groupings, frequently referred to as "outfits," occupying and using from one generation to the next the same grazing and farming areas.

Also we have one fairly unique case in the southwest, where although the reservation was formally allotted in the 1920's, near the end of the allotment era, the Indians never really accepted the allotment idea and continued with their customary tribal land use practices. Today nearly all original allottees have voluntarily surrendered their allotments back to tribal ownership and control.

On the other hand, in many of the allotted reservations particularly, the concept and pattern of individual ownership have become a definite part of the Indian attitude toward land. Many of these Indians live with and generally think and act like their non-Indian neighbors. Why, therefore, should not their land holdings be held in the same way with the same freedom to sell, lease, or otherwise dispose of? Furthermore, as the acculturation process goes on and the gap between Indian and non-Indian narrows, which it is doing at a rapid rate in many places, and as more Indians move to industrial areas and establish themselves permanently away from reservations, the pressure for individualizing and isolating the member's share of the tribal assets, to these lands or royalties from minerals or other tribal income, is inevitably increasing.

So far as the individual trust allotments are concerned the question of complete individual control is one between the individual Indian and the Secretary of the Interior.

The Secretary has authority at present to grant patents in fee on application to any Indian over twenty-one years of age who holds land in trust patent. The Secretary also has authority to issue certificates of competency in those cases where the allotment patent was a fee patent but subject to restrictions on alienation. Such patent in fee or certificate of competency gives the individual complete control of his land, and though there is some evidence that an increasing number of individuals securing fee patents are retaining their land for their own use and even are pledging them to secure operating loans from commercial banks just as their non-Indian neighbors do, there is depressing evidence that in the great majority of cases the land is very soon disposed of to non-Indians and the proceeds soon dissipated for day-to-day expenses. The Secretary also has authority on application to sell the allotted lands of an individual at supervised sale, and this is resorted to in cases where administrative control over the proceeds of sale is advisable to protect a family or to insure the carrying out of a repurchase or other contract agreement.

The Secretary's decision to issue a patent or authorize a sale takes into account two principal factors: (1) the reasonable competency of the applicant to handle his own affairs and (2) the effect of sale or alienation on the remaining Indian holdings as far as proper land use of administration is concerned. Should the Secretary after his investigation decide against removing restrictions or authorizing a sale, appeal by the applicant can be and is frequently made to Congress through the Indian's congressional representative, and the Congress may by law direct the Secretary to issue a patent. Such directives have occasionally been vetoed by the President, as was the case several times in the Eightieth Congress.

So far as tribal land is concerned—and even on many of the allotted reservations some amount of tribal land is to be found —the question of individualizing the member's interest so that he can withdraw his share is constantly arising. The inability so far to devise an equitable, workable plan for individual withdrawal from the tribe has precluded the adoption of so-called "emancipation" legislation, which is being sought by some tribal members and is urged by a number of legislators. Some tribes, because of increased income, or money recoveries from successful claims against the government, may be able to buy out the per capita interests of withdrawing individuals and thereby retain the tribal holdings intact for those who remain on the reservation and for their children, but for many tribes this will not be possible because of limited financial resources, and in such cases individuals desiring to leave the reservations must either forego payment for their share of the tribal estate—which under the present application of the law is simply a life estate—or work toward the goal of individualizing and distributing all tribal assets in order to obtain that share.

To forego one's share in a tract of land, even if the land is relatively invaluable, is an action not readily taken by any individual, whether Indian or non-Indian, and even to pack up and leave a reservation where, after all, even an insufficient or unusable parcel of trust land affords some chimerical sense of ultimate security is not psychologically easy. This psychological fact, many persons will maintain, so binds the individual Indian to the reservation and, on the poorer reservations, consequently so dooms him and his family to a substandard existence that the only desirable solution is to cut cleanly and irrevocably through this unhealthy dependency by dividing up the tribal estate and freeing the individual. On the other hand, such liquidation of tribal assets almost inevitably assures the disintegration of the group and the break-up of the reservation,

and this is opposed by many reservation residents who wish and struggle to maintain such tribal unity and as much of the tribal homeland as they can.

The solution to this countrary problem is not in immediate view, but it is a certainty that in any harmonious solution of it both time and understanding will be required. Much more is involved than the mere issuance of a fee patent or a certificate of competency to an individual Indian. Critically involved also are the understandable pride of the survivors of small, closely-knit groups, once sovereign, and their struggle to maintain group integrity; the nature of the continued responsibility of the federal government for services to such individuals or their families; the attitudes and new responsibilities of the state and local governments. It is not a simple problem.

A point is frequently made by some of the "free-the-Indian" advocates that the overprotective policy of the government—that is of the Bureau—is such that it prevents the proper development and use of resources "locked up" on Indian reservations. An examination of the record readily disproves this, though many persons who make the charges against the Bureau aren't really interested in what the record shows. Through leases, permits, and sales the land products and sub-surface oil and minerals of most reservations are being exploited at rates which compare favorably with the developments on other similar areas and in accord with good conservation practices. Some tribes are in fact relatively quite well off financially as a result of income derived from their oil, minerals, timber, or other land produce. Were all reservations as fortunately situated as the Osage in Oklahoma, the Klamath in Oregon, the Menominee in Wisconsin, we would undoubtedly still have an Indian problem, but it would not be of the same order as the one we now have and it would have a sounder economic base on which to plan. It is not true that national resources are not available for national need because they are on Indian lands or in Indian ownership.

The present general policy of the Department of Interior is to promote the retention in Indian ownership of Indian lands and minerals and to assist the Indians in the conservation, development, and beneficial use of such resources. The pressures for relaxing federal trusteeship and supervision are many and from diverse sources, but it is not foreseeable to me that the government will ever again embark upon any over-all program so disastrous to Indian economic welfare as was the compulsory individual allotment scheme. Many Indians, however, both on and off reservations, are more desirous of, and more prepared for, assuming complete control of and responsibility for their lands than they were fifty years ago, and for these Indians some procedure for voluntary withdrawal and relinquishment will undoubtedly soon be provided. In many areas of strong tribal control, on the other hand, there is reason to believe that the tribal governments, with their constantly increasing abilities to adjust to the demands and the competition of the non-Indian culture which surrounds them, will be able to work out tenure arrangements that will continue tribal title with only use and occupancy rights in the individual or the family. Wholly apart from whether or not in the years ahead the federal government withdraws its trusteeship over Indian land holdings, which it is its announced purpose eventually to do, it is my guess that several decades hence there will still exist in America among many Indian groups land tenure patterns that will vary little in principle from what was the common land-holding pattern in America three centuries ago.

These five thousand words I have just finished reading are but a short syllable compared to what has been said in the past and what will be said in the future on the subject of Indian lands. It is a complex problem, legally, morally, and economically, and with strong emotional biases; such problems tend to become wordy. But it is not insoluble, and not the least hopeful of all the present steps toward a solution are the efforts of the Indian people themselves, tribally and individually, to come to grips with the problem. These efforts are of a piece with the efforts of many similarly situated people in all parts of the world today to adjust themselves to new crises and face up to new responsibilities. In these efforts they need all the help and encouragement that any democratically-conceived government can give them.

NATIONAL LAND POLICY AND THE DEVELOPMENT OF AGRICULTURE: THE AMERICAN EXPERIENCE

 Maurice M. Kelso

AGRICULTURE at any time and place is a product of natural environment, social institutions, and the technical knowledge and goals of the cultivators. In this paper, we are concerned only with the influence of a closely-related group of social institutions upon agriculture in the United States over the past 150 years. That closely-related group of institutions is known as land policy.

Land policy is an important part of the institutional framework within which the development of agriculture takes place. In a democratic society such as the United States, land policy expresses the goals and wishes of a majority of the citizenry towards the use and control of land. These goals and wishes contain many mutually contradictory features—frequently illogical and inconsistent—but the policy at any given time and place expresses what the majority wants relative to land use and control more than it wants any other alternative set of policies.

Land policy is a composite of many things related to land use and control. Concerned as it is with the use and control of land, it expresses itself primarily through the landed property institution.

Property in land regulates the relationships between individuals, between groups, and between individuals and their government so far as their relationships stem from their mutual relationship to land and its products. Property in land controls, liberates, and expands the opportunities for individual or group action relative to land; it denies people access to some and grants them access to other alternatives relative to the use of land and the enjoyment of its fruits.

We are concerned here with a description of the structure of alternatives in land use and control made available by land policy in the United States over 150 years and an analysis of the problems it has created in American agriculture in the Mid-West and Far Western states.

History of Land Policy

There are two persistent threads that run through the entire history of American agricultural land policy. First, the use of land and the enjoyment of its fruits shall be placed in the hands of individual persons (private property). Second, these individuals shall be as free at all times to choose how they will use and dispose of the land area in their control and how they will enjoy its fruits as is consistent with the rights and privileges of the rest of the individuals who make up the society (unrestricted private property).

There has never been in America and there is not now any important questioning of private property in agricultural land as a fundamental social institution. The history of land policy in the United States is a story of slow change in stubbornly-held judgments as to what degree of restriction on the private land owner and user is consistent with the basic belief in unrestricted private property.

The strength of this private property belief relative to agricultural land is set in bold relief when it is realized that all land outside the thirteen original states, with minor exceptions, was the property of the United States government. It was public property, not private property. For 150 years land policy in America was primarily concerned with the conversion of this public property into unrestricted private property. Only in very recent years has there been any noticeable stirring for change in that historic policy.

PERIOD OF SALE: 1789–1862

For the first seventy years, public land was sold into private ownership. This period of sale divides into two periods—one when sale for public revenue was a dominant consideration and the other when sale as a means to encourage settlement was the dominant consideration.

Sale of land for public revenue: 1789–1841.—From the start there was no questioning that the public land should be placed in private hands. But in the beginning the new government of the United States needed revenue; the vast area of land owned by it represented a valuable asset; what was more natural than that it should sell these lands for revenue purposes? So, to maximize its revenues and cheapen its costs of sale, it decided to survey its lands and, as rapidly as the survey progressed, to auction the surveyed lands in relatively large blocks. It set a minimum price of two dollars per acre and hoped at first to sell these in blocks of thirty-six square miles (about 23,000 acres). It hoped thus to speed its sale, to maximize its net revenue, and to leave to the buyer the slower and speculative task of sub-dividing and selling to individual settler-farmers. For fifty years this sale for revenue purposes persisted. The saleable unit was reduced until finally an individual farmer could buy as little as forty acres; the price was reduced, finally, to $1.25 per acre. But the restriction of sale to lands that had been surveyed and restriction of the method of sale to auction persisted throughout the period.

From the beginning, a strong body of public opinion contested the idea of sale of the public lands for revenue purposes. Almost to a man those people living west of the Allegheny Mountains and a sizeable body of opinion in the original thirteen states thought the land should be disposed of to encourage settlement. Pioneer families were continually pushing ahead of the area surveyed, settling on tracts, developing homes and farms, only to have the tract sold from under them or to be forced to buy their own improvements when, finally, the land was put up for auction. Conflict was sharp, often violent. But the federal policy of sale at auction after survey remained. Those who settled ahead of the survey were "squatters" with no legal claim to the land and no protection at law. But the conflict over policy persisted and the strength of the opposition grew.

Sale of land to encourage settlement: 1841-1862.—In 1841 the first change in policy occurred. For reasons which we will not elaborate, it finally became possible in 1841 for settlers to buy land upon which they may have settled before it was surveyed. They could claim up to 160 acres at the stated price of $1.25 per acre. Land not claimed by settlers was auctioned in tracts from 160 acres upward, at the minimum of $1.25 per acre. Now it became possible for settlers to move freely westward, pick their parcels of land, settle on them, develop them for farming and homes with assurance that when

the survey and the sale reached them they were protected in their claims and would need to pay no more than $1.25 per acre for the farms they had developed from the wilderness.

Still the westerner had not achieved his goal of free land, but he had achieved his goal of public land disposal to encourage settlement with sale for public revenue secondary.

Under the policies of this period of sale, that area of the United States from the thirteen original states westward to western Iowa and east Texas was settled. It was an area of humid climate, in the main heavily forested, although in its western parts it reached the humid prairies. It was an area in the main very fertile, but required clearing of dense forests or draining of vast areas. Areas of 80 to 160 acres were as large as could be prepared for agriculture by a single family; the simple techniques of farming could be applied only to small tracts of this size. Once cleared or drained and in production, tracts of this size were ample, because of their productivity, to supply the meager requirements of the pioneer families.

The tracts were large enough for that day and age, and land was readily and cheaply available to any family who wanted to endure the hardships of pioneering and land development to carve out a farm and home of its own.

PERIOD OF FREE LAND: 1862-1934

The "free land for settlers" agitation that had persisted from the beginning attained victory in 1862 with the passage of the Homestead Act. Any person who had not homesteaded other lands could obtain a tract on any federally-owned land by simply filing a claim to it, provided the tract was within the lawful limits of size and provided the claimant met certain simple conditions regarding the development of the land or residence thereon.

The Homestead Policy dominated public land disposal during the era when settlement expanded across our great western plains. Settlement under the period of sale had reached the zone of transition from the humid "prairie plains" to the sub-humid plains. In the area being settled during the fifties, 80 to 160 acres made a very acceptable farm, for reasons just given above. In fact, 160 acres was a "large" unit under those conditions.

The Homestead Act set 160 acres as the maximum a family could claim under it. Under the conditions of the times, 160 acres was a liberal allowance. But even before the Act was passed in 1862, the area of settlement had moved into the sub-humid plains. A farm area of 160 acres was still suitable, but now it was approaching a suitable minimum rather than a suitable maximum. Treeless plains needed no clearing; drainage was unnecessary; rolling grass plains could be cultivated in broad areas; and the advancing technology made it possible now to till larger expanses per farm.

In the North immediately after the Civil War, settlement exploded westward. The settlement frontier moved rapidly across the plains. But as it moved westward, aridity increased sharply. The 160 acre limitation became rapidly obsolete. By the eighties, the last of the area for which 160 acres was suitable even as a minimum was settled. The advancing line of settlement faltered. A culture rooted in a humid, timbered, well-watered environment moved out into an alien environment.

Political power was lodged in the humid, timbered "East." The "East" could not understand (and never has understood) the problems of semi-aridity. A farm area of 160 acres, ample for humid area people, continued to be the area allowed for free homesteads. Grudgingly, it was increased after 1904 to 320 acres, then to 320 acres to husband and 320 acres to wife, then to 640

acres. But such increases in allowable size always came too little and too late. The needs for successful settlement changed faster, as settlement pushed westward, than did the policy under which the land could be settled. An area of 640 acres was the largest the allowable homestead tract ever became, and it was farther out of line with the needs of successful settlement at the end than the smaller 160-acre tract had been at the beginning.

In 1879, John Wesley Powell, agent of the federal government, studied the western public lands and recommended to his government that homesteads of 2,560 acres be permitted and that the homesites for such homesteads be grouped along the water courses. But his report made not a ripple on the surface of land policy formation of the period.

Conflict with prior European users of the plains.—As settlers pushed westward during the period of sale and during the first years of the period of free land, they met no human opposition except that from the alien native culture. But when the settlement wave pushed westward into the semi-arid plains, it found a territory already fully occupied, not by an alien race, but by Europeans. The agricultural system followed by these prior settling Europeans was different from any system of agriculture that had been followed by those now pushing westward from the humid East. The new settlers didn't understand it; the citizenry of the humid "East" didn't understand it. Conflict was inevitable. In this experience, we find one of the most revealing examples of the influence of customs and beliefs on land policy and on the agriculture that develops under it. The clarity of the example deserves our attention for a few moments.

The Spaniards settled Mexico, beginning as early as the northern Europeans had settled the east coast of North America. The Spaniards came from a semi-arid environment. A pastoral agriculture and the development of water where it was a limiting factor were parts of their cultural heritage. The Spaniards occupied northern Mexico and pushed into west Texas and all the arid southwest by the early 1800's. Use of a semiarid country with pastoral methods of agriculture came naturally to them. They developed a pastoral-irrigation agricultural economy in all that territory now embraced in the southwestern United States.

By the time of the American Civil War, northern European settlers from the eastern United States had reached central Texas. The Spaniards had been driven out of Texas in the 1840's. They had left their lands and cattle behind. The cattle had been running wild and multiplying for twenty years by the time of the Civil War.

Following the disruption of the southern economy in the United States brought about by the Civil War, many southern men went into west Texas and "put their brands" on these "wild" cattle. They picked up the Spaniards' methods of agriculture and became pastoralists. It is significant that most of the western livestock man's equipment and terminology has been Spanish from that day to this. The heavy saddle, the curbed bit, the leather "chaps," the big hat, the throw rope, the words "hackamore," "lariat," "riata," "chaps," "cavvy," "cinch," "conch," "remuda," and even the term "ranch" are all Spanish in origin.

Within five years following the end of the Civil War, west Texas was largely occupied and the Texas pastoral economy was firmly established. By 1870 it began its explosion northward—an explosion as dramatic and even more rapid than the explosion westward of "homesteaders" more than a decade later.

By the 1890's, European Americans with their cattle and sheep had occupied all the Great Plains, all the southwest, and all the intermountain desert country. The entire territory was fully "occupied." But to a humid society, agriculture was crop farming —pastoralism was alien. The land in this entire western country (outside of Texas) was federally owned. It was disposed of under policies laid down by the federal government. The federal government was dominated by its citizenry from a humid environment. They could not understand—did not even recognize—pastoralism as agriculture, as farming. The pastoralist never could obtain, under the homestead laws, more than 640 acres when several thousand were required. Fencing of the public land was illegal; developments to enhance its productivity for livestock were impossible because the user had no legal protection to his claim to such improvements. The range was fully occupied when the homestead farmer came in from the mid-eighties onward. But the occupying pastoral economy had no legal claim or protection. It was pushed out and back by the advancing wave of homestead farmers until only in areas too dry or too rough even for the optimisms of homestead settlers could it survive. Even in these areas it never, during the homestead period, secured any tenure control over the land it used with the exception of headquarter and key water-controlling tracts it could secure legally and often illegally by homesteading. Every place that optimistic homesteaders thought to be flat enough and wet enough to plow was settled in 320 to 640 acre tracts by 1920.

Remember that, when in the humid area of the United States, the settler got on land ahead of the legal wave of settlement. After 1841 he was protected in his claim and could get title to the land he occupied. No similar protection ever was even considered for the pastoralist in the Great Plains. Customs and beliefs expressed through land policy forced the development of a crop farming agriculture and the partial destruction of a livestock agriculture.

Water as a special policy problem in the West.—In the humid area of the United States, water was not a limiting factor to occupancy and use. It received no special treatment at the hands of policy. Water was simply part of the land on which it occurred. It was surplus relative to needs for it. As a consequence, it was alien to "eastern" thinking that water required any separate or distinctive treatment at the hands of policy. As the western states were created, water was transferred to the control of the states, although land remained largely in the hands of the federal government for management and disposal. No distinctive federal policy attached to water. Note here again the influence of custom. "Land" was important to eastern-minded people; so they retained control over it; water wasn't; so they let control over it pass into the hand of the settlers in the person of their state governments.

In the arid western country, water was often a limiting factor to successful settlement. There was no precedent in the eastern humid part of the United States for institutions required to control and use water when it is scarce. Institutions suitable to the purpose grew out of the needs and purposes of the people in the arid areas. Water was scarce relative to the needs for it and its control was in the hands of the local units of government. Water tenure institutions grew up under the idea that a land owner might claim (appropriate) use rights to sufficient water from a near-by stream to farm his land adequately. The first claimant to water on a stream had first rights to use the water he claimed regardless of other claimants above him on the stream. In case of water shortage, all later claimants had to quit using water from the stream to supply earlier claimants.

Thus developed the doctrines of appropriation of first in time, first in right; the property device of water rights; the enforcing mechanism of "filing" the water claim with a unit of local government. There also developed the notion of "beneficial use" under which a person can "claim" no more water than is reasonably necessary for the use of the land he tills.

But irrigation requires large capital investments. Developments that could be completed relatively cheaply were completed by private individuals at a relatively early date. By the turn of the century, demand was heard for devices that would bring larger blocks of capital into irrigation development than were available to private land occupiers. In 1902, the federal government entered into the development of irrigation on western lands. Under federal policy, the government built the necessary works, assessed the costs against the lands benefitted by the water thus made available, collected the charges from the settlers over an extended period of years, and supplied government-developed water to no more than 160 acres of land belonging to a single farmer.

Many federally-financed irrigation projects have been built. Many problems have been encountered—inadequately sized farms, developments on lands unsuited to irrigation, failure to provide adequate drainage works, charges higher than the settlers could pay off even over long terms and without interest. These problems have not yet been solved. In recent years, additional new and different problems have arisen, such as the relationship between power development, flood control, navigation and irrigation uses of water. Our American society is a long way from solving the policy problems associated with water resources in the West.

Size of Holdings

From the beginning, the people of the United States have held a deep-seated prejudice against "large" land holdings and tenancy in agriculture. Always the ideal has been the "family-size" farm tilled by its owner. National policy has never purposefully encouraged large estates and tenancy. Neither has national land policy ever restricted land ownership for reasons of race, creed, or color.

National land policy from the start right down to this day has attempted to structure land policy in a way to encourage "family-size" farms and owner-operatorship. Not that land policy has always been successful in this regard. We had, at the same time, the policy of unrestricted private property; when the family owner-operator obtained his farm, he could do with it as he pleased. Hence, by sale and foreclosure, consolidation into sizeable farms took place and ownership by nonoperators grew considerably.

National land policy has attempted to further this family-size farm ideal through several channels. This has been done, first, by the policies under which it disposed of its land to private persons—160 to 640 acres per homestead and not more than 160 acres per family irrigated by federal irrigation water; second, by supplying credit for land purchase by farm families under easy credit terms; third, by placing certain limits on the amount of federally-owned grazing lands individuals were allowed to use.

It is obvious that America is a nation of family farms pretty largely because of these historic policies. It is just as obvious that the nation's concern over these policies has often, especially in the sub-humid area, led it to extremes that have been quite detrimental to its welfare. It is also obvious that the ideal of unrestricted private property has sometimes conflicted with the ideal of family farm ownership—when it has, it has prevailed. In other words, the ideal of unrestricted private property has been held to be more fundamental than the ideal of family farm owner-operatorship.

Change in Basic Land Policy

The goal of the entire history of land policy in America has been unrestricted private property in family-size units for all agricultural land. Beginning fifty years ago, the first tiny crack appeared in this basic goal. But not until the past twenty years has the emerging change been widely debated.

About 1900 those of the remaining public lands that were forested or that were of high watershed value were withdrawn from homestead entry by Presidential order, and the national forests were born. These national forests are publicly managed for forestry and watershed protection and for any other uses that do not conflict with these uses—primarily such supplementary uses are grazing and recreation. These lands are not "used" by the government but are managed by the government as landlord for private use under suitable rules and regulations. For the first time, extensive areas used for agricultural purposes were permanently removed from among those resources available for private property. Here, again, an interesting example of the influence of customary thinking emerged. It was possible for many years after the national forests were established for individual persons to file claims to lands within these public withdrawals and, if the federal agency responsible for their management classified them as "agricultural" (meaning crop farming land), the individual could obtain private title to them under a procedure similar to homesteading. But if such lands had important other use values for forestry, watershed protection, or recreation, the claim to them by private individuals could be denied. Note that lands important for grazing purposes only were not considered as "agricultural" lands. Furthermore, the area any single individual could claim was kept within the size limits set by the homestead law; thus a further obstacle to claiming them for grazing purposes was continued.

In 1934, the homesteading era came to its virtual conclusion. There remained in the western states about 185 million acres of lands available for homesteading that had not been claimed by private persons for reasons of aridity, rough topography, or other conditions that limited their adaptability for farming purposes. These lands were outside those areas that had been withdrawn from homesteading for national forests or other special uses.

From the beginning of western settlement, as described earlier, there was no legal device by which livestock grazers could obtain any form of tenure control over the public lands available for homesteading. But for seventy years, grazers had used the public grazing lands under no form of public regulation whatever. Any man with livestock could turn them on the public domain; he could put on as many head as he wished and could leave them as long as he wanted. He couldn't practice conservative use because if he left any grass ungrazed, some other stockman could graze it off with his stock; he couldn't fence it or develop water or do anything else that would increase its productivity.

In 1934, these 185 million acres of land available for homesteading were withdrawn from homesteading, and their management and development for livestock grazing begun. Under the 1934 law, three means to dispose of or to regulate the use of these lands were provided:

(1) Any lands classified by the federal government as suitable for "farming" or for other private use (such as "desert homes") may be "homesteaded" by private claimants in tracts of suitable size up to 640 acres. Here again the tract size limitation and the definition of "farming" excludes livestock grazing from the operation of this feature of the law.

(2) Any "isolated tracts" too small or too isolated from other areas of public lands to be efficiently managed by the federal government may be sold or leased to private applicants.

(3) The remainder of the acreage (about 140 million acres) is included in "federal grazing districts" wherein the public land is managed and developed for grazing purposes, and use rights to specific parts of it are assigned to individual stock grazers for a fee. These lands are retained in public ownership, managed by the federal government as landlord, but their use is put in the hands of private individuals as tenants.

Through this act and the earlier forest reservation acts, many millions of acres of agricultural lands, largely in the western states, are no longer available for private ownership but are available for private use under rules and regulations prescribed for their management and control.

It is interesting to note here again, however, that there has not been and is not now any change in that persistent thread in national land policy that favors private ownership of agricultural land. The emergence of these public tenures over agricultural lands in the West is a result of the recognition that some uses of land can be furthered only by public ownership (forestry, for example). But it arises also with respect to grazing land because the American society has not recognized extensive livestock grazing as a form of agriculture and so does not apply its agricultural land disposal policies to grazing lands. The result is that lands adapted to extensive livestock grazing that have not been disposed of to private ownership for "farming" use remain in public ownership for pastoral use.

Regulation of Private Land

For 150 years, national land policy provided practically unfettered use and control of agricultural land by its owner. Except that the product of the land and its capital value were subject to taxation, that public rights of way could be imposed on private land, and that the land could be acquired for public purposes without the consent of its owner, the private owner could sell, give away, mortgage, and use his land in any way he pleased without regulation by the government.

As recently as fifteen years ago, a change, faint and ill-defined, appeared in this historic policy. The change is still faint and ill-defined, but it is receiving public attention. Increasing concern over wasteful use of our basic agricultural resources and with troublesome social problems growing out of unregulated human relationships relative to land has led to certain policy actions and to wide public discussions over the merits of public regulation over private uses and relationships growing out of private property in agricultural land.

A few states within the United States have adopted police power regulations over the use of private agricultural land to reduce the seriousness of certain social problems with which they were faced. Primarily, these regulations have been directed at the control of settlement and occupancy of rural lands to reduce the extent of isolated family living. The public problem arose because of the modern social policy that all families should be supplied with roads and schools. Isolated settlement greatly increased these costs, and so some states have regulated occupancy of isolated tracts to reduce the costs of these public services.

Some states have given considerable attention to the problem of landlord-tenant relationships in agriculture. In many states, consideration has been given to legislation designed to regulate or at least to alter the institutional framework within which landlord-tenant relations take place. The goal of such considerations has been to stabilize tenancy, to encourage conservational land use on tenant-operated farms, to encourage socially more efficient production, and the social and economic betterment of tenant farmers. Not much has been actually accomplished along these lines, and what has

been done has occurred in only a few states, but that they have been seriously discussed in legislative councils is a marked departure from previous years.

The federal government has encouraged state governments to set up a governmental device within each state through which co-operative investment in land could be made and regulation of land use could be effected to attain conservation goals. In every state in the United States, soil conservation districts are now authorized and in most states such districts have been formed. Primarily, these districts have functioned as devices for co-operating with the federal government and through which federal funds for conservation purposes can be channeled. But many of these states grant the power (so far practically unused) to the districts to institute land use regulations in the interest of conservation covering all privately-owned lands within their boundaries. Here again, change in the basic policy of unfettered private ownership is hardly noticeable, but that the need for such power has been debated and the permissive power has been legislated are of great significance.

Agricultural Policy Today

American land policy unquestioningly accepts private property in farm land; it accepts the idea of public ownership of certain kinds of nonfarm lands such as mountain watersheds, recreational lands, and forests. Its relation to grazing lands is confused; it classifies them separately from farm lands when used for extensive grazing purposes and accepts the idea of public ownership for them when so classed, but it classifies them as farm land when used as "farm pastures" and applies the policy of private ownership to them under these conditions. Because of the confused status of grazing lands, especially in the area of extensive grazing, a violent public debate swirls and eddies around the issue of public or private ownership.

Though accepting the idea of private ownership for farm lands, in American land policy there are the stirrings of changing ideas to restrict the freedom of action of land owners and land users in agriculture in the interest of conservation, protection and strengthening of the "family-size" farm, and improvement in the social and economic status of tenant farmers. These stirrings are a forewarning of a growing break with the traditions of the past 150 years when unrestricted private property in farm lands was as unquestioned as private property still is.

But these stirrings of change are yet vague and ill-defined; they are the reflection of disturbing underlying problems in American agriculture and land use for which the American society is seeking solutions by institutional changes new and untried in the United States. How far these changes will go, how fast, and in what direction are not yet clear. But the yeast of change is working and some expansion of the mixture seems inevitable.

Mid-West Agriculture

Farming in the corn belt characterizes American farming to people all around the world. It is here that we find all that is best in American farming—prosperous, stable, productive, family-size farms, each farmer on his own farm or working in reasonably close partnership with his landlord.

In part, these characteristics of corn belt farming are a result of the high level of productivity of the corn belt soil and climate; in part they derive from the historical consonance of federal land policy at the time of settlement with the natural conditions of the area.

The natural environment of the corn belt was one of humid, level prairies and woodlands. The prairies and much of the woodlands were highly fertile. It was, and is, one of the most productive agricultural areas in

the world. Some of the land required no clearing of timber, though much of the prairie land required extensive draining. Its natural environment was conducive to stable, prosperous farming if any area in the United States or in the world ever could be. It was blessed from the beginning.

Land in the area was made available to its first settlers at low or no cost. It was available in tracts big enough for small but reasonably adequate farms. Sizes of farms have increased over the years—slowly, it is true, but enough to keep up quite well with technological advance and with the increasing productivity that followed clearing and draining.

The federal land disposal policy at the time of settlement encouraged owner-operatorship. But the owner-operators being unrestricted, as described earlier in this paper, owners were free to become absentee and operate their farms through tenants on the land. They also were free to consider the land they owned as a financial asset to be bought and sold or to be exploited for maximum money gain.

As a result of these historical conditions, the leading land policy problems of the corn belt have been (1) a serious amount of exploitative land use with fertility depletion and erosion damage dangerously widespread, (2) unstable tenancy arising from the reluctance of both owners and tenants to tie themselves to long-term arrangements that might prevent the owner's selling or changing tenants or the tenant's moving to another farm, and (3) socially inefficient farming resulting from the distortion of farm production towards crops and livestock that require a minimum of fixed capital investment and a short turnover. After all, neither an owner nor a tenant is going to invest in dairy barns and milk houses and a well-bred herd of dairy cows (even though dairying might produce more income if operated on a long-run stable plan) when each wishes to leave the way open to dissolve their agreement from year to year. They will mutually prefer to raise and sell corn for cash or engage in hog production.

Except for these problems in the corn belt, we find what is best and considered most typical of American farming the world around.

Western Agriculture

The basic factor to understand in appraising the development of western agriculture is that the institutional framework within which western agriculture developed was in large measure ill-adapted to the conditions of the area. These ill-adapted institutions were partly implanted on the West by the federal government dominated by the humid East and partly were planted on itself by the settlers in the West who were themselves products of the humid East. The struggles of agriculture in the West ever since it was first settled have been concerned with trying to live within an institutional framework familiar to the nation and to the settlers in the area and with slowly, gropingly, and with considerable pain, adjusting those institutions to the hard facts of the semi-arid western environment.

In the first place, the system of agriculture (pastoral) best adapted to a major part of the West never was given any friendly institutional environment. The development of the western pastoral economy and its status today has been largely in spite of, not because of, the institutional framework within which it functions. Major Powell's recommendations (referred to earlier) were totally ignored by the United States Congress and by the settlers in and coming into the area.

In the West, the pastoral industry never received from the federal government any grant of legal control over the land areas necessary for carrying on a pastoral business. That the industry survived at all was due to the existence of federal lands so obviously unsuited to crop farming that they never were homesteaded and hence did not pass into private hands. On these public lands, on the national forest reservations set aside in the early years of this century and on such tracts of private land as he could buy, the pastoral agriculturalist could find a place to graze his livestock. But out of this circumstance grew the struggle over public landlord-private tenant relationships that persists into the present. There was no precedent in American agriculture to guide the solution of this problem. Everywhere else in the United States, agriculture took place on private lands, and where tenancy arose, it was a tenancy on land of private landlords. In the West, public landlordism with private tenancy just grew without plan and without precedent as to how best to do it; we simply stumbled into it.

But the particular form that public landlordism took on the grazing lands of the West—though it just grew without plan and precedent—became fixed in custom both of the bureaucracy and of the livestock producers. Emerging demands for modification of public grazing land tenures meet all the resistances that customary ways of doing things always meet. Bureaucracy and many stockman users of the public lands don't want any change—but many stockmen do. And from them come the expressions of dissatisfaction and the demands for change in public grazing land policy.

We come to the second maladjustment between agricultural institutions and the environment in the semi-arid West. Crop farming was established under the mistaken institutional policy that 160 acres, 320 acres, or even 640 acres, was adequate for family-size farming and was all the land that one family should get from the federal government. Once a pattern of settlement based on farms of these sizes became established, adjustment to a pattern of more adequate farm units was slow and painful. It was a harsh process compounded of financial failure, heartbreaks, and abandonment of farms and homes to "open up" the settlement pattern and create "vacuums" into which the surviving farmers or new outsiders with adequate capital could move. Thus were larger, better-adapted farms built up.

Adjustment of farm sizes in the Great Plains also followed upon the growth of technological knowledge as to how to produce under semi-arid conditions. Such technological knowledge developed both by trial and error of farmers themselves and by planned research in the agricultural experiment stations. Summer fallow and power machinery made larger farms necessary.

Farm size adjustment in the Great Plains has almost eliminated the 160 to 640 acre "farms" of the homestead era. For the first time in the history of the West, its farms are in reasonably good adjustment with the environment. As farm sizes come into adjustment with their environment, the farms become financially more secure but at the cost of increasing social isolation, higher costs, or growing inadequacy of social services— schools, roads, medical care, community organization, electricity, etc.

Policies relating to water are the third and last of the problems of agriculture peculiar to agricultural development in the western states. Water for irrigation is, in most of the West, the limiting factor to agricultural development. Control of water is vested in the states—not in the federal government as was the case originally with all land in the area. To bring water under regulation and control and make its use available to private land-holders, the institution of water rights has grown up. A water right is a claim to use a certain amount of water out of a stream for irrigation purposes—the claim is filed with and recorded by a unit of government. The first claim filed, regardless of how far down the stream it is located, has first right to any water in the stream to fill its claim. The claimants to water usually file their claims against enough water to insure adequate irrigation of their lands.

Out of these conditions relating to water in the West, wasteful use of critically-limited supplies of water has often resulted. The first claimant to water in a stream is often located downstream from later claimants. When supplies are limited, enough water must be allowed to pass upstream claimants to fill the right of the downstream claimant of higher priority together with enough additional water to allow for evaporation, infiltration, and other losses during passage of the flow down the stream. When supplies are limited, they may be used more efficiently on lands up the stream rather than on lands down the stream, but the principle of "first in time, first in right" sometimes interferes.

Also, early claimants laid claim to as much water as they could conceivably justify as necessary for proper irrigation of their lands. Only the relatively weak principle of "beneficial use" restricted the amount they could claim. "Beneficial use" has usually been defined as that amount of water customarily considered as necessary under the prevailing methods of irrigation in the community. It is apparent that as methods of irrigation have changed, amounts of water may become excessive. Not infrequently, the plentiful supplies available under early rights have been influences retarding the adoption of changed and more efficient use. The laws of the several states are not uniform in their handling of this problem. Allowing claims to water to be freely bought and sold would tend in time to get water and land together in amounts and priorities that would enhance the efficiency of water use. This is now possible in some states and not in others.

Limited water supplies, somewhat wastefully used, resulted in the early exhaustion of cheaply developed supplies. For some years now, the only sources of additional supplies of irrigation water require large and high-cost investments. The only source of funds for such investments has been the public treasury and primarily the federal treasury. The use of federal funds for this purpose has raised the following issues that are current today:

(1) Competition between regions within the United States for water development, for development of resources other than water, and for use of the not inexhaustible supply of federal funds.

(2) Costs of water development have become so high that the irrigation farmer is not able alone to pay the whole cost of development. This has raised the difficult issue of reimbursement of the public investment and the related issue as to how the costs of development should be allocated for reimbursement among the highly diverse and widely spread beneficiaries, who include many more than the new farmer-settlers on irrigation developments.

THE story of land policy and agricultural development in the West is a revealing account of the maladjustments and problems that arise when a society moves into a radically different environment. Tenacious holding to social arrangements that are familiar, though holding to them may be painful; making adjustments in social arrangements only under the hammer blows of adversity and making them then by trial and error attempts to find more workable arrangements —these characteristics typify the development of agriculture in the West.

THE LAND TENURE AND AGRICULTURAL DEVELOPMENT IN THE SOUTH

John H. Bondurant and Frank J. Welch

THE GEOGRAPHIC area usually referred to as the South includes thirteen of the forty-eight states of the United States lying principally south of the Ohio and Potomac rivers in the eastern United States and south of the states of Missouri and Kansas in the Midwest. Most of the South has a semi-tropical climate; southern Florida, a small area of the mouth of the Mississippi River, and the lower Rio Grande Valley have a tropical climate. Except in western Oklahoma and Texas, the South has an average annual rainfall of forty inches or more; some parts have sixty to seventy inches.

In the semi-tropical area the growing season between killing frosts ranges from about six months in the northern part to nine months on the south Atlantic and Gulf coasts. In general, from the standpoint of climate, the South is naturally adapted to the production of tobacco in the northern, cotton in the central, and rice, sugar cane, winter vegetables, and citrus fruits in the extreme southern and tropical sections.

Practically all the South, except the alluvial soil along the Mississippi River, has Red and Yellow Podzolic zonal soils of the great soil groups. Largely because of origin, topography, elevation, chemical composition, structure, and subjection to erosion the soils of the South vary widely in suitability for agricultural use and in natural productivity. Under these conditions have developed about twenty-six agricultural subregions. There are many fertile upland soil areas such as the Kentucky Bluegrass, the central basin of Tennessee, the Shenandoah Valley of Virginia and the Black Prairie of

Texas. Also, the Mississippi Delta has a high natural fertility. But, in general, the soils of the South are of medium to poor grade and require constant effort to maintain fertility and protect from severe erosion. Relatively heavy rainfall especially in winter, and frequent winter freezing and thawing, plus a high percentage of cropland in row crops, have washed topsoil from millions of acres of farmland. In the Southern Appalachian Mountains and other similar areas, and in swamps, bogs, and sandy soils along the Atlantic and Gulf coasts are millions of acres suitable only for forests, game refuges, and recreation in their present state. Compared with the Midwest, the South has one-third as much first-grade land, about half as much second-grade, and somewhat more third-grade land.

Historical Setting

The South was settled principally by English-speaking people. In Virginia, one of the first colonies, land grants from the English government were made directly to individual settlers. For every person transported across the Atlantic to Virginia, it was the custom to give the party responsible fifty acres of land, provided the person transported remained for three years. The only other requirements were that the land must be occupied, nominally at least, for a year and that a quit rent be paid to the sheriff. If these conditions had been adhered to, the cost of transporting emigrants would have curtailed the acreage accumulated by individuals. But land was plentiful, and false lists of settlers and lists of ships' crews or lists from old record books were frequently used to acquire large estates without incurring any expense for transportation. About the same system of granting lands to individuals was later developed by the Carolinas and by Georgia.

In the eighteenth century, most of the land was acquired for settlement by direct purchase. This method also was favorable to the ownership of land in large estates. Furthermore, the law of primogeniture, which required that all land of a deceased person should descend to the oldest son, was in force at that time in some of the Southern states, and this greatly influenced the perpetuation of large estates and plantations. By contrast, inheritance customs in New England and in other northern states were generally unfavorable to the establishment and perpetuation of large landed estates. In the northern colonies land grants were usually made to the governor of the new settlement for distribution to individuals, and the custom of equal division of estates among surviving heirs was established much earlier than in the South. However, despite the origin of the big plantations in the South in settlement policy, their continuance was principally for economic reasons, as will be indicated later.

Even though land settlement policy and cheap land encouraged the establishment of large estates, the majority of farms in the colonies were small and were cultivated with family labor, and most of the early settlers in the South were farmers. The farmer produced most of the food and clothing needed by his family and secured building materials for his house and barns. But very soon attention was given to production for export, much earlier than in the northern states.

The accessibility to settlement and dependency upon water navigation for transportation encouraged early settlement along the coast and on navigable rivers. This was further encouraged by the production of tobacco, rice, indigo, and later cotton, for export.

Negro slavery, introduced in 1619 into Virginia, spread rapidly to other areas. The large amount of labor required per acre for tobacco and rice and the ownership of much of the land in large estates and plantations created a wide demand for slaves in the South as the acreage of these crops expanded.

Large plantations continued to be a distinct feature of Southern agriculture for three centuries—the seventeenth, eighteenth, and nineteenth. The principal crops produced on the plantations, and in the South as a whole, were tobacco, cotton, rice and sugar cane. Two major economic factors were underlying causes of the long survival of the plantation:

(1) There was a continued strong world demand for cotton, tobacco, rice and sugar. In the nineteenth century cotton production greatly exceeded that of all other crops, largely as a result of the invention of the cotton gin in 1793 and the introduction of the cotton mill into New England in 1790. But throughout the period the strong demand in foreign countries for the above crops was such that they could be raised in almost unlimited quantities. These crops required fertile soil, and tobacco grew best on freshly cleared land. Most of the South originally was covered with forest. The practice of moving to new ground when production per acre declined, and for production of the better grades of tobacco, required ownership of enough land for both current and future tillage.

(2) The large amount of physical labor required by the four principal crops produced was partly offset by cheap labor, especially the use of slaves. To be efficient the farm requires supervision of labor. In tobacco production one person could supervise a large number of workers. Rice was grown with mass, unskilled laborers where white workers did not thrive. Cotton followed the pattern of tobacco and rice, being even more suited to mass employment of unskilled labor.

The location of the different types of plantations was largely determined by climate, soil, and water transportation facilities. To-

bacco was produced in the upper South, rice in the Carolinas and Georgia, hemp in Missouri and Kentucky, sugar cane in Louisiana and a few valleys in Texas, and cotton in a belt of varying width from the Carolinas to eastern Texas. Although the production of rice and sugar cane was confined to plantations, cotton, tobacco, and hemp could be profitably grown on small farms in the nineteenth century and later. These small family farms although scattered throughout the South were most numerous in the upper South and in the Piedmont.

The invention of the sewing machine in 1846 further expanded the demand for cotton and led to a westward movement of cotton production. Low prices for cotton in the 1840's had encouraged abandonment of much land which had been severely eroded by one-crop farming in the mid-south. Many farmers, especially young men, moved westward to obtain more productive, free land. However, about this time the farmers who remained in the area began major changes in crop and livestock production which in more recent years has spread throughout the South.

At this point, background for the events which followed seems desirable. Prior to 1865 slaves provided most of the farm labor in the South, though there were a few tenants and farm wage workers, especially in the subregions which produced very little cotton or sugar cane. White farm operators, especially on the larger farms and plantations, were apathetic toward physical labor. Generally, slaves received reasonably satisfactory food and clothing, and the average slave performed only a moderate amount of work in a day. They received no formal education, but were trained to produce crops, care for livestock, and perform domestic service for their owners. They remained in a low stage of civilization. The principal differences between a slave and a free agricultural laborer were outside the realm of food, clothing, shelter, and work. The difference was that the slave was ordered to work, his food and clothing were rationed, his movements were restricted and watched, he was sometimes punished, and he might be sold. By contrast, the free agricultural laborer could move about from one place to another within the limits of his knowledge and ability; he worked when he chose to, and provided his own clothing.

Post-Civil War Developments

The South probably reached its lowest point in agricultural development in the years immediately following the Civil War of 1861–65. The farm operators had no labor force at their disposal, farms had been mismanaged, and property destroyed over a four-year period. Fences were in need of repair, and farm buildings, sugar houses, and cotton gins were in poor condition, damaged, or destroyed. Fields were abandoned and grown up in broomsedge, weeds, bushes, and briars, and livestock herds and work animals were greatly diminished.

Four million Negroes were free and invested with new civil rights; this number represented nearly a million Negro families beginning a new livelihood, most of them with no money or property. They could neither read nor write, and had no business and little social training.

Most farm owners had no money; many of them had old debts to pay, along with the necessary physical reclamation of their depleted property.

Figuratively speaking, a widespread vacuum existed on Southern farms: an agricultural region of small and large farms with depleted resources, no dependable labor force outside the farm operator's family, no money, debts to pay, and no established source of credit. Such was the situation in the South in 1865. Into this vacuum went forces which played a major part in the development of the South.

The lack of an efficient labor force added to the financial distress of Southern farmers and forced many of them deeper in debt. The employable labor force included both Negro and white laborers. Lien laws were enacted to help the farmers, the recently freed slaves, and other farm workers. The purpose of these laws was to furnish a basis for credit. To obtain operating capital those who had mortgage-free land could give a lien on it; those who had livestock could get their year's supplies on this security. Those who had neither land nor livestock could rent land and work stock, farm on a cropshare basis, and give a lien on the prospective crop to the landowner or to the local merchant for necessary farm supplies and subsistence goods.

The alternative to renting land and operating capital was to work for wages at different wage rates according to the ability of the worker and under the supervision and direction of the employer. To the Negro the wage plan was unpopular—a semblance of the old slavery regime; and to the farm owner-employers this plan required more capital and expensive supervision.

In this situation world trade was demanding large amounts of cotton, tobacco, and other southern crops, but there was no central source of credit within the area, and under the chaotic conditions very little private capital was risked from outside the South. There was no Economic Cooperation Administration to help the South restore its prewar economic position.

With the large demand for agricultural products, the heavy labor requirements to produce them, the prostrate credit position of farm owners and local sources of credit, and the large immobile labor force it was inevitable that through the new lien laws and their implementation sharecrop production and the plantation furnish system, plus a large proportion of widely scattered, small owner-operated farms, became the principal tenure system of the South. Perhaps the only alternatives would have been exportation of the free Negroes and a resultant decrease in agricultural production or government-sponsored direct financial assistance and long-term loans.

The production of tobacco and especially cotton under the treacherous operation of the lien laws soon involved the farm owners heavily in debt. They were responsible to the merchants for the supplies and subsistence goods furnished the share worker. They mortgaged their farms, and when cotton was high they bought land, mules, and other merchandise, much of it on credit. Interest accumulated, and a steady pressure was kept on the production of cotton for the world market. On many farms the production of grain and livestock declined. Finally, the large expansion of cotton production pressed down its price.

One cannot adequately evaluate the post-Civil War Southern agriculture without giving consideration to the country store. The local merchant was one of the most tangible factors in the complex one-crop cotton, tobacco, and sugar cane system of Southern agriculture. To a large proportion of the new share tenants he was banker as well as merchant. He furnished the farm people with supplies and subsistence goods on credit, and for most Southerners the country store was the place where they came in contact with the outside world. Some of the merchants, no doubt, sized up their trade and took from the farmers unreasonable credit charges, but the preponderance of evidence indicates that the merchant was only a part of an inefficient tenure and subsistence furnishing system.

The Southern farmers, after having been forced to do without many consumer's goods for four years or more, were ready buyers when goods became plentiful. Since they were without money, they took advantage of the new lien laws and bought large quantities of merchandise. Thus the new credit legislation encouraged the country merchant to buy all kinds of merchandise. His business was further expanded by the sale of cotton at the crossroads villages rather than in the larger towns and cities. As a substitute for cash the merchants exchanged small amounts of manufactured goods for equally small amounts of a variety of farm products—and thus became not only the principal source of merchandise and credit for the farmer but the buyers of most of his farm products as well. These crossroads centers became an important factor in the changed economic system, and they maintained their place in the agricultural economy throughout the South for at least a half-century; in many Southern communities they still maintain today an important status despite improved roads and motor transportation which encourage trade in the larger towns and cities.

In general, the tenure system and agricultural economy which developed after the freeing of the slaves were maintained with little change for half a century. New types of tobacco and new cotton varieties expanded the markets for these products and helped maintain a relatively strong demand for them. In the meantime, new systems of farming and new nonfarm industries were developing in various parts of the South. The Mexican boll weevil entered the South from Mexico to devastate the cotton fields and greatly reduce yields before control measures could be developed—and cotton production moved still farther westward.

Between 1870 and 1914 cotton prices were relatively stable, and with the exception of unusually low prices from 1890 to 1902 they followed rather closely the wholesale price index of all commodities. Prices for tobacco, rice, and sugar followed a similar pattern. For the half-century prior to 1914 the tenure system, the one-crop farm economy, the expensive, elusive credit facilities, and the inroads of erosion on a generally susceptible soil, enhanced by lack of maintenance of soil fertility, were contributory causes of persistently low per-capita incomes and constant depletion of farm resources.

Race problems persisted throughout the period prior to 1914. The liberties which the Negroes took with their new freedom, the attitudes of both whites and Negroes toward each other, and lack of adequate educational facilities were augmented by low incomes and the general lack of economic opportunity in most of the South. In general, alternative opportunities were conspicuously absent as compared with other regions of the United States. In this relatively stagnant economy of the South it was only natural for old prejudices to be kept alive and for various components of the economy to be referred to as reasons for the relatively poor economic conditions which prevailed.

World War I and Depression

In the period from 1914 to 1932 cotton and tobacco prices gyrated with the almost constantly changing price level of wholesale commodities. The war prosperity from 1914 to 1920 was soon offset by the widespread agricultural depression of the twenties. Strengthening of farm product prices for a brief period in the late twenties served to make more severe the financial distress of most Southern farmers in the years 1932–34, brought about by world-wide depression.

During the 1914–32 period four significant developments occurred in Southern agriculture: (1) Cotton production expanded rapidly in the Southwest. (2) Thousands of white owners and laborers became share tenants through loss of farm ownership. In the ten leading cotton states in 1933, 60 per cent of the cotton producers were share tenants; this was probably the peak year for tenancy in the South. According to Rupert B. Vance, the number of tenant families totaled 1,792,000; of this number he

estimated that about 61 per cent were white tenant families. (3) Demand for cotton decreased because of the introduction of rayon and other synthetic fabrics. The consumption of rayon in the United States increased from 2.7 million pounds in 1912 to 39.4 million pounds in 1923. (4) Exports of tobacco from the Southern states decreased by more than one-fourth from 1920 to 1933.

Such were the conditions in the cotton and tobacco producing areas of the South at the beginning of world depression in the thirties. In the depression cotton consumption fell sharply, and the annual carry-over of American cotton increased from 5 million to 13 million bales. Prices dropped, and the gross farm income from cotton declined from $1,470,000,000 in 1928 to $431,000,000 in 1932, with the result that the average gross income per farm family growing cotton fell from $735 to $216. Similar changes occurred in the consumption of tobacco and in the income derived from its production.

A New South

In spite of the early colonial development of the plantation system and the concentration of agricultural production for three centuries on a few staple crops, the agriculture of the South in 1950 formed a very heterogeneous pattern. Throughout the thirteen states there were about twenty-six type-of-farming areas distinctly different in agricultural products, soils, crop production, and farming methods. Cotton is the chief product in only five of these areas. Farms range in size from ten-acre or less, home-use, subsistence farms in the Southern Appalachians to cattle ranches of several thousand acres in Texas. Although the majority are family farms, on large plantations or cattle ranches several hundred workers frequently are employed. Cotton yields by areas range from one-half bale to two bales per acre; tobacco yields from 750 to 1500 pounds; corn from 10 to 80 bushels per acre. Tobacco is typically produced on relatively small farms. Tobacco production on one-acre farms totals more than that on all other tobacco farms combined.

Some of the larger type-of-farming areas which produce cotton as a major product are the Piedmont, with low yields and medium-sized farms; the Brown Loam, with loess-deposited, erosive soil of medium productivity and small to large farms; the Delta, with fertile land and large farms; the Texas Black Prairies, with large, productive, cotton-livestock farms; and the Southern Appalachians, with small, low-producing subsistence and part-time farms.

Paralleling the gradual movement of cotton production westward was the beginning of basic changes in the agriculture of the South. On the more level acres of the Delta Area of the Mississipi Valley and in the Southwest, cotton could be produced more cheaply than in the older areas of the Southeast. The soils in the Old South were eroded and depleted in fertility. The boll weevil also worked its way across the older areas; it reduced cotton production an estimated 30 per cent in 1929. New crops were introduced. Soil improvement and maintenance practices were introduced. Livestock numbers were increased on many farms.

Under the impact of the above conditions many new developments brought about changes in the agriculture of the South and a new tenure pattern. Production of winter vegetables and citrus fruits was developed and expanded along the warm coast lines, following the introduction of refrigeration for freight and express railroad cars. The building of interstate highways to population centers of the East and Midwest and the development of truck transportation led to the expansion of peach production in South Carolina and Georgia. Sweet potatoes and peanuts likewise became important crops in the South with U.S. markets. Hydroelectric power developments in the Carolinas

enabled many New England cotton mills to move south and draw upon the abundant labor supply. Mechanized farming was emerging on many large farms. Practically all these and similar developments encouraged an increase in owner-operated family farms utilizing principally the labor of the farm operator. The demand for one-crop tenant farmers began to decrease; many such farmers obtained employment in nonfarm industries, both local and outside the area.

Though practically all these devolpments occurred prior to 1933, their impact upon Southern agriculture was only fragmentary up to that time. In the South in 1930, 42.8 per cent of the total employment was in agricultural occupations as compared with 14.6 per cent of the total employment in other parts of the country.

Agriculture and the New Deal

With the beginning of the New Deal in 1933 the U.S. Government created the Agricultural Adjustment Administration "to relieve the existing national economic emergency by increasing agricultural purchasing power." Following this enactment the adoption of the Domestic Allotment plan for crop reduction with land rental and price parity payments, for those who voluntarily reduced their cotton acreage, occurred after the 1933 cotton crop was planted. To avoid an increase in annual carry-over for 1934, emergency action was necessary. By lease contracts with the Secretary of Agriculture cotton farmers plowed under 25 to 50 per cent of their 1933 planted cotton acreage. For this acreage they received a rental payment of about eleven dollars per acre, varying somewhat according to cotton yields. The price of cotton increased to ten cents per pound. Crop receipts and government payments doubled the income from cotton as compared with 1932.

Largely because the landowners received a land rental payment, they benefited more than the share tenant producer. Because of the reduced cotton acreage, fewer tenants were needed. Some of them became farm wage workers and others began to seek other employment rather than share in the lower acreage allotted to the farm and divided among the share tenants. The cotton acreage allotment and price parity programs continued for several years. Beginning in 1934 similar acreage reduction programs were enacted for tobacco and some other crops not widely grown in the South. These programs also were continued with resultant reductions in labor requirements for crop production.

This brief discussion of the AAA probably oversimplifies the impact of the early agricultural program of the New Deal on Southern agriculture. These initial programs set the pattern for subsequent agricultural legislation which, along with other developments, was to have a revolutionary effect on land tenure and agricultural production in the South. Paralleling the government-sponsored crop reduction program were other governmental programs for stabilizing and reconstructing the U.S. economic system. Some of these measures greatly benefited the half-million or more tenants and their families who were no longer needed for crop production, as well as millions of other low income families throughout the South. Other programs provided new sources of credit for farm owners and many tenants.

Among the more important of the non-farm government-sponsored national recovery programs was the Civil Works Administration, later succeeded by the Works Progress Administration. These agencies provided relief funds to unemployed families by furnishing employment principally at government expense on community-sponsored civic development projects. A large proportion of Southern tenant families and low income farmers were employed on these projects in one way or another until this

work was discontinued in 1942. By this time many former tenants had moved to nearby towns and cities in order to more adequately qualify for employment. This change made them nearer work opportunities, lowered transportation costs, and usually increased their standard of living. Although the cost of part of their employment was at government expense, it furnished income to destitute families, and some training for future jobs in private employment. In brief, it bridged the gap between underemployment and unemployment, on the one hand, and subsequent industrial employment which will be referred to in more detail later.

The AAA farm program was declared unconstitutional by the United States Supreme Court in 1936, and the governmental program for agriculture was changed from an emphasis on acreage allotments to emphasis on conservation of the soil. In the South, however, the acreage allotment programs for tobacco and cotton were also maintained largely in their earlier form.

The soil conservation emphasis provided new impetus to the shifts in farming that had begun in the South many years earlier but were temporarily halted by depression. New crops, improved pasture, more livestock, and, in general, better balanced systems of farming were encouraged by this program of subsidizing the conservation and improvement in the productivity of the soils of the South.

Although less spectacular than the other government programs and directly affecting fewer farmers, the role of the Farmers Home Administration in making loans to farmers, primarily to relatively low income sharecroppers and tenants, to improve their productive efficiency and economic well-being through the purchase of fertilizer, limestone, seeds, livestock, and machinery has been one of the most important types of assistance to income improvement in Southern agriculture. Also, through forty-year amortized loans this government agency has enabled tenants to become land owners. By 1940 farm owners constituted 50.7 per cent of all farm operators, as compared with 43.1 per cent in 1930. These United States government policies and programs and other related enactments paved the way for the rapid development of Southern agriculture in the past decade.

Practices and Technology

Along with the New Deal farm programs came an increased interest of Southern farmers in new farming methods. Some of the land formerly used for row crops was now available for other use. Increased yields were desired on allotted acreages of cotton, tobacco, and other crops. Government payments for conserving the soil through the use of approved practices called for information on alternative opportunities in land use and other changes in farming systems.

Results of agricultural research at state agricultural colleges and experiment stations were made available to millions of southern farmers through county agricultural agents, through vocational agricultural teachers in high schools, and by the press and radio. This coupled with the above developments resulted in a wide adoption of improved practices and an increased use of technology in agriculture. New and more profitable systems of farming were developed. The demand for new information on farm technology greatly increased. In soil improvements, for example, millions of tons of agricultural limestone and thousands of tons of high analysis phosphate were applied to potential forage cropland. For the fourteen-year period 1936–49 in the thirteen Southern states 50 million tons of limestone and 9.5 million tons of phosphate (20 per cent equivalent of phosphoric acid) were used on farm land. Mixed fertilizers for harvested crops, particularly row crops, and winter cover crops for control of erosion and to prevent soil leaching were widely used, as well as many other improved practices. The use of tractors and a variety of tractor appliances increased. Mechanized cotton pickers, which would equal the work of thirty-five to forty persons picking by hand, appeared on cotton farms, especially in the Mississippi Delta and the Southwest.

World War II Influences

The South has a high birth rate. During the period 1935–39 the population increase was 80 per cent higher than that needed to replace itself. This causes a backing up of population on farms when migration is low and emphasizes the importance of opportunities for employment off the farm.

The entry of the United States into World War II accelerated the changes already underway in land tenure and systems of farming in the South. The most important new factors were more favorable prices for farm products and employment opportunities in nonfarm industries. The need for war munitions was greater than the increased need for foods and fiber from southern farms. Relatively heavy stocks of farm products were on hand, stored in warehouses throughout the country. Earnings of United States factory workers rose 42 per cent from 1940 to 1942. Farm wages, which were relatively low in 1940, rose 69 per cent in the same two-year period. Several million tenants, other low-income farmers, and underemployed or unemployed workers in villages and towns throughout the South sought industrial employment. In 1945 farm owner-operators constituted 58.2 per cent of all farm operators as compared with 50.7 per cent in 1940 and 43.1 per cent in 1930.

Employment Opportunity

With the revival of economic activity in 1939, and later the war boom itself, migration out of the South increased greatly, despite the fact that prices of cotton, tobacco, and other farm products increased. The high wages in war plants outside the South acted as a powerful magnet to cause a net migration of almost 3 million people to other regions. Many veterans of World War II found employment outside the South. Thus the South lost more people from 1940 to 1948 than it had lost in the whole generation before 1940. In addition to the large migration out of the region, the war caused very large movements of population within the region, as workers left farms, towns, and villages to work in shipyards, war factories, and in building army camps. In 1940 only 34.9 per cent of total employment in the South was in agricultural occupations as compared to 42.8 per cent in 1930.

During the period 1939 to 1948, there were important changes in the production pattern of the major crops. There were decreases in acreage of corn, cotton, soybeans, tobacco, and miscellaneous crops and increases in acreage of hay, wheat, peanuts, rice, and truck crops. The acreage of peanuts increased by a million acres.

The most important increases in yields per acre came in cotton and tobacco. Cotton yields increased 93 per cent from 1929 to 1948, tobacco yields by 74 per cent. Corn yields increased 31 per cent and wheat 8 per cent.

Other significant changes occurred between 1940 and 1945. Farm population declined 26 per cent and acreage per farm increased 6 per cent. The number of farms with tractors increased 84 per cent, while the number of farm workstock declined 34 per cent. Beef cattle numbers increased 31 per cent, milk cows 7 per cent, chickens on farms 5 per cent. Sheep and hog numbers declined about 15 per cent.

As previously indicated, significant changes occurred in the tenure pattern for agriculture in the South. The number of tenants reached a record peak of 57 per cent of all farms in 1930; by 1944 they had declined to only 42 per cent. Conversely, owner-operators occupied 43 per cent of all farms in 1930 and 58 per cent in 1945. In 1950, the number of all tenants had declined to about 35 per cent of all farm operators in the thirteen Southern states.

By way of summary, there were many important changes in the agriculture of the South, especially during the last ten years. Large shifts in farm population have occurred, with a decline of more than 25 per cent. Tenancy declined by about 15 per cent. Cotton and tobacco acreages declined but total production increased slightly. Most other crop acreages, except corn, increased both in acreage and total production. Livestock numbers increased both absolutely and in relation to the rest of the country. Wheat acreage increased by 6 million acres and the production of citrus fruits doubled. In spite of the large decrease in farm population, total farm output in the South increased 23 per cent from the years 1935–39 to 1947.

The Future

The South has made phenomenal progress both in agricultural and industrial development in recent years. The rate of industrial expansion has exceeded that of any other U.S. region. Although agricultural output increased 23 per cent, changes in types of farm products and farming methods were the most significant.

Even with these developments the per-capita income of the thirteen Southern states in 1950 was estimated at $1,024, as compared with the United States average of $1,436. In the poorest states the average per-capita income was only about half that of the most prosperous states outside the South. In the past, however, this income disparity has been much greater.

Some of the causes of the low incomes and resultant low living standards in the South are low productivity of manpower in agriculture, inefficient use and underdevelopment of resources, depleted soils and high rate of soil erosion, lack of capital, high rate of natural increase of the farm population, relatively inadequate education and health facilities, adjustments required to increase the rate of farm mechanization, and lack of alternative employment opportunities off the farm.

The nonfarm employment opportunities available both in and outside the South have been an important factor in agricultural improvement. An increase in the rate of nonfarm employment opportunities would encourage farm mechanization, as it has in the past. Further mechanization of farming in the South including the cotton-picker, the flame-cultivator, the tractor and other farm equipment, is needed. It has been estimated that these technological developments would displace 2,150,000 farm workers by 1965. The cotton-picker and flame-thrower would reduce the manpower production requirements per bale of cotton by 75 per cent—from 191 man-hours per bale to 48 hours; these changes alone would displace 550,000 farm workers.

Changes in farming methods are necessary for improvement and maintenance of most Southern soils. Relatively expensive fertilization and other soil improvement and erosion control practices are needed throughout the South before its agriculture can adequately compete with that of other regions. The restoration and improvement of millions of acres of land in various stages of erosion is a major problem; considerable capital from outside the region would be required.

For farming to pay its way and provide satisfactory net incomes to farm people it is necessary that farm manpower be used efficiently. In 1948 the average cash farm income from farming per farm person in the South was about $600, as compared with $154 per person in 1940. Farm production expenses were approximately 70 per cent of the cash income in 1939 and at least 50 per cent of the cash income in 1948.

In the past decade or more the trend has been toward an increased number of family-size owner-operated farms and fewer plantations, sharecroppers, and tenants. However, with modern power and equipment a large proportion of these family farms need to be increased in size. Instead of one-crop farming and low labor efficiency there is need for enough land to support both cotton, or tobacco, and livestock, or some other combination of farm enterprises that will produce a higher net income to the farm family. Also, small specialty farms requiring intensive labor on an efficient basis may further develop with increased industrialization and new markets—for example, commercial broiler production.

In 1947 the capital required for developing minimum-size, efficient single family farm units was estimated at from $8,000 to $22,000 per farm, depending largely upon the type of farming. For multiple family units in the Mississippi Delta area from $60,000 to $90,000 would be required. For mechanical equipment, farm tools, and drainage systems and other alterations necessary for efficient mechanized operation an additional $38 to $55 per acre would be required. Almost complete mechanization of farming could be accomplished in some areas and distinct improvement could be made in all areas. Adequate credit facilities are a necessary requisite for these changes to efficient-size family farm operating units.

The larger, more mechanized farm units, using considerable capital to attain production efficiency, need a high level of managerial performance. But alert farm operators using typical resources have already demonstrated the pattern for this more efficient agriculture in all the various subregions. Thus the needed adjustments are supported by both research information and practical accomplishments. With these adjustments the physical volume of production would be increased by 50 per cent, achieved with a one-third smaller farm population. Therefore, the physical production per capita of the farm population would be increased by two and one-fourth times. This would, no doubt, greatly increase farm family incomes and standards of living.

Even though Southern agriculture has made distinct progress in recent years it is believed that a much higher level of efficiency can be obtained. This can be done largely through higher crop yields, more efficient livestock production, improved pastures, more land and other resources per farm family, increased mechanization and improvements in labor efficiency, balanced and well-developed farm organization, and a higher level of managerial performance.

These developments would encourage a higher proportion of owner-operated family farms, varying in size according to type of farming. An improvement in the general distribution system for agricultural products and farm supplies and better educational programs for adults and children would greatly encourage these developments. Through the application of scientific knowledge, a better combination of production factors and improved management practices much additional progress can be made in Southern agriculture.

In this discussion on the future of agricultural development and land tenure in the South a high level of general economic activity and relatively full employment in the United States was assumed. Also assumed were approximately parity prices for farm products, especially cotton and tobacco, and an acreage control program for these crops.

Part XIV   RESETTLEMENT OF PEOPLE ON THE LAND

THE LAND SETTLEMENT PROGRAM OF FINLAND

⑨⑨⑨⑨   *Kaarlo Uolevi Pihkala*

As a CONSEQUENCE of defeat in war, Finland was compelled to adopt an emergency program to provide farms, homes, and productive work for nearly 11 per cent of its total population, who left the territory surrendered to Russia. The subject of this paper is mainly the land settlement part of this emergency program. Some historical background will be given by brief reference to earlier land policy and programs.

Land Reform to 1918

The Finns, in their homeland and elsewhere, are traditionally attached to the land and land clearing to carve cultivated land out of forest and peat areas. This is the history of the settlement of Finland—hard work of individual families seeking a livelihood by their own work on the land. Thus, they cleared from 1920 to 1929 roughly 600,000 hectares, or approximately 20 per cent of the cultivated area, with almost no aid of machinery. Since the last war, with some mechanization, 140,000 hectares have been cleared for cultivation. In short, 740,000 hectares have been cleared in the years of Finnish independence, or about one-fourth of the present total of cultivated land.

The state sponsorship of land settlement, until the end of the last century, was on a minor scale only. There was significant agricultural overpopulation in the beginning of this century, before the advent of industrialization. While only 23 per cent of the rural families were independent owners, about 43 per cent of families were without land, and 34 per cent were tenants. Most of them were small leaseholders paying their rent by day labor. This kind of leasehold caused much social grievance and great insecurity of occupancy.

After the parliamentary reform (1907), the leaseholders gained more security by approval of a law (1909) concerning special kinds of tenancy. The claims for more far-reaching reform, intensified by the unfortunate events of civil war, led to the approval of a new law (1918) which entitled the leaseholders to buy out on very favourable terms the land they had cultivated. This was real land reform. It made about 67,000 small tenant farmers into independent landowners and provided some 55,000 cottagers with ownership of their dwelling sites. It is a very remarkable stage in the history of land tenure in Finland. The most socially undesirable forms of tenancy were totally wiped out. Common opinion in Finland is that this reform has remarkably strengthened the self-esteem and patriotic feelings of our agricultural population.

The principle of compulsory expropriation of land was applied for the first time in this law of 1918. It presupposed compensation—maybe this compensation was rather formal, in consequence of inflation, which cut the value of money by 90 per cent. Once approved, this principle survived in the more recent settlement laws, though compulsory expropriation was applied only in very few cases.

Land Settlement Policy 1918–39

During the first years of independence, there was much enthusiasm for improving the social conditions not only of leaseholders but also of other landless rural people. As a result, the Land Settlement Act, sometimes called *Lex Kallio* after Prime Minister (later President) Kyosti Kallio, was passed in 1922. This law provided for acquisition of land, by the state or communal aid, for any Finnish citizens who met certain conditions and who otherwise could not become an owner of a farm or dwelling site. The acquisition of land was on a voluntary basis, with the financial support of the State Settlement Fund empowered to grant loans for the buying of land, construction of buildings, and for working capital. If the applicant could not find a reasonable opportunity to get land, he was entitled to ask the Communal Settlement Board to acquire land for him from state-owned lands or from land owned by the church, municipalities, corporations, or private persons. Compulsory expropriation of land was presumed if land could not be obtained otherwise.

Certain preferences and limits too complex for discussion here were specified in the law of expropriation. Those liable were, first, the owners of neglected farms, the real estate speculators, corporations whose activity did not exclusively concern agriculture, and, finally, the other landowners beginning with the owners of the largest estates. There was, in principle, no limitation on expropriation, except the maximum size of holdings established according to this law (twenty hectares of cultivable land and the forest land necessary for home needs). This limit was to be applied only in the case of absentee owners who had neglected rational cultivation. Other land could be expropriated only according to limits of a progressive scale (1 per cent to 50 per cent), if the total area of the estate,

without waste land, exceeded certain limits (in South Finland, two hundred hectares).

The Land Settlement Law of 1922 was amended in 1936 by a new law, whereby the expropriation from private land was presumed, only for acquisition of additional land, to enlarge holdings that were too small. The maximum size of settlement holdings, in terms of cultivated land, was reduced from twenty to fifteen hectares.

The significance of compulsory expropriation in the settlement policy between the two world wars was negligible. The expropriation was used only for establishing 29 new holdings and acquiring additional land for 112 small holders. In contrast, the total number of new holdings established by state aid was 41,171, and the number of additional allotments, 17,573. It is clear, therefore, that voluntary operations or grants from state land were overwhelmingly dominant. (See Table 44.) The state and local governments bought many large holdings and divided them for settlement purposes. Of the number of new holdings established by settlement measures only about 26,000 were classified as agricultural holdings. As the number of farms having more than one-half of one hectare of arable land increased during the period 1901–41 from about 200,000 to about 300,000, the "normal-time" settlement measures account for one-third of the increase in the number of new holdings.

The industrialization of the country, aided by emigration, absorbed the excess rural population during the first half of the twentieth century. The agricultural population, in fact, decreased slightly while total population grew rapidly. A much larger part is now classified as ownership than in the beginning of the century.

Resettlement After World War II

It is widely known that the people of those areas which were ceded to Russia by the Peace Treaty of Moscow in 1940, by

TABLE 44

NORMAL-TIME LAND SETTLEMENT IN
FINLAND, 1899–1944

Land Settled On	Number of New Holdings	Number of Additional Holdings	Total Area in Hectares
State-owned land	6,503	2,145	341,700,000
Land Purchased by state or local governments	6,280	1,333	253,400,000
Land purchased by applicants	28,359	13,983	602,400,000
Expropriated land	29	112	2,000,000
Total	41,171	17,573	1,199,500,000

the Armistice Agreement in 1944, and the Peace Treaty of Paris in 1947 spontaneously left their homes and emigrated to the territories still under Finnish sovereignty. This population (mostly inhabitants of Karelia, eastern province of Finland) totaled 480,000, of whom 230,000 were farm people. The latter comprised about 40,000 families who had tilled about 300,000 hectares and whose entire holdings had been over 1.5 million hectares. Only a few of these families had owned medium-size or large farms; the average size of their farm in the lost territories had been somewhat less than eight hectares, cultivated land.

The problem facing the Finnish people was to furnish these families with the means of livelihood without the economic burden becoming too heavy for the rest of the people, on top of the reparations and other heavy burdens of war. It had to be done

within resources of Finland, a country with large forests but comparatively small agricultural resources. The agricultural area—fields and natural meadows—is 2,724,000 hectares, only about 9 per cent of the total area, while the productive forest land is about 62 per cent of the total area of the country and waste land about 19 per cent of the total. This includes also peats, to a large extent cultivable after draining but situated mostly in the northern part of the country which is climatically favorable for farming. Various estimates show that in the southern part of the country at least 760,000 hectares are cultivable after reclamation, while in the northern part, 1,200,000 hectares of open peat land are cultivable.

Before the war, of the total area of the present territory 35.2 per cent was owned by the state, 1.4 per cent by municipalities, 0.8 per cent by the church and other religious bodies, 7.5 per cent by corporations, and 55.1 per cent by private owners. Only about 11 per cent of the state-owned land was situated in the southern half of the country, and because of unfavorable climate only a fraction (0.6 per cent) of it was agricultural land. The state and other corporate owners were thus largely owners of forestal resources.

About 93 per cent of the tilled land was privately owned, of which only a few of the owners did not cultivate it themselves. The statistics of holdings of various-size classes show that only 12.6 per cent (288,000 hectares) of arable land belonged to holdings with more than 50 hectares of plow land. These holdings numbered about 3,200 and included also state- and corporate-owned units. Middle-size farms—with 15 to 50 hectares of field area—were more than twelve times as numerous and consisted of 865,000 hectares (37.7 per cent of total cultivated area). If simple distribution methods were used, these groups would be first under consideration as potential sources of land.

Principles of Resettlement

With strong unanimity seldom found among Finnish people, the principle of resettling displaced population was approved after the end of the winter war (1939/40). There was discussion only as to how this principle should be applied in the resettlement program with least disadvantage to national economy. There were two opposing opinions on the methods of resettlement. One of these held that the resettlement should be based largely on land reclamation with public aid, while the other aimed mainly to divide and redistributte the existing cultivated land. From a purely economic point of view, the former was favored because the capital values of existing buildings and machinery could be better retained and the extension of cultivated area would increase the total capacity of agricultural production. The supporters of this view stressed also that the burden on landowners would be more equally distributed if cultivable forest land were taken into account when determining the quota of land to be given up for settlement. Many farms of considerable size, if measured in forest area especially in the lake district of middle Finland, were very small in terms of cultivated area. The opponents of this opinion stressed the necessity for rapid realization of the settlement program and the social dangers eventually arising from the settling of Karelians in areas (in central and northern Finland) where climatic and soil conditions differ from those they had been accustomed to farther south.

There were different opinions, also, concerning the use of state and corporate land for resettlement purposes. The Social party generally opposed the use of state and community land for settlement. Only a very few persons supposed that the resettlement program was attainable through voluntary operations alone.

The Resettlement Act of 1940

In June, 1940, only three months after the Peace of Moscow, the first emergency law, the Rapid Resettlement Act, was passed by the Diet. According to this law, the citizens in the ceded territory who had earned their livelihood or a substantial part of it by agriculture or fishery were entitled to land if they had not been land speculators or had not neglected their farms. For persons whose holdings had been too small or of uneconomic size, the allotments could be to some extent larger than their holdings on the ceded area. On the other hand, the maximum area of cultivable land for new holdings was fixed at 15 hectares. The number of applicants was 38,873, but only 28,939 were entitled to agricultural holdings (over 2 hectares of cultivable land). The law gave broad powers for land expropriation. The state was first among the owners obligated to turn over all the land for colonization. Next came the municipalities, religious bodies, business corporations, and private persons classified as speculators or as having neglected their farms. Next after these, in order of obligation to turn over the land demanded, was the ordinary farmer who had more than 15 hectares of cultivable land and appropriate forest areas. They were due to surrender land down to that limit.

Modesty and rational deliberation were displayed by the executive committee. It was composed mostly of young surveyors and graduates in agriculture and in forestry. A certain degree of elasticity was permitted by the fact that the law allowed land surrenderers the right to buy land from other persons who were not obliged to surrender land and to use that land to fulfill the obligation. The price of land was to be determined at the average current price of land used for agricultural and dwelling purposes during the period 1934–38.

The supporters of the idea of land reclamation as a basis for resettlement established in 1940 a joint stock company (Pellonraivaus Oy) to perform land clearing with modern machinery and reclamation. This company, which later got a large part of its capital from the state, has contributed very much to the adoption of modern methods in land clearing. Still, by far the greater part of the land clearing is done by the individual farmer using horse, grubbing hoe, and brawn.

According to the plan for resettlement, about 170,000 hectares of cultivated and 161,000 hectares of cultivable land were needed for this purpose. Only about one-half of the planned area was acquired before settlement activities were interrupted by the second war (1941). The number of established new holdings was 8,422, including 2,334 dwelling sites—not regarded as agricultural holdings—and 603 part-time holdings. Of all these holdings, 7,752 were inhabited at the outbreak of the second war.

Legislative Measures 1941–44

The ownership rights in the ceded areas were restored by a special law, passed in December 1941, after the Finnish troops had reoccupied the lost territory. The earlier owners of land were regarded as owners if they gave up their rights to new holdings. This law encouraged the return of Karelians to their home regions, and only 982 of them retained the new holdings which were established according to the Rapid Resettlement Act.

Because of the vast war devastation, much reconstruction work was necessary. The Karelians rebuilt about 22,000 farm buildings, among them 7,357 dwellings. Loans totaling 11 billion marks, or 27.5 million dollars, were granted for this purpose.

At the same time, legislative measures intended to improve the size and parcelling of Karelian small holdings were effected. These were regarded as important, especially in the regions which were totally devastated during military operations.

A special committee was appointed in 1941 to outline the settlement policy after the war. It studied not only the problem of possible rehabilitation of the land expropriated according to the Rapid Resettlement Act, but also the problem in a broader sense and especially how to meet the settlement requirements of the disabled ex-servicemen, war widows, war orphans, and front-line veterans. The committee included in its recommendations, published in 1943, a special settlement law to meet the needs of these groups.[1] The proposed law was rather radical, including compulsory expropriations, though only in a minor degree. To anticipate the policy outlined in this project, a law was passed early in 1944 in which all voluntary transfers of land to the people belonging to the above-mentioned groups were to be taken into account in any future legislation dealing with expropriation quotas.

Land Acquisition Act of 1945

The military defeat in 1944 with still greater loss of territory called forth the same problems as were met in 1940, but in still more acute form. The number of displaced persons was increased by the families of Petsamo and Porkkala areas, the latter area being leased for a fifty-year period. The country's financial condition was much worse than in 1940, and the fertility of the soil was to a large extent depleted by the lack of fertilizers. There were new claims for land, encouraged by certain wartime promises to front-line soldiers. An inquiry in 1945[2] indicated a total number of applicants for land of more than 208,000; which number was reduced to 156,000 when the applicants who did not meet conditions of the law had been eliminated. Only 46,000 of the applicants were from ceded areas. The rest were from among the land-hungry who were eligible for land under the new law.

Claims were advanced, the approval of which tended to limit the area where compulsory expropriation could be effected. Thus, the Swedish population living in certain regions on the southern and western coast demanded that the Finnish-speaking farmers should not be placed in Swedish-speaking or bilingual communes to any extent which would alter the linguistic character of the population. The Karelians who lost their homes in the south claimed that the northern limit of their settlement on a compulsory basis should not be drawn farther than the Kokkola-Joenauu line (about lat. 64° N.). These matters are mentioned in passing merely to illustrate certain practical difficulties encountered.

A special committee, appointed in 1944, drafted a proposition for a new radical resettlement law, which, as to land expropriation, was based on almost the same principles as Rapid Resettlement Act.[3] When this draft was considered in the Council of State, a counter-proposition was presented. Its purpose was to save the agricultural holdings from too heavy expropriation by fixing a progressive scale. This scale provides for different sizes of maximum farm limits of expropriation. The forest land was also taken into account and was converted into the equivalent of cultivated areas. According to this proposition, about 125,000 hectares of cultivated area were to have been used for resettlement, with reclamation satisfying the rest of the land requirement. To encourage the establishing of farms on cultivable forest and peat land, a special award was provided.

The Land Acquisition Act, passed in May, 1945, was based mainly on the principles drafted by the committee. Those first entitled to land were all displaced persons having owned or leased land on long-term conditions in the ceded territory. In the second place were put disabled ex-servicemen, war

widows, and war orphans, and, in the third, all ex-servicemen with families who had taken part in military operations. Leaseholders and agricultural workers losing their employment in consequence of land surrender were also included in this group. To obtain an agricultural holding persons in the second and third groups were required to have such experience and skill in agricultural work as was regarded necessary for independent cultivation of the land.

The maximum size of agricultural holdings given to a single person in southern Finland was 15 hectares of cultivated or cultivable land with a forest area producing normally 75 to 125 cubic meters of timber yearly (corresponding to about 25 to 40 hectares of average forest land). Within localities where possibilities existed for permanent nonagricultural earnings, provision was made for dwelling sites with cultivable areas not exceeding one-half of 1 hectare or part-time holdings not exceeding 2 hectares. Larger types of part-time holdings with areas of 2 to 6 hectares in size were fixed for localities offering good marketing possibilities and other conditions for intensive farming or adequate subsidiary earnings from industry, forestry, fishing, etc. Additional land in the form of cultivable land, not reclaimed, was to be given to persons in the above-mentioned groups if their holdings were too small and if it seemed likely to be serving the purpose.

Landowners obliged to relinquish land were divided into two general categories—primary and secondary, as under the earlier law described above. The primary group consisted of the state, owners of neglected farms, real estate speculators, corporations, the church, local governments (municipalities), foundations, and "amateur" farmers by occupation. The secondary category consisted of farmers proper, those deriving their livelihood chiefly from farming.

The lands belonging to primary surrenderers were subject to expropriation without any limitations, except that the land inevitably needed for public agricultural education and scientific institutions or industrial or recreational purposes was to be saved, and the "amateur" farmers were allowed to keep an area corresponding to the size of the dwelling site. For secondary surrenderers, a minimum limit equal to the maximum size of settlement holdings was fixed in the Land Acquisition Act. If the owner had two or more children who were not earning their livelihood outside of farming, the area corresponding to the size of the agricultural holding (fifteen hectares of agricultural land) was to be allowed for the second child and half this amount for each of the other children.

As the law sought to avoid measures which were apt to weaken the productivity and profitableness of agriculture, a scale for land expropriation for secondary surrenderers was fixed by Resolution of the Council of State, June, 1945, and amended July, 1946. According to the latter, the maximum percentage of surrender was fixed on a basis of the total area of cultivated land,

as well as cultivable meadow and open pasture land, both converted according to a value equivalent to that of cultivated land. This percentage varied in different size classes, as shown in Table 45.

If the above-mentioned area was less than twenty-five hectares, and if the farm had cultivable land, the surrender should not be greater than would allow for the owner a total of twenty-two hectares of cultivated and cultivable land.

According to the law, compensation for the land was to be paid on the basis of "justifiable current" local price levels prevailing at the end of December, 1944. In practice, this price level was fixed, using the estimates of taxable income made by the Ministry of Finance in co-operation with the Research Bureau of the Board of Agriculture and local authorities, and compensation was not to be paid in cash, but with state bonds payable after fifteen years and yielding 4 per cent interest. The inflation later wiped out four-fifths of their value, but those bonds could be used instead of money when paying the very heavy Second Property Expropriation Tax, which was in the nature of a capital levy. Hence, the landowners, on the average, probably did not suffer more than did other owners of property.

A special law, the Voluntary Acquisition Regulation Act, encouraged the voluntary transfer of land to the persons entitled to get land according to the Land Acquisition Act.

The recipient of land had to pay the state for it in annual installments, beginning after the holding had been five years in the hands of the new settler. The annual payments were 5 per cent, of which 3 per cent was regarded as interest and the rest as amortization.

The Karelians got compensation for their property losses according to a special Second Indemnity Law. This was given in the

TABLE 45

PERCENTAGE OF LAND SURRENDER IN FINLAND ACCORDING TO SIZE CLASSES

| | PERCENTAGE OF SURRENDER | |
Size Class (hectares)	By Lower Limit	Part Exceeding Lower Limit
25–35	10	45
35–50	20	53
50–100	30	60
100–200	45	75
200–400	60	80
400–800	70	90
800–	80	90

form of state bonds, which contained guarantees against inflation. Those bonds were to be used for payment of land, but only according to their original face value, to prevent speculative operations in those bonds in payment for land. The law provided that the displaced population should be settled, as far as possible, in areas where natural conditions were similar to those to which they were accustomed. Moreover, it provided that former neighbors should be resettled, as far as practicable, in the same locality in order to retain their social relations.

The settling of Karelians in Swedish-speaking communities was limited according to the "language paragraph" of the law, designed to preserve the language composition. In addition to the Swedish-speaking families of the Porkkala area, only about one thousand families have been located in these communities. The landowners of these communities, however, have been obliged to perform or support land reclamation operations, and therefore have not escaped the economic burden of the resettlement program.

The law provided, also, special subsidy for settlers willing to establish new holdings on cultivable land. This subsidy in the beginning amounted to from 200,000 to 280,000 marks (2,200 to 3,100 dollars), but has been increased during the depreciation in the value of money. For land clearing, other subsidies have been granted.

A special law was approved at the time of the Land Acquisition Act to provide the necessary credit for resettlement. According to this law, the recipients of the land were entitled to get loans from the State Settlement Fund for purchases of land, land clearing, construction of buildings, and purchase of machines and implements. The loans were granted, to the extent the budgetary means were available, through co-operative credit societies or savings banks, and the state guaranteed repayment of a part, at maximum 25 per cent, and in exceptional cases 35 per cent, of the amount of offered security. The interest on these loans has been the same as on other loans granted by the Settlement Fund, i.e., 3 per cent, which is a very low rate in Finland.

In addition to these, some other related laws were enacted. These include the Preliminary Land Clearing Act, authorizing regional boards under the supervision of the Ministry of Agriculture to perform land clearings on suitable areas; the Common Forest Act, under which the establishment of common forests in districts where scarcity of forest land made it difficult to provide individually-owned parcels; and the Pasture Act to promote co-operative pastures, improved and used according to modern methods. The last two of these forms of land use have as yet been applied only to a small extent; the common forests comprise at the present time 59,000 hectares, or 3.1 per cent of the total area of established holdings, while the co-operative pastures have an area of hardly 1 per cent of the total area.

Execution of Land Acquisition Act

The administration of the Land Acquisition Act has been entrusted to the Department of Land Settlement in the Ministry of Agriculture. Local organs include the land redemption boards, responsible for expropriation measures, and the settlement boards, with the duty to locate the applicants for land. The first of these boards has a surveyor engineer as chairman, a graduate in agriculture, and a forester as expert members, and two lay members as representatives of land recipients and land surrenderers. The settlement boards have a graduate in agriculture as chairman, one representative of the land surrenderers, and two of the land recipients as members. Both boards are situated in the same locality and work in close co-operation.

At the beginning of resettlement activities

there were 147 boards of both kinds. The intermediate stage in this organization consisted of eight supervisory bureaus and eight courts of appeal. The setting up of the re-settlement farms, i.e., the next phase of execution following upon the creation of the new farms, was managed by the local organizations of the Central Association of Agricultural Societies. This organization aided the settlers with the design of buildings, planning of roads and drainage construction, and land clearing, and gave advice on all management problems. Most extensive drainage and construction work was performed by the local organization of the Engineering Division of the Board of Agriculture. Some executive proceedings were entrusted also to provincial forestry boards and the Pasture Association.

In the execution of the Land Acquisition Act, up to the end of 1951, a total of 1,911,-000 hectares of land were acquired.[4] (See Table 46.) This is about 12 per cent of the area of southern Finland, the two northern provinces excluded. Of this total area, 507,000 hectares are taken from state-owned land and 614,000 hectares from other nonprivate owners. The land bought or expropriated from private owners consisted of an area of 790,000 hectares, including 195,000 hectares of cultivated land, as compared with 87,000 hectares from nonprivate owners.

Of the transactions up to the end of the year 1951, voluntary operations embraced an area of 589,000 hectares. Most of this area was land subject to expropriation; but more than one-fifth of it was bought from owners who were not liable to expropriation. Only about 63,000 hectares of expropriated land were classified as neglected land and 4,200 hectares as owned by land speculators. The number of land units formed or transferred according to the Land Acquisition Act and the law concerning volun-

TABLE 46

Land in Finland Acquired by Voluntary Transactions or Compulsory Expropriation Through 1951, Including Areas Acquired Under the Rapid Resettlement Act*

Owner Group	Agricultural Land	Potentially Cultivable Land	Forest Land	Waste Land	Total	Percentage
State	20.1	49.2	398.8	39.0	507.1	26.5
Municipalities	15.3	14.0	76.4	2.9	108.6	5.7
Churches, etc.	18.2	15.5	66.4	1.6	101.7	5.3
Corporations	33.6	59.9	303.7	6.8	404.0	21.2
Private Owners	194.7	110.6	467.1	17.3	789.7	41.3
Primary Surrenderers†	(39.9)	(28.0)	(141.2)	(7.1)	(216.2)	(11.3)
Secondary Surrenderers	(106.7)	(58.6)	(208.6)	(5.4)	(379.2)	(19.8)
Others‡	(48.1)	(24.0)	(117.3)	(4.8)	(194.3)	(10.2)
Total	281.9	249.2	1,312.4	67.6	1,911.1	100.1

*In thousands of hectares.
†Amateur farmers, land speculators, and owners who have neglected cultivation.
‡Including owners not liable to expropriation and owners having surrendered under the Rapid Settlement Act.

TABLE 47

NUMBER AND AVERAGE SIZE OF LAND UNITS IN FINLAND FORMED BY OR TRANSFERRED
ACCORDING TO SETTLEMENT LAWS, 1945–1951

	Number	Average Cultivated (hectares)	Av. Area Cultivable (hectares)	Average Other Land (hectares)	Av. Total
Agricultural holdings:					
6–15 hectares	27,641	7.1	6.5	33.4	47.0
Part-time holdings:					
2–6 hectares	14,297	3.0	2.3	14.3	19.6
0.5–2 hectares	21,039	0.7	0.3	0.8	1 8
For fishermen	677	2.2	0.8	10.1	13.3
Dwelling sites	30,787	0.1	0.0	0.1	0.2
Common pastures	1,545	1.8	5.0	2.8	9.6
Common forests	59	. . .	. . .	1,000.0	1,000.0
Additional areas	24,648	0.6	0.7	5.4	6.7
Other areas	4,538	. . .	. . .	4.0	4.0
Total	125,231	2.2	1.9	10.9	15.0

tary transfers was, up to the end of 1951, around 125,000. (See Table 47.) This included around 28,000 agricultural holdings with potential cultivated areas of 6 to 15 hectares, about 36,000 part-time holdings with from 0.5 to 6 hectares of cultivable area, about 31,000 dwelling sites, and about 25,000 additional areas to be turned over to existing small farms to enlarge their holdings.

TABLE 48

LAND UNITS IN FINLAND BOUGHT BY OR CONTRACTED TO PRESENT HOLDERS, BY CATEGORIES
OF LAND RECIPIENTS, JAN. 1, 1952

Land Recipients	Agri. Holdings	Part-time Holdings	Dwelling Sites, etc.	Total
Displaced families	19,622	13,362	5,168	38,152
Disabled ex-servicemen, war widows, and orphans	1,126	3,737	5,157	10,020
Ex-servicemen with families	6,072	16,053	20,233	42,358
Former leaseholders and agricultural workers	826	2,773	855	4,454
Recipients of additional land	. . . . . .	. . . . . .	23,487	23,487
Total	22,646	35,925	54,900	118,471

An idea of how the new holdings are distributed to different groups of land recipients is given in Table 48, which shows the number of farms either bought by or contracted to present holders. (Most of the expropriated land is first contracted to future owners for five years.)

Displaced families have received about 38,000 holdings, the total figure of land units being 118,000. As the families of the first-mentioned group deserving land have generally been resettled by now, about 18 per cent of the families belonging to this group have given up their intention to acquire land.

Though the displaced families thus form only about 32 per cent of the recipients of land, their share of the total amount of land is larger—about 59 per cent, as shown in Tables 48 and 49. Their share of the cultivated land is 63 per cent.

At the present time, some statistical data are available to show how the execution of the Land Acquisition Act has changed the number of holdings and the acreage in the different farm-size groups. According to these data the number of farms with 100 hectares or more of cultivated area has been reduced from 790 to 227 and those with

50 to 100 hectares, from 2,500 to 1,281. About 170,000 hectares, or about 60 per cent of the cultivated area of these size classes, have been transferred to size classes under 15 hectares.

Economic Burden of Resettlement

The execution of the Resettlement Program has been a heavy economic burden. The government has taken the responsibility for extensive road construction and drainage operations. Only a very small part of the cost of these can be put on the shoulders of land settlers. About 9,000 kilometers of new roads have been planned and 8,200 already built for the needs of about 37,000 new farms. The drainage operations are planned for an area of 200,000 hectares, of which 149,000 hectares are drained.[5] During the years 1945–51, 3.9 billion markkas (20.6 million dollars) from the public budget have been used for these purposes.

The state has paid for establishing subsidies for such land recipients who have voluntarily taken holdings on uncleared forest and peat land (called "cold" farms) in an amount of 2.89 billion markkas (15.3 million dollars). At the end of year 1951, the number of such farms was 11,800,

TABLE 49

Land Area in Finland Bought by or Contracted to Present Holders, by Categories of Land Recipients, January 1, 1952*

Land Recipients	Agricultural Land	Potential Agri. Land	Other Land	Total
Displaced families	172.7	130.2	741.1	1,044.0
Disabled, widows, orphans	13.0	12.1	63.2	88.3
Ex-servicemen	62.2	56.1	295.3	413.6
Leaseholders and workers	10.3	7.4	44.3	62.0
Recipients of additional land	15.0	16.1	125.8	156.9
Total	273.2	221.9	1,269.7	1,764.8

*In thousands of hectares.

whereof about 1,000 were still without holders.

In addition to these, special subsidies for land clearing have been paid by the government. These subsidies amounted during the same time to 3.73 billions of markkas (19.19 million dollars). With this subsidy, more than 140,000 hectares of uncultivated land were put into cultivation. The state has also provided large sums of money as loans to land recipients. The amount of loans granted during the years 1945–51 is 29.8 billion markkas (181 million dollars).[6] Most of this sum (around 25 billion markkas) is granted for construction of buildings. During this time, 45,000 new dwellings, 21,700 barns, and 38,000 other buildings were constructed.

The loans for purchase of land amounted to 2.6 billion markkas, while those for equipment were, according to the statistics, 2.4 billion, and for land clearing 100 million markkas.

It has been calculated that by the end of 1951 the total amount of public funds used for resettlement in form of loans, compensations, and subsidies will have reached a total of 52.3 billion markkas (278 million dollars).

Financial Position of Settlers

According to an investigation of around 4,000 agricultural holdings established under the Land Acquisition Act, the average cost involved in acquisition of land, in the construction of buildings, equipping the farm, and land clearing amount to an average per farm of 2,325,000 markkas (10,060 dollars). This figure refers to average holdings, with potential cultivable area of 12.2 hectares, of which 5.9 hectares are under cultivation, and with total area of 39.8 hectares. The cost of buildings was 57.5 per cent of all costs. The other costs were, in order: land, 15.9 per cent; equipment, 12.8 per cent; land clearing, 12.8 per cent; other, 1.5 per

cent. The value of family labor constituted 19.1 per cent of the computed costs, while invested capital was 11.9 per cent. The part of loans from Resettlement Funds was 34.0 per cent and private loans 5.2 per cent, while various subsidies contributed 12.3 per cent. This investigation shows that resettlers are rather heavily indebted, their debts being about 40 per cent of the value of investment.

Consequences of Resettlement

The land reform programs of Finland up to the Winter War of 1939/40 were matters of deliberate choice in public policy, and the results have been good from the standpoint of economic, social, and political considerations. The resettlement program after the war was an unavoidable consequence of the war with the loss of territory in which lived about 11 per cent of the population. These people left their homes and farms and moved into the Finland that was not lost. The consequences of their resettlement cannot be judged in economic terms alone. Yet some of the farm-economic results may be noted in conclusion.

The splitting of middle-size and large holdings in a country in which these holdings have been regularly operated by the owner and only seldom exceed the optimum size of management means diminished possibilities of mechanization. Very large capital values are lost in buildings and equipment than cannot be used fully after reduction in the amount of land in the farm. This is true especially in cases where there has not been the possibility of compensating the loss of land with new land clearing. Increase in the number of farms on the same cultivated area has led to an increased number of workers and draught animals. According to the statistics, we, in fact, have in the present territory about 55,000 more horses than before the war.

On the other hand, it has been pointed out that the expropriation of cultivated land, in most cases, has concerned the most distant fields of farms subject to expropriation. These fields had often been extensively used, and adding them to new farms situated nearby may lead to more intensive cultivation and higher yields. This may compensate to some extent for the disadvantages of the fragmentation of holdings.

The reduced average size of farms probably will, to some extent, alter the composition of farm production. The small farms tend to produce relatively more animal products than larger ones which often have specialized more in cash crops. This may increase our imports of grain and cause a need for larger exports of animal products and thus create new marketing problems.

The large sums spent for execution of the resettlement program were, of course, not always used very profitably. If alternate use of this money, for example, for improving machinery, extending drainage, etc., had been possible, it might have been economically more advantageous. It must be pointed out once more, however, that our resettlement program was an unavoidable emergency program. We were compelled by very hard facts to adopt such a program in order to redress the economic loss and social injustice that the war had heaped upon a large part of our people. To have done otherwise than to meet this challenge by some such program as that which I have attempted to describe might have brought consequences far more serious than the fiscal burdens and the farm-economic maladjustments to which I have alluded.

LAND TENURE PROBLEMS IN THE RESETTLEMENT OF REFUGEES IN WESTERN GERMANY

Siegfried H. Palmer

To UNDERSTAND the peculiar difficulties of Germany's land tenure problems, it must be mentioned that today there are about 48 million people living in the Federal Republic of Germany; but of these, 9.4 million people did not reside in Western Germany before World War II. They are newcomers, and may be subdivided by origin as follows: 7.6 million expellees came from the east provinces of Germany (Silesia, East Prussia, etc.) and other European countries (the Balkans, Baltic states, and Poland). One and one-half million German refugees have fled from the Soviet Zone of Eastern Germany to seek safety in the Federal Republic of Western Germany. Their number is increasing daily by 800 to 1,000 persons. There are 300,000 non-German refugees from Eastern Europe who refuse to be repatriated and who, like the German refugees

from the Russian zone, seek asylum in Western Germany. There is a constant influx of such refugees from the East.

If we add to all these the 4.4 million German expellees from Eastern Europe living in the Soviet zone of Germany, we arrive at a figure of 13.8 million uprooted people living in the four occupation zones of Germany. Three million more Germans have perished during the mass flights and expulsions in the last period of war and the following months. If applied to American conditions, this would mean that the states of Massachusetts, Connecticut, Rhode Island, New York, and New Jersey would have to absorb the entire people of Canada, stripped of all their possessions.

Under the emergency conditions of the years 1945-47—with unanticipated and unpredictable arrivals of mass transports from the East—the expellees were channeled to the predominantly rural provinces bordering the Soviet zone of occupation. The urban centers of trade and industry were largely in ruins due to air warfare. Hence, almost 85 per cent of all expellees had to be accommodated in rural areas, especially in the states, or Laender, of Schleswig-Holstein, Lower Saxony, and Bavaria. Unavoidably, this herding together of newcomers resulted in an inequitable distribution, since the three Laender contain but 61 per cent of the former indigenous population of Western Germany. Moreover, the expellees found standing room only in these Laender without industry, and most of their unemployed burden these financially weak agricultural states.

Of the total number of expellees, 25 per cent formerly engaged in farming and forestry, among them 270,000 families as independent farmers. Nearly 50 per cent of these groups are formerly self-employed expelled people.

Up to June 30, 1951, 15,080 independent farm families from the East have been rehabilitated by aid of the Refugee Settlement Act (Fluechtlingssiedlungsgesetz) of August 10, 1949. We may expect this number to increase by 5,000 more families by the end of this year, since sufficient means could be provided for their rehabilitation. Thus not quite one-tenth of the former independent farmers from the East have found an opportunity to resume their customary pursuits. Our problems have to be seen in the following context.

According to the census of 1949 there are about 2 million farms and woodland holdings in Western Germany, occupying about 34 million acres (13.5 million hectares) of agricultural land. But more than 30 per cent of these holdings have less than 5 acres of land each and cannot be considered as independent farmsteads, unless they are garden or vineyard units. Of the whole

agricultural area, two-thirds belongs to holdings under 50 acres and 18 per cent to holdings with less than 12.5 acres, i.e., holdings which are for the most part smaller than an economic unit. Most small holders of this size group must engage in a secondary occupation. To holdings of more than 250 acres belong 4.2 per cent of the whole agricultural area. This percentage was considerably higher in Germany east of the Elbe River, amounting up to 30 per cent for the whole area. In Western Germany, large estates are mainly located in the British zone, especially in Schleswig-Holstein and Lower Saxony.

The German legislative authorities in the different German Laender issued various land reform laws, inaugurated by the occupation powers, in the years 1946 to 1949. They provided for the obligatory surrender of land for all owners of more than 250 acres in the Laender of the American Zone. In the Laender of the British zone the big landowners have to surrender the whole surplus of land over the size of 250 acres, including forest land. In the U.S. zone they have to deliver a certain percentage of their land exceeding the 250-acre limit, according to a tabulation of progressive amounts by size of holdings. Necessarily, only a little land was made available for settlement of expelled farmers. First, the land of the large estates which was leased to small tenants could not be taken away from them, but was to be converted into properties in order to maintain the local farm. However desirable this was, the measure did not help the have-not refugee. Furthermore, the law and the subsequent decrees had to provide for legal appeals and injunctions on behalf of big landowners. This, and the provisions for compensation, caused considerable difficulties. Thus land reform and settlement moved slowly and on a small scale. In Western Germany up to June 30, 1951, about 3,500 new holdings have been provided for expellees on land made available by the land reform. Permit me to compare this with what Finland has done after the war.

A few days ago, we heard a paper about the way the 4 million Finns have solved the task of integrating the evacuees. We admire the heroic accomplishment of this Finnish resettlement work. We Germans envy Finland not only because of this but also because Finland in the hour of defeat continued to be a state with a working administration. The Finnish representatives, under the impact of common misfortune, one day could resolve—and at that unanimously resolve—to enact incisive laws stipulating surrender of property and land and compensation for the expellees from Karelia. If I may be permitted to draw this comparison and to comment in this way, I do so because I had the opportunity to study these issues in Finland this last September. Finns told us: "At this time we were all Karelians." The difficulties came only later, when conditions were improving.

The initiation of a thoroughgoing agrarian reform requires the great hours, when all realize the urgency and true proportion of overriding issues. This to my mind is the renewed lesson of the Finnish example.

Now, I will describe another way, after Germany became the Federal Republic in 1949. One of the basic principles of the Refugee Settlement Act of August 10, 1949, is to eliminate weaknesses in the present land tenure law. Furthermore, poorly managed or only partly cultivated farms were to get into the hands of capable farmers from the East. Such farms include those owned by single, aged people whose sole interest may be just to earn a living without fully exploiting the capacity of their holdings (for instance, by not investing in fertilizer, repair of buildings, etc.). Usually these single, aged people have no heirs, or the descendants have taken nonfarming occupations and do not intend to take over the parental farm. I should like to emphasize that these social conditions do not necessarily lead to neglect of intensive cultivation, although they may tend to do so. We have termed such farms "blind alley farms" (auslaufende Hoefe). For social reasons as well as for reasons of agricultural output it seemed desirable to promote in such cases the voluntary transfer of the land or farm to an expelled homeless farmer from the East. This has led to good results. "Blind alley farms" in the hands of refugee farmers in a short time have taken on a new appearance and have yielded higher output. There are one or two such "blind alley farms" in almost every West German village. There are also farms which have been given up by the heirs who were not interested in farming and who either sold them or permanently rented or let them out. These are so-called "deserted farms" (wueste Hoefe). The farm buildings which might still be usable were to be placed at the disposal of refugee farmers in order to make use of the capital invested in buildings. The third category of farms which were preferably to be made over to the expellees were farms of absentee owners or of nonfarmers. Compulsory seizure of such farms might easily lead to injustices. Whether or not the refugee was able to take over such a farm was decided mainly on purely economic grounds, since the parties concerned were free to negotiate on a voluntary basis. To encourage the surrender of land to refugee farmers, the Refugee Settlement Act provides various tax privileges to the landowner. First, the landowner is exempted from the income tax with this part of his income gained from the lease of land to a refugee farmer up to the income of 2,000 Deutsche Mark. Second, the landowner is freed of paying the so-called Soforthilfe-Abgabe, the special tax levy in aid of refugees and expellees, but only for this part of his property which is given to the refugee farmer. To secure the aged landowner, the state is warrantor for the payment of rent under the lease contract with a refugee farmer. This is a first step to solve a problem existent in our agriculture, namely, the problem of security for the aged people in order to reach a quicker transfer of landed property to the younger generation.

For the refugee farmer himself, who lacks the needed capital, the law also provides certain privileges. First, for installment and equipment purposes he can get a state loan free of interest, to be repaid after a period of three years in annuities of 4 per cent. Second, for the improvement of run-down buildings or for the establishment of new living space the refugee farmer can also get a state loan under the same conditions. Both loans should not exceed 5,000 Deutsche Mark each. But in many cases there are additional funds available for the same purpose from other sources.

This has proved a strong incentive for such land transfers, and it has been more effective than compulsion could have been with time-consuming appeals and injunctions. In order to minimize bureaucratic interferences, great weight was put on voluntary and independent operations. The grant of tax privileges for landowners and of public loans for refugees, to be sure, depends upon the settlement authorities' endorsement of the contract of tenancy or purchase, but the preparation and the conclusion of these contracts is left to the parties concerned. Thus, the refugee, too, is expected to show initiative of his own. Certainly this was not always easy for the refugees from the East, who may have drifted into out-of-the-way places, but they were free to seek the advice of the private real estate agents, and they also helped each other through their self-help organizations and information service. There was a further difficulty. In most cases, refugees or evacuees from the cities had been billeted in the farm houses under consideration. The new farmer, how-

ever, needs the space for himself and his family. Therefore, a statutory provision provides for a loan to the departing tenant, enabling him to build, alone or in partnership, a residence near his place of work. This serves both parties. Moreover it contributed gradually to reduce tensions caused by the overcrowding of rural areas by masses of refugees and evacuees. The urban man, billeted in a farmhouse or a village and wanting to return to his customary urban occupation, could move back to town; the refugee farmer could leave his barracks for the newly acquired farmstead.

The following figures present some results of the Refugee Settlement Act.

Of the total area of land settled with refugee farmers, 25.9 per cent were "blind alley" farms, 7.9 per cent deserted farms, and 66.2 per cent land of other absentee owners.

The type of establishment of the refugee farmers was as follows: 23.1 per cent new settlements, 45 per cent tenant farms, and 31.9 per cent purchased farms.

The size of the agricultural holdings by size groups was as follows: Holdings below five acres represent a relatively large proportion of the total, namely, 35.7 per cent. They comprise in the main the so-called Aufbaubetriebe and the cottages of land laborers (Landarbeiterstellen). Aufbaubetriebe are small farmsteads, with certain arrangements for future enlargement of buildings and land allotments. If this is not realized, we have here part-time farmers. We had to accept this type of settlement, since it is better for the homeless expellee farmer to have a place to live in and garden land of his own than to continue indefinitely to live in unsatisfactory conditions. Certainly it is a makeshift adjustment by the standards of our agricultural goals. Fortunately the remaining 64.3 per cent of the land is in holdings sufficiently large to guarantee independent farming. Most of them offer to the expellee some substitute for his lost farm.

Now, let me conclude. I tried to be short. But I want to emphasize that there are many other projects or proposals which could contribute to the solution of our refugee problem. There are projects of land reclamation, irrigation, and dike building on the coast of the North Sea and the promotion of emigration.

But all these measures in Germany, as well as in other countries, can be carried out only if the necessary capital is made available. Let us hope that the further development of political events will go on in a peaceful way—to provide the necessary capital, needed now for other purposes, for these most important tasks.

INDIAN EXPERIMENTS IN LAND RECLAMATION AND THE RESETTLEMENT OF POPULATIONS

 Aditya Nath Jha

THE YEAR 1947 brought freedom to India but with it a number of serious problems. The settlement of displaced persons (a problem following directly from the division of the subcontinent) was a burden so severe that the world doubted seriously the ability and the capacity of the young republic to shoulder it. The other task, no less heavy, was to make a determined drive for self-sufficiency in food.

The state of U.P. (Uttar Pradesh)—with a population of over 60 millions—about 3 per cent of the world population, nine times that of Australia, more than five times that of Canada—received to a greater extent than any other state the impact of the problem of displaced individuals, and to it fell the greatest share of the burden of the problem of food.

To clear the decks, as it were, for the battle for food, far-reaching measures of agrarian reform were introduced and the Extension Service was reorganized—twin admissions of the fact that the answer to the food problem lay with the cultivator, who had to be given the necessary incentive and the knowledge and means for increasing production. The new program aimed at intensive production in the land already under plough, plus extension of cultivation to new areas.

It is the object of this paper to give an idea, however sketchy, of the state's land reclamation and settlement scheme, which program would bring over a half-million acres of new land under cultivation.

In pursuance of this program, 160,000 acres have already been reclaimed and settled in different tracts of the state. The problem in these tracts was fivefold: (1) to make the areas healthy by launching an intensive anti-malaria drive; (2) to reclaim land, mostly covered with weed and scrub jungle, by mechanical means; (3) to build residential quarters for the new and mostly destitute settlers; (4) to give rehabilitation loans and grants on a generous scale; (5) to provide irrigation and healthful drinking water facilities.

One cannot do better than describe one of these schemes, typical of the rest.

The story of the Tarai, until the reclamation scheme was adopted, was a very depressing one. The unhealthiness of the tract and the depredation of wild animals had discouraged everyone in the past. The area was sparsely populated, and the influenza epidemic of 1918 caused a great decline in manpower, and from that time may be dated the commencement of the more rapid deterioration. Life in the whole of this submontane tract was one of continual struggle for existence against the depredation of wild animals, the rank and vigorous Tarai vegetation, the enervating climate, malignant malaria, bad drinking water, high death-rate and infant mortality, low birth-rate, appalling scarcity of means of communications, and lack of even ordinary amenities of existence. An ever-dwindling population made heroic efforts to stem the tide of deterioration, but conditions were so precarious that even minor calamities set deterioration in motion. This was the problem which faced the government intent upon ameliorating the condition of the inhabitants. As the end of World War II hove in sight, the question of the returning soldiers began to loom large on the horizon, and the advent of the National Government expedited the scheme for development, contemplating both the reclamation of the tract and the colonization of the area. Begun for the rehabilitation of ex-servicemen, the scheme was later thrown open to persons displaced as a result of the partition of the country, to landless laborers, and to a handful of persons trained in the agricultural colleges and schools.

A detailed scheme for the reclamation and colonization of the tract was prepared and approved by the government in August, 1947, and with the help of a few units of the state and the Central Tractor Organization the work of reclamation was begun on January 4, 1948, under a new Colonization Department created for the purpose.

The scheme envisaged the development of over 100,000 acres of land (165 square miles) in two phases. The first phase is now over, with the reclamation of about 35,000 acres of land. A central state farm, perhaps the biggest in Asia, comprising 16,000 acres of land inclusive of a dairy and fodder farm and an orchard covering 1,000 acres, has been established in the most difficult area, while the remaining land has been allotted to over 1,600 families—all of whom have

been provided with well-designed residences, the cost of which will be recovered from them in 25 years.

Sixteen new villages have been founded and seventeen more are in the process of being laid out and will soon be completed.

Thirty miles of tar-macadam all-weather roads and over fifty miles of fair-weather roads have been constructed.

Extension of canals was neither possible nor desirable in a tract which was already damp. The proper solution lay in the establishment of a series of tube wells energized from a powerhouse to provide irrigation as an insurance against drought. Sixteen tube and artesian wells have been installed, and it is proposed to have one tube well for each one thousand-acre block. A power house has been constructed with a capacity for generating six hundred kilowatts of electricity, and a properly planned town is being established.

Malignant and pernicious malaria was the scourge of the tract. As a result of the excellent work performed by our Anti-Malaria Unit, the incidence of malaria has been reduced to negligible proportions. This is a remarkable achievement. The highly successful malaria operations have not only succeeded in making the area reasonably healthful for settlers but also in obliterating any fear of the sickness which discouraged even Extension workers from going to this area in the past. The settlers gained confidence, and the health of the people has continued to remain very satisfactory.

Twenty Land Settlement Co-operative Societies have been formed for the different categories of the settlers, and more are in the process of formation. The settlers have been given loans for the purchase of agricultural stocks and implements and for the construction of one-room tenements and other essential requirements. Two Consumers Stores have also been started. Loans to the extent of 100,000 dollars have already been advanced to the Societies and more loans are being given.

It is proposed to have belts of forest along the several streams of the Tarai in order not only to prevent erosion but also to provide timber and fuel reserves for the colony.

According to the statistics collected recently, there are 3,400 children (of the settlers) who are expected to go to school. Nine primary schools and one secondary school have been established.

A fleet of eighty tractors is being maintained by the state mainly for dealing with the "follow-up" work after the initial reclamation. Both a field and a base workshop have been set up for field repairs and major overhauls of tractors and other equipment.

The Tarai area is now a smiling country with flourishing cultivation and a contented population happy at finding a new home. There are still many problems to be solved, and the work of development is in progress.

The financial side of the picture is as follows.

1. The total expenditure incurred on (1) roads, culverts, bridges, powerhouse, etc., (2) anti-malaria measures, (3) provision of housing and potable drinking water facilities, and (4) reclamation operations in the Tarai Colony up to the end of the financial year 1950/51 has been less than 3.5 million dollars.

2. The total area under cultivation is approximately 35,000 acres, while another 29,000 acres have been cleared of scrub jungle. The cost of follow-up operations in this latter area of 29,000 acres will not exceed 4 million dollars.

3. Out of the entire area thus reclaimed 16,000 acres are to be maintained as a state farm. Approximately 4,000 acres out of this area are to be used purely for growing cultivated grasses for government cattle and the cattle of the surrounding countryside. Notwithstanding the fact that only 6,000 acres are at present under state farming, the audited accounts for the agricultural year 1950/51 have shown a net profit of 160,000 dollars. The state farm (excluding the 4,000 acres of pasture land) should ultimately yield a net profit of approximately 400,000 dollars annually.

4. Briefly, the financial position of this colony, once the work is completed, should be as follows: total capital expenditure (approximately), 5.0 million dollars, total grant from the central government, 0.6 million dollars, leaving a balance of 4.4 million dollars.

To the 400,000 dollars annual net profit on the state farm should be added the total land revenue of approximately 60,000 dollars on the reclaimed land. This means an annual return to the government of approximately 10 per cent. This figure does not include the irrigation rates that will be paid by the cultivators on the facilities for irrigation provided them. Thus, in short, even if we ignored the tremendous advantage secured in the matter of rehabilitation of displaced and landless persons and the very considerable increase in food production secured by these operations and judged the entire Tarai reclamation scheme as a purely business proposition, the expenditure incurred has been a sound investment. In the above calculations the sale proceeds of food grains (amounting to 1 million dollars) so far credited to the government have also been ignored.

APPRAISING EXPERIENCES IN THE RESETTLEMENT OF POPULATIONS

Report of the Working Party

Chairmen, *George W. Hill and Carl C. Taylor*

THE COMMITTEE believes that the evidence on population clearly indicates that there is a real need for a more adequate balancing of the world's rural population and the resources available for this population. The committee is equally certain that these problems vary from region to region in the world and that solutions or projects should be conceived on a regional rather than a world-wide basis. In some regions there is a greater need for a realignment or redistribution of population within a region, whereas in other regions there is a clear need for international movements of people.

The committee also believes that whereas the history of migration has been one in which peoples moved freely and spontaneously from one political orbit to another the complexity of the modern world compels any sizeable migrations to be guided or controlled. International agencies and support are playing an increasing part in the guidance of international movements. A corollary phenomenon to the spontaneous movement of peoples in past decades was that it was characterized largely by movements of individuals, whereas guided migration means greater emphasis upon group movements. Furthermore, whereas little control was exercised by national governments in previous decades now the complexity of the problem requires close supervision of the movements both on the part of governments of the emigrating countries as well as immigration countries.

The situations which now exist in the world, in the Middle East and Far East for example, which have thrown millions of the world's population into distress, are ample evidence that international groups or agencies have a mandate to try to arrive at some rational means to guide and expedite human resettlement to avoid the cost which these unsolved problems are now taking in dollars and human lives.

✦ Minimum Requirements

Whether the problems call for movement of peoples from one country to another or within a country there are certain minimum requirements which must be considered so that the movements will produce the result which all people strive for—a decent standard of living and freedom of religious and cultural expression.

Successful resettlement programs on both a national and international basis have demonstrated the need of careful and competent surveys and studies prior to the movement of peoples. These surveys have included data such as the following:

A. Land, including its topography, quality, types of drainage, etc.

B. Water resources, both subterranean and surface sources, for human consumption and irrigation.

C. Mineral and other natural resources as supplementary or complementary sources of employment.

D. Demographic and social studies of the composition, social preferences of the existing and potential immigrant population.[1]

E. Elaboration of local patterns of settlement and farm sizes in accordance with the requirements of an average family taking into account the necessary income and capability to work, as well as the soil conditions of the various regions.

F. Elaboration of regional settlement plans in accordance with the economic (agricultural) capacity of absorption of the region with due regard to the necessity of land reforms and the differences in approach in cases of governmental settlement, credit assisted settlement, and independent (private) settlement.

G. Preparation of plans for social and administrative services on the basis of careful studies of the sociological requirements in order to enable a smooth integration of newcomers in the new settlement areas. The important needs to be covered are education, language, religious services, health, technical assistance, etc.

H. Economic projections as to the potential future contribution of the newly built-up rural sector to the national economy as a whole to assure a smooth integration of the new production into the total national economy.

Successful implementation of resettlement projects requires that adequate provisions be made for the preparation of the lands to be used for the colony—including land clearing, deforestation, and levelling, and the laying out of a suitable system of roads, drainage and irrigation or irrigation systems. In the case of government-sponsored colonies, these services will be made available by the respective government agencies; in the case of private colonies, the government should exercise sufficient control so that these essential services will be assured for every colony.

When lands are to be made available to settlers or colonists, the following provisions should be a minimum part of every such project to be considered:

1. Land units of appropriate size should be either sold against installment payments according to the capacity of the settler over a long period (ten to thirty years) or given in hereditary lease.

2. Loans should be available to settlers for the following purposes: (a) erection of dwelling houses and farm buildings under suitable terms of payment; (b) improvement and preparation of soil (three to five years); (c) purchase of farm machinery and implements (three to six years); (d) operation expenses for crops (maximum of eighteen months); (e) tree (fruit) plantations; credits to be repaid not before ten years in equal rates each year during the five years following the beginning of production; (f) financial support or subsistence of the settler during the first year of settlement—to be repaid after two years.

3. Co-operative organization of settlers should be encouraged.

4. Technical guidance should be freely available to all the new settlements.

In all resettlement projects, the welfare of families should be an uppermost consideration. Excessive fragmentation should be avoided when land redistribution is undertaken; likewise, safeguards should be established to forestall the accumulation of lands by those who are either not interested in their proper use or who already possess units of adequate proportions.

Social and cultural islands should be avoided in resettlement schemes; likewise, every new settler should be fully conscious of his moral and social responsibilities toward his adopted land.

Adjustment of immigrants to a new land is not a one-way process; on the contrary, it implies rights and obligations upon both the individuals and governments concerned. Individuals must participate sincerely and honestly in their settlement programs. Governments, at home and in the new country, should be prepared to make their facilities available to settlers at all times; and regulations of resettlement and immigration should be consistent with the plans, ideals, and requirements of people undergoing the resettlement process.

Whereas the foregoing comments apply to the general problems of resettlement, countries faced with an immediate pressure of population and having no suitable resources at present levels of technique to absorb excess populations must be concerned with effective programs of emigration. In such countries, it would be advisable to consider the consummation of bilateral agreements with countries desiring new immigrants. These agreements should be based upon careful studies of the composition and abilities of the available emigrant population on the one hand and the potential resources for successful assimilation of immigrants in the receiving country on the other.

The committee is painfully aware of the limited time which it has had to study a problem of the magnitude of resettlement of people on an international scale, and recommends that plans be made whereby an effective attack can be made on the problem. This will call for future meetings, but more important, for concrete, effective proposals on the part of world governments for the alleviation of the problem.

Part XV — FINANCING LAND SETTLEMENT, LAND REFORM, AND FARMING OPERATIONS

FINANCING LAND SETTLEMENT IN RECENT GERMAN HISTORY

Siegfried H. Palmer

TODAY'S SUBJECT matter is supposed to adduce experiences and principles derived from the history of financing the redistribution of land. Consequently, I shall try to elaborate those developmental phases and measures from the colorful history of rural settlement in Germany which are of general significance also for other countries. In recent reports certain financial problems have been raised in a similar context.

The Prussian government, in 1886, was entitled by law to dispose a special fund of over 100 million marks with the object of promoting denser settlement in the territories of Eastern Germany. Provision was made (1) for buying large estates suitable for the establishment of viable family farms, (2) for utilizing suitable land of the public domains and of state forests for the establishment of such farms, and (3) for publicly subsidizing the establishment of new farmsteads and new communities, their churches and schools.

In the main, this program was carried out, with some extensions, until 1919. About 24,000 new settlements for peasants and land laborers were established, and additional land was given to small holders to raise their holdings to the size of subsistence farms (family farms). This program claimed a total area of about 617,500 acres (250,000 hectares) of an assessed value of about 340 million gold marks.

Establishment of Rentengueter

A new legal device, the so-called Rentengut, was created at the time. Its purpose was to provide applicants for settlement who were without funds with opportunities for self-employment and social ascent. This legal device facilitates the acquisition of a new farmstead, or merely of the requisite land, not by payment of a lump sum but by payment of an obligatory and fixed annual rent. This was the foundation of a method of financing which made the purchase of land, or of a new farmstead, not dependent upon moneyed wealth but on the ability to cultivate the land profitably year in, year out. Ever since, this principle has been followed and extended. To be sure, there were some initial difficulties, but over the years a suitable and smooth method of financing rural settlement has been established on this basis.

One of the difficulties was that the seller of the land was unwilling to accept for payment an annual rent instead of a lump sum. Therefore a later amendment stipulated that the Rentenbanken (mortgage banks) which had previously been established in the various provinces were entitled to compensate the seller for the cession of his rent claim by means of Rentenbriefe (certificates) to the amount of the capitalized rent of the Rentengut. The quotation of these Rentenbriefe at the stock exchange later were guaranteed by the state at a certain level, hence could be cashed at any time.

The settler in his turn had to pay his annuities to the Rentenbank. Apart from a few exceptions the bank could cancel neither the rent nor the capital of the Rentengut. The settler had to pay his obligatory rent until he had paid off the purchase price of the farmstead or of the land, plus the accumulated interest. Depending on the general economic conditions and the incurred obligations for payment of purchase price and interests the settler had to pay his annuities for about forty-five to seventy years. Provision was made for that settler who wished to pay off his long term credit in larger sums in a shorter time.

The settler was free to dispose of his place only after having completed all payments. Without permission of the settlement agency the settler could neither sell, mortgage, nor divide his holding. This gave not only greater security to the creditor but also served to check parcelment customary in certain regions of Germany. Besides, the restriction aimed at checking the detrimental fragmentation of the area of cultivation into widely scattered plots. Since Professor von Dietze has presented informative details concerning these stipulations of the Rentengut enactment (committee on inheritance and land distribution) I shall confine myself to this brief reference.

There was further difficulty which at times resulted from the following: Since the Rentenbriefe had to be sold in order to finance the acquisition and settlement of landed estates they could not be issued before the so-called *rezess* had come into force. This *rezess* is the final contract comprising all agreements made at the establishment of the so-called Rentengueter. Only therewith the Rentenbank had the necessary security. The signing of the contract, for various reasons, could take as much time as three years. Meanwhile the requisite capital for the purchase and establishment of the new farmstead had to be advanced privately. The landlord had no interest to alienate land without receiving prompt compensation, and the settlement agencies had only limited means to finance the purchase and establishment of the new farmstead during the transitional period. Therefore, the government advanced so-called Zwischenkredite (intermediary credits). These credits were advanced from the beginning of the settlement project to the signature of the *rezess*. They served the preliminary financing of construction work. They were paid back to the state by converting them into long term credits, that is, interest yielding Rentenbriefe (rent-certificate). Further stipulations provided that the intermediary loans when converted into long term loans could be used fully for financing new settlement projects. At last a revolving fund had thus been established which facilitated the continuous promotion of settlement. Whoever engages in this will appreciate stable financial resources and independence from budgetary allocations.

In these provisions the state in the last analysis is not the sole creditor and financier of the settlement projects. Private capital is made to contribute by placing the Rentenbriefe in the open market. This, however, applies only to those settlement costs which are covered by continuous interest and redemption payment. This part of the total costs has been termed the profitable part. Dependent on economic conditions, building costs, etc., occasionally not all investments were covered by the long-term loan. In this case the government, in order to cover this so-called "unprofitable" part, had either to grant additional means and write them off as lost or it had to stipulate that the settler had to pay back also these sums after having redeemed the profitable part, that is, after about fifty to seventy years. Usually the administration allowed such "lost" grants for canalization and drainage work, rural electrification, the construction of streets, schoolhouses, and churches in newly established villages.

In order to attract private capital and thus promote the financing of settlement projects the legal limit for mortgaging Rentengueter (settlements) was kept high—higher than is customary for any other credit institution. An act for the promotion of settlement in 1916 fixed the mortgage limit for family farms—that is, farms managed completely or in the main without non-family help—at nine-tenths of their assessed value. Nevertheless, the quotations of the Rentenbriefe were fairly high as the state gave additional security. Time has shown that the question of security is no problem at all, and of all possible entries of losses this column shows least. Besides, this stipulation increasingly eased the strain on public finance by attracting private investment capital. This result was desirable as the expansion of the whole settlement activity stimulated the demand for public financial aid.

One might add further details about the interrelationship between agricultural long term loans and short term intermediary loans in the various developmental phases. Especially the influence of the general price level and of interest rates would merit closer attention. But it does not seem to be necessary in this circle of experts. The point I wished to make with regard to the German experience with this method of finance is the following: first, public financial aid is necessary; only later private investment capital can be drawn into the process. Agricultural settlement is no field for profitable business ventures, hence the state has to shoulder the risk. Our experience has taught us that security rests largely on the correct selection of qualified and efficient settlers.

Fair Rent

A further principle in the financing of rural settlement projects is that of a fair rent. Between the two world wars this principle has increasingly proven itself. It means that the proprietor of the Rentengut, that is, the new settler, should be expected annually to pay off purchase price and interest charges to the amount which a well-managed comparable farm could afford to carry without economic harm. Thus one sought to avoid overburdening the new settler. It was argued that the settler should visualize freedom from debts and therewith complete social independence as an attainable goal of his life's work. For, all settlement promotion aims at establishing viable farmsteads, especially family farms, and therewith aims at creating independent forces which can play their part in a democratic society.

Hence when drawing up plans of finance one proceeds from the calculation of the fair rent of the future Rentengut and one figures the extent to which the profitable part will cover the cost of the settlement project and what possibly "lost" subsidies will have to be granted. For such calculation comparative farms and experiences are available so that a fairly reliable basis for calculation can be established. To be sure, economic conditions during the next years are uncertain; the situation of the capital market and the tax yield cannot be predicted with certainty. Hence this risk, too, must be shouldered by the state. Quite a few settlement projects in the past became more costly than anticipated through unforeseen price increases.

The Role of the Banks

The question of how to go about finance, whether to use private banks or state banks may be answered briefly by presenting the result of a rather intricate development in Germany. In 1930 there existed two special financial establishments. The Prussian, later Deutsche, Landesrentenbank mainly concentrated on long term settlement loans and on the conversion of public intermediary loans. These credits, however, were primarily issued by another bank, the Deutsche Siedlungsbank (settlement bank). This bank was directly subject to the control of the then Reichs ministry of food and agriculture (REM). Certain funds of its budget were earmarked for the promotion of settlement and were placed at the disposition of the Deutsche Siedlungsbank. This bank in turn distributed intermediary credits among settlement agencies according to rules and regulations of the Reichs ministry. Neither bank had other tasks. Hence they dealt exclusively with settlement finance in the broadest sense. These credit institutions were not banks in the usual sense but rather administrative action agencies commissioned by the respective Reichs department. This arrangement has turned out well. Unfortunately the various postwar changes in administrative structure and jurisdiction have thus far prevented the restoration of the former setup. But the well-proven arrangement is ubiquitously and urgently demanded, and may well be expected to be carried through.

Thus far I have presented some experiences and principles derived from the history of the financing of German settlement up to World War II. It seems to me that some of these points of view are maintained by the Farmers Home Administration of this country or have been incorporated in the respective legislative acts of Congress during the 1930's and 1940's. In Germany up to the beginning of World War II the main point was rather to establish new farmsteads, especially in what was then Eastern Germany. The American legislation in contrast—so it would seem to me—aimed rather at strengthening economically the already established farms. In Germany, according to the Reichs Settlement Act of August 11, 1919, further settlement measures were envisaged in order to strengthen the small holding of peasant and part-time

farmer and to raise them to subsistence farmers. To this end they were to receive land allotments from large landowners, who were placed under the obligation to surrender some of their land. Another goal was to make independent proprietors out of tenants so far as this could be handled in the framework of a settlement project. In prewar Germany, however, the main emphasis was placed on the establishment of new farms. This was the primary purpose of the above-mentioned loans and grants.

After World War II and on the basis of land reform and settlement enactments, particularly in Southwestern Germany, the so-called Anlieger, or neighboring smallholders, have often been given land from large estates. In many cases these have been lands that they had been leasing for many decades. The big landowners, especially in Southwestern Germany, had leased a great deal of their land to the medium-size and small peasants who could maintain themselves only by renting additional land. This explains why in some regions of Western Germany the obligation of large landlords to surrender land benefited the small-holders and not the many thousands of landless aspirants to settlement, especially not the expelled German farmers from the East. This being so, one is most eager to give what land is available for settlement to the expellees and no more to residents of old.

The Question of Compensation

The compensation of the landowners was regulated by a new law only after the currency reform. This act used as a basis for calculation the so-called Einheitswert, a figure for tax assessment. This figure is estimated on the potential net output (Reinertrag) over a number of years. There have been times when compensation was paid in terms of the so-called Verkehrswert (that is, the actual market value). Nowadays this value in some regions of Western Germany is twice that of the assessed value. To be sure, the nature of fair compensation will always remain a controversial issue. Expropriation without compensation as was carried through in the Soviet zone for proprietors of 250 acres (100 hectares) and more was out of the question in Western Germany as a Rechtsstaat affirming the right of private property. Compensation according to the market value (Verkehrswert) undoubtedly would provide an incentive for the owners voluntarily to offer even land not subject to obligatory surrender, and certainly considerably fewer protests would be raised before the administrative courts of law against the compulsion to surrender land.

Loss of Settlement Funds

The question why there is no provision for a higher compensation for land in Western Germany can simply be answered as follows: The settlement fund which had accumulated during the years before World War II has been liquidated or has shrunk to next to nothing through the currency reform of 1948. Besides, the capital market since then has not yet been able to re-absorb the low interest rent certificates. Conditions in this field are slow to return to normal, and thus far only high interest loans for industrial purposes could be placed in the capital market. This phenomenon is familiar in Germany since the stabilization of the Reichsmark after World War I. At that time, too, rent certificates could be placed in the capital market only four to five years after the currency reform.

For all these reasons the single Länder thus far had to take the initiative to promote settlement projects and therewith also to compensate the landlords for their obligatory surrender of land for settlement. It was they and not the federal government at Bonn who had to vote the necessary funds to compensate the landlords. Now the tax income

of the predominantly rural Länder best able to set aside land by land reform is lower than the tax income of highly industrialized West German Länder such as North Rhine Westfalia comprising the Ruhr industries and mines. Besides, most of the newly arrived expelled population from the East were first quartered in rural districts, in communities below 2,000 population and not in the cities, since most cities have suffered great destruction through the air war. Hence the low-tax-yield rural Länder were primarily burdened with the greatly increased welfare expenditures for the expellees. The possible grant of an initial loan for the financing of rural settlement up to the moment when a sufficiently large settlement fund has accumulated could be helpful indeed. Numerous thorough and well-prepared projects could be undertaken and the hopes of many an expellee could be fulfilled.

Financing Refugee Settlement

The Refugee Settlement Act (Flüchtlingssiedlungsgesetz) represents a new endeavor to settle the land hungry expellees from the East and simultaneously to husband capital outlay. This act of August 10, 1949, encouraged not only the settlement of expelled farmers from the East on newly established farms but, in addition, facilitated the taking over by expellees of existing farms, of residential and utility buildings, of former farmsteads. The latter provision especially saved the otherwise necessary capital layout for residential and utility buildings.

In Western Germany there exist in wellnigh every village one or two farms which are managed either by widows or by single and aged people. They either have no male heirs or their children have taken up nonfarming pursuits and have no intention to take over the parental farm at a later time (rural exodus). Various provisions (Vorschriften) of the Refugee Settlement Act make it easier for the aged people to make over their farm to a qualified farmer from the East. They can do so by leasing or selling the farm to the expellee. Also, proprietors unwilling to farm themselves or able to do so only temporarily are encouraged by tax privileges to have an expellee manage their farm. Thus, the legislator chose not the road of compulsory surrender of land but that of providing economic incentives for making over the farm to expellees. This is justified economically because usually such farms are in poor condition. One may well expect an able farmer to cultivate such land more intensively. The expelled farmer who at long last resumes his vocation strives to build a new life for himself and his dear ones and is only too eager to prove to his new neighbors that he has the know-how of a good farmer.

The new farmer receives a 4 per cent loan payable in annuities after three free years. This loan permits him to purchase the necessary implements, to improve run-down farm buildings. Thus far these credits were paid out of diverse public funds, especially out of the so-called Soforthilfe Aufkommen (representing a special tax levy in aid of refugees and expellees.) In addition to these credits, the ECA has allowed means to be used for this purpose—thus far about 12 million German Marks—out of the ECA counterpart fund alloted to Western Germany. Furthermore, the West German Länder and the Bonn government have made financial contributions. All in all, during the last two years, up to June 30, 1951, about 170 million Deutsche Marks have been publicly provided in execution of the Refugee Settlement Act. These sums have sufficed to help 15,080 expelled farm families to re-establish themselves in the West in their customary occupational pursuits. Of these families 3,482 have been established on newly created farmsteads, 6,781 families were able to rent farms, and 4,817 purchased farms of their own.

It is hardly possible to state in dollars and cents the tax increment accruing to the government from the re-employment of the newcomers. Whatever such public benefits may be these families have ceased to be public charges and have become productive citizens.

The above figures show that the methods and principles of the Refugee Settlement Act (based on voluntary endeavor) have been a success. This is no ground for complacency. Unfortunately there are 250,000 more families (or about 1 million people) who have lost their former farms and could not be satisfied in Western Germany. There is little hope to place all of them in the reduced area of crowded Western Germany. By now quite a few of these families have taken up other occupational pursuits or are too old to begin farming anew. Nevertheless, considerably more farm families could undoubtedly have been rehabilitated had larger funds been available. What stands in the way are the familiar and diverse social obligations of the government to provide means for low cost housing, relief for widows and waifs, etc.

In this connection permit me to point to the following. The execution of the Refugee Settlement Act has shown that joint heirs and other absentee owners frequently are willing to surrender their land when offered sufficient security or adequate compensation. Indeed, so-called ceasing heirs or proprietors holding on to their land primarily for the reason of security would readily surrender more land if they were assured of security. Hence authorities consider resuming at a later time issues of especially guaranteed rent certificates, in order to compensate ceasing heirs or other proprietors with these capital assets. Besides, the leading German farm organizations are agreed upon establishing a special fund for such purposes. Unfortunately, the accumulation of such a fund is a slow process. Even though so far no money for settlement purposes has been paid out this attempt of the farmers at self-help seemed to me worth mentioning.

The Sonne Report

Under the leadership of the New York banker H. C. Sonne, an American committee of experts has prepared a report on the knotty problem of resettlement of expelled farmers and has submitted its recommendations to the Bonn government. The Sonne report recommends opening up and offering to expellees as settlement land, at a cost of about 220 million Deutsche Marks, about 100,000 acres (40,000 hectares) of waste land and brush land approximately, and 75,000 acres (30,000 hectares) of moor land. Within a six year period 34,450 full-time farms and 65,550 part-time farms shall be established for the expellees at an additional cost of 2 billion, 410 million Deutsch Marks. These new settlements shall be established either on new ground or by taking over existing farmsteads.

Thus the report assumes that about 100,-000 more farm families desire to resume farming. This agrees with the estimates of German experts. But German tax yields alone can hardly provide even for this reduced number of candidates for resettlement. The federal government in Bonn has gratefully welcomed the work of the Sonne committee, since the report has clearly shown how difficult it is to integrate the expellees. Recent history has taught all of us a lesson about the political dangers inherent in uprooted masses of expellees who have been deprived of all hope and property. The task is to join forces in an unceasing struggle against hopelessness, embitterment, and resignation. The great safeguard against Communist attempts at infiltration is to establish independent and self-employed proprietors.

FINANCIAL ASPECTS OF LAND REFORM IN THE FAR EAST

 Arthur Bunce

I AM GOING to take you to another part of the world, quite different from South America and very different indeed from Germany. I might say that the financial problems of land reform vary tremendously all over the world. They even vary tremendously within the Far East. I am going to try to bring together some of the basic factors affecting the financial measures to be used in attaining some of the objectives of land reform and rehabilitation.

In South Korea, for example, about 70 per cent of all the farmers were tenant farmers in 1945. Their level of living was extremely low. The average size of farm for the whole of Korea was about four acres. The average in South Korea, in the better rice growing areas, was about two acres. The level of living of the people was that of extreme poverty. The rent paid by the peasant ran as high as 60 per cent of the crop. This went largely to absentee landlords. You had a permanently depressed, poverty-stricken mass of people. You had a small class of wealthy land-owning aristocracy. In the case of Thailand, you find the picture is entirely different. Land ownership is fairly widespread; the farmers are fairly well-to-do. In certain areas in Thailand there is actually a shortage of farm labor. There is not the pressure of population on the land in Thailand that there is in Korea. In both Korea and large areas of Thailand the main crop is rice. The patterns of agriculture include small individual farms. When you move to Malaya and Indonesia you find an entirely different pattern of agriculture: a situation associated with the production of specialized crops for export—largely rubber. Rubber estates present an entirely different problem in land reform than do small holdings in the rice growing areas.

Neither Korea nor Thailand has a market for stocks or bonds such as exists in Germany. The program that was so excellently presented on the land and resettlement program in Germany is completely impossible in most of the Orient because there is no market for securities such as those which financed the program developed in Germany. It seems to me that in considering the financial problems of land reform we have to consider a whole series of interrelationships. There is no solution applicable to all countries. Only as we study a particular country, and in many cases a particular area within a country, can we develop a financial solution and program of land reform which is workable because it will fit the conditions existing in that country.

The first problem that always arises is the question of whether the land reform should proceed through private sales or through government purchase and government sale. If you desire to keep the reform program within the ordinary economic framework and have voluntary sales, then there are certain things which may be done to speed up the liquidation or sales by absentee landlords. I will just mention these very briefly. First of all, a government can give the tenant security by enacting a law which makes it compulsory for the landlord either to give a long term lease or a permanent annually renewable lease. The landlord is restrained from renting the land to the highest bidder and cannot evict the present tenant except for explicitly stated causes. Secondly, the government can reduce by law the amount of rent paid by the tenant

for the land. In the case of Korea one of the first actions of military government was to issue an order limiting all rent payments to one-third of the crop. Such measures give the farmers higher incomes and security of occupancy. They also bring pressure on the landlord to sell his land because it is no longer as profitable to hold it. Whether he will sell or not will largely depend upon the alternative investments available. On the other hand, there are difficulties in using this method of encouraging private action. Measures that I have mentioned are exceedingly difficult to enforce, particularly if the farmers are unorganized and compete against each other to obtain the use of a small area of land. In the case of Korea we knew, for example, that many of the tenants, while only paying one-third of the crop as rent, made the landlord large gifts. This was not breaking the law, but it certainly didn't allow the tenant to become rich. In general for the Far East, I would say the government has to act directly, either by confiscating or by purchasing the land and then selling or distributing it to the farmers; reliance on the factors which will encourage the individual to sell the land is too slow. The people in the Orient today do not want to wait.

Now let us look very briefly at the various factors which affect investment in land. In the Orient one of the most important factors is prestige. A man who owns land has social position. Many people own land and keep holding land when they could earn a much higher return on their capital by a different type of investment, because being landlords means they belong to a type of feudal aristocracy. Where you have that attitude and that feeling it is almost impossible to expect the private individual to take steps to sell his land. It makes government action essential.

The second factor affecting investment in land is, of course, the great security of land holding. When there is inflation, the value of land rises; when there is destruction, land is not destroyed. Even in Korea with all the fighting backward and forward and the general destruction in cities, the land is still producing.

A third factor affecting rent, and this is one that is sometimes lost sight of, is the question of whether alternative investments for capital are available. It is certainly true in most of the Oriental countries that there is a tremendous need for capital; they need capital to develop mineral resources, to establish industrial plants, to expand commerce, and to develop banking and financial institutions. In many cases the Orient is underdeveloped, and one of the basic problems is to raise enough capital so that their own resources can be developed by their own people.

A fourth factor, which again is closely related to rent, is the question of the managerial and technical experience of the people. You cannot expect alternative investments to develop when the people in the country are not familiar with the development of mining, industry, and trade. In many cases, under the colonial systems of the past, Asiatic countries have been kept as primary producers of raw materials. There has been little investment in manufacturing and the development of other resources. The result is that there is a lack of experience, both in the fields of management and technical "know-how."

A fifth point, which in a way summarizes many of the others, is the question of comparative returns from investment in land and in other capital developments. Where a landlord, for example, receives as rent 60 per cent of the total crop, the value of that land, if you place it on the basis of earning power—say at 3.5 per cent—is extremely high because you have high returns associated with security.

A sixth factor, which is always important,

is the question as to whether the farmer is living on a subsistence level or whether he is in the position to save toward the purchase of his own farm. In the case of Korea, I would say that 90 per cent of all the farmers were so poverty stricken that they had to scrape from year to year to pay off their debts and have food to carry them over to the next crop. There was no opportunity whatever for the farmer to save in order to buy his land. He had absolutely no hope.

Now let us review briefly the various methods of acquiring land in order to carry forward a land reform program. First of all, there is the obvious and simple method of confiscation. This is the method that has been followed in many cases by the Russians and by the Communists in North Korea. All the land held by the landlords in excess of the amount they could work themselves was confiscated without compensation. In North Korea the land was distributed free of charge to the tenants or the farm workers and a very high tax was collected. In the case of North Korea, however, the farmers did not really own the land. They were not given that piece of paper which we call a deed. Actually, the farmer only had the right to farm the land, and he could be removed from that land if he did not farm it effectively according to the desires of the Communist leaders. The result was that the land reform in North Korea became a means of keeping the farmer in line politically. If he didn't do as he was told, he was removed from the farm. This program applied not only to absentee landlords but also to small owner-operators. During 1946 and 1947 up to 2 million refugees came down from North Korea. Many of them were small farm operators who had lost their land and were thoroughly dissatisfied with the land reform program which reduced them to a tenant of the state. There you had farmers fleeing from a land reform program which is something new in this world. I might say that the land reform program in Communist China is very different from that which was formulated in North Korea. According to present regulations in Communist China the farmers have the right to sell their land. They also have the right to borrow on their land. In other words, they are following a policy of creating independent owner-operators rather than state tenants holding their land only as long as they follow orders issued by the local committee.

Generally, the idea of confiscation without compensation is not acceptable within a democracy; we must, therefore, review the various means of purchasing land in order that the government may control it and distribute it to the tenants. The first thing I would like to make quite clear is that it is very difficult to draw a line between confiscation and purchase; it all depends upon how much you pay for the land. If a government enacts a law which pays to the landlord a very small part of the sale value of the land, then it is almost confiscation; such a program, even though called "purchase," in actual effect amounts almost to confiscation. In other words, a land reform act may pay an owner nothing and take his land or it may give him 5 per cent of its value or any percentage up to its full value. In Germany, of course, they paid the full value. In South Korea I think they paid very much less than the full value. The general terms of the Republic of Korea land reform program were that the owner of the land was given 150 per cent of the total value of one year's crop. In other words, he was allowed 30 per cent of the crop over a five year period. When in the past he had been receiving up to 60 per cent of the crop per year, 30 per cent of the crop for a five year period is almost confiscation.

The terms that are settled upon in a land reform program will depend upon many factors. First of all, it will depend upon the political power of the land owning class. It will depend upon the strength and organization of the tenants. There will be the inevitable struggle of the tenant against the landlords, and the solution will reflect the strength, politically, of these two groups as well as a general sense of what is just under the circumstances. Many tenants will say that they have been suppressed and exploited for centuries and demand that the landlord class be liquidated; they will claim that there is no justice in maintaining high payments by the tenants in order to reimburse what they call a parasitic exploitative aristocracy. A person's general concept of moral and ethical values will, in many cases, depend on how close he is to the poor tenant or how close he is to the rather well-to-do and usually better educated landlord. I should say that what would be considered reasonable terms of purchase would have to be determined in the light of all the economic facts regarding a particular country. I think it is impossible to lay down any general rules except that it will have to be a compromise.

The second big problem in purchase is how to pay for the land when it is bought. The government can pay the landlords cash, and when sufficient income is not available it may be tempted to print money. If there is a large amount of land involved, the result may be inflation, which will certainly not be to the advantage of the economy as a whole. Purchase by cash, therefore, is by and large limited to countries where the area to be purchased and the amount to be paid out is relatively small. Where there is large scale tenancy and large amounts of land to be purchased for redistribution, the government can seldom pay cash without endangering the whole economy. The other alternative, of course, is to give the landlords bonds; then the government can determine how those bonds may be used. Obviously, if the bond can be cashed, paying bonds is the same as paying cash. Therefore, the bonds must be restricted, and they can be restricted in many ways. A bond can be made non-transferable; it can also be made nonredeemable, even by the government. The result is that the landlord obtains a bond, usually paying a relatively low rate of interest, and he may be obliged to hold it. In the areas where capital is greatly needed in other fields, holding such bonds does not increase the investment capital of the country. It is, therefore, highly desirable that, instead of having rigid restrictions on redemption, the government allow the bonds to be cashed for stated purposes, such as investment in industrial projects. This opening up of new sources of capital for investment may be a very important supplementary program to land reform. Also, the government might allow the bonds to be used for the purchase of foreign exchange to bring in capital goods or employ foreigners where necessary to provide the technical knowledge for the particular industry or development of resources.

Just as there are several ways of obtaining the land, so are there several ways of distributing it to the farmer. First of all, one of the easiest methods of distributing land is to make grants free of charge; instead of attempting to collect from sales, the government may rely upon tax collections in order to obtain revenue. Where the government has to purchase the land, then it should distribute land free to the farmers only if a return to the government is obtained through taxation.

The other alternative is to sell the land to the tenants; here again you can establish various means of payment. You can have payments to the government for the purchase of the land extending from a period of five years to as long as fifty years. In the case of Japan they have a very much longer purchase period than they had in Korea. The tenant in Korea, under the government land reform program, is paying 30 per cent of the crop for only five years. This was definitely a reaction of the Korean government to the insistence and the power of the peasants, who form a very large majority of the population. That is not quite free distribution, but it is purchasing the land in five years with payments lower than the legal annual rent!

Again, the terms of payment that should be used should be determined in the light of all the conditions existing. Where the government has to buy the land, it will usually have to secure some income from the tenant purchaser in order to pay the previous owner. In Korea the government adopted an extremely simple formula. The tenants were sold the land at a payment of 30 per cent of the crop for five years, and the landlords were forced to sell for the same amount—30 per cent of the crop for five years. The landlords were given bonds which could not be redeemed; all they could obtain in any one year was 30 per cent. An exception was made so that these bonds could be turned in to the government for the purchase of industrial and commercial properties, a very large amount of which were held by the Government of Korea after being taken over from the Japanese at the end of the war. In Korea one of the basic objectives of the land reform program was to transfer capital from land into industry and commerce; unhappily, the invasion from the north prevented this from being fully implemented. However, some progress has resulted and some bonds have been turned in and exchanged for industrial property.

There is very little time left and I must review briefly a few other specific points, again using Korea as an illustration. One of the basic problems faced in land reform in Korea was the fact that it was conducted during a period of extreme inflation. In other words, the value of money or the value of a fixed asset such as a bond was declining very rapidly. The question was raised as to how to compensate the landlords with bonds; cash would add to the inflationary pressure, and at the same time the inflation would reduce the value of a bond with a fixed money value. It was decided that the bonds to be issued and paid to the landlords should be in terms of rice. The landlord was given a bond which was equivalent to a certain quantity of rice, and each year when he obtained his income from that bond in settlement, he obtained not a fixed sum of money but a sum of money equivalent to the quantity of rice. Because the price of rice in the Orient always reflects inflationary trends, the landlord's return fluctuated with the change in the value of money. In the Orient rice is one of the most stable indices of money value there is, and this solution was an important factor in persuading the landlords to accept the land reform program.

There is another experience in Korea which I believe you would be interested in. I mentioned that a government could bring pressure on individuals to sell land by passing certain laws. Military government did this in Korea; rents were reduced to one-third, and the landlords knew that a land reform was inevitable. Because of the reduced income and fear of the terms of the land reform, great efforts were made by the landlords to sell their land at reasonable prices and long terms rates to their tenants. The tenants were so land hungry that this looked attractive to them and many were purchasing on the landlords' terms. The Assembly of Korea then passed a law prohibiting the sale of land by landlords while the land reform was being implemented!

It has been estimated that, if it had not been for the attack from North Korea, tenancy would have been reduced from 70 per cent in 1945 to only about 5 per cent in 1950. The remaining tenants would have occupied land owned by churches, schools, and the government. The land reform program would have been complete.[1]

⟡⟡⟡⟡   DISCUSSION

PEDRO BERNAL—The gentleman who spoke about Korea mentioned that in Colombia there were national lands, which could be distributed by the government without receipt of compensation. That is what is being done in my country. Anyone who wants to take over and develop some of these national lands can get them from the government, provided he works them. The government also gives him additional land equal in amount to that which he has worked. This additional land is given him so that he can extend his activities, making his holding larger and more productive. The only expense connected with this is the legal expense—the amount of money he has to pay the lawyer for the necessary proceed-

ings. This point seems to be cleared up, but it might be worth while to discuss further the different methods of financing the distribution or redistribution of land.

In most countries, there is not enough capital to pay for bonds issued to pay for the lands which are distributed or allocated. Consequently if these bonds are to be placed in the open market, they are going to suffer a depreciation. This might be another means of confiscation. In case that the bonds are not to be negotiable on the open market the owner will have to hold them pending redemption of them by the government or some other agency. In such a case the land owners will not willingly accept paper which will be of such limited uses. The issuing of bonds works very well in rich countries that have money markets, but it does not work well in countries where those conditions do not exist. We are, however, issuing negotiable bonds in Colombia in the case of housing programs, for both rural housing and urban housing. The result is that those bonds have gone down to about 83 per cent of their value. Consequently the man who expects to be paid in such bonds attempts to make up the difference by charging more for the construction. This is the way he tries to get his money back. Actually the depreciation of the bonds has been limited by the practice of the issuing bank in buying some of them on the side. In this way they keep up the value and limit the depreciation. However, it prevents the banks from using their capital in some other way. Under these conditions, which are probably present in other countries, I would like to ask the gentleman who spoke about Korea if in his judgment bonds should be issued in Colombia for the purchase of land.

MR. BUNCE—I am very pleased to hear that in Colombia they are following the system of distributing the land to the peasants who agree to till it, giving them also an additional area equal to that which they clear for cultivation. I think that is very similar to our old homestead law. With reference to bonds, I would like to point out first of all that the issuing of bonds for land and the issuing of bonds for the erection of housing are two quite distinct and separate things. When you issue bonds for a housing program, those bonds have to bring in money, because the money has to be spent to build the houses. In the case of bonds issued for land, the land is already there. What you are doing is giving the present owner a bond for an asset which is there. The bond itself need not in any way represent cash that has to be brought in. It is simply a certificate of indebtedness of the government; and when those bonds are

issued to the owner, then the conditions attached will determine the amount of compensation the owner is going to get. And as I pointed out before, that compensation to the owner can run all the way from 100 per cent of the market value all the way down to 25 per cent or less of the market value. Actually the solution will largely be determined by the political powers and pressures within a given country. I do not know the situation in Colombia sufficiently well to form any judgment as to what conditions should be attached to those bonds. It's the sort of question you could answer only after very intensive study. Certainly the political power of the land owning class might be so strong that it would be impossible to get any movement forward in the land reform program unless they receive a very high compensation.

Another method of handling this problem of very large land owners who wish to hold that land is to use the system of taxation. If the land is not being used for productive purposes, but is rather being held for speculation or for the growth of population, a tax based on what the land should be producing (if it were used) would force the owner to use or sell it. Another way has been used extensively in England. They have in England very high death duties, which have caused the families to split up their great estates. Where the government takes 80 per cent of the property the levy cannot be paid out of revenues from property. It must be sold. So various methods can be used. And I only wish I could visit Colombia and discuss this in detail, in light of the political situation that exists, and the basic ethical justice of how much these people ought to be given in terms of equity.

G. R. YTTERBORN—It is a comment rather than a question which I wish to make. We have had in Sweden since the beginning of this century a system by which the government has loaned money to farmers who have been unable to obtain credit from the regular credit institutes—that is, the savings banks, the co-operative trade institutes, and the commercial banks. The money which the state has loaned has been obtained by selling bonds. But this method can be applied only in countries where there is a bond market—not in other countries. But in Sweden recently we asked ourselves, why should the government actually borrow money from the money market and, in turn, lend it to the farmers? Why shouldn't the farmer go directly to the credit institute? We introduced such a reform in 1948. The government guarantees the payment of the loans only if the lender fails to pay. The program seems to have worked rather well. I would like Dr. Bunce to comment on this problem by indicating how generally he thinks such an approach would work. It seems to me that it makes the whole process much easier. The government doesn't have to work with money; it doesn't have to work with the security papers and all those things —these are done by the regular credit institutes; yet the government is always standing behind, as the final guarantor for these loans.

MR. BUNCE—I think that the program in Sweden of using your institute and the stable institution methods of financing is thoroughly sound and should be used in those countries where that approach is possible. The point I brought out this morning was that in two countries I know very well—Thailand and Korea—there is no money market, no investment market, no security exchanges, and no government bonds are issued and sold. Such an approach as followed in Sweden, is, therefore, impossible under those conditions. Another factor which is tremendously important is the level of living of the farmers, who have to be in a position to make such payments that they can redeem that paper issued by the commercial institutions. Where you have a farm

group on an absolute subsistence level, almost a starvation level, the possibility of putting it on a commercial basis is negligible.

I would like to say one other thing, coming back again to this problem in Colombia —which is really a very, very fundamental issue at this conference—and that is: In a program of land reform, particularly where the situation is such that the high rents of the past have made it impossible to compensate the landlords by cash at the full value of the land, you may be forced to give them some form of paper which cannot be redeemed for cash because of the inflationary effect it would have. But if you have to adopt such a program, then I believe that at the same time it is very desirable for the country to adopt a general economic development program which calls for development in the segments of the economy as well as in agriculture. In other words, if you make available alternative investment opportunities for sterilized capital which is held by the landlord, then the opposition to such a program will be greatly reduced. In Korea the landlords were very antagonistic to the whole land reform program; however, they were such a small minority of the population that the politicians did not dare to listen to them. But the fact that the government made it possible to exchange the bonds for the purchase of investment capital and the landlords were not just simply expropriated or given a small payment for five years made the bonds more acceptable. The South Korean government offered the landlords the opportunity to invest in cotton mills, wholesale firms, warehouses, and manufacturing industries of various types, which had been owned by the Japanese and were taken over by the Korean government. I think that land reform is not in itself and cannot in itself be an adequate answer to the problem of development in many countries, certainly not in the Orient. We need the development of all kinds of resources in many areas in the Orient, and a land reform program where the owners of the land are compensated by bonds and at the same time permitted to cash those bonds in for the purchase and development of industry can be one way in which the antagonism of the landlords can be offset. This means that you have to develop as supplements to land reform and rehabilitation programs, a general development program which will create alternative investment opportunities.

JAMES G. MADDOX—I would like to make a comment in terms of what I believe might be a practical solution to the problem in countries like Colombia. There are several such countries in Latin America. The government will not take kindly to progressive tax measures of the type that was mentioned here this morning. However desirable that might be, it is politically impossible to get very far with that proposal. There are very low real estate taxes in these countries, and in some no taxes whatsoever on farm real estate. Yet it might be possible to get through a moderate land tax on the farm solely or a general property tax. If this could be combined with the program suggested, namely, paying the land owner with bonds—which I think should be negotiable —these countries could develop some of their public domain lands. I would suggest that the same agency both issue the bonds and receive the revenue from this new real estate tax levy.

Land settlement and farm development requires more than the distribution of wild land. The mere fact that several countries of Latin America stand ready to give land to a small squatter type of farmer provided he will clear that land up, does not really do the job of clearing the jungle and developing large areas of land. These latter tasks require engineering work, much of it on a large scale. Therefore to meet the financial needs of a comprehensive farm development program, it seems necessary not only to pay for the privately owned land with bond issues but also to have funds to assist in the development of all new lands to be cleared up and brought under cultivation. It is my suggestion that the funds needed by the agency for development which cannot be recovered from the recipients of the farms should come principally from a modest property tax. This type of program would require administration of very high quality, and it is here that the principal weakness of the suggested procedure would likely be found.

Nevertheless I bring these suggestions forward as providing the basis for practical and expedient programs in several of the Latin American countries. Initially such a development agency would need an appropriation of some capital. Thereafter the finances should be kept within manageable limits (a) by the receipt of the suggested real estate tax revenue, (b) by not paying too much for the purchase of land to be developed, (c) by not spending too much for the clearing and developing of new land, and (d) by recovering funds from the purchasers of farms. By skilful financial management it should be possible to maintain the bonds at par at the same time that new lands were brought into cultivation. All of this could be done, I believe, without any substantial real inflation, beyond let us say the inflation in the currency needed in the way of increased purchasing power to complement the expansion of production facilities. It is my judgment that a balanced approach of this kind on a modest scale could be undertaken now in several of the Latin American countries. But if you limit the thing simply to progressive taxation or to the issuing of nonnegotiable bonds to the landlord putting pressure on him to sell, the program is not nearly so acceptable as a well-rounded approach such as I foresee as a possibility.

OTTO SCHILLER—I would like to have a

comment on what the man [Mr. Bunce] has said about the agrarian reform in northern Korea. We were told that the landlords have been expropriated of their lands beyond the size which they can work themselves, evidently about the size of the family farm. It seems to me to be a very generous way of expropriating landlords, in a country under Soviet rule, because in the Soviet zone of Germany the landlords have been expropriated completely; not only were they not allowed to keep a portion of their property for their own cultivation, they were not even allowed to live in their former residences. They were banished to a distance of at least thirty kilometers from their residences where they lived before, and even the registers for real estate are gone. Also in recent years, even the houses and barns where these landlords lived have been systematically destroyed to the last stone, to eliminate entirely all traces of the former landlords and make it impossible to re-establish the old order even in the case that the political structure might be changed. If I understood well the comment of Dr. Bunce, the North Korean program was quite generous to the landlord.

M. L. DANTWALA—In India, I think we have one of the biggest programs of the purchase of land from landlords; and though I have not got my statistics here, the estimated compensation was to the tune of something like 4 billion rupees. From this you can see that the program is probably the biggest in history for the purchase of land in any part of the world. But that is not what I wanted to emphasize here. I want to make two comments. We have devised some amendment to the system of compensation. We vary compensation according to the size of ownership. We give to the biggest landowner three times the annual rent and to the smallest thirty times the annual rent in the same region. On points of law maybe that may not be justified, but

from the other point of ethics this sort of discrimination between the big and the small owner is, I think, justified. One more thing that I might say: You will observe probably that this very small compensation is not much different from confiscation. In discussing this point it will be well to remember that in countries like mine the proprietary rights or the ownership rights of these landlords are not well established, and, therefore, if we pay them a nominal compensation it does not mean confiscation for the simple reason that most people would refuse to accept the idea that they had any ownership rights originally. Therefore in appraising these reforms it would be better to also convince ourselves about the ownership rights of these people before commenting that this legislation is confiscatory.

One small point is about the negotiable and the nonnegotiable bonds, as we call them. As far as I can see, it makes no difference that a bond that you give is a negotiable or a nonnegotiable. I understand that if the bond is made negotiable it will depress the market and the value will depreciate. But when the bond is nonnegotiable, the credit of the issuing authority is depreciated—it's not the value of the bond, it's the credit. And in India, for example, this legislation is undertaken by the states. So when the states made this proposition that they would issue nonnegotiable bonds, it was observed that as far as immediate inflationary results were concerned, nonnegotiability will take care of that. But what about the future credit of the state, if the government wants to borrow for other purposes? The very fact that it has issued nonnegotiable bonds will reduce the credit of the issuing authority.

I might tell you also about another difficulty. Most of the legislation which was passed by the state governments was declared unconstitutional because it did not provide for cash payments. Such proposed laws were declared unconstitutional a second time because of discrimination between one landlord and another—by the proposal to pay three times the value of the property to one and thirty times to another. You may be interested in the remedies—how we overcame and bypassed both these things. The key idea is that we based our compensation primarily upon the need for rehabilitation. Now a more substantial rehabilitation allowance is given to small farmers; consequently we can pay the compensation at a uniform rate and vary the rehabilitation allowance. So we got rid of that difficulty.

I would like to comment on the idea of the bonds being made convertible for definite purposes. The government in one of our states has said these bonds would be made negotiable—could be cashed—if they were invested in the co-operative movement. That is in line with the suggestion that has been made.

CHAIRMAN [1]—It seems to me that the residue of questions that we have here is an indication of the interest there has been in the topic this morning and of the value of the contributions that have been made not only by our speakers but the audience as well. I only wish there were time for a word of summary of the discussion, of the great amount of ground that we have covered, but I am sure that any effective effort at summary would be almost as lengthy as the program itself. We have wasted very little time this morning, I'm sure you will all agree. Yet it does seem to me worth emphasizing one or two points.

Surely we had good indication this morning of the difficulty and, indeed, the potential error of generalization. The problem, as we have seen, in the old and settled countries is very different from the problem in the new and developing lands. We've had a good deal of emphasis on one important difference; that is to say, the existence of an effective capital market. Another difference has been implicit, which I would like to make explicit; namely, a difference in the juridical and ethical standards which are involved in the problem of land reform. In countries like Germany, England, and Sweden land titles are firm; they represent ancient common law and attitudes toward property. We are inclined to carry such conceptions over to our consideration of the less developed countries and consequently to carry over an approach to land reform in the countries where land may be held in rather recently acquired large estates. Yet we carry over such ideas with some possibility of difficulty and even error. We have heard the case made very effectively in the instance of Korea for a type of land transfer which would be intolerable by the standards of the older countries. But this becomes tolerable in a country like South Korea because it represents an alternative to something much more violent, something even farther from western standards of law and morality. There has been a good illustration of that in the area immediately north of the parallel, the area where the Communist land reforms have been carried out. We should strive to see the differences in standards of economic practice implicit in the instruments we use. But we will also err if we do not see the differences in the juridical and ethical values which must be brought to bear in the solution of this intensely practical problem.

I have one other comment to make. I hope that sometime attention will be given here to this problem of inflation. I'm a little disturbed, frankly, at the way in which virtually all of the speakers have said that such programs must be carried out in a manner by which inflation is avoided. That has been set down as an absolute value. Now, I'm a college professor on a fixed income, and I'm no friend of inflation. During the last war I invested two or three years of my life in the very difficult job of administering price control in this country—and administering price control in the United States is a task second in difficulty only to the task of administering land reform in the Orient. But, it seems to me that we must be careful also of establishing absolute bans of that sort. As a matter of fact, in some of the less established countries—I'm sure Mr. de Sousa will permit me to say this of Brazil—inflation is the normal thing; price stability would be abnormal. The economy has been adjusted to progressive inflation in considerable measure; and if it is necessary to risk inflation for land reform, that question should be at least examined on its merits. I am sure Professor Hibbard would agree with me when I remind the Americans present that in the 1830's and the 1840's an enormous amount of land transfer in the United States was facilitated by what we call the free banking period. Almost anybody, whatever his credit standing, could go to a bank and get a loan of almost any amount for the purpose of buying land—and did. As a result, an inflationary process distributed a great deal of land to a great many people who in a context of price stability and hard money might never have come into the possession of it. In this, I'm exceeding the prerogatives of a chairman only to remind you, as I would like to remind myself, that in a free discussion of a problem of this sort no absolute bars should be put up even against something that is so difficult to contemplate as inflation.

PROBLEMS OF FINANCING LAND DISTRIBUTION

Report of the Working Party

 Chairmen, *John K. Galbraith and Walter A. Morton*

General Considerations

FINANCING OPERATIONS

THE PURPOSE of a land distribution program is to make land available to farm families in units of adequate size. Usually, the successful execution of the program will also call for the extension of credit to farmers for the purpose of acquiring equipment, buildings, and other items of capital. In financing land distribution, the government acquires credit for the above purposes from various segments of society. In turn, it extends credit to the new farm owners for the acquisition of land and capital, and it acquires from them obligations to repay such advances, usually in the form of mortgages.

The government usually pays the large landowners in bonds when land is purchased from them for distribution purposes. This in effect forces the landowners to lend to the government in the amount equal to the price they receive for their land.

The government may distribute land out of the public domain. Activities necessary to prepare it for distribution may include clearing the land, building roads and schools, reclaiming, draining, or irrigating land, etc. The government may attempt to raise part of all of the funds by borrowing.

The new owners may be in need of large amounts of additional capital in order to set up economically sound farms. Technical advice and supervision is probably needed if the farmers are to make the best use of credit. This need for advisory personnel in connection with credit extension makes this form of credit expensive and unavailable from the usual sources.

The workshop felt that such credit should come from general governmental appropriations and should be administered by an agency working closely with farmers, rather than by a financial institution. However, it also recommended that the amortization payments made by the farmers be available for reborrowing to acquire capital.

Acquiring credit.—By receiving payment in bonds, the landlords become the original lenders. However, if the bonds are negotiable, they can be sold to other investors. Whatever the form of bonds, the program needs to secure results such that the value of the bonds will be secured by real assets representing the ability of the new farmer owners to repay their debt to the government.

In raising credit from the general public, the program will have to be carried on in such a way as to promote the confidence of the creditors in its financial soundness.

DISTRIBUTION AND TRANSFER

A program of distribution of land to family farmers is distinct from transfers of land occurring in private transactions in the market. In the latter case the two parties come to a mutual agreement, because each one of them, presumably, improves his position by the transaction. The previous owner sells his land in order to use the proceeds of sale for other purposes. The buyer buys with his own savings and with credit made available to him, primarily from commercial channels. By contrast, a land distribution program has to deal with farmers who usually do not have sufficient savings and access to credit and with landlords who may not have other alternatives for using their accumulated wealth.

Nevertheless, the workshop felt that within these limitations the land distribution program should be carried out in a financially sound manner. One aspect of this is building the confidence of the credit market in the investments being made in the course of the program. An important

contribution toward this could be achieved by working with the new farmer owners so as to help them to create economically sound farm units which are able to pay off their debt obligation.

The workshop suggested that these two aspects of the program be carried on by separate agencies—a land bank and a land distribution agency. The land bank would borrow money, issue bonds to the land distribution agency, to be used for payments to landlords, lend to the land distribution agency, and secure from it mortgages on the new owners. By investing as a sound financial institution, the bank would seek to attract funds from the public and from the commercial banks.

The land distribution agency would be concerned with carrying out the objectives of public policy. It would purchase and distribute land, and it would advise and supervise the farmers. The agency must be able to win their confidence. It cannot, however, operate on a profit basis, and may even be in need of subsidy to finance some of its expenditures. It should not, therefore, be subject to regulations governing banking institutions which are designed to promote financial soundness. As part of its program it will spend whatever funds are contributed as subsidies from government revenues. Some subsidy will be needed in the work of the agency concerned with extension of credit to farmers for the purpose of acquiring capital. The necessary technical assistance and supervision make such credit expensive, but such expenses should be treated as being for an educational purpose. This is one of the important conditions for the success of the land distribution program. Therefore the workshop felt that the extension of credit for capital formation to the new farmer-owners be administered by the agency and should be closely integrated with its other activities. The joining of functions of advice with the extension of loans would make it more likely that the advice will be followed.

OTHER RELATED CONSIDERATIONS

In instituting a land distribution program a number of decisions must be made about the actual content of the program. Such decisions will determine the costs and investments that need to be made, and will allocate these to the different groups affected by the program. The major decisions are whether to use land from the public domain or from large landed property, what should be the extent of government participation beyond mere distribution of land, to what extent should the costs of the program be paid for by society as a whole through government funds, and whether there should be a partial or complete confiscation of the property of landlords.

Price to the new farmer-owners.—The cost of land to the government depends on the price paid to former landlords or on the costs of preparing the land for distribution out of the public domain. The price which the new farm owners can afford to pay may be considerably different. Also, it may be the aim of public policy to sell the land to farmers at a subsidized price, if the society is rich enough to shift this burden to the general public.

The workshop felt that the price to farmers should not exceed an amount that they could reasonably be expected to pay. That is, the price should be based on the capitalization of the payments that farmers can make out of expected incomes on the farm units created by land distribution. The price should not necessarily be related to the incomes made by previous owners. It was also proposed that where the cost of distributing land from the public domain is lower than the price by the above criteria the price should equal the cost. Others objected to this and were in favor of the uniform standard of capitalized payments in all situations.

Public benefits and expenses arising out of the program.—The opening of new lands by clearing, reclamation, or irrigation involves the creation of new communities, the building of roads and schools. Such activities benefit others besides the farmers who acquire new land. Many of the purely administrative expenses, including surveying and registration of the titles, may be considered to be investments necessary to insure the success of the program. Again, subsidies necessary to cover the discrepancy in the price paid the landowners and those charged the new farmer owners may be considered to be public expenses for the promotion of public standards of social justice.

In summary, many of the expenditures connected with a land distributon program may be in the nature of investment, but the achievement of results from them and the accrual of benefits to different groups may be so uncertain and so difficult to measure that such expenses should be covered from general government revenues.

Confiscation of the property of the landlords.—The workshop heard a report on the Mexican Revolution, which confiscated the landlords' property in the land that was taken away from them. Much of this was justified as a return of land to the Indian communities, from whom it was illegally seized in the past. Other land was confiscated in effect because the bonds issued for it were never honored. Today it is the general conclusion in Mexico that the revolution provided the only possible solution. However, the rapid distribution of land was attended by haphazard methods, great social unrest, disruption of production, and loss of life.

It was also suggested that Mexico was an example of a case where the landlords possessed power in the social structure that enabled them to exploit the labor attached to the land through custom and lack of alternate opportunities.

In many countries, the land distribution program confiscated most of the landlords' assets, not because of measures so designed, but because of inflation. In some of these cases inflation may have been due to the program, but it could also have arisen for other reasons.

Distribution of land from public or private domain.—The two alternatives can be compared on the basis of the cost of land. However, additional criteria have to be considered. Distribution of land from the holdings of large landowners does not involve the creation of new communities or the building of new roads, schools, and the extension of other government services. There would be less uncertainty in previously settled areas because the resources and markets of such areas are known. On the other hand distribution of public land would make possible the creation of farm units of economic size without great reorganization of previously established patterns. Also, the opening up of new alternatives to farmers employed by large landowners would tend to improve the terms offered by landowners to tenants and hired workers and might even lead to unprofitableness and the breaking up of large property.

A report from the Philippines is instructive about the nature of some of the costs associated with settlement on public domain. The first government program started in 1913 without any government subsidies to settlers. It failed. A subsequent attempt, which also failed, provided for subsidies to cover the cost of transportation to the settlers. By contrast, a successful program, operating from 1939 until the outbreak of the war, was based on government activities in road building, malaria control, clearing small parcels of land for each settler subject to a fee, and extending credit of 1,000 pesos to each settler.

The workshop inclined to the belief that costly land development should not be undertaken as long as less expensive private land is available in settled areas. This is especially so if some of the private land is cleared but not used. However attention must be paid to the considerations discussed above. In older countries, opening up new lands may be the only way of meeting the demand for land.

Operations of the Bank

GENERAL CONSIDERATIONS

It was the feeling of the workshop that the land bank should be confined to financing operations based on secured assets. It would start with an initial appropriation from the government, but its operations would have as its assets mortgages on the land sold to the new farmer owners and unsold land and as its liabilities bonds given in payment for the land to previous owners or sold to the public. Land would be sold to the farmers at a price which they can afford to pay out of future earnings. That is, it would be based on a capitalization of possible annual payments. Because of the need of farmers for building up their capital, it was proposed that they could reborrow their amortization payments. Thus they would be increasing the capital on their farms, while the principal of their debt to the bank would remain the same. The interest payments of the mortgaged farmers would be used by the bank to pay interest to the bondholders; any repayments on principal of the mortgages could be used to retire bonds; while the continued bank ownership of mortgages, secured by land, would provide the basis for refinancing bond issues by tapping the available savings of the country. The above set of transactions attempt to retain for the former landlords the wealth which they had accumulated in land (at least to the extent of a price for land that the farmers are expected to pay), but the landlords are removed from the management of the farms.

With slight modifications the above description could be applied to a program of clearing land on the unsettled public domain for distribution to farmers. In this case land would also be sold to farmers for a price which they could afford to pay out of future earnings. The farmers would pay for the land by giving mortgages to the land bank. The land bank would sell bonds to the public to cover some of the costs of clearing. Any excess of the costs of clearing over the proceeds from the sales of land would have to be covered by a subsidy from government revenues.

In summary, the land bank is intended to operate in financial markets in such a way as to promote faith in the soundness of its operations, to secure the participation of whatever savings are available in the country in the land distribution program, and thus to minimize the danger of inflation.

CREDIT INSTRUMENTS

Negotiable bonds.—It was felt by some participants of the workshop that the bonds issued by the land bank should be made negotiable. The bond issues would be secured by real assets, while the bank would operate under ordinary banking procedures so that the value of the bonds could remain at levels approximating face value without any guarantee by central banking authorities. Negotiable bonds would make it possible for some of the previous landlords to turn their bonds over to other savers. The success of the program would prevent inflation. Absence of success, when it is due to lack of sound financing operations, would probably lead as a final result to inflationary creation of money to pay off bondholders.

In the case of negotiable bonds provisions would have to be made to prevent the previous owners from repurchasing land. This can be achieved by reserving to the bank the right to repurchase any land offered for sale by a new owner.

Bonds and mortgages payable in commodities.—Despite sound operations by the bank, inflation could still be due to government expenditures to subsidize costs connected with a land distribution program (such as subsidies to cover the difference between higher price paid to previous landlords and the price charged to new owners or costs of supervision and technical assistance to new owners) or due to other reasons unrelated to the program. Because of this the workshop was interested in possibilities of "purchasing-power" bonds and mortgages, or bonds and mortgages providing for amortization and interest payments in terms of fixed amounts of principal agricultural crops. It was felt that of these two types of bonds, the latter would be simpler to administer and easier to understand. Mortgages providing for payments in fixed amounts of coffee have actually been used in Colombia.

Bonds guaranteed by the central bank and money creation to pay for the land.—There were objections to any guarantees of bonds by the central bank of the country. Such guarantees are likely to lead to the repayment of bonds with inflationary money created by the central bank.

Initial creation of money to pay for the land bought from previous landlords is almost certain to be inflationary. This would not be true if the money could be used by the former landlords to repurchase land, and the proceeds of sale would extinguish the mortgage. But such transactions would of course nullify the land distribution program. Neither would money creation be inflationary if opportunities existed for rapid development in the nonagricultural sectors of the economy and if the new money would be used for these purposes. However opportunities of this kind are very unlikely, especially in an underdeveloped country.

Nonnegotiable bonds.—It was also proposed in the workshop that the bonds used to pay previous landlords be made nonnegotiable. This would prevent repurchase of land or the necessity of immediate creation of new money, which might arise if negotiable bonds were guaranteed. However bonds of this type would prevent former landlords from turning their wealth into other investments. If there is little faith in the ability of the government to maintain the value of the money, then payment in nonnegotiable bonds would be regarded as equivalent to confiscation.

Bonds of limited negotiability were also proposed. For example, bonds of this kind issued in the Korean land reform could be used for the purchase of seized Japanese industry, but could not otherwise be sold. The former landlords, who would own the bonds, would typically not be inclined to invest in industrial development. Thus provisions for limited negotiability were thought necessary to prevent declines in prices of these bonds which might affect unfavorably the market for other government securities.

In summary, the workshop was inclined to favor the use of negotiable bonds in conjunction with the operations of a land bank on the lines of a sound financial institution. However, provisions preventing former landlords from repurchasing the land and limits on negotiability of the bonds were deemed worth-while. Also, since inflation could be due to reasons other than land distribution, the workshop thought that bonds and mortgages payable in commodities might be worth-while. Instruments of this nature can carry a relatively low rate of interest due to diminished risk. In addition, some opinion was expressed in favor of nonnegotiable bonds.

Land Distribution Agency

The land distribution agency is concerned with the execution of a program decided on by public policy. The content of this program determines the financing needs. What is significant for this workshop is that successful operations of the agency and of the new farmer-owners make for the solvency of the financing arrangements. It is with this in mind that brief statements are made about the operations of the agency, even though the subject matter below is largely covered in other workshops.

PURCHASE AND DISTRIBUTION

The workshop felt that it was important to have a procedure for arriving at values of the land which would be considered fair by the parties concerned. The guiding principle would provide that the value of the land should be set according to the earning capacity of the settler. The land would be valued by experts, and impartial arbitration boards would be available to pass on contested decisions.

The workshop recommended that the agency should be granted the power of eminent domain in those countries where this power is available. In cases where voluntary sales are not made, this would enable the agency to obtain land through judicial procedure after payment of just compensation. However, in the United States this power could not be used to obtain land at other than fair market prices.

In some Latin American countries the government may seize unused private land. In Colombia uncultivated land is subject to seizure by the government after ten years. However the owner can keep twice as much land as he cultivates. Peru has a similar law, with the difference that the owner must be paid for seized land. The workshop felt that, where available, these laws should be used for purposes of land distribution.

The workshop also stressed that the land should be distributed to the new owners in sizes sufficient to form economic units. In certain circumstances it might be preferable to set up proportional-profit or co-operative farms.

METHODS OF OPERATION

Supervision of use and technical assistance.—Farmers benefiting from land distribution will be in need of an extension program designed to help them make the best use of their resources. The land distribution agency should provide capital to the farmers along with supervision over its use. This capital can be extended on conditional terms, making its availability contingent on efficient use.

Conditional occupancy.—Similar to conditional lending of capital, the occupancy of the land can also be made conditional through various tenure provisions. The land distribution agency can retain the ownership of the land and rent it out to farmers. Another method would postpone granting of full ownership rights to the farmer until after a certain test period. Farmers may be prohibited from selling, leasing, mortgaging, or dividing their land, and their uses of the land may remain subject to supervision. A useful provision would reserve for the land distribution agency the right of first purchase if the new owner wants to sell his land.

CONTINUING AIMS OF DISTRIBUTION

Preserve ownership by operators.—To protect the achievements of the program, the agency may stand ready to purchase land which the owners desire to sell.

Weed out inefficient farmers.—The purpose of the program is to make land available to qualified farmers. In private transactions the creditor and seller are protected against the inefficiency of the buyer of land and the risks of price changes by requiring down payments. However, these provisions in a land distribution program would work against its purposes. The agency should set up a program to help the new owners with organization of the farms and with management. Control over use of borrowed funds

and conditional reservations on ownership may help the agency to promote better farming practices and will enable it to remove inefficient operators.

Provide flexibility for future reorganization of agriculture.—Some participants of the workshop stressed the fact that it is difficult to estimate what is likely to prove the most efficient type of farm organization as the country undergoes development. In these cases the land tenure pattern should not be frozen. They therefore proposed that the agency retain ownership of the land and rent it out. Thus it can retain considerable power, which may be used in the future in different types of farm organizations.

GENERAL ISSUES IN SUPERVISION

The proposals for technical assistance and supervision come up in connection with a land distribution program because of their importance for the success of the program and because of their contribution to the development of the country. In the United States very fast development resulted from private initiative, though there was a good deal of waste of resources, which underdeveloped countries with limited resources could not afford. Even more important is the inventiveness, initiative, and the general attitude of the people. This is a very complex issue that can only be evaluated in the context of the resources and the culture of each country.

Financing Authority

In order to finance the redistribution of land among small landholders each country should establish a land bank or a land authority. This institution shall be an independent authority provided with safeguards which minimize the possibility of political influence on its decisions. The initial funds shall be provided by the government from the budget and shall be large enough to enable the bank or the agency to carry out extensive operations without requesting additional funds from the legislature, except for a specified continuing yearly appropriation obtained from a special property or land tax. This agency should be so constituted that it can attract foreign loans.

This institution will have the power to issue long-term, open-end, negotiable mortgage bonds. These bonds will be used to purchase land for subdivision from large landholders. The recipients of the bonds will have the choice of either retaining the bonds and collecting rent on them or of selling them in the open market. The rent paid by the farmers to the lending institution could be re-lent to the farmer as long as productive investment is possible.

The government will also allocate large tracts of the public domain to the land bank or the agency. The bank, in co-operation with other appropriate government agencies will prepare the land (the more highly developed the country, the more extensive will be the preparation possible) for sale to small landholders at prices not higher than the cost of preparation or the capitalized value of the rent, whichever is lower. Long-term credit will be extended to the buyer, and the bank or agency shall hold a first mortgage against the land. The settler is to receive continued technical assistance and supervision from the proper authority. The government shall not start clearing public domain for settlers if the cost of preparation would be higher than the price to be paid for land already owned by third persons.

The following procedure shall be used by the bank or agency in acquiring large estates for subdivision:

1. A board of experts, banking and agricultural, will determine what land is to be purchased and the price to be paid for it. The price paid for the land will be the estimated economic rent of the land capitalized to the new settler.

2. Where the government has the right of eminent domain it should make extensive use of this power in acquiring land at fixed prices.

3. In those countries which have laws authorizing the government to acquire title to unused land at no charge, this power should be used to the full and the land put at the disposal of the agency mentioned above, for sale to small landholders.

Land sold by the agency should be sold in economic units capable of supporting the farm family and large enough so that modern farming methods, where possible, may be utilized. The farmer may remain on the land if he complies with systems of use recommended to him. In those areas where the soil, terrain, climate, etc., require the use of heavy capital equipment, i.e., expensive farm machinery, to secure the greatest economic utilization of the land, the land settlement should be carried out in such a way as to encourage the establishment of proportional-profit farms or agricultural co-operatives. In settlements of this type, disposal or subdivision of the land by settlers would have to be subject to approval by the appropriate government agency.

In selecting settlers—nationals or foreigners—the agency should make sure that those selected are qualified farmers and that adequate extension facilities are available to aid the new settler. In addition the settlement contract should provide that the settler must remain on the farm for a specified minimum time.

Although this presentation has been one dealing with the sale of land to new settlers, approximately the same procedure could be used in renting land to new settlers if the country is one which has determined that long-term leases to tenants are preferable to the outright sale of land. If land is rented, all leases should terminate at the death of the farmer-tenant. First preference should be given to the son of the former operator, if he is a qualified farmer, when the government agency again leases the land to a farmer.

The plan suggested here will be noninflationary if the result of its application is increased productive capacity and if it is coupled with general development of the economy.

The plan suggested here is applicable to a country in which there is a well-developed money market, where bond issues may be floated, and in which judicial and ethical considerations arising from political instability do not constitute a serious problem.

PROVIDING CREDIT FOR FAMILY-SIZE FARMS

Report of the Working Party

Chairman, *William Murray*

THE PROBLEM of providing efficient credit facilities for family-size farms could easily be the subject for study and discussion for at least six months. During the course of the conference we were able to devote only three afternoons to this subject. With delegates from fifteen different countries in attendance—from Asia, Europe, and the western hemisphere, in good mixture—it was clear that we could hope only to bring out the most urgent and important problems in this field. The discussion was carried out in the following manner:

1. Every attending delegate described in the first session the most important problems of providing credit facilities in his own country.

2. This was followed by a survey of how and where adequate capital can be obtained for meeting the various kinds of credit needed by the people who farm the land.

3. The organizations of the various credit systems in the different countries were outlined and compared.

4. The main points discussed during the sessions were summarized, with special attention to the sources of credit and to alternative remedies for undesirable situations in credit arrangements.

The situations and problems discussed at the first session can be summarized as follows.

From Argentina there was reported a need for credit facilities in order to enable tenants to become owners. The total sum of capital required for this purpose is estimated at 26 billion pesos. Moreover, credit is short for the acquisition of land and for its cultivation.

In Iran the Agricultural Bank provides credit for small farmers, most of whom do not own the land they cultivate. The basis for these credit possibilities is small. As a matter of fact, it is not possible to provide the implements necessary for better farm management and to raise agricultural output.

Germany is facing the severe problem of having to resettle approximately 270,000 refugee farm families coming from throughout Eastern Europe and from the Eastern regions of Germany, where before the war they cultivated their own farms. For this purpose a tremendous amount of capital is necessary, which cannot be provided from present German resources. Furthermore, credit facilities are needed for machinery purchase and soil improvement and, especially, for long-term credit for drainage and reclamation purposes, and to make possible financial settlements for those heirs who do not remain on the farms.

The most important credit problems of Paraguay are: (1) improvement of farms (enlargement to economic size), (2) aid to small farmers (machinery, equipment, etc.), and (3) transfer and resettlement of people from overpopulated areas to less densely populated ones.

Bolivia and Colombia both described situations in which they have had little experience in providing agricultural credit. In Bolivia there are few possibilities of getting credit in an interest rate as low as 6 per cent.

In Cuba there is the Bank of Agricultural Development, able to provide loans of a total sum of 25 million dollars. A special fund of 5 million dollars was assigned to enable tenants to purchase the land they cultivate.

The situation in Lebanon exhibits the same picture as to lack of capital. The Agricultural Bank, the only money-lending agency in Lebanon, lends money at a rate of interest of 9 per cent per annum. The conditions that must be met in order to get a loan are more than arbitrary. The peasant who gives a loan agent a good dinner stands a better chance of getting a loan. Also, the rates of interest are increased as the borrower's need for credit increases. A borrower who is desperate is charged an exorbitant rate of interest, with rates as high as 10 per cent per month or 120 per cent per year on short-term loans. The same country reported rates of 9 per cent on long-term loans totaling no more than 40 per cent to 45 per cent of the value of the security.

Credit facilities in the Netherlands are much better than those mentioned above. The loans granted by the savings banks are based on security usually consisting of mortgages on immovables. This kind of credit is not accessible to all small farmers, since 50 per cent of the farm area is rented.

Haitian small farmers can get loans only from private money lenders. In most cases these are the middlemen through whose hands the agricultural export products go and who demand rates of interest of 10 per cent to 40 per cent per season, depending on the necessity for the loans. The government feels an urgent demand to create a sound credit system. There is, however, little to report about the efficiency of any government-sponsored credit system to date, because of the distrust of the illiterate farmers for every kind of credit agency.

In Japan three new banks were recently established for agricultural credit. Private credit is neither popular nor common, as a result of a law prohibiting land purchase from nonagricultural persons.

The main problems in Italy are lack of capital sources and exorbitant rates of interest.

In Finland the co-operative credit system prevails. It provides two kinds of credit: (1) credit for resettlement purposes, at an interest rate of 3 per cent, and (2) credit for other agricultural purposes (machinery, reclamation, etc.).

The delegate from the Gold Coast reported the existence of savings banks only. They provide credit especially for cocoa-growing farmers, who export the crop to overseas countries.

In the second session the gathering dealt with the cardinal problem: *How and where to get the necessary funds to fulfill the needs of the family-farmer and to permit an expansion of credit facilities.* There was general agreement that most of the countries represented are in urgent need of capital for agricultural purposes. Three types of shortages can be distinguished: (1) countries with over-all shortage of capital, (2) countries with shortage of capital in rural areas, and (3) countries with capital shortages for certain agricultural purposes.

Among the countries with an over-all shortage of capital the following were represented in this working party: Bolivia, Colombia, Germany, Haiti, India, Iran, Japan, Lebanon, and Paraguay. In these countries, the supply of capital for agricultural purposes is very low, especially for reclaiming land, for purchasing land so that tenants may become owners, for compensation and rehabilitation grants to landlords whose large estates were broken up; in short, for all purposes where long-term credit is needed.

After this clarification there followed a discussion of various experiences in providing capital for family-size farms. In the reports of the different delegates the following sources of capital were described:

Private savings banks.—These institutions tend to demand high interest rates and do not fulfill the conditions needed for an agricultural long-term credit system.

Co-operative bank system.—The delegate from the Netherlands reported on this system. In that country co-operative banks were founded nearly sixty years ago, patterned on the Raiffeisen system. Every village in the Netherlands has its Raiffeisen Bank, which collects the savings of the farmers. From these savings, loans are provided to farmers in need of capital. Two kinds of deposits are possible: call-money deposits and savings deposits. With call-money deposits, the money is available on demand, which results in a lower rate of interest. With savings deposits, there are restrictions to prevent withdrawal of the entire deposit. A Central Bank functions as a clearing bank which organizes the transfer from banks with surplus to those with too little money. The weakness of this system lies in the fact that during a period of bad economic conditions not enough money is available to meet the need, because the farmer-investors prefer to have their money in cash to avoid losses.

State-sponsored banks.—These banks provide loans at lower rates of interest and receive their funds from government budgets.

Credits from foreign countries with capital surpluses.—Referring to the last point, the Italian delegate pointed out that it may be necessary to co-ordinate the different sources in any one country in such a manner that the call for international capital may be limited to particular needs. In addition to this, he suggested that the following points be distinguished:

Short-term credit needs in underdeveloped countries where usury prevails and in abnormally developed countries with unsound economic and social conditions.—To get the necessary capital in countries falling within this classification, it is usually only a problem of organization and control of credit institutions. Normally, there exists no need of capital from abroad, and agricultural credit may be obtained from internal sources. Only in underdeveloped countries or in developed ones in years of economic depression is foreign capital necessary.

Medium-term credit needs for normal agricultural operations (machinery, livestock, etc.) and for exceptional operations (extraordinary technical improvements).—The first kind of credit should be available without difficulty. The distribution of this type of production credit depends only on the organization of credit institutions. As to the second type, the financing of extraordinary technological developments requires not only capital from abroad but also an intervention of the state in providing special funds in order to reduce interest rates, to prolong the repayment of borrowed capital, and to safeguard the investor. With regard to such security, an American participant in the working party suggested that a sharp distinction be made between single-security capital (i.e., the lender is secure, but not the farmer who carries out the investment) and double-security capital (i.e., a credit system that protects the borrower as well as the lender). For instance, when it is obvious that the farmer can repay the loan, then he should get the loan. In case there is no clear evidence about his ability to repay, he should get help and assistance to make repayment possible. This system of double-security capital has proved its value in Paraguay, where a special branch of the Agricultural Bank provides its loans according to this principle. The source of capital is small and the need is great. Consequently only 10 per cent of the farmers in Paraguay have been reached by this system. Nevertheless, it deserves study and support, for this 10 per cent has made considerable progress in improving their farms.

It is readily understandable that countries having severe deficits of capital should direct their eyes to richer ones that could transfer surplus funds to them. Accordingly, the next question raised in our discussions was: *What arrangements can be made to transfer capital from countries with surpluses to those with lack of capital?* To begin with, it was recognized that the number of countries having surplus capital is small. To supplement their normal capital exports there are some international organizations which under certain conditions may bring efficient help. Among them are: (1) the International Bank for Reconstruction and Development, an organization that provides loans to banks or other countries in order to permit them to undertake programs of technological development; (2) the Import-Export Bank; (3) the Rockefeller Foundation (restricted to certain countries); (4) ECA "counterpart funds" (consisting of the equivalent, in local currency, of the dollar value of goods contributed under the ECA, now MSA, programs); and (5) GARIOA funds (available only in occupied areas as Japan and Germany). The third part of the discussions dealt with the different developments and organizations of credit systems. In order to get at the problems involved, the discussion was centered on the following three topics:

1. Under what conditions do private banks reach the family-size farms?

2. What can be done to overcome the evils of unrealistic terms, the high rates of interest, and the inaccessibility of banks?

3. What are the relative merits of different banking systems; e.g., co-operative banks, private banks, and government-sponsored banks?

In most countries of the world, a private bank is interested in loans to farmers only if high rates of interest and security of repayment are provided. For example, private bank credits in Japan are not common because the law prohibits the purchase of land by nonagricultural people. As a result those who have invested money in agricultural credits have no security, either in movables or immovables, in case the borrowing farmer is unable to repay his loan.

With reference to double-security credits, as mentioned above, the Italian delegate emphasized the need for bank people to study the credit problems of agriculture and to go to the farm people, instructing them about the possibilities of credit and assisting them in an efficient utilization of capital. This would actually be a type of social work by the banks. How far away we are from this ideal in some countries is illustrated by the case of Lebanon, where the middleman in the marketing system takes profit from the lack of other credit facilities. Several delegates expressed a conviction that this middleman system, upon which the farmer is often entirely dependent because of the lack of other possibilities, should be abolished and replaced by sounder banking systems.

With regard to co-operative banking systems, one delegate stated that a co-operative bank would not succeed in his country because the farmers were not yet ready for it; therefore legislation should provide for some other type of credit institution. On the other hand, the experiences of other countries have demonstrated that the co-operative banking system is a desirable type. In many countries they have had a long, hard way to go until they gained the significant position they have at the present time.

How the co-operative system works may be shown by some examples.

In Japan, co-operative banks have attained an influential position. Their funds are obtained from the Bank of Japan, a semi-official bank. The need for short-term credit for agricultural production purposes is covered by these facilities.

In Finland, the capital for credit co-operatives comes from the government, which guarantees the security of these investments in an amount of 25 per cent to 35 per cent. It was pointed out that the plan of procedure for making use of these credits is adequate; but the supervision, which means guidance and technical assistance, is not.

The Agricultural Cooperative Credit Bank in Egypt provides short- and long-term credit at interest rates of about 4 per cent for short-term loans and about 5 per cent for longer term loans. Half of the funds come from the government, the other half from private sources. In the most recent year loans totaling 30 million dollars were granted.

In Colombia an institution of the same kind has been founded by the government. In the past year credits totaling 75 million dollars were available, which were granted to 150,000 farmers. There are 130 branches of this credit institution throughout the country, and every farmer may easily take advantage of their facilities. Credit is provided especially on long- and middle-term bases.

In the above-mentioned four countries the co-operative banking institutions are government-sponsored, and provide supervision and technical assistance to the farmers, thus assuring security of the loans both to investor and borrower. This solution avoids the bad effects of credit systems observed in Haiti and Lebanon, where, because of the lack of competition and of government supervision, the system tends to exploit the credit-seeking farmer.

In conclusion, the working party agreed that the procedure of granting loans to family-sized farmers should avoid (1) too high rates of interest, in order to permit the extension of credit to that particular group of peasants who are so low in the scale of human existence that they frequently have no will, desire, or ability to improve their lot, (2) unreasonable and unrealistic credit terms and conditions which are not adapted to the needs of the farmer, and (3) inaccessibility to credit facilities, so that farmers can obtain their needed credit without unreasonable effort or expense or resort to the use of influence.

Part XVI

EQUITABLE TENANCY ARRANGEMENTS IN A PROGRESSIVE AGRICULTURE

THE INFLUENCE OF WESTERN CONCEPTS ON INDIAN TENURE: INTRODUCTORY COMMENT

B. Natarajan

THIS IS A really important day with papers from representatives of three great countries. Britain, France, and the United States have evolved different types of land tenure systems. In Britain you have the big landlord and the tenancy system of the leasehold, which has worked wonderfully in the British situation. In France you have developed the peasant proprietorship, which idea was responsible for a great revolution, and which has changed the political and economic face of several countries. And you have in the United States the conception of the family farm, which to us in the Orient is something offering hope, but which is very much of a delusion also. It is a hope because we feel in the family farm lies the future success of a democratic way of life; but yet it is a delusion, we feel, because we will have probably a long way to go before we can ever achieve the family farm. So we have to see the relative merits of these systems in the historical context of these three countries. One thing is certain: these three concepts have affected history considerably. The English concepts of the landlord, the freehold and leasehold tenancy, were taken over to India by Lord Cornwallis, who thought that if Indian landlords were created on the model of English landlords we would have here a very healthy agricultural system. So he introduced the zamindari system, but it did not suit the circumstances. The landlords became mere rent receivers and were not the agricultural pioneers that

England sought. Tenancy degenerated into rack renting. Again, the concept of the peasant proprietorship of farms travelled to India, strange as it may seem, through an Englishman, Arthur Young, who said, "The magic of property turns sand into gold." His ideas were taken to India through students who were trained in the Haleybury College, where Malthus and other people were teaching as early as 1805. And these Indians repeated Arthur Young's ideas, and thus he won what is called the ryotwari system of tenancy, or the peasant proprietorship. So the two major systems of land tenure in India; namely, the zamindari and the ryotwari both came from Europe, one from England through Lord Cornwallis and the other from France through England and Arthur Young. Both of these have had profound influence in creating the agricultural economy, in laying down the agricultural setup, in the country. But these things did not exactly suit us.

The genius of the country—the history of the country—was different; and conditions differed. We have gone our own way, and we have to devise new forms that will suit our conditions. Now, as I told you, the concept of the family farm is dangling before us, and I do not know how far we can translate it in practice. But these three concepts have been very vital, historically as well as practically, in shaping the features of the world. So we look forward to a very interesting discussion this day.

EQUITABLE TENANCY ARRANGEMENTS IN A
PROGRESSIVE AGRICULTURE: THE BRITISH EXPERIENCE

John Stuart Hill

IN WRITING a paper on the subject of equitable tenancy arrangements I must, of necessity, be influenced by my knowledge and experience of rural estate management in England. It therefore seems desirable first to provide a little background before discussing the specific matters which arise out of the words "equitable tenancy arrangements." The existing arrangements, so far as England is concerned, have been gradually built up over a long period and have been influenced by the pattern of land ownership, land tenure, and farming practice, and changes, social and economic, which have taken place.

I do not intend to quote many statistics, since these are readily available in various publications; but perhaps it will be helpful to observe that the population of England and Wales is about 43.5 millions, which gives an average density of about 750 persons per square mile. The close concentration of the industrial population in large towns and urban areas, however, leaves about 24 million acres under crops and grass on holdings of upwards of one acre. The number of holdings concerned is about 367,000. About 1.25 million persons are regularly engaged in agriculture. I should perhaps explain that my remarks relate to England and Wales (exclusive of Scotland and Northern Ireland) because Scotland and Northern Ireland have their own agricultural departments. While there is close contact and consultation between these departments and the Ministry of Agriculture and Fisheries, my subsequent remarks on legislation and procedure relate to England and Wales. Moreover, the general all-over picture is not appreciably influenced thereby.

Before the late war imports of food and feeding stuffs accounted for 45 per cent of our total imports, and in terms of calories for human consumption we were producing about 30 per cent of our requirements. At the beginning of 1949 our production in these terms had been increased to about 40 per cent. Our aim by 1952 is to achieve a higher level of agricultural production than ever before; that is, to produce in terms of calories for human consumption one-third more than was produced before the war and to save the equivalent of 4 million tons of imported feeding stuffs.

It will, therefore, be clear that our most immediate problem and task in relation to land management and farming is one of increased production so that the agricultural industry can make its maximum contribution towards the job of balancing the national budget.

The present pattern of land tenure derives from Norman times when the land tenure was the English manorial system— medieval manor comprised of the lord's demesne, the homesteads and lands of the freeholders or yeomen, and of the unfree tenants, the cottages of the workers, the open field, woodland, and water. The eighteenth century witnessed a great improvement in agricultural estate use by enclosure and layout and also in the development of farming practice. Incidentally, it was in the year 1727 that the first manual on the subject of land agency was written. By the nineteenth century British agriculture was famous by comparison with then existing standards, and the industry was prosperous. Depression occurred later in that century, the immediate cause being the importation from the New World of corn and meat necessary to feed the rapidly increasing industrial population, but at a price with which the English farmer could not compete.

This depressed economic position of British agriculture persisted in a greater or less degree until the outbreak of the first world war. This is not to say that fine stock was not reared and that our export trade in pedigreed animals was not maintained—we know it was, and, as in every walk of life, the particularly efficient and progressive man made good; but, in general, farming was carried on on a basis far below full production, large areas previously under cultivation reverted to grass, and the economy, excluding the period of the first world war, was one of low costs and low returns. In fact, between 1870 and 1937 the crop acreage dropped as follows: cereal crops, 47 per cent; root crops, 46 per cent; and rotation grasses, 19 per cent.

During the greater part of this period the often-maligned large landowner did much to enable his tenants to exist, and thus to ensure the land being farmed at all, by allowing them to remain in occupation at rents which afforded him little or, doubtless in some cases, no return on the capital invested in his land, and in not a few instances by positively assisting him to carry on.

Prior to 1914 the break-up of many medium-size and large estates was in progress for economic (pressure of taxation and death duties), personal, and other reasons, and this process was greatly accentuated towards the end of and in the years immediately following the first world war. That war made farmers prosperous but did not improve the position of landowners. As the result of newly found prosperity many tenant-farmers purchased their farms, soon to find that, with the repeal of the Corn Production Act and other causes, a heavy depression again returned to the agricultural industry. Many who had purchased at the high prices then obtaining and had taken up a large proportion of the purchase money on mortgage and in addition had, of course, assumed the landowners' liability for the maintenance of permanent equipment, found themselves unable to carry on. At the present time, of the aggregate number of farms and of the total area of farm land approximately one third is in owner-occupation, the remaining two-thirds being farmed by tenants.

Certain measures of relief—notably marketing schemes and some import regulations—somewhat improved the position of the farming industry in England after 1931 and before the second world war. Having made this brief reference to landownership and agriculture, I will now say a very few words about the pattern of the countryside.

England is mainly a country of small farms, about 80 per cent not exceeding one hundred acres in area, about 18 per cent being between one hundred and three hundred acres, and about 4 per cent above this acreage. They are not set out in squares or rectangles, but are often of irregular shape, and sometimes are made up of scattered areas of land. In many parts of the country a field of, say, twenty acres is the exception rather than the rule, and sizes of enclosure run between five and fifteen acres. This means, of course, that there is a lot of fencing on the normal farm, mostly hedges, and in the lowlands, ditches or rhines, and on some of the hill farms, loose stone walls. The type and inherent quality of the soil differ widely and frequently, so that hardly anywhere are there large areas of uniform land. We also have our frequently varying altitudes with, as is common elsewhere, the less productive land at higher levels. In the main, mixed farming (with livestock) is practiced, dairying (liquid milk production) being predominant. A large number of farms are devoted almost entirely to the production of milk, and those which can be placed in the mixed and stock rearing groups very often also produce and sell liquid milk, while the production of vegetables for human consumption is often a side line on farms which are suitable as regards situation and soil. In the recent past, there has been relatively little corn-growing except in the eastern countries, though during and since the late war we have had to do much in the way of taking the plough round the farm for the purpose of wheat production and more especially, taking the long-term view, for the production of protein-content cattle feeding stuffs which previously had been largely imported but which for economic reasons it is not now practicable to purchase from overseas.

It can, I think, be fairly stated that until recent years farm buildings erected long ago were, and in fact often still are, being relied upon in the main to serve the requirements of the farm. There has been very substantial new construction of, and improvements and adaptation to, cowhouses and dairy equipment in connection with essential requirements for clean and tuberculin-free milk, but much still remains to be done to bring up to date other farm buildings. Many of these old buildings are substantially erected and in fair condition, and still serve the industry well, but they are progressively becoming less suitable to meet modern requirements, particularly as to convenient layout and the increasing necessity of saving labor (man hours) in the tending and feeding of stock. Thus, there is a constant demand for improved and up-to-date accommodation, and, moreover, landowners have now statutory duties in this respect to which reference is made later on.

It will not perhaps be out of place to mention the medium through which landowners and their tenants usually do their bargaining, air their grievances, and settle their differences. The person who generally can claim to be counsellor and friend to each in their relationship of landlord and tenant is known as a land agent. Usually land agents are qualified by examination and belong to professional bodies of which the three principal ones serving the agricultural industry in England are the Royal Institution of Chartered Surveyors, the Land Agents' Society, and the Chartered Auctioneers' and Estate Agents' Institute. In the case of large estates there is often a resident land agent who is a full-time employee of the landowner, but many estates and small ownerships are managed by a member of a firm in general practice as land agents, valuers, and auctioneers, while there are not an inconsiderable number of small owners who consider they can manage their affairs successfully without obtaining professional advice. The existence of these professional men, trained in practical land agency and in the application of the law of landlord and tenant, undoubtedly has influenced through the years the maintenance of equitable landlord and tenant arrangements.

The rights of the two parties in their relationship of landlord and tenant, and in the event of their dispute, the legal position between them, has been governed by the following four matters: (a) the contract of tenancy, either in the form of a lease for years, or, much more frequently, in the form of an agreement for a lease which conveys an annual tenancy requiring twelve months' notice by either party to terminate it; (b) an unwritten law known as the custom of country which came into operation mainly on the termination of the tenancy; (c) common law with regard to a few matters, if these were not otherwise covered under contract or custom; and (d) statute law, viz., Acts of Parliament passed from time to time since the first Act in 1875, under the title of Agricultural Holdings Acts.

This legislation has been designed to secure fair dealing between landlord and tenant both during the term of the tenancy and upon its termination. Its main trend has been towards giving the tenant more security of tenure, freedom to crop as he pleases provided he maintains the fertility of the land and puts his tillage area into proper rotation in the last year of the tenancy, freedom to carry out improvements, and freedom to receive adequate compensation for such improvements when he quits the holding. Provision was also made for compensation for disturbance to be paid by the landlord if, as a result of a notice to quit given by him, the tenant left the holding, unless it could be shown that this tenant was not farming in accordance with the rules of good husbandry. The important provisions were operative despite any agreement to the contrary, and a method of settling disputes by reference to an arbitrator, instead of by recourse to the courts, was laid down.

I now come to the second world war, which compelled a drastic reconstruction of our agricultural economy in the interests of intensive production, particularly of foods and feeding stuffs which previously we could import. I do not intend to dwell on what was then achieved. I refer to the period because it helped to provide the pattern of administrative machinery through which our postwar agricultural policy is carried out. As is widely known, County War Agricultural Committees were set up under emergency wartime powers.

These committees were given as a temporary measure extensive powers of direction and control of food production, which they exercised in their respective counties on behalf of the Minister of Agriculture and Fisheries in whom those powers were actually vested. Apart from the issuing of directions for cropping and the breaking up of permanent pasture, the taking of possession, temporarily, of land and farms and directly farming such of them as could not otherwise have been cultivated, they had to acquaint themselves with all the needs of farmers and in so far as possible arrange for their supply. During the war years the arable area was increased by 6 million acres to 15 million acres, and the yearly importation of feeding stuffs was reduced by 1.5 million tons. The substitution of mechanized power for horse power on farms was greatly accelerated; for example, the number of tractors increased from about 55,000 in 1939 to 190,000 at the end of the war. It is now about 300,000.

We have had to take stock of the broad, long-term economic position of the country and firmly face the fact that the clock could not be put back and that we were obliged to produce an all-over policy for the agricultural industry which would not only provide the incentive and the means to maximum food production but would also be capable of being implemented. Also, this had to be provided for by democratic methods and within the framework of the existing pattern of British agriculture and land tenure. As a result there was passed by Parliament the Agriculture Act of 1947, which may be termed a new deal for the agricultural industry and which brings the state into the picture as the guardian of the interests of the community as a whole. Thus there became four partners or interested parties—the landowner, the occupier (whether he is also the owner or a tenant) in his capacity as a farmer, the agricultural worker, and the state. In fact, the position of the agricultural worker does not enter largely into the subject matter of this paper, but I would mention that statutory provisions and consultative machinery exist for the improvement of his status as regards wages, housing, and the possibility of his ultimately becoming a farmer.

Whereas previous legislation affecting landlord and tenant had been designed primarily for the purpose of insuring fairness between those parties, the Agriculture Act of 1947 is much wider in scope. Its purpose is to provide for all those working on the land or connected with it, the machinery through which they can increase the efficiency of agriculture and thus step up food production and ensure the future prosperity of the industry. The Act comprises five parts.

Part I is devoted to provisions for securing assured markets and guaranteed prices for agricultural produce and thereby ensuring stability in the industry. The greater part of the farmers' output is purchased by the Ministry of Food either directly or through authorized agents.

Part II is devoted to securing that landowners fulfill their responsibilities to manage the land in accordance with the rules of good estate management and that occupiers or tenants fulfill their responsibilities to farm their holdings in accordance with the rules of good husbandry.

The rules of good estate management require a landowner to manage his land in such a way as will enable an occupier or tenant of the land reasonably skilled in husbandry to maintain efficient production as respects the kind of produce and the quality and quantity of it. In particular, this places a responsibility on the landowner to provide, improve, maintain, and repair fixed equipment on the land in so far as is reasonably necessary to enable efficient production to be secured.

The rules of good husbandry require a tenant to maintain a reasonable standard of production, both as regards the type of farming and the way it is carried out, and to preserve the fertility of the land. To crop and stock the land properly, to keep stock and crops free from disease and pests, and in so far as the liability is his under contract or statute to carry out necessary works of maintenance and repair.

Part III is devoted to the relationship of landlord, tenant, and the state, which for a time had to be read in conjunction with previous landlord and tenant legislation. A consolidating act, the Agricultural Holdings Act, 1948, now sets out the law in this respect.

Part IV is devoted to the provision of Statutory Tenant Holdings by Local Authorities—notably the Councils of counties who for the past fifty years or so have been entrusted, under various smallholdings acts, with the provision of smallholdings for prospective farmers with limited capital at their disposal. Perhaps the principal difference between the smallholdings provisions of the 1947 act and the previous smallholdings legislation is that in the selection of tenants from applicants for smallholdings preference must now be given to bona fide agricultural workers, whereas previously the majority of those settled on statutory smallholdings were sons of small farmers. Facilities also exist for making loans to selected applicants who have insufficient capital of their own to stock the holding. Since the inception of smallholdings legislation about 450,000 acres have been acquired by county councils for this purpose in England and Wales.

Part V provides for the setting up of an Agricultural Land Commission for the purpose of managing and arranging for the farming of land vested in the Minister of Agriculture on behalf of the state. Such land comes into state ownership by various channels, usually because for one reason or another it could not or would not be adequately developed to enable it to be farmed in accordance with the rules of good husbandry if it remained in private ownership. This part of the Act also provides for the setting up in each administrative county in England and Wales of Agricultural Executive Committees, who act as agents of the Minister of Agriculture. These Committees, first set up in 1939 to deal with wartime food production requirements, are thus retained and are responsible for administering, in the interests of good estate management and of good husbandry and thus of adequate production, parts II and III of the Act.

These Committees are in constitution nicely balanced as between representatives of agricultural interests. They consist of a maximum of twelve members, five appointed directly by the Minister and seven from panels nominated by the interests concerned. They are the judges, on behalf of the Minister, of farming and estate management efficiency, subject to a right of appeal in some instances, by an aggrieved landowner or farmer, to the Agricultural Land Tribunals.

It is most necessary to appreciate that the primary object of the Act as regards securing efficiency in farming and estate management is to secure this by means of help and advice to the parties concerned and that the ultimate sanction of dispossession of either landlord or tenant is not put into effect until every chance has been given to the defaulting party to profit by advice offered on problems of farming and management. In this connection either may be put under supervision for a period to enable him to remedy deficiencies, and it is only after he has had full opportunity to do so that the question of dispossession arises.

In connection with the availability and tendering of advice I should explain that agricultural research in Great Britain is largely financed and co-ordinated by the state, and its results have been available to farmers for many years. The war years, however, showed that an adequate advisory service to farmers is essential if maximum food production is to be obtained, and in 1946 a National Agricultural Advisory Service was set up. This Service will in due course employ some two thousand officers. Subsequently, an Agricultural Land Service was instituted with a much smaller complement, and in this connection it will be appreciated from previous remarks that many

landowners already have the service of professional private land agents. It is through these two services, the NAAS and the ALS (incidentally, the ALS performs other duties, notably in connection with the management of land held by the Land Commission and with the provisions of smallholdings), working in close co-operation with the County Agricultural Executive Committees that technical advice on farming and estate management problems is obtainable at no direct cost to farmers and landowners.

In relation to equitable tenancy arrangements, the position thereof now is that by way of a contract of tenancy between landlord and tenant and by way of legislation which can be invoked to provide for any deficiencies or remedy any unfair provisions in a contract of tenancy or to operate between the parties in default of a contract, fair terms on all matters between landlord and tenant can be assured, and the state can be well served in the interests of food production. Some of the practical effects are that the tenant is afforded a very secure tenure, in that, broadly speaking, he cannot be turned out of his farm if he is cultivating it in accordance with the rules of good husbandry. He can, if he so desires, have his rent adjusted from time to time (not more often than every three years) by reference to arbitration; that is, by the assessment of an independent arbitrator who is a professional valuer, appointed by the Minister of Agriculture from a specially selected panel of valuers. A tenant can carry out improvements adjudged to be reasonably necessary for the proper working of the holding and secure adequate compensation for them from his landlord when he quits the holding. He is also assured when he quits the holding of adequate compensation for matters which we call tenant-right and which comprise harvested and growing crops and tillages left for the benefit of an incomer and also for the unexhausted value of manures applied to the land and the unexhausted manurial value of feeding stuffs consumed on the holding. The landlord has the same right as the tenant to refer to arbitration the question of what rent should properly be paid for the holding and also to claim on the termination of the tenancy for any dilapidation or deterioration to the holding due to default by the tenant.

It is not practicable in a paper of this length, if indeed it is appropriate to its title, to touch upon many aspects and activities designed to assist the agricultural industry. But perhaps I should mention that loan facilities exist for both farmer and landowner apart from those provided by the banks and that substantial grants and aids have been, and are being, made by the government in relation to such matters as the Attested Herds scheme, Drainage and Water Supply, Hill Sheep and Cattle Subsidy, Hill Farming Grants, etc. In this paper, therefore, I have endeavored to concentrate on the land tenure and tenancy aspect, at the same time conveying some idea of the agricultural background which influences these matters, and I can only hope that to some extent I have succeeded in putting a comprehensible picture before you.

Finally, I should like to express my thanks to our hosts for taking the initiative in making this conference on land tenure and allied problems possible. I am sure we are all finding it most instructive, interesting, and enjoyable.

LANDLORD-TENANT RELATIONS AND FRENCH LAW

Albert Alexandre Costa

ORIGINALLY under the Civil Code farm leases were drawn under the general principle of complete freedom of negotiation. The contracts entered into by the interested parties had the force of law and were to be executed in good faith. Property rights were of an absolute nature.

In the course of the nineteenth and twentieth centuries, however, a slow evolution took place in the relations between tenants and landowners. In many cases, especially those where a shortage of farm labor was involved, contracts were drawn up after free discussions in which each of the interested parties defended equally his respective rights.

But it was nonetheless true that because of this principle of the freedom of contracts the tenant might find himself deprived of certain advantages which he had arduously acquired if the economic circumstances were so oriented. The celebrated phrase of Lamenais frequently came to mind: "In many cases it is liberty which oppresses and the law which brings freedom."

Prompted then by a desire for justice and by certain social and economic considerations, French legislators were led to draw a status of farm tenancy which was incorporated in the ordinance of October 17, 1945, itself modified by various subsequent laws—notably by those of April 13, 1946, and December 31, 1948.

We shall discuss, in turn, regulations concerning farm tenancy contracts, those concerning sharecropping contracts, and finally the regulations common to both these kinds of contracts.

Tenancy Contracts

Farm tenancy, which is found in 33.5 per cent of the total area of the country and in 544,000 individual farms, may be characterized as the association of the real estate capital of the landowner and the material capital of the tenant. The risk incurred in operations is borne by the latter. The rental fee remains fixed during the whole length of the contract.

In order to avoid the serious consequences resulting from fluctuations in farm prices and currency values, the law stipulates that the rental fee must be expressed in terms of a fixed quantity of farm products. At the time of the drawing up of the lease the interested parties must agree on whether these farm products will be handed over in kind by the tenant or whether the payment shall be in an equivalent sum of money.

The choice of farm products which are to serve as a basis for calculating rental value is also regulated. The contracting parties are obliged to consult a list of eight local or regional farm products which has been drawn up for each department by an advisory commission on farm leases made up of an equal number of representatives of the government, landowners, and tenants.

This group, after having drawn up the list of farm products, decides likewise on the quantities of the various products which will represent the normal rent value of the properties to be rented.

The prefect, after having reviewed and in some cases modified the results of the commission's work, issues an order on the results. If he considers that the commission has not fulfilled its tasks he may take the place of the commission and draw his own conclusions.

The decision as to the rental fee thus fixed is only advisory, and the contracting parties may agree to raise or lower it, if for instance, the quality of the land of the work to be carried out by the tenant merits such action.

The contracting parties, however, must advance very prudently. Under the law either of them, who at the time of the drawing up of the lease accepted a price which is above or below the normal rent value by as much as 10 per cent, has the right before six months have elapsed to request a re-evaluation by a competent tribunal. At the time of any renewal of the rent it is likewise the same court which will fix the new rental fee in case there is any dispute over it. Once the rental fee has been set as outlined above, no further fees nor service of any nature can be required of the lessee.

In case of the loss of at least half a harvest by an act of God, the tenant may request a reduction in his rent unless previous harvests have made up for this loss. If this latter is not the case the setting of the amount of the reduction cannot take place before the lease has run out, at which time a general settlement for all the years the lease has run is made. The judge may, however, as a temporary measure, allow the lessee to omit rental payments where the loss suffered has been considerable.

Sharecropping Contracts

Sharecropping is a contract under the terms of which a landowner contributes the real estate capital and all or part of the material capital, while the sharecropper contributes his labor. Contracts of this nature, which are restricted to the region south of the Loire River, have been decreasing in number. At the beginning of the nineteenth century they were found in about 50 per cent of the land under cultivation. By 1892 this figure had fallen to 12 per cent, and at present it is 10.5 per cent, with 138,000 farms concerned.

Under this system of farm operation, sometimes the sharecropper was his own operator; sometimes the owner, who lived on the property, co-operated directly with the sharecropper in running the farm. Sometimes over-all supervision of a number of sharecroppers on a large estate was put in the hands of a resident operator.

The law now specifies that in each departement the advisory commission on farm rents, previously mentioned, may either set the conditions under which the sharecropper may himself direct farm operations or define carefully special arrangements where the landowner himself has a hand in farm operations.

In interpreting this regulation the advisory commission has allowed the sharecroppers considerable latitude in so far as the actual carrying out of the year's farm program is concerned. On the other hand they have generally insisted that the said program be drawn up in accord with the landowner. Where there have been disputes the courts have been called on to force a decision.

The law specifies that farm products shall be shared on a basis of one-third to the land owner and two-thirds to the sharecropper. Exceptions to this rule may be made by the courts, especially in the case of vineyards and orchards which have entailed a large investment on the part of the land owner. The tenant cannot be held to any further payment whether it be in kind, cash, or further services beyond the fixed rent in farm products or in cash which has been agreed upon. It should be noted that this division of farm produce on a one-third–two-thirds basis does not apply to the livestock, which continues to be shared equally under special "livestock contracts" which are regulated directly by the Civil Code.

French legislators, believing that farm tenancy is more desirable than sharecropping, have set up a system under which, at the request of one of the interested parties, sharecropping contracts must be converted into farm tenancy.

The request for the conversion, which will affect the whole farm property, including farm equipment and livestock, must be made at least a year before the expiration of any of the three-year periods coming within the rent or of the expiration of the lease itself. Its effect will be to substitute a farm lease for a sharecropping contract beginning with the first day of the farm year as construed at the time of the request for conversion. The only way a land owner can oppose such a request for conversion is to claim the land again directly for his own use.

Tenancy and Sharecropping

DRAWING THE LEASE OR CONTRACT

The law specifies that such contracts must be drawn up in writing. If there is no written lease, the contracting parties are automatically bound by the clauses of a model contract which has been set up for each departement by the before-mentioned advisory commission.

An inventory must be made listing various real estate or other improvements which may be made to the farm. Under such an arrangement it is easier to determine at the end of the lease any payments which are due the farmer for the various improvements he has made.

CONDITIONS OF LEASE

Various measures intended to guarantee to the farmer and his family some measure of stability include the length of the lease, which must run for a minimum of nine years, with the possibility of an automatic renewal for nine years if the farmer so desires.

The landowner can contest the renewal of the lease by giving due notice eighteen months before its expiration, but he can do so only if he backs up his action with serious and legitimate charges or if he is making the cancellation with a view to a permanent, personal operation of the property. The lease may likewise be cancelled if a son or daughter, becoming of age, is ready to operate the farm. In such cases the cancellation may be made at the end of one of the three-year periods without waiting for the end of the lease. The contract, however, must specifically mention the possibility of cancellation after any of the three-year periods of the lease.

If the land owner is to operate the property personally, such cancellations are limited to one. Land owners, however, retain the right to cancel as many contracts or leases as they have adult children. The serious and legitimate reasons which a land owner may use to refuse renewal of a contract of lease are, on the one hand, repeated failure to make the rental payments, whether they be in cash or in kind, unless a case of absolute necessity is involved, and, on the other hand, any action on the part of the tenant which may compromise the sound operation of the farm, especially failure to provide sufficient manpower for the needs of the farm or refusal to make farm improvements which have been approved by a three-fourths majority within the advisory commission on farm leases.

The security of the farmer's family is further guaranteed by the fact that in case of the death of the tenant, the lessor may call for the cancellation of the lease or contract only in case the former has no surviving wife, parents, or children under sixteen at the time of his death, and who either live or work on the farm with him or have a reasonably adequate theoretical and practical knowledge of farm operation.

The stability thus guaranteed the farmer and his family has aggravated many land owners who have spoken of it as a veritable derogation of property rights. Historical precedents, however, cannot be neglected. Direct contact with the land has always created a kind of right over the land. Legislation which is intended to stimulate farm production has had to give some recognition to these rights. The example of the declining Roman Empire in this respect is very clear. The colonial peoples who cleared the land were granted perpetual right which, later, became the hereditary lease.

Ancient French law offers a similar example. When the great Carolingian rule was breaking up in the ninth century, each farmer, free man, colonial, or slave received a plot of land which he cultivated. The concession, which was somewhat precarious at the time of its granting, became strengthened with time; a new form of land tenure appeared on the scene, copyhold tenure, which conferred on its holder a perpetual right and which, for the same land, enjoyed an existence which was parallel and rival to the "eminent domain" of the owner and which the French Revolution was to suppress.

But if the legislators desired to grant the tenant the stability which he deserved, they have nonetheless taken away any possibility of this by their suppression of transfer and subletting fees. Henceforth, the farmer who gives up a farm lease can no longer make money on the deal. The only indemnity he will receive will be that which is paid him by the landowner for any improvements he has made on the farm.

INDEMNITIES TO TENANTS

Indemnities granted to departing tenants do not figure in the Civil Code. Jurisprudence has tried in vain to base it on the theory of unjustified excess profits. It was not until the law of July 15, 1942, that one found any mention in official texts of an indemnity for appreciation. The statute on farm leases after having repealed the law of July 15, 1942, set forth two series of regulations, the first applying to all indemnities, the other applying individually to each kind of indemnity.

Among the regulations common to all indemnities, it should first be noted that the farm improvements which justify the granting of an indemnity must be derived from the work of the lessee. Proof that the improvements have been made must result either from the before-mentioned inventory or from any other method of proof which is allowed by common law. Payment must be made at the time of the end of the lease without any reference to the cause of the termination of the lease.

Regulations concerning specific indemnities deal with (1) crop improvements, (2) real estate improvements, (3) an indemnity paid for planting.

As for crop improvements, the indemnity must equal the expenses of the lessee if the effects will continue after his departure. Any profit he may have derived from these improvements is, of course, taken into account.

As for real estate improvements (buildings and works), the indemnity equals the sum which these improvements would cost at the time of the expiration of the lease, with a deduction made for depreciation. Expenses of a luxury nature are not taken into account. Special regulations have been set up to consider economic conditions which result in an important variation in the cost of these improvements between the time of their execution and the date of expiration of the lease.

Planting justifies, first, an indemnity to the resultant increased rental value for a nine-year period and, secondly, payment of any expenses, including labor, which the lessee may have incurred in the planting.

It should be noted that no matter whether the improvements consist of planting, building, or works, they justify an indemnity only if they have been authorized by the lessor or, in certain cases, a court having the proper jurisdiction.

The lessor is held responsible for guaranteeing the permanence and quality of the plantings (trees and vineyards). He must bear likewise any charges for heavy repairs, and must pay the real estate tax and any fire insurance premiums for the buildings being rented. Only minor repairs and those not resulting from depreciation, faulty construction or building materials or cases of absolute necessity are to be borne by the lessee.

The lessee may join a growers' co-operative. During the effective duration of the lease he is authorized to make temporary exchanges of units which will result in better farm efficiency. He may group together several contiguous units, eliminating within the limits of the rented property any embankments, hedges, ditches, and trees which divide these units, provided, of course, that these operations, likewise, result in better farming efficiency.

In connection with this, the lessee cannot stand in the way of full ownership exchanges of tracts of lands from the estate with other tracts of lands or landed property for the purpose of arrangements similar to reparceling operations, provided that the tracts of lands or landed property newly rented be put under cultivation to replace the tracts thus ceded.

The law grants the lessor hunting rights on the property he has leased. On the other hand he must contribute payments to a fund which will be allocated to various farm and farm building improvements.

Conclusion

The above regulations guaranteeing as they do the farmer's stability, the fixing of a fair price of rent, and finally the constant and progressive efficiency of the farm are of a nature to render useless any agrarian reform in a country such as France of chiefly middle-size farms. It appears fairly sure that land owners will be less and less interested in purchasing land whose rent is low and, which once deduction has been made for various charges, will yield the owner only a very meagre income (from 2 per cent to 5 per cent). Farmers are likely to be more inclined to invest their capital more advantageously in the purchase of farm machinery and in various improvements which will justify an indemnity at the end of the lease.

The legislators have given the scales one final tip in favor of the tenant farmer by granting him certain pre-emptive rights in the case of the sale of the rented farm; thus, the tenant is granted a priority for purchasing the land which he has under cultivation. In case of disagreement the lessee may even have an estimate of value set by the proper court of arbitration unless the land owner decides on sale by auction, in which case the lessee can buy the property if he is able to meet the price of the highest bidder.

Certain special courts empowered to solve questions concerning farm leases have been set up and are made up of two lessors and two lessees, presided over by a professional judge.

The legislators have hoped that justice thus administered in collaboration with the interested profession will be of a nature to avoid law-suits and to facilitate the concilia-tion of interested parties to the dispute.

But on the whole these regulations apply only to normal farm leases. The law has been specific in the case of certain anti-economic situations. Tracts of land below the maximum fixed by prefectoral decree and after approval by the advisory commission on rural rents, which have been rented separately, do not, for instance, come under the regulations in force for leases of a nine-year length with the right of renewal. The lessor, thus, can make the necessary arrangements in order to include them in a unit which will be economically justified.

In conclusion, it should be pointed out that in this brief summary it has been possible to give only a general idea of French legislation relating to farm tenancy and sharecropping. Other forms of farm leases and contracts of special or local character have had to be left out of the discussion.

THE PLACE OF TENANCY IN THE AGRICULTURE OF THE NETHERLANDS

Cornelis D. Scheer

AGRICULTURE in The Netherlands is progressive in some ways, namely, in methods of production, in equipment, and in quality and quantity of its labor force. As a result it has high yields per acre.

On the other hand, it is not progressive in bringing more acres into cultivation, for the gain of land by reclamation and otherwise is outnumbered by the losses for nonagrarian purposes, such as airfields, roads, expansion of cities, and so on. According to recent figures, these losses amount to about 6,250 acres a year, taking away in eight years the whole gain in land of the newly reclaimed polder of the Wieringermeer.

Since 1879 the population has increased by 250 per cent, to more than 10,286,230 people, living on 33,000 square kilometers, or 315 persons per square kilometer. Since the war the population has been increasing at a rate of about 1.65 per cent a year. According to generally accepted expectations, this rate will in the next 20 years gradually slow down. The expected maximum population to be reached in 1970 will be about 12,000,000 people, or 365 persons per square kilometer.

The main source of this growth is the rural population having a considerable surplus of births over deaths. Investigations have shown that in the purely agricultural villages only about 30 per cent of farmers' sons over fifteen years of age leave the farm for nonagrarian occupations. In villages under the influence of industrial areas, about 45 per cent do so.

To maintain a status quo in the labor

supply 67 per cent of these people should leave the farms. This figure is an average; in fact, there are differences in different parts of the country. But only in a very few villages is there a status quo in the labor supply.

The staying-at-home of these people can be explained by the firm grip the family farm holds on the sons. This is particularly important because the family farm is the predominant type of farm by which agriculture in The Netherlands is run. Other factors of resistance are the preference for being a master rather than a servant and the tradition that a farmer's son becomes a farmer. Table 50 shows the development of land use in The Netherlands in the past 40 years according to the main profession of the land users.

Since the demand for labor did not increase at the same rate, this development has had a number of consequences. First of all, on most of the family farms the labor performance is low, or in other words, yields per laborer are low. A recent investigation, covering the sandy soils, with 40 per cent of the land of the whole country in cultivation, shows an average labor performance for the adult worker amounting to about 2,200 standard hours a year, 2,900 hours

being normal. A simple computation shows an under-employment of about 24 per cent. In other family-farm regions, similar figures have been found.

In the few regions where hired labor is employed, the sons of the farmers and their laborers are not so closely tied up with the farm. Birth and death rates in these regions are showing lower surpluses than we find in the family-farm districts. As a result there is some equilibrium between supply and demand of labor and aside from some seasonal unemployment a pretty high labor performance.

Some other districts with greater land-ownership are showing similar conditions. Here the farmer knows that only one son can be his successor when he retires. So he is induced to look at other possibilities than the farm business for his other sons, and he does.

A particular form of land tenure in one district of the country has the same effects. Here the farmer owns the house and other buildings and has a permanent, hereditary, and transferable right to use the land—a right which cannot be terminated by the landowner. The farmer has to pay to the owner a fixed annual rent and certain incidental fees, for instance, when the farm is

TABLE 50

NUMBER OF LAND USERS IN THE NETHERLANDS, 1910–1948,
ACCORDING TO MAIN PROFESSION OF USERS

Main Profession	1910	1921	1930	1948
Farmer	148,844	163,075	175,025	197,186
Horticulturist	15,488	18,800	24,565	38,490
Subtotal	164,332	181,875	199,590	235,676
Laborer	86,099	76,185	57,078	49,268
Nonagrarian	25,474	103,332	115,413	84,724
Grand Total	275,905	361,392	372,081	369,668

transferred. So he, too, is induced to look for other possibilities for his second, third, or other sons, and he does, too.

During the past forty years there have also been considerable shifts in the size of the farms. The number of farms larger than fifty hectares or smaller than ten hectares has decreased; the number of farms from ten to fifty hectares has increased. For lack of figures on different types of farms, further details cannot be given.

A very serious consequence of the population pressure in the rural areas has been the splitting up of a great number of farms into scattered parcels of small and impractical size. About 30 per cent of the land under cultivation has to be re-alloted for this reason; about 4 per cent has been dealt with up to now. Another bad consequence of the disproportion in the man-land ratio that is to be noted brings us to our main problem of tenancy. The increasing labor supply led to an ever-increasing demand for land. As a consequence, prices and rents of land rose, duration of the contracts shortened to one or two years, continuation was often impossible, remission in cases of serious crop losses was not given, nor was compensation given in cases where the farmer had made improvements to the farm or the land.

The fight for a change of the tenancy law began in the nineteenth century, but it was not until 1937 that this change was made. In the next part of this paper we shall go into the methods by which the government with this Act of 1937 has tried to give the tenant more social and economic security and to improve the efficiency of farming.

In the third part of this paper we will try to give an appraisal of these arrangements. This is particularly important because the major form of the relationship of man to the land in The Netherlands has become lease of land. In 1948, 56 per cent of the land in cultivation was in lease. As a matter of fact, this rate, being an average,

is different in different parts of the country, and in different types and sizes of farms. In the coastal provinces this rate is higher than in the other provinces. In horticulture relatively more land is leased than in agriculture.

Tenancy Arrangements Since 1937

Since the French Revolution land has been leased under a free contract. The provisions the law contained could all be waived by contract, including the provision to safeguard the tenant in case of serious crop losses.

To reach its target, the new act of 1937 contains a certain amount of mandatory provisions which cannot be waived by contract. Since then, arable and horticultural land, including the buildings on it, can only be leased on a contract of a provided form and content. Every mandatory provision has its own sanction.

First of all it is provided that the contract, and every contract of modification, has to be approved by a public board—the Land Chamber. This Chamber is appointed by the government and consists of tenants, landowners, and economic and juridical experts. Every province has its Land Chamber. Appeal is possible to the Central Land Chamber consisting of representatives of tenants, owners, and experts. The approval of the contract and, in particular, of the rent is granted when the general interests of agriculture are not hurt and the net revenue to be expected when management is proper guarantees the tenant a fair gain (Art. 41). When contracting parties eventually do not agree with the modifications desired by the Land Chamber, the contract is declared null and void or is altered by the Chamber. Thus the Land Chamber can reduce rent when the tenant has no guarantee of a fair gain by proper management.

The rent must be expressed in a certain amount of Dutch currency for a certain period and may not be made dependent on the prices of products or on other factors. If requested, the Land Chamber can give its approval to fix the rent otherwise (Art. 11).

Every three years a revision of the rent may be requested by both parties if they do not agree. The Land Chamber decides and alters the rent if demanded by fairness (Art. 38).

Major repairs are the responsibility of the owner, but everyday minor repairs must be taken care of by the tenant if it has not been agreed otherwise (Art. 20).

The law compels the owner to insure buildings, whereas the tenant has to insure livestock, equipment, and stores (Art. 23).

Compelling provisions are also made in respect to the duration of the contract.

Individual parcels of land, so-called loose land without a farm, must be leased for at least six years; and farms—land with buildings on it—must be leased for at least twelve years. Shorter periods may be allowed by the Land Chamber in exceptional circumstances or for special purposes (Art. 10).

The tenant is entitled to continuation of the lease at the end of these terms when the owner is not willing to continue (Art. 30). His request for continuation will be refused, however, when (1) he has not been a good tenant; (2) his landlord has a well-founded complaint about the behavior of the tenant toward him; (3) the owner wishes to designate the land for nonagrarian purposes in the public interest; (4) the owner wishes to operate the farm or to use the land himself, or his descendants are wishing to do so. In this case there has to be a weighing of interests.

Death of the tenant or owner does not break the contract (Art. 33).

At the termination of the lease, the tenant has a claim for compensation by the owner for the improvements he has made to farm or land (Art. 27). Of course this claim is limited. The compensation shall not be higher than the increase in the value of farm or land on account of such improvements, and the compensation shall be reduced in proportion to the benefits from these improvements already enjoyed by the tenant. This claim cannot be waived by contract.

As to the formal side, the law provides a written contract. If there is no such contract, the tenant does not have to pay the rent and he can claim back all the rent he paid without obligation. By request of one of the parties, the Land Chamber writes the contract.

Finally, a few words have to be said here about the ways of dealing with disputes between parties. If there is any dispute about the contract—even about the existence of a contract—a special court called Tenancy Court is resorted to. Like the regional Land Chamber, this court also consists of representatives of the tenants and owners and of experts. Here, too, there is a possibility of appeal to the Central Tenancy Court, the members of which are the same as those of the Central Land Chamber.

Appraisal of Tenancy Arrangements

As said above, the tenant can claim (1) minimum duration of the contract for farms with the land of twelve years, for land without buildings, six years; (2) reduction of rent in certain circumstances; (3) reimbursement for improvements; (4) continuation of the lease.

The owner cannot ask the tenant to waive these rights; they are inalienable rights. Great authority has been given to the Land Chambers and Tenancy Chambers. Jurisdiction is provided by a mixed court of career judges and expert laymen. In many respects the tenant enjoys almost as much security as the owner-operator. His interest in maintaining or improving the productivity of the farm is about as great as that of the owner.

He is pretty sure of the fruits of his labor, or he can count on reimbursement of expenses for improvements.

If the tenant is not a good farmer, the landowner can appeal to the judge, and measures can be taken to remove him.

It is clear that these arrangements have solved many of the existing problems. It may be clear, too, that these arrangements can have no pretense of solving the problems of under-employment, of farms of too small size, and of reallotment.

To solve these problems, other steps have to be taken; and such steps have been taken, for some of them. It is not my intention to deal with these steps, since they are beyond the scope of this paper. Morever, there are problems to be solved, some of them very important, in the field we are discussing. Furthermore, there have been some unfavorable repercussions.

The strong protection of the tenant has decreased the interest of the owners in improvements and has not improved the personal relations between tenant and owner. Then it is pretty difficult for an owner to remove a bad tenant.

But the greatest problems have arisen around the approval of the rents. In fact the Land Chamber is confronted with the question of how to find a rent guaranteeing a fair gain to the tenant when he manages his farm property. Apart from terminological questions, it is clear that the rate of rent is tied up with the net revenue of the farm.

This question has arisen because the law not only sets aside free contracts but free competition in renting land, too. This was done while free contracts and competition gave inacceptable economic and social results. It now becomes the duty of the Land Chamber to provide an acceptable solution for the rate of the rents in any individual case.

Unfortunately the law has not given the Land Chamber a clear statement of its norm, nor a suitable measure to solve the question just mentioned. Moreover, it is hard to see how it will be possible to give the farmer any guarantee for a fair gain by manipulation with the rent, the latter being only one of the factors of the cost of production. The results have been subjective valuations and lack of uniformity throughout the country in the rents of similar objects. In the meantime, returns have risen appreciably; but rents have not risen more than 10 per cent to 20 per cent above the level of 1940, fixed during the war.

Speaking in general, the government has failed in finding a practical method of determining what is called a fair gain for the tenant; at the same time the present procedures are injuring the sound interests of the ownership. Not only a general level of rents is missing, but a relative leveling of the different kinds of farms and lands is missing, too.

A second important difficulty has arisen from the large number of oral and unapproved contracts. The cause of this phenomenon is the fear of a number of tenants to request aid from the Land Chamber, against the will of the owner. This is a very weak point in the whole arrangement; for these are the tenants who need the protection of the law most of all. As a result, there is considerable renting of farms and lands in the black market and a number of contracts expiring within twelve or six years without continuation, and without reimbursements for improvements, if made, and lastly without reduction of rent in certain circumstances. For these and other reasons, the act is now being considered.

In conclusion, although considerable progress has been made in the improvement of the social and economic position of the tenants, it must be said that an act only aimed at curing the symptoms without really effecting a cure by getting at the roots of the problem can only have limited results.

EQUITABLE TENANCY ARRANGEMENTS IN THE UNITED STATES

H. C. M. Case

ONE CAN HARDLY understand land tenure or tenancy in the United States without a little historical background. Few laws are significant in relation to tenancy. Compared with some other parts of the world, the settlement of agricultural lands and the development of many agricultural techniques in the United States are relatively recent. Throughout the nineteenth century desirable agricultural lands were made available to settlers for only a small filing fee or at a low cost. It was not until the beginning of the twentieth century that strong competition to gain control of land developed. With the competition for land came tenancy, which had not previously been considered an important problem because land had been both plentiful and cheap. Since the early days of this century, however, farm tenancy and leasing have become an important consideration affecting American agriculture.

Farm leasing provisions must necessarily change over a period of years because of the changes that take place in the techniques of agricultural production. During the past fifty years a large number of the farms of every type in the United States have changed from horse and mule power to mechanical power. Much of the farm work that was formerly done by hand is now being done with mechanical power. Such operations include milking cows, husking corn (maize), cutting corn in the field for silage, baling or chopping hay in the field, harvesting small grain, and many others. This change to mechanical power has greatly reduced the heavy work formerly associated with farming—much of which was done by the farm family. It has also increased the cash cost of operating farms.

The Rise of Farm Tenancy

The first census record of tenant farming in the United States was obtained in 1880. Before that time tenancy had not had any great impetus because farmers could still settle on free land in the areas west of the Mississippi River. But by 1900 the more desirable farmland had passed into private ownership and tenancy began to increase at a rapid rate in many areas. In the early 1900's there was only a relatively small amount of tenancy in the New England and Middle Atlantic states, as well as in the Western states. In the Western states land was not too high priced, new irrigation districts were being opened up, and it was still not too hard for a man to acquire a farm of his own. Tenancy had not attained alarming proportions in these areas as a whole.

The situation in the South was somewhat different. In this area, commonly called the Cotton Belt, cotton was being produced by cropper tenants. This form of tenancy—which some people contend was not really tenancy but a method of paying labor by giving it a share of the product—was an outgrowth of the Civil War. Prior to 1860 most of the cotton in the United States had been produced by slave labor. With the freeing of the slaves, who owned no property, cropper tenancy developed.

Under cropper tenancy, the owner of the land provides equipment, seed, and shelter and finances the cropper tenant until the new crop is made, when the cropper is paid for his share of the crop. Hence the name cropper tenancy. This system still persists in the South, although there is also an increasing amount of tenancy as we know it in other parts of the United States. An evolution is, however, taking place. In cotton production, machines are replacing the hoe and one mule, and cropper tenancy is beginning to diminish or to take on new aspects.

Besides the South, the North Central States is the area in which tenancy is most prevalent. This region, which includes about two-fifths of all the farm land in the United States, produces about two-thirds of the food sold in commercial markets, including three-fourths of the corn, oats, wheat, soybeans, milk, and eggs. Because of the importance of this region agriculturally, the rest of what I shall have to say about tenancy will apply particularly to this area, which is commonly referred to as the Midwest.

Tenancy in the Midwest, which averaged about 20 per cent of all farms in the area in 1880, had increased to about 35 per cent by the beginning of World War I. In the thirteen states making up the area, tenancy now varies from about 50 per cent in the western part to less than 20 per cent in the east (Michigan). (See map, page 147, *Illinois Bulletin* 502.)

In the eastern and southern part of the area, the percentage of tenancy has become fairly well stabilized during the past forty years, but in the western part there has been a phenomenal increase. This represents a maturing of the agriculture in the western section. Much of this land was settled about the close of the last century, and tenancy did not develop until it had been transferred to succeeding generations. The depression of the early 1930's has also been responsible for some of the increase. In 1920 land prices were high, and many purchasers assumed large debts that increased rather than decreased. The result was foreclosure of many farms between 1930 and 1934. During this period continual changes took place in the characteristics of tenancy.

Objectives of Land Tenure

The early land policy of the United States encouraged the operation of farm land by those who owned it. As early as 1821 the policy of the federal government was to sell land to those who would operate it. Various federal acts, including the Preemption Act of 1841 and the Homestead Act of 1862, were designed to encourage individuals to settle on the then abundant supply of undeveloped land. In setting 160 acres as the amount of land one person could acquire by homesteading, the Homestead Act contributed to the establishment of economic-size farm units, since 160 acres was a good unit in the Midwest for the farm practices followed up to 1915.

Some time ago a group of midwestern agricultural economists and representatives from the United States Department of Agriculture attempted to outline briefly what they considered to be a current statement of good land tenure policy. This policy, which emphasizes income, security, and opportunity for farm people is as follows:[1]

Income. It should be possible for qualified farmers to become owners or renters of farm units that will provide an equitable reward for intelligent management, necessary labor input, and the use of necessary capital, and that are large enough and productive enough to support families at levels comparable to those of other major population groups.

Security. Farm families should have the opportunity to enjoy such degree of security in the occupation of their land, whether owned or rented, as will enable them to be effective members of their communities and give them reasonable protection from financial distress resulting from extreme climate hazards and economic depressions.

Opportunity. Farm families should have such further opportunities as are necessary to enable them to develop their best personal talents, to participate actively in community life, and to enjoy adequate social and cultural facilities.

Farm tenancy is an important phase of land tenure especially in an area like the Midwest where, for some entire states, approximately 50 per cent or even more of the land is operated by tenants. Under such conditions the opportunity for the tenant to attain the objectives stated above depends upon a number of things, among which the following are important: (1) productive land; (2) adequate size of business; (3) efficient management; (4) co-operative planning; (5) adequate financing; (6) good business arrangements; (7) a fair sharing of expenses and income; (8) good living conditions; and (9) pride in the farm and community.

Criticisms of Tenancy

Tenancy as it is found in the North Central States is neither all good nor all bad. Some of its good points include the following:

1. From the early days many farm operators have preferred to pay for the use of good land instead of going to new areas where land might be obtained free or at low cost. Their chief reason for this preference was the social and economic advantages to be found in settled areas.

2. Retired farm operators often prefer to leave their savings invested in land, as it is the principal form of investment to which they are accustomed. In fact, many a farm operator does not retire, but retreats from the farm as old age comes on and it becomes necessary for him to let a younger man do the major part of the work.

3. To be successful in farming, a man must operate a reasonably good-size unit. Therefore, when he buys land, he needs to buy a considerable acreage. Tenancy reduces the amount of capital a man must have in order to operate an economic-size farm. A man with limited capital can use it to better advantage as operating capital than to invest in land.

4. Tenancy serves as a means of passing land on from one generation to the next. In many communities a third of the tenants are related to the land owners.

5. Tenancy affords an opportunity for the young or inexperienced farmer to test out his ability before making a heavy investment in land.

6. Many farm operators thrive better as tenants under the supervision of a wise owner than when they attempt to direct all of their own efforts.

7. Some land owners render a valuable service to the community by providing better living conditions for tenants than the tenants would provide for themselves, especially if they attempted to buy land with limited capital resources. Some tenants remain tenants on a good farm after they purchase farms of their own which are in turn rented to another tenant.

8. There are many other reasons, such as temporary health conditions, leaving a community to educate children, and others, which lead some owners to rent their farms for a period of time, although they may later return to operate them.

Although these points justify having a considerable percentage of tenancy, the following objections to it may also be stated:

1. A large percentage of tenancy has certain detrimental influences on the development of the best social life of the community. That is, because many tenants do not feel permanent, they often do not give their best effort toward the development of sound community life.

2. Where the owner does not give wise attention to his property, tenancy may result in the neglect of land, buildings, and equipment, and an exploitative type of production.

3. In some areas farmers' co-operative efforts have been retarded by the large percentage of tenant farmers.

4. Some landlords own land only as a

speculative investment and do not appreciate the problems involved in developing the land to its full productive capacity.

Need for Improving Farm Leases

Many changing conditions which give rise to the need for improving farm leases, include the following:

1. Since the war more farmers are ready to retire, and more young men are starting than under normal conditions.

2. Many young men who should make good tenants lack sufficient capital to begin farming and need leases adjusted to their financial condition.

3. The care of the soil because of the heavy use it received during the war and the difficulties arising from erosion, requires well-developed plans for soil improvement involving the expenditure of more capital.

4. On many farms buildings are in poor repair and wasteful of labor, or more equipment is needed when livestock production is undertaken to fit into an improved cropping plan.

5. An improved level of living reflected in such improvements as better housing, electricity, running water, and sewage disposal requires capital investments and lease provisions to provide for their maintenance and perhaps some sharing of such costs.

6. The use of mechanical power and newer types of machines, including combines, corn pickers, pickup hay balers, and field ensilage cutters, raises questions involving the provisions of farm leases.

7. Changing price relationships, especially labor costs and other cost items in relation to farm income, may require adjustments in farm leases, especially on farms which have heavy cash expenses.

Types of Leasing

The following are five principal types of leases in the Midwest:

1. The cash lease is a rental agreement in which the tenant pays cash for the use of the farm and improvements. Less than one-sixth of the rented farms in Illinois, for example, are leased on the cash basis, and much of the cash leasing is confined to the Chicago dairy and truck crop area. A cash lease contains high risk for the tenant, who guarantees to pay a definite sum of money for the use of the land regardless of the income he is able to make from the farm. Under a cash lease, rentals usually lag as price levels change. Thus, the tenant is at an advantage as net farm income increases and at a disadvantage as income decreases. This difficulty may be partially overcome by adjusting cash rentals with the changing price levels and by making adjustments for crop failures.

Some landlords prefer a cash lease, since it requires less supervision, although they usually receive a lower return than under other forms of leasing farms. A tenant may prefer the independence of a cash lease, because he is sure of receiving the benefits of any superior management he possesses and because in good years it is likely to be more profitable to him than other forms of renting.

2. The crop-share cash lease is the most common type of lease in the Midwest. The tenant gives a share of the grain crops and pays a cash rent for pasture and hay land. Some variations in such leases occur from farm to farm, such as a tenant renting small areas of cropland on a cash basis. Many landowners and tenants prefer this type of lease because both parties share in the uncertainty of crop yields and the prices of farm products. This type of lease gives a landlord more opportunity to supervise the farm, and he has more interest in its operation.

3. The share lease is very similar to the crop-share cash lease but is more commonly used where single fields are rented or where the untillable land has little or no rental

value. This type of lease often results in exhaustive systems of farming because the land is usually rented for only one year without a written contract, a definite rotation of crops containing legumes is frequently lacking, and part or all of the crops are often hauled away from the farm.

4. The livestock-share lease is growing in popularity with the growing need for systems of farming which will maintain the productivity of the farm. Under a livestock-share lease the landlord shares in the ownership of livestock, except that work horses may not be shared. As is true of other forms of leases, the tenant usually furnishes the labor and the major part of the power and machinery, and the landowner furnishes repairs for buildings, fences, new buildings, insurance, and real estate taxes. Other expenses for the purchase of feed, seed, and veterinary bills are shared. Many landlords and tenants prefer the livestock-share lease because both parties share all risks and are mutually interested in all phases of the farm business. It makes possible a more productive system of farming and provides for the most economic use of roughages and low quality crops.

Landlords consider that they are able to attract the best tenants under such leases, while many tenants consider it an advantage for the landlord to share in furnishing operating capital and better permanent improvements. They are likely to be furnished because the landlord is anxious to obtain good returns from all farm enterprises. Successful livestock production requires good buildings and other equipment. Other kinds of leases usually do not provide for increased rentals to pay for depreciation and maintenance of the kind of buildings that are needed for a good livestock program. A livestock-share lease automatically takes care of this need if the tenant is a good livestock farmer.

5. The term "manager-operator agreement" is used to cover many instances where the owner furnishes the farm and most of the equipment. The manager-operator of the farm usually does not have all of the needed capital, and various arrangements are entered into, which are more fully discussed in Illinois Circular 587, *Father-Son Business Agreements*. Contract forms are also outlined in this circular.

There is no essential difference between a manager-operator agreement and a father-son agreement. Both provide for profit-sharing, and contract forms are largely interchangeable simply by substituting a few words—for example, owner for father and operator for son. Advantages of manager-operator agreements include the continued operation of the farm, which is fully equipped and stocked and the maintenance of well established herds. It gives the owner close supervision of the farm and is a convenient means of transferring the management of a well-organized farm to another operator. From the standpoint of the operator, it gives him an opportunity to grow into the management under the supervision of a qualified owner and gradually to obtain a larger share in the enterprise.

The Amount of Rent Paid

In general the amount of rent paid, whether a share of the income or cash rent, depends upon the productivity of the land and the desirability of the farm. In Illinois, for example, over 90 per cent of all share-rented farms in the northern two-thirds of the state pay half of the grain crop as rent. One-third of the grain crop is the usual rent given in the southern part of the state, although hay is divided on a fifty-fifty basis. Between the two areas there is considerable share rent paid on the basis of two-fifths of the grain crops. This rental is also found in small areas of mixed soil conditions. Even in the area where half of the grain crop is normally given as rent, there are a considerable number of farms where the landlord receives only two-fifths of the small grain, including soybeans, as rent, but frequently the tenant pays the cost of seed and harvesting when the smaller rental is paid.

In addition, it must be recognized that farms within a community vary widely in their productivity. There is just as much reason for a variation in the rental paid within a community as there is for the wide differences in different parts of the state. It may cost the tenant just as much or more to farm a low-producing farm as a good one.

In many cases adjustments are made in other rental practices to keep the lease fair to both parties; for example, many landlords and tenants on less productive land in southern Illinois share livestock on a fifty-fifty basis, but the landlord owns half of the machinery and equipment and pays other expenses that are not common to other areas in order to equalize the contributions of the two parties.

What Is a Fair Lease?

The fairness of a farm lease or a profit-sharing arrangement depends mainly on whether or not the income from the farm is divided in about the same proportion as the expenses and other contributions of the landlord and tenant where the operations of the farm as a whole are considered. With continually changing price and production relationships, it is not possible to keep a lease in balance every year. In prosperous periods tenants bid for farms and are, thus, partially responsible for higher rents.

It is accepted generally in leasing farms that the owner furnishes the farm and fixed improvements, while the tenant furnishes the labor and the major part of the equipment. The other items of expense are shared in different ways in different lease agreements. There is need, therefore, to appraise the contributions of the two parties to determine whether the sharing of both the ex-

penses and income provides an equitable arrangement between the parties.

Farm rent paid either in cash or as a share of the produce normally varies from one area to another in a way which is largely the outgrowth of custom, while custom in turn has been influenced by the productivity of the land and the tenant's normal costs of operating the farm. As the agriculture of an area becomes older, the changes in methods of production, the development of serious problems of soil conservation, changes in types of farming, and changes in technological developments give rise to questions of adjusting the provisions of the lease to provide for a more equitable division of expenses and income between the two parties. Differences in the original productivity of land have been recognized between regions. This is indicated by the differences in the share of produce or the amount each gives as rent in different parts of midwestern states. For example, there are large areas where one-fourth, one-third, or one-half of the crop is given as rent to the landlord.

On the other hand, even though the soil of a community may have been similar when the land was developed for farm use, differences in the income from farms within the same community result from the degree of care that has been given over the years to the land and improvements on the land. Under such conditions custom is not a safe guide in developing a lease for a given farm. It may, for example, cost a tenant as much to operate a farm that will not produce more than half as large yields as another farm in the same community. These differences in the productive value of farms in the same community become more marked as an agricultural region becomes older. When it becomes necessary to make more provisions for the improvement or conservation of the soil, many questions arise concerning equitable leases. Also there are frequent questions concerning whether well-improved farm buildings do not justify a higher rental than mediocre buildings.

One method of determining whether a particular farm lease is equitable or not is to estimate the total contributions which both the landlord and the tenant expect to make toward the annual cost of operating the farm in question. If records are available from the farm for several years, these estimates may be made with considerable accuracy. Caution must be used in placing valuations for various items on a comparable basis. For example, if conservative valuations are used for labor, equally conservative values should be placed on land and other capital items. If such records are not available for a given farm, data from records of similar farms may serve as a basis for estimating the contribution of the two parties.

Under all forms of leases the landlord furnishes the farm and makes all the fixed improvements. His major contribution is represented by a fair interest return on a conservative valuation of the property; hence, judgment must be exercised in estimating both the value of the property and the rate of interest to be expected on that valuation. Likewise, the operator of the farm furnishes his own labor and management and the labor of members of his family on which a valuation should be placed. Such items may be difficult to estimate, although there are many items of farm operating expenses that can be quite accurately estimated for a given farm. Such estimates also serve to set forth the importance of unusual provisions which may be written into farm leases.

There are two ways of securing an equitable farm lease. The first assumes a fixed division of income between landlord and tenant and then proceeds to adjust the division of expenses and other contributions in order that they may be in the same proportion as the division of income. The second involves a listing of a fair evaluation of the contribution of each party and then sug-

gests that income be divided on the basis of the relative contribution of each. Either approach to the problem is based on the same assumption; that is, that the landlord and the tenant should share the income of the farm in the same proportion as they contribute to the expense of its operation.

Problems in Dividing Expenses

FERTILIZER COST

The cost of purchased fertilizer is an item which may be subject to considerable discussion from the standpoint of how much of the cost should be borne by the landowner and how much by the tenant. It might be stated that, if soil fertility is badly depleted when the tenant moves to the farm and the farm is renting on a basis comparable to more productive farms, the landlord might well assume the responsibility for the purchase of "long-time" fertilizer, such as limestone or rock phosphate, to bring the farm up to a higher level of production. At the other extreme, if a farm is highly productive when a tenant moves to it, it may be reasoned that the tenant should contribute his share toward maintaining its productivity, as he is participating in the advantages of a highly productive farm compared with many others in the same community.

There is no one arrangement for "long-time" fertilizers, such as limestone and rock phosphate, that applies equally well to all farms for the following reasons:

1. Farms vary in productivity, and the landlord should pay more of the cost on a poor farm than on a productive one if the division of crops is the same.

2. Some farms have had one or more applications of limestone or rock phosphate from which the present tenant has received benefits. In such cases, the tenant may well share the cost of subsequent applications, with proper provision made in the lease for reimbursement to the tenant for the unexhausted portion when he moves away.

3. The division of governmental payments makes a difference. The landlord may prefer to pay the total cost and receive all the practice payments for application of limestone and rock phosphate.

4. The facilities for getting the materials delivered and spread need to be considered. For example, in some communities limestone is trucked directly from the quarry to the farm and spread, the entire cost appearing on one bill, while in other communities the limestone is shipped in by rail, and the trucking and the spreading are distinct operations. Furthermore, the tenant may have trucking and spreading facilities on the farm and assume that share of the cost.

5. Leasing arrangements in the area are strong influences that need to be considered. Some of them, however, may be based on tradition and need to be changed.

6. There may be other offsetting agreements in the lease. For example, in return for an excessive amount of repair work on buildings and fences to be done by the tenant, the landlord may agree to pay for all of the limestone and rock phosphate. On the other hand, because of low cash rent for hay and pasture, from which the tenant may gain the advantage under cash leases or grain-share cash leases, the landlord and tenant may agree to share the costs.

Normally the cost of "quick" fertilizers, from which the major value is realized in the same year they are applied, is shared by the landlord and tenant in proportion to the sharing of crops. The cost of spreading limestone and fertilizers has been handled in various ways, sometimes being shared by the landlord and tenant, while in other instances either of the two parties may bear the expense.[2]

Since many farm leases do not make adequate provision for arrangements between landlord and tenant for soil conservation practices, a supplemental agreement, or "rider," is often needed. Such a form is being prepared. When it is ready, it may be procured from the county farm adviser or direct from the University of Illinois.

TRACTOR FUEL COST

The cost of tractor fuel may be questioned as a charge against a tenant under a livestock lease. In a livestock lease if the farm work were done by horses, they would probably be fed from undivided grain. The landlord would be contributing half of the cost of feed, although the tenant would furnish the horses. When the work is done almost entirely with tractors, it may be reasoned that it is fair for the landlord to make some contribution to offset the saving in the cost of feed for work horses. Many landowners do not like to be involved in securing an accounting of the cost of fuel. Some landowners are making a contribution of fifty cents to one dollar an acre for cropland to help pay for the cost of tractor fuel. Such contribution is based on the net cost of about ten gallons of tractor fuel per crop acre. Other landlords are making larger contributions to include part of the cost of truck fuel and the farm share of electricity. The amount of the contribution should naturally depend somewhat upon the size and productivity of the farm, kinds and numbers of livestock, mechanization of the farm, and other factors. On a heavy livestock-producing farm where power is used for grinding feed and many other purposes there may be a justification for the landlord's paying a larger amount toward the cost of fuel. In some instances landlords make concessions in other expenses to offset part of the tenant's power costs.

ADJUSTMENTS FOR LABOR

In the operation of a dairy or poultry farm a very large amount of labor is required with most types of farming. Because of the labor involved, the income from dairy and poultry products may be divided on a basis of sixty-forty or fifty-five–forty-five respectively between the tenant and landlord, or in other instances the landlord may furnish more than half of the dairy herd or poultry flock or make some other major contribution to equalize the contributions of the two parties.

It is seldom advisable for landlords and tenants to share hired labor expenses except where close blood relationships exist, as with father and son, or where the ability of the tenant to supervise hired labor has been proved.

COST OF COMBINING

The practice of sharing the cost of combining grain and soybeans, which is prevalent in Illinois, is an outgrowth of sharing threshing cost. One should recognize the fact, however, that the two methods of harvesting are not strictly comparable. The combine replaces much man labor which was formerly contributed by the tenant. On the other hand, the combine leaves the straw in the field where it is well distributed for fertility maintenance, but it may involve an additional expense to the landlord for picking up straw if a livestock-share lease is used.

The most common practice over the state is for the landlord and tenant to share in the combining cost as they share the harvested crops. Variations from this plan are the following:

1. The landlord pays the going rate per bushel for threshing. This practice is most common where there is a great deal of threshing done.

2. The landlord pays seventy-five cents to two dollars an acre for each acre combined. This practice for example is most common in east-central Illinois and on farms where the tenant owns the combine. Thus, the landlord is not paying the tenant a profit due to high custom rates.

3. The landlord pays none of the combining cost, but the tenant may get a larger than normal percentage of the crop. For example, at the south edge of the cash-grain area it is common practice for the landlord to furnish none of the seed oats and to pay none of the combining cost on the crop and to receive two-fifths rather than one-half of the crop harvested. The same practice also applies to soybeans on individual farms in various areas of the Midwest.

4. The landlord may pay none of the combining costs but make other concessions like charging low cash rent for hay and pasture and providing a superior residence for the tenant's family.

ADJUSTING CASH RENT

The change in cash rent for hay and pasture, especially on crop-share and cash-lease farms, frequently fails to keep pace with changing prices for farm products. Some landlords and tenants agree to base the cash rent per acre on the market value of a definite amount of one or more of the principal products produced on the farm—for example, corn, milk, etc. In such case, the parties to the lease should agree on the amount of the product or products that would have been required to pay the cash rent per acre for a fairly normal period, for example, 1935–39. If for this period the cash rent were six dollars an acre and No. 3 corn (the agreed-upon product) were valued at sixty cents a bushel at harvest time, the quantity would be ten bushels of corn. Then to this quantity the landlord and tenant may apply the price for a given date, such as December 1, to get the cash rent per acre.

In some cases the cash rent is kept low in return for other contributions made by the tenant, such as paying for part of the clover and grass seed, doing more than the normal amount of work on farm improvements, and doing a superior job of farming. The cash rent may also be low because the landlord gets a part or all of the seed crop harvested, or because the hay crop is divided and the cash rent applies only to a small acreage of pasture.

In any event the productivity of the land should be considered in agreeing on a fair cash rent because the production of hay and pasture per acre varies just as much as the production of other crops.

These instances serve as examples of some of the problems involved in making farm leases. They indicate the need for considering the lease as a whole as well as its individual parts and, also, the need for definite written agreements. Leasing arrangements should be the result of forethought rather than afterthought.

Farm Leasing Practice

The rental conditions in any community need to be studied carefully, because different areas adopt different customary arrangements that may vary considerably from those of another area, especially when the soil or type of farming differ.

In local areas not enough attention is given to variations in productivity between farms because of the way in which the soil has been managed over a period of years, variations in the original characteristics of the soil, and differences in the improvements on the land.

These factors are well illustrated in the mimeographed report, *Farm Leasing Practices in East-Central Illinois*. Similar reports have been prepared for other parts of Illinois.

IMPROVING FARM ECONOMIES THROUGH REGULATION OF LANDLORD-TENANT RELATIONS

Report of the Working Party

Chairman, *John F. Timmons*

MOST OF THE world's agricultural lands are tilled by persons other than the owners. This separation of ownership and operatorship creates serious problems of land use, security of tenure, and divisions of the produce from land. The welfare of rural people as well as the amount and efficiency of agricultural production depends largely upon the amelioration of problems inherent in and growing out of landlord and tenant relations.

The working party's approach to this problem was fourfold. First, the nature and objectives of landlord and tenant relations were analyzed. Second, landlord-tenant relation problems were delimited. Third, remedial measures were considered. Fourth, application of these measures to problems of particular countries was attempted. The discussions on these four points were focused on the situations in each of the ten countries represented in one or more sessions of the seminar. These countries included France, England, Germany, Italy, Uruguay, Paraguay, The Netherlands, Argentina, India, and the United States.

Nature of Relations

Landlord and tenant relations were interpreted broadly as including all formal, contractual, legal, customary, and informal arrangements involved in and surrounding the use, improvement, and occupancy of land operated by persons other than owners. They may pay for the use of the land in cash or with a fixed amount of the produce, or by paying shares of the produce as rent. Laborers working for wages were excluded under this interpretation. Owner-operators were likewise excluded.

Regulation of landlord and tenant relations was interpreted to embrace all formal and informal controls which might be used for improvement of these relations. Laws, administrative controls, education, and custom were brought in under this interpretation.

Function of Rent

The function of rent was discussed in terms of (1) allocating land, capital, labor, and management resources toward the end of efficient and full production of agricultural produce and (2) dividing returns from this production among the contribution resources in such a way that each contributor received the productivity of his contribution.

Objectives of Relations

In keeping with these functions expected of rent in the agricultural economy, landlord and tenant relations were viewed as the means for carrying out these functions. Within this setting the objectives of landlord and tenant relations were interpreted as providing for (1) a fair rental or division of income or produce between landlord and tenant; (2) adequate security of expectation for the tenant to use and improve the land in keeping with good husbandry practices and to assume his role as a citizen in a democratic community; and (3) establishment of practices and improvements necessary for the proper operation of the land both now and in the future.

Situations Within Countries

In Egypt the combination of land scarcity and the large number of prospective occupiers resulted in landowners obtaining an amount of cash rent or share of crops that left the tenant insufficient income for a reasonable standard of livelihood. Also, there was little security of tenure and no compensation for improvements. The latter was not a very serious matter, since the holdings were in the main small areas of unimproved but fertile irrigated land. Moreover, it is important to add that under recent legislation Egyptian landowners have broad social obligations to provide housing, health centers, schools, and related facilities for the benefit of a community comprising these tenants, although these obligations have no direct relation to the terms of tenancy of land.

In Uruguay leases for livestock farms were limited to three years and for cropping farms to five years. These terms were too short to enable a tenant to plan his farming operation satisfactorily and carry out necessary improvements. More security of tenure should be given to a satisfactory tenant. Further, such compensation provisions for improvements as at present exist apply only to dairy holdings. Good farming requires that a tenant of any holding should be enabled to carry out improvements necessary for its proper working (if the landowner is unwilling to do so) and should be assured of adequate compensation for improvements executed by him.

In the U.S.A. most leases are for only one year with a provision for a thirty-day notification if the lease is to be terminated. One state, Iowa, has a four-month notification period. Much more security of tenure is needed, in the interest of encouraging more livestock production, longer-term cropping systems, and land and home improvements.

In Germany, farms are generally leased for terms of eighteen years. Leases for less than nine years are exceptional. Thus, tenants in the majority of cases are able to obtain the benefit of improvements carried out by them. As to rent, this could be adjusted by the courts after hearing from landlord and tenant, following an application by either of them for rental revision. The tenant has no statutory right to compensation for improvement.

As regards France and England, statutory provisions ensure adequate security of tenure, and a proper measure of compensation for improvements carried out by a tenant. Legislation also enables a periodic adjustment of rent to be made in the event of changed economic conditions in the farming industry.

On the question of remedial measures and appropriate action to secure them there was general agreement that no hard and fast rules could be laid down. Suitable action depends not only on the existence of apparent injustice but must be based on careful consideration of all the surrounding circumstances. These include the economic structure of the country concerned, the degree of underpopulation or overpopulation, the proportion of the population which, for the time at least, must rely upon the cultivation of the land for its livelihood, and the availability of land to meet this demand. Certain broad principles, as stated below, were, however, agreed upon.

Regulation of Arrangements

The amount of rent in cash or in kind to be paid a landowner, or to an intermediate person, should follow the general pattern of the productivity of the resources including labor, capital, management, and land contributed by each party. In those countries where population pressure on land is intense, some deviation in rent from the marginal productivity principle should be made within the short run to provide families on the land with reasonable levels of living in keeping with the general economic development of the country concerned.

In relaxing the productivity principle of determining rent in the short run, care must be exercised that minimum levels of living in agriculture, relative to other needs for labor and capital, are not fixed at a point that will prevent labor and capital resources from moving into other industries where the marginal productivity of these production factors would be greater. To do so would prevent general economic development and would increase the problem of population pressure on land in agriculture.

Since rental rates and shares tend to remain fixed through custom, arrangements should be made for the adjustment of rents, from time to time, upon application for adjustment by either landlord or tenant to an independent body or court of neutral position.

Regulation of Tenure Security

To encourage better use of land and to provide the tenant with security of tenure on the land, the tenant should not be subject to eviction at the will of the land owner or intermediary person. Certain minimum conditions for eviction, such as gross neglect and mismanagement on the part of the tenant or the landlord's direct operation of the land for himself, might be set forth. If the landlord endeavors to evict a tenant for reasons other than those approved, he might be made liable for the disturbance of the tenant's security, and certain appropriate penalties might be imposed.

Application by the landlord for the removal of the tenant might be made to an independent and neutral body or court whose recommendation on the applications would be final. In the event the decision was to remove the tenant, he should be compensated for disturbance costs and provided with a sufficient period of notice in order to become relocated on other land or in another occupation.

It was suggested that in Uruguay, for example, the lease might be made for seven years with an option to renew for additional seven-year periods. In Egypt a lease for six years with the possibility of rent adjustment every two years was suggested as an appropriate application of security of tenure regulations.

Regulations for Land Improvements

With regard to permanent or long-term improvements in the nature of fixed equipment necessary for the proper working of the land, the tenant should have the right to carry them out (if the landlord is unwilling to do so) and on quitting should be entitled to compensation. The measure of such compensation should be the increase in the value of the land (or holding) which is attributable to the improvement or improvements.

With regard to short-term improvements, including the unexhausted value of lime and artificial manures applied to the land and the crops remaining on the land when the tenant quits, compensation should also be paid on the basis of their fair value to the landlord or to an incoming tenant. Disputes between landlord and tenant regarding the right of a tenant to execute improvements in the nature of fixed equipment and regarding the amount of compensation payable for any improvement should be settled by an independent person or body.

Experiences in England and France suggest the workability of legal provisions permitting compensation for improvements by tenants and their possible application in other countries.

With the application of modern technology, agriculture is rapidly involving longer-term planning and investments. In making these long-term investments of fertilizers, buildings, water supplies, fencing, grasses, and tree crops, the tenant must be assured of getting full benefit from the improvement he makes. This can be achieved by assuring the tenant that he can remain on the land long enough to get full benefit, or that he will be compensated by the owner or incoming tenant for unused benefits remaining when the tenant leaves the farm.

Means for Carrying Out Regulations

Several means of complementary nature exist for carrying out the foregoing measures. Legislation forms the backbone of regulatory measures. However, complementary programs of an educational nature are necessary in order to make legislation serve the needs and to provide for carrying out the legislation. Both legislative and educational programs should be preceded by research and studies to provide the basis for corrective measures. To supplement legislation, education, and research there is need for organizational steps to organize and carry out the programs. For example, local landlord-tenant boards or courts may be formed to hear and recommend changes in rents, compensation provisions, and eviction action.

Part XVII   CONSOLIDATION OF FRAGMENTED HOLDINGS

LAND CONSOLIDATION PROCEDURES: A
COMPARATIVE ANALYSIS

Excerpt from the Report of the Working Party

Chairman, *Constantin C. von Dietze*

LAND CONSOLIDATION is a means of increasing the productivity of the three production factors—land, capital, and labor—in agriculture. Also, the legislation in different countries reflects the tenure pattern of the country concerned. It is obvious that consolidation work should ultimately aim at bringing about the most favorable conditions for the operator whether he be tenant or owner.

Land consolidation is in itself a stage in the economic development of a country. As there is an interrelation between the population pressure in rural areas, the existing tenure pattern, and the development of industry, the tendency for an increase or decrease of the fragmentation phenomenon should be reflected in the desire and possibilities for consolidation work. In many underdeveloped areas, however, there may be other more fundamental issues to be solved first before consolidation work can be undertaken—for example, landlordism. The Japanese experience should be noted here. Moreover, consolidation (which only deals with the fragmentation problem) does not have the same objectives in all countries. A difference may be noted between the objectives for an underdeveloped country with subsistence farming and a well-

developed country with commercial farming. Between these two extremes we may find a range of other forms.

In a country like India, for example, the main task of agriculture in the immediate present is to obtain the highest output per acre so as to supply the growing population with enough food. By consolidating the fragmented lands the output per acre may be increased and more acres made available for farming. It was reported that large areas of agricultural land in India have gone out of cultivation because in some areas fragmentation has reached a stage where people do not think it worth while any more to cultivate these fragments. Even subsistence farming becomes impossible under these circumstances. Since land is scarce and labor plentiful, the policy in India is to conserve the one and make full use of the other.

❬ The full advantages of a consolidation scheme in decreasing substantially the demand for labor in agriculture will only be realized if there are alternative employment possibilities. In a country where industries are being developed, land consolidation is a means of cutting labor waste, and any excess labor is likely to be absorbed in industrial work. ❭

IMPORTANT ASPECTS OF CONSOLIDATION IN FRANCE

SSSS   Jean Roche

THE OBJECT of this brief report is to explain the methods used in France to remedy the disadvantages resulting from an excessive parcelling of farm lands. The results already obtained by legislation indicate that the legal measures already taken are well adapted to the widely varying conditions found in French farms.

In France parcellings are found which have been made inevitable by the physical aspects of the land, as in mountainous regions, for example. There exist parcellings justified by certain crops (fruits, vegetables, flowers); but there exists also a considerable amount of land where the parcelling is irrational and detrimental to cultivation. The causes of this parcelling are numerous and diverse, as in all lands which, like France, have an ancient agrarian civilization, a large rural population, and certain inheritance laws.

It should be noted in any case that in France parcelling seems to have no relation to the form of land tenure and that parcelling is found in land tenancy, sharecropping, and owner-managed farms. It exists in the family-size farms as well as in the large farms with permanent hired personnel. The discussion which follows will explain briefly the French system of land tenure, parcelling, the evolution of French legislation concerning farm consolidation, the legislation at present in force, and the technique of consolidation operations. In conclusion, we shall give a summary of results obtained in France to date in the program of farm consolidation.

Tenure Situation in France

According to 1948 agricultural statistics, the area of the land surface of France is 55,104,054 hectares. This area may be divided as shown in Table 51. The total area of France is 55,104,054 hectares. The area under cultivation comprises 39,405,504 hectares (71.5 per cent of the total area). Forest lands comprise 11,112,296 hectares (20.2 per cent of the total area). And the area

TABLE 51
LAND IN FRANCE SUITABLE FOR AGRICULTURE

Kind	Area (in hectares)	Percentage of Area Under Cultivation	Percentage of Total Area
Plowed land	18,949,320	48.0	34.35
Pasture land	12,301,864	31.3	22.4
Woods and orchards	463,808	1.15	0.8
Vineyards	1,550,424	3.95	2.8
Pools and small lakes	104,223	0.25	0.15
Uncultivated land	6,035,865	15.35	11.0
Total	39,405,504	100.00	71.5

neither under cultivation nor wooded is
4,586,254 hectares (8.3 per cent of the total
area).

Agricultural statistics show that the agricultural lands have changed very little since
1862. Since that date there has been simply
a reduction in the area of plowed lands and
vineyards and an increase in pasture lands
and forests. There has been a marked decrease in lands lying fallow during this
same period.

On the other hand, the number of farms
shows a marked decrease. Farms numbered
5,672,000 in 1862; by 1948 there were only
2,471,000 farms. The average farm size has
increased from 8.75 hectares in 1882 to 14.18
hectares in 1948.

The Distribution of farms in France according to their size is shown in Table 52.

TABLE 52

DISTRIBUTION OF FARMS IN FRANCE
ACCORDING TO SIZE*

Size (hectares)	Number of Farms	Total Area (hectares)
0–1	250,000	122,000
1–5	670,000	1,800,000
5–10	520,000	3,820,000
10–20	545,000	7,600,000
20–50	382,000	11,200,000
50–100	78,000	5,170,000
100–	26,000	5,350,000
Total	2,471,000	35,062,000

*Source: 1948 Agricultural Statistics.

The farms of from 5 to 50 hectares occupy 63 per cent of the land under cultivation and represent 59 per cent of the total
number of farms. A comparison of statistics
since 1862 shows that the very large farms
have a tendency to break up and that the
small farms tend to consolidate and form

medium-size farms. Farms of less than 5
hectares, for example, have decreased from
4,034,000 in 1862 to only 920,000 in 1948,
a decrease of 75 per cent.

In so far as the method of land tenure
is concerned, the distribution for 1946 is
shown in Table 53.

TABLE 53

DISTRIBUTION OF LAND IN FRANCE IN 1946
ACCORDING TO TENURE

Tenure	Percentage of Farms	Percentage of Area Under Cultivation
Owner-operators	65.2	53.9
Tenants	26.2	33.5
Sharecroppers	6.6	10.5
Others	2.0	2.1
Total	100.0	100.0

One can say in summary that a great
share of the French agricultural land is
composed of small and medium-size farms
and that owner-operation is very common.
Owner-operation is very frequently found in
the medium-size farms, while tenant farming is more likely to be found in the large
farms.

Parcelling of Farms

French farms are in general very much
parcelled. If on the cadastral survey of certain communes in different regions one colors the parcels belonging to the same farm,
one is immediately struck by their great dispersion, most often without any relation to
the location of the farm buildings; the form
of the parcels is irregular, many are simply
enclaves; their average size is small, generally under one hectare. But this parcelling
of farms, throughout the country, shows va-

riations which may be grouped in three main types as follows:

1. The first group, which is found in the north and east of France, has predominating elongated parcels of rectangular form arranged in clusters. This type of parcelling is ordinarily associated with areas where the farm population is concentrated in villages.

2. In the second group, which is characteristic of certain wooded regions in the west of France, the parcels have no regular form and correspond to areas where the rural population is dispersed.

3. In the third group, very frequently found in the Mediterranean region, the parcels are of various irregular shapes and are associated with areas where the farm population is concentrated in villages.

But over a large part of the country, these various types are all present, depending on the different types of agricultural lands within any single departement. The degree of parcelling varies in different regions.

In certain extreme cases farms are literally pulverized. One can get a more precise impression of parcelling by referring to information furnished by survey documents. If one refers to the old surveys made for the most part between 1810 and 1850 the number of parcels was 126 million for 53 million hectares of taxable area, or a surface of 24 ares for an average parcel.

A study of the value of survey documents made in 1891 showed 151 million parcels for the same taxable area; the size of the average parcel was 35 ares. There has been no more recent general study, but it is known that the survey revisions made between 1931 and 1948, affecting 18,515 communes, showed 36 million cadastral parcels for the 22 million hectares under consideration, or an average area of 60 ares per parcel.

The number of parcels reached a maximum at the end of the nineteenth century, but it was considerably less in 1948 than it was at the beginning of the nineteenth century. One can say that, in France, contrary to a widely prevalent opinion, parcelling shows a marked tendency to be on the decrease; consolidations have become much more numerous than have divisions. The variation in the average area of the parcel corresponds very well to the decrease in the number of farms and the increase in their average size, noted since the general agricultural study made in 1882.

If one considers now the variations in the average size of parcels in the different regions of France, one notes wide divergencies. Although each departement has agricultural regions of very different kinds, a study made by departements of the average size of parcels is very instructive. For instance, this average is only twenty ares in the Meuse in eastern France. On the other hand, it goes as high as seventeen hectares in the southwest, in the forest region of the Landes. It is striking to notice the relation between the average size of the parcel and the different types of agricultural organization which we have already pointed out.

In the twenty departements of the north, of the east, and of the region around Paris—where one finds the open-field system associated with areas where the farm population is concentrated in villages—the unenclosed parcels, of elongated regular form, have an average size of considerably less than one hectare.

The same may be said of the southwest and of the Rhone Valley, which are likewise regions where the rural population is concentrated in villages, but ones in which the unenclosed parcels have an irregular form. On the other hand, in certain wooded regions of western and central France, where the fields are enclosed and where the rural population is dispersed, the average size of the parcels is higher, but their form is irregular, and the enclosures which surround them are often detrimental to a rational cultivation of the soil.

This is only the over-all picture, for there exist regions now in transition and in which one finds mingled all of these different types of parcelling.

Without assigning an absolute value to these figures, one can conclude that in more than a third of the departements the average size of a parcel does not allow efficient mechanical farming.

The general agricultural survey of 1929 gave by departements the land areas in which parcelling was detrimental; the total area so indicated was 10 million hectares. It is difficult to set a limit on the size of consolidation operations, but one may say that, taken all in all, the 1929 estimate is not exaggerated.

Evolution of Land Legislation

One can distinguish in this evolution three periods: (1) the period of individual decisions, (2) the period of majority decisions, and (3) the period of commission decisions.

PERIOD OF INDIVIDUAL DECISIONS

The harmful nature of parcelling for agriculture was long ago recognized in France, and as early as 1697 a consolidation was effected in Burgundy. There were others in Lorraine from 1778 up to the Revolution. Their good results may have been appreciated by certain enlightened agriculturalists, but the great majority of farmers remained indifferent. These operations had to be carried out with the unanimous consent of the interested parties, for there existed, at this time, no special legislation. This was continued by mutually-acceptable consolidations which took place in Lorraine between 1860 and 1901 in thirty-five communes, at the time of a general verification of the official survey of these communes.

A law of June 21, 1865, affecting landowner associations allowed mutually acceptable exchanges of parcels within the confines of the association, but the unanimous consent of the landowners was always indispensable, and this explains the meager results obtained. Finally a law of November 3, 1884, granted certain tax exemptions to encourage mutually acceptable exchanges.

PERIOD OF MAJORITY DECISIONS

A law of December 22, 1888, changed the law of 1865. This new law allowed the formation of landowner associations with a view to the verification of the official survey as well as the building of roads. These operations could be carried out when they had been voted by three-fourths of the landowners possessing two-thirds of the land area.

Although the word "consolidation" is not found in the law, true consolidating operations were carried out under this same law, especially in the east of France. This law marked the beginning of the period of majority decisions in legislation. During World War I the reduction of farm labor available and its consequences forced Parliament to find a legal solution for the problem of excessive parcelling. A law of November 27, 1918, provided expressly for "consolidation of agriculture properties"; it entrusted consolidation to an association of landowners who could make decisions either by a majority of one half of the landowners possessing two-thirds of the land area, or a majority of two-thirds of the landowners possessing more than half of the land areas. The manner in which the operation was to be carried out was set forth in detail in the law. Under this legislation consolidations affecting 54,000 hectares were carried out in 120 communes, but this legislation still required the agreement of a majority of landowners, and such was often very difficult to obtain.

PERIOD OF COMMISSION DECISIONS

After the war of 1914–1918 the necessity for putting back into production rapidly the land of those departements which had been devastated gave birth to consolidation legislation applicable only to those departements. Consolidation was now to be decided on and carried out by an appointed commission which included landowners and government representatives presided over by the *juge de paix,* that is, a conciliation magistrate. For the first time, public and private interests were reconciled. In the years 1920 to 1941 this law brought about the consolidation of an area of 365,000 hectares in 565 communes. This law has served as a model for the legislation which governs present agricultural consolidation.

Present Legislation

The law governing present operations is that of March 9, 1941, validated by an ordinance of July 7, 1945. The group authorized to carry out consolidation operations is a communal commission which includes an equal number of representatives of the interested parties and of government officials, presided over by the *juge de paix* of the canton.

The government employees are delegated by the Chief of the Agricultural Engineering Service, by the Departemental Director of Agricultural Services, by the Departemental Director of Direct Taxes and of the Cadastral Survey, and by the Chief of the Waters and Forest Administration. The representatives of the interested parties are the mayor, or one of his assistants whom he designates, and three land-owning farmers of the commune. These farmers are appointed by the prefect on the recommendation of the Director of Agricultural Services and are chosen from a list of from four to eight land-owning farmers provided by the farmer associations and under conditions set forth by the law. An employee of the Rural Engineering Service serves as secretary of this commission. This communal commission chooses a land surveyor to carry out

the various technical operations here involved.

The checking on the operation of the law and the verification of work done are carried out by the Rural Engineering Service.

The expenses occasioned by consolidation operations are borne by the state. Once the consolidation operations have been carried out, the interested parties are asked to make a contribution towards the expense. At present this rate is 20 per cent.

In the carrying out of consolidation, the communal commission is called on to make certain decisions. These decisions are brought to the attention of the interested parties in the course of the inquiries. The law specifies very exactly the time allowed and the form for such notices. Any complaints by the interested parties in the course of this inquiry are considered by the communal commission.

If the interested parties wish to appeal the decisions of the communal commission they may do so before the departmental commission on land reorganization and consolidation. This commission has authority for all cases within a single departement.

This departmental commission is very similar in composition to that of the communal commission. The departmental commission makes final decisions in cases of appeals. However, the interested parties may bring before the "Conseil d'État" the decisions of the departmental commissions for technical proof, for exceeding their powers, or for violation of the law.

The request for consolidation may be made by any landowner or farmer who is concerned; the same possibility is granted government bureaus dealing with agricultural or cadastral affairs. After a preliminary investigation by the Rural Engineering Service, the prefect may appoint a communal commission on consolidation. This latter, after an investigation, makes the decision as to whether consolidation should be carried out within any specified area.

Once the commission has made its decision, consolidation becomes obligatory for all landowners within the specified area. The communal commission proceeds then, following the principles set down by law, to the technical operations (to be described later) which should give each landowner after the consolidation a land area equivalent in productive value to the one he owned previous to consolidation.

The new parcels must (1) be sufficiently large; (2) be as close as possible to the farm buildings; (3) be of a shape to make cultivation profitable; and (4) be placed advantageously in so far as access to the fields and drainage are concerned.

Indeed, the efficiency of a consolidation can not be measured solely by the reduction in number of parcels previously cultivated by each farmer. These parcels must likewise, by their form and their ease of access, be easily adaptable to mechanical farming. Numerous experiments have shown the influence of the form of the parcels, of their area, and of the strips on farm costs.

At present in France it is believed that a parcel of from one and one-half hectares to two hectares permits the efficient operations of a tractor of the ordinary type. The best form seems to be that of a rectangle whose two smaller sides are bordered by roads. This area corresponds to a minimum width of fifty meters and to a length of from three hundred to four hundred meters. For larger parcels, it would seem that the square form is the most efficient.

The economic significance of a consolidation operation is considerable. Numerous studies have shown a decrease in farm costs of as much as 30 per cent and increased production of as much as 15 per cent. The rental value increases sometimes by 40 per cent, and the same is true of the marketing value.

The regrouping of parcels likewise facilitates land improvement projects, such as drainage and irrigation. It makes feasible the establishment of co-operatives for the use of heavy agricultural machinery such as combines. From a social point of view its importance, while difficult to evaluate, is nonetheless considerable.

Technical Operations in Consolidation

Consolidation, touching as it does so closely property rights, calls for a thorough verification of land deeds and rights.

The communal commission, after having proceeded with drawing the lines of the possible consolidation, seeks to determine clearly the legal ownership of the land. This operation starts with the cadastral survey documents. The law provides, indeed, that the limits of the area under consideration be those which are found on the cadastral survey or those which result from an official court survey, if such exists.

Once the exact limits of each one's property rights have been set, an estimate of land value is made. It is an estimate which is made not of the market value nor of the rental value but of the value which the law defines as the natural value of productivity.

This classification does not take into consideration certain transitory super values which may increase momentarily the value and productivity of the property. These transitory super values may be the basis for a request on the part of the owner for a special cash payment.

Once the results of the classification are known, after the investigation, it is possible for each land owner to establish what is known as the total real value.

As a general rule, the area found in the cadastral survey documents is not that which really exists on the ground. It is then necessary to determine the exact surface of the group of properties. That is why it is necessary to carry out a topographic survey of the whole area under consideration. Of course, at the time of this survey the limits of the old parcels will not be taken into consideration since they are to disappear, but it will be necessary to allow for, on one hand, the putting through of a system of roads, and, on the other hand, the setting up of the limits of new parcels when special terrain features (such as slopes, trees, existing roads, railroads, quarries, etc.) are concerned.

The extent of the network of roads is very important, since this is what will form the skeleton for the consolidation and will determine the orientation of new parcels.

Once the land owners' rights are clearly defined, the commission then divides the area among the owners in order to obtain a rational regrouping. By applying rigorously the principles laid down by the law, and in seeking for each group of small parcels what is called the ideal location for grouping, little by little one can determine the location of new parcels.

It should be pointed out that since, as previously indicated, the surface set forth on the cadastral survey and the surface really existing on the land are almost never exactly the same, the area and value of each piece of property must be multiplied by a corrective coefficient generally inferior to the unit. This corrective coefficient takes into consideration also that the area necessary for the creation of new roads must be taken away from the total area concerned.

The time necessary to accomplish this work of redistribution (which necessitates the constant collaboration of the communal commission, of the interested parties, of the official land surveyor, and of the Rural Engineering Service) is quite variable, depending on the commune. It is not unusual for several successive preliminary proposals to be made before the acceptance of the final project.

Once the commission has defined the project and the new parcels have had their limits drawn, the project is submitted to the interested parties for any objections they may have. These objections are passed on by the communal commission, whose decisions may be appealed to the departmental commission. The commission's decision puts into operation the consolidation. As previously mentioned, further appeals are possible to the Conseil d'État, but they may not prevent the land owners from taking possession of the new parcels.

The next step is the transfer to the new parcels of any mortgages on the old ones and the drawing up of the official report of consolidation operations.

The law of March 9, 1941, has likewise settled a number of other points. In particular, it has specified that the results of consolidation be incorporated in the cadastral survey documents, that special measures be taken to avoid any later division of parcels so consolidated and, finally, it regulated the consequences of consolidation in so far as the relations between landowners, tenant-farmers and sharecroppers are concerned.

Results Obtained to Jan. 1, 1951

The results have been very interesting. Statistics are available for one departement in the Paris region concerning a grouping of thirty communes therein, scattered throughout the departement and representing very well its agricultural characteristics.

The total area of the 39 communes is 51,325 hectares, of which 33,873 hectares have been consolidated. This area is shared by 7,083 landowners, each of whom owns an average of 4.78 hectares. Here are found 808 farms, whose average of 40 hectares is above the general average for the country as a whole. Before consolidation there were 64,-323 parcels averaging 52 ares. The average number of parcels owned by any one person was 9.08.

After consolidation the number of parcels has been reduced to 16,004, averaging 2.11 hectares. The number of parcels hence has been reduced by 75 per cent. The average number of parcels by individual owner is 2.25. All enclaves have been suppressed. Two hundred ninety-eight kilometers of roads have been put through. It should be noted that this group of communes were especially broken up and that the average area of a parcel before consolidation was inferior to the average for the country as a whole.

The general situation of the problem of consolidation in France as of January 1, 1951, may be summarized as follows: 1,484 requests for consolidation for 1,082,242 hectares; 1,405 operations in progress for 1,069,-277 hectares; 725 operations completed for 525,833 hectares. The total number of cases is 3,614 for 2,677,352 hectares.

Consolidation operations are most numerous in those regions where the agrarian structure is that of open and elongated fields and where the rural population is grouped in villages. Consolidation operations are growing in the regions of enclosures (the Breton peninsula and the west especially). They are still very scarce in the regions of open and irregular fields (in the southwest and southeast).

The first operations under the law of January 9, 1941, took place in 1943. For the period from 1943 to 1950 their budget went as high as 7,966 million francs.

The average length of time necessary for an operation has been reduced since 1943. At present it is somewhere between two and three years, depending on the importance of the commune and the difficulties met. This time lag still appears somewhat long and it

is hoped it can be reduced in the coming years to one and one-half years.

The cost per hectare for a consolidation operation at present is 3,750 francs. The cost to the landowners concerned has been set at 20 per cent of the expenses. In 1950 this cost averaged 750 francs per consolidated hectare.

Conclusion

One can say that consolidation has been a success in the open-field regions and in the north, the east, and in the Paris regions where increasing mechanization made apparent the great disadvantages of parcelling.

Elsewhere, in wooded regions for instance, operations have been carried out or are in progress which one might call test operations. Their outcome will be of the greatest importance in determining the attitude of farmers in these regions to consolidation. Both the technical difficulties rising out of the terrain features and the land tenure system and the individualist spirit of the French farmer must be surmounted.

In those regions, especially, consolidation must be accompanied by the building of a network of roads which can be used by mechanical equipment and which are easy to maintain. This is indeed a difficult task in regions where there is a predominance of steeply embanked, narrow roads, lined with hedges.

However this may be, one can say that progress has been constant; the technique for the application of the principles of consolidation has been perfected.

FRAGMENTATION OF LAND HOLDINGS AND MEASURES FOR CONSOLIDATION IN GREECE[1]

 Euthymios Papageorgiou

BEFORE GOING into my paper, I wish to express as the Greek participant my gratitude to the American government, which through

the Economic Cooperation Administration is so helpful to my country. I thank also the ECA and the U.S. Department of Agriculture for the invitation to this conference and the University of Wisconsin for the hospitality in this wonderful University city surrounded by its splendid area. I would like to congratulate the American government, which in the field of its world human policy took the initiative to call here this conference. The words "human policy" here are important. I hope, or I almost believe, that America does not forget the philosopher Diogenes, who by daylight with a lamp ran through the streets of Athens looking for the man, but for the man, as he said, with goodness, good will, and humanism. The world conferences support this humanism. An exchange of knowledge between the countries of the world is very important. In my opinion, it is one of the best paying investments that the Economic Cooperation Administration has made.

In spite of the great difference between the land tenure conditions of America on the one hand, and of other countries and particularly of the European countries on the other hand, the exchange of knowledge and experience will be very useful also for the American delegates. They will know the land tenure problems of the other countries and the measures which have been taken or must be taken there to solve the above-mentioned problems. Thus the American delegates will be prepared to prevent their prosperous agriculture from developing such problems.

This study was adopted to avoid repetition and to limit this paper to an easily readable length. It will present to you briefly the fragmentation of land holdings and the measure for consolidation in Greece. This paper will be divided into six parts as follows: (1) general land tenure conditions, (2) fragmentation of land holdings, (3) causes of fragmentation, (4) effects of the fragmentation, (5) measures for consolidation of fragmented holdings, and (6) conclusion.

General Tenure Conditions

Greece is an extremely agricultural country. Sixty-two per cent of the total Greek population makes its living from agriculture. The agricultural character of Greece is based not only on the high percentage of its agricultural population but also on the large number of agricultural holdings, which are nearly a million.

It is true that there are some other countries, such as the Soviet Union, the Baltic States, the Balkans, Poland, Mexico, India, which have this agricultural character still more pronounced. These countries, however, have far more fertile and larger areas under cultivation than Greece, and in most cases with sufficient acreage for each farmer to produce enough agricultural goods. In contrast, Greece with its limited acreage under cultivation and the moderate fertility of its soil finds itself, as regards agricultural resources, in an inferior position when compared with the above-mentioned nations.

The land area is approximately 33 million acres, or about four acres per person. We have a density of about sixty persons per square kilometer of the whole land area. There are many mountains which are rough and rugged and often scarce of vegetation. Only about one-fourth of the land is arable. This allows only about one acre per person which can be cultivated. The agricultural production is relatively low, and for this reason in recent years it has been necessary to import about one-third of the food supply. Taking five persons as an average of Greek agricultural families, we have five acres of arable land per family. To this we must add another piece of land which, though not cultivated, is however used as pasture, building site, court, roads, and so on. Thus we have the total acreage of the agricultural holdings, which does not exceed an average of ten acres for all agricultural holdings in Greece.

Land tenancy is not a serious problem in Greece. Today only a small number of big farms remain unexpropriated. Most of them are experimental farms. Consequently the land in its greatest part belongs to its cultivator. The percentage of all the kinds of tenancy is 20 per cent. The tenants include those holding from the different corporations, the state, banks, welfare organizations, monasteries, and especially the monasteries of Saint Athos near Thessalonike.

Fragmentation of Holdings

The really serious problem is the smallness and the fragmentation of the holdings. Under smallness is understood the cases where the farmer does not possess enough acres to occupy and to feed his family. By fragmentation is meant a holding which consists of several plots, often scattered over a wide area. The problem of fragmentation of the Greek holdings is a disadvantage because the fragmentation is closely cognate and combined with the smallness of the holdings.

TABLE 54

Distribution of Agricultural Holdings In Greece by Size*

Size (hectares)	Number of Farms	Percentage of Total Number
0–2	565,783	59.3
2–4	212,544	22.3
4–6	83,989	8.8
6–8	35,261	3.7
8–10	17,627	1.8
10–	38,163	4.1
Total	953,367	100.0

*Source: 1929 Census. Present distribution may show an increase in the lower groups.

Table 54 analyzes the distribution of agricultural holdings by size.

It is clear from Table 54 that the holdings up to four hectares, or ten acres, in size comprise 81.6 per cent of the total holdings. It is also clear that of the total distribution the smallest holdings have the highest percentage with 59.3 per cent.

The holdings in Greece are not only too small; at the same time they are fragmented. The fragmentation varies in the different regions of the country. There are regions (such as the region of Attica and the region of Peloponnese) where the most holdings consist of from fifty to one hundred parcels. These parcels have a surface from one-eighth to one-fourth of an acre, and the transport from one plot to another and from the plots to the residence or to the buildings of the farmer takes one or two hours of time.

Causes of Fragmentation

Over the centuries when land is inherited and divided into smaller and smaller plots to be farmed by individual owners, serious problems often occur. The causes of fragmentation are of two kinds: (1) physical and economic and (2) social.

Physical and economic conditions may compel separation of plots, as in some mountainous regions or as in some dry farming and irrigated regions, or as in regions with different fertility of soil. In certain low-lying areas which are liable to severe early flooding, it is advantageous to have a small patch of higher land for use as seed nurseries or for use to obtain food earlier. In the case of farms consisting primarily of hill pastures, it may be highly advantageous as well as convenient for the farmer to possess a small area of valley land, which may be used as intensive pasture, for production of feed crops, and for farm buildings and residence.

On the other hand, the farmer in Greece lives always in a village and not on his farm.

In this case it is important that a portion of the farm be used for purposes requiring close and constant attention, as gardens, tobacco fields, and so on, which should be near the place of residence.

Fragmentation is created by causes which are not connected with agriculture but which are due to the construction of railways, roads, game preserves, airports, canals, reservoirs, establishment of forest, or national parks.

Another cause of fragmentation in Greece is the fact that industry has not been greatly developed, and so the land has been the principal object of investment. In other words, the lack of balance between agriculture and other fields of the national economy became a potent influence on the process of fragmentation.

Because of historical and traditional causes, the Greek farmers live in villages, and so the agglomeration of the houses of farmers in villages was often a cause of fragmentation. Furthermore, conditions which greatly facilitate progressive fragmentation are the growing population and the existence of the right of the landholder to transfer and alienate his right in the land freely and, in particular, the right to subdivide or add to existing holdings. Such rights or customs are derived from Roman Law, but their application became much more general as a result of the profound influence of the Code Napoleon and of the Mohammedan Law on the legislation of Greece.

Generally, long-established cultivation, shortage of land, unrestricted rights of transfer, a pressure of population on the land, and living away from the farm are thus conditions that encouraged excessive fragmentation.

Effects of Fragmentation

The fragmentation in Greece, combined with the smallness of the holdings, is associated with lack of full employment for members of the cultivating classes. After some investigations in different typical farms in different areas of Greece, we discover the low employment of the members of the agricultural family. The average employment of the investigated holdings was only 50 per cent of the available labor of the agricultural family. And so we see that the problem of unemployment is more severe in the country than in the cities.

The effects of the under-employment of the agricultural family are malnutrition and misery, combined with social and biological danger. The Greek holder for these reasons tends to emigrate to the towns or to other countries in order to supplement his earnings by other work.

The several and very small plots of irregular shape have the effect of hampering cultivation and of causing unnecessary waste of land. Time is wasted and extra expense involved in moving workers, animals, and implements to and from the farmstead and from one plot to another, in carrying seed and manure to the various fields, and in moving crops from the fields to the threshing floor, stockyard, or barn.

The supervision of the work, animals, and crops is rendered more difficult. Expenses on fences, water supplies, buildings, and so on are often much greater. Drainage and improvement of the soil or prevention of soil erosion may be rendered impossible. The fragmentation of the farm limits the choice of crop rotation by compelling the adoption of a system of cropping which allows all to have access to their scattered fields at the same time.

The fragmentation is not always a disadvantage, however. Where fruits, vegetables, and flowers are farmed intensively, a moderate degree of fragmentation diminishes the risk of damage from frost. A fragmented farm has a greater variety of soils and growing conditions and can cultivate more crops. In spite of the advantages of the fragmented farm, the disadvantages are greater in number and in importance. Furthermore, the advantages of the fragmentation are exceptions to the general rule, while the disadvantages can be found in all conditions.

Measures for Consolidation

In 1917 Greek agricultural legislation tried to restrict the subdivision of holdings when the owner died. According to this law the holding which was derived from expropriated big farms after the death of the holder should be transferred only to one heir, who was able to pay the others if there were any.

But this new law was valid only for a short time because it was believed to be against the customs of the country and because it favored only the one heir while the others had to leave the farm and look for other work to win their bread. On the other hand, the new holder was so surcharged with debts that he was obliged to sell his holding by auction. In fact, the most important cause which stopped the validity of the above-mentioned law was the 1.5 million Greeks who came to Greece from Asia Minor as refugees after the Greek-Turkish War in 1922. After this time the pressure on the land was great, and industry which could occupy the surplus of population was not developed.

In a few areas the village farmers have recognized the disadvantageous effects of fragmentation and have "pooled" their land and have put into practice the essential soil and water conservation practices on the slopes. They have found a way to do what seemed impossible, and this plan must be adopted in more areas if food and feed supplies are to be increased. In this connection the extension of the use of co-operative farming will be important.

In other areas, as in the Island of Carpathos of the Dodecanese, there is the custom of the sole heir. The other heirs have to leave the farm and find work anywhere they can.

The conditions today for the introduction of a law of the sole heir are not so unfavorable as in the year 1917 and after. Today some of the great soil-improvement works in North Greece have been finished and others are under construction. The extension of irrigation in many areas has made much progress; both improvement work and irrigation have brought a large and fertile area into cultivation. Also the intensity of cultivation and essential progress of Greek industry have been increased.

All the above-mentioned favorable factors, combined with the progress of the home industries and the local agricultural industries which can and must be made soon, will relieve the pressure on agriculture and will, we believe, help to consolidate the holdings by prohibiting subdivision.

By introduction of the one-heir farm, a system of long-term loans would be essential to enable him to pay off the other heirs if there are any. At the same time the state would need to take care to help the other heirs to find other work. In this case their payment from the sole heir could be low, and the charge of the new farmer need not be great. This system might be a satisfactory method of preventing subdivision, and such a system of loans may also well be an essential counterpart to the smooth working of any restrictions placed on the free subdivision of holdings.

After the introduction of measures which restrict the subdivision of the holdings, we can proceed to prescribe a minimum area which provides full employment and feeds the agricultural family. This prescription is not so difficult, but it must be worked out very carefully by competent workers to prescribe the minimum area suited to all types of farming and to all types of land.

Before this land reform takes place it will

be necessary to prepare the farmers, because the success of the consolidation finally depends on the education of the rural population in these matters.

Conclusion

After all these thoughts and reasoning we come to the conclusion that Greece must consolidate its holdings by changing basically its national economy by supporting home, agricultural, and local industry and by restricting its agricultural population. The Greek agricultural population may be reduced slowly from 62 per cent to 45 per cent with no danger to its general vitality, because the 45 per cent will be enough to provide the healthy population needed.

By such a reduction of the agricultural population and by a corresponding increase of the other industries we shall achieve the following: (1) The average acreage of the agricultural holdings will be increased from ten to fifteen acres. (2) Employment could be found for the farmer in his spare time. (3) Farm and national economy would be placed on a sounder basis. (4) Many of the agricultural products would undergo an industrial process, thus obtaining a higher value. (5) Progress should be made and better standards reached in our national and, more particularly, agricultural life.

We know from our history that the Greeks are good sailors, merchants, and tradesmen. We should not therefore have an agricultural small-holder living in misery and poverty. Let us hope that with the assistance of our American friends we shall be able to lighten his burden and increase his prosperity.

REALLOCATION OF LAND IN THE NETHERLANDS

Philine R. Vanderpol

FRAGMENTATION of farm holdings is found throughout the Netherlands, but it is most serious in the eastern and southern parts where owner-occupancy is prevalent. In this sandy region where the Catholic religion prevails and families usually are large, the system of inheritance by which each heir receives an equal portion of the estate accounts for the excessive parcellation of the land. Due to subdivision of the farms, the average size of a parcel in the province of Brabant is three-quarters of an acre. It is estimated that nearly a third of the agricultural area of the Netherlands needs consolidation.[1]

The best consolidated farms are found on the land which was newly reclaimed from the former Zuider Zee, where the holdings have been well planned and established in single blocks.

The prevailing parcellation is the outgrowth of various farming systems. Accordingly, the following four categories of parcelled-up land can be distinguished:

1. The "esschen," or blocks of cultivated land, around which villages and farms are situated in a ring.

2. Land belonging to scattered farms and divided into parcels in such a way that the different lots of the same owner are not contiguous.

3. Land adjoining to farm buildings which line the roads or the dikes. This situation occurs in the northeastern part of the country where the moorland was dug off and the underlying soil was put under cultivation. The farms were constructed either along the roads or along the dikes which protect the lowland from the canals. When at the partition of an estate there was no

room for the heirs who did not inherit the old farm to build a new one along the same road or dike, a new farm was built right behind the old one on the same lot. Thus it could happen that in Staphorst, a small town in the province of Overijsel, the farms are situated in three or four lines, one closely behind the other. The principle of equal partition among all heirs made a simple division of the land impossible, since the heir receiving the part most remote from the farms would be worse off than the others. In a case where the owner left three heirs, the estate, therefore, would be divided into three-by-three parcels in order that each heir might receive land in each zone of distance from the farms. As a result agricultural undertakings in that region consist of long and narrow strips, and in many cases an owner has no other access to his land than across his neighbor's strip.

4. The fourth category is formed by the former common pastures, which were often situated at considerable distance from the villages and farms. In the years after the first world war many commons were turned into arable land.

In the years around 1920 the need for increased agricultural production made itself felt, and the problem of parcellation and its remedy, reallotment of the land, were taken up by the government. Until that time the consolidation of land could be effected only by the unanimous agreement of all owners concerned. Reallotments had therefore been rare. In 1924 a Reallotment Act was passed which made possible reallotment by majority vote of the owners concerned and which created the legal framework and a detailed procedure for consolidation of farmholdings. Yet, by requiring that a reallotment proposal be adopted in the general assembly of owners by the twofold majority vote of more than half of the owners, representing more than half of the land included in the reallotment, the act

defeated its purpose. This requirement, which in many cases could not be met, and the often considerable costs of a reallotment, which depend on the length of new farm roads and canals, account for the fact that until 1937 only 36 applications for reallotment had been filed, covering an area of 11,841 hectares. The effects of these applications, shown in Table 55 demonstrate the inadequacy of the reallotment provisions.

TABLE 55

APPLICATIONS FOR REALLOTMENT OF LAND IN THE NETHERLANDS, TO 1937

Status	Number	Area (in hectares)
Rejected by parties concerned	11	2,478
Remain undecided	4	687
Adopted	21	8,676
Total	36	11,841
Carried out	17	6,458
Being put into effect	4	2,218

Moderate estimates based upon the few reallotments that had been brought to a successful conclusion, calculate the increase in the production capacity of reallotted land at 20 per cent.[2] Consequently, reallotment of an area of 500,000 hectares would result in an increase in agricultural output equivalent to that from acquisition of 100,000 hectares of new land. This prospect justified the matter to be taken up again, and in 1938 the Reallotment Act was amended to the effect that adoption of a reallotment was henceforth possible by the vote of more than half of the owners or by the vote of the owners representing more than half of the land included in the project. At the same time the state assumed a larger proportion of the costs than it had done so far. Subsidies may be as high as 100 per cent of the costs charged to the owners, as was the case in the following instances.[3] In the province of Limburg a block of 366 hectares was parcelled up into 1,600 lots of an average size of 23 ares. Reallotment proceedings were taken up in 1941, but, owing to the war, the completion lagged until 1945. By then the reallotment costs had risen from the original 90 guilders per hectare to 180 guilders, due to the lack of manpower and the increase in wages and prices of material. With the help of a state subsidy amounting to the balance of the actual and the estimated costs, the project of reorganizing the block into 370 lots of an average size of 1 hectare could be completed.

Since the passing of the 1938 Act the number of applications for reallotment has been rising steadily. In 1936 there were seven applications; in 1937, ten applications; in 1938, twenty applications; and in 1939, there were sixty-two applications.

In the province of Limburg applications for reallotment of an area of 12,000 hectares had been filed on September 1, 1944.[4]

Reallotment Procedure

Reallotment of land, except when brought about by an agreement of all parties concerned, enfringes the sovereignty of some of the land owners, and the law's objective is therefore to secure proper protection of all rights involved as well as to prevent private interests from hampering the development of agriculture and the furtherance of general interests by refusing co-operation. The public interest is protected by the Minister of Agriculture, who has been empowered to deviate in some cases from the rules set in the Reallotment Act and who under certain conditions may prescribe consolidation of land even against the will of the owners. The private ownership rights, on the other hand, are protected by the right of parties

concerned to appeal to the judiciary or to the Crown.

The following public authorities play a part in reallotment procedures: the Minister of Agriculture, the Provincial Executive, the Central Committee for Reallotment, the Local Committees for Reallotment, and the Council of State. Since the functions of these officials and bodies cannot be well understood without comprehension of their place in the country's administration as a whole, it seems appropriate to give a short explanation of the Dutch policy.

The Netherlands is divided into twelve provinces, the administration of each of which is with the Provincial States, a body elected by the province's inhabitants. The Provincial States have a limited power of legislation, notably in the field of the administration of the polders (land below sea level which has been reclaimed from the sea or lakes and is enclosed by dikes), but their function is mainly executive. The Executive Committee of the Provincial States, which will be referred to below as the Provincial Executive, plays an important part in reallotment procedures.

The general administration of reallotments has been entrusted to a Central Committee for Reallotment, the members of which are appointed by the Crown. Two-fifths of the members must be appointed upon recommendation by certain agricultural societies designated by the Minister of Agriculture. The execution of reallotment is committed to Local Committees, the members of which (maximum five) are appointed by the Provincial Executive. They are assisted by a surveyor of the Land Registry, designated by the Minister of Agriculture.

An appeal to the Crown by a party concerned is heard by the Council of State, which is an advisory body to the Crown. Its committee on Contentions proposes the decision on the issue to the Crown. If the

Crown and the Minister of Agriculture do not see fit to conform their decision to the Council's proposal, both their and the Council's decision must be published in the Official Journal of the State.

Reallotment of land is effected either upon agreement of the owners concerned or by virtue of the law. The purpose is the furtherance of agriculture, horticulture, forestry, cattle raising, or peat-digging.

REALLOTMENT AGREEMENT

Three or more persons may pledge themselves in writing to join the real property as the owners of which they are entered in the Land Registry and to reallot this block among themselves. The rights to the reallotted land are acquired by registration of the deed of reallotment.

If parties in the agreement later appear not to be owners of the land, although they are registered as such, the agreement still retains its validity, and the real owners are substituted for the persons who were considered proprietors.

Parties may join the agreement by bringing in capital in order to receive a lot, as well as the reverse.

REALLOTMENT BY LAW

Several restrictions have been made as to the type of property which can be included in a reallotment. Cemeteries within thirty years after their closure, monuments and their grounds, property situated in a built-up area, and land destined for building purposes may not be taken into the block. Land being used for military purposes may be taken in only with the consent of the Minister of Defense. Buildings, parks, and land in other use than for agriculture, horticulture, forestry, cattle raising, peat-digging, hunting, or fishery may not be included against the owner's will, except for the case that maintenance of this rule would impede proper reallotment of the adjacent land.

Owners are entitled to receive lots, the value of which in proportion to the value of the block is as close as possible to the proportion of their brought-in property's value to the block's value. The difference in value, if any, may not exceed 5 per cent of the sum the owner is entitled to, against his or his mortgagee's will, and is paid in cash. However, the Minister of Agriculture is empowered to determine that the difference in value can be in excess of 5 per cent in cases where the general interest demands this and viability of the undertaking is not impaired. The Minister is also empowered to prescribe that the presumable share of the owner in the reallotment costs, as estimated by the Central Commission, be charged against the value of land due to him. Against his or his mortgagee's will the deduction may not exceed 5 per cent of his due, and the profitability of the enterprise may not be imperiled.

The lots the owners are to receive must be of a quality and destination similar to that of the property they brought into the block, and preferably consist of this property wholly or in part, provided that an arrangement to this effect will not impair the result of the reallotment.

Each lot must be constituted in such a manner that it has a way out and, if possible, is adjoining to a public road or watercourse.

Public roads within the block and watercourses, as well as structures that go with them, become the property of a public body designated by the Provincial Executive, which also sets rules for the administration and upkeep of these roads and waterways. No compensation is given for the land which is taken from the block for the construction of roads and canals, since the smaller size of the owner's new property will be offset by its increased value on account of the improved accessibility.

Owners and tenants must allow their land

to be entered, dug or measured upon if the Central Committee judges this necessary. If opposition is encountered, the mayor or county judge can have the operations carried out under protection of the arm of the law. Damage resulting from these actions is compensated by the government.

The main lines of a reallotment procedure are as follows: After the application has been approved by the commissioned authorities, the plan is adopted by the General Assembly of owners. The rights of each owner are determined and the land is appraised; a plan is then drafted of the roads and waterways to be constructed and of the parcels to be created. After this plan has been approved by the Central Committee the execution of the reallotment is commenced and a deed of reallotment drawn up for the transfer of ownership. A detailed account of the procedure is given below.

Application for reallotment.—Applications for reallotment are made in writing either by one-fifth of those registered as owners or by agricultural associations of corporate status active in the field of agriculture, horticulture, forestry, cattle raising, or peat-digging, or by the state, province, municipality, or polder board (a body commissioned with the administration of a polder).

The application, together with a map of the block, is sent to the Provincial Executive, who forwards it to the Central Committee. After investigation of the matter this Committee returns an advice, as the result of which the block may be enlarged or reduced. The Provincial Executive may refuse the application by motivated decree, a copy of which is sent to the first five signers of the application. Each person concerned has appeal to the Crown.

If the application is approved, the Provincial Executive preliminarily determines the block and the project for roads and water-courses. The Central Committee then makes out a list of the persons registered as owners, which list is deposited for public inspection at the town clerk's offices in the municipalities in which the block is situated. All owners are notified of the deposit, which is also publicized in at least two newspapers. Objections can be brought before the Provincial Executive.

Adoption of the reallotment.—An assembly of the owners, convened by the Provincial Executive, acts on the reallotment plan. Convocations are sent by registered mail and point out that failure to partake in the voting is considered a consent to the reallotment. No one can allege that he has not received the convocation, which is, moreover, publicized. The Central Committee is represented in the assembly.

Adoption of the reallotment plan requires the votes either of the majority of the owners or of the owners of more than half of the block. Yet, if public interests demand reallotment urgently, the Minister of Agriculture can prescribe that the reallotment be put into effect, even when the necessary votes have not been obtained.

The adoption is publicized, and owners and tenants are hereafter prohibited from taking any action which might lower the value of their property without the permission of the Local Committee. Infringers of this rule are liable to a fine up to one thousand guilders.

After adoption of the reallotment plan a start can be made with the construction or improvement of roads or watercourses. Landmarks may be placed; timber can be cut down; earth, gravel, or other material can be taken from the land or brought upon it; land can be drained, opened up, or reclaimed; buildings may be torn down or constructed if the Central Committee judges this to be in the interest of the reallotment. Damage resulting from these actions is compensated. Owners and tenants are bound to allow the aforementioned actions on their land, and can, in case of refusal, be compelled to do so by the arm of the law at the command of the mayor or county judge.

Delimitation of rights and appraisal of land.—Reallotment is executed by the Local Committee which establishes a list of all parties concerned, with a delimitation and qualification of each right, and nominates valuators who appraise the lots.

The Central Committee grades the land and determines the value per hectare of each grade. In accordance with this gradation the valuators classify the land and peg out the boundaries of each grade.

The reports of the Local Committee are deposited for public inspection and publicized. Objections may be brought before the Local Committee. If no objections are raised, the rights and valuation are definitely established.

Objections are dealt with by the Local Committee. If no agreement can be effected the documents are sent to the investigating judge of the Court, who convenes all parties concerned. Parties between whom no agreement is reached are referred to the Court.

Execution of the reallotment.—As soon as the list of parties concerned and the appraisal of the land have been established, the Local Committee proceeds to draft a map of the roads and waterways to be built, which map is sent to the Central Committee and finally to the Provincial Executive, who determines the decisive plan for roads and watercourses. Their construction can then be put in hand.

The Local Committee also drafts a plan for reallotment, which must be approved by the Central Committee. The plan comprises the following points: the lots to be created, allocation of these lots, compensation for the allocation of a less valuable lot than was brought in, provisions as to special rights, tenancy or leases which may cling to the land, indemnification for damage resulting from digging, etc. upon the land, apportioning of the costs of the reallotment among the lots, and provisions concerning the occupation of the land.

The boundaries of the lots are pegged out, and again each person concerned can bring objections before the Local Committee. If no objections are raised, the reallotment plan is definite. In case objections are raised and the Local Committee does not succeed in bringing about an agreement, the investigation judge convenes parties and, if needed, refers them to the Court, which decides the matter in the last resort.

The deed of reallotment and the transfer of ownership.—The deed of reallotment is drawn up by a notary public; the ownership of the allocated land is acquired through registration of this deed.

The costs of the reallotment.—Part of the costs of a reallotment is paid by the state, notably the costs involved in the functioning of the Central Committee, the Land Registry and the assemblies, the expenses of the publications, and all expenditure incurred in case no reallotment is brought forth.

All other costs are incumbent on the owners. The money is advanced by the state, and the debt is apportioned among the lots in proportion to their size. These lots are then encumbered with a debt to the state. Five per cent of the amount due is annually paid off over a period of thirty years. However, the debt can be redeemed in any year for its value at that time.

Reallotment and Tenancy

The Reallotment Act frequently falls short of its goal of implementing the establishment of the most favorable agricultural conditions, owing to its being primarily concerned with ownership rights. In situations where ownership and exploitation of the land are not in one hand, the welfare of agriculture is dependent on the conditions of tenancy rather than on the consolidation of property.

Although tenants are recognized as parties concerned and may voice their opinion on the reallotment projects, too little consideration is given to their interests. Article 19 of the Reallotment Act rules that "in each reallotment regulations be made as to the rights of lease and tenancy which cling to the properties." In the interest of the consolidation an owner can be compelled to accept certain parcels of land, but it is held that "regulation of tenancy" does not imply that tenancy relations can be established against the will of one party. It is considered a serious shortcoming of the law that no provision has been made for the reorganization of tenancy conditions along with consolidation of ownership, particularly in cases where parcels without farm buildings have been leased out. For in the consolidation of a leased farmholding the interests of owner and tenant are the same, but reallotment of a block including leased parcels is likely to be prejudicial to the tenants of these parcels, both if they are owned by farmers whose holdings are situated in the block and when they are the property of absentee landlords.

In the former instance the owner leased out the parcel because it was not adjoining to the body of his holding; in case of a reallotment he will want to unite his two properties and to exploit his undertaking as a unit. He will therefore either cancel the lease or await the expiration of its term, but in both cases the tenant is dispossessed.

In the latter case, when the parcel is owned by an absentee landlord who owns several scattered parcels in the area, the situation as a rule is such that these lots are leased out to various tenants and that one tenant cultivates lots of various owners. If a reallotment consolidates the properties and the tenancy contracts are transferred from the formerly owned land to the newly acquired parcels, fragmentation of tenancy will replace fragmentaton of ownership.

As a solution of this problem it has been recommended that a provision be added to the Tenancy Act to the effect that a "regulation of tenancy" as required by the Reallotment Act may henceforth give rise to a duty for parties concerned to accept a reorganization of tenancy conditions if this is deemed essential for the success of the reallotment.[5] The consent of the Land Chamber or Tenancy Chamber would guarantee proper preservation of all rights involved.

ASPECTS OF CONSOLIDATION WORK IN
THE NETHERLANDS

 Jan M. van Rossem

THE PROCEDURE of land consolidation work in the Nethelands has been very thoroughly described by Philine R. Vanderpol as part of a study of world land tenure systems undertaken by the FAO in collaboration with members of the staff of the University of Wisconsin. Since all delegates have received a copy of this study, I may start out from that paper and discuss some of the actual problems of consolidation work in my country.[1]

However, we have to start off with defining as exactly as possible the meaning we in the Netherlands attach to this word. In a land consolidation scheme a number of different parcels are joined together in one block whereby all property boundaries are imagined to have been eradicated. Not only are the individual properties subsequently replanned, but also, the system of roads and waterways is overhauled and improved, if necessary. The arrangements for the control of the water level will be improved in such a way that in summer and winter the water level may be considered to be under the best possible control. Every new parcel will have a way out to and possibly adjoin a public road or watercourse and have, if necessary and possible, proper drainage facilities. Also, the land itself is improved by carrying out of necessary reclamation work. Consolidation thus embodies an all-round improvement of land.

The following general rule applies to the parcelling out: Every owner is entitled to receive property the value of which in proportion to the total value of the block is as close as possible to the proportion of the value of his original property to the block's total original value.

Deviation from this rule, however, is possible if proper completion of the consolidation scheme would be endangered. The difference in value, however, may not exceed 5 per cent of the value of the property. As long as the interests of the consolidation scheme are not affected, every owner will receive property of the same kind and with the same possibilities for use as he formerly had, and as much as possible it is tried to return to him his original property. I will now discuss some aspects of the consolidation work.

It has been suggested that the consolidation procedure requires too long a time. At present a consolidation scheme in my country takes three or four years after the vote has been taken. It was noticed that some farmers had the inclination to pay less attention to the fields they would have to hand over on the completion of the scheme. In the new law which has been presented to Parliament by Royal Message of January 19, 1951, certain provisions will facilitate an early handing-over of the parcels without waiting for the final plan dealing with matters of compensation, special rights, etc. to be adopted. Also some articles deal with the possibility for provisional handing over of properties. Of course it would be possible to speed up the procedure considerably by increasing the 5 per cent limit on the difference in the value of property before and after. The work of the local committee would be very much simplified. On the other hand, some owners might find themselves after the completion of a scheme with a considerably smaller-sized farm. It is felt that this would seriously undermine the confidence of the farmers in the fair way the consolidation schemes have hitherto been carried out.

It has been suggested that The Netherlands consolidation law should be an example of perfectionism. There might be some truth in this, but I would like to point out that our farmers have confidence in the way this law is being carried out, and they are willing to co-operate. Our government wishes to preserve this state of affairs and tries to find a compromise between the desire for a quick and efficient dispatch of the work and the desire to safeguard all justifiable interests against any possible administrative procedure at will.

The second topic with which I will deal is that of the financial aspects of consolidation work. First of all, I wish to state that in our country, as well as in many other European countries, we have government controlled rents. An equitable tenancy arrangement needs a state control of rents. Any tenancy arrangement which aims at the protection of the tenant will be a dead letter in the law if there is not at the same time a control of rents. Now in our country because of various circumstances the rents are kept at a low level. This has a bearing on our consolidation work. The costs of the work are partly met by the state and partly by the landowner. The state pays for such expenses as those of the central committee, the assistance of the Land Registration Service, the expense of meetings, publications, etc.; also, all expenditure incurred in case no reallotment is brought forth is borne by the state. All other costs are borne in principle by the owners. I wish to underline the words "in principle" because these costs are often so high that without a state subsidy the work would not be taken on. The state subsidy amounts to the difference between the cost of the consolidation scheme that would be borne by the landowner and the (calculated) private economc increase in value of the landowner's property. This subsidy can, however, not amount to more than 75 per cent of the costs. In general the consolidation subsidies now amount to approximately 70 per cent of the cost. This is a profitable arrangement for the owner-operator, but this may not be so for the owner who leases his property.

All property in a consolidation scheme is charged with a consolidation rent (special assessment). The costs which have ultimately to be met by the owner are advanced by the state, and the debt is apportioned among the lots in proportion to their size. These lots are then encumbered with a debt to the state. Five per cent of the amount due is annually paid off over a period of thirty years. This is the consolidation rent (special assessment). Now if the owner could charge this consolidation rent, or at least the main part of it, to the tenant he would not object, but this might not be the case because he has to get an approval to raise the rent from the Land Chamber (Grondkamer). These boards may be reluctant to approve an increase in the rent by a substantial part of the consolidation rent. The reason for this I cannot start explaining because I would have to embark on some very complicated aspects of our rent control policy. But I would like to add just one thing: the tenant profits by

the consolidation scheme; is it fair to let him pay for it? I might go one step further. Even if he pays for it, would it be fair if the landlord not only gets back the money he invested but also a small part of the extra profits the tenant makes on his improved lands? By putting these questions to you I have let you enter into the realm of a basic issue in our national policy: How shall we divide the cake? And we are able to discuss this question in our country because the government has enough power indeed to divide the cake. You will understand that these issues are of a political nature. The consequences for the technicians are very real. The landowner who leases his land lacks the incentive to co-operate fully in a proposed consolidation project. The improvement to the land seems to the owner less economic because of the (at a low level) controlled rents. The result of all this is that the meetings where the vote on the consolidation scheme are to be taken cause anxiety to the men who are in charge of this work. Some schemes are voted down; in some cases we succeed by the skin of our teeth; and I am glad to say in the majority of cases we still get a comfortable majority. But at the same time I may remind you of the fact that we only require the votes either of the majority of the owners or of the owners of more than half of the block.

Now I would like to draw your attention to some aspects of education and extension work in consolidated areas. It is often thought that agricultural problems in a backward area may be solved by a consolidation scheme only. Indeed, fragmentation, bad drainage, and road conditions, as well as shortcomings in the reclamation of the land, often cause low yields. But I wish to stress that the farming techniques are of equal importance. I think one can say that there is an interrelation between the educational level of a population group and the way they use the land. In an area which may be termed backward with regard to agriculture, the farmers are backward too. This state of affairs cannot be improved except by an all around land improvement scheme. Our experience has taught us that consolidation of the land does not in itself bring about higher production. Therefore education and extension work necessarily have to go with land consolidation. Never have education and extension services had a better chance to tackle the problems of the people and their ways of farming than they have in consolidated areas. The establishment of demonstration farms by the extension service in the consolidated areas is of great importance. If possible all the farmers should be covered by the county agents on an individual basis, meetings should be organized, sons and daughters should be shown the way to winter schools and courses. Attention should be paid to credit facilities, because the better layout of the farm enables the farmer to use modern machinery. Often the fertilizer stock in the soil is at a very low level, and bringing it up to standard requires substantial investments. The formation of co-operatives should be stimulated. In short, consolidation in the proper sense of the word should also take in its stride a far-reaching education and extension program and the promotion of such agencies as better credit facilities and co-operatives. Only then will the conditions have been established which will enable the farmer to benefit to the fullest possible extent from the consolidation scheme.

Finally, I may elaborate somewhat on a point Miss Vanderpol quite rightly makes in her paper; namely, that our Reallotment Act of 1938 as amended in 1941 falls short of its goal of implementing the establishment of the most favorable agricultural conditions, because it is primarily concerned with ownership rights. In the explanatory memorandum to the aforementioned draft Consolidation Law of 1951 the government has

again pointed out that the consolidation law is concerned primarily with ownership rights and that for various reasons the Tenancy Act should deal with the possibilities of a scheme for reallocation of tenancy rights.

However, the draft law does contain some provisions with regard to tenancy. By the legislation of 1938 and 1941 new lease contracts could only be established on a voluntary basis—that is to say, only where the owner and the prospective tenant came to an agreement would a new contract be established. There was, however, a provision that lease contracts could be abolished in the interest of the consolidation scheme. In the absence of provisions to establish new lease contracts against the wish of the landowner, it was found to be often very difficult indeed to establish satisfactory tenancy arrangements in the consolidation area. One tenant often may work parcels of different owners. The joining together of these parcels can usually not be combined with an efficient parcelling out of the ownership rights. The draft law not only gives the administration the right to abolish existing tenancy contracts but also the right to fix new contracts if on a voluntary basis so proper results can be obtained. However, these provisions do not make it possible to force lease contracts on an owner who did not lease land before the consolidation scheme was started. Fundamentally the agreement is still voluntary; but if the draft law is accepted by Parliament, there will be a possibility to force on the landowner a new tenant. The draft law contains provisions for appeal against decisions in this field by the administration. These appeals will be handled by the tenancy courts (Pachtkamer), which are special courts for dealing with tenancy conflicts. You will agree with me that these arrangements have considerably restricted the right of property in our country. I will not deal with this any further, since a discussion of this issue is essentially a discussion on conflicting private concepts of human society in this world.

As a postscript to this statement a comment on the ratio of progress of land consolidation may be meaningful. According to figures released by the *Cultuur technische, Dieust,* Utrecht, Holland, through 1950 reallocation has been completed on 67 blocks comprising 42,846 hectares, and reallocation

has been undertaken in 62 blocks comprising 68,379 hectares. Reallocation is under consideration on 249 blocks comprising 267,055 hectares (but has not yet, at this time, been voted on).

Currently, consolidation is proceeding at a rate of 10,000 hectares a year. Eventually this may be stepped up to 15,000 or 20,000 hectares a year.

ASPECTS OF LAND CONSOLIDATION IN JAPAN

     Setsuro Hyodo

THE TOTAL area of Japan is smaller than that of California in the United States, and only 14 per cent of Japan's area is used as cultivated land. Moreover, Japan has a population of 83 millions. The intense population pressure in rural districts and lack of urban employment opportunities cause intense competition for land.

Characteristics of fragmented lands in Japan are as follows: (1) The average farm size is 0.8 hectare. (2) The average area of a parcel of land is six ares (600 square meters). (3) The farmer has an average of ten to twenty pieces of land. (4) The total distance to parcels of land is about four kilometers (one way).

History of Consolidation

From olden times land consolidation has been initiated by the learned or experienced people in some districts of Japan, but it was not very popular in the rural communities. The Japanese law of 1901 on cultivated land consolidation enabled owners of agricultural land to organize co-operatives for the consolidation of their lands. But the number of landowners who did not cultivate their lands and only rented them to the tenants was very large, and most of them did not want to contribute to the improvement of

the productivity of the land by consolidation. In short, overwhelming forces of landlords hampered land consolidation in spite of good legislation. The necessity for land reform under such conditions still remained.

In carrying out the land reform, land consolidation was considered necessary in order to improve the productivity of the land. But in a rural community land consolidation is very difficult to execute in a short time. The government therefore decided to postpone land consolidation until the land reform had been completed.

The government did prepare, in the meantime, the necessary legislation for land improvement, including land consolidation. The name of this legislation is the Land Improvement Law, which came into effect in June, 1949. It should be noted that this law was drafted to expedite land development, because land development is one of the most important policies in Japan since the end of the war. Japan's food supply is far from self-sufficient. Because of population increase, improvement in diet, calamities of nature (natural disasters), and increased use of land for nonagricultural purposes, Japan has to import 3 million tons of foodstuffs annually. Therefore the increase of the production of staple foods is an important goal for Japan's agricultural policy. This must be brought about by increasing the productivity of the land through land development. The government launched a three-year economic sufficiency plan for the period 1951–1953, under which reclamation of lands of 150,000 hectares, reclamation of waters of 170,000 hectares, irrigation-drainage for 1 million hectares, utilization of fertilizers on 70,000 hectares, land consolidation (farm boundary adjustment) for 170,000 hectares, etc. is undertaken. This will result in an increase of 1,160,000 tons of rice and barley in 1954. The total expenditure for the three-year period amounts to 230 million dollars. However, the monetary and budgetary situation does not permit the completion of this plan. Assistance from foreign funds might meet the situation.

Procedures in Consolidation

According to the Land Improvement Law, a local agricultural commission, a local agricultural co-operative association, or a local land improvement district can take the initiative for land consolidation with the consent of half of the land owners in the district concerned. These organizations may draft the consolidation plan and may request the approval of the Prefectural Governor and present the plan for public inspection. According to this plan, the farmers get the same value of land as they had but in a case where the farmer gets value in land, he shall get money him for the loss.

es of Consolidation

enactment of the Land Improvement Law, contrary to what we might we can find only a few instances of al land consolidation. We must consider the reason why land consolidation has not been executed smoothly, and our discussion should be concentrated on this point. In my opinion the reasons for the difficulties in Japan are as follows:

Rural people persist in holding on to their lands which they inherited from their ancestors. They do not want to move to any other place. This pattern of feudalistic thinking may perhaps be changed through education.

Every parcel of land has different values according to situation, productivity, water facilities, etc. Especially in Japan, where the main crop is rice, water facilities are most important for cultivation. For instance, water facilities vary according to the distance from the river or canal. Accordingly, without the construction of new canals there is no hope of equalizing the value of different lands. Land consolidation cannot be accomplished without construction of agricultural facilities such as canals. This is the reason why land consolidation goes hand in hand with agricultural development schemes. Financial help will be necessary to increase water facilities.

A further motive for consolidation is that farmers can use machinery on consolidated holdings. However, at present Japanese farmers cannot introduce machinery because they do not have money enough to purchase the machinery, and they have cheap family labor which substitutes for machinery.

In some cases Japanese farmers prefer fragmented parcels of land to spread the risk of damage from typhoon, flood, frost, etc., which constitute a severe danger to their farms. Preventive measures and insurance against these damages should be established in order to promote the land consolidation.

CONSOLIDATION OF HOLDINGS IN SWEDEN

G. R. Ytterborn

IN SWEDEN the first law on consolidation of holdings, the Land Partition Law, was passed in 1757. It provided for consolidation of the holdings in a village upon the request of only one of the owners in that village. The consolidation was to be brought about in such a way that each holding would consist of not more than two, three, or, at most, four fields. The houses of the holdings were to remain in the village, which meant, especially in the case of large villages, long distances between the farmhouses and the fields.

A new consolidation law was passed at the beginning of the nineteenth century, called the One-Partition Law. However, it was valid only in the southern part of Sweden. According to this law the holdings should consist of only one piece of land with the farmhouses located on that same piece of land. In 1827 the law of reallotment, the Law of *Luga skifte,* was passed, and this law with some amendments still exists. The law valid at present is to be found in the Law of Division of Land in Rural Areas of 1926. According to this law, every owner of land in a village is entitled to demand that his land be consolidated. If anyone in the village is not willing to participate in the consolidation of holdings in that village, the case will be tested and the following procedure carried out:

1. If the village land is divided or reallocated according to older laws, the latest one being the One-Partition Law, the holdings in that village should be consolidated if through such a process the production and the value of the land will increase and if the economic advance of the consolidation is higher than the cost of it, which is most likely to be the case. If the village land

is divided or reallocated according to more modern laws, there must be a majority, both in the number of farmers and in the acreage they represent, voting in favor of the consolidation proposal. In addition, the case has to meet the conditions mentioned above.

2. The village land is mapped.

3. The land is evaluated or appraised. That is, the value of the land is graded according to a certain scale.

4. A scheme of consolidation is prepared. This must be done in such a manner that each owner of land obtains the same amount of economic area that he had previous to the consolidation. However, a difference of 2 per cent (maximum) is allowed to be paid in cash.

5. In the consolidation scheme each holding is to be given the most practical shape possible. In order to obtain that, some of the farmsteads may have to be moved from the big village.

6. If any land owner is not satisfied with the scheme, he may appeal to a local special court consisting of a judge and three farmers. Any landowner not satisfied with the decision of the local court may appeal to the Royal High Court. The owners of the land are bound by law to contribute to the aggregate consolidation expenses according to the value of the land they may own in the village; government subsidies are granted individuals according to their needs up to 50 to 60 per cent of their costs.

The prevention of continued fragmentation, including the fragmentation of once-consolidated holdings, is the aim of the 1926 Law of Division of Land in Rural Areas. According to this law, a landholding could not be divided unless the new holdings, with regard to size and quality, will

be permanently suitable for their purpose. This means that a holding could not be legally divided in case of inheritance or for other purposes if the above-mentioned conditions are not met. In principle, a family farm cannot be legally divided.

However, such farms are sometimes divided illegally by the heirs or by other co-owners. In course of time such divisions have had to be recognized and made legal. At the present time there is a committee working on this legislation, and that committee will probably recommend that any such division of land made after a certain time should be declared illegal and not be recognized.

Consolidation according to the laws mentioned has spread over all Sweden, and most of the land is consolidated. However, there are still villages in need of consolidation. The majority of present-day consolidation is to take place in connection with enlargement of the farms. It may be done in such a way that the government agency buys some farms in the village, either in the free market or by using its priority right of purchase. In working out the consolidation scheme, the land bought by the government agency will be added to the farms that are now too small to form economic farm units.

Further fragmentation is not considered likely in Sweden since there is not the population pressure on the land that exists in many other countries. Sweden is a highly industrialized country, and alternative employment possibilities are thus offered to any excess rural population.

ASPECTS OF LAND CONSOLIDATION IN GERMANY

Otto Schiller

IN WESTERN and Southwestern Germany there is the greatest need for land consolidation. Until 1937 every state had its own legislation. The 1937 Reichsumlegungsordnung is still in force, but a draft-law has been presented to the Bonn Parliament.

One of the basic issues which the new consolidation law brought up was whether a consolidation scheme should be entirely voluntary or whether the Administration should have the power to order it where no voluntary vote is taken. Although preference is given to voluntary application from communities concerned, it was decided to retain this right for the Administration in case the national interest warranted the start of a consolidation scheme (new main roads, airports, etc.).

There are more applications filed than the Administration can deal with. Nevertheless one should always keep in mind that the majority vote overrides the minority, but that this minority can seriously slow down procedure by appealing from administrative decisions. There is a special Court of Appeal.

Progress on land consolidation is shown by the following figures: reallocation has been completed for 3,882,000 hectares, or 26 per cent of the total area; reallocation is needed for 7,266,000 hectares, or 48 per cent of the total area; no reallocation is needed for 3,859,655 hectares, or 26 per cent of the total area.

In most countries consolidation aims at two to five plots per farm. Experience in Germany has taught that although it was advantageous to have all the land in one parcel, the farmers usually make new subdivisions because of crop rotation. Since in many areas of Germany the farmer has his twelve o'clock break on the farm, there is no disadvantage if the plots are of such size that they will keep the farmer busy for half a day. Early land consolidation procedure in Germany therefore did not reduce the number of parcels substantially; for example, the number of parcels was cut down from one hundred to eighty-five. New roads were constructed, and the parcels were given a better form. However, these consolidated areas now are often in need of reconsolidation because of the advances in agricultural techniques. Even in new consolidation schemes, however, each farm has its land usually in at least six parcels, since the farmers wish to have land of different soil quality for pasture, arable land, orchard, a bit of horticulture, etc. This has proved to be advantageous for the agricultural machinery co-operatives too. Less time is lost by these co-operatives in driving from one farm to the other if the land belonging to one farm lies in six or more parcels. The quality of the soil determines the time of ploughing, harvesting, etc. This six-parcel system also helps to speed up the work of consolidation.

Should land consolidation be planned in such a way that the areas where fragmentation is at its worst are consolidated first, or should consolidation be carried out only in those areas where it has been requested by the local farmers? Although in the first case more complete results may be obtained, the psychological resistance will increase substantially too.

In large areas of Western Germany and neighboring Western European countries land consolidation is a particularly complex problem because a part of the peasantry for more than a century has been involved in a process of sociological transformation which is still under way. With the penetration of industrial enterprises into rural areas a great many peasants or their descendants have taken up other occupations, either permanently or seasonally, or for a certain period of their lives. Therewith a part of the cultivated area is now in the hands of small holders who cling to their property but

actually have become part-time farmers. In these districts there are so-called "workers' residential communities" (Arbeiterwohngemeinden) which consist nearly entirely of nonfarmers or part-time farmers.

In such communities where the majority are so-called "peasant-workers" (Arbeiterbauern) the fragmentation of land is particularly widespread. Therefore, the question often is not so much how to consolidate the land of the farmers with regard to efficient management but rather how to deal with the land of nonfarmers in socio-economic perspectives.

Hitherto this growth of a stratum of industrial workers who are at the same time part-time farmers and attached to the soil has been considered desirable for economic and social reasons. The close link between industry and agriculture as developed especially in Southwestern Germany has brought forth a special type of industrial worker whose landed property provides some additional income which in times of crisis or of restricted industrial production guarantees his subsistence. From the point of view of industry it is desirable to preserve this kind of worker who by his landed property and by permanent residence is a stable and reliable factor and less exposed to radical influences than is an urban proletariat. From the point of view of agriculture and food economy this is, however, desirable only so long as it guarantees the proper use of land. But that is the case only as long as the small land owner takes a genuine interest in his farm work and as long as his wife and children, who have to do the main work, are able and willing to do it. But in many cases the small land owner considers his landed property primarily as a secure asset, safe from inflation. He avoids selling or leasing his land in order to have some secure property and a reliable source of food supply in case of war or distress.

Of late, occasional serious neglect of land

by small holders has been noted. This had happened before in time of business prosperity. Under present conditions, however, these cases have to be considered as rather grave symptoms, the more so since the younger generation is obviously not as willing as the older one to shoulder the burden of part-time farming.

The slackened interest, if not in landed property but in its use, would have influenced the real estate market to a higher degree had there been less political insecurity and, especially, no Korean war. Nevertheless it is indicative that in some rural communities small land owners offer plots for sale or lease under favorable conditions without always finding buyers or tenants. To be sure, we should not generalize from these instances. But, if the small holder once came to believe in a long period of peaceful development the situation on the real estate market would change remarkably.

Land consolidation faces especially difficult problems in communities largely consisting of part-time farmers. The land of small proprietors consisting of only one or two parcels can not be consolidated but can only be regrouped. Consequently the psychological resistance against land consolidation usually is strongest among the small land owners.

In communities consisting almost entirely of small proprietors and part-time farmers, land consolidation is less urgent and cannot lead to a considerable reduction of fragmentation. In communities where the land of the farmers is interspersed with the parcels of small land owners, these parcels should be concentrated next to the village.

At the same time the question arises whether to promote the gradual transfer of land from part-time farmers to full-time farmers. It is hardly to be expected that the "peasant-worker," a result of the sociological process just described, in the long run will be preserved in the present form and

to the same extent. The social and moral benefits, together with attachment to the soil and the work on the land, can largely be gained even if the land owned is comparatively small and used as garden land, in the form of allotment gardens. If the property of the small land owner is so large that instead of gardening he has to farm it on a larger scale with the help of his own inadequate or hired draft power, then the result proves the more unsatisfactory the more agronomy develops.

The shift of parts of the peasantry to other occupations will continue, in line with natural developments. But the transfer of land from farmers to part-time or nonfarmers, which is connected with this process and leads to further fragmentation of land, should be restricted as far as possible. It is, for instance, a task of education to persuade the nonagricultural co-heirs of landed property not to use the inherited land themselves but to leave it to the one heir who remains a full-time farmer. Furthermore, suitable provisions of agricultural or tax policy might serve to promote the sale or lease of property of small owners who do not garden and who may or may not farm it, in order to increase and strengthen the holdings of full-time farmers. In the long run a satisfactory solution of the consolidation problem can be reached only if combined with a gradual up-grading of the size of holdings.

As soon as the real estate market operates in the normal way, it, too, might possibly contribute to land consolidation. In some cases, able farmers have known how to consolidate their holdings effectively by purchase or barter, before an official consolidation procedure was extended to their community. In a South German community, for instance, with prevailing small holdings and great fragmentation, a nonresident contractor within the last ten years succeeded in building up a consolidated farmstead of approximately seventy-five acres on the out-skirts of the village land. He bought or leased all available parcels in the community and traded them for parcels needed for rounding out his consolidated block. This contractor gave an interesting example of what private initiative can do in the midst of highly scattered community land. Such opportunities might be exploited also in other communities and should be made use of by government agencies for consolidation purposes.

In many communities with large acreage and a great number of land owners, a satisfactory solution of consolidation can be found only if some farmsteads are moved to the outskirts of the community area. In Switzerland this is often successfully practiced; usually the size of the farmsteads concerned is increased. In the long run this is the most efficient way of changing the size of the holdings in such communities and of spreading out the narrowly built villages. Possibly the transplanted farmsteads can be settled in the form of hamlets.

Consolidation must not only be considered a matter of land surveying aiming at regrouping of land in the most effective way, but it must also be treated as a matter of agricultural policy. Hence, before initiating a consolidation project the economic and social conditions in the community concerned should be analyzed. This analysis should show the social groups in the community and their landed property. An analysis should be made of full-time farmers, part-time farmers, nonfarmers owning land, and, furthermore, of the number and distribution of tenants in the area, of the land of absentee owners, etc. On this basis a plan for the regrouping of the different types of land should be worked out. In addition one should examine whether land utilization in the given area corresponds to the natural and economic conditions, whether, for instance, ploughland should be changed into grassland, whether pasture should be reforested, or whether land should be set aside for heifer pasture or orchards. Only such planning, similar to the methods of zoning, will allow the surveyor to draw a consolidation project offering a satisfactory and permanent solution.

Closely connected with this is the question, discussed in a different context, of how to impede the fragmentation brought about by inheritance after the consolidation has taken place. This is not only a matter of legislation but also of education which in various respects should contribute to the promotion of land consolidation. Thus it is, for instance, a task of the educator to eliminate psychological resistance against consolidation in order to prevent land owners who have been coerced by majority vote to participate in the consolidation from impeding and delaying the procedure through unreasonable grievances.

A further task of education is to advise the small holder in the efficient use of lease of his land and to advise the farmer how to adjust the organization and management of his farm to the new conditions following consolidation. Land consolidation is a very complex matter and shows to what degree education, advising, and research are essential to the solution of the land tenure problem. Certainly this conference will help to clarify the ways and means of reaching this goal.

Part XVIII   INHERITANCE AND THE TENURE PROBLEM

THE ROLE OF INHERITANCE IN THE TENURE PROCESS

Abstract of the Report of the Working Party

§§§§ Chairmen, *Jacob H. Beuscher, Constantin C. von Dietze,*
and *Charles L. Stewart*

THE WORKING party on inheritance was concerned with the whole problem of passing the family farm from one generation to the next. The group attempted no formal recommendations for solving particular problems. It took as its purpose to exchange experiences, to get firsthand insight into practical problem situations, and to search for common threads running through inheritance problems in widely different societies. Certain aspects of the role of inheritance in land tenure were passed over lightly in the short time available; there was little consideration of the positive role of education and communication in changing inheritance patterns. Other relevant aspects of the problem were presumed to be covered by other working parties: those on land consolidation, taxation and public regulation, and certain technical features of titles and deed registration.

Attention was given chiefly to the problem of excessive subdivision brought about by inheritance, but the working party also dealt in less detail with other aspects of inheritance, including (1) the effect of inheritance laws upon very large holdings; (2) future effect on agricultural areas being newly settled; (3) the problem of increasing numbers of people in succeeding generations supported from a given acreage, even though it is not physically split up by inheritance.

Where inheritance laws are in effect, a variety of devices can be used to alleviate their effects. Certain considerations to be borne in mind when framing measures to alleviate the effects of inheritance were discussed, such as, for example, the following:

1. The special importance of understanding fully, and giving appropriate weight to, established traditions, customs, and values. As a corollary to this it is important to study how the inheritance process actually operates as distinguished from the law in the books. Besides, planning measures to alleviate the effect of inheritance practices should not be viewed simply as a law drafting job but as a task to be undertaken on a broad basis by a team of social scientists.

2. The economic ideal is to get the farm consisting of both movables and immovables transferred as an economic unit and going concern, with the least possible disruption.

3. Freedom to dispose of property by will or *inter vivos* transfer makes it less necessary that the laws governing inheritance correspond to the traditions and feelings of the rural population.

4. Uniformity of inheritance practices throughout a single country is not necessarily desirable.

5. Clear differentiation between (a) intangible rights of ownership and (b) the actual thing owned will help spread the idea that two or more persons can, at the same

time, own undivided shares in the same farm without physical partition. Wider acceptance of this idea will reduce parcellization.

Mr. BEUSCHER remarked in the first session upon the importance of land tenure patterns and specifically upon the role of inheritance in maintaining or modifying these patterns. As inheritance, he specified the following: (1) transfers of land *inter vivos* and the family settlements that often go with them, including so-called "support contracts"; (2) disposition of property by landowners after death, by will, and, *per contra,* limits in law or custom on such disposition; (3) law or custom regulating disposition of land in the absence of will or other arrangement; and (4) arrangements made among co-heirs of property.

Mr. PONCE DE LEÓN stated his conviction, growing out of participation in many cases at law in Peru, that the subdivision of land into parcels which are too small is a problem, but one which can be limited through legal means, primarily perhaps through the ancient custom of inheritance by the oldest son, or through other methods.

Mr. LE RICHE outlined a dual problem in Libya. In part it rises from the subdivision of land itself into smaller and smaller parcels and in part from fractionating ownership into the equivalent of shares, which however may relate to particular portions of a property, such as specified trees or buildings. The ensuing discussion underscored the importance of Islamic law and custom as factors conditioning land holdings and inheritance.

Mr. HILL expressed a general concern in England with the problem of preventing the splitting up of economic farming units and particularly with the arrangements sometimes made in avoiding it, whereby the owner-occupier who inherits the farm may be obliged annually to pay sizeable sums to his sisters or brothers or may sell off

parts to discharge his obligation, which may result in an undue burden comparable with rent or cause fragmentation. He pointed out that its practical seriousness as regards ultimate management and production is mitigated by a recent English statutory requirement that land be farmed in accordance with the tenets of good husbandry and managed in accordance with the rules of good estate management. Failure to meet these standards can, under the law, lead to dispossession of a farmer or a landowner and in the latter case in acquisition of the land by the state at its fair market value. Ensuing discussion brought out, further, that the abuse of land for the purpose of meeting payments stipulated as a condition of inheritance or for other purposes is in principle at least held in check by the machinery available to ensure good farming and land management. There is also a statutory provision, which has not yet been put into operation, but which can become operative if considered necessary, controlling the splitting up of farms by sale.

Mr. VAN ROSSEM mentioned the work now being done by Professor Meyers of Leiden University in the Netherlands toward revision of the code of civil laws. It should be expected that a revision of the inheritance laws will also be considered. Although a wise inheritance policy for agricultural land could be considered an important step toward prevention of further fragmentation of farm land, so far agricultural interests have not taken any steps on this issue. This is probably mainly due to the fact that the laws governing inheritance are deeply embedded in the habits and customs of the people. It will probably be very difficult indeed to change these laws, as religious sentiments are also involved. It is even questionable whether a change of the inheritance laws would change the customs now existing in the field of inheritance of land. The basic fact remains that in certain parts of the country an excess agricultural population leads to the continuous subdivision of land. An effective educational program should point out to the people that an agricultural holding of an economic size cannot be subdivided without seriously endangering the living standard of the farmers. Attempts should be made to encourage the small farmers to break with the custom for their sons to commence work on the farm as soon as they have completed the required elementary schooling at the age of fourteen. When the children are grown up they are small farmers by profession and they cannot learn another trade any more. In the small farm regions, schools should be established where the boys can learn an occupation which enables them to find a job in the nonagricultural industries. An effective industrialization program is of the highest importance. Mention was also made of the possibilities which lie in a change in the law governing death duties. Death duties in the Netherlands have reached a high level and now play an important part in the financial arrangements which have to be made after the death of a person. It requires little imagination to state that a substantial reduction of the death duties on an owner-operated farm when this is passed on to only one son might keep the farmers from having the farm divided up in equal portions after his death. Arrangements could be worked out also for tenant-operated farms. Mr. van Rossem was of the opinion that a heavily mortgaged farm resulting from the equal portion system represented no very satisfactory solution to the problem of the subdivision of land. The consequences of the inheritance laws are worthy of study by agriculturalists, and this should not be left to legal authorities alone. The issue is in fact a sociological problem with far-reaching economic consequences.

Mr. Schiller suggested that in many instances neither inheritance theory nor inheritance law will square with practice and that the latter, representing what actually takes place, warrants the most careful consideration by this group.

Mr. Natra observed that, in his opinion, the problem of land use in Thailand may be less severe than elsewhere inasmuch as there still exist reserves of unimproved wasteland. Although no legal restraints are now applied in Thailand to inheritance, he thought that legislation of some type may be required in the future.

Messrs. El-Ricaby and Samara outlined some of the salient features of Islamic law as it affects inheritance in Syria. The son receives from the father double the share of the daughter and a widow one-fourth of the property if there are children, one-half if there are none. In the case of state lands and in the case of the miri (the title to which belongs to the state and which in the European sense is not held fully by the occupier) inheritance laws divide the right equally among male and female. No minimum limit exists for the size of any landholding. These have in some cases become very small. An estimated 1.2 million hectares (roughly 3 million acres) are held in units smaller than 10 hectares each. The recent constitution of Syria contemplates a maximum size of holding to be set by statute, and a draft now under consideration sets such limits at 50 hectares for irrigated land and 500 hectares for nonirrigated land. Heirs cannot be cut off by will, and even though the father be deceased, grandchildren under Syrian law, as under American, inherit the father's share from the grandfather. Prior to 1909 trees were inherited in accordance with the Moslem law, while the miri land itself was inherited on equal share basis. After 1909 the trees were subjected to the miri inheritance.

Mr. Fakher outlined the major problems in Iran as arising not from those lands where legal ownership is separate from the actual farming of the land and where sub-division by inheritance does not directly affect the pattern of farming but from owner-operated holdings. Specifically, he said, farm families are large. Children customarily stay with the family and work on the farm. All of them are entitled, under the law of inheritance, to a share from the land. Productivity and income are low. Since life expectancy is low among this group, there is a strong probability that the heir will in turn pass his farm on in perhaps a dozen years (after becoming legally old enough to own land), and that minor children will inherit it. Consequently, a considerable fraction of these farms is at any given time in the hands of individuals not yet competent to manage them and farm them properly. This discussion also dealt with the necessity of maintaining the farm enterprise as a whole, capital goods as well as land. Moslem law distinguishes between movable and immovable objects, and under Iranian law the shares of the heirs in the two categories may be different. Thus the wife shares in the movable objects but not in certain immovable ones.

A specific instance of application of Iranian land policy was presented. By royal edict certain Crown lands were ordered sold to private individuals under long-term payment provisions. Among the interesting problems raised by this disposition were the following:

1. If long-term payments run for twenty-five years, who will meet the residual payments after the farmer's death?

2. What is the minimum economic size of farm to be created? This is a matter requiring a perfectly definite answer, yet it depends upon type of farming, productivity, skill of management, and other factors which cannot be arbitrarily determined.

3. Since there were more people desiring land than the available lands could carry, selections must be made on the basis of qualifications and ability. Yet the probability must be recognized that the land will pass to others within the purchase period. What guarantee can there be of continuing competence?

In assessing these problems, a fivefold concept of essential farming elements was suggested, consisting of land, water, labor, seed, and equipment.

Mr. Astorga described a limitation in Chile on transfers of land *inter vivos,* chiefly because, as a result of speculative holdings around the cities, land was being held out of agricultural production. In this way the population centers have progressively suffered the loss of their normal, legitimate areas of supply. The law now prohibits sale of land in portions smaller than fifteen hectares (thirty-seven acres) without permission from the government. Concerning inheritance after death, the very rigid laws of inheritance tend on the one hand to facilitate breaking up of the latifundia, or large estates. On the other hand the same inheritance provisions tend to break parcels of economic size into tracts that are too small. A study now in progress will re-examine inheritance provisions and ways by which the size of holdings might be protected. Mr. Astorga expressed interest in the English plan whereby the state asserts its interest in sound management and good husbandry on the farm.

Mr. Costa indicated that the purpose in present legislative trends in France is to give preferential treatment to the heir who lives on the land, provided he continues to live on the land and provided his farm is an economic unit. Decisions on this latter point, made by the local prefect, are inherently difficult and are constantly becoming more so by virtue of the effects of machine cultivation. A professional group interested in the scientific study of agriculture, the SESTO, is now attempting to arrive at some recommendations for objective standards for farm size, for ascertaining full employment of a farm family, and for evaluating land productivity under machine methods.

Mr. Jha sketched the basis of inheritance and land problems existing in the United Provinces of India. By far the large majority of land is held in three-acre to four-acre units. Ninety-four per cent of the farm units are smaller than ten acres, in his view a practical minimum for economic farming. The minimum suggested by recent legislation of six and one-fourth acres as an economic unit is larger than 85 per cent of the farms—37.8 per cent of cultivators work less than one acre each.

For more than a hundred years there has been interest in separate legislation concerning tenancy rights, as distinct from proprietary rights. A committee report of 1847 made the following three recommendations along these lines:

1. The smallest cultivated unit should be a "survey field"—a unit of assessment deriving from the area that a pair of bullocks could efficiently cultivate, of the order of four acres of good rice land and varying to perhaps eight or ten acres of dry land.

2. When occupant of a survey unit died, one heir only should inherit.

3. Tenancy rights to the entire survey unit should be transferred, i.e., the whole unit should go in order for any rights at all to pass.

No actual steps were taken to carry out these recommendations, chiefly because they left no provision for younger sons and other dependents. Nevertheless, since 1847 all Indian states have made attempts of one sort or another such as the following, largely without success, to prevent excessive subdivision: (1) maximum limit on size of holding, an effort to find some additional land; (2) limitations on transfer of tenancy rights, e.g., permitted only to another of the same village; (3) where total area of tenant's

holding falls below a set minimum, the holding to be held at law indivisible.

With respect to the United Provinces specifically, he outlined the following provisions of the Act of 1950 which are intimately related to the inheritance process. This act is now being tested in the courts.

1. Sales are prohibited to anyone who already has thirty acres or who, with the proposed purchase, would have more than thirty acres.

2. Holdings smaller than six and one-fourth acres are to be held indivisible.

3. Where two-thirds of the cultivators of uneconomic holdings in any one village (which usually runs from one thousand to fifteen hundred acres total) desire to form a co-operative, the remaining third are obliged to join.

4. Sublease of holdings are prohibited.

Mr. Tep Youth characterized one-half of the farms of Cambodia as poor. Fifty per cent of owners have less than one hectare, 10 per cent have two to three hectares, 5 per cent have three to five hectares. Other holdings run between five and fifty hectares; very large holdings are rare. Subsistence cultivation is a common pattern, occasionally supplemented by off-farm labor. No laws restrict the inheritance of land or the size of holding, and heirs commonly make arrangements within the family. Since about 1948, a beginning has been made in the introduction of machinery. Although no agricultural co-operatives exist, they may offer a means for purchasing and maintaining machinery, and the government is now studying this possibility.

Mr. von Dietze, in summarizing important points of view that appeared in the different statements, suggested that we have to see that inheritance should not lead to an excessive subdivision of land. Out of this major point of view, a series of problems arises. These problems are set forth in outline form below.

I. How can inheritance be avoided altogether?

  A. By a joint family system. Its disintegration has taken place gradually, or has been brought about suddenly, as, for example, in the Stolypin land reform of 1906–14. Should we say that a joint family-system does no longer present a form of land tenure feasible in our days and that individual ownership by a family head is to be preferred?

  B. By corporation systems, as they are being tried in India or in Puerto Rico.

  C. By private landlords who, in feudal times, were owners of the land operated by tenants as well as of the equipments of peasant farms.

  D. By state ownership of the land. This leads to socialist or even communist systems of land tenure.

II. Where inheritance takes place:

  A. Should the inheritance laws be compulsory or should they give freedom? The Roman law gave freedom in making wills in this particular. In this regard, the French Code Civil is not based on Roman law. Most of the European Codes contain a combination of compulsory rules with a certain freedom of disposal either by will or *inter vivos*. In French Law, the compulsory portion is a little higher than in German Civil Law. Moreover, in France all children are necessarily co-heirs of the land, while in Germany the compulsory portion consists in a share of the value of the estate. Instances of nearly complete compulsion were *Reichserbhofe* and *Fideicommiss*.

  B. Generally, the inheritance laws should be in harmony with the traditions and the feelings of the rural population, especially if they are compulsory. If they give freedom of disposal, the actual situation may widely differ from the rules the codes provide for intestate successions. Harmony with the feelings of the population concerned is particularly important where those feelings are supported by religious teachings and commandments.

  C. To preserve the farm as a current unit of production is an economic point of view. It is of major importance for a satisfactory situation on the land. But the human point of view, appreciating the family traditions as the basis of social life, as it is advocated by anthropologists for the British Colonies, should not be quite overlooked.

  D. Indivisibility of farms is to be distinguished from the indivisibility of consolidated lots of land. Undivided farms are incompatible with an equal succession of all children, while consolidated lots of land may be preserved undivided even when each child gets an equal share in the land. However, there are great practical difficulties which should be dealt with in the Working Party on Land Consolidation during the third week of this conference.

  E. Even within an individual country, the inheritance law need not be uniform for all regions or for all sizes of holdings. It may be advisable to have different rules in various regions, or for land operated by part-time farmers, for medium-size farms, and for large estates.

  F. In the case of large estates the inheritance law can bring about or induce their subdivision.

Mr. von Dietze then described the Prussian Rentengut (ownership arrangements of the rental holding type), answering a good many questions. In the eighties, Prussia—as did other European countries—embarked on a policy of creating small holdings, some on newly reclaimed land, most of them by subdividing large estates. For that purpose the Prussian government refrained from reviving divided ownership, but created a new type of ownership, e.g., the Rentengut. Its holder was made an individual owner, but under the following conditions:

1. He had to pay annuities for a period of up to sixty-nine years. As long as these annuities were not paid off fully he practically could not mortgage his holding to other creditors without the consent of the public corporation that had laid out the small holdings.

2. This consent, moreover, was necessary for selling or leasing the holding to strangers and for splitting it.

3. If the small holder violated the rules of good husbandry, the named corporation could repurchase the holding. In fact, this happened very seldom, but indirectly, this right of repurchase had some good effects.

4. The Rentengut was under a special inheritance law. Its rules were not far from what had been practiced by rural families on medium-size farms for centuries. They were binding only in case of intestate succession.

Under this inheritance law, there was no right of primogeniture. But provision was made that one child could take over the holding without incurring too high a debt to his brothers and sisters. To this purpose, this one child, whom the parents could choose, got a pre-share of one-third, and the holding was valued below the marked value, at a "brothers and sisters value." For instance, if the market value was 24,000 marks and there were four children, the assumed "brothers and sisters" value was 18,-000 marks, and the pre-share to one child was 6,000 marks. This left a remainder of 12,000 marks to be divided equally among the four children. Consequently, the burden of actual payment would be 9,000 marks.

Under civil law, the burden, in the case of intestate succession, would have been 18,000 marks, and even if there was a will cutting down the three other children to their compulsory portion, not less than 9,000 marks.

Though the Rentengut was introduced for newly created small holdings, its application was extended to old holdings whose owners agreed to its terms, e.g., in order to get rid of creditors whose conditions were harsher than those of the government. In Eastern Germany, up to 1933 altogether roughly 5 per cent of the agricultural area came under Rentengut law.

Mr. Hill was asked to comment on the English Small Holdings Acts as a supplement to Mr. von Dietze's summary of ways in which inheritance is avoided entirely. It was pointed out that these Acts do not impinge directly on inheritance, but were rather the result of legislative attention beginning in 1892 to the problem of land hunger. Recently the principle of meeting land hunger has been somewhat altered to that of providing a means whereby agricultural workers may become farmers on their own account. Administered by the County Councils, the program has since its inception, provided some 26,000 holdings in an aggregate area of about 250,000 acres. The authorities buy land in the open market, provide necessary fixed equipment, and set a fair rental based on open market rentals. Since land rentals in England are insufficient to return all of the calculated annual costs—interest on the investment, amortization on buildings, maintenance, and improvements—the annual deficit which may at the present time run as high as 180 pounds per holding per year is met out of public funds, 75 per cent by the national government, 25 per cent from local rates. The deficit runs very roughly equal to the rental. The tenant has absolute security of tenure, subject to stipulations of good husbandry and satisfactory production, during his lifetime. On his death the holding is assigned by the County Council to the best qualified man from the list of applicants, preference being given to agricultural workers over other applicants.

MR. LE RICHE outlined the Gezira scheme used in a certain large-scale irrigation area in the Sudan. Lands are leased for a period of forty years with option of renewal (where for one reason or another they are not purchased outright) from private owners by the government. In turn the lands are subleased to individual farm operators, with annual renewals. The state assumes the role of lessee to overcome fractionation of ownership resulting from the Islamic code. When an owner of a share dies, occupancy of the land is not affected, no matter how numerous his heirs. The rent paid by the state is based on an appraisal of the original value of the dry land, nearly all of which lay fallow. The government assumes responsibility for dams and irrigation works and supervises its sub-lessees closely, stipulating, for example, the crop rotation and fertilizers to be used. It was noted that almost the entire present value of the land held under these arrangements is a function of water supply rather than of land alone. The original owners, where they were actually on the land, have been given preference in leases. The rentals paid to the state are a 40 per cent share of the cash crop, cotton.

MR. EL-RICABY elucidated further the Syrian practices on the state-held miri land. A three-year lease with option to buy the right to use (but not ownership) of tracts up to fifty hectares is given, subject to certain conditions: (1) punctual payment of small, frequent ten or fifteen yearly installments; (2) building a dwelling and dwelling on the land itself; (3) planting trees.

Priority is given to local peasants on state domain lands, and the rights of use, once acquired, can be bequeathed, subject to the miri provisions described in an earlier session. It was noted that the miri institution

was abolished in Egypt over a century ago.

MR. FAKHER described the projected program, by his Imperial Majesty the King of Iran, which will ultimately affect some three thousand selected villages, in the best agricultural areas and covering in the aggregate one-fifteenth of the total arable area of the country. Purchase payments are nominal, running perhaps 40 per cent of what they would be if he were a tenant. The discussion brought out several further aspects: that no restraint on the Islamic rights of bequest is involved; that water, being essential to land but not divisible as the land is, offers a possible means of indirect control and a powerful stimulus to co-operative institutions. It was pointed out that there are certain governmental regulations in Iran, that the state may make recommendation for improvement of land and, should the owner fail to comply, the County Council may do so, at the expense of the owner, in certain cases.

MR. PONCE DE LEÓN stated two problems of central interest in the discussion: (1) Is it true that inheritance frequently gives rise to excessive subdivision? (2) Is control of inheritance in fact a way to control this problem? Concerning villages in Peru, he said the country is large but decidedly broken up. The coastal area is sandy and dry, with some very fertile arable land lying along the streams and in the foothills. The Sierra, the backbone of the Andes, also has scattered cultivated lands in the valleys lying at elevations from 9,000 to 20,000 feet. Erosion is a problem, as is transportation. The third region, on the east, is jungle, with very scattered population, great difficulty of transport and communication, and with a very small share of the land under cultivation. The Peruvian tradition is one of deep attachment to the land, and frequent disagreement is met among heirs.

In response to questions from the group, village lands were described as a special aspect of Peruvian culture with a long history. The ancient Incas based land division on family, redistributing fields each year among families according to an appraisal of needs, i.e., an "economic unit," in modern terms, adapted to the family. The Spanish conquerors undertook to impose fixed measures of land and permanent distribution, and the ancient institution of tupu fell into disuse.

The ancient system of agriculture of the Incas was phenomenally successful, with hillsides terraced in cut stone, with bridges and canals, and with more than sixty species of plants in cultivation, including potatoes, corn, and quinua. Under the ancient system there was no great disparity between rich and poor, but the old system of land distribution according to family needs was eliminated, even while the latifundia were being created.

The republic is pledged to break up the great landholdings. Land reform is likely to be on a small-holding basis, however, rather than on the ancient basis of village and of family within the village.

MR. STEWART observed that in Mexico, the ejidos, or village lands, today constitute half the agricultural land in Mexico. Discussion brought out that though the name persists, these have been modified in major respects from the original village holdings to which the name of ejidos originally applied.

MR. PONCE DE LEÓN observed further that some scattered Peruvian villages still hold lands in common, but that a more widespread heritage of the past is the community spirit of mutual help. The government's attempt to organize community co-operative sheep-raising has been made more successful by the resemblance to ancient tradition.

MR. BEUSCHER described the Tenant Purchase Act of the middle thirties in the United States. The Farm Security Administration of the federal government sold land under lease-purchase contracts running

forty years and containing stipulations for adherence to a management program on the farm set by FSA. Although the total acreage was negligible, these provisions are of interest as a means which might conceivably have been used to prevent subdivision of the farm unit by inheritance during the forty years.

In contrast, the practical means by which undue splintering is prevented under the common law in customary use in the United States starts with the concept of the heirs' "undivided shares." The state does not assume any initiative in dividing either title or income from property. Each of the heirs has an undivided share, and each has a right in the absence of the assertion by the others of their rights, to the whole farm. From the legal dogma that all have equal rights to all of the farm—a logical impossibility—follows the practical and socially useful consequence that the heirs are forced to come to agreement. If they do not, their recourse lies in the courts. Their lawyer will tell them that it lies within the discretion of the judge whether to divide the farm into four separate units and that in all but rare cases the judge will refuse to divide the farm. Instead, he will order it sold at auction by the sheriff to the highest bidder and will order the proceeds of the sale to be divided among the heirs, deducting court costs, sheriff's fees, etc. At this point, almost without exception, the disputants see that it is in their own interest to arrange among themselves to operate the farm or to sell the farm privately as a unit. It does tend to burden the farm, it was noted, with a heavy indebtedness, but tends to prevent undue subdivision.

MR. SCHILLER pointed out that usually one believes that inheritance subdivision must lead to rapid fragmentation of land. The circumstances must be examined in each case, however, in ascertaining whether this is actually the consequence. Investigations over the last one hundred years in some communities, where inheritance subdivision by tradition and custom has taken place, have shown that the average size of holdings and of parcels in this period has remained about constant. The breaking up of holdings has been balanced by other tendencies toward consolidating holdings and an equilibrium has resulted. Nevertheless, even in areas where such balance has been attained, as farms are consolidated into larger units better adapted to modern farming practices, the tendency toward dispersion becomes stronger while larger field units can more easily be subdivided than small parcels prevailing before. From this a need for legal protection arises. In some parts of Germany there are legal provisions setting a limit, for instance one-fifth of one acre, beyond which subdivision of field parcels is not allowed. Furthermore, German postwar legislation provides that title to land cannot be registered without approval of the local agricultural agency. Although this approval cannot be denied in cases of inheritance subdivision, there is a certain degree of effectiveness in avoiding unreasonable and unjustified subdivision of land.

LAND REFORM AND AGRICULTURAL PRODUCTION

Report of the Working Party[1]

Chairman, *Rainer Schickele*

LAND REFORMS should be designed to give farm families greater security on the land, better opportunities for education, personal development, and self-expression, and higher living levels. To achieve these goals, and at the same time contribute to the economic progress of the country as a whole, land reforms should disrupt production processes as little as possible and should facilitate increased agricultural production over the years ahead.

The discussion brought out the following principles and fundamental issues which should be taken into account in the planning of land reforms. Changes in land tenure systems and their probable effect upon agricultural production are discussed under three main headings: (1) changes in tenure status of farm families, (2) adjustments in the farm sizes and numbers of farm families, and (3) market deliveries and capital formation as affected by land reforms.

There is, of course, much interaction between these three aspects of land tenure policy. Details of legislative, financial, and institutional improvements must be determined by each country in the light of its cultural, political, and economic peculiarities. But it is hoped that many costly mistakes might be avoided if the following principles and issues are realistically considered as land reform programs are developed in the various countries.

Changes in Tenure Status

Many land reform programs call for a transfer of land ownership to the tenants or laborers now occupying the land. The aspiration of farmers to own their land appears to be almost universal. Under some circumstances, however, the mere transfer of ownership to the farmers may bring a decrease in production. What are these circumstances, and how can adverse effects upon production be avoided?

There are three typical situations requiring different types of measures of those areas where, at least for the time being, no major changes in the total number of farm families in a certain area are contemplated.

NO LANDLORD SUPERVISION OR CAPITAL

There are many areas where tenant farmers cultivate the land and operate their enterprise on their own, without supervision or help from the landlord. The landlord furnishes the land and all or part of the improvements upon the land such as buildings, irrigation systems, etc. Under these conditions, landlords usually re-invest none, or very little, of their rental income in land improvements or working capital.

√ Transfer of ownership to the tenants is likely to stimulate agricultural production, where the landlords are merely rent receivers, and the tenants have customarily provided implements, draft power, seeds, etc. and have managed their farming units with little or no supervision from the landlords. The greater security and the incentives of ownership will induce farmers to improve the land and, if possible, production methods. Examples: Japan, India, Paraguay, Colombia, USA.

Tenant rights legislation in economically highly developed areas in Europe has shown that by providing tenants with security of occupancy, freedom of management and rent controls, the same beneficial effect on production can be achieved without transferring ownership to the tenants. Under such conditions, tenants sometimes prefer to continue renting the land instead of using savings to acquire ownership title. Such a situation has the advantage of avoiding expropriation and compensation of landlords and the attendant financial burden on the government and on the tenant and of reducing the danger of subdividing farms through inheritance into uneconomic units or of speculative land sales on the part of new farmer-owners. Also, the sizes of farm units may be more readily adapted to changing conditions under tenancy than under farmer-ownership. Examples: England, France.

In many areas, the alternative of a tenant rights and rent control program may be politically less feasible and less acceptable to farmers than ownership transfer, because land ownership has become a symbol for security on the land, for social status, and for greater well-being. Examples: Caribbean Islands, several Latin-American and Asiatic countries.

The discussion brought out this principle: Where the landowners contribute little or no capital and management to the production process, transfer of ownership to the farmers will have no adverse effect upon production, and is likely to stimulate production incentives—provided the debt and tax payments do not exceed the former rent.

WITH LANDLORD CAPITAL AND SUPERVISION

Where the landlords actively contribute to the production process by furnishing equipment, seed, fertilizer, livestock, etc., and by giving managerial guidance, merely the transfer of ownership to the tenants or farm laborers is likely to reduce the production, because the tenants or workers are accustomed to being supervised and depend upon the landlord for various forms and amounts of capital. Such experiences have been observed in the Philippines, the Caribbean Islands, and other countries.

The most important requirement for success under these conditions is that tenants be given, along with a better tenure status, effective assistance in improving their skills and management and in obtaining necessary capital for operation.

If under such conditions tenants are to be given ownership, provisions for technical guidance and production credit are essential for sustained production. Examples: Paraguay, Costa Rica.

Various alternatives to an immediate ownership transfer to farm families might be considered, such as the following:

1. Establishment of co-operative farming enterprises, with the government furnishing necessary supervision, technical guidance and production credit, and with as democratic a participation as possible on the part of the co-operator-farmers. Title to the land might be retained by the government at least until the continuation and improvement of the production process are assured. Competent supervisory and technical personnel will often be a limiting factor. Example: India.

2. A program of tenant rights providing tenant security, rent controls, and supplemental production credit for tenants, coupled with technical advice by government agencies furnished directly to tenants. The ownership may remain with the land-

lords (as in England, France and various other countries), or may rest in the government (as in the Gezira scheme in the Sudan).

3. A program of profit sharing among workers, the manager, and the owner. This may be applicable especially in plantation agriculture. Example: Puerto Rico. The owner can be the government or a private concern. Such a program may also provide for small garden plots and houses to be owned by the plantation workers. In Costa Rica, this was done in some areas in order to attract and keep a sufficient number of workers for the plantations—however, without the profit-sharing device.

The discussion brought out this principle: Where the landowners fulfilled major production functions by contributing capital and management, a land reform program should provide for someone to continue furnishing such contributions to the farmers or workers at least as effectively as the old owners, and at least until the farmers have become sufficiently skilled to assume the managerial responsibility themselves. This will usually involve government sponsored technical guidance and production credit as an essential phase of the program.

Adjustments in Farm Sizes

In many areas, land reform requires redistribution of land into different operating units, which often involves changes in production methods and types of farming. In some areas, farm sizes are so large and so extensively utilized that a larger number of families could make an acceptable living from the land than are now present, even without requiring much additional capital equipment. There are other areas where farm sizes are so small that no mere change in tenure status could lift the people above their present level of abject poverty. These situations raise the issue of determining maximum and minimum size standards for

settlement and tenure improvement programs.

All the issues and principles of ownership and tenancy rights and their effect upon production discussed in the previous section apply here likewise.

ECONOMIC FARMING UNITS

Wherever large estates (latifundia) are broken up into smaller units or undeveloped lands are reclaimed for new settlement, maximum limits are set for the newly created holdings in order to provide opportunities for as many farm families as the land can support. Often, minimum limits are also established so as to prevent the creation of many under-size units on which the farm families could not support themselves. The subdivision of large estates into too many uneconomic units has often resulted in the failure of the program and in severe hardship for the settlers. Examples can be found in the agrarian history of many countries in Europe and the Americas.

Too frequently have these size limits been determined by political expediency and population pressure, with insufficient regard to physical characteristics of the land and economic conditions of production.

The following criteria for determining size limits should be useful in developing a land distribution program.

✓ Land productivity varies widely even within small areas. An allotment of ten hectares of very fertile soil may represent an economic size several times larger than one of one hundred hectares of poor grazing land. The size ranges established by law have often been too narrow to allow for wide variations in land productivity.

✓ Intensity of farming, especially with respect to capital application in the form of seeds, fertilizer, machinery, and livestock, is an important factor. An increase in capital application can increase the economic size of a holding on the same physical area. Whenever such an increase in intensity of farming over the present customary level is contemplated as a basis for determining the area size-limits of holdings, specific provisions should be made in the program to make production credit and technical guidance available to farmers.

✓ The *level of living* which the minimum size of holding can be expected to support for an average farm family should not be lower than what farmers would consider reasonably satisfactory in the area. In no case should it be lower than what the modal group of farmers has experienced in the past.

✓ *Outside employment opportunities* in villages or on larger neighboring farms might justify the establishment of holdings smaller than would be needed without such sources of supplemental income. In developing a land distribution program for such part-time farming units, the reliability and remunerativeness of outside employment should be carefully appraised. Examples: Italy, USA.

The discussion brought out this principle: In establishing size limitations for land distribution programs, limits in terms of area (e.g., hectares) should be kept sufficiently flexible to allow for variations in land productivity, farming intensity, income requirements of farm families, and outside employment opportunities. Where possible, size limits should be expressed in terms of appraised land value—if these values reflect differences in land productivity and degree of intensivity of farming adequately. Example: India. Where size limits are established on the basis of more intensive farming, specific provisions for making production credit and technical guidance available to farmers are essential.

FLEXIBILITY IN FARM SIZES

Land distribution programs where the land was transferred to farmers in fee-simple ownership have often experienced poor results. Inheritance customs can lead to uneconomic subdivision and fragmentation (see France, Germany for instance); sale of the holding by the farmer-owner can lead to tenancy and to farm sizes much larger than needed to support a family adequately, thereby undoing what the land reform was intended to achieve. If the holdings are too small, farmers are in danger of getting forced into debt to a point where they lose their farms through foreclosure. Examples: USA, Costa Rica, Philippines, Haiti.

There may be various possibilities for meeting these dangers and facilitating adjustments in economic farm sizes (both with respect to area and capital intensity) in the various countries.

Government retention of certain rights in land may be feasible. For instance, the government may retain the right to purchase the farm when the owner wants to sell. The government then can resell the farm to another qualified farmer-owner or to neighboring owners for enlarging their under-size units. Another possibility might be for the government or a government supervised agency to retain ownership and to grant farmers long-time leases with security and fair rents designed so as to induce production incentives and interest in improving the land on the part of the farmer.

Prohibiting the sale of farms to nonfarmers, or giving farmers priority or an option to purchase ahead of any nonfarmer, is a method which may have some merit in certain areas. Examples: France, India, Japan. This, of course, will reduce the supply of private credit available to farmers for land purchase, and therefore will call for adequate government sponsored credit facilities.

Special farm enlargement loans enabling farmers on under-size holdings to purchase additional land have been used successfully. Example: USA. A related measure is the allotment of parts of an expropriated estate to neighboring under-size holdings so as to round them out into economic farm units. Example: Germany.

Discouragement or prohibition of hereditary subdivision below critical size limits might be desirable. This may involve provisions for real estate credit or for related tenancy as a means of compensating co-heirs, and statutory changes in inheritance laws.

CO-OPERATIVE ORGANIZATIONS

There are conditions where, at least for a transition period, some co-operative arrangements might be used to prevent decreases in agricultural production and to actively hasten the introduction of better production methods. Particularly where the holdings are of necessity too small and where production methods have been very primitive, co-operative measures can be very helpful in the following two respects:

1. Fuller utilization of scarce machinery and other capital equipment through co-operative use can increase production for human use, and hence the income of farmers on under-size units. Saving of draft animals, better tillage with larger machinery, uniform use of superior seed and breeding stock can contribute substantially to production on under-sized units. Examples: India, several European countries.

2. Developing managerial skill can be enhanced by co-operative methods. Technical guidance and introduction of superior production methods can be made more effective. It is important, however, that individual incentives to work and learn should be preserved as much as possible. Active participation by the individual farmers in the co-operative activities, and rewards proportional to their individual effort should be deliberately encouraged.

The discussion brought out this principle: Care should be taken that in the process of land distribution sufficient flexibility be provided for desirable adjustments in farm sizes according to production and family income needs, and for protection against uneconomic subdivision of holdings, land speculation, unwarranted foreclosures, and reestablishment of large estates and insecure tenancy. For this purpose, the government may be justified to retain certain rights in the land, but not more than necessary to assure the continuation of economic farming units and efficient production methods. Where holdings are very small and production methods primitive, co-operative organization of certain farming functions can at least in part overcome the disadvantage of under-size units and hasten the adoption of more efficient production methods.

Market Deliveries and Capital

Land reforms usually entail changes in rental rates and land taxes, which in turn may affect the delivery of agricultural production to the market on the one hand and production incentives of the farmers on the other. These aspects are particularly important in areas where agriculture is not highly commercialized, where consumption habits of the farm population are traditionally fixed, and where the urban section of the economy offers but few and exorbitantly priced goods and services of use to farmers.

In discussing the effect of changes in rents or taxes, let us assume that where expropriation of landlords is involved, the fiscal arrangements for compensation are handled separately, by issuance of bonds or payments of cash out of the government's treasury.

RENT, TAXES, MARKET DELIVERIES

In areas where the tenant or small owner uses most of his share of the land's produce directly for his own family livelihood, deliveries of rent, debt, or tax payments by the farmers constitute the bulk of farm production entering into market channels and available to the country's nonfarm population or export. This proportion in many areas has been between one-half and two-thirds of the farmer's crops, in other areas higher or lower, depending upon productivity of the land and socio-political factors. The share remaining for the farmer is often so small that it barely feeds him and his family, leaving but little that he may bring to the market in exchange for nonfarm goods for his use. Hence, for generations, many farmers in these areas have become accustomed to a very low living standard providing only bare necessities of life.

If these deliveries in payment of rent, or interest and amortization on the land purchase loan, or taxes are reduced, the amount of agricultural production coming on the market may be affected in various ways.

Farm production may remain the same, but as a result of lower rents or taxes,[2] the farm family can consume a larger proportion of the land's produce directly, by eating more and better and building up some food reserves for lean periods. This reduces market deliveries, at least in the short run, and forces nonfarm people to bid up prices, import more or export less of agricultural products, and consume less themselves.

Farm production may increase, if not immediately, perhaps after a year or more, as a result of the farmer's better nutrition, health and work capacity, his greater incentive to improve the land (particularly if he has become an owner), his greater personal interest in higher output, and the increase in prices of agricultural products as mentioned above. Market deliveries, however, will regain the former level only when the production increase has become at least as high as the increase in the farm family's home consumption, and if goods and services of use to the farmer are available in exchange for his land's produce. Herein lies the great importance of bringing city products, both for consumption such as movies, household goods, clothes, and for

production such as tools, fertilizer, high-grade seeds, within reach of farmers, in order to induce farmers to produce more and sell more in exchange for goods they need and want. If the farmer cannot buy such goods, he has no incentive to produce more than he needs for his own home use. This was demonstrated even in highly commercialized areas during the last war and postwar years, as in France, Germany, and other countries whose industries were badly damaged.

Farm production may decrease, if rents or taxes are reduced to a very low level, and farmers lack ability or interest in increasing their own income and consumption. With smaller rents or taxes, they can afford to produce less and still maintain their former rate of consumption. To prevent such a decline in production and market deliveries, the government should provide means for stimulating farmers' incentives to produce more and improve their living standards, so that the self-interest of farmers is awakened to replace the compulsory force of high rents or taxes. Technical guidance, education, and availability of city goods and services for farmers can become effective means for changing traditional consumption habits and stimulating production incentives.

The type of rent or taxes may influence production incentives. If it is a fixed amount, the farmer's incentive to produce more is stronger than if it is a proportional amount of the crop. Payment in money is often more desirable than in physical produce, because it brings the farmer in direct contact with the market and develops his marketing and bargaining skills. However, since in many areas farmers are illiterate or very poorly educated, they are entitled to protection from unscrupulous dealers and merchants.

We discussed the various possible results of a reduction in rent or tax payments because this is the usual direction of change under recent land reforms. These recent reductions in the share farmers must deliver have been very substantial, between one-third and one-half in some areas. Examples: Japan, India, Argentina. In areas of tense agrarian unrest, rents have often been so high that they left farmers in dire poverty, a situation which did not stimulate initiative and production incentives, but rather made for low production as farmers had nothing left for land improvement and often felt that higher production brought more advantage to the landlords than to themselves.

The discussion brought out this principle: The reduction of rent or tax payments in areas where farmers' market contacts are few and not highly commercialized is likely to bring about a reduction in market deliveries of agricultural products, unless provisions are made for stimulating farmers' interest and ability to produce more and sell more in the market. Such a decline in market delivery could seriously damage the nonfarm sector of the economy. Hence, it is important to accompany a reduction in payments with measures designed to induce farmers to produce more and sell in the market an additional volume of produce at least equal to the payment reduction. Efforts of government and trade to bring an increased amount of goods farmers need and want into the rural areas and at prices in reach of farmers promise to be most effective for this purpose. Movies, clothes and household goods for consumption, simple tools, farm equipment, fertilizers and improved seeds for production, have now or will soon have a great appeal to farmers. Technical advice on improved production techniques can hasten the awakening of farmers' interest in new types of capital equipment, fertilizer, seeds and breeding stock. No land reform program should miss any opportunity for awakening such interest.

RENT, TAXES, CAPITAL FORMATION [3]

In large areas of the world, the rate of net capital formation on the part of most farmers has been close to zero for centuries. Their income was too small to allow for savings, and often they lacked technical skills, education, managerial incentives to invest whatever little savings they might have made into land improvements and better production methods. The function of capital formation, therefore, was left in the hands of the landlords, creditors, and the government.

Where land ownership was concentrated in the hands of large estates or wealthy landlords or the governing class, only a tiny proportion of the rents or taxes was used for the immediate necessities of life by these owners. Much of their income went into luxurious mansions, jewelry, works of art, and many other nonproductive uses characteristic of wealthy leisure classes. A considerable part of their land income may have been invested in domestic and foreign industries and contributed to capital formation there. Some of the land income was, at times, invested in land improvements, irrigation works, and various kinds of capital equipment for agriculture. This rate of reinvestment of land income into agriculture on the part of the landowners has usually been quite small indeed, otherwise agricultural production techniques would not have remained so primitive over such vast areas of the globe.

Any major increase in agricultural production requires an increase in capital investment in one form or another. Such new capital formation should be facilitated by any land reform program.

If rent or tax payments by farmers are reduced, the rate of capital investment in agriculture may be affected in various ways.

The investment function may shift from the landlord or previous owner to the tenant or new farmer-owner. To bring about such a shift, the farmer who remains a tenant must feel secure in his occupancy, and his investment in the land must be protected by appropriate laws or terms of contract; the farmer who becomes an owner must be made to realize that ownership implies the function of investment in the farm enterprise and that he can no longer look toward the landlord for capital investment. Regardless of the farmer's tenure status, he will usually need technical guidance and production credit to fulfill this function. Capital investment in agriculture by landlords whose tenants have been given rights of security and compensation for improvements and whose rental receipts have been reduced will drop sharply as a result of these tenure changes in most cases. Investments by expropriated landlords, of course, cease altogether. Whether the net rate of capital investment after the tenure reform will be larger or smaller than before depends on (a) the amount formerly furnished by the landlord and (b) the farmer's income remaining after payment of rent, debts, or taxes and family living expenses. This farmer's excess income available for investment in the production process is bound to be very small indeed, especially on uneconomic sizes of farm units. Hence, special credit provision should accompany land reform programs.

The government may find it necessary, in many cases, to supplement the farmer's rate of investment by grants, production credit, or direct land improvement works. Without such a program, a land reform, however well designed otherwise, can hardly be expected to result in significant production increases.

Real-estate credit for financing ownership transfer is unproductive in itself; it does not provide the farmer with any operating capital and land improvements. For these, production credit must be extended, together with technical guidance.

Compensation for expropriated landlords, and reduced rents for remaining landlords, result in lower incomes of these groups and a virtual cessation of agricultural investment from this source in the affected area. This income reduction may also cause lower rates of investment elsewhere in the economy. The government, therefore, should stimulate increasing rates of investment by other groups and, if necessary, participate itself in capital formation in crucial fields of activities.

The discussion brought out this principle: Reduction in rent or debt payments to remaining or expropriated landlords will reduce their rate of capital investment within and outside of agriculture. Production investment by farmers is likely to increase, but in some areas probably not sufficiently to offset the investment decline from the former landlord group. This holds particularly where landowners contributed formerly considerable amounts of capital, and where the size of the farm units is very small. To facilitate production increases in agriculture, land reforms must be accompanied by public policies stimulating the rate of capital formation within as well as outside of agriculture.

APPRAISING THE ADEQUACY OF LAND TENURE
SYSTEMS FOR AGRICULTURAL PRODUCTION

Thomas F. Carroll

LAND TENURE is a complex set of relationships between men, embodying their various rights in the use of land. We want to look at land tenure from the point of view of agricultural production and to suggest ways in which the merits of alternative tenure institutions may be more intelligently judged. It is important, however, to realize from the start that the manner in which land is owned and the rights to its use distributed is intimately tied to many facets of life within every culture. The lower a society stands on the ladder of economic development, the greater the relative importance of land as the prime resource. In the so-called underdeveloped countries, the relationships of land tenure are woven into the lives of most of the population with a thousand strands. Thus, in the areas where tenure problems seem to be most crying, their identification and solution is perhaps also most involved and difficult.

Since tenure systems form the institutional framework within which land is used, tenure is one of the basic factors which determines the efficiency of farm production. Over and beyond its role in production, tenure affects the social content of living of the farm population, and tenure is also closely bound up with the political institutions in every country. These three aspects of tenure, the economic, the social, and the political, are, of course, highly interrelated, but they are the customary points of view from which the adequacy of any tenure situation may be discussed.

The student of modern economics is interested primarily in how well the existing tenure system functions in terms of social welfare criteria. In such an approach there is room for a whole set of desiderata, ranging from efficiently produced food and fiber to such values as personal income distributions or the preservation of the nation's natural resources. Unfortunately, the tools for calculating the sum total of satisfaction under alternate tenure systems are lacking. Even if it were possible to express some of these values quantitatively, the complexities of translating available theoretical analysis into empirical work are baffling. This is the reason why it does not seem fruitful to discuss land tenure simultaneously from every angle. Much of the constant confusion in this field comes from our tendency to ask sweeping questions which we are not equipped to answer, such as: Is this or that particular system of tenure "better" for society? Are family farms desirable? Is communal tenure to be preserved? Is collective farming a "failure"? It seems much more meaningful, though by no means easy, to begin looking at land tenure institutions from specific points of view, such as their role as hindrances or facilitators in the farm production process, or in what way they contribute to certain social needs. By specializing in the analysis, our task of synthesis is greatly facilitated. Through such means we can hope not only to come up with practical guides for policy, in terms of certain goals, but also to be in a position to point up conflicts between various goals and thus present the alternative choices to society for policy making.

Perhaps it is well to state here that appraising social institutions, like anything else, is a comparative process. Land tenure systems are not good or bad, efficient or inefficient in themselves. They can only be judged adequately when compared to possible alternate systems, either already existing or as synthetic models which fulfill certain criteria more or less fully. Our primary criterion here will be sustained productive efficiency. We will attempt to help answer such questions as: Which of two existing tenure systems contributes the more to long-term productive farm practices? Is it likely that a proposed change in some tenure institution will increase agricultural production? It is immediately clear that even partial answers to such questions are enormously helpful in policy making. Even when social and political criteria predominate in attempting to change existing systems, society is always interested in what is likely to happen to production. Furthermore, one might advance the hypothesis that high production per person and concomitantly higher material income are not only directly or indirectly the lion's share of total welfare the world over but that in the more underdeveloped areas increased efficiency in farm production is a prerequisite to much of what is desired in the way of nonmaterial human goals.

How Tenure Affects Production

When we relate tenure to production, the usual difficulty in distinguishing between means and ends is largely resolved (or rather suspended). Our aim is to judge any land tenure institution from the way it contributes to the efficiency by which inputs (land, labor—including management—and capital) are transformed into farm products the community wants.[1] Thus, family farming or the "freehold system" is, in this context, not a goal in itself but only insofar as it is conducive to efficient farm practices. Similarly, tenancy, or more particularly share cropping, is not necessarily "bad" in itself but may be found wanting when submitted to the test of economic production efficiency (quite apart from any social desiderata).

There are various possible measures of farm efficiency. From the point of view of agriculture as a whole, long-run farm production per person has much to recommend it as the best single measure. High production per person is invariably associated with high income per person and is thus a criterion of general economic development. It is important to recognize, however, that the efficiency pattern of an individual farm depends on factor costs of which labor is only one. Although there are real conflicts in maximizing returns over costs between firms and agriculture as a whole, we are not here concerned with this difference.[2]

In an economy where prices are expected to reflect consumers' wishes and to guide the allocation of resources into productive channels, farmers can maximize their returns in a manner consistent with the wishes of society by (1) employing techniques of production and combining the productive agents in a way which will minimize their costs and by (2) extending the total scale of operations in a manner consistent with their costs and returns.

If the tenure system in some manner impedes these processes, we can say that production-wise it is imperfect.[3] In what way tenure affects these postulates of efficiency depends greatly on local conditions. In every culture and in every region tenure institutions and farming are linked up in a somewhat different manner. Yet perhaps it is possible to translate economic principles into more workable criteria, which, in general, could be applied in every part of the world. There have been several attempts to make such lists of criteria, although few are more than a random selection of economic and social means and ends.[4] They invariably include "security" to tenure, conservations, and "just" rewards for labor. We shall try to summarize most of the major criteria under three headings. In line with our objective, the list is made up of factors influ-

encing efficient production and contains social requirements only insofar as they *more
directly* relate to production. There is obviously no hard and fast rule for such a
division. Vertical social mobility of labor
for example is included because the functioning of an "agricultural ladder" by which
able men can ascend to entrepreneurial roles
is directly tied to the incidence of efficient
management. Our three major criteria are:
(1) economic size and layout of farms, (2)
human incentives and opportunities for sustained economic production, and (3) favorable conditions for capital formation and
productive investment.

Production Criteria of Tenure

ECONOMIC SIZE AND LAYOUT

To the extent that the size and layout of
farms is due to the prevailing systems of
tenure, a critical examination of tenure features yields valuable insights into the causes
of rural inefficiency the world over. It must
be remembered that farm size (economic,
not acreage) is often the result of factors
other than tenure alone. This is particularly
true in the areas where heavy population
pressure has resulted in very small farms.
By and large, within an agricultural region,
any tenure system operates through a characteristic pattern of farm sizes. Changes in
tenure relationships are likely to change this
pattern, and, conversely, farm sizes cannot
be moved closer to optima without calling
for tenurial alterations. This close interdependence needs to be studied closely, whenever appraisal of a particular tenure problem is attempted. The key question is:
Which one of the available choices of tenure
arrangements is most conducive to the establishment of optimum sized farm units?[5]
We need not be concerned here with techniques to determine optimum farm size.
Examples of too small or too large farms
at the ends of the scale are well known.

In the Central Valley of Chile both very

large and very small farms exist side by side.
From the point of view of farm management efficiency, the very large haciendas are
wasteful of land, while the minifundos
(small holdings) are wasteful of manpower.
Output per man on both types of farms is
lower than on medium-size properties. Both
extreme types of holdings are intimately
linked with certain historic tenure characteristics.[6]

It is not always easy to point out such
obvious economic deficiencies in the scale of
farming. Many of the tropical plantations
show high economic efficiency measured in
a variety of ways. In most places the argument against the plantation system is motivated by social considerations.[7]

A similar but somewhat more easily per-
ceivable criterion is the layout of farms.
Fragmentation and poor coherence of lands
belonging to production units is a frequent
hindrance to farm efficiency. In many places
such obstacles to production weigh heavily
against the existing tenure system.[8]

Examples of tenure-caused fragmentations
are common in all parts of the world. In
Europe inheritance customs according to
which the heirs demand the physical subdivision of the estate into parts of equal
value cause the well-known strip-farming effect. It is estimated that in France alone,
as a result of the equalitarian legal codes, 10
million hectares of land are excessively
broken up.[9]

INCENTIVES AND OPPORTUNITIES

Whatever the system of tenure, it must
provide the "decision makers" and all the
owners of resources with incentives to employ their resources fully and ingeniously.
There is no system of tenure which automatically assures such incentives. The role of
tenure for proper production incentives becomes crucial in the majority of situations
where ownership and farm operation are in
separate hands. "Who profits by a situation

in which a landlord will not repair a leaking roof because it leaks upon his tenant, and the tenant will not repair it because he expects to move to another farm before another season?"[10] Such problems are common in every country. Incentives must be present for all levels of farmers from owners down to day laborers. It is very important to find out how many and what kind of such productive incentives function through the tenure process.

Much of what is necessary for a proper set of farm incentives passes as "security of tenure." A certain amount of security in tenure arrangements has an unquestionably beneficial effect on long-term production practices such as maintenance of capital equipment, soil conservation, and proper animal husbandry.[11] Security of tenure also contributes to proper type-of-farming adjustments in line with the best environmental possibilities.

Another set of conditions within the realm of human relationships which have a great influence on production can be described as "occupational opportunities." It is good common sense to help those who have the best abilities and inclinations to take the most responsible places in farming. Top quality entrepreneurship and workmanship should be brought forward through the tenure process. For greater security of tenure and the proper type of productive incentives we ask for a certain measure of stability from a tenure system. For occupational opportunities, we would like the same system to be endowed with dynamic qualities as well.

Incentives and opportunities for responsible, intelligent, and productive farming seem to be most frequently deficient in situations where ownership and operation are in different hands. The largest body of tenure literature deals with landlord-tenant relationships. It is also in this field where perhaps the greatest amount of confusion and misinformation prevails. Social and economic considerations are jumbled, and no yardstick for scientific appraisal is applied. The simplest relevant rule of production economics requires that the returns to productive factors must be proportional to their respective contributions to the process.[12]

The role of tenure institutions in this postulate of efficiency is chiefly through the contractual relationships between the participants in farming: the owner, the manager, the tenant, the share-cropper, the inheritor, etc. Each ought to contribute to the sustained production process according to the best of his ability, reap proportionally the rewards, and share proportionally the risk involved.[13]

Closely linked with such incentives and opportunities is the question of how well the tenure system encourages farmers to keep abreast of rapidly changing technology, and to adjust their operations to dynamic economic conditions. The more developed a country is, the greater the significance of such flexibility. One of the most difficult things to change is the scale of operations. In countries where few alternative occupational opportunities exist and the population pressure is great, most farmers must continue to farm on a relatively small scale. In an expanding industrial economy, however, where there is a constant movement of labor out of agriculture, a lag develops between the actual scale of farming and the most economic size of units. Under these conditions the tenure system must not impede a more rapid changeover to increase the farm business. There are strong indications that a slower than desirable change in this direction is taking place in the United States.[14]

CAPITAL INVESTMENT

The third major set of factors which link the tenure structure to production involves capital investment in agriculture. In line with the general scope of this paper, we are not concerned with investment in agriculture vis-à-vis other branches of the economy. What we focus on is the way in which tenure institutions affected the most productive employment of available capital resources in farming. The chief criteria in this respect are the conditions which enable farmers to invest sufficient capital to complement their labor and land resources most productively.[15]

If the tenure system is such that a large portion of agriculture's earnings are diverted into unproductive expenditures, a change in tenure might bring about a better allocation of capital. This charge is levelled frequently against certain agricultural economies of the feudalistic type. Redistribution of income in this sense does not necessarily contribute toward increased productive efficiency of farming, but it may often do so. It all depends on what proportion of the new income will be used productively by the new recipients and on how much of it would be spent on purchasing consumers' goods or even leisure.[16] At any rate, the conditions of tenure which influence capital formation in the various sectors of agriculture are of major importance in determining farming efficiency.

Beside the criteria which ask that capital in the form of income be allocated within agriculture in a productive way, there are also other requirements directed toward facilitating the efficient absorption of outside capital. The institutions involved in the agricultural credit mechanism are not, strictly speaking, part of the tenure structure itself. Yet, tenure and credit are so closely interwoven that a given situation in one clearly determines the way in which the other can function and develop. To illustrate this point it is only necessary to recall that the customary way of inheriting land in many places (especially in Europe), in order to prevent fragmentation, is for the sole owner to go into debt to all the other heirs. This way the new owner might start out farming with a debt load that he will never be able to repay.[17]

There are many ways in which the tenure arrangement presents definite obstacles to the operation of a productive credit system. Nonexisting or unconfirmed titles, landlord-tenant contracts that offer little security, absenteeism, haphazard settlement, and other features of existing tenures are examples. Short-term leases, for instance, without adequate provisions for the sharing of benefits from unexhausted improvements limit the beneficial effects of a well-conceived source of outside credits. But on the other hand, the lack of sound credit or certain defects in the credit system itself frequently impede desirable changes in tenure arrangements and perpetuate the ills of inefficient land holdings. The examination of these problems is beyond the scope of this paper.

Taxation occupies a position vis-à-vis land tenure similar to that of credit. Although not directly a part of tenure systems, taxation policies are strongly influenced by them and, conversely, many of the maladjustments in tenure cannot be resolved before the tax policy is revised. An example of a situation where taxation and tenure are closely interdependent is the often negligible land tax in areas where land is held for nonproduction purposes as investment or for prestige reasons. Such is the case in many Latin American countries, where often tracts of good land close to markets are cultivated extensively or not at all, while poorer and often more erodable land is destructively exploited.

How to Apply Production Criteria

Land tenure is now a focal point of social troubles. The pressure to change prevailing institutions is mounting. People in many places believe that the tenure system stands in the way of social betterment. There is also a growing interest in economic development. Tenure systems are believed to be major obstacles to such development.[18] In this kind of an atmosphere, where change is so strongly desired, scientific advice is at a premium. All of the so-called land reform measures have been carried out allegedly for the economic and social advancement of the rural population. Under the weight of political pressure most of them, however, have disregarded or were obliged to disregard the most elementary principles of production economics. The underdeveloped countries of the world are now divided into two types —those that have pushed through quick political land reforms and those that have done little or nothing in reforming their agrarian structure. If the latter want to avoid the mistakes committed by others, they have to begin looking seriously at their own land tenure situations in the light of such criteria as proposed in this paper. By doing so, the following things may be clarified:

1. In what way are the present tenure systems linked up with the dynamics of agricultural production?

2. What practical changes are necessary in certain tenure systems to help increase the efficiency of agricultural production?

3. What other changes are needed to supplement tenurial reform?

When we know what to look for in analyzing tenure's role in production, and when we know what questions to ask, the next problem becomes: What methods to apply? The selection of methodology is important not only in formal research but in everyday intelligent decision making. The proof of the quality of any judgment is its validity in experience. Abstractions and models can suggest working hypotheses, but experience is the supreme test. Altogether too little is known about the quantitative aspects of land tenure. Statistics are collected to throw light on no more than a superficial and often artificial classification of tenure

status. The fact that so many acres of land are owned by so many individuals tells very little of what we really want to know. Evidence in support of ideas in the field of tenure can be obtained in three ways: (1) analysis of consequences of historic changes, (2) comparison of existing alternative tenure institutions operating under a similar socio-economic environment, and (3) introduction of partially controlled changes through pilot projects.

The analysis of historic change is only possible where sufficient data on past events are available. Such is very seldom the case. Introducing tenure changes under controlled conditions on a limited scale is a very important tool of analysis. Such pilot projects may be established for newly reclaimed or settled areas, integrated river valley development schemes, or in connection with other comprehensive development projects. The main disadvantage of such work is that the results are slow in accumulating.

The principal practical method of doing land tenure work remains the critical examination of the existing tenure structure and the discovery of strategic operating factors which contribute to the realization of stated objectives. The objective with which we are concerned here is farm production efficiency. No intelligent decision concerning changes in the existing institutions can be made unless data are gathered in the field through farm management surveys and by other methods on the interrelationship between tenure practices and those factors which are responsible for farm efficiency.

Productive efficiency is actually only one of several criteria in economic analysis. In order to get a more complete picture of the effect of a given institution, one would have to consider also distributive efficiency and consumption efficiency. And what about the social criteria and political criteria of land tenure? Obviously there is need to develop and to refine such criteria parallel to those suggested for economics. Any analysis of complex social problems would be unrealistic without a many-sided attack. The causative factors responsible for a particular tenure element can only be discovered by enlisting the aid of history, law, psychology, sociology, anthropology, and geography, as well as economics. This is indeed a big order.

In the foregoing we have discussed tenure from one generalized point of view only. Just as the sweep of our key criteria, which had to be broadly drawn, points up the need for further refinements and adaptations to specific situations in the field, likewise the single-mindedness employed in showing analytical possibilities should not diminish the necessity for interdisciplinary approaches.

In summary, the following suggestions have been made:

1. It is desirable to appraise the merits of tenure systems from the point of view of agricultural production.

2. Three main generalized criteria of tenure for farm production efficiency are offered: (a) economic size and layout of farms; (b) human incentives and opportunities for sustained economic production; and (c) favorable conditions for capital formation and productive investment.

3. These criteria have to be refined for analyzing specific tenure situations, but they represent a useful framework to help in asking strategic questions.

4. There is no substitute for purposefully collected data of field origin in applying testing and revising such criteria.

5. Production criteria for tenure work must be supplemented by further intra-economic and extra-economic approaches.

Part XX THE CO-OPERATIVE APPROACH TO TENURE REFORM AND AGRICULTURAL DEVELOPMENT

THE POSSIBILITIES OF CO-OPERATIVE FARMING

S. M. Akhtar

THE SIGNIFICANCE of co-operative farming as a subject of discussion before this conference is twofold: First, it represents one of the alternative social forms which could be suggested as a solution of serious land tenure situations in certain countries which necessitate more or less drastic remedies. Second, this method of social change, while involving effective transformation of the economic situation, has the additional advantage of preserving such values as individual incentive and democratic procedures during and after the change. These two values, it is assumed, are nearest to the hearts of those gathered here.

It is necessary not only in the interest of clear thinking but also in the interest of correct action that the concept of co-operative farming should, as far as possible, be clearly defined. The danger of confusion lies in two directions. On the one hand, co-operative farming is something more than the mere use of the co-operative principle in meeting some of the subsidiary needs of the agriculturist. For instance, in Pakistan, India, and elsewhere co-operative societies have been supplying the cultivator with purchase, sale, and credit facilities either through separate or multipurpose organizations. Such societies do not represent activities which could be called co-operative farming. They may be brought under the general term, agricultural co-operation. A co-operative farmer must undertake some or all of the farming operations co-operatively

through pooling of resources of members, partially or wholly. But mere pooling of resources is not enough. This leads us to the second direction in which confusion may arise.

The other and the more serious confusion results when the term "co-operative farming" is identified with "collective farming." It is not easy to distinguish between the two because sometimes the difference may be only in the spirit in which they are worked. It may be mentioned here that the basic characteristics of all co-operative organizations may be said to be three, whatever the purpose of a particular form of co-operation.[1] First, the membership of a co-operative organization must be voluntary. If coercion is used for making members or for keeping members within the society it ceases to be co-operative. Second, the decisions of a co-operative society must be arrived at democratically, directly or indirectly—the latter when the general assembly of the members makes decisions through its executive committee or a manager under its democratic control. If such a committee or a person becomes an autocrat or is dictated to by an external authority, the organization ceases to be co-operative. The third distinguishing feature is equally important, though it is frequently overlooked by writers on this subject. A co-operative form is not merely actuated by the profit motive in its activities. It is concerned as much with the moral welfare of its members as with enhancing their material resources.[2] In this respect a co-operative society is distinguishable from a joint stock company. The latter may possess attributes of voluntary membership and democratic control, but it is primarily activated by the profit motive. For instance, it is indifferent regarding the quality of the person who buys its shares as long as he has the purchase price to pay. From this also comes the fact that the profits shared by members of a truly co-operative society are in proportion not to the material assets contributed by them (which are rewarded on a uniform basis) but in proportion to the co-operative spirit shown by the members—in other words in proportion to the use made by the members of the society for the common good.

Keeping these attributes of a co-operative organization in mind, it would be easy to see how and why co-operative farming is something distinct from collective farming. The most typical instance of collective farming is the Soviet collective farms, called Kolkhoz, which the Russians insist are "co-operatives" in character. Confusion arises here because things are different in practice than they are in theory. "Legally," says Lazar Volin, "the Kolkhoz is intended to be a self governing organization, managing its own affairs within the limits set by government plans and regulations . . . In practice, however, the government and party officials are in the habit of appointing, dismissing and transferring officers from one Kolkhoz to another at will, and the Kolkhoz general assembly actually has little or no voice in the management of its Kolkhoz affairs."[3] The same applies as regards membership, which is voluntary only as a matter of theory.

Now suppose a collective farm is organized in which membership is voluntary and control democratic. Could it then be called a co-operative farm? Here a difference of opinion exists among experts. Some feel that a co-operative farm should have the additional attribute of preserving individual rights of the members in the assets, in the form of land equipment, etc., which they contribute to the farm. Others do not regard this condition as essential. In a collective farm all assets are pooled and no individual rights in them are recognized. The members receive payments only in proportion to the labor performed by them on the farms. In extreme cases like the Communal Settlements in Israel (Kvutza) even this right is denied to the members. And the principle of "from each according to capacity and to each according to need" is followed. But this example is not of collective farming because membership is voluntary and control democratic. Should it be the extreme case of co-operative farming where everything is pooled—consumption as well as production?

It would appear, therefore, that co-operative farming cannot hinge upon the degree of pooling of resources that may occur. This should be left to the will of the members. If they are free to enter or leave the organization and decide through the democratic procedure that specified or all resources contributed by them should be pooled, such a pooling will not detract from the co-operative character of the farm. It is likely, however, that human nature as it is, in most cases the members, especially when they are small landholders to whom such a system will appeal the most, will like to keep their ownership rights in land in one form or another.

We may say, therefore, that co-operative farming is a system of agriculture in which a number of persons form themselves into a co-operative society for purposes of carrying on their farming operations through mutual assistance, voluntarily and democratically deciding the necessary degree of pooling of resources required by the needs of the situation facing them.

Degree of Pooling of Resources

Now, assuming that membership is voluntary, control democratic, and purpose of the society mutual assistance in farming, the degree of pooling of resources that will occur will depend upon such factors as the amounts and kinds of resources possessed by the members, their ideals and traditions regarding individual possession of such resources, their trust of each other, the methods and technique of production contemplated, etc. In actual practice a variety of forms of farming co-operatives have arisen in various countries as a result of different degrees of pooling of assets or common use of land or equipment by members. These forms may be arranged as follows:

1. Co-operatives may be formed for mechanized cultivation only. Such societies exist in France, Norway, The Netherlands, and England. The idea is to use the co-operative principle for modernizing and re-equipping agriculture through the use by members who cannot afford their own machines of co-operatively owned mechanical devices. In France, for instance, there are threshing societies and societies for mechanized cultivation. We are told that average cost of threshing by this method has proved to be 30 per cent lower than by the old method of threshing through contractors.[4] Under such a system the machines are hired by a member from a co-operative society to be used on his plot which is under his individual control and management.

2. Co-operation may be extended to common operations on an individually owned or occupied holding. Thus leveling of land, taking out of deep-rooted weeds, ploughing, sowing, hoeing, etc. may be done co-operatively by machinery, keeping the identity of individual plots separate. The harvesting is usually left to the individual so as to give him incentive for additional care of his land. In fact it is possible to preserve the separate character of harvesting even though the process of harvesting is combined by a particular method of laying out plots as shown by Professor Schiller's experiences in this connection. If farming operations are to be done co-operatively while individual members' rights to production from particular plots are to be preserved, the land belonging to or occupied by individual owners in the first instance will have to be pooled and then reallotted in the form of convenient strips in one or more than one place. Under the system described by Professor Schiller,[5] these strips were allotted to groups of members in such a way that they could be operated upon co-operatively by the group concerned without losing their identity. The number of places in which one individual's strips will lie will depend upon the various kinds of lands or the system of crop rotation relevant to the locality. A variety of arrangements are possible under this category of co-operative farming. The essential point is that the land is not pooled, in order to preserve incentives for those people whose attachment to private ownership or occupancy in land is strong. This is the most suitable system for most of the communities of small holders or small tenants found in countries of Asia and the Far East. The system is already at work in varying degrees in India, Pakistan, Israel, etc. There are differences in certain details which we may ignore for the present.

3. A more advanced system of co-operation implies the pooling of all assets, including land, for joint farming. Here, if the rights in land are preserved at all, they only consist in a title to rent of the area contributed by the member concerned, in accordance with the principles decided by the farming society. The rent may be limited to a certain percentage of the produce or determined in some other way. It may be paid as an item of costs or as a share in profits after other costs including that of

labor (as in some joint farming societies in India) have been accounted for.

The most typical of this form of co-operative farming is met with in some countries of Eastern Europe.[6] In these countries (except perhaps in Jugoslavia) this form is supposed to be a transitional stage in the way of the establishment of collective farms on the Soviet model. It is difficult to say how far the element of voluntary membership and democratic control exists at the moment. Theoretically these societies are formed by small peasants on their own initiative and membership is voluntary, while they are supposed to be democratically operated. It is expected that gradually the amount of rent paid to members will be reduced and ultimately abolished. If this process occurs with the full consent of the members it should not affect the co-operative character of these organizations. But it is difficult to believe that the members would willingly forego their rights in land. If such rights are socialized it will be due to pressure from above, and hence it is difficult to call these farms co-operatives.

This, however, does not mean that this model, if its voluntary and democratic character is preserved intact, cannot be introduced in other countries. It will depend, however, upon the extent to which members can be persuaded to substitute titles to rent in place of titles to specific plots of land without affecting incentives. The system is being tried in Mexico.

4. A still more advanced form of co-operative farming is one in which all assets including land are pooled and the remuneration to members is determined only by the quality and quantity of work done by them during a given period. This system is most suitable for people who have owned no land and work on area leased from the state or some other source. But it is expensive to run.

The most advanced type of co-operatives,

if this name may legitimately be applied to them, are communal settlements of the type found in Israel. But such organizations are unique and can only succeed under a strong community feeling inspired by religion or an equally strong force. It cannot be recommended for common adoption.

Factors Determining Success

So far we have been considering the main features of co-operative farming and the various models of it which have been tried in various countries. It should be remembered, however, that apart from the Russian system, which we shall regard as collective rather than co-operative farming, the co-operative principle has been applied to the farming processes only by a small number of peoples. The system is still in its experimental stage. What degree of success it will ultimately achieve will depend on a variety of factors psychological, historical, and geographical. Secondly, it should not be forgotten that co-operative farming is not being suggested as a substitute for economic-size independently owned and managed farms such as are found in many of the states of U.S.A. and elsewhere. It is being suggested as a remedy for a pathological situation in some agriculturally backward countries, who have failed to make adequate use of scientific methods of agriculture on account of their uneconomic size of the units of cultivation. It is being recommended as a safeguard against more drastic remedies which have been applied in certain parts of the world at enormous cost in terms of human misery and sweeping away of values such as respect for the individual personality of man. Hence we have stressed its voluntary and democratic character. In introducing this system, on the other hand, it is the difficulty of reconciling the necessity of maintaining this voluntary and democratic character, especially in communities which are educationally and socially underdeveloped, with the pressure of the immediate need for such transformation, which will be the chief barriers in the way of its success. What then are the possibilities of adoption of this system by the countries which need it so badly?

Whether given communities will take to this system and make it a success will depend upon a large number of factors, among which may be mentioned the following: (1) the quality of the leadership in the country inside and outside the governmental machinery, (2) the traditional habits and ideals of the mass of the people, (3) the particular form of co-operative farming selected for the locality concerned, (4) the methods adopted for the implementation of particular schemes, and (5) measures taken to preserve what has been achieved in the first instance.

Situation in Pakistan

I shall now take up each of these factors and analyze its implications with special reference to a concrete situation as it exists in my own country.

We are faced with the following situation: The area of the country is about 360,-000 square miles and the population is 75.5 million souls, 90 per cent of whom are illiterate. About 85 per cent of the people depend upon agriculture, and cultivated area per head of the population is a little over one-half of one acre. The area cultivated per family whether of tenants or of peasant proprietors varies, but the vast majority of holdings are uneconomic in size—very few of them would be over ten acres each; holdings of less than five acres are very common. These holdings are not only small but are also fragmented. Half the total cultivated area is owned by absentee landlords and is cultivated by small tenants. The other half is owned by peasant proprietors. Of the three parties associated with the ownership of cultivation of land, none of them

makes capital investment in land: the landlord because he thinks he gets enough by allotting his estate in small parcels, the tenant because he has neither the resources nor the incentive for investment, the peasant owner because of lack of capital. In any case the small unit of cultivation is hardly amenable to scientific farming even if there were incentives and financial resources. Only very simple and primitive methods can be applied on such lands. The result is as should be expected from such a situation: low productivity per man as well as per acre, small income, chronic shortage of funds, indebtedness, low state revenues, low standard of living, and lack of minimum social amenities like medical aid, education, etc. Undernourishment, ill health, high incidence of mortality, etc. are the final consequences. One factor has been accentuating the other. A vicious circle of poverty leading to lack of resources for abolition of poverty has been created. Half-measures of legislative regulation of tenancy, credit, and marketing have brought in very limited success. The problem needs tackling at the source, at the production end and at the population end, which means encouragement of new sources of production through industrialization, reorganization of agriculture, and control of population growth. It is the second line of policy which is relevant to the present discussion.

Co-operative farming is suggested as a method of reorganization for reasons already given. What are the chances of its adoption and success? Let us proceed with the factors already mentioned which will determine this success.

Nature of Leadership

First, as regards leadership. Our leadership is in the hands of two kinds of people: the landlord class and the educated middle class inside as well as outside government administration. With some isolated exceptions, the landlord class will not favor any radical change in the present land tenure system, obviously, because such a change sooner or later will involve their relinquishing their rights in large estates which they do not cultivate themselves. On the contrary, they will do everything they can to counteract any tendencies that may favor a change of this kind. The educated middle class is sympathetic to the peasantry. Many of them have sprung from the same stock. Others feel that an equitable solution of our agricultural problem is a condition precedent for our national advancement. They have only to be convinced that co-operative farming is the only way out of the present difficulties, and they will take up the cause of educating the mass of the villagers regarding the advantages to be derived from the new system. The educated middle class will supply the initiative where they are in a position to do so.

Social Habits and Ideals

As to the traditional habits and ideals of the mass of the people involved, three of them are relevant in this connection. First, their passionate desire for and attachment to individual possession of land. This desire has historical and psychological reasons behind it. They will thus hesitate to pool their land and may insist on having their individual plots to gather their own harvest. Second, they have a strong feeling for social equality which is their cultural trait derived from the Islamic concept of brotherhood. This will be a force in favor of the change. Third, they look up to the government for initiative for any important change. This habit has historical reasons behind it and can be turned into a positive asset if tactfully handled. Attempts, however, shall have to be made to develop greater initiative in the people through education and propaganda if permanent results are to be achieved.

Selecting the Form

The particular form of co-operative farming adopted must fit in with the psychological attitudes and environmental factors existing in a particular locality. Obviously among small peasant owners the rights in the landed property must be preserved. Where land does not belong to the members, for instance, where large landed estates have been acquired from absentee landlords or where it is crown land, either allotments may be made in return for rent, or land may be pooled and cultivated by the peasants in return for a fixed wage plus a share in the final net profits. Perhaps the most commonly acceptable form would be where land is allotted to individual families to be worked upon by them with the help of the machinery co-operatively owned. This will represent something like the pattern of farming described by Professor Schiller in his widely discussed article. All objections raised against his system appear to be objections against co-operative farming as such and should be dealt with at that level.[7] Here we have assumed that for a particular situation co-operative farming is the only way out.

The system under which land is pooled and is worked by "brigades" of laborers will involve detailed keeping of accounts, and is not likely to suit a community in which literacy percentage is negligible. Even if record keepers and other administrators required were available, the system would be expensive in addition to being less satisfactory from the point of view of incentive.

Methods of Implementation

As regards the method of implementation the watchword is gradualness. Gradualness in this context has two aspects, geographical and constitutional. Geographically speaking, the co-operative system of farming need not be introduced in all parts of the country and among every agricultural community all at once. It can be tried first in those areas in which conditions are most favorable and social and political barriers of the weakest resistance. For instance, vacant crown lands may be granted to cultivating communities on the condition that they operate them as a co-operative village. This is already being done in certain parts of the country. For instance, in the "Thal" area—a newly opened canal colony in the Punjab—ex-servicemen and refugees from India have been settled in co-operative villages. In some other portions of the province, land left by migrating non-Muslims has been treated in the same way. In all, over 200 co-operative societies have been formed which cover 237,920 acres of land, including 25,809 acres of virgin soil broken recently. They have a membership of 11,765 families. These societies help their members in the economic as well as social fields. Through them the members purchase seed and other of their agricultural and domestic requirements. Through them they also satisfy their educational and religious needs. They further aim at providing dwelling houses, laying roads, lighting and drainage facilities. They are in the process of becoming full-fledged co-operative farming societies. This also represents an instance of the other aspect of gradualness, i.e., the constitutional aspect. By this I mean evolving a farming co-operative society by stages. There is already a movement towards the creation of what are called multiple co-operative societies which aim at supplying more than one need of the members co-operatively. The first step should be the encouragement of such societies. These will meet the needs of the villager in the matter of purchase of implements, seeds and manures, supply of credit, and marketing facilities. The only link that will remain will be the extension of co-operation to the farming processes. This need not necessarily involve the pooling of land or even the use of heavy expensive machinery. Some machinery, however, could be used without creating a surplus labor problem. Such operations, for instance, as levelling of land, destruction of deep-rooted weeds, etc. could be mechanically performed. As through expanding industrialization some population is shifted away from agriculture, mechanization may be extended to ploughing, sowing, harvesting, etc.

To return to the geographical aspect, the next step after establishing co-operative farming societies on vacant land will be to persuade village communities of peasant proprietors to transform themselves into co-operative villages. Inducements can be given in the form of reduced water rates, lower rates of land revenue, extension of social amenities, such as better schools, hospitals, and roads, etc., supply of improved seed, artificial manure, and improved implements at concession prices. Once the superiority of the new system has been established by experience the people will take to it easily.

The greatest difficulty will arise when the system is extended to areas now opened by large absentee landlords. Here the first step will have to be to transfer the ownership of these lands to the state, the co-operative village, or the individual cultivators as may be regarded best under the circumstances. Transfer of land rights to cultivators as individuals may be the most preferable course. This change will be resisted by the vested interests even though they will be compensated. This resistance may be a serious barrier because the landlord class is still politically powerful in spite of the introduction of adult suffrage. But with the spread of education and new ideas and the success of co-operative farming in nonlandlord villages the public opinion will get strong enough for the necessary legislation to be passed. Moreover, the landlords themselves may agree, fearing that a stage may develop when they may have to part with their lands without compensation. It is contemplated that the compensation to the landlords will be paid partly in cash and partly in bonds redeemable over a period of, say, twenty years. If the ownership rights are transferred to the members they will pay the price of the land in easy instalments over a similar period. Similar will be the case if proprietary rights in land are transferred to the co-operative village taken collectively.

Maintaining Achievement

Finally, steps will have to be taken by the state to create conditions for the continued successful functioning of co-operative villages after they have come into being. The state will arrange for the necessary technical and general education and over-all assistance and supervision. The co-operative villages will be integrated into the general plans of development of the country. They will serve both as organs of carrying out the democratically arrived at decisions of the community as a whole and will also reflect the public opinion of the local community for the guidance of those in authority.

CO-OPERATIVE FARMING IN INDIA

𝔖𝔖𝔖𝔖   *M. S. Menon*

ONE OF THE main reasons for the backwardness of India's agriculture and the consequent low conditions of the rural masses is the small size of individual agricultural holdings and their scattered distribution. The average size of an agricultural holding in India is between three and five acres. In the state of Bengal, 42.7 per cent of the families have less than two acres. In Madras, 74 per cent of the holdings are below two to four acres. In Uttar Pradesh and Punjab the majority of holdings are below five acres. In Bombay, 49 per cent of the holdings have less than five acres. The man-land ratio in the country has undergone progressive diminution. According to the Census Report of 1921, the number of acres per cultivator was 4.91 in Madras, 3.12 in Bengal, 3.09 in Bihar and Orissa, 2.96 in Assam, and 2.51 in Uttar Pradesh. The net area sown per head now is in the neighborhood of 0.7 acre.

What is of even more serious consequence than this progressive diminution in the size of holdings is the composition of each holding. It is common to find a holding of ten to twelve acres scattered in twenty to thirty plots. In some of the states, the average size of a field does not exceed one-fifth of one acre. The land thus presents a crazy-quilt of disjointed pieces, unfenced and unprotected, with large areas rendered unproductive by a crosswork of boundaries, and cultivated by small holders, who have individually neither the resources nor the chance to improve the land.

Co-operative farming had not received much attention in the country until lately, either at the hands of administrators or the public. The previous governments, before the advent of the popular government, were mostly engrossed in the collection of land revenue and the maintenance of their authority. And, as the landed aristocracy helped them in both, they were loathe to disturb existing rights in any manner, and did not encourage any measure which might savour of an encroachment on vested interests. Moreover, the country's food position, with imports coming in steadily from

Burma and other countries, was secure, and the clearance of vast areas of barren land and their conversion into arable areas for increasing the food resources of the country had not become so pressing. Conditions since then have materially changed. In the new political framework, only democratically organized institutions have a chance of survival. The old methods of disorganized production and disorderly marketing have to give place to a more orderly system, consciously directed by, and in the interests of, the producer. The attempt to organize agricultural production on co-operative lines represents thus an effort to bring order in the largest field of human endeavour in the country, which till now has remained the most disorganized. Its immediate importance lies in the urgent necessity to increase national production for making the country progressively self-sufficient in food and industrial raw material. As a permanent measure of improvement, it affords the best means of rationalizing agriculture and attaining a higher order of social and economic life in keeping with the principle of democracy and self-government.

It is difficult to give a standard definition of co-operative farming. Whatever form is attempted, it must embody the distinctive traits of a co-operative organization: (a) it must be one for mutual assistance; (b) the management must be democratic; and (c) it must distribute income in proportion to the use which each member makes of the association. If the society is one for purchase and sale, the value of the goods the member purchases and the value of the goods he sells through the society should determine his income; if it is one for joint cultivation, the value of the land he brings into the common enterprise and the share of the labor he puts in should form the basis on which his proportion of the proceeds is determined. There is one important distinction between a co-operative and collective organization

which has to be kept in mind: in the co-operative, whatever form it might take, ownership rights are definitely recognized and paid for, either in the shape of rent or dividend or some participation in profits; in the collective, ownership rights are forfeited either to the state or to the collective unit and do not carry any claim to a share of the proceeds. The co-operative thus represents a golden mean between the capitalist organization with its stress on individual rights and the complete collectivist system under which all individual rights of property are suppressed and are merged in collective or state ownership. In the co-operative, therefore, ownership may still remain individual, but the use of the material requisites of production may become socialized. How far such collective use would extend would depend upon a number of factors such as (1) the prevailing system of land holding in the area and the size of the existing farming units, (2) the kind of crops grown, (3) whether diversified or single cropping is pursued, (4) whether the farming clan in the area is homogeneous in social and economic status, (5) the degree of technical skill available, and above all the degree of co-operative spirit manifest among the farmers.

Generally, co-operative farming societies in India are classified in four categories: (1) co-operative better-farming societies, (2) co-operative joint-farming societies, (3) co-operative tenant-farming societies, and (4) co-operative collective-farming societies.

A co-operative better-farming society consists, like any other co-operative society, of ten or more members who join together for the promotion of common interests through the adoption of improved methods of farming. Except for certain specific purposes, the members own and independently work their lands, although they may agree to a common plan of cultivation drawn up by the society.

A co-operative joint-farming society represents a much closer association of members in the common work of the farm and in the business aspects of farming. The objectives of the society are: (1) to encourage the members to pool the land and work it jointly in compact blocks, (2) to prevent their physical subdivision and fragmentation, (3) to arrange for joint purchase of requirements and joint sale of the produce, (4) to arrange for the necessary finance for carrying on its operation, and (5) to undertake land improvement and all other activities (like the starting of subsidiary industries, etc.) calculated to improve the economic lot of the members. Ownership remains individual, although the property is worked in common and is generally recognized by the payment of an ownership dividend from out of the proceeds, or by payment of rent, or by some method of evaluation entitling to a claim on profits. The wages may be on the basis of daily work, or evaluated in terms of work-day units calculated on the basis of the possible time required to complete a given task. The balance of the proceeds after paying for the interest on loans and deposits, charges for working expenses, allocation to cover losses, and depreciation and land assessment, cesses (taxes or rates) and rent, is distributed somewhat in the following proportion: (a) 25 per cent is carried to reserve fund, (b) a percentage is distributed as dividends to members on their share-capital, (c) the balance of the net profit is paid to members in proportion to the wages earned by them or the assets brought by them into the common pool.

A co-operative tenant-farming society is generally organized by the society taking over land either on lease-hold or free-hold and dividing it among members, who work the land as tenants of the society on the basis of a fixed rent. A cropping plan is laid down by the society, but the actual cultivation of the land is left to each member, who tills the land independently, the society providing the supplementary services of purchase and sale and the provision of credit.

A co-operative collective-farming society is a combination of tenant-farming and joint-farming organizations. The society takes land on lease or free-hold, which the members cultivate jointly under the direction and management of the society. The proceeds, after the usual deductions, are distributed among the members in proportion to the wages earned by each member.

Earlier attempts at organizing co-operative farming in India were confined mostly to societies for better farming and to land improvement societies. Better-farming societies are generally on a limited liability basis, and their area of operations covers a whole village or group of villages. The members include residents of the area, who are either owners of land or tenants. There were 125 such societies in the Punjab during 1947/48, 95 in Bombay, 23 in Madhya Pradesh, and a few in other states.

There were few instances of successful ventures in joint co-operative farming until recently. Due to the enthusiastic efforts of a Bengal civilian, Mr. S. K. Dey, some joint farming societies were organized in the district of Nadia in Bengal in 1940/41. The members of the society transferred their respective proprietary rights in their lands to the society by executing sale deeds. The market value of the lands so transferred was credited to each member as his fully paid-up share capital entitling him to a proportionate share in the profits. The society entered into separate agreements with the landlords, constituting itself as the tenant of the plots and undertaking to pay any arrears of rent or cess (tax) that may have existed at the time of transfer. There was no pooling of the cattle, implements, or other equipment owned by the members. Each cultivator-member was expected to bring his own cattle and implements to work with. He received wages for his labor at the current wage rates. There was no compulsion regarding his working on the land himself. The management of the society was, as in other societies, entrusted to a committee elected by the members. Some societies had advisory bodies composed of the Agricultural or Cooperative Department officers, other officers engaged in rural reconstruction work, and nonofficial enthusiasts of the area. The Nadia experiments were inconclusive because (1) the lands which the members held outside the co-operative farm claimed their prior attention; (2) the management was ill-paid and lacked driving power; (3) the members were disinclined to work on the farm themselves; (4) there was no proper arrangement for the storage of produce, which for the most part was kept in private houses without sufficient safeguards; and (5) the members were not sufficiently educated in the value of joint effort and relied too much upon outside initiative. Like many other experiments which drew inspiration from one man, the societies withered when that leadership was withdrawn.

A good deal of success has been achieved in Madras by land colonization societies. They are generally organized on a tenant-farming basis. Land is allotted on lease at the rate of ten acres per member and divided among them on an approved plan, each member also getting a house site. Subdivision and fragmentation is obviated by requiring each member to nominate a single heir acceptable to the society, in whose absence the property will revert to the society. The government has provided them with grants and loans for sinking wells and for purchasing bullocks, manure, and implements, constructing houses, and even towards share capital. There were thirty-nine of these tenant farming societies in Madras in 1949/50. The societies, however, have

few of the characteristics of a real venture in "joint" co-operative farming.

A real beginning in the organization of farming co-operatives on a systematic plan has been made in the state of Bombay. A special officer, Captain S. P. Mohite, was appointed by the government in 1947 to investigate the possibilities of organizing co-operative farming societies in the state in the light of existing crop practices, distribution of land, prevailing land tenures, etc. Based on his report, the government of Bombay has drawn up a scheme for the organization of different types of co-operative farming societies suited to each particular area. During 1949/50 there were eighty-two co-operative farming societies in the state, of which twenty-two were of the joint-farming type.

In Bihar, joint cultivation of sugar cane on scientific lines is being attempted. The members of eight cane growers' co-operative societies have agreed to surrender the right of cultivation of their plots to the co-operative farms formed by them. The land of each member is classified according to its quality, and the profit earned is distributed according to the area and the quality of the land. The assessment of the quality of the land is generally done at the time a person joins the farm. In employing labor, bullocks, or implements, preference is given to persons who have joined the scheme. The rate of compensation for utilizing labor, bullocks, or implements is based on the prevailing rate in the locality.

An instance of a successful experiment in co-operative joint farming is the society organized at Mouza Akola in the state of Madhya Pradesh. The ground has been well prepared by a multipurpose society, which has been in existence since October, 1947. A group of eleven members has organized a sub-society for co-operative farming by pooling about 113 acres of land. The members have agreed to work the scheme for five years and have executed agreements in favor of the society, which have all been registered. According to these agreements, the society will have full possession of the fields during the period of the scheme, and no member is allowed to create any encumbrance. Cultivation and harvesting operations will be carried on jointly by the society. The net profits of the cultivation, after providing 10 per cent as "bullock depreciation fund," 5 per cent as "plough and implements depreciation fund," and 10 per cent as "crop stabilization fund," are distributed among the members in proportion to the area and fertility of the land of each member. On this basis, the members have decided from the start the percentages of net production to which each member will be entitled at the end of the season.

In Uttar Pradesh, the colonization of the vast areas which are newly being reclaimed in Yanga Khadir and Naini Terai is being attempted on co-operative lines. There were fifty-two land settlement societies in the state in 1949/50. Two co-operative farming societies have also been formed in the Jhansi district of the state and have been working successfully since 1947/48. The members of the societies have pooled their tractor-operated land for purposes of joint cultivation. The managing committee of the societies lays down the cropping plan, apportions the work among the members, elects local leaders for blocks of one to fifty acres, settles wages, and attends to other details of work. The net profits, after the usual dividend, are distributed on the basis of the average of land pooled. A system of efficiency bonus for good work and deductions for indifferent work has been devised to maintain the standard of work at the desired level. It has been claimed that the earnings of those who have contributed both their land and their labor to the society have more than doubled compared with what they used to obtain before the society was formed.

Most of the states in the Indian Union thus have schemes of one kind or another for extension of co-operative farming. Government has encouraged the formation of such societies by various means: (1) the services of government officers and experts have been given free to some of the societies; (2) free grants and loans are given for the purchase of agricultural requirements and subsidies for meeting management costs; (3) government lands are assigned to the societies; (4) rebate is given on land revenue in some states; and (5) priority in the provision of irrigation facilities and roads and other civic amenities is promised to villages which agree to manage their land on a co-operative basis.

Co-operative farming societies are also being encouraged by legislative action. In the Cooperative Societies Acts in Uttar Pradesh, Hyderabad, and Bombay provision is made for the application of a small measure of compulsion to bring a recalcitrant minority into the scheme if a certain percentage of farmers holding a major area in the locality come forward to form a co-operative farming society. Notable exceptions are also made in favor of co-operative farming societies in regard to the maximum size of holdings prescribed under the acts recently passed in some of the states. The tenants in Bombay, Hyderabad, and Sawrashtra who have joined a co-operative farm cannot be ejected even when the landlord requires the land for personal cultivation, as long as the society continues to function. These and other concessions are expected to encourage the small-holders to pool their resources and form co-operative societies and overcome the disadvantages of uneconomic size. Under the stimulus of all these encouragements, a total area exceeding 50,000 acres has been brought under co-operative farming of one kind or another in the different states in India during 1949/50.

A COMPARISON OF COLLECTIVE AND
CO-OPERATIVE FARMING[1]

Otto Schiller

THE COLLECTIVE farming system is one of the most striking features of the economic and social order which has been developed in the Soviet Union in the course of more than thirty years. The singularity of this new farming system often has not been recognized sufficiently. Some persons hold that this system is only a variation of the co-operative form which has been developed in other countries. The communists themselves are supporting this erroneous idea by representing the "kolkhoz" system for propagandistic reasons as a co-operative form, or trying to introduce it via transitory co-operative forms into countries under their control.

The terminological difficulties are augmented by the fact that in English the adjective "co-operative" stands also for "joint." In order to arrive at the proper conclusions it is necessary to shed light on the principal distinction between the collective and co-operative system and to realize to what extent it is possible to develop forms of co-operative management in the agriculture of other countries without approaching agrarian communism.

There are certain analogies between the collective and the co-operative form, but these analogies cannot efface the principal difference. This difference consists in the fact that the co-operative is an association of free and autonomous economic units, whereas the collective enterprise consists of members who have lost their economic autonomy.

The co-operative of Western pattern is to support the enterprise and the business activities of the members, as expressed in the German law of co-operatives. This aim can only be reached if there are autonomous enterprises of the members who associate in order to support their individual enterprises. It cannot be the purpose of a genuine co-operative association to dissolve the individual enterprises and replace them by a joint enterprise. If the association goes so far that individual enterprises cease to exist this is no more a co-operative but a joint enterprise, that is, a collective one.

In the beginning of the collectivization of Soviet agriculture there have undoubtedly been some co-operative features. For instance, during the first period the so-called co-operative for joint cultivation played a certain role as a transient form. In this co-operative the land but not all inventory was pooled. Even after joint cultivation the fields occasionally were harvested individually. But soon this transitory form as well as another, the so-called agricultural commune, then in practice, were superseded. Since then the unique form of organization in collectivized agriculture is the so-called agricultural artel, commonly called the kolkhoz.

During the first period every member of a kolkhoz could claim a certain share according to the value of the inventory he had contributed, and he had the right to pecuniary compensation of his share in case he left the collective. This bespeaks of the co-operative idea. Soon voluntary withdrawal from a kolkhoz and the claim to a share became illusory.

A small holding of one-half of one acre to one acre and a small number of livestock left to the kolkhoz members for private use hardly justify one to ascribe a co-operative nature to the kolkhoz. The kolkhoz is not to serve these small holdings but, on the contrary, it is opposed to their interests. This conflict of interests repeatedly has caused drastic measures on the part of the Soviet government. As the relationship of the industrial worker to his factory is not changed by his cultivating a community garden so the relationship of the kolkhoz member to his kolkhoz remains unaffected by his having a private small holding.

The peculiarity of the kolkhoz shows most clearly in the manner of compensation of its members and their share in the output of the collective enterprise. The share is not calculated according to the communist principle, i.e., as an equal share or a share according to the needs, neither is it calculated according to the capitalist principle, i.e., according to the value of the contributed property in land, livestock, etc., but the share is calculated according to the principle which the communists call socialist, i.e., according to the work done. The contribution in labor is calculated in labor units according to the amount and quality of work done with detailed norms for all working processes. The value of the labor unit is not determined by fixed norms but varies according to the surplus which remains for distribution after the delivery obligations and the requirements of the kolkhoz have been met.

These features of the sharing system resulted from the necessity to relieve the state of the business risk of collective agriculture. The transformation of all agriculture into state domains ("sovkhozy"), which during the first period was seriously considered, would have caused the necessity for the state to guarantee fixed wages to all former peasants who then would have been transformed into land laborers. Thus the state would have had to bear the business risk of all agriculture. High state subsidies would have been necessary, at least during the first period. The sharing system introduced in the kolkhozy leaves the entire risk to the members, the labor unit being evaluated lower in case of poor results. Furthermore this system offers the opportunity to finance all investments needed for the development of the collective farms out of the output without burdening the state budget. Such investments do not burden the wage account of the collective farm, since the amount of wages in money and kind available for distribution depends on the surplus alone and not on the sum of labor units worked.

This particular trait of the sharing system is not in accordance with the basic principle of the kolkhoz as described above. How many labor units the individual member earns during a year depends on his own work, but the value of this labor unit depends on the work accomplished by all members. The kolkhozy usually are large farms with more than one hundred members; therefore an individual accomplishment above average is hardly apparent in the total accomplishment. If, for instance, during the harvest, the tractor driver is found wanting and the harvest thereby is delayed, this can reduce considerably the whole output of the collective farm without an efficient member working at another place being able to help it. This dependence on the accomplishments of others in the long run paralyzes the will to work even of industrious members.

Another factor which deprived the kolkhozy of its original quasi-co-operative character was the establishment of the machine tractor stations (MTS). The machines and implements which formerly were privately owned by the peasants in the course of the collectivization had been expropriated in favor of the kolkhozy. Later on the heavy machines like tractors were expropriated from the kolkhozy in favor of the *state*-owned MTS. Now the kolkhozy have to pay for the work of the state-owned machines a considerable part of their output, that is, 10 to 20 per cent of the "brutto" output. They are completely dependent on these state institutions and thus can be included the better into the system of total state planning. In this way joint economic initiative based on joint incentives cannot develop, in accordance with the real spirit of co-operative movements.

Of late the establishment of mammoth kolkhozy and so-called agro-cities has set in by way of combining several kolhozy and concentrating the kolkhozy population in these new rural centers. This removes the kolkhozy still further from their quasi-co-operative origin. Apparently even the individual small holdings of the kolkhoz members are to disappear by and by, if the establishment of agro-cities, which is now only beginning, will be continued.

The present state of Soviet economy shows still other features contradictory to co-operative principles. These features, however, are not necessarily an integral part of collective farming. Whereas a genuine co-operative is based on voluntary membership, in the Soviet Union membership in the kolkhozy is practically compulsory. Yet it seems possible that in other countries, as for instance, in the Eastern European satellite states a collective farm may be established on a voluntary basis; individual cases of this kind have been reported from Poland. Nevertheless, such voluntary association cannot be termed co-operative.

In the Soviet Union collectivized agriculture has become an integral part of the state-planned economy, leaving no room for any joint or co-operative initiative. The state, thereby, succeeded in subordinating and exploiting agriculture for its own aims.

In the Soviet Union compulsory cultivation programs and delivery quotas are still prevailing. The greater part of products is collected by the state at prices which are far below the level of the free market or of consumption goods. This underrating of agricultural products procures a good deal of the state budget.

It is, however, not impossible that compulsory delivery of agricultural products will someday be abolished. The character of the collective farms thereby would not be basically changed. Furthermore, of late, experiments with joint farming have been carried through also in other countries, where these particular features of the present Soviet economy do not prevail. Yet, in these countries joint farming enterprises due to the character and organization of the latter should be considered as collective farms and not as co-operatives.

The main difficulty in organizing a joint enterprise is how to handle properly the sharing of the members in the income and how to combine this with the sharing in the risk. Among all possibilities of finding the proper solution of this problem the sharing system developed in the Soviet Union on the basis of long practical experience theoretically seems to be the most reasonable because it is based on the economical principle of sharing according to work done. As mentioned above, this principle actually has been deviated from by the kolkhozy in one decisive point and therewith the will to work is paralyzed. This is the main reason for the far spread discontent among the kolkhoz members. Another reason for discontent is the low payment for kolkhoz work, which will prevail as long as the exaggerated delivery demands and low prices for agricultural products prevail.

Everywhere the peasant is a firm believer in property striving for independence. Hence a collective economy will meet with his emotional resistance from the start. On the other hand, the co-operative idea of self-help by voluntary association which does not efface economical independence appeals to peasants. It is significant that communists try to overcome the individualistic thinking of peasants by using co-operative slogans.

It must be admitted that the kolkhoz system, in spite of its inner weakness, is capable of achieving technical and economical improvements. To be sure, the economical achievements of collectivized agriculture have benefited the state more than the kolkhoz members. Their standard of living can hardly stand comparison with that of a land laborer of the Soviet state farms or with that of an agricultural laborer in Western countries.

Even if a reduction of the exaggerated demands of the state should bring about a gradual change herein, the kolkhoz system would not thereby be justified. Ultimately it is not the question of economic efficiency or of form of organization, but it is the question whether individualism or collectivism should prevail. Peasantry represents not only a certain form of economy but also a certain way of life. Within peasantry those character traits and moral forces are most pronounced which resist the tendency of collectivism and of being levelled down into a uniform mass.

The kolkhoz system has little to do with the cooperative idea of the West. On the other hand the peasantry must be freed from its isolation and social ossification and a workable and organic social idea must be presented by the West to counter the crude social scheme of the East. Many beginnings of such a social idea are embodied in the spirit of the Western co-operative movement.

A COMPARISON OF THE MANAGEMENT PROBLEMS
OF INDIVIDUAL AND COLLECTIVE FARMS

Report of the Working Party

Chairman, *Kenneth J. Bachman*

THE PROBLEMS of management of individual farms depend upon the size of the farming unit, the degree of requirements for the proper conduct of farm operations, the access to the sources of supply of these requirements, their efficient use on the land, the facilities available for the disposal of the produce, and the general economic set-up in which the unit functions. In general, where the farms are of economic size and managed by an enlightened class of peasantry, the problems are not serious; each unit can function efficiently within its own orbit, and the sphere of associated action will mostly be confined to the provision of supplementary aids to production. The problems of farm management, however, in areas where holdings are subdivided into small uneconomic units and cultivated in dispersed plots, where capital is very scarce and technical knowledge of the peasants very limited, are of a different order. In these areas, some means have obviously to be found of bringing the resources of the individual cultivators together, which would enable farming to be done on a more rational basis. This is suggested not only so that the small, individual farms may have the economies accruing from the larger scale of operations but also so that the scarce resources in land, technical knowledge, and available capital may be better utilized and that the resulting increase in the efficiency of management may lead to an increase in farm production.

The management of small strips of land under the conditions described above on an absolutely individual basis in isolated units is economically wasteful and socially undesirable and requires modification. In discussing alternative forms of the organization of farms, some understanding of terminology is essential. There is, however, one initial difficulty which has to be contended with. The terms are used with such varying import in different countries that what is described as co-operative in one may savour of being collective in another. The working party discussed what should be considered as distinguishing features of the two types of associations in the opinion of the representatives of each country, but could come to no agreed conclusion. One view on the precise limits of co-operatives and collectives was that, when different business units formed themselves into a co-operative, the units were not amalgamated, but preserved their identity, whereas in a collective the whole enterprise of all the units was coalesced into one. Another distinction was sought on the basis of the degree of regimentation and compulsion used and the extent to which freedom of decision and action was abrogated. It was, however, pointed out that collectives may also be voluntary and democratically managed and, except in the Soviet sphere, function as independent organizations with no interference from the state. It was also pointed out that some of the co-operatives of the more inclusive type may pool the land and the other resources of the members and work the farm as one unit and apportion the income on some agreed joint basis between the members but differ very little, in point of management and operation, from the collectives. Still another distinction suggested was based on whether ownership rights to land were recognized or not in the new organization. If ownership rights were recognized by some form of payment, and only the use of the land was made on common basis, the association, it was said, could be called a co-operative. If individual ownership rights were forfeited and replaced by collective property rights, either of the state or of the group, the organization became

collective. The borderland in some cases, however, was so indistinguishable that it was considered not worth while to labor the point, but that it would be useful to consider what particular type of organization was evolved in each country to meet the needs of the situation, whether they went by the term co-operative or collective. It was, however, decided that large-scale state collectives, where regimentation of the productive resources is imposed by the state, are unsuited to the conditions of all the countries represented.

The problems of management on individually operated farms and co-operatives or similar groups are legion. Within the limits of the time at the disposal of the working party, it was deemed necessary to concentrate on those problems which pertain to the practical operations on the farm and to further restrict discussions to those problems of management that are generally confronted in the actual processes of organizing co-operatives. This question was considered under four heads: (1) how will the actual processes of farm work be carried on under the system adopted; (2) how will the management be constituted; (3) how will earnings be apportioned; and (4) what forms of farm layout would facilitate co-operation. The first question considered was: To what extent can individual farming activities be brought within the ambit of co-operatives in order to secure better efficiency of management and working processes, in the light of each country's own experience?

The experiences of each country on these aspects of management and operation of farms naturally differed according to local conditions and the objectives which each country or group of people sought to attain. In somes countries, co-operative farming was undertaken for specific purposes; e.g., the common use of machinery. Since there was no common urge for a fundamental change in the method of organizing farm work on a co-operative basis, some of these attempts were evanescent and ceased when the specific objectives were in some degree attained. In some countries, the co-operative movement started with credit and ended in discredit. In others, as in Israel, considerable success has been achieved in different types of organization, suited to the requirements and objectives of various groups of settlers. The "small-holders settlement" represents one such type, which combines co-operative as well as individualistic elements, the proportion of each varying with the needs and aspirations of particular groups. At one end is the middle-class settlement, largely individual in character, handling co-operatively only certain limited enterprises, such as purchasing, marketing, irrigation, etc. At the other end were settlements which practiced a much higher degree of co-operation and came very near to communal or collective settlements. The individual households are still separate and the seclusion of family life is retained, but all other agricultural activity is pooled and operated in common. In between, there are intermediate types which go further than joint purchase and sale and adopt a certain amount of compulsory crop planning and rotation, but still retain individualistic features in a greater degree than the more socialized type.

A far higher degree of co-operative living than all these is represented in Israel in the type of organization called the kvutza. The kvutza was an experiment to escape from the highly individualistic, acquisitive form of life characteristic of modern Western society and evolve a socialist order based on collective production and a common household for all members of the settlement. In the kvutza, there is virtually no private property, no personal compensation for work done, and no individual allocation of profit. To compare the degree of efficiency in the various places and over different periods work is classified by productive and unpro-

ductive days spent in the various branches. Constant efforts are made to increase the number of days spent in "productive" labor; i.e., in production proper as compared to the number of days spent in household work, children's care, etc.

The Jewish settlements are unique examples of community living, helped by the Jewish National Funds, organized by an enlightened class of people, and inspired by a spiritual desire for a particular order of social life. The Hutterite Fraternity Farms and similar rare types of community settlements have, however, shown that such organizations can work only on some strong ideological basis. In most of the other countries, which are thickly populated and where land has been held under tenant-landlord relationships for centuries and is worked on an individual basis, attempts to evolve a better system of land management and land use present considerable problems of organization and technical operation. Within each country itself, the physical and economic factors may vary so much from region to region that different systems may probably have to be tried to suit each particular need. In India, for instance, a variety of forms of co-operative management is being tried. These range from associations for specific purposes or for the general improvement of farming, frequently called "better farming societies," to complete joint farming in which the land of all members is pooled and managed as one unit and the produce shared on the basis of the assets brought in by each member.

A variant of the co-operative form of management of lands is found in the land settlement organizations formed in Italy for the proper cultivation of land expropriated from the big landlords. The settlement of these lands by groups of peasants organized in co-operation is carried out by an agency which divides the lands into convenient blocks according to the physical configuration of the region. Possibilities are also being considered of redistribution of land every year among the members within each group who cultivate each block.

The Ejidos of Mexico are another example of a different mode of organizing agricultural production and land management in a country where about 65 per cent of the population depends upon agriculture and there is a large class of landless men side by side with small and big landlords. Groups of co-operative settlements were established on lands which either originally belonged to the eligible participants or were expropriated from the wealthy landowners on payment of compensation. The constitution of the Ejidos is democratic; membership is based on fulfilment of requirements prescribed by law; and the land acquired is given to the group. The members or the President of the Republic may decide whether it should be worked individually or collectively. In the collective Ejidos, the work is done in common, but consumption and all other aspects of life remain largely individual. The National Bank of Ejidal Credit functions as a banker, agricultural expert, and technical advisor.

In areas where collectives are sought to be organized on the soviet model, a more elaborate arrangement for division of work, supervision of operations, accounting of the work done and its remuneration will have to be made. Each performance is converted to work-day units classified according to certain norms set for each operation and credited to each member, which entitles him to a participation in the net income. At the other end of the scale are the comparatively simple types of co-operatives formed for undertaking some specific farm operations on a common basis.

What farm operations and which of the resources of the individual farmers should be combined and brought within the co-operative organization, would thus vary from country to country according to local conditions. No particular standard of combination can be prescribed for universal adoption. The distribution of income will likewise depend on the particular type of organization adopted and the degree to which individual interests are subordinated to community or collective interest. In advanced communal settlements like the kvutza income is divided according to the need of the family and work is not compensated for separately. In collectives of the soviet pattern, a special method of valuing and paying for work done in units known as work-days is followed. The evaluation of the unit depends upon the nature of work and skill involved in its performance. Special bonuses in the form of additional work-days are given for an increase in labor productivity over the average of the collective farm. In the ejidos, compensation for work may be on the basis of wages or may depend on the number of days worked and on the proportion contributed to the income. Or again, as in some of the experiments in India, the income may be divided, after allocations are made towards the reserve land, depreciation fund, etc., in proportion to the quality and the area of land brought under common management, labor being paid for at the prevailing market rates. In the Italian settlement schemes, the member gets the produce he grows on the land allotted to him.

It is not easy to say which of the forms of remuneration is more desirable, as the system adopted would depend on the situation obtaining in each country. Theoretically, division of income according to work done may serve best to preserve incentives to good work and lead to efficient management of land. But in areas where land has for long been cultivated by a class of peasant holders deeply attached to their small plots, it will be difficult to persuade them to surrender their individual pieces of land to the common pool in return for remuneration for work done, unless they expect to get profits of cultivation over and above the usual rent. In areas where land is cultivated in small fragments the most pressing problem is not that of labor, but the reallocation of land in more compact blocks, which would give a sizeable unit of production. It would be far easier if this could be taken up as the first objective, and the assets brought in this manner to the common pool definitely recognized and paid for.

The constitution of management will likewise depend upon the form of organization adopted. In the co-operative, the executive committee or board of management will be elected by the general body, and may have a manager who may or may not be a member of the co-operative. In many of the societies organized in India and elsewhere, an agricultural officer and a co-operative officer are available to the executive manager for consultation and guidance. In the co-operative settlement of kvutza in Israel, the general assembly, which is the supreme authority in the settlement, elects committees for all phases of community life. In the ejidos of Mexico the internal administration is in the hands of two committees, one executive and the other supervisory, both of which are elected by the General Assembly. In the Russian kolkhoz, although in theory the general meeting of the members elects the board of management, in practice they are imposed by the Soviet party. The board appoints brigade leaders for supervising the work of each team and seeing that the assignments are completed.

The problems of farm management are thus a result of several factors: the peculiar systems of land holdings and land tenure prevailing in the different regions, the availability of capital and other resources, the concentration of population, the physical aspects of the land, the aspirations of the people, and the general economic situation. In the very nature of the case, the discussion of this working party had to be in a large measure the record of the experiences of the several countries represented, rather than an attempt to evolve any formula for common adoption. Only certain very broad generalizations can, therefore, be ventured.

1. Under the conditions obtaining in the bulk of the countries represented in the group, individual farming by a large class of small, under-resourced farmers made for progressively deteriorating standards of management and cultivation. In intensively populated areas with deep-rooted traditions of ownership rights, the organization of large farms on a collective basis involving the merging of all personal rights is not a workable proposition. Further explorations must be made of the possibilities of some alternative forms of co-operative management which will preserve individual incentive and promote associated effort in desired directions.

2. In general, it would be wise to move by stages. It would be better to begin with simpler types of co-operation organized for specific purposes, wherein the problems of management are not very taxing, and move forward toward more extensive forms, as more and more experience is gained.

3. The resources combined in co-operatives will vary greatly. The principal limiting factors will be the degree of their scarcity, the alternatives open for their use, the prospects for increasing their supply, and the difficulties of bookkeeping and administration involved.

4. The method of distributing earnings may also vary with conditions. Some method of relating the distribution to participation in work and recognition of superior performance should eventually be attempted. Within this framework, the methods adopted should be as simple as possible and should not make excessive demands on administrative requirements.

5. The physical structure of the farms is

an important factor in facilitating co-operation and should, therefore, be given primary
consideration.

6. The traditional co-operative procedures
for the election of the management committee offer the best means of self-discipline
and democratic working of the farms.

THE POSSIBILITIES OF CO-OPERATIVES AS
MEANS FOR STRENGTHENING THE
POSITION OF THE INDEPENDENT FARMER

Report of the Working Party

Chairmen, *Henry H. Bakken and Marvin A. Schaars*

ABOUT ONE-HALF of the countries represented in the working party are in Asia,
one-fourth in Europe, and one-fourth on the
American continent. Participants from each
of the countries reported upon the major
problems facing co-operatives in their respective countries. These problem areas
were reported to be the following:

1. Obtaining adequate finances for establishing co-operative associations in the fields
of credit, marketing, purchasing, and service.

2. Devising ways and means to supply
credit to farmers who may be termed "high
credit risks" and who do not presently
qualify for loans under existing credit society or production credit association practices.

3. Consolidating credit societies and
spreading the base of ownership of shares
in the societies.

4. Educating farmers as to the necessity
and possibilities of co-operative organization.

5. Solving the problems of co-operative
organization where there is a lack of (a)
capital, (b) technical "know-how," and (c)
leadership.

6. Resolving the issue as to whether compulsory co-operation or strictly voluntary co-
operation is the proper method of initiating
co-operative action among peoples handicapped by a lack of education, capital, and
experience in co-operative endeavor.

7. Developing unions of co-operatives.

8. Avoiding stagnation of co-operatives.

9. Preventing top-heavy administrative
control of co-operatives.

10. Clarifying the tax position of co-operatives.

11. Supervising loans of credit societies so
as to make certain that loans are used for
productive purposes.

12. Consolidating land holdings through
co-operative organizations.

13. Whether multipurpose societies are
superior as a form of co-operative organization in villages to single commodity or specialized service associations.

14. Determining the proper and respective roles of government, co-operatives, and
private traders in the rural economy.

15. Co-ordinating the growth of the co-
operative movement in order to have a balanced approach to all sectors of co-operative
activity.

16. Instituting an objective research program as a basis for undertaking and guiding the direction of co-operative development.

17. Giving serious attention to an understanding of basic principles of co-operation.

18. Fostering a sound public relations
program about co-operatives.

19. Existence of competition between co-operatives in serving farmers in the same areas.

20. Failure of local associations to federate with others for the solution of common problems beyond the local sphere.

21. Planning for and bringing about better membership understanding and membership relations.

22. Recognizing the limitations as well as merits of the inherent conservatism of co-operatives.

Many of these problems and the need for their solution if the movement is to be a vital force in strengthening the position of the independent farmer were common to most countries; other problems were especially acute in some countries but less so in others. The need for credit and organizations that can supply it at fair rates to farmers is undoubtedly the major, if not universal, problem in most countries.

Credit and Financing

A brief description of the institution for developing credit facilities and serving the needs of co-operatives in the United States was outlined by the moderator. Much of the discussion that ensued centered on the operations of government banks established for the purpose of financing co-operative associations, including their structural organization features, interrelationships with other credit agencies, and their mode of operations.

Comments and observations emanating from the conferees were directed in particular to the solution of the three major limitations prevalent in underdeveloped areas: First, from what sources should initial capital be obtained to make it available to the indigents? Second, what should be done about extending credit to those who have become improvident and indolent as a consequence of a vicious system of exploitation in centuries past? Third, how can the extension of credit be properly administered or supervised to avert its dissipation after it has been placed in the hands of the borrowers?

It appeared to be the consensus of the group that governments in general have recognized their responsibilities toward those underprivileged classes and have in some measure attempted to alleviate their unfortunate circumstances. The difficulty, however, is to avoid paternalistic tendencies. The protective hand of the government should be limited to creating basic legislation and providing the necessary "grubstake" (i.e., the creation of favorable circumstances in which growth can occur) to help its indigent citizens to help themselves.

Some positive measures should be taken to eliminate excessive interest rates and in particular the practices of usury. The main objective in each nation should be that of releasing its agrarian people from a perpetual state of peonage and to make it possible for them to ascend progressively toward a state or economic independence. The ownership of the land and the machines which they use to till the soil would be a manifestation of success in this objective. One solution to this problem appears to lie in a proper pattern of organization. But perfection of organization is not enough; it must be evolved in proper sequence and propitiously timed. This implies that, initially among the unsophisticated, the remedial procedure must be projected from the top down to the prospective co-operators. This requires expert techniques, a trained leadership, and infinite patience to endure some failures and relapses. It should be noted that this experience is already a reality in some countries.

The problem of obviating the misuse of funds by reloaning them for higher interest is simply an administrative detail. The major issue is to eliminate the cause and this has been partially solved by the establishment of numerous voluntary savings and credit societies similar to the credit union movement in the United States and the Raiffeisen system in Germany.

Marketing and Purchasing

The development of marketing and purchasing associations varies a great deal by countries. In some areas, as in northern Europe and in North America, Australia, and New Zealand, significant developments have taken place; but in other areas, the marketing and purchasing associations are considerably overshadowed by the credit societies. Multi-purpose societies which combine credit, marketing, and purchasing at the village level are generally considered preferable in Oriental countries to single commodity or single function associations which ordinarily predominate in western countries. Both types of societies are deemed to have their place, depending upon the economic environment in which they are to function. The great diversity of commodities marketed co-operatively indicates the wide applicability of this technique in selling. Procurement societies—or, as they are also called, purchasing associations—have contributed to the economic welfare of their members.

The underlying philosophy behind co-operative marketing was also discussed. Specifically, the issue was raised as to whether the goal of such organizations was to establish monopolies with price-fixing powers or whether the basic aim is to achieve business efficiency and to take the conditions of the market as they are found, with the goal of placing the farmer in the best possible position relative to them. The former position would entail the necessity of having all or a substantial proportion of the supply under the control of the association, in order that arbitrary price fixing and monopoly control might be exercised. The latter position envisages the possibility of benefiting farmers through such practices as reducing costs

of distribution, careful timing of the flow of goods to market, developing expanded market outlets, grading, etc. without having a certain percentage of control of the supply. It was pointed out that, as a result of product differentiation, co-operatives also engage in monopolistic competition, and that as a result of the very nature of co-operation, competition between individual farmers is eliminated. It was pointed out that for export purposes of some commodities, co-operatives in some countries have requested of their governments the sole authority to engage in export operation as a means of more effectively representing the interests of all producers in the world's competitive markets. In addition to the thought of "business efficiency" as a driving force for marketing associations, the desire of "business honesty" was also included in the discussion by the working party.

The integration of business operations on a vertical, horizontal, and complementary basis was also discussed as a means of strengthening the position of co-operatives, both from the standpoint of improving business efficiency and providing more dependable service for co-operators. The degree to which integration can be accomplished, especially of the complementary type, depends in no small measure upon the financial strength of the organizations, their business experience, and the economies which may be attained from spreading out into new fields. Integration of co-operative purchasing with co-operative marketing associations as is done by numerous co-operatives in the United States does not fit the pattern of organization in all countries.

The issue of having labor unions unionize members of co-operative associations to bargain for them with their own co-operative or other handlers of farm products was not a problem experienced in the countries of the conferees represented as it is in some sections of the United States.

Taxation

The concerted attack upon co-operatives in the United States growing out of the federal income taxation issue was discussed. The arguments of the critics of co-operatives and the counter arguments presented by co-operatives were mentioned. Apparently the issue is not a major one in most of the countries.

Service Associations

The possibilities of strengthening the independent farmer's position through organizing service co-operatives were discussed. Such service co-operatives as insurance, telephone, electricity, artificial breeding, auditing, health, and hospitalization associations were included in the discussion. Although co-operative auditing services are provided in some countries, the need for such associations is nonexistent in countries where the co-operative registrar's office includes auditing of the books of co-operatives as one of its principal functions. The expansion of co-operatives in the service fields has practical limitations in many countries. However, the opportunities in this field of co-operative action deserve careful consideration if a balanced co-operative program is to be undertaken by farmers.

Part XXI SUPPLYING FARM MACHINERY THROUGH STATE STATIONS AND CO-OPERATIVES

MACHINE-TRACTOR STATIONS IN SOVIET RUSSIA

Lazar Volin

THE PIONEER role which Soviet Russia played in the development of machine-tractor stations is well known. As a matter of fact, co-operative ownership of tractors by the Russian farmers in the 1920's even preceded the organization of machine-tractor stations (usually abbreviated as M.T.S., as it will appear here henceforth). However, since the 1930's, tractors and complicated machinery belonged as a rule either to the state farms or to the M.T.S. This was a consequence of the rapid forced collectivization of Russian peasant agriculture, a subject with which I deal in another paper in this volume. Here I would only like to point out that the M.T.S. has been an integral feature of Soviet agrarian collectivism.

The credit for establishing the first machine-tractor station must be given to the Russian agronomist, Markevich, who was a manager of a Soviet state farm near Odessa. In 1927, he took the initiative of assigning ten tractors with the necessary agricultural implements and operators to work on a contractual basis the land belonging to peasants of four neighboring villages. This unit served as a pattern for the organization of other M.T.S. One of the requirements of the contract was the voluntary consolidation on a co-operative basis of the small, scattered peasant holdings into large fields suitable for tractor operations. Markevich, who was "purged" by the Kremlin a few years later, was the real pioneer of this important Soviet agricultural institution. He ex-

pounded this idea in a little book entitled *Mezhselennye Mashinno-Traktornye Stantsii,* published in 1929, which became a classic on the subject.

The Soviet Government, which, in the late 1920's was determined to collectivize small peasant agriculture, to transform it into large-scale farming, was quick to perceive that the M.T.S. could be a powerful lever for accomplishing this objective, especially since the pooling of tractors and other equipment made possible their greater utilization so much needed at a time when Russian agriculture was severely handicapped by critical shortage of draft power. This shortage resulted from the wholesale slaughter of horses and other livestock by the peasants during the forced collectivization campaign.

Maximizing the use of tractors and other farm equipment by concentrating them in a central unit—the M.T.S.—and thus economizing or making more effective the capital investment in agriculture is, no doubt, of first importance. However, this is not the whole story. For the Soviet M.T.S. is not just a farm-machinery custom work agency, but is a powerful arm of Soviet technical direction and control of collective agriculture, as well as a highly important source of revenue to the state.

Each M.T.S. is a separate unit, having a certain number of tractors, combines, and other machinery. It is headed by a director appointed by the Minister of Agriculture.

There is a political vice-director, whose functions are similar to those of the political commissars in the Red Army. The staff of an M.T.S. is made up of mechanics, bookkeepers, and agronomists, as well as tractor drivers and combine operators. The latter two categories are recruited from members of the collectives and trained for their work in special schools. The collectives also provide all other labor necessary to assist with the field work of the tractors and combines, such as workers delivering fuel, water, etc.

The M.T.S. are usually divided into several so-called tractor brigades, each consisting of three to five, or more, tractors with necessary implements and personnel. A tractor brigade is usually assigned work in one or several adjoining collectives. The tractor drivers are paid partly by the state and partly by the collectives, and the remainder of the personnel are paid by the state.

The collective farms, as a rule, do not own tractors, combines, and other complicated machinery, but must rely on state-owned M.T.S. The collectives are thus divorced from their modern power-machine base, which is completely controlled by the government. The amount of work to be done by the M.T.S. each year is determined, as in the case of all other Soviet enterprises, by the government plan. In addition, an M.T.S. is supposed to conclude agreements with the collectives each year, specifying in detail the kind and amount of work to be performed and the time required for its completion. Likewise, the contribution that the collective is to make, such as the amount of labor to be assigned to help the M.T.S. in its field work, is stated in the agreement. These agreements follow a standard form approved by the government. In practice, however, the agreements were often not lived up to; sometimes they were not even concluded.

As a high Soviet functionary stated, in 1947, "Some M.T.S. have stopped entirely making agreements with the collectives and others conclude such agreements with much delay and only as a formality, the agreements made not being observed." Official criticism of this sort has been repeated year in and year out. The fact of the matter is that the so-called agreements with the M.T.S. are not really voluntary contracts with respect to which a collective can exercise a choice. Actually, government plans determine the relationship between the M.T.S. and the collectives. The collective is therefore confronted in the M.T.S. with a monopolist supplying essential services— albeit, a public monopolist closely regulated by the state with regard to both the rates paid and services performed. But experience with the M.T.S. has shown that, as far as the character of the service is concerned, effective regulation has been most difficult.

In their desire to service more and more acres, the M.T.S. have often neglected the quality of the field work and the improvement of yields per acre so much stressed by the Soviet government. A member of the powerful Politburo, Andreev, complained a few years ago:

Our machine-tractor stations are little interested in improvement of yields, in good soil management, in timely seeding and harvesting. The existing system of evaluation of the work of M.T.S. in terms of hectares converted to plowing equivalent, and the system of incentives for the M.T.S. personnel, results in the M.T.S. striving to complete as many light operations as possible instead of the difficult plowing work. . . . One must ask what good do the state and collectives derive from such a fulfillment of their plan by M.T.S. if it results in low yields? The objective, after all, is not just to dig the soil a little but to create actual conditions for growing a good crop and to harvest it in good time with combines.

This disappointment will be even better understood when it is remembered that the M.T.S. are supposed to direct and guide collectives in the introduction of improved farm methods and practices.

In view of the great dependence of collectives on the M.T.S., the damage caused by the slipshod work by the latter cannot be exaggerated. Good and timely or poor and delayed cultivation of the collective fields by an M.T.S. may spell the difference between good and poor crop yields, between success or failure of the collective to meet its production and distribution goals.

A stock claim of Soviet spokesmen has been that tractors are more effectively utilized in Soviet Russia than in the United States and other countries where they are privately owned, because they are used longer during the year. This is correct as far as statistical averages go. Much of this advantage in the Soviet Union is offset, however, by the use of several workers where one would do the job in the United States and by frequent breakdowns and idleness of tractors and combines as a result of poor care, inexperienced or inefficient operators, poor repair work, shortages of spare parts and fuel, and other factors. Inadequate repair facilities and care of tractors and other machinery and in many cases lack of M.T.S. storage facilities have contributed to excessive wear and tear on machinery. Every winter, repairing and overhauling tractors and combines has been a campaign that required major official attention.

It is not surprising, therefore, that the high cost of operation of the M.T.S. has been a constant source of preoccupation for the authorities concerned. Among factors contributing to high cost, considerable prominence has been given to wasteful use of fuel by tractors. This is caused by unsatisfactory adjustment of machines, wasted motion of tractors, lack of proper fueling equipment, and inadequate storage and transportation facilities.

The extent of tractor mechanization of farm work varies among different operations and different regions. The greatest mechanization was achieved in plowing and other heavy types of farm work. But little progress was made in mechanization of some important farm operations—such as haying, for example, notwithstanding the usefulness of machines in avoiding delays and other difficulties that usually beset the Soviet hay harvest and reduce the much-needed forage supply.

Among the farm operations performed by the M.T.S., harvesting of grain by combine has held a special place in official interest. Stalin even devoted one of his infrequent speeches to the subject at the conference of the best combine operators held in Moscow in December, 1935. Combine operators, even more than tractor drivers, came to represent the aristocracy of farm labor. The steeply differentiated system of payment, with liberal bonuses for exceeding the standard task, made it possible for some of the best operators to earn during the relatively short season several times more than the average annual wage in the M.T.S.

The attention focused on the combine is explained, in the first place, by the fact that delayed, inefficient harvesting with resulting large crop losses constitutes one of the weakest links in Soviet collective agriculture. Complete mechanization of the harvest was, therefore, looked upon as the way out of such difficulties; though the results have often been disappointing because of the inefficient operation of combines. Weedy fields must be mentioned as one of the worst enemies of combines in Russia.

In the second place, harvesting of grain by state-owned combines, eliminating the intermediate threshing center and extra transportation and handling, facilitates and speeds up government collections of grain. From the combine, grain can be shipped directly to the government procuring center. This may not only result in economies but also make for a more certain supply. For it must be remembered that the "struggle over grain" and other farm products between the Soviet government and the peasants, though it changes its form, has never really ceased since the beginning of the Soviet regime.

In addition to field work, the M.T.S. are also helping at present with a number of other operations, such as planting tree shelter-belts, constructing water reservoirs and irrigation canals, improving pastures and meadows. Mechanization in animal husbandry and poultry raising, which depends on use of electric power, is still in its infancy in the Soviet Union.

The M.T.S. are state-financed both with respect to capital investment and current expenditures. As a rule, they are paid in kind for their services to the collectives. M.T.S. are paid in cash for only certain minor operations. Each M.T.S. operation is paid at a specified rate per hectare, which varies with the officially estimated yields of crops per hectare for a district or group of collectives and increases with higher yields. Beginning in the 1947 season, the rate of payment was reduced where the M.T.S. delayed work—a means of penalizing tardy M.T.S. For harvesting grain by combines a certain per cent of the outturn is charged.

An important fact to remember is that the officially estimated Soviet figures of yields per hectare of crops since 1933 are preharvest figures. The figures are based on the standing crop, and do not take into account the heavy harvest losses common in the Soviet Union. Thus, official estimates of crop yields (on the basis of which the collectives pay in kind to the M.T.S.) are invariably higher than actual harvested outturn, the so-called barn crop. This is true even when there is no exaggeration for propaganda or fiscal purposes, from which these figures cannot be considered free. Under such conditions, payments to M.T.S. are especially burdensome in years of poor crops. Collec-

tives that are serviced by M.T.S., however, deliver 20 per cent less grain as compulsory procurements or tax in kind than those which are not serviced.

The payments in kind to M.T.S. make up an important part of the supplies of grain and other farm products acquired by the government. Grain collections of M.T.S. constituted, on the average, more than a third of all grain procurements from the collectives during the period 1935–37.

It is implicit in what was said above, that agricultural mechanization in Soviet Russia and its principal institutional form—the M.T.S.—have highly significant political as well as economic and technical functions to perform. From Lenin's days down, the Soviet leadership has manifested an unbounded enthusiasm for that American invention, the tractor, to which was later added the admiration for another American invention, the combine. Lenin, as early as 1919, toyed with what he called a fantasy of 100,000 tractors as a bait to attract peasants to collectivization. The tractors, however, were not to be had in those years of revolution and civil war. Even ten years later, when the Soviet government decided to collectivize speedily Russian peasant agriculture, it did not wait for an adequate supply of tractors and machinery.

But it soon became clear that the tractors had to be enlisted to fight the shortage of draft power and the crisis of underproduction, which the collectivization policy of the Soviet government made acute. Unlike other countries, in Soviet Russia the tractor was not displacing the horse because this was economically advantageous on the basis of price-cost calculations. The tractors were thrown in as rapidly as possible to repair the wide breach on the agrarian front which developed as a consequence of the destruction of horses during collectivization. Despite the often inefficient and uneconomic use of tractors and combines, judged by

Western standards, it must be acknowledged that the M.T.S. helped to overcome this crisis. They contributed materially to the expansion of the Russian crop acreage during the 1930's, though much less so to the improvement of yields. The fact that the M.T.S. were affected most adversely by the war, accounts in no small measure for the slowness of postwar agricultural recovery in the Soviet Union.

In conclusion, I would like to point out that what strengthens significantly the posi-tion of the M.T.S. is that by divorcing the collective farms from its power-machine base, making the Soviet agricultural economy so thoroughly dependent on the government for draft power, machines, fuel, and tech-nicians, mechanization has greatly helped Communist control of Russian agriculture. But I hope that the day will come in Russia when M.T.S. will be stripped of their po-litical functions and will become genuine servants of the Russian farmer.

EXPERIENCES IN OPERATION OF FARM MACHINERY CO-OPERATIVES IN GERMANY

Otto Schiller

THE PAPERS which thus far have been pre-sented at this conference have brought out clearly that agriculture in big areas of the world is largely managed in holdings smaller than what has here been termed "economic units." This holds especially for countries with dense rural population such as South and Southeast Asia, but it holds also for large regions of Europe. The small size of agricultural holdings is indeed one of the world's greatest land tenure problems. The problem has become crucial with the exten-sion of mechanization into agriculture. The small size of agricultural holdings constitutes the main obstacle to a rapid spread of mecha-nized work processes in agriculture. The gap between the methods used in small holdings and those used in fully mechanized large-scale farms is widening steadily. The small holder meets difficulties in using farm machinery because of the small size of his holding, the fragmentation of its fields, and because he lacks the necessary capital.

The attempt to adjust the size of the holding to the requirements of the machine, as the Soviets have done by establishing huge collective farms, cannot be considered the solution of this problem. On the con-trary, in the free world the agricultural ma-chinery and its utilization have to be ad-justed to the given size of holdings.

This is a matter of machine design as well as of managerial and social organiza-tion. In recent years machine design in Europe has made great strides in this direc-tion. We may point to the so-called Bauern-schlepper, a light tractor which can be profit-ably used even in middle-size farms. In re-gions of prevailing small and dwarf hold-ings, however, the solution of the problem can hardly be expected from the ingenuity of machine designers. Rather, agricultural policy has to establish the prerequisites for increased mechanization of agricultural small holdings by legislation, organization, and by financial and educational measures.

Considering the small holders' lack of cap-ital, obviously the joint use of agricultural machines is the most important organiza-tional device for promoting mechanization among them. In Germany and in other European countries the following forms of organization have been developed for this purpose:[1] (1) the private machine owner-operator working for a fee for the farmers, (2) public institutions owning machines, (3) co-operatives owning machines as a side line, and (4) co-operatives or associations specializing in agricultural machine operations.

The private machine owner-operator in Germany predominantly concentrates upon threshing machines, tractors, equipment for fighting insects and plant diseases, for steaming potatoes, etc. In Germany, with about 2 million holdings of more than one-half hectare there are about 7,000 such businesses in operation.[2]

In Western Germany publicly owned machines are important only in the field of fighting insects and plant diseases. The plague of the Colorado beetle during the mid 1930's, for instance, caused the government to intervene directly via the offices for plant protection (Pflanzenschutzämter). Today this fight is being carried on mostly by publicly owned machines.

In the Soviet Zone of Germany more than 500 public machinery stations (MAS) with about 8,000 tractors have been established after the Soviet model.[3] Just like the MTS in the Soviet Union these MAS serve also political purposes.

For some time the German co-operatives, that is, mainly the credit and the marketing co-operatives, as a sideline have engaged in the operation of large agricultural machines, such as threshing machines, tractors, seed cleaning machines, etc., which they lease to members for a fixed charge much in the way the private owner operator does. In the small holding areas of Southwestern Germany, for instance, this form of tractor operation and maintenance is customary in rural communities. Most small holders, however, avail themselves of the tractor of the co-operative only for transportation purposes or in order to meet seasonal peak demands. That is why the use of the tractor did not essentially change the farm organization nor

reduce the number of draft animals. Consequently, the maintenance of agricultural machines as a side line of large co-operatives, offers in many cases no satisfactory solution to the problem.

Co-operatives or other associations for the special purpose of joint use of machinery would seem to have better results. These machines become a stable element of the respective farmers' equipment and consequently cause a change of farm organization and a reduction of draft animals. Partners can readily agree to use jointly machines which are not in demand by all at the same time, as for instance, threshing, seed cleaning, washing machines, and machinery for plant protection. Such machines can be used also by a larger number of partners who usually associate in the legal form of a co-operative society.

Other machines, however, have to be used during definite periods (as for instance the tractor, if used for tillage and harvesting) and require a small number of partners. Therefore, in Germany the legal form of the co-operative usually is not practicable since the German law for co-operatives prescribes a minimum number of seven members. Generally, tractor partnerships are confined to two to five members who legally contract a partnership or simply make a gentleman's agreement. It is of importance that the capacity of the tractor correspond to the acreage of the partners to guarantee the efficient exploitation of the tractor. In contrast to the private machine owner-operator the partners usually charge merely the operating costs of the machine without charging for amortization and for capital interest. The mutual aid of rural neighbors operates similarly: a prosperous farmer may regularly cultivate with his machines the fields of one or several of his neighbors.

In Southern Württemberg during the last two years, eighty-two so-called Betriebsgemeinschaften, that is, partnerships of usually three farmers, have been tentatively established with public support. The government helps them to buy a tractor, and the farmers, in turn, are held responsible for its efficient utilization and for orderly bookkeeping which will be examined by the government agency.

At first glance it might appear as if the Soviets had found the most simple and entire solution for the problem of joint machinery use via the system of kolkhozy. Actually this is no solution of the problem but rather its elimination. Our problem is not to liquidate the small holders but to help them. Consequently, no form of joint machinery use which eliminates the independence of the small holders can be considered a satisfactory solution of the problem. There are, however, ways and means of joint use of machinery which have nothing in common with the methods applied by the Soviets. Hence, it would be a mistake to reject any and all forms of joint use of machinery for fear of taking the first step toward the collectivization of agriculture. If one realizes the difference in principle between collectivistic and co-operative methods of work and respects the limits which must not be trespassed in applying co-operative methods, then the joint use of machinery certainly does not represent the first step towards collectivization but rather one of the most important means of challenging the advance of communism by economic and social support of the small holder.

The efficient use of agricultural machinery is difficult because various special machines are used only for a few days of the year and consequently their capacity is normally exploited only very little. Machines such as the seed cleaning machines can hence also be utilized co-operatively to advantage by large farms. A further difficulty results from the fact that a whole series of agricultural operations are seasonal; hence, the utilization of machines not belonging to the farmer

himself fails to guarantee him the timely performance of the work. This is the main reason why partnerships for such machine operations as mentioned before can extend but to a small number of farms.

Often the problem of mechanization in agriculture is seen too exclusively in the perspective of the large-scale farms, and, accordingly, undue significance is often ascribed to the tractor. An analysis of German small holdings, however, shows that by far the larger part of the annual work of a farm family is spent not in the field but in the house, farmyard, and stable. Many of these operations can be mechanized also on the single small farm. Since this concerns work which is less rigidly time-bound there exist still great opportunities for the joint use of machinery, such as, for instance, the installation of co-operative laundries, bakeries, etc.

The problem of machine utilization on the small farm differs in another point from that of the big farm. The large estate tends to save as much labor as possible and to mechanize completely all operations. On the small farm a certain potential of human labor is given from the start. This work potential shall and will be utilized to an economically and socially justifiable extent. It would be no service to the small farmer if mechanization were to make him and his family members partly idle, especially if he would have to pay in money for co-operative machine utilization what he saves in labor. Hence, the farmer will be interested in the joint use of machinery only to the extent to which it frees him and his family from oppressive work or to the extent to which he has opportunities to use his saved labor for intensifying his farm or for profitable employment off the farm. Therefore, one can count on regular joint use of farm machines on the part of small farmers only to the extent to which they do not consider it to be an avoidable expenditure. Many a farmer in financial distress will try to save at the wrong place and will, say, use his cows for long distance transport rather than use the tractor of the co-operative, even if his saving should be lower than the loss incurred by the drop in milk output. In some cases provisions are made that the partners are obligated to a minimum use of the jointly-owned machinery. This minimum time is calculated in the charge for use of the machinery.

The diffusion of farm machinery and its joint use is often blocked by the generally strong individualism of the farmer, who dislikes to become dependent upon others. Hence, he will, wherever possible, prefer to have his own machine, even if this should mean uneconomical over-investment. Such excessive investment in diverse machinery can be observed in many rural communities of Germany. This tendency has been re-enforced by his lack of desire to save and by uncertain political conditions. In times of crises this over-investment can become very detrimental for the respective farms. Great educational and advisory endeavors have to be made in this field, too, to steer agriculture in the proper direction. This requires also that our educators and advisors come to realize more than heretofore that agricultural progress under present-day conditions must be sought not merely from technological but also from economic and social perspectives. It is necessary to strengthen the community spirit among small holders in order to pave the way for the diffusion of the joint use of machinery.

An essential prerequisite for the efficient use of machines on small and middle-size holdings is the consolidation of scattered plots. Where strip farming prevails the machine cannot be used efficiently because of the necessity frequently to shift from one small parcel to another. Meeting this drawback by common crop rotation, therefore, has been considered and occasionally has

been tried out. Common crop rotation permits farms linked through joint use of machinery to cultivate their neighboring fields with the identical crop. The machine then can operate without loss of time on the parcels, either consecutively or, in certain operations, even jointly. Principally such work procedures can be endorsed only if individual harvesting of the single plots guarantees the independence of individual farms, the preservation of private property in land, and personal interest in landed property. Otherwise one gets dangerously close to collectivistic work procedures even if formally retaining private property in land. Generally, the peasant is not merely interested in the legal concept of private property in land but in the security of independent land utilization by himself and his heirs.

Recently the author published in *Land Economics* a report on experiences made under special conditions, and on a big scale, outside of Germany with the introduction of common rotation and work procedures of joint machine utilization resulting therefrom. Hence, details of these experiences are out of place here, but two other examples may serve to illustrate experiences which recently have been made in Germany with such work methods.

Early in the 1930's nine farmsteads of a small Württemberg community were organized into a machine co-operative under the guidance of the agricultural college of Hohenheim.[4] The nine farms were obligated to follow a common scheme of crop rotation. So far as the unconsolidated field layout allowed for it, neighboring plots were cultivated with the identical crop. Ploughing, sowing, and mowing on these neighboring plots were performed in a single operation by means of the jointly-owned tractor, occasionally disregarding the boundary lines separating the parcels. But it was insisted upon that each farmer carry off and thresh the yield of his plot individually. This procedure worked out fairly well during the experiment. When, however, the farmers were left to themselves they soon dropped this method of operation, especially since obligatory cultivation programs then introduced in Germany changed the crop rotation, and the cultivation of field vegetables and of oil seeds was taken up by the respective farms. Besides, this system of operation was justified only for so long as the co-operative had only the then prevailing iron-wheeled large tractor which demands a rather large area for operation, especially for turning around. The later type of tractor with rubber tires, which is smaller and more mobile, can operate efficiently also on small plots of no less than one-half hectare. Using this type of tractor the co-operative could attain economic efficiency through avoidance of idling by way of common crop rotation even if the identically cultivated plots were worked on consecutively instead of together.

After World War II, a similar experiment has been made in a new settlement of German refugees near Stuttgart. Here conditions were more favorable inasmuch as one was not handicapped by strip farming on widely scattered plots and was able from the start to systematically adjust the layout of fields to the requirements of common crop rotation. In laying out ten settlement farms on an even and homogeneous area of a former maneuver ground, one proceeded by dividing the square area into ten rectangles, one next to the other. Hence, each settler received one coherent piece of land of about six hectares. Then, in a right angle to this, the area was subdivided, in chessboard fashion, into twelve strips, representing the fields for crop rotation, so that a unified twelve-field crop rotation scheme resulted for the ten settlers. The jointly-owned tractor of the settlers, bought with the help of a government loan, could without difficulty accomplish the different work operations in a single move across all ten fields. During the initial phase, before the settlers were sufficiently prosperous, this procedure worked out all right. Soon, however, it became apparent that the schematic use of a common crop rotation handicaps the deployment of individual initiative. One settler would be more interested in livestock than the other, hence would require a different crop rotation emphasizing fodder; another one with a large family would have a better chance for engaging in hoe and vegetable cultivation, etc. Thus, as soon as the settlers had gained an economic footing of their own they dropped the common crop rotation and acquired draft animals of their own in order not to be dependent exclusively on the common tractor.

It is also reported from Holland that the peasants of a machine co-operative in Northern Brabant have taken up common crop rotation, and it is reported from France that fourteen machine co-operatives in the Isere valley have introduced this method.[5] There is no detailed information available about the results of these experiments.

The German examples mentioned above do not seem to speak for common crop rotation as a means for the economic use of agricultural machinery in small holdings. But these few examples do not warrant a final judgment. Other experiences which the author had occasion to observe indicate that under certain conditions a common crop rotation can foster joint use of machinery. To be sure, it has to be flexible, leaving a sufficient margin for modifications, especially in the fields cultivated with hoe crops, to make allowance for the varying requirements of individual farmers. The utilization, for instance, of irrigation equipment, which for small holdings cannot but be jointly used, would presuppose common crop rotation. The cultivation of special crops requiring the use of special machines, such as, for instance, flax comb machines, can benefit from common crop rotation. The same holds for crops which require a joint and simultaneous fight against insects and plant diseases. In this context we may point to the practice used during the consolidation of vineyards in Switzerland and in some German communities, namely, to concentrate grapevine plantation in the most suitable sections of the community areas, fixing the width of rows and choice of species in order to facilitate the mechanization of operations by pulleys, by joint fight against pests, etc.

In conclusion, it may be said that for large farmsteads it is preferable to own their machines, and even for middle-size farmsteads the light tractor (Bauernschlepper) as an all-round implement can be a profitable investment. Threshing machines, seed cleaning machines, special equipment for fighting pests, etc., will be profitably maintained by co-operatives or associations, even in the case of large holdings. The joint use of machinery will, however, mainly apply to areas of prevailing middle and small holdings, although offering but a partial solution to the land tenure problems of such regions. To be sure, the small and middle-size farms can be more readily won for technical progress through the joint use of machinery, but in the long run the larger family farm (under German conditions a size of roughly twenty-five to seventy-five acres) may well prove itself as the more effective and desirable economic unit. The polar opposite to the kolkhoz is not the small holding dependent upon co-operative support but the strong family farm, which is considerably above the minimum size of an economic unit and can hold its own without outside support. Although we must make every effort to improve the small holding by joint use of machinery and by other means, we should, at the same time, make use of all means of agricultural policy which lead to a gradual change in land tenure in favor of larger family farms.

THE DUTCH EXPERIENCE WITH FARM MACHINERY CO-OPERATIVES

ƧƧƧƧ *Cornelis D. Scheer*

ONLY IN THE last four years farm machinery co-operatives have been established, and they are developing rapidly in number. Earlier, they hardly existed in The Netherlands.

In respect of some agricultural farms of larger size, primarily run with hired labor, people had established a small number of co-operatives or similar forms of joint use of threshing machines. But most of these farmers were employing their own set of machinery and implements, others hiring these machines from individual owners.

The same can be said of the mechanization in the dairy farms as to haying and milking, though from the beginning of this century the production of dairy products moved away from the farm, partly in co-operatives, partly in non–co-operative mechanized plants.

In general, farm machinery was employed individually and not co-operatively and, on the whole, at a small scale.

There are different causes for this initiation. Part of our farms are family farms, and in most of them there is more-or-less excess labor. These farmers are afraid to raise their expenses without being able to find productive employment for the labor who will be set free if machines are employed. Moreover, these farms are often small and fragmented and, therefore, unsuitable to use machinery efficiently.

But after the war the scene changed. Wages increased considerably, increasing costs of labor on the family farm—at least when the regular force had to be supplied with hired labor in the peak seasons. Moreover, farm machinery has been improved and several types more suitable for farms of small size have been developed. Finally, our government in its drive to improve the efficiency of the smaller farms set up in 1947 a system of premiums for farm machinery co-operatives.

Since then a great number of these co-operatives have been established. At the end of 1950, 403 co-operatives were in action, covering a cultivated area of nearly 300,000 acres. About 85 per cent of these co-operatives were established in the districts with the greatest number of small-size farms.

These co-operatives invested about 1.2 million dollars in farm machinery. In over 60 per cent of the number the investment totals not more than about five dollars per acre. In farms of around twenty acres, a very popular size on the sandy soils in the eastern and southern part of the land, this means one hundred dollars for each farm, as an average.

When we keep in mind the cost of a medium-size tractor, these co-operatives are cutting down the capital equipment needs of these farmers to at least one-fifth, with a reduction of 80 per cent.

Some Experiences

What are the experiences with these co-operatives? Since they have been only a short time in operation, not much can be said. The most important question is: what is the best size of these co-operatives? In answering this question two considerations have to be kept in mind. There are several motives for establishing a co-operative of large size, but there are several motives for a small size, too.

In a large co-operative underemployment of machinery and implements can be less than in a small one. More members mean fuller employment of the equipment.

A large-size co-operative can be run by a paid manager with paid personnel. Maintenance and small repairs can be done by this personnel out of season, when business is dull. Fuel and oil can be bought on easier terms.

On the other hand, more members mean a longer time to wait their turn. There will be many complaints when the weather is fine for plowing, threshing, and all the other activities dependent on good weather. So there has to be some equilibrium between the two in keeping costs low and keeping members quiet. Experience has taught that for this reason the number of members has to be relatively small.

Running the co-operative by a paid labor force may keep some costs on a low level, but their labor force is doing many things that could be done by the farmers themselves. When these farmers, or their sons, have some experience they are able to drive a tractor themselves, earning the wage the hired driver should have earned. Moreover, it is impossible to give these hired drivers or a manager full employment the year round; this means increasing costs.

Anyway, farm machine co-operatives run by a manager with hired personnel have not been successful in our country and have been suffering great losses, partly due to the particular postwar circumstances, partly due to internal inefficiencies.

This brings us to another question. Does it pay, and do they pay?

The question is very difficult to answer because of lack of exact figures. For our farmers are not able or willing to figure out these questions in their cost accounts. Nevertheless, hired ploughers, threshers, etc. are cutting their costs down to a low level as soon as these co-operatives are put in action. And this perhaps points out that it pays to the farmer. But do the co-operatives themselves pay, too? About this question more can be said, for most of them employ bookkeeping and cost accounting methods. It must be said that most of them have had very poor results, a great number of them suffering more or less losses.

Different causes of these losses can be mentioned. Very often they charged their members on a level below costs of production and had to charge them for a second time at the end of the year, according to their rules. In particular, poor bookkeeping, underestimating of costs, rising prices of fuel, oil, repairs, etc. gave rise to these losses.

Another problem will arise in the near future when the machinery or implements have to be substituted by new ones. For most of the co-operatives neglected the rising substitution value of their equipment,

charging their members on the basis of the old lower prices. More capital will have to be put in, and rates will have to be raised once more.

Summary

After the war farm machinery co-operatives developed rapidly in the small-size farm districts under the pressure of changed conditions and with some government aid.

Roughly speaking, these co-operatives cut down the farmer's capital equipment needs to about one-fifth of previous amounts.

Farm machinery co-operatives run with a manager and hired personnel do not pay.

Apparently, these farm machinery co-operatives have to be worked on a scale farmers themselves can run. They can pay when charges are on a rate according to proper cost accounting, and if so, they are paying to the farmers, too.

FARM MACHINERY CO-OPERATIVES AND CUSTOM SERVICES FOR PROVIDING CAPITAL EQUIPMENT TO SMALL AND MEDIUM-SIZE FARMS

Report of the Working Party

 Chairman, *Preston E. McNall*

THE MEMBERS of the working party discussed these topics in the light of their various experiences. The report is here presented in the nature of a summary of these experiences.

1. Countries with low or moderate incomes per farm relative to machinery prices make the most use of machinery co-operatives and stations. Here farmers need to buy machinery carefully and make full use of the machines bought.

2. Tractors, especially for the heavy operations in preparing the land for seeding, are very useful and are used on many small farms under various co-operative arrange-

ments or government ownership. Tractor co-operatives usually comprise only two to five farmers.

3. Spraying for weeds, insects, and diseases, and seed cleaning are in the public interest and are well suited to co-operative or government-owned machines. Western Germany, for example, has seven thousand publicly owned spraying outfits.

4. In farming areas with large and high-income farms, such as occur in many parts of England and the United States, most of the machines are privately owned. The larger machines, such as combines or threshing machines, pickup hay balers, corn pickers,

and field forage harvesters, are used by many farmers for doing custom work. Even these expensive machines which cost from fifteen hundred to three thousand dollars are being used more and more on single farms, not because the cost per hour of use would not be reduced by using them on two or more farms but because many farmers are not under enough economic pressure to force them to operate their farms at the lowest cost per unit of production. Fifty years ago these same areas in the United States used their large machines (such as threshing machines and corn shredders) many more days per year than they do now in 1951, and most of them were either co-operatively owned or were used for custom work. It was not uncommon then for one man of the neighborhood to own all the custom-employed machinery. However, a trend toward individual ownership of machinery may be expected wherever farm incomes increase. High progressive income tax rates and monetary inflation encourage extravagant purchases of machinery, a part of the costs of which may be entered yearly as farm expense.

5. Cost comparisons that are useful can often be made easily and directly. Thus three neighboring farmers in Sweden bought one tractor co-operatively. Each farmer had two horses before buying the tractor, after which each sold one horse and replaced the horse with a cow. The product of each cow for the year was worth more than one-third the cost of the tractor. Hence the tractor more than paid for itself.

6. In the United States, the cost of machinery given average usage may be computed as follows: The annual cost of interest (at 4 per cent), insurance, taxes, housing, depreciation, and repairs amounts to 10 per cent to 15 per cent of the new cost. Repairs amount to about 1.5 cents per hour per 100 dollars of new cost.

7. Custom rates in Wisconsin in 1951 for combining grain and for corn picking averaged about 5 dollars per acre. Pickup balers were 10 cents to 13 cents per 50 to 80 pound bale. Field forage harvesters supplying also two tractors, two wagons, one blower, and two men were 10 dollars per hour.

8. Special provision must be made for repairs and servicing of new types of machinery in areas where they have not been used before. Fuel must be supplied for power machinery. These seemingly obvious problems have been overlooked in some areas that began mechanizing. This has resulted in the most inefficient use of many of these machines. Short courses of one week or longer have been especially useful in teaching young farmers how to repair and operate the new machines. These short courses are usually given at agricultural schools.

9. The desirability as well as the type and extent of mechanization is influenced in some countries not only by the size of the farms and the income level of the farmers but also by the ability (capacity) of the local economy to absorb into other activities the manual labor released from agricultural production through mechanization. Labor inefficiently employed is more desirable than idle labor.

The labor set free by machinery should be used in industries or services unless people need, or can afford, more leisure. In Sweden the use of farm machinery reduced labor requirements 50 per cent in twenty years, but there were no problems of unemployment because industries developed in the meantime which absorbed the surplus farm labor. In The Netherlands certain areas have used the labor saved by more mechanization to increase the intensity of their farming. Considerable quantities of greenhouse products are being produced with the labor saved by mechanization.

10. Some of the European countries finance the joint use of machinery through co-operatives or through some banking sys-

tem. In Sweden, privately owned machines are subsidized by the government up to 25 per cent of the cost if they meet certain requirements in doing custom work. However, these subsidies are withheld for five or six years in order to induce the machine owners to continue doing custom work.

11. Consolidation of holdings and an increase in the size of holdings generally favor the economical use of machinery. Some improvements have also been made in the use of machinery in areas handicapped by scattered, small fields, by planning to plant adjacent fields to the same crop. In that way each operation of ground preparation and seeding can be done at one time with a company or government-owned tractor and other suitable machinery.

MANAGEMENT PROBLEMS OF LOW-INCOME FARMS

Report of the Working Party

Chairman, *William E. Hendrix*

THE FIRST part of the workshop was devoted to a statement by the participants of the management problems of low-income farmers in the countries represented in this workshop. Early in the discussion, questions were raised as to the meaning of the terms "low-income farms" and "farm management." It was evident that what we call low-income farms in some parts of the world would represent a very high level of production and income in others. Hence it was the consensus of the group that at best the concepts of low income and poverty are highly relative ones, but ones having reference to situations where production is too low to fulfill basic human wants and to provide the standards of reasonable human living.

Farm management was broadly defined as a field dealing with the problem of how to use scarce resources to maximize want-satisfying goods and services or standards of living, whether through production for direct consumption or through a market economy.

In describing the management problems of low-income farms in the various countries, it was very early evident that there are many different degrees of scarcity of the basic factors—land, labor, and capital—essential to agricultural production. Specifically, two extreme kinds of situations were distinguished: (1) areas where land is a very limiting factor and where labor is abundant and (2) areas where land is plentiful but labor is scarce.

A great scarcity of capital, itself a result of the low level of production and incomes, characterizes both of these situations. Too, agriculture in both ranges from highly self-sufficing kinds to highly commercialized types.

In the heavily populated areas, it was the consensus of the group that emphasis should be placed upon raising productivity per acre of land rather than upon labor-saving machines and other labor-saving methods of farming. It was indicated, however, that by co-operative effort, mechanical power could often be substituted for animal power to a large economic advantage, enabling farmers to dispense with draft animals and to use a larger part of their land to produce crops for food or market instead of feed for draft animals. Better food storage and preservation practices were indicated to be other highly pressing needs.

Some members of the group expressed the view that in the more heavily populated areas very little progress is possible unless the population pressure can be greatly relieved, that gains in productivity on farms would very quickly be absorbed by population increase. Industrialization was seen as the most likely solution of the population problem.

Discussion revealed also that low production and incomes, instead of being peculiar to densely populated areas, is perhaps equally as acute in many under-populated areas of the world. In these areas, land is plentiful, but farmers lack the capital and the knowledge of farming techniques essential to effective use of the available land. In these areas, it was agreed that labor-saving machines and techniques may be adopted and that more extensive kinds of farming need to be developed. On the other hand, the scarcity of capital requires that emphasis be placed upon the simpler techniques needing very little skill and capital, rather than stressing the more spectacular improvements. Among such simple but needed advances are: better seeds, better fertilizer practices, better insect control measures, and better tillage practices. Attention to better spacing of plants, for example, has been known to increase yields appreciably.

Increased attention to "better management of cash money" was suggested as a need in some areas where farmers are loath to use even the money they have for farming practices which would pay. This situation is observed particularly in politically unstable areas and in areas where crop failures are frequent. It is a way of meeting risks and uncertainty in areas where the problem is mainly one of survival. Bookkeeping, budgeting, and farm planning were discussed as other ways of helping to improve the situation.

It was the consensus of the group that the problem of raising the productivity of low-income farmers is not merely one of helping these farmers to adopt the machines, forms of economic organization, etc. which characterize highly productive farming. Rather, it is essential that we distinguish the major features of this problem wherever it occurs and that we orient both research and educational activities with careful attention to the needs and abilities (financial and otherwise) of the low-income farmers. Failure to distinguish the problems of low-income farmers from those of the more productive ones and failure to develop research, educational, and action programs specifically oriented to the needs and capabilities of the low-income farmers are undoubtedly associated with our limited success in eradicating rural poverty, even in highly productive nations like the United States.

Part XXII THE MANAGEMENT OF PUBLIC LANDS AND THE PUBLIC CONTROL OF PRIVATE LAND USE

THE MANAGEMENT OF PUBLIC LANDS

Abstract of the Report of the Working Party

Chairman, *Marion Clawson*

PARTICIPANTS in the workshop discussed the structure and management pattern of the publicly owned lands in their own countries. Programs for records of title were considered; it was apparent that adequate records have not been achieved in all countries. Also discussed were the ownership of mineral rights and water rights and methods by which ownership of water rights may be acquired.

It was noted that the public ownership of land may arise within a country in any one or a combination of several ways. Land may be owned by the central government of a country primarily for historical reasons. Also, in some countries land is publicly owned because certain types of land are believed to be or have been demonstrated not to be suitable for private ownership, at least under the prevailing social institutions. While it may be argued that any physical type of land might be privately owned on a permanent and indefinite basis, it has been true that our social institutions have not always proven adaptable to meet the needs of private ownership for certain physical types of land.

Purchase and management of land by a country may be entered into as a part of a land reform program. For instance, it might be desired to subdivide large estates as a means of increasing agricultural production and as a means of increasing the welfare of the actual tillers of the soil. While it might be possible to force the breakup of such estates through the operation of law, it could be simpler and more effective for the central government to purchase such lands, make such improvements as are necessary, and subdivide and settle the lands. Likewise, the central government might more readily have adequate capital for the improvement of these lands.

Public land management may arise from the reverse of the preceding, from a program of land consolidation. In many countries of the world, inheritance practices and other factors have led to a highly fragmented land ownership. Farms in these countries characteristically consist of several small and scattered tracts. Consolidation of these tracts into farms of one or a few larger tracts is essential to agricultural progress. The simplest way to accomplish this may be that the government purchase the small tracts, consolidate them into efficient farms, and resell them, perhaps to the same persons who owned the land originally.

A somewhat similar situation might arise in the case of badly depleted lands. It may be simpler and better for the central government to purchase such lands, rehabilitate them, and dispose of them to private individuals than to attempt their rehabilitation while in the hands of their present owners. Much the same reasons or factors would

629

apply here as in the matter of subdivision of large estates. If depleted land were purchased and rehabilitated, its sale to private individuals should be surrounded by such conditions as would reasonably seem to promise no repetition of the depletion process.

A government differs from an individual as a landowner in several respects. A government has political powers in addition to those economic powers of a private landlord. Further, a government frequently is in a monopolistic or semimonopolistic position, since, where it owns a large proportion of the land in a country, it may be the sole source from which individuals may obtain land.

A government normally is not interested in profits alone from the land. The administration of the land is affected by the government's policy of utilizing the lands in such a manner as to be of service to its citizens.

Considering the relationship between the government and its citizens, it was noted that the use of the land should be pursuant to sound standards established by legislation. This legislation should (a) express the social policies of the country and (b) be adapted to the physical characteristics of the land itself.

In a discussion of the framework of legislation and regulations governing state-owned land, it was suggested that it is desirable for legislation affecting the public lands to be in broad terms and the details with considerable flexibility left to administrative regulations and procedures.

In the United States, a flexible plan is followed to some extent, but has not been attained in every respect since there are over five thousand public land laws, many of them detailed and inflexible. Of these five thousand laws, about five hundred have current applicability.

It appeared that most other countries followed a system which combines more or less broad legislation with more detailed regulations. In Costa Rica and Libya, however, the land is managed largely by the executive power without legislative standards.

The Chairman expressed the tentative conclusion that it is desirable to have simple and general written laws which express the social policy of the country and to have clearly established administrative procedures to carry out those laws.

To obtain proper land management, technically competent permanent staffs must be maintained. Further, management of the type found in the United States requires the co-operation of local users of the land. This is obtained most frequently by setting up advisory boards of local people who do not have the responsibility for managing the land but who do give advice on management problems. Further, the responsibility of the managing agency is to a considerable degree put on a local level by the decentralization of duties and responsibilities.

Another element which is essential to proper land and resource management is the making of adequate inventories. To manage lands properly such things as the amount and types of trees and forage, the grazing capacity of the land, seasons of proper use, productivity, soil conditions, and topography should be known. Management plans, either complete or partial, can then be made on the basis of these factors; timber can be cut on a substantial yield basis; grazing can be permitted without damage to the soil; plans can be made for combatting fires.

In the comparison of country experiences with reference to the ownership of water and mineral rights, it was found that generally similar patterns were followed, despite differences in detail. In the arid countries, water is controlled separately from the land, although there are instances where water rights have become appurtenant to the land.

In most countries, however, the state retains control of water rights, while recognizing in practise, customary or past uses.

In the case of minerals, their ownership is generally separated from the ownership of the surface (the United States being to some extent an exception to this general rule). It is not uncommon, but by no means general, to give some sort of limited preference to surface owners when the state disposes of mineral rights.

A number of the participants presented formal comments on the practises of public land mangement in their respective countries. This summary report concludes with notes on four countries. More extensive comments on the management of public lands in a number of countries follow.

Syria.—The state lands consist of state-owned lands, such as lands on which state buildings are situated, parks, lakes, etc. These are administered by the state for its use. Some state land may be leased by and later bought by peasants. Preference is given to those in the locality. Other public lands are the waste lands. Legislation is now under consideration for the use and disposal of these lands. The situation is rendered difficult because in recent years some Bedouin chiefs have seized large areas of waste land. The minerals in the lands are owned by the state and are disposed of by the state, but the land owner has a priority in leasing the minerals. Considerable forested areas are owned by the state. Cutting is controlled by selective marketing. Free permits are available for village purposes, and timber may be purchased for commercial purposes. There is some replanting and natural regrowth, and the state maintains reforestation nurseries.

Philippines.—The government has a program of acquiring large estates owned by religious organizations and of redistributing them to the people who till them. There are also large areas on Mindanao Island which are government-owned and are available to homestead settlers. The government also has projects involving the clearing of land and turning it over to settlers. Under the constitution, minerals and forests are owned by the state, which may dispose of them. Minerals are reserved when land is disposed of.

Colombia.—Most land is owned by the federal government, although small areas around cities are owned by the cities. Over large areas between the centers of population the land is largely unused and is very difficult to farm. Persons clearing land are granted twice the area they clear. Since 1870, the government has reserved all minerals. Owners of land acquired before 1870 have the mineral rights in that land.

Australia.—Public lands are owned by the six states and are under different systems and laws, although there is a general similarity in policy. Grazing land has been retained by the government since an early date. Much arable land has been alienated in family-size farms. Some states, notably Queensland, have adopted policies of perpetual leases; others permit choice between absolute ownership and perpetual leases.

THE MANAGEMENT OF PUBLIC LANDS IN IRAN

Mohammad Reza Ghavam

IN IRAN all lands which have not been registered as private property belong to the government. A distinction as to the type of government-owned land should, however, be made. The government owns land which has come into its hands as a result of confiscation or purchase. This category of land usually possesses water and has been inhabited for some time. It has also been registered. The other kind of government land is the sort which is not inhabited and on which no farming is done but which with irrigation becomes arable. This sort of land is estimated to amount to 24 million hectares.

Fifteen years ago the government sold to the peasants in ten-year installments all the land in the province of Sirtan which could be irrigated by the Kirman river. It is also now selling the land available in Khuzirtan province to corporations or private individuals on condition that they should plant a citrus garden of a certain size in each farm. Irrigation is now made available by pumps which draw water from the Karum river. A dam is under construction by the Independent Irrigation Corporation, an institution under the general supervision of the Ministry of Agriculture, and it is hoped that it will soon be completed. As regards the other kind of government-owned lands, namely those which have been confiscated or purchased, the policy until ten years ago was to sell them. The practice has, however, been abandoned, and it is hoped that they will be sold to farmers. At present they are either rented or managed by officials of the Ministry of Finance.

Grazing lands owned by the state are either rented annually or managed by officials of the Ministry of Finance.

All mines, including oil, are owned by the government; but when minerals are discovered on private property, the owner is given a share.

It is clear that the Iranian government's intention is to divide up all the lands at her disposal among the farmers, but forests will definitely be excluded from this plan. An Independent Forest Corporation under the general supervision of the Ministry of Agriculture is responsible for all the forests, including those privately owned. It issues permits for the cutting of trees and export of timber. It is also responsible for reforestation. It is equipped with fire-extinguishing machines, and it has at its disposal forest guards whose duty is to prevent damage from being done and to extinguish fires.

THE MANAGEMENT OF PUBLIC LANDS IN LIBYA

J. E. le Riche

DATA ARE available only for Tripolitania, but Cyrenaica and the Fezzan closely follow the same pattern.

1. Privately owned land including Arab gardens and oases amounts to 401,286 hectares.

2. Afforested land owned by the state amounts to 4,050 hectares.

3. Remainder of the territory belongs to the state, but certain villages and tribes have acquired by tradition the use of defined areas for grazing and shifting cereal cultivation.

In area, Libya is about one-quarter the size of the United States.

Since the occupation in 1943 no land has been disposed of by the administering authorities.

Legislation to this end is being drafted and will be submitted to the Libyan government for consideration.

Administration is directed by the Ministry of Agriculture through its own officers or through Provincial Commissioners.

The afforested areas are retained by the state, and the use of these areas is denied to all persons. Grazing is not allowed; any other exploitation is controlled by the Forestry Service under the Director of Agriculture.

The writer agrees with Mr. Marion Clawson that these principles must be based on the following points: (1) broad but sound legislation in conformity with the conditions obtaining in any particular territory; (2) a high order of administrative integrity coupled to this legislation.

ORGANIZATION AND ADMINISTRATION OF THE STATE DOMAIN LANDS IN CAMBODIA

Tep Youth

To PROVIDE a better understanding of our topic, some general information on Cambodia is given first.

Cambodia is a small country situated in the southwest of French Indo-China. It has an area of 17,550,000 hectares and a population of 3.5 million inhabitants. The population is concentrated in the plain and valleys of the Mekong River and its tributaries. It is very scattered in the mountainous and forest regions. The average population density per square kilometer is 19.

The lands under cultivation are cut up in small parcels.

Constitution of State Lands

The lands of the state domain were established in 1903. They comprise free lands and those abandoned by their holders for five years. They are considerable, representing at the present time three-quarters of the total area of the country. They are divided into two groups: public property of the state and private property of the state.

The first, comprising, notably, land and river communications, lakes, ponds, etc., are inalienable and imprescriptible. They can cease to be public property by appropriation.

The remainder of the state-owned lands come into the second group of the domain. These are the lands in which we are interested in this study.

Methods of Granting Lands

The lands of the state's private property are subdivided into (1) lands which the state intends to keep permanently as National Domain—these are forest reserves (3.8 million hectares), fishery reserves of the lakes (150,000 hectares), and parks of a tourist nature in which are found historic monuments like the park with the ruins of Angkor and (2) lands which the state allows to be granted for private use. These latter comprise arable lands, forests, and grazing lands.

The ways of granting arable lands, under the legislation now in force, are of three forms, as follows:

1. *Grants subject to payments.*—That is to say, the state sells the lands. Under this method, sale is made to any person of age and qualified to acquire lands in Cambodia (Cambodians and citizens of the French Union) and to companies organized under the laws of France or Cambodia. No limitation of area is imposed. Land of any area can be bought provided that one can furnish proof of sufficient financial capacity to exploit it.

The sale is always effected by adjudication at public auction, with the starting price fixed by the Minister of Agriculture. The applicant can make use of the privilege of outbidding, on condition that he has previously publicly given notice of his intention. This privilege costs him an addition of one-fifth of the highest price offered by another person.

After the sale, the land is granted only

provisionally. Its assignment to the buyer in positive ownership is effected only when the buyer has fulfilled the terms and conditions imposed, especially the improvement of the land and the payment within the time set (variable according to the area—three to fifteen years).

2. *Free grants.*—These grants are limited to three hundred hectares. For considerations of procedure and of the financial ability of the applicants, this category is subdivided into classes of (a) grants of more than ten hectares (granted by the Ministry of Agriculture with three to five years allowed for improvement of the land) and (b) grants of ten hectares or less (granted by the head of the province involved) with two years allowed for improvement of the land.

It is to be noted that (a) the members of a single family (wife and minor children) cannot claim the award of a grant separate from that of the head of the family and (b) a person who has already bought from the state land of an area of more than three hundred hectares cannot obtain a free grant.

The procedure for arriving at definite ownership in the first category (grants subject to payments) applies also to free grants.

3. *Permit for cultivation.*—This is an authorization for free cultivation of state land of ten hectares or less. This method is, in principle, reserved for poor people who do not have the financial means to bear the expense of a request for a free grant.

The beneficiary of this permit will be able to become owner of the land only after confirmation by the Administrative Commission for Registration of Lands.

Land grants of whatever type are of the surface only. The subsoil remains always in the ownership of the state. However, if the owner of the surface applies for permission to exploit the subsoil in competition with others, priority of concession is always reserved to him.

With respect to water, there are no regulations. The owners may use freely whatever sources of water supply are found on the land.

With respect to forests, those forests not reserved by the state cover a very considerable area—about 4.5 million hectares. They represent one of the natural riches of the country. They are exploited for firewood, for the manufacture of charcoal, for building lumber and woodwork, and for the extraction of wood oils. In a normal period, their annual production is distributed as follows: lumber, 150,000 m³ (cubic meters); firewood, 300,000 steres (cords); charcoal, 15,000 tonnes (tons); wood oils, 280,000 tanks (18 liters each).

These yields, for a small country like Cambodia, not only satisfy local needs but also permit of export of a large part.

Thus the forests are not exploited independently. The state directs this through the Service of Waters, Forests, and Fisheries. This Service fixes the limits of the zones for the project and the species authorized to be cut.

Woodcutting is carried on in all seasons of the year. To facilitate removal, however, it generally takes place during the dry season.

Cutting permits are granted by sale at public auction with a base starting price. They are granted free, however, for timber which is indispensable to the construction of dwellings for inhabitants of moderate means.

With regard to grazing lands, the state has not set up national grazing lands. All lands belonging to the domain where grasses grow are at the disposal of cattle-raisers and of the inhabitants. The animals have free access to them even in the forest reserves.

However, under the methods of granting arable lands, set forth above, grants are accorded only to persons qualified to acquire lands in Cambodia. Therefore, foreigners are prohibited from taking title to the lands. However, foreigners may occupy such lands, either by ordinary lease for three years, or by long-term leases.

Administration of State Lands

The lands of the state are administered in part by the Minister of Public Works and Communications and in part by the Minister of Agriculture.

Management of the lands which are state public property devolves upon the Department of Public Works. As for the rest of the state lands, their management is the responsibility of the Minister of Agriculture, who administers them with the assistance of the Service of Water, Forests, and Fisheries, the Service of Land Surveys for the Surveyed Territories, and interested provincial heads.

Despite the legislation in force for the administration of the state-owned lands, irregular trespassing on these lands for agricultural cultivation or for the cutting of wood always continues to exist. However, the damage caused by these elements is very slight. The most serious damage to the forests is that caused by brush fires started by careless hunters or, most frequently, by people living in the forests. The latter, in order to have more land for the cultivation of rice necessary to their subsistence, do not hesitate to set fire to the forests. They err thus from ignorance, heedless of the destruction of one of the natural riches of the country.

With a view to eliminating these irregularities and scourges from Cambodia, the following measures should be taken:

With regard to the trespassing on the state-owned lands destined for agriculture, it is indispensable to expedite the completion of the work of registering the lands in order to have an exact inventory of the appropriated lands and the state-owned lands. This inventory once established, it would be easy for the Land Survey Service, entrusted at the present time with land registration, to administer the state-owned lands by annual register.

As for brush fires, the Service of Waters, Forests, and Fisheries should, in the first place, make the inhabitants understand the bad effect of their conduct and then try to group them in villages near the forests by putting lands at their disposal for the cultivation indispensable to their subsistence and, finally, should take severe action against delinquents.

For extinguishing fires, no effective method has yet been found. The Royal government is counting heavily on American help through the ECA (superseded by MSA) to equip the Service of Water, Forests, and Fisheries with airplanes and with fire-fighting materials. (To my knowledge, this Service is at the present time investigating the possibility of sending some inspectors to the United States in order to learn fire-fighting techniques.)

Suggestions

This memorandum makes no suggestions, for the sole reason that Cambodia is a new country. Its independence is very recent. It goes without saying that those responsible for its administration do not yet have the desired experience in all fields. On the contrary, they have many things to learn in order to introduce into their country judiciously the fine results obtained from methods tried out in other countries.

THE MANAGEMENT OF PUBLIC LANDS IN COSTA RICA

Manuel M. de San Román

IN COSTA RICA a division of the different types of property has not yet been made officially, but generally we can define them as follows:

1. *Private property.*—All the land which is under private ownership is private property.

2. *Municipal lands.*—These are lands which belong to the different municipalities in the country, the majority of which were lands handed over by the government and located in public lands with the idea that these institutions should subdivide them and sell them in order to raise funds. Much of this land has already been sold to private individuals, but in theory more than in practice, because the majority remains uncultivated or occupied by squatters.

3. *Institutional lands.*—These are lands which belong to autonomous or independent institutions which act in the public interest. Included in this classification are lands belonging to the church, which for the most part are urban properties.

4. *State lands.*—These are lands which the government has bought from private individuals or from autonomous institutions in order to distribute them among the settlers or the squatters. This classification also includes the lands located on public lands which have been surveyed, whose titles have been registered in the office of property records in the name of the state, in order that the latter may have greater legal guarantee over these lands which were public at one time.

5. *National lands.*—These lands, also called public lands, belong legally to the nation, and any citizen of Costa Rica who is of age can use them or rent them. They are not clearly defined as to boundaries, nor surveyed, since information is lacking about their extent and location.

All these types of land are recorded in the Office of Property Records and some are registered in the National Geographic Institute, with the exception of the so-called public lands.

The majority of state lands are occupied by squatters and will be distributed to them. Other lands are unoccupied, and it is intended to establish settlements under technical direction. Still other lands are destined for parks (about one hectare within a town), and here roads, public buildings, etc. are included. Some land of this type is leased for the exploitation of timber.

National lands are located along the coast on a strip 1,606 meters (one mile) wide in some cases and in others only 200 meters. There is also a strip of 2,000 meters along each border with the neighboring countries of Costa Rica. All these lands are inalienable, and they are to be leased for cultivation, for the exploitation of timber, or for the use of salt makers or fishermen.

The rest of the public lands are all over the country, and any citizen of Costa Rica can request thirty hectares. After five years, provided he fulfills the legal requirements, he can acquire the title to the property. These lands can also be leased for cultivation, up to 250 hectares for agriculture and 500 for livestock raising or for the exploitation of timber.

Rents are low, and they are fixed in every case after a thorough study of the land requested. In some special cases the land is put up for auction and allocated to the highest bidder.

All these lease contracts call for an accompanying plan of investment, but this condition of lease is almost never satisfied.

According to the Constitution, the subsoil belongs to the state, and only the state can exploit it or grant concessions on it for its exploitation, through contracts approved by Congress. The only exception to this rule is the exploitation of gold, metals, and other minerals, which are specified in the law and can be exploited by private individuals.

Timber which is found on the lands of the state or on the so-called public lands is turned over to private individuals for its exploitation through concessions of up to 500 hectares, without a technical plan for its exploitation. A fee is paid by cubic measurement (on the basis of a log of 18 by 18 by 144 inches) according to the type of wood. At present, in order not to paralyze the lumber industry, these concessions are granted for three months, renewable upon recommendation of the executive branch of the government; legally they are frozen until the passage of a forestry law.

Surface and underground water belongs to the public domain. For its use, either for irrigation or to produce electric power, a permit must be obtained called "concession for water utilization." This permit can be modified at any time to the benefit of public interests.

Public lands are handled by the judicial branch of the government and by the executive branch of the government through the Ministry of Agriculture and Industry.

Water is under the National Service for Electricity and the Ministry of Agriculture.

Timber, state lands, and the subsoil are administered by the Ministry of Agriculture.

In the Ministry of Agriculture and Industry all these functions are centered in the Agrarian Department. At this time a law is being prepared with the idea of unifying all these matters under one organization, and the Ministry of Agriculture and Industry will be the one to handle such delicate functions. This idea of centralizing everything related to the subsoil, soils, forests, and water will be incorporated in the future in a Ministry of State, or what would be more ideal, into an autonomous organization. In either case the name would include the term "Natural Resources." Under this head would also come the services of the General Office of Statistics and the National Geographic Institute. The principal objective is to avoid a duplication of functions and work, thus saving effort, and to create a definite policy of responsibility for the conservation of natural resources for the future good of the nation.

Political history has shown that in Latin America it would be desirable to centralize the management of all natural resources into one autonomous organization responsible for the future protection of the economic potential of natural resources.

PUBLIC REGULATION OF LAND USE IN MEXICO

Antonio Tapia

ALMOST TWO-THIRDS of all the land in use in Mexico belongs to the government. The exact amount is very difficult to give because of the opening of new areas to cultivation in the last ten years, as a result of the big irrigation projects of the Mexican government.

Usually the government allots this land to farmers to cultivate. The government took this land from big landholders at the end of the Mexican Revolution in 1921; subsequently it was granted to farmers for their use. There was no charge for the land, although there are some prescriptions. The farmer is not allowed to sell or give the land to anyone, nor to divide it. If for a period of two years the farmer abandons the land without making any use of it, except in case of illness or for other valid reasons, the government takes it back and allots it to somebody else.

The water usually belongs legally to the state, and all use of it requires permission. Rates for the use of water from the big government irrigation projects are very low, based on the cost of maintenance of supervision. The farmer pays according to the volume of water he uses.

All the subsoil belongs to the government, and the development of any product such as oil is in charge of federal agencies. In the case of mineral products in Mexico, the owner of the surface is entitled to exploit his subsoil if he wishes, but must first have the permission of the government. When a mineral is found in land that does not belong to anyone, then permission is granted the one who first declares the mine.

The state retains no land for its own use. With the exception of the national parks, all land may be used by private persons or agencies if they wish.

In the case of forests, in Mexico it is forbidden to cut a single tree without a permit from the government, even on private property. This is because so many trees have been cut for the manufacture of charcoal since its use was discovered. Now, gas and oil and their development have ended this irrational exploitation, and the government is working on a great reforestation project.

THE PRINCIPLES OF PUBLIC LAND MANAGEMENT IN THE UNITED STATES[1]

 Marion Clawson

The administration of publicly-owned resources for use by individuals raises some serious problems in a democratic country. Public ownership and private use of resources are not incompatible with the democratic system of government or with a system of private property, but they do impose some particular and serious problems. We present here some principles which we consider appropriate as criteria for evaluating a democratic program in the United States.

First of all, public-land management under these conditions should be governed by sound basic legislation. Such legislation should be in conformity with the natural conditions of the land. The government should not seek by legislation to accomplish something which is physically impossible nor should it fail to take advantage of the physical adaptability of the land it owns. For instance, if some of the federal land contains valuable minerals, the laws for its administration should provide a workable system for the extraction of such minerals. The basic legislation should, moreover, clearly express the social policy of the country. For instance, if land ownership by the actual tillers of the soil is a major social objective of the country, its laws should be designed to facilitate and insure such land ownership.

In the second place, definite regulations based upon law are essential. The laws should not attempt to be so detailed and so specific as to cover each situation. They should, instead, be rather general in character, clearly expressing national policy, but leaving many of their details of operation to the administrator. He, in turn, should prepare definite and specific regulations in as simple and clear terms as possible to cover the activities of his agency and to provide the public with instructions for obtaining the use of the particular lands and resources.

Third, there must be an efficient, decentralized administration of the publicly-owned lands if they are to make their maximum contribution to the welfare of the people who seek to use them. All aspects of administration relating to a particular area should be centralized in a single office or place located as close as possible to the land in question. In many forms of administration, both public and private, there is a conflict between functional specialization and area administration. It is significant that in the administration of publicly-owned resources of the United States, all agencies give dominance to the consideration of area administration; that is, fire control, timber sales, grazing administration, and various other specialized programs are generally all consolidated at the local or operating level into a single administrative office or function. Specialization by function usually occurs at higher levels in the organization, but at the local level area considerations predominate.

In the fourth place, publicly-owned resources must be available to all private users on an equal basis. In many instances, the amount or volume of publicly-owned resources is inadequate to meet all of the demands by all of the individuals who would like to obtain these resources. Under these circumstances some individuals will obtain federal resources and others will unavoidably be deprived of them. When this is necessary the choice should rest upon objective grounds. In general, conditions may be established under which publicly-owned resources may be obtained. One such condition is often the willingness to pay more for these resources than any other applicant is willing to pay. Timber is generally sold by competitive bidding. The methods of administration can be varied and adjusted in many ways to encourage and provide accessibility of resources to all interested individuals.

Finally, in a democracy the federal agencies which exist to serve people must establish and maintain democratic relationships with those people. The previously enumerated steps aid in attaining this goal but do not insure it. In addition, direct working relationships with the public are necessary. One of the best devices in this connection is the use of advisory boards of informed local citizens to advise and assist the administrators. Another important matter is to provide a system of appeals from the decisions of local administrators so that the citizen who feels he has been unfairly dealt with has some ready recourse. Still another matter is the provision of accurate and understandable information to the public through newspapers or other means of mass communication.

Federal land administration in the United States has sought to achieve these goals. On the whole, notable success has been achieved. But it must be admitted that in some respects practice is, or has been, far below ideals. Legislation has sometimes been unclear, conflicting, unnecessarily detailed, or no longer appropriate; classification of land, and application of suitable laws, became general only with the Taylor Act in 1934; administration has sometimes been centralized in Washington or other remote location; resources have sometimes found their way into the hands of a favored few; and administrators have not always been as democratic as they might have been. Recognition of inadequacies may be the first step in their correction.

A basic characteristic of federal land management in the United States has been that the land, though publicly owned, has been used by private individuals. Practically none of the federal land is withheld from use of some kind by individuals. The timber cut from federal land is cut by private lumber operators, manufactured by them, and sold by them. The grazing of livestock on the federal lands is carried on by private individuals who own their own livestock. In most cases grazing on federal land provides feed for the livestock during only part of the year, and during the rest of the year the livestock secure their feed from privately-owned land. Minerals are removed from public land by private operations. A substantial part of the federal land is used for recreation and sightseeing by individuals. There has never been any substantial organization and operation of federal enterprises to use the federal lands (except for military training), and with very few exceptions all use is made by private individuals. Such use is under license, permit, lease, or other form of specific agreement or arrangement.

A second major factor is that most federally owned lands in the United States are used for more than one purpose. This is known as the multiple-use principle. A well managed forest area will have important values as a watershed for the streams which arise within it and flow through it. It is likely to provide a suitable habitat for game and other wild animals and also to provide desirable recreational facilities. It can often be used for the grazing of livestock also. Likewise, areas chiefly valuable for grazing may have many similar values. There are some areas of high value for one purpose which cannot be used for other purposes without impairing their value for their chief purpose. For instance, the national parks have been closed to grazing, lumbering, and mining operations in order to prevent their impairment for scenic and recreational purposes. There are a few watershed areas of such importance for this purpose that they are closed to other uses. However, this single-purpose use is in the minority. In most instances, possible conflicts among uses can be resolved satisfactorily.

A major reason for federal ownership of much land in the United States is precisely because of its possibilities for multiple-purpose use and because such use is more likely and more satisfactory under public than private ownership.

Another major factor of federal land management in the United States has been the existence of a competent and efficient organization for actual administration of the land. If the social objectives which the country had in mind in providing public-land ownership are to be fulfilled, it is essential that an appropriate mechanism of government be created and maintained to carry out these objectives. In general, the land managing agencies in the United States are outstanding.

There are several factors involved in a competent and efficient organization. First of all, there should be properly-trained personnel in sufficient numbers, and they should be assured of reasonably secure tenure in their jobs. A civil service system based upon ability, knowledge, and merit—rather than upon political favoritism—is generally considered essential. If there is to be an adequate organization, there must obviously be sufficient appropriations to carry on the necessary work. A country does not gain much by proposing to have an adequate system of public-land administration and then refusing to appropriate the funds necessary to provide such a system of administration. In general, particularly in a moderately large country, decentralized operations in public-land administration are desirable, if not essential. The man on the ground must have the authority to carry out the necessary land-administration actions. His decisions and his actions should be taken within a framework of policy and instructions provided by the central office of the land-administering agency. In general, experience has been that public-land administration is most effective when all aspects of administration are combined into a single operating unit or office at the local level. For instance, a land administering agency may have specialized problems of forestry, grazing, mineral production, and the like, which will necessitate a specialized staff at some level in the organization. However, at the actual operating level—on the land itself—all of these functions should be combined and co-ordinated under a single administrator or office responsible for a clearly defined area of land. Federal land administration in the United States has been very largely in the hands of career, civil service employees; it has, on the whole, been moderately well supported financially by the government; and it has been notable for its decentralization and for its area, as contrasted with functional, administration.

In order to administer public lands satisfactorily, the responsible agencies must have accurate knowledge of the characteristics of such land. This may include soil surveys, range surveys, erosion surveys, forest inventories, and many other specialized surveys or inquiries as to the characteristics of the land. Although the body of such knowledge is rather great, there are many inadequacies in our knowledge about the federal land in the United States. Moreover, the kind of information needed is continually changing. As our economy develops, our population grows; consequently, the demand for federal land increases. The process of inventory is a continuous one.

The responsible federal agencies have management plans for the area under their jurisdiction. These plans are based upon the best information available to them. Management plans may be general and comprehensive in character or they may be more limited and specific. For instance, an agency should have a fire-control plan for all lands on which there is a serious threat of destructive fires. This fire-control plan may be to some extent independent of other plans, but is to some extent correlated and integrated with it. Likewise, there may be a program

for the control of soil erosion and for the restoration of eroded areas. These various specific programs should be integrated into a comprehensive over-all program for the management, use, and development of a particular area.

A sound and comprehensive public-land management program necessarily includes several parts. First of all, it should include conservation of the land itself and of its resources. Conservation is taken to mean the greatest possible present use of the land and its resources without impairment of future uses or with the minimum possible impairment of such future uses. For most of the renewable resources such as forests and forage, it is usually possible to enjoy complete or reasonably full present utilization without any impairment of future use of the same resources. In the case of nonrenewable resources such as minerals, present use inevitably means diminished future use. In this case, conservation largely means avoidance of waste and full utilization of such resources as are used, including utilization of moderately low grades of resources. Conservation essentially includes full present utilization, full future utilization, and a balancing of present and future utilization where the two are in conflict.

Essential to conservation and complementary to it is the protection of resources of public lands from waste and destruction. Practically, the two greatest threats against which public lands must be protected are fire and erosion. Since a substantial part of the publicly-owned lands are forested or are covered with other native vegetation which can be consumed by destructive fires, fire protection becomes an extremely important part of public-land management in many countries. Prevention of undue loss by fires is in one sense conservation, although the latter is more generally applied to constructive uses of the resources. At any rate, fire protection is often essential and is basic to other management efforts. Likewise, much public land, particularly grazing land, is subject to the serious hazard of soil erosion. Some erosion, and in many cases a great deal, occurs without consideration of the use of the resources involved. This is the so-called geologic erosion which is often most pronounced in relatively low rainfall areas. Other erosion may be accelerated or induced by man's use of the land, including grazing, forestry, and the like. In either event, protection against erosion is essential. There are other and less important ways in which lands may require protection as a prerequisite to conservation and management programs.

Federal land-management programs in the United States have generally given full consideration to the conservation needs of the land. Their record is outstanding.

TAXATION AND PUBLIC REGULATION OF PRIVATE LAND USES

Report of the Working Party
Chairmen, *Harold M. Groves and Raymond J. Penn*

THE SUBJECT of discussion during these meetings of a group representing eight countries was the relation of land taxation and regulation to problems of land tenure. The first two sessions were devoted to a discussion of taxation. The last session, led by Maurice M. Kelso of Montana State College, dealt with land regulation in the United States.

Taxes and Land Tenure

It was found that taxation bears on land tenure in the following three principal ways:

1. Taxation may be used as one of the means to accomplish land reform.

2. Taxation should be adapted to any land reform which is carried out, in order to protect such land reform. Tax legislation should be such as to maintain any given land settlement program.

3. The land tax system, along with the tenure system, should be adapted to technological changes which might occur as well as to the general economic climate (capital resources, etc.).

Tax Systems Affecting Tenure

A system of graduated taxes on the total land value that a person owns is like an income tax, except that the base is land and not income. Such a system is used in Australia and New Zealand. Some farm organizations in the United States advocate such a tax.

A system of graduated inheritance or estate taxes has an effect similiar to the graduated land tax. At the time of transfer of property, such a tax causes liquidation and changes the size of property. For that reason, land in the United Kingdom is exempted from death taxation so as to avoid fragmentation.

In the United States we find homestead exemption in some areas. This favors owner-occupied land as contrasted with tenant-operated land.

Frequently land is weighted more heavily in the tax base than improvements. It was agreed that the distinction between site values (land) and improvements (including fertility) is a very important one. From an incentive point of view, it is desirable to encourage that which is not fixed in supply —i.e., improvements—and let the major tax burden rest on that which is relatively fixed in supply, namely, the site itself.

Tenure and Efficient Operation

The working party considered the question of what is desirable from the point of view of tenure and efficient operation. One of the problems was how to determine the basis of land value taxation so as to promote efficient use. As a basis of land value the "annual" value or the market value of land may be used. Both are based on objective standards, independent of the production and income achieved by the present owner on the land taxed. Annual value is derived from the annual rent which can be obtained from the land in its present use by an average man. Thus, cultivated land would be assessed at a higher value than uncultivated land if annual value assessment is used; but this would not necessarily be the case if market value were the basis of assessment. The market prices land on the basis of what it can produce. In the case of these taxes on objective land value, the land owner can gain by being a better farmer or encouraging better farming. In addition, market value means assessment of land at its highest possible value in terms of the best available use, thus promoting change to the most remunerative uses as well as increasing efficiency in any one use. (Some members of the group felt that land which is not operated in its "proper" use should be taxed particularly heavily.)[1]

In contrast to these are the subjective taxes, based on the results actually obtained by the present occupant on the land. If the tax is related to present production, the incentive to the land owner to develop the land is greatly diminished. Thus if taxation were based on the income from land or even on the gross product, the taxpayer could not lighten his tax burden by improving his farming methods.

Some objectives which emerged from the discussion could be summed up as follows:

1. Some form of graduated taxation is called for to achieve redistribution and parcellation, if that is desired.

2. If the tax power is to be used merely so as not to discourage development and optional use, a proportional tax on market value (or "potential capacity") suffices.[2]

3. If the tax power is to be used so as to force development, a progressive tax on uncultivated land to get owners to produce or else to pass the land on to others who will produce is called for.

4. Consumption (or sales) taxes on agricultural products may raise the cost of living without necessarily affecting land values. But full use of land is not encouraged by such a tax. Depending on elasticities of supply and demand, the tax may also impede the development of agricultural production, apart from its regressive and capricious incidence.

Timing of the Tax

As a special case, the question of timing of the tax in relation to receipt of income was discussed, to cover cases where crops take more than one year to be harvested. Here it was agreed that a tax on the basis of output would be preferable to one on the value of the land. Otherwise a tax may have to be paid out of borrowed funds; and, most important from the conservation point of view, it would be undesirable to have taxpayers attempt to "get out from under" a tax by overcultivation. Here a severance tax may be in place. In the case of forest lands, for instance, a certain percentage of the value of the timber, when sold, may constitute the proper tax.

This principle may be extended in other directions. Land of all kinds may be exempted for a number of years for developmental and incentive reasons in conjunction with higher rates on unused land. The group saw a certain degree of danger in such exemption programs, which are in effect subsidies, if political pressure groups were to promote them and use them. Nevertheless the principle is useful when applied for limited duration to develop new projects.

General Tax Application

The workshop agreed that taxes and regulations should not be applied to individuals but should be general, that is, should be "reasonably" related to the purpose of the legislation rather than to individuals as such. Unless the classifications used in taxation and regulation are reasonable in relation to the ends sought, discrimination may result.

The United States Experience

MEANS OF REGULATION

The means of regulation are (a) police power, (b) eminent domain, (c) taxation, and (d) public expenditures.

Police power is the power of the government to limit personal liberties and property rights for public purpose. Public purpose has been defined in such terms as protection of public health, morals, and safety, and the promotion of public welfare, convenience, and general prosperity. The actual content of these definitions emerges out of legislation and court review. Regulations under police power, as long as they further public purpose, may take away income or value of property without compensation. One of the important uses of police power is in zoning regulations. In the United States the police power is exercised only by the states and their subdivisions.

Eminent domain is the power of the government to acquire property needed for a public purpose without consent of the owner but with just compensation. Eminent domain might be exercised by an irrigation district to acquire land for irrigation ditches.

Taxation can be used to regulate land use through special taxes on special forms of land use, tax exemptions, and graduated taxes. Special taxes on land used for forestry have been used to promote forestry.

Public expenditures can be made on projects on private lands to promote public welfare. An example is soil conservation payments.

LIMITS OF REGULATION

The legality of regulations is tested in the United States by the courts under the "due process" doctrine. This test seeks to evaluate whether legal procedure was followed in the enactment of regulations, whether the purposes sought are indeed for public welfare, and whether the regulations are reasonable methods of attaining these purposes. Land uses existing prior to the regulation are usually protected against abolition; this protection is accomplished by zoning. Judicial review of regulatory measures is designed to protect individuals from arbitrary or discriminatory regulations.

EXAMPLES OF REGULATION

By general governmental units.—Examples of this kind of regulation are land use zoning and weed control.

By special districts.—Examples are soil conservation districts, irrigation and drainage districts, and grazing districts.

Range of activity.—There is a great deal of difference in the degrees of control exercised under the various regulatory activities. The soil conservation districts do very little regulating. Instead, by agreement with the Soil Conservation Service of the U.S. Department of Agriculture, they make available to farmers in the district free technical advice and assistance in adjusting the farm organization to soil conserving practices. In this case the aims of the program are furthered by direct subsidies and by making available to farmers services necessary to initiate soil conservation farming. At the other extreme would be land use regulations which depend on police power to prohibit certain uses and on the power of eminent domain to acquire for public ownership whatever land is necessary for the execution of the program and which raise local taxes to cover the expenses of the program. Irrigation districts regulate the use of water, acquire lands for necessary storage, ditches, and other facilities, and collect taxes on assessments for their services.

ISSUES IN REGULATION

Local participation.—The participation of local people in drawing up the purposes and methods of regulation would help to get better regulatory laws, related to the experience of local people with the problems which the law attempts to deal with. Also, it would help to make enforcement easier. Opportunity to express local views should be provided in setting up the program and during its administration. Adequate protection should be provided for the rights of those who oppose or may be harmed by the program.

Technical assistance.—The issue of the role of the technicians comes up in any program based on local recognition of problems. The technicians must provide the technical assistance necessary. They can provide ideas which would make possible better decisions by the people and the administrators. They may attempt to determine the direction of the program based solely on their own judgments. The latter course is likely to lose the lessons of local experience and the help of local leadership.

Representation of broader public interests.—Outside groups and the general public are usually affected by land use regulations. It is extremely difficult to provide for the recognition of these interests in locally administered regulations. Sometimes there are no organized groups to press their claims; again, such interests may be uneconomic in nature, as efforts to preserve the natural beauty of an area. As such, they suffer in comparison to more easily evaluated and more vocally pressed local interests. The balancing of different interests may be achieved at a higher level of government.

A Note on Police Power

The term police power is rather unfortunate in that it seems to imply enforcement by the arbitrary action of the police. Actually it has nothing to do with methods of enforcement; violations of police power regulations are not criminal offenses, and are controlled by civil action calling for the assessment of damages or for injunctions to prohibit such activities. The term refers to the power of government to enact regulatory measures for the promotion of public purpose.

METHODS OF TITLE REGISTRATION AND THE
MAKING OF CADASTRAL AND BOUNDARY SURVEYS

Report of the Working Party

 Chairmen, *Earl G. Harrington and Jacob H. Beuscher*

THE DISCUSSION was, in most instances, general in character. It avoided, to a large extent, minor details of procedure. It sought suggestions for solutions to problems confronting the countries represented. Each person present explained the methods and procedures in his own country as a necessary preliminary to a discussion of suggested improvements.

Cadastral Surveys

The working party agreed that a glossary of surveying terms agreed to by surveyors in the various countries would avoid confusion. It also suggested that consideration be given to the definitions of the many types of surveys, including cadastral surveys, listed in *Modern Cartography,* published by the United Nations, Department of Social Affairs, in 1949 (Sales No. 1949. I. 19). This valuable publication treats cadastral surveying, geodetic surveying, photographic surveying, and other types of surveying under the following headings: (1) a short definition of what is involved in the cartographic activity under discussion; (2) a short statement on characteristic methods; (3) the principal uses of the technique under consideration; (4) an account of relevant existing international organizations; and (5) a bibliography of books dealing with methods.

The working party also gave attention to the important matter of qualifications for surveyors. The "Report of the Conference of the British Commonwealth and USA Survey Authorities" held in Wellington, New Zealand, in November, 1950, was examined. Special attention was paid to the qualifications listed on pages 18 and 19 of this report. The working party concurred in the comments in this report that there be international affiliation between qualified surveyors with a view toward exchange of literature and views, advice in connection with qualifying examinations, and hospitality in helping visiting surveyors from foreign countries.

There was considerable discussion of the constantly improving techniques for aerial photography. It was the view of the working party that techniques of aerial photography are now sufficiently advanced so that aerial photographs are a definite aid (1) as a preliminary to all types of surveying; (2) as a basis for mapping areas to be used for land reclamation and settlement programs (The delegate from Chile explained that his government had used aerial photographs in mapping more than four million hectares in Chile.); and (3) in land management

work of various kinds as follows: (a) Land classification. Here again the experience of Chile is an important case in point and other countries are making important use of aerial photography for this purpose. (b) Timber evaluation. In the United States maps based on aerial photography are presently prepared on a scale of 20 inches to a mile (5,280 feet) for this purpose as well as for making cadastral surveys and for the classification of land. (c) Estimating the cost of reclamation and settlement projects. (d) Preparing for land consolidation programs. The delegate from France reported that aerial photography of the land to be consolidated is now being used, thus avoiding the high cost and delay of a detailed survey of all of the existing strip fields and parcels. The working party was informed that Germany particularly could speed up its land consolidation program by using aerial photography for this purpose. Such photographs, especially if local residents are asked to participate in the marking of fields before they are photographed and in the study of the pictures after they are taken, provide an excellent "extension" device to interest the people most concerned in the consolidation project.

Because aerial photographic techniques are being rapidly improved, it was agreed that whenever a government has occasion to contract for aerial photographic work, the specifications should be carefully drafted to provide for the use of the newest techniques, whether the photography is to be "general purpose" photography or "specific" photography. In this connection attention was called to the bibliographical material on aerial photography listed on page 70 of the United Nations publication, *Modern Cartography,* mentioned above. Even now it is contended by some that aerial photography using the most modern techniques gives an accuracy for surveying problems of one to fifteen hundred.

Mr. Harrington suggested that members of the working party call the attention of their respective governments to the solar transit used by engineers of the United States Bureau of Land Management, Department of Interior. Though the initial cost of this instrument is in the neighborhood of eleven hundred dollars, the experience of the Bureau of Land Management shows that use of the instrument has resulted in an average reduction of surveying costs by 20 per cent. For further information about this new transit see the 1947 *Manual for the Survey of the Public Lands of the United States,* prepared by the Bureau of Land Management and available through the Superintendent of Documents, United States Government Printing Office, Washington 25, D.C., at a price of $2.50. The solar transit can be obtained from any large American instrument maker.

Attention was also given to the crucial need for permanent monuments marking the boundaries of the areas surveyed. The initial additional expense of erecting permanent monuments is well merited when it is remembered that poor monumentation has caused much bitter feeling and thousands of law suits and disputes. The United States government is now in some areas sinking copper rings below the monument itself so that these can be found through the use of mine detectors if the monument is removed. It had also been suggested that radioactive matter might be deposited under monuments so that the monument point can always be located through the use of a Geiger counter.

Finally, it was concluded that cadastral surveys are nowadays always made for definite purposes such as reclamation and settlement as in the case of Chile, or forest exploitation. Therefore it is impossible to say that any single type or method of cadastral survey is best. In general, the techniques used by the surveyor in the countries represented in the working party are the same, but the type of survey being made varies depending on the purpose of the survey conducted. This is as it should be. For example, in Alaska the United States is now modifying its historical rectangular survey system to meet the special settlement problems.

Title Registration

Basic differences between systems of title registration were uncovered. In some countries the land transfer instrument is legal and final between the parties to it, once the instrument is delivered, even though it is not recorded. In these countries recordation of the instrument in a public office protects the transferee from possible claims of persons who acquire later interests in the same real estate. In other countries the instrument of transfer must be registered in order for the transfer to be valid even as between the parties to it. In some countries registration is based upon an official index to the real estate records, arranged alphabetically according to the names of the parties to the transfer. In other countries the official index is based on the survey description of the land involved. In general, members of the working party felt that the latter type of index was to be preferred.

It was pointed out that in a country which has long been settled, it would be exceedingly difficult to change a long-established, though inefficient, recording system to a more efficient system. The very slight use that is being made of the Australian type "Torrens" system approved for use in nineteen of the forty-eight American states is an instance in point. Nevertheless, the working party thought that in connection with the opening of new land for land settlement, and also in connection with land consolidation and land reform programs, the possibility of drafting into the basic legislation a special and efficient system of title registration should be given careful attention. It was suggested that this be done even though the result might be two different systems in some places—one for old lands and the other for new, consolidated, and "reformed" land. In the case of new or reclaimed land there is no long history of ownership and it should be relatively easy to start afresh with a new system for registering such land. Titles to consolidated land or land being acquired for land reform programs must be investigated by the government anyway; it should be relatively easy to subject it to an improved system of registration after such investigation.

In addition to a tract index, as above mentioned, the working party felt that the following are marks of an effective title registration system:

1. Specially trained personnel subject to careful supervision who become specialists in the handling of registry problems.

2. A single office in which are registered all instruments affecting real estate titles.

3. Registration made a condition to the transfer of land even as between the parties to the transfer.

4. Registration relatively conclusive in cutting off competing claims to the land. This will make time-consuming and expensive title examinations unnecessary and should permit quicker and easier land credit where real estate is being used as security.

5. Microfilming and photostating to save time, expense, and to avoid errors.

6. In some countries where a high rate of illiteracy prevails, state help in the drafting of real estate documents.

CADASTRAL SURVEYING AS A BASIC TOOL IN LAND MANAGEMENT[1]

 Earl G. Harrington

MANAGEMENT of lands and their resources, transfer of property and title, appraisals, development of areas, defining the limits of jurisdiction between nations and states, all construction work on land, determining boundaries of areas for taxation purposes, and in fact every activity dealing with land are to a large extent dependent upon cadastral surveys.

Cadastral surveys are defined by the Pan-American Institute of Geography and History—published by the United Nations in the document entitled "Modern Cartography, Base Maps for World Needs, 1949"—as follows:

Cadastral surveys in general create, re-establish, mark and define boundaries of tracts of land. Such surveys, unlike scientific surveys of an informative character which may be amended with changing conditions or because they are

not executed according to the standards now required for accuracy, cannot be ignored, repudiated, altered, or corrected, and the boundaries created or re-established cannot be changed so long as they control rights vested in the lands affected.

The official record of a cadastral survey ordinarily consists of a drawing or map and a written description of the field work. The drawing represents the lines surveyed showing the direction and length of each of such lines; the boundaries, description and area of the parcel of land; and, as far as practicable, a delineation of the topography of the region, including a representation of the culture and improvements within the limits of the survey.

This definition, published by the United Nations, should govern all countries with respect to what is meant by a cadastral survey.

The basic methods employed in cadastral

surveying are similar in most countries; that is, each individual tract is marked on the ground by natural or artificial monuments; the boundaries are measured and their bearings determined, and a description and area are given for each parcel of land. Generally a plat or plan of survey is prepared. However, different plans of survey have been adopted by nations with respect to the types of surveys executed—whether some form of the rectangular method, survey by irregular metes and bounds, or a combination of the two methods—and as to the size, configuration, or unit of the lands disposed of or administered.

There is no doubt that the modern cadastral survey is better than the survey made 150 years ago. We have better instruments; durable monuments are established; accuracy is considered a major factor; surveys are being adapted to land types; it is essential that the survey be properly related to the adjacent boundaries and that a proper plat or plan be prepared, etc. However, improvements and new methods are still needed. The development of mineral resources in submerged off-shore lands—ocean beds—is taxing the ingenuity of the land surveyors or cadastral engineers to work out methods to define and describe individual tracts in such areas.

Factors in Cadastral Survey

The primary purpose of a cadastral survey is to mark and define the boundaries of tracts of land and to furnish a proper description and area. The major factors to be considered in making a good survey are noted below.

TYPE OF SURVEY

Cadastral surveys generally are made for a definite purpose. The type of survey must first be determined. This, to a large extent, depends upon the character of the area

to be surveyed and the development of that area. The need for the survey generally involves some form of land management.

ACCURACY

Accuracy as measured today was not an important factor in executing early surveys. The requirements for accuracy at the present time should to a large extent be based upon the character of the area being surveyed and its value. Since the established monuments mark the boundaries, not the reported bearings and distances between those monuments, it would not be good business and it is not necessary to require the same degree of accuracy in rough mountainous areas, valuable for grazing purposes only, as is required in agricultural areas or mineral areas where high values are involved. Lands of a comparative low value should not be burdened with the cost of a survey of an accuracy that is not needed to administer or manage the area. The actual cost of a survey bears a direct relation to the character of the area irrespective of the value of the land. The surveyor must necessarily weigh all elements involved before determining the allowable error of closing.

MONUMENTATION

The importance of good monumentation cannot be overemphasized. The monuments constitute the evidence on the ground of the boundaries created or re-established by the cadastral survey. These monuments govern regardless of the accuracy required in making the survey in the first instance. It is a principle of law that corners once established, designated, and used to mark land boundaries cannot be changed if there are existing valid rights based upon those corners. The construction engineer can remove a defective foundation and rebuild; errors appearing in those surveys which supply information for the public can be corrected and new data supplied; but an original cadastral survey which creates boundaries cannot be changed so long as it controls rights vested in the lands affected.

The acid test of a corner monument is that of lasting quality or durability. Consideration also must be given to the cost of monumentation. It is possible, if cost is not a factor, to construct corners that would withstand corrosion from the elements and insofar as material substance is concerned would be considered everlasting. Monuments of this type would in many cases cost more than the value of the land. Such procedure would not be good land management. The land should not be burdened with such excessive costs. Soil characteristics have to be considered in selecting the type of monumentation.

The Bureau of Land Management has adopted a standard monument for surveying the public land based upon studies and experience which is satisfactory and which under most site conditions will last many years. This standard monument is manufactured from wrought iron or copper-bearing steel pipe filled with a core of concrete and with a brass cap riveted to the top of the post for appropriate marking of the position of that particular corner. Under present specifications, the corner monuments are thirty inches long, two inches in diameter, with the lower end split and the two halves spread to form a flange. The monuments weigh about twenty pounds and the cost of manufacture is about $2.50 per post. The metal post is set about twenty-two inches in the ground and surrounded by a mound of native stone, if stones are available. Witness monuments and reference monuments are also established if the true point for the corner falls in a position where the monument may be destroyed by either natural or artificial means.

Consideration should also be given to depositing at the base of all monuments a piece of metallic material or some radioactive material subject to location by an electronic detector.

CONTROL FOR MAPPING

All geodetically-established control points should be connected to the corners of the cadastral survey at the time the field work is executed. Based upon these connections, the precise latitude and longitude of each monument can be computed. The vast monumented net of cadastral surveys will provide control for practically all types of mapping projects.

FINAL SURVEY RECORD

The final survey record consists of field notes describing in detail the processes of survey, and the results on the ground, and the plat, which is a graphic representation of the surveys made in the field. The plat shows the courses and lengths of survey lines and relief, drainage, and culture. Its basic function is to designate and describe areas in specific terms and to serve as the legal basis for all transactions involving the public lands. The legal significance of the plat in this respect is as important as it would be if incorporated and made a part of the original patent itself. The scale of the plat or plan depends to a large extent upon the data shown thereon.

Surveys and Land Management

Adequate surveys are necessary for the administration of lands. It is obvious that an administrator must know where the land is, if he is to administer it at all. The problem of the public land administrator is particularly complicated in those areas where there are tracts of privately owned land within the boundaries of the federal land holdings—a very common situation. It is also essential to know the character of the area and the portions suitable for agriculture, grazing, forest, or other purposes. A good cadastral survey will locate and mark the boundaries of the land on the ground. The plat, or plan, if properly prepared from aerial photographs and the field notes of the survey, gives the designation and area of each individual unit and indicates by appropriate symbol a delineation of the topography of the area, including a representation of the culture and improvements within the limits of the survey. This gives the administrator a general idea of the type of land being administered. The cadastral survey is in fact the first step in any form of land management.

Part XXIII RESEARCH AND STATISTICS FOR TENURE ADJUSTMENT PROGRAMS

ON THE MAKING OF TENURE RESEARCH SURVEYS

Excerpt from the Report of the Working Party

Chairmen, *Joseph Ackerman and Joe R. Motheral*

THE REPORTS presented in the plenary sessions of the world land tenure conference have offered striking evidence of the significance and urgency of the land tenure problem throughout the world. Without exception, spokesmen who have described the conditions of tenure in the various regions have suggested—sometimes explicitly, sometimes implicitly—the need for programs of land reform. While the specific measures proposed have been as varied as the problems themselves, unquestionably the common denominator in terms of corrective techniques may be summed up under a broad land reform heading.

Thus the spirit of the conference is not alone one of full and free discussion. It also possesses a forward-looking quality of the sort that leads to policy adjustments, and thus it might well provide the intellectual basis for the advancement both of education and administration in the area of land tenure. If such proves to be the case, how well grounded in factual analysis are land policy revisions likely to be? And how much simply the outgrowth of emotionalism generated by a violated sense of justice?

There is no questioning the sincerity and the good intentions of land reform advocates nor, for that matter, of the essential validity of their arguments. To appraise critically the existing systems of tenure and to launch a rational program of remedial measures,

however, are two quite different undertakings. Even the appraisals at this conference have been handicapped by the inadequacies of available research materials. It is only reasonable to assume that programs based upon incomplete or misleading information would be even more seriously handicapped and, indeed, might frustrate the laudable purposes toward which they are directed.

Little imagination is required, therefore, to appreciate the importance of research as a policy guide. The evidence presented at this conference clearly reveals the imperfections—and frequently the total lack—of existing land tenure research materials.

Unfortunately, the factual base is often weakest in the very countries in which the aspirations for economic and social change are strongest. Intelligent adjustment calls first for systematic study of the problems. Research provides not merely the knowledge which necessarily accompanies successful administration; it also serves to enlighten the people whose welfare is at stake and whose informed co-operation is essential to economic reformation.

These, then, are the values of research in land tenure. The interest manifested in the subject by this working party was proof enough of the recognition by professional people of these values. Parenthetically, it might not be amiss to impress upon other responsible men in governmental and administrative positions the vital role of research as a foundattion for purposeful action.

Problem Characterization

The selection of the study and the formulation of the problem are the first two major steps in the development of a land tenure research project. It was recognized by the working party that many countries have not yet compiled the basic statistics needed for planning and executing an intensive analysis of tenure problems.

The procedure here has been to inventory briefly some of the outstanding land tenure problems, to select two of these for more detailed consideration, and to develop each of these two problems in the approximate sequence normally followed in a formal project statement. This procedure was modified, in numerous particulars, and at the same time enriched by the varied backgrounds of the participants. What at first glance might appear to be departures from the rigorous model generally accepted by social scientists in one culture may in fact represent a more practicable approach to scholars coming from another culture. It will be apparent that efforts to blend these diverse methods into a single, logical frame of reference were not always successful, but the real aim was a common understanding. This was substantially achieved.

Briefly stated, some of the problems suggested by the working party were as follows:

1. Impacts of inheritance laws upon the pattern of land tenure.

2. Maldistribution of land ownership and control.

3. Shortcomings in the living conditions, income, leasing arrangements, and opportunities for advancement of sharecroppers and other landless groups.

4. Lack of individual responsibility and initiative associated with certain communal forms of tenure.

5. Lack of adequate credit facilities to support advancement in tenure status.

6. Difficulties of capital accumulation under systems of widely dispersed peasant holdings.

7. Complexities of the problem of limiting size of agricultural holdings and hence income.

8. Relationship of types of tenure to the alleviation of population pressure.

9. Evaluation of the merits of co-operative farming.

10. Problem of developing meaningful definitions and classifications of such phenomena as part-time farmers and absentee landowners.

11. Extension of technical knowledge to peasant workers in order to equip them for the tasks of managing operators.

12. Determination of optimum operating scale under peasant proprietorship, both in the present and with allowance for future population growth.

13. Evaluation of reclaimed and realloted land and of land for taxation purposes.

14. Evaluation of land in cases of expropriation for public purposes and for private purposes in cases of selling, inheritance, renting, and mortgaging.

15. Inequitability of rental rates.

16. Causes of excessively high rates of tenancy under conditions of relatively low population pressure.

17. Confusion resulting from inadequate land survey and title records.

18. Retardation of tenure progress due to exorbitant interest rates for production credit and family living expenses.

19. Unwieldly and poorly enforced laws relating to the acquisition of ownership.

Selecting the Study

The foregoing list of problems was regarded as being neither all-inclusive nor precisely stated. It did furnish the basis for further discussion and for the selection of problems to be outlined in more detail. The two which were selected were in the general areas of (a) the relationship of types of tenure to the alleviation of population pressure and (b) an approach to the inequitability of rental rates through land evaluation.

Dividing into two sub-groups, the working party proceeded to concentrate on each of the problems selected for more thorough-going examination. It was agreed that in this activity, as well as in the work of the larger group, complete freedom would prevail with reference to preparation of the statements and, if deemed advisable, revision of the problem itself. The latter occurred in both instances.

For example, the first project originally was proposed in connection with a country which has an excess population in relation to its area of developed resources and the status of its industrial development. The question of the precise meaning of "population pressure," however, placed that subject high on the roster of terms to be defined and, if possible, converted into some measurable meaning. This, in turn, led to a decision to recast the inquiry so as to cover the tenure-population relationship regardless of the degree of population pressure. The second project was modified even more considerably as the sub-group progressed with its deliberations. One of its major concerns continued to be the technical problem of land evaluation, but its major interest shifted to the strategic place of sound procedures determining land values in the consolidation of fragmented holdings.

Both projects are outlined in rather general terms. While each is based on problems which the working party considered important and as having significant tenure content, the main purpose of these statements is to illustrate the processes by which a plan of work for any tenure project of a similar nature might be developed.[1]

Project Number One

The title of the project was "A Study of Land Tenure Reforms as a Means of Alleviating Population Maladjustment."

Note: This general title is mainly for purposes of identification. In adapting such a project to any given country, the scope and hence the title should be focused upon a more definitive area of inquiry. For example, if the land reform under consideration is that of conversion to a system of small peasant proprietorships, this should be indicated in the title as well as in the balance of the statement. Similarly, the population problem should be identified; e.g., a surplus rural labor force, maldistribution of people in relation to the location of resources, or the loss of an historic migration outlet. A further refinement would be the naming of the areas to be surveyed within the country.

PRIMARY CONSIDERATIONS

Note: The sub-group engaged on this project statement found it somewhat easier to suggest the problem through a series of related questions which are asked more or less in the descending order of their magnitude. It is the aim of these questions to provide a narrowing focus which culminates in sample hypotheses that might be subjected to testing.

1. What specifically, constitutes population pressure (or population deficit)?

2. What objective criteria may be employed to determine (a) whether population pressure exists, and (b) the intensity of such pressure?

3. What are the probable impacts of population maladjustment upon land tenure?

4. What are the prospects of land tenure reform alleviating the population maladjustment?

5. What kind of land tenure reform measures would likely provide maximum relief?

6. What factors other than that of land

tenure are essential to a major population adjustment?

7. What is the role in the solution of the population problem of the following: (a) population policy; (b) intensification of agriculture—reclamation, irrigation, farm technology, chemurgy; (c) market development; (d) migration—both internal and external; (e) expansion of nonfarm economic activities.

SPECIFIC CONSIDERATIONS

1. What are the principal weaknesses of existing forms of land tenure with reference to the population maladjustment?

2. What types of tenure would produce optimum results in the effort to relieve the problems?

Note: Choices of tenure forms to be analyzed, together with an indication of their respective characteristics, may be drawn from the following:

1. Individual farm owner operators: (a) ownership of the land; (b) important decisions made and risks assumed by the family group (family head); (c) a self-contained agricultural unit with no labor or only occasional labor from outside the family; (d) major part of family income derived from labor on the farm; (e) sense of responsibility in conducting the work on the land; (f) favorable conditions for the conservation of soil and other resources; (g) identification with sound social institutions in an area farmed under this type of tenure.

2. Tenant operators: (a) exploitation of land by non-owners; (b) tendency to reduce opportunity for the attainment of ownership; (c) unfavorable cultural conditions and labor exploitation, sometimes conducive to class struggle.

3. Community farming: (a) common use of land according to specified agreement; (b) co-operative buying and selling; (c) tendency to minimize individual responsibility; (d) sense of group relationship.

4. Industrial farming: (a) machinery rather than land the most important agent of production; (b) use of farm workers as mere tools of production, creating a monopoly in favor of a small group, accelerating the trend toward pauperism, and strengthening the demand for land; (c) a large number of workers per unit; (d) a one-crop system of production.

FORMULATING THE HYPOTHESES

Working hypotheses are clearly stated assumptions about the problems which are to be subjected to testing. A first requirement is that a hypothesis should be grounded in logic and theory, and it is further assumed that the character of the hypothesis will be conditioned by the observation and experience of the research worker. Thus, in the hands of social scientists hailing from widely separated regions of the world, the task of formulating meaningful hypotheses becomes almost insuperable.

The function of the working party becomes mainly one of classifying and emphasizing the importance of hypotheses in the development of the project plan. Thoughtful students of research methodology repeatedly have called attention to the significance of the working hypothesis in all phases of project operation. It is apparent that lack of relevance in the hypothetical formulation and absence of continuous reference to the hypothesis as the study progresses constitute the greatest single weakness in most studies of land tenure. Therefore, the necessity for care in stating and utilizing the hypothesis can scarcely be overstated.

Beyond this word of caution, the working party does not purpose to offer further discussion on this important section in the project statement. More complete treatment of the subject may be found in several reference works (notably, L. A. Salter's *A Critical Review of Research in Land Economics,* University of Minnesota Press, 1948).

The preceding list of related questions concerning the problem implies that the working party accepted a certain theoretical framework for this inquiry and would be able, following the selection of the region or country to be studied, to develop hypotheses appropriate to the study. The country, however, remains unnamed, and the group can only propose illustrative hypotheses. Two examples are submitted as follows:

1. Community tenure forms, combined with cottage industries, provide the most feasible vehicle for absorbing surplus rural labor in productive enterprise during a transition from low-level to high-level industrial development. (Under conditions of heavy population pressure.)

2. Individual peasant proprietorships, on a unit operating scale that is economical, offer the necessary incentives for effecting internal population transfers and correcting population maladjustment. (Under conditions of low population pressure.)

HISTORICAL REVIEW

The pattern of the institutional fabric will differ in each country with respect to the conditions of its population and land tenure. A review of the historical development of prevailing tenure systems and of the factors which account for the present character of the country's population should precede the detailing of techniques for conducting the study. Four points are worth mentioning in connection with the historical review:

1. Literature bearing on the subject should be summarized and appraised, and a bibliography should be prepared.

2. In this phase of the project a special effort should be made to utilize the values of disciplines other than agricultural economics. This background material should include the most revealing works available in such fields as history, geography, sociology, and law, the objective being to add depth to the breadth of the economic analysis. No source which helps to explain the behavior of people in terms of population and tenure problems should be overlooked.

3. While the main weight of the historical review would rest upon literature produced in the country under study, foreign references also should be utilized where they can contribute to a clearer understanding of the evolution of social and economic processes within the country. Inter-nation migration and the cultural flow of significant tenure practices, for instance, cannot be evaluated entirely from a single, national vantage point.

4. The conjunction of institutional factors in the locale under observation should be oriented about the working hypotheses, precisely for the reason that the latter emerged in the first place from insights gleaned from the environment. Order and control of the subject matter of the investigation demand close adherence to specified hypothetical boundaries, even in an interpretation of the background.

SECONDARY STATISTICAL MATERIALS

The conference Working Party on the Collection and Use of Agricultural Statistics on Tenure has grouped under major headings the items on agricultural statistics which should be reviewed in trying to study land tenure in a given region. Their report proposes a minimum body of basic statistics in agriculture. In many countries, however, including some employing large census bureaus, such complete statistical information is not available. In such cases the following procedures are advisable:

1. To select the most reliable statistics relevant to the problems under consideration.

2. To compile a "deficit list" of factual information which should be obtained.

3. To study the means (budget and personnel) necessary for overcoming the deficiency in statistics within a reasonable period of time.

4. To reconcile available statistics with the urgency and time dimensions of problem analysis; in short to make the most of what is on hand while updating and enlarging the tenure content of the agricultural census.

In addition to tenure statistics, demographic data of particular relevance to this project include (1) long-time population trends, (2) vital and migration statistics, particularly statistics on external migration, (3) selected data on internal migration, if possible through comparisons with two or more censuses, and (4) occupational patterns of the areas of study, in relation to population density.

OBSERVATION AND SAMPLING

The choice of the unit of observation necessarily will be conditioned by the selection of the country under study as well as by the emphasis to be placed upon certain population and tenure factors. However, the working party strongly favors observing the recommendations of the United Nations with regard to the use of standardized international units. The obvious choice in this instance is the family, since the family is the one institution that possesses attributes common both to population and land tenure. The preferred interpretation of "family" is that which identifies the family as the smallest homogeneous unit of social organization.

Defined as a miniature of the universe, the sample must be determined in light of the larger complex which it represents. Hence, it is impossible to generalize with any degree of assurance about sampling procedure without first identifying the area of study. General guidance on sampling is available in numerous professional publications, to which qualified research persons usually have ready access. Since this project embraces the concept of relationships internal to the unit of observation, it may be presumed that attention would be given to all of the recognized tools of investigation including the case method.

FORMATION OF THE SCHEDULE

The schedule is an observation device. As a formal method for obtaining facts in a form that is objective and standardized, it should provide the means by which statistical analysis may be carried forward with precision. The schedule has the following three main functions:

1. It serves as a reminder to the enumerator of items to be covered in the study.

2. It brings the reports of different enumerators into the same uniform pattern.

3. It clarifies and isolates the various elements of importance in and among the units of observation, in order that the sequence of relationships between the constituent factors may be observed.

Characteristics in the design of a schedule for the study of land tenure in relation to population problems are not fundamentally different from those followed in any study in the social sciences. However, in a general study as suggested here for adaptation to conditions in different countries, it is emphasized that the utmost care should be exercised to bring the schedule into the range of circumstances prevailing in a given region. This requires more than technical knowledge in schedule preparation on the part of the research worker. It suggests a background of training and experience suitable to the locale in which the study is to be conducted.

Among the principles that should guide the organization of the schedule, the following are particularly noteworthy:

1. The number of questions should be rigorously limited to those which are pertinent to testing the hypotheses.

2. Questions should be clear, specific, and within the range of understanding of prospective interviewees.

3. Insofar as possible, the material should

be cast in measurable quantitative terms that are familiar to the interviewee.

4. Questions should be so formulated in order to minimize bias in the answers, presenting to the interviewee a full range of alternative answers, only one of which would be clearly applicable in any given case.

5. Means of corroboration, i.e., "internal checks," should be provided where possible.

6. Intimate or embarrassing questions should be avoided, but the least impersonal inquiries should be reserved for the latter part of the schedule and presented only after rapport has been established with the interviewee.

7. Consistent with point 6 above, the questions should be arranged in logical sequence.

In the present study much of the basic data would be provided by secondary sources. The schedule, however, should produce information that is either attainable from no other source or which is needed to explain or confirm more general statistics. Hence, certain minimum contents of the proposed schedule might be visualized under the following brief outline:

1. Identification data
   a. Name, location, cultural or ethnic identity, and sex of interviewee (assumed to be family head)
   b. Tenure status
   c. Size of farm
      1) Size of this family's operation
      2) Size of total operation
   d. Type of landlord
   e. Class of operation
2. Family composition and characteristics
3. Level-of-living items
4. Crop and livestock organization
5. Inventories of real estate and equipment
6. Credit data
7. Tenure history of the family
8. Ownership data
9. Leasing arrangements

10. Labor organization
11. Social participation

CONDUCTING FIELD WORK

The type of field organization should conform to the general needs of the inquiry. Four features of the plan of organization are worthy of special attention: (1) field staff requirements, (2) pilot survey, (3) duration and stages of inquiry, and (4) adequate community understanding.

Field staff requirements.—These cannot be exactly prescribed without keeping in mind the particular needs of each zone as to the extent of the sample selected for intensive investigation, the statistical material available for utilization as sources of secondary data, and the intensity of the problem. Following the determination of these prerequisites, the requirements of field operations may be accurately assessed.

Normally, the research staff would include a major supervisor (government official or university professor) and a team of field recorders or enumerators who will actually approach the people for personal interviews. A good investigator, besides his specialized knowledge of economics and statistics and his practical training in the field, ideally should possess a combination of qualities—an infinite capacity for taking pains, a keen and observant eye, an all-absorbing interest in his work, an objective outlook, sympathy for those with whom he has to deal, patience, ability to take rebuffs in good humor, and a knowledge of the customs, manners, language, and mode of living and working of the people. The field recorders likewise should be given sufficient training and instructions on the precise implications of the terminology and the items used in the schedule. As a check on the qualifications of the field recorder, the project supervisor or supervisors should accompany him on his interviews for a period of training.

Pilot survey.—The execution of the project will take some time, perhaps a year or two. This being a long process, in order to obtain some advance idea of the findings of the project within a reasonable margin of error, a pilot survey should be undertaken during the first two months. This is pretesting, which, besides affording valuable experience as to the difficulties to be encountered, will pave the way for the planning of detailed questions.

Duration and stages of inquiry.—The period of the project is the cumulative total of the time consumed by the various essential stages of inquiry. These stages consist of preliminary planning, the pilot survey, the main study, and the processing and publication of results. An approximation of the time requirements of the project considered here would read about as follows: four months' preparatory work, two months for the pilot survey, six months for the main field enumeration, and one year for processing, analyzing, and publishing the results. These time requirements would vary markedly with the circumstances.

Adequate community understanding of the project.—For successful completion of the project, the collaboration and co-operation of the public is vital. Adequate publicity to make the people conscious of the needs, objectives, and methods of study should be arranged as an integral part of the project.

ANALYZING THE DATA

Guidance on the matters of processing and analyzing data is available in many publications on statistics and sampling. However, the stress put in this workshop on the formulation of hypotheses needs to be related to this phase of inquiry.

These hypotheses, which have served to determine what data need to be collected, now guide the use of data in classification, comparisons, and statistical tests. The analysis of data proceeds by determining which hypotheses singled out social processes leading to significantly different results. Such conclusions point the attention to possible methods of achieving desirable results or they indicate areas of social interaction in which control must be attempted to achieve more desirable results.

An important part of every study, which contributes to further inquiry, lies in the failure of some of the hypotheses to lead to significant analysis of the data. This, together with hints derived from experience during the collection of data, may promote a deeper understanding of the problem by suggesting further analysis of previously overlooked factors.

UTILIZATION AND PUBLICATION

Findings of the project should be presented in the media which have been proved to have the most effective educational values. These include a wide variety of outlets, but it is especially desirable that the current international aspects of land tenure be observed in the presentation. In some cases, publications should be prepared in three languages besides the official language of the country concerned and otherwise arranged in conformity with the U.N. recommendations on published material.

In addition to the international audience, such consumers within the country as agricultural leaders, government agencies, educational organizations, the press, radio, and commercial and industrial interest groups should be reached if possible. The working party on information at this conference should be in a position to furnish some highly useful counsel on techniques for publicizing the findings of such a project.

THE COLLECTION AND USE OF AGRICULTURAL STATISTICS ON TENURE

Report of the Working Party

〄〄〄〄   Chairmen, *Marshall Harris and Charles L. Stewart*

THE WORKING Party on The Collection and Use of Agricultural Statistics on Tenure restricted its deliberations to a consideration of the collection of mass statistical data on land tenure. This was done in recognition of the assignment during the second week of the conference to the Working Party on The Methodology and Value of Land Tenure Research Surveys. The working party endeavored to survey various ways and means of collecting and using tenure statistics, but not to encroach upon the methods and uses of research surveys. The party also took into consideration the inclusion of tenure-related items in the 1950 World Census of Agriculture. It was felt, however, that a fairly complete coverage of items should be made even though some duplication might occur.

The first activity of the working party was to list major headings of various tenure and closely related items that might well be collected whenever the opportunity presented itself in any country. The basic objective was to present an over-all list from which any country could select the items most pertinent to local situation. The following major headings were listed:

1. Form of tenure under which the farm operator holds the land.

2. Characteristics of the farm operator as to age, sex, educational attainments, marital status, and labor supply, including family and paid laborers.

3. Characteristics of the owner (usually landlord) of the land operated by tenant, cropper, manager, or someone else other than the owner.

4. Kind of rent paid, whether cash, fixed amount or share of production.

5. Physical and economic facts about the farm.

6. Use of the land in the farm.

7. Type of farm, based upon sources or amount of income or whether managed in single or multiple units (plantation system).

8. Types of ownership, including characteristics of owner, methods of acquiring the land, and types of interest the owner has in the land.

9. Capital used in acquiring ownership of the land and in operation of the farm: source and amount.

10. Length of occupancy by the farm operator.

11. Types of debt: amount, rate of interest, and other terms.

12. Facilities available to the farmer: housing, farm equipment, and household equipment.

13. Situation of farm roads, distance to market, electricity, etc.

14. Off-farm work and other sources of income: type and amount.

15. Information available to the operating farmer: sources, kinds, and media.

16. Fragmentation of the farm land: number, size, and distance between parcels.

17. Farm expenses: types and amounts.

These major headings were amplified by listing pertinent subitems, with appropriate cross-references where duplication occurred, as shown in the following outline:

A. Tenure of operator
   1. Owner-operator

(a) Full owner

(b) Part owner, part tenant

2. Manager (salaried)

3. Tenant

4. Subtenant

B. Characteristics of operator

1. Age

2. Color, caste, etc.

3. Sex

4. Size and structure of family

5. Religion

6. Place of residence

7. Educational attainment of operator

8. Length of occupancy (see item J, below)

9. Proportion of time used on this farm, on another farm, at nonfarm activities (see item N, below), or unemployed

10. Proportion of income received from work on this farm, from work on another farm, or from nonfarm activities (see item N, below)

C. Characteristics of landlord

1. Types

(a) Individual, corporate, public body or agency, religious and charitable institutions, whether absentee or resident

(b) Operator-landlord, whether absentee or resident

2. Area owned

3. Value

4. Residence of landlord

5. Kinship to operator, that is, landlord rents to son, son-in-law, grandson, etc.

6. Age, sex, and other personal characteristics

7. Length of time landlord and his ancestors have owned this land

D. Kind of rent paid

1. Cash per unit

2. Share

(a) Crop share

(b) Livestock share

(c) Mogharassa—an agreement between tenant and landlord whereby the landlord supplies the land to the tenant on which the latter plants trees. The agreement has a fixed period after which the tenant becomes entitled to a share in the trees planted, and in certain cases also to a proportionate share in the land on which the trees were planted. The amount of the tenant's share depends on the social and economic conditions of the locality, on the types of trees, and on the integrity and good will of the landlord.

3. Share-cash, that is, a combination of share and cash

4. Standing rent, being a fixed quantity of product per unit

5. Combination of any of the above methods

E. Physical and economic facts about the farm

1. Area owned; area rented

2. Value of real estate with separate values for land, farm buildings, dwelling

3. Mortgage debt situation (see item K, below)

4. Taxes and real estate assessment for local improvement and similar charges upon the land

5. Road type and distance from community center (see item M, below)

6. Irrigation

(a) Area covered

(b) Irrigation charges: kinds, purposes, and amounts (construction and/or operational charges)

F. Land use

1. Cropland: showing total area and whether harvested or fallow

2. Pasture land

3. Woodland and forest land, showing

whether pastured or not pastured

4. Other land, including waste and idle land

G. Type of farm (operating unit, whether single or multiple)

  1. Classified as to sources of income

    (a) Crops: cotton, tobacco, etc.

    (b) Livestock: dairy, beef, poultry, etc.

    (c) Mixed farming

    (d) General farming

  2. Alternative—classified as to size or amount of income (illustrative figures are as used in United States, 1950, for each country an appropriate scale would be necessary)

    (a) Large scale (25,000 dollars and over)

    (b) Commercial:

      (1) Large family (10,000 to 25,000 dollars gross income from sale and home use)

      (2) Medium family (5,000 to 10,000 dollars gross income from sale and home use)

      (3) Small family (2,500 to 5,000 dollars gross income from sale and home use)

    (c) Small farms (1,200 to 2,500 dollars)

    (d) Subsistence (1,200 dollars or less)

    (e) Part-time

    (f) Residential

    (g) Other

H. Types of ownership

  1. Type of owner of the land, such as public, individual, religious, charitable, co-operative, corporate, partnership, communal, collective, ejidal, or prescriptive

  2. How the owner acquired the land, such as by purchase, inheritance, government grant, expropriation, or foreclosure

  3. Type of interest the owner has in the land, such as life estate or life lease, fee simple, purchase, contract, undivided interest, or joint ownership

I. Source of capital used in ownership and operation

  1. Land purchase capital

    (a) Borrowed

      (1) Banking institution—government or private

      (2) Money lender

      (3) Co-operative

    (b) Owned

      (1) Savings from farming or from nonfarming

      (2) Inheritance or gift

J. Length of occupancy

  1. Year occupancy began

  2. Month occupancy began

  3. Length of lease

K. Debt and interest

  1. Real estate (land)

    (a) Amount

    (b) Interest rate

    (c) Term—length

    (d) Type of security: mortgage, note, crops, livestock or personal

    (e) Purpose of loan

    (f) Methods and terms of repayment

    (g) Underwritten or insured loans

  2. Chattels and personal:

    (a) to (g) same as above

L. Facilities

  1. Housing (dwelling)

    (a) Number of rooms

    (b) Running water and sanitary facilities

    (c) Electricity

    (d) Other (specify)

  2. Farm

    (a) Buildings: barn, silo, shed

    (b) Equipment: preparation, seeding, cultivation, harvesting

    (c) Source of power: hand, animal-drawn, or mechanized

M. Roads
   1. Type of road and surface
   2. Who maintains road
   3. Condition of road
   4. Distance to market where farmer:
      (a) Sells major products
      (b) Buys major requirements
N. Off-farm work and other sources of income
   1. On other farms, whether regular or part-time
   2. Industries, whether skilled or unskilled
      (a) Home
      (b) Other
   3. Pensions, etc.
   4. Amount of income from each source
O. Source of information available
   1. Government
      (a) Written
      (b) Oral: meetings, groups, individual or radio
      (c) Motion pictures—visual aids
      (d) Demonstrations and exhibits
   2. Nongovernment
      (a) to (d) same as above
P. Fragmentation
   1. Number of parcels
   2. Distance from residence and between parcels (by specified distances)
Q. Expenses
   1. Operation on an annual basis
   2. Capital—long-term and fixed
   3. Taxes
   4. Family
   5. Rent
   6. Management
   7. Interest

The working party also discussed ways and means of collecting the desired statistical data. The weight of the discussion was in favor of adjusting procedures to the local situation as to funds available, ways of collecting data, and customary practices. The following topics were discussed:

1. Collecting data by questionnaire, whether by (1) personal interview or (2) mailing to farmers. Personal interviews were preferred to mailing the questionnaires to farmers. The problems presented by poor roads, low level of literacy, and reluctance to fill out questionnaires, were considered. However, costs and frequency of enumeration may indicate preference of mailing the questionnaire under certain conditions.

2. Whether to interview farmers individually or in groups. Individual interviews were preferred to group interviews, but cost might be reduced considerably if one enumerator could handle several respondents at a time.

3. Advantages and disadvantages of complete coverage or sampling the total. If a sample is used, what method of sampling should be followed—block or cluster samples as compared with a random percentage sample? Sample enumerations have much to offer and might well be used more frequently.

4. Whether to go to the farmer or have him come to some designated headquarters, such as school, government office, church, or army post. Local practice varies considerably from country to country. In many areas it is not necessary to go to the farm to get the data. However, the enumeration may be more accurate if the interview takes place on the farm.

5. Who should do the interviewing (enumeration), a trained technician or others?

6. Who should give the data—the operator or the landowner?

7. Best part of the year to do the enumeration, and the period of time over which it should extend.

8. What is the best unit of observation—the farm, the farm operator, or the landowner? It appeared that many of the data would refer specifically to the farm (operating unit) and its operator, but that some of the data needed in improving the land sys-

tem would have to be concerned with the landowner, if he was not also the operator.

9. The form of the questionnaire and the wording of each question were mentioned as important items, although time did not permit exploration of these matters.

10. It was recognized that the tenure items, as herein proposed, would generally become a part of a much larger questionnaire, and would have to be integrated with other items. This integration would increase the value of the enumeration.

11. Should tenure data be collected in conjunction with local law enforcement, tax assessments, and similar activities? It was recognized that this is the practice in some countries, that it reduces the cost, and that it makes possible annual or frequent enumerations. However, certain difficulties have been encountered; for example, enumerations related closely to taxation have not proved successful because many people tend to withhold information in the interest of obtaining a lower tax assessment. For this reason the tax assessor or collector and the census enumerator probably should be different persons.

A short time was spent on how the statistical data should be processed and used. The discussion centered around the following topics:

1. The relative merits of local versus central tabulating. In some areas where the data are tabulated locally and final results are sent to central headquarters, it was found that the data became available much earlier than if all the tabulating had to be done at a central place. It was recognized that local tabulating was more easily handled when the items were few and the definitions clear. The problem is one of balancing accuracy, timing, and costs.

2. The place of special surveys in the collection of tenure statistics. The matter was divided into two distinct aspects: (a) detailed research surveys, and (b) special enu-

merations to supplement regular censuses. The importance of supplemental enumerations, frequently on a sample basis, was recognized.

3. The use of agricultural statistics on land tenure. The primary use of mass statistical data is for the purpose of describing the existing tenure situation. The description can be presented in statistical tables, in a graphic summary, and in narrative form, depending upon the audience and the purpose of the presentation. Mass statistics may also be used for analytical purposes. In this connection, they are more readily usable for problem-defining than for problem-solving purposes. The latter data usually are gathered in special research surveys.

The Working Party on The Collection and Use of Agricultural Statistics on Land Tenure, after full discussion during its three meetings during the week of October 8, 1951, suggests to the conference on world land tenure problems that for satisfactory planning for the solution of land tenure problems it is necessary that each interested country obtain the following minimum list of statistical data on the land tenure situation, using appropriate and available methods. It is further suggested that this list may be modified in light of local conditions and circumstances pertaining to each country.

A. Who owns the land
  1. Types of owner—for example, public, individual, religious, co-operative, etc.
  2. Area owned
  3. Absentee or not
  4. Occupation of owner
B. Type of farm and land use
  1. Cropland, by major crops
  2. Pasture land
  3. Woodland
  4. Waste and idle land
  5. Irrigated area

6. Livestock by number and kind
7. Number of parcels into which farm is separated
C. Tenure and characteristics of operator
  1. Owner operator
    (a) Full owner
    (b) Part owner, part tenant
  2. Manager
  3. Tenant
  4. Subtenant
  5. Cropper
  6. Personal characteristics, such as sex, age, size of family
  7. Length of occupancy of operator

D. Facts about the farm
  1. Area—owned and rented
  2. Value of real estate
  3. Debt—source, amount, terms, and interest
E. Kind of rent paid
  1. Cash
  2. Share
  3. Combinations
F. Off-farm work and other sources of income
  1. Source
  2. Amount

THE FUNCTION OF PROBLEM FORMULATION: COMMENT ON TWO POSSIBLE PROJECTS IN TENURE RESEARCH[1]

Don Kanel

FORMULATION of problems, whether done implicitly or explicitly, underlies all organization of research work. This presentation will be an argument for doing this explicitly.

A problem is formulated by a series of propositions about relevant interactions of resources, technology, and social processes. Such propositions are hypotheses. They are derived out of knowledge accumulated through past research and experience, using these terms in a broad way to describe past attempts to describe, analyze, adjust to, and control the world around us.

A problem arises when we do not feel that we can go ahead with action until we have given some thought to the situation facing us. We do not have full confidence in our knowledge of that situation; if we did we would have gone ahead to take care of it. On the other hand, we can formulate a problem; this implies that impressions arising from previous experience and our previous thinking enable us to formulate the mere dissatisfaction with the situation into a hypothetical statement of the problem.

This formulation is a tentative statement of what are the relevant means and obstacles in the situation and what are the alternative ways of controlling these or adjusting to them. We shall not feel confident of undertaking action until our confidence in this analysis of the problem has been strengthened. The work of research can be described as being directed by our hypotheses to analyze data considered to be relevant, to conclude from such analysis whether or not the data are relevant, or else to reformulate the hypotheses and undertake further study until we are satisfied with our understanding of the problem and with the adequacy of proposed solutions. Our conclusions are still tentative, but are accepted as better guides to action. Action based upon these conclusions tests them further, possibly suggesting new hypotheses for study. Thus problem formulation, analysis, and action interact with each other.

Not all research is instituted in immediate connection with pressing social problems. However, the theory of the method of the social sciences can be discussed most easily by dealing with examples of studies designed to contribute to the process of determining public policy.[2]

For the purpose of discussion, two examples of possible situations will now be introduced. The emphasis will be on the relation between the problems arising in these situations and the types of research capable of making the best contribution to the determination of policy. The first situation is one in which it has been decided to carry out a land reform, creating family-size farms of owner-operators by dividing among them the land taken away from large property holders. However, to define the scope of the program and to provide general guides to administrators, information may be wanted about such items as land available for distribution from large properties, types of large specialized farming units unsuitable for division, numbers of landless and land-poor farmers, etc. In this case there is an implied acceptance of the suitability of general procedures of distributing land from large property to working farmers. Research serves to define such details of the program as the amount of land which landlords can retain, special types of farms eligible for exemption from the program, and the size of new holdings to be created.

The second example is a situation in which it has been decided that the ownership of family-size units of land operated by tenants will be transferred to them, but that co-operative farming will be organized on those farms where previous landlords carried on irrigation and other types of farming depending on specialized centrally-controlled equipment and on co-ordination of work, principally by the supervision of hired labor. It is desired to find out in more detail which solution should be applied to different areas and different types of farming.

The first case is intended as an example of a problem which requires the collection of relatively few items of data from a representative sample of the whole population. The ability to carry out successfully this program depends primarily on the use of methods already considerably tested in experience and not so much on the additional research to provide the details. The important feature of this example is that essentially the problem has been analyzed and the solution devised on the basis of knowledge already available. Land reform programs have been carried on in broadly similar ways in other countries. The policies adopted in the past have provided rather uniformly for maximum acreage that can be retained by landlords and for exemption of specialized farms. The various actions that will be undertaken in the program are known; further research is simply expected to answer how extensive these operations will be.

We may assume for the moment that the solution adopted in the second case was also based on considerable previous experience, so that the feasibility and adequacy of this policy was generally accepted. Then there would be need for the collection of relatively few items of relevant data. These data would determine the distinctive situations to which one of the two adopted solutions would apply. The information collected should make it possible to distinguish between operating units on which a tenant family is fully occupied on its own portion of land from other cases where tenants, sharecroppers, or laborers spend part or all of their time on the landlord's land under central supervision. Family farms owned by operators will be the solution applied to the former situation. Additional data are needed to indicate whether central supervision of labor in the latter situation provides merely central management or whether it is needed to enable extensive specialization of labor and the use of important items of indivisible capital. The former solution is still applicable when central management is not crucial, but co-operative farming would be tried in the remaining cases.

Sampling surveys are well adapted, and guidance is available from principles of sample design, for setting up studies needed in the above examples. The data needed have been carefully defined in the formulation of the solution; after collection they should be able to provide the answers which are expected of them. The conclusion may be that the program is feasible and the details of it can be worked out from the data. Or the collected information may disclose that the means are not sufficient for the program contemplated. However, in this latter case there may be very little information in the study suggestive of other relevant alternatives, besides the obvious need for more analysis.

For the purpose of further discussion, the example of a situation in which a co-operative farming policy is being applied will now be expanded by additional illustrative assumptions. This addition will include in turn the specification of the assumptions on which the original policy was based, and the example of an important variable which may have been overlooked in the above problem formulation.

The co-operatve solution suggests itself for those farm units which need central management over indivisible equipment and specialized workers. Continued large-scale production should secure higher incomes for the members than the less suitable family farms. At the same time the democratic structure of a co-operatve gives the members a vote over its policies. In addition the powers of the government to regulate, tax, and acquire the property of its citizens for purposes of public policy are deemed capable of separating former landlords from the control and ownership of the large farm units. Thus it is proposed that the program can be carried on by instituting time-tested procedures. The legal processes available to the government will permit acquisition of the private property of large landlords, and co-operatives will maintain these large units of land under central management while giving farm laborers control over the policies of these organizations. The resulting situation is thought to provide the continuity of efficient production with improved security and welfare of the farm people.

The full acceptance of this analysis would be evidenced by a willingness to apply the above policy. This problem formulation leads to the acceptance of a solution based on previous knowledge. In order to implement the program, some collection of data would be required, but this research would not be designed to test the general adequacy of the adopted solution.

However, people drawing on experience of action programs among farmers, on previous studies of farm problems, or on known experiences in other countries might suggest that the above formulation overlooks probable difficulties. Thus they may suggest that a land reform program will bring to the farmers expectations of freedom from dominance by landlords, of a chance to escape poverty, and of the dignity of a more secure place in a reformed society. Only disillusion is likely to result in the new co-operatives from the relations between trained technicians, officials, and managers on the one hand and the ignorant farm laborers on the other. In the performance of the joint tasks the inferior position of the latter would continue without any immediate identifiable gains in income. The opportunities for visible gains would be rather in the slackening discipline on the joint tasks, making it possible to do additional work outside the co-operative or to devote effort to individual garden plots. Thus there would be no identification of effort with the share in the gains of the co-operative; production is likely to suffer, while the power of the individual farm laborer will indeed increase, primarily because of his greater ability to oppose the control of managers elected by him.

Consideration of the above hypotheses prior to a decision on policy would point to the need for additional research in several relevant directions. It would be significant to find out how farmers have responded to contact with technicians in extension programs. They may already be acquainted with benefits from improved methods and thus have faith in government-promoted programs despite the lack of visible short-run gains. Again, there may be traditional institutions for providing self-help and regulating social conduct. These have already worked out methods of securing co-operation among members, so that they may be the best agencies for taking over the management of the large land units. Or acquaintance with local people and analogies derived from the experience of organized labor may suggest that it would be better to separate the function of making production decisions from the function of protecting the interests of farm laborers in the common product. This may be because it might prove easier to rally farm laborers around issues raised by their grievances. Trusted leaders can develop, who will press these grievances but who in addition will develop policies that do not reach for unachievable gains. On the other hand government ownership of the large-scale units can vest the management function in government officials and technicians who will represent the public interest in efficient production.

Thus the lack of tested procedures for executing this program requires that other experiences, which may be related, be incorporated in the formulation of the problem. This would increase the scope of research to the testing of hypotheses proposing alternative solutions. It might suggest that it would be feasible and worthwhile to experiment with local projects. Further, the lack of previous experience would favor setting up research in such a way that other opportunities and obstacles not suggested by the original hypotheses would have a chance to show up.

The preparatory work would thus fulfill two functions. The problem formulation may be so tentative and of such limited scope that it would be inadvisable to decide what policy to adopt without further study. On the other hand the hypotheses direct the work of collection of data by determining what is relevant, while the extreme tentativeness may suggest the need for studies that make possible the reformulation of the problem.

The tentativeness of problem formulation does not necessarily preclude mass collections of data from large populations. For example, there may be a number of hypotheses, and it is believed that some of them will provide a useful formulation of the problem. They indicate the relevant data, and the useful hypotheses can be chosen by statistical analysis of correlation and tests of significance. Such studies have provided useful descriptions of our environment, and possibly have given us means to think about the broad features of social behavior. However, by themselves they have rarely given useful guides for new solutions. More specifically, they have not been suggestive of ways to control and adjust to problems for which there are no settled solutions. Rather they have indicated those broad patterns of similarities in behavior which arise because individuals and groups do have to work out solutions for getting along together in societies in which they live.

The attempt to collect "all" data in the hope of deriving a solution from this information is especially invalid. Actually this means that the research worker has his own ideas of what is relevant, despite the lack of an explicit statement of the problem. This is so, since it is impossible to collect "all" data. On the other hand, his underlying assumptions about the interrelations are not held in a tentative way. If this research worker had been pressed to propose a solution before the study, he would have probably derived it from these assumptions—subject to the test of the study. The analysis of the data makes possible the acceptance or rejection of the solution of the problem that the research worker would have formulated. However, this test will probably not be made, since it was not recognized that underlying assumptions are operating and need to be tested. Probably some of the previously held assumptions will appear as explanations advanced to explain the correlations found in the study. But these explanations will be less valid in the absence of a conscious test of these hypotheses against other possible hypotheses. The only function that this "blind" collection of data might perform is in showing up unexpected correlations which challenge future study to provide explanations of the interrelations producing them.

The need is for case studies which avail themselves of the experience (experimentation) of many people. There is no sharp contrast between sampling studies based on a definite statement of what data are relevant and case studies. Pre-testing, which can be used with different types of studies, is a device for the reformulation of the problem. What is important is the range in the tentativeness we attach to the validity of different portions of our accumulated knowledge. When this is very tentative, case studies or intensive studies of local areas and groups are valuable because of the opportunity they provide for flexibility in the reformulation of hypotheses during the collection of data. Such case studies provide opportunities to shift emphasis to new data during the interviews themselves

and during the stay in the area studied.

When our knowledge is very tentative, the wide ramifications of a proposed policy lead into unknown directions of human interrelationships. The most strategic ones cannot be determined easily. What is to be hoped is that hypotheses drawn out of an admittedly inadequate experience, will direct attention to the problem in such a way that inadequacies in the initial formulation will show up.[3] The conclusions of a useful analysis would very likely provide significantly different solutions as alternatives to the original policy. It might be concluded that the proposed programs are well suited to local experimentation and that this would be worth while before a more general action is undertaken. Experimental action by private individuals or under state programs, where it is already going on, is a very important and but little exploited area for research. There is need for increasing the awareness of research workers to look at new departures for meeting old problems which are constantly being made. The impact of these experiences must be carefully analyzed, separating out extraneous influences, analyzing the varieties of problems that have been overcome or that will have to be overcome elsewhere, so that the conclusion can be a meaningful statement of an alternative.

The purpose of these intensive studies is to provide better and more useful conclusions. The accumulation of such conclusions is not in opposition to collection of mass data representative of large portions or of the whole population. On the contrary, the intensive studies lead to the formulation of better questions and the designation of relatively few strategically relevant data to be collected in sample surveys. Both types of studies can contribute to the working out of better policies.

Part XXIV   ENLISTING THE PARTICIPATION OF
THE PEOPLE IN LAND TENURE ADJUSTMENT

CHANNELING THE DESIRE FOR IMPROVEMENT
IN TENURE STATUS

Report of the Working Party

🙟🙟🙟🙟   Chairman, *John H. Kolb*

THE DISCUSSION in this group turned about three central points of interest: (1) the meaning and importance of desire in relation to land tenure; (2) the forms and causes of desire for improvement in tenure status; and (3) some methods and techniques necessary to order and channel desires.

Importance of Desire

The desire for land on the part of man appears to be nearly universal. "Hunger for land," it is sometimes called, and the more agrarian a people is, the stronger this desire seems to be. Land and man's relation with it often dominates the capital structure and the social systems of whole nations. Moreover, land in many countries is valued not for itself alone; its possession stands as a symbol of security, a badge of prestige, and a form of power. Something of this general feeling is expressed in the slogan of Dr. Sun Yat-Sen of China, as quoted by a member of the working party: "Equalization of land a right, and land to the tiller." Exceptions to this general attitude are found in those situations where there is ignorance of possibilities or where sheer inertia born of generations in serfdom veils hope for improvement.

The desire for access to land is not to be confused with various specific forms of tenure systems such as complete individual ownership, crown lease, or even co-operative plans based upon some earlier communal or tribal arrangements. Practices, customs, traditions, and the cultural values of different countries have much to do with the particular forms of tenure which are most sought after or desired. The point for consideration in this working party was the importance of the desire itself or in some instances the lack of it.

The importance of desire is found in relation to action. What moves people to action, what is the motive power—motivation—whereby they seek to exercise their recognized or hoped-for rights? Desires spring from deep aspirations, earnest wishes to obtain something which is felt to have high value, great worth, in this case improved tenure status. The agreed purpose of the group therefore was how to help people get from where they are to where they desire to be with respect to freely agreed-upon objectives, and to do it in an orderly and disciplined manner.

A corollary point of view found its way into the discussion, not always by explicit statement but certainly by implication; namely, that access to land, "land to the tiller," is not only an assumed right but an implied responsibility. Rights and responsibilities both involve moral issues. One of the great deans of American agriculture, Liberty Hyde Bailey, once said, "The morals of land management are more important than the economics of land." He regarded the right use of land as a criterion of whether a nation is truly civilized. The same attitude is expressed in many forms of religious literature, as for example, by the early Hebrew psalmist who declared, "The earth is the Lord's." The same idea is found in early Roman law. It is likewise found in some contemporary legislation whereby a careless cultivator may be punished or, in extreme cases, deprived of his land.

The meaning, whatever its source of expression, is quite clear. Not simply individual persons or even separate generations are involved in man's relation with the land. There are certain continuing values associated with land which must be recognized and respected. This would seem to suggest that property in land should be of a different character and content than property, for example, in stocks and bonds or in capital goods such as buildings and machinery. This point of view has found legal expression in many countries.

Thus, the meaning and importance of desire in land tenure relations are deeply personal and emotional, as well as highly social and moral in nature. Both are strongly conditioned by the historical and cultural experiences of any particular people at any particular time and in any particular place.

Forms and Causes of Desire

For the development of this point, the discussion turned to the experiences and opinions of members of the working party. Only a few highly summarized statements can be included here, and these simply as illustrations.

A member from Pakistan observed that in some areas of some countries the desire for tenure improvement was latent, unable to rise to the level of expression in action.

This was because: (1) A belief prevails in a kind of Divine dispensation to accept what is, without question. (2) There may be no hope for improvement, since there is no experience or knowledge of what is better. (3) Feudal systems in certain areas have tended to fix status and render change difficult, if not impossible. However, changes are coming about because of (a) political activities and rivalries of leaders and the extension of voting powers; (b) expanding channels of communication; for example, newspapers, radio, travel, education; (c) the increase in peasant meetings and the resultant demands for improvements, even through direct action.

A member from China reported that for centuries land ownership has been regarded as a measuring stick of social standing as well as economic power. The desire for improvement has been especially strong since the 1926 revolution. It has taken the form of demands by peasant associations and here and there has erupted in sporadic violence. On the other hand, there is reluctance to own land when exorbitantly high taxes are imposed as under present communistic control.

In Colombia, a member of the group explained, there had been a long history of active desire for individual family ownership of land. It had been kept alive through civil wars and by political propaganda, and so there is strong belief that ownership gives families security.

A member from Peru described the strong desire for land which is found there in the Indian communities and among sharecropper families. It has a strong social basis and extends beyond legal considerations.

A member from Costa Rica expressed the opinion that the desire for individual ownership of land was already so strong that certain misuses had resulted. Therefore the emphasis should be placed upon means for the better ordering and more proper disciplining of present desires.

A member from Mexico pointed out the problem of not having sufficient good land for distribution among the "ejidatarios." The desires were present, but means must be found for their satisfaction within the legal framework of the recent agrarian reform.

In Paraguay, a member said, there is a tradition and an active memory of land ownership in the hands of operating families. Therefore, there is now a strong desire for the repossession of land on the part of tenants and sharecroppers. The people and their government are in agreement about the desirability of such reforms, and are seeking to work out acceptable agrarian policies.

In the Philippines, a member used current reports to show that fully one-half of the number of farms are still operated by tenants in spite of five decades of liberal public land policies, including homestead settlement provisions. Among many families tenancy is now accepted as a permanent status and not as a step to ownership. However, there has been a desire for improvement in the tenants' conditions as shown by certain unrest, refusals to pay rent, and the formation of political parties with land reform planks in their platforms.

In Sweden, a member explained, the desire for direct individual ownership of farm lands is disappearing. This is due, he thought, to increasing mechanization of agriculture and the industrialization of the whole country. The desire of farmers for improvement finds expression through the organization of unions and associations and in seeking political action. Here is further illustration that gaining ownership and improving tenure status may not be one and the same thing in every situation; securing better tenure arrangements may be the goal to seek.

Thus, it is evident that the causes underlying desires regarding land are complex. Even in countries where there is relative freedom of choice and where mobility is comparatively easy, people do not shift about or change their status without reasons. In generalized terms, there are at least three fundamental forces which tend to influence people's behavior: (1) Personal experiences. People do not exert themselves about things of which they have no knowledge or with which they have had no experience, either direct or indirect. There must be some contact with what is better. (2) Group pressures. People do not usually act separately and alone. They respond to such group incentives as prestige, power, recognition of their own importance, desire for family survival. (3) Cultural systems. Not all people respect the same customs, traditions or codes of conduct. Both individually and collectively, they are part and parcel of established patterns of human life and behavior. These patterns have the force and sanction of law, religion, public opinion, and other institutional establishments.

Techniques to Channel Desires

Time did not permit the presentation of experiences and opinions regarding this third point, but only a brief enumeration of some rather generally recognized ways and means such as the following:

1. General improvement in political status through an extension of voting and citizenship privileges.

2. Legal measures to insure rights of owners and tenants in respect to their relations with land.

3. Extension of numerous means for credit, short term and long term.

4. Fostering co-operative movements.

5. Responsiveness of governments to the changing needs of land tenure arrangements.

6. Expansion of communication and education facilities and techniques, including those for better land use and greater con-

servation of natural resources of the country.

7. Assumption of responsibility for education and improvement at the local community level, through private organizations and reaction to public policies.

8. Readjustments and, in cases of necessity, the redistribution of land in relation to changing population requirements.

Conclusion

Finally, the firm conclusion was reached that the focus of attention must be upon the interaction of man and land. It is not simply the land, but the man on the land, that creates problems. In many circles, policies of land reform have been discussed and put into effect with little or no attention given to their social basis or to their direct human consequences. In other quarters, population policies have been considered quite independent of their land or other natural resource implications. It was agreed that it is now full time to recognize the interrelation of man and land and the interdependence of policies affecting land tenure and population. Population changes are not automatic, without reason, or unresponsive to forces influencing other forms of human behavior. They also yield to study, prediction and policy making, as the evidence presented in the discussions of this working party so amply demonstrates.

INFLUENCING RURAL PEOPLE

Selections from the Report of the Working Party

Chairmen, *Charles E. Rogers and Dorothy Cochran*

EARLY IN THE planning of the land tenure conference it was recognized that improvement in landholding practices frequently depends on how well rural people understand and support proposed changes.

Accordingly, along with workshops on other technical questions in land tenure, a series of four workshops on information methods was planned.[1] Each of the workshops had a central theme: first week, reaching the low income farmer; second week, the availability and productivity of credit; third week, consolidating scattered holdings; fourth week, honoring the attitudes and values of farm people.

The aim of each workshop was to give the participants some practical experience in information media and methods and to encourage them to look critically at the information needs of land programs in their own countries.

The information tools that can be used effectively in a land tenure program differ widely from one country to another and are greatly influenced by the stage of economic development of a country.

Newspapers and magazines depend upon a rather high degree of industrialization. Radio, although less affected by the whole economy, requires that receivers be available in the hands of the people you want to reach. Filmstrips and motion pictures must rely upon projection equipment. Above all, the level of literacy in a country sharply limits what you can do and the tools you use.

No matter what the country or culture, however, there are certain principles of information practice upon which there can be general agreement.

The information workshops necessarily dealt with specific tools and techniques, but the real goal was to bring out some of these general principles which could be applied in almost every land.

Some of the points on which the delegates

agreed are given in the paragraphs which follow.

Laws Need Public Backing

Information or education is a vital part of any land tenure program, since most programs must be widely understood to be effective. In no country can a law be effective over a long period unless it has public understanding, acceptance, and support.

This principle is more obvious in a democracy than in a dictatorship, but even a dictatorship finds it hard to enforce a law which is unpopular or not understood.

As an example of legislative change in social usage, the delegates from Iran mentioned that unveiling of women in their country was unpopular at first, but that public acceptance has now become almost universal.

The way in which this program caught public approval was of interest to the group, for it illustrates an information technique. The queen and the daughters of His Majesty came out first without their veils. Then other women leaders "came out," and soon it became more of a custom to go without the veil than to wear it.

Support Information with Action

Workshop participants emphasized the importance of tying the information program to a sound action program, backed with necessary legislation or other support. Unless the farmer has some means of doing what the information program urges him to do, the program is of little value. An action program without an information program is not much good, nor is an information program with no plan for action. Every land tenure program should include an information program backed with sufficient funds and qualified personnel to do the job.

The Japanese land reform is an example of what can be accomplished when information and action programs are used together. Laws were passed. Local land commissions were set up. Prices were set. Credit facilities were worked out. And to explain all these rules and the obligations of landlord and tenant under the reform program an extensive information program was launched.

A pamphlet called *ABC of Land Reform* (this pamphlet was studied by the workshop) was sent to each of Japan's six million farmers. Posters were put up in villages, on public bulletin boards, at meeting houses, and along the roads. Filmstrips were used, and a movie was made showing the advantages of land reform.

The Ministry of Agriculture has an information section. There is also an information section in each of the forty-six prefecture or state offices. The information specialist works with the agronomist and the land tenure expert and the administrator. The Japanese realize that a good information officer may not always be a good agriculturalist, and a good agriculturalist often is not a good information specialist. But together the two officers can do much.

Channels Are Unlimited

Any channel of information is a potential channel for carrying agricultural information. In planning an agricultural information program, it pays to ask how the farmers of the country now get news and information. How do they learn of an election, of a new law, of a wedding, of a flood or other disaster? These are the channels for spreading agricultural information, too.

Church, school, and community organizations may have something to offer the information program.

Song and dance are sometimes methods of spreading agricultural information. The calypso, a type of ballad song very popular in the Caribbean area, can be used there as a channel for information on better farming methods.

In Burma and other countries where there is an innate interest and talent for drama and the dance, these forms of art can be used for farm information.

Reach Opinion Leaders First

Every community has opinion leaders, and a good step to a successful information program is to contact and convert the community opinion leaders first. People understand and feel secure within their own communities; so they are more likely to accept a program which originates at home, through leaders they trust.

The priest in most Greek villages is a man who grew up in that community, and this makes him acceptable in the eyes of local people.

In Moslem countries, getting the support of the village priest for a program is tantamount to success, especially if in endorsing the program he can refer to appropriate passages in the Koran which back up the idea.

A county agent does not need to originate in the village where he works to be accepted by the people. But to combine his job as adviser with that of tax collector or other enforcement official is usually unsatisfactory. The county agent proves himself a friend of the farmers over a period of years, and once his ability is proven he is a valuable leader and information channel.

The participants agreed that a county agent must be a diplomat as well as adviser on farming matters. In most lands, when he meets a farmer he must ask about the family. If a child is ill, he remembers the next time he sees the farmer to ask about the youngster's health. Only after this kind of discussion, which establishes him as a friend of the farmer, can the county agent successfully suggest an improvement for the man's farm.

The county agent's wife and family must also be models for the community. One of the European participants pointed out that if the county agent's wife washes clothes in a way which is not acceptable in that locality, the prestige of the county agent falls, too.

Work Through Young People

In dealing with some problems which seem insoluble due to deep-seated prejudices and traditions, it may be better to aim at the younger generation. Young people are often more willing to accept new ideas than are older people. For this reason, the need for agricultural schools and colleges and for farm youth groups such as the 4-H clubs must be emphasized.

In some countries young people are reached through the schools, and they in turn teach their parents. In Iran, school children form farmers' youth clubs to learn and show others how to farm better than with the old ways. In one Iranian project district agricultural demonstration areas are host to all school teachers in the district every Thursday. The teachers are given seeds to take back. Every school has a garden, and the teacher gives each boy two portions of seeds, one to plant in the school garden and one to take home for planting there.

The climax of the garden project comes at harvest time when contests or fairs are held. Each boy is judged by three standards: whether he raised the product all by himself or had some help with it; the quality of the vegetable or other crop; and how well the boy can explain both the theory and the practice of raising the product.

The spirit of friendly competition makes the contest very heated. Each boy tries to outdo the next in gathering information and improved seeds.

The prizes for the contests are sweets, both for the boy who wins and for his school. This stimulates school spirit and competition between schools, and the parents cannot help but be interested in better farming methods.

This experimental project was carried on in more than fifty villages around Tehran, and officials and teachers from other provinces were invited to see how the experiment worked. A half-hour film on this project has been made by the United States Information Service.

Doing and Seeing

All workshop participants agreed that the best teaching method is always the demonstration. The best type of demonstration is one in which the person who is to be persuaded can actually participate.

A farmer who has never seen a long-handled hoe will learn its advantages best if he can hold it in his hands and use it. The next best demonstration is one in which he sees the hoe demonstrated by a neighbor or someone he knows and trusts.

If it is not possible for him to actually see it demonstrated, pictures of the process with an explanation may be helpful. The first method is much to be preferred, however.

Demonstration farms, a device used in many countries, are better when the farmer-demonstrator has no outside capital or guarantee against failure. As long as a farmer knows the demonstrator is taking no financial risk in trying a new method the farmer will say, "I could do it too under those circumstances, but I can't risk it or I might go broke trying this new method."

Campaign Methods Effective

The individual is influenced in proportion to the number of different ways in which the same idea is brought home to him within a relatively short period. A farmer may first hear of an improved practice on a radio program, then see an article about it in the paper, then talk to a farmer who has tried the method, then attend a meeting where a movie demonstrates the practice. If all these contacts are made within a relatively short time, the farmer is more likely to be influenced by the idea and try it for himself.

A state-owned agricultural broadcasting station reaches the whole population of Uruguay. The Ministry of Agriculture broadcasts market news and farm information, along with entertainment features. Uruguayan farmers also receive popular bulletins from the Ministry of Agriculture, free on request. Vocational education, youth organizations, and general agricultural extension services supplement the radio program, so that every farmer hears or reads about important farm programs through several communications media.

The Task Is Complex

Since land tenure problems themselves are very complex, the information problem for land tenure improvement is also complex.

It is relatively easy to design an information program to teach a farmer the value of using commercial fertilizer. It is much harder to plan a program which will convince farmers that they should consolidate their fragmented holdings.

Land tenure problems often involve tradition, religious beliefs, and other deep-rooted values and attitudes of farm people. Their solution may require cash transactions where cash is not readily available. Sometimes these transactions must be between rural and city people or between wealthy landlord and poor peasant. These differences in class and position make the solutions to the problems even more difficult.

Affection for particular land is a recurring problem in land reform. Near Tingo Maria, in Peru, some of the people live around mountain lakes on the small patches of good land next to the lakes. Obviously, there is not enough good land for all these people to make a good living here.

It would be better if some could be persuaded to go down to Tingo Maria, where the government is opening up land for cultivation. It will be difficult to achieve this transfer, though, because the aborigines love this particular land. The earth is one of their gods, and their fathers and grandfathers for many generations have farmed *this* land. It seems more important for them to stay on the land they know and worship, though this means a poor living, than to leave all that is familiar and go to new lands, lush though they may be.

In a resettlement project in Thailand, a few farmers were persuaded to leave their village because of the good opportunities in the newly-opened area. But after they had earned some money, they all returned to their former villages to live.

Be Specific on Goals

The workshop stressed the importance of good planning. You must know what persons or groups you are building the information program for, and what specific suggestions the program will give them.

Administrative Support

It may be easier to win administration support for an information program by starting with a job where the results can be easily demonstrated. One successful information program is a good talking point in building another program.

The Farmer's Point of View

The successful information program for farmers must be planned from the farmer's point of view. It will answer the questions he would likely want answered, in the language he knows and understands. It is only natural that the over-all economic benefits of the program will mean less to him than how *he* can benefit by it. Such is the farmer's point of view.

Politically Unsettled Areas

Most of the discussions of information methods dealt with countries where the government is well established and reasonably secure.

Politically unsettled areas present different problems. These were not discussed except to point out that some media and methods not used in any other regions have to be adapted for those parts of the world where there is political unrest and where the usual channels of communication are disrupted.

Organizing Information Programs

People use three significantly different kinds of symbols in communicating with one another: (1) the written word, (2) the spoken word, and (3) pictorial presentation (photograph, drawing, graph, chart).

To use any of these three in an information program requires special skills. Someone with "art sense" is needed if the information program is to make much use of illustrations. Ability to handle the written work is required for bulletins and circulars and for newspaper and magazine articles. Writing ability and also a suitable radio or platform voice and manner are needed if the spoken word is an important part of the information plan.

Most nations are faced with limited funds for an agricultural information program. The obvious steps, then, are to determine which media are available and most useful in reaching farm people, to decide where the written word, the spoken word, and pictorial presentation are required, and to allot staff and budget accordingly.

The United States, for example, has a well-developed network of community weekly newspapers which reach small towns and rural areas. Its daily newspapers blanket the larger communities and also reach out to agricultural areas. Its farm magazines go into almost every rural home. It has a high proportion of people able to read and write. It is natural, then, that information programs in the United States will lean heavily upon the written word and that an agricultural editorial office must have staff members who can work with newspapers and magazines and other staff members who can write and edit publications for distribution to farmers.

Other nations will use entirely different combinations of media for reaching rural people. Iranian participants in the conference, for example, describe the tea house as an important communication center. It is over a cup of tea that Iranian farmers and villagers talk about farm practices and land policies. In other lands, the market place serves as a discussion center. A good information program cannot overlook such avenues for reaching people.

Many areas whose economic development is as yet limited have a high proportion of people who cannot read. This calls for heavier stress on the spoken word (through radio or some other channel) and pictorial methods (posters, illustrated talks, exhibits, films and filmstrips).

The organization of an agricultural information office in almost any country must begin with a person or persons who have writing skill.

Even where the written word is not capable of reaching the bulk of the population, written materials will be the backbone of any information campaign. Moreover, levels of literacy are improving all over the world, and a great change can be expected in many countries even within the present generation.

Brief and pointed publications are important for agricultural information in most countries.

There is in many lands a tradition of sober, serious, dignified, and stilted manuscripts, dealing with farm problems but written by someone remote from the farm. This is not conducive to effective communication of ideas in a modern world.

Shorter publications, which have a clear-cut purpose and are written with a particular audience in mind, seem to be more likely to get results.

Films and filmstrips have the advantage of carrying conviction. To see something done in a movie is almost like seeing it done in real life, and is more believable than a verbal report. But most countries have the handicap of limited facilities for projecting films and filmstrips.

Some have overcome this by the use of mobile cinema trucks, which go from town to town presenting agricultural films and other programs of interest.

The usability of radio will depend upon the kind of broadcasting activities carried on in the country. Almost every nation tells of the great usefulness of radio in reaching country people. Even areas of primitive economic development usually have some access to radio reception, and this is likely to increase in coming years. In agricultural radio, it is less important to have a broadcaster who has a "professional radio voice" than to have someone who understands farming and likes farm people. However, a great deal can be done about improving the quality of broadcasts to farmers. For one thing, persons can be employed who are trained in the psychology of verbal communication and in the physical requirements of radio broadcasting.

A nation studying the establishment of an agricultural information program must decide what media are available or can be developed to reach farm people, study the question of equipment, and determine what additions in equipment are needed to make the program effective, and find technicians in information methods who are trained in handling the kind of symbols that are to be used in the program.

A Check List in Planning

Every land tenure program is a program of change. Moreover, man's usual resistance to change is intensified when institutions and values of long standing are involved.

How can needed changes be made quickly and efficiently and yet with full public understanding and general support? The answer to that question is the blueprint for a successful information program.

Interviews and discussions with tenure conference participants suggested the following check list which might be used in deciding what tasks the information program must undertake:

1. What are some of the land tenure problems that different countries face?

   A. Size of farming units
      (1) Fragmented holdings
      (2) Uneconomic holdings—farm units too small
      (3) Great population pressure on the land
      (4) Concentration of land in the hands of a few
   B. General land policies
      (1) Colonization or resettlement on newly-cleared lands necessary
      (2) Heavy tax burden on farmers
      (3) Institutionally-owned land not being used efficiently
   C. Owner-operator relationships
      (1) Absentee ownership
      (2) Absence of written contract
      (3) Lack of security for tenant on the land, no long-term arrangements
      (4) Indebtedness to landlord which makes it impossible for tenant to move to another farm in an attempt to improve his status
   D. Other problems
      (1) Lack of credit at reasonable rates
      (2) Confusion in ownership of land, lack of clear title, etc.

2. What are some of the possible solutions to these problems?

   A. Regulation by government
      (1) Requiring written contracts between tenant and landowner (encouraging long-term lease arrangements)
      (2) Fixing fair rental rates
      (3) Setting minimum size for holdings
      (4) Preventing further subdivision and fragmentation of land
      (5) Requiring consolidation of fragmented holdings
      (6) Forbidding absentee ownership of land
      (7) Requiring owner-cultivation of land
      (8) Requiring clear title for land ownership
   B. Development of services to individuals
      (1) Formation of co-operatives, for credit and marketing, for producers and consumers, for consolidation, etc.—eliminating the middleman
      (2) Development of stronger extension or advisory services for farmers
      (3) Supervised credit by a government agency
      (4) Development or expansion of government credit banks for small farmers
   C. Broad economic policies
      (1) Government purchase of land for resale to owner-cultivators
      (2) Lowering of tax burden on farmers
      (3) Government subsidy payments to farmers for improved practices
      (4) Opening of new agricultural lands for colonization or resettlement
      (5) Industralization in urban centers

and development of cottage and home industries to relieve population pressure on land; create good industrial climate

(6) Development of roads and waterways and better communication

D. Education and information

(1) Better technical information—for farmers, general public, and administrators

(2) Improved education for children through schools

3. How can information or education help to solve land tenure problems?

A. By promoting a wider understanding of the existing problems and their causes

B. By familiarizing farmers with existing legislation and government services, such as extension or credit agencies, which can help to improve the farmers' land tenure situation

C. By motivating farmers to take advantage of opportunities to improve their status

D. By building public support for land tenure improvements, including needed corrective legislation and enforcement of existing laws

4. What are the requirements of a good information program?

A. A good information program must be based on a sound action program, backed with necessary legislation and support.

B. Use local leaders; make the program acceptable to the farmers by making it appear to have local origin.

C. Use the information channels by which the farmer gets news and information now in addition to any new channels which may be introduced.

D. Reach the farmer by a variety of channels and media; appeal to him through the eye, the ear, and by personal contact.

E. Use the demonstration method whenever possible; it is the most potent teaching tool.

F. Appeal to the young people of the country with programs which are difficult or impossible to sell to older people.

G. There should be a definite policy of providing funds and personnel for the necessary educational work in connection with every project in land tenure launched by the government.

H. Professional information specialists must be employed to direct the information program for most efficient results.

I. When possible, choose as the first information program a job where the results can be easily demonstrated.

J. Remember that any program aimed at the farmer must be thought out from the viewpoint of the farmer; he is not interested in the over-all economics of the program or how it will benefit his country—he is interested in how the program will benefit *him*.

What Two Workshops Did

REACHING LOW INCOME FARMERS

The low income farmer is not usually reached by the co-operative or at meetings called by the county agent or by many of the normal channels for farm information.

The appeals or motivations of the low-income farmer are much the same as for all farmers, however, two of his main goals being social prestige through a better living standard or by ownership of the land which he farms and better financial returns.

Lack of incentive may sometimes exist because farmers in a backward area do not realize that other farmers have higher living standards.

Another barrier to improvement is a fatalism among farmers about what they can do to improve their own status. They wait endlessly for the government or the landowner to make improvements, but do not try to improve themselves.

One constructive attitude an information program can encourage is a belief in the strength of co-operation with other farmers. The best persuasion is, of course, a successful demonstration.

Demonstration farms are excellent teaching devices for the low income farmer as well as for other farmers. It may be necessary, however, to provide transportation if the low income farmer is to attend.

The low income farmer can be reached at gathering places such as the tea house, the coffee house, or the market place. In Moslem countries the county agent can reach all the farmers of the village at the weekly religious service in the mosque; he speaks to the assembled group after the service.

Personal contact by the county agent is always one of the best ways of reaching the low income farmer, but the initiative must usually come from the county agent. Participants pointed out that in an underdeveloped country a county agent can serve fewer farmers than in a country where he has such varied channels as the press, radio, and farmers' bulletins to help him.

Simple printed leaflets can be effective information tools even in countries where literacy is low, participants agreed. These are best if they have many illustrations which tell the story in addition to the text. If a boy brings a leaflet home from school, his parents are immediately curious as to what it says, and they ask the boy to read it aloud. In almost every village there is at least one person who can read, and if any one in the village receives written material he loses no time in getting to the person who can read it to him.

If the information being spread is of great interest to the farmers, it will travel fast. If they see no direct benefit or no way to use the information, it may never be spread.

In some cases the poor living standard of the low income farmer may in itself be the incentive for an improvement program. Complacency is never a stimulus to change, but discontent is usually the cause of change. This one factor was largely responsible for the widespread development of co-operatives in Sweden during the depression of the 1930's, the delegate from that country pointed out.

The low income farmer is the least educated farmer in most communities. Thus the information program built to reach him must depend more heavily on audio and visual aids and demonstrations than on printed matter. These aids can be radio or posters or loud-speakers in the market place or a mobile van which shows movies and slides.

A special device for reaching the low income farmer is supervised agricultural credit. The principle of this type of credit is that a loan is given a farmer on condition that he talk over possible farming improvements with the credit agency representative and agree to make his farm pay off the loan by using improved methods. Technical advice is given the farmer and his wife and family. By the time the loan is repaid, the farm family has learned the value of improved farm practices and has graduated from the low income class. It is then eligible to get credit through normal commercial channels.

Workshop participants agreed that the idea of supervised credit is a good way to reach low income farmers, but they pointed out that there must be government capital to back this program.

The delegates from India noted that more than 70 per cent of the farmers of his country could not pass the eligibility requirement of the U.S. agency for supervised credit, the Farmers Home Administration, since the FHA demands that the farm be a potential economic unit, large enough to support the farm family which lives on it. The case of India is typical of many countries with great population pressure on the land, he said. The FHA representative who met with the workshop suggested that in this situation the loan might be made to groups of farmers with joint liability.

Before you can reach the low income farmer, or any other group, you must know what they think, Prof. Ralph Nafziger of the University of Wisconsin School of Journalism told the group. He discussed the need for public opinion research, especially by any institution which depends on the public for support. Some of the techniques and the theory of measuring public opinion were also described.

BUILDING INFORMATION PROGRAMS

The project of the week was to develop an information program to convince the farmers of a village in Greece that they should consolidate their fragmented holdings.

Believing that one of the strongest propaganda appeals is the demonstration of a successful practice, the participants built three information pieces on the success story of a village in Greece where a consolidation program had been effected. These pieces were a leaflet, a flannelgraph, and a filmstrip.

The leaflet was in the form of a story, told in the first person by a farmer named George, who is from the village of Vraila where consolidation has taken place. George tells what his farm was like before and after consolidation and says, "My farm isn't as big as I'd like it, but it's better and easier to farm."

He tells of all the inefficiencies of scattered plots and of the advantages of his larger fields after consolidation. George's story raises and answers many questions which

might occur to a farmer in Greece who was hearing about consolidation for the first time.

The flannelgraph is a visual aid which is little known in most countries; yet it is a simple and inexpensive tool which makes almost any story or lesson vivid and interesting. The principles of the flannelgraph were demonstrated to the workshop by Prof. Joseph Elfner of the University of Wisconsin Horticulture Department. Prof. Elfner uses a flannelgraph in his work as extension landscape architect to demonstrate good and bad arrangements of trees, flowers, and shrubs around a farm home.

After the demonstration, the workshop participants constructed a flannelgraph demonstration to convince Greek farmers of the wisdom of consolidation.

Sheets of colored paper were pasted to squares of cotton flannel, and shapes representing the farmer, his horse and cart, his village, his farm lands, his cow and a sheep, etc. were cut from the various colors. The farmer in this case was cut from blue paper. All of his farm land was represented by strips of blue paper also.

The village where all the farmers live was represented by a yellow mass, and roads were narrow strips of green. The cow and sheep were cut from red to make them show up against a white background. The farmer's horse and cart were cut from blue also to show that they belong to this farmer. Trees to mark the orchard area were cut from green, and other trees marked pasture land in the hills.

The background for our flannelgraph was a piece of white cotton flannel, one yard from top to bottom and one and one-half yards across. The principle of a flannelgraph is that flannel will stick to flannel, even when the board it is mounted on is in an upright position. Thus the flannel-backed paper forms stick to the white flannel material which serves as the background.

The first thing the audience sees at the opening of the flannelgraph demonstration is the layout of the village and the roads leading out from it, as on a map. The demonstrator then puts the farmer on the road leading out of town, gives him the horse and cart, and says that this is the farmer starting out for his day's work in his fields.

This farmer has a good-size farm, but it is not very convenient to farm, since it is so fragmented and scattered. The demonstrator then puts on perhaps thirty narrow blue strips, representing the farmer's lands. Some strips are near the village and are very good land. Others are in irrigated areas. Others are in an area which needs draining. Some land far from the village is in pasture. Some fields have one type of soil and some another. One field is a valuable orchard. These fields are described as the demonstrator puts the blue strips around the village.

The demonstrator also tells how the farmer's land happened to be in such small and widely separated fields, through inheritance and continued subdivision of land generation after generation. He describes the farmer's work-day as being inefficient because he has to spend so much time moving from one plot to another. A lot of land is wasted, too, the demonstrator shows, due to the need for so many fences and rights-of-way. All the strips of land which are not on the road must be reached by crossing someone else's small strip.

Then the demonstrator shows how this bad situation can be remedied. If all the farmers of the village get together and consolidate their holdings, each farmer can have a few big fields to cultivate rather than many small ones. At this point the demonstrator picks off the board five or six strips in the area near town and puts them together. Another five or six are grouped together in the irrigated area. Another group further

from town represents good arable land, and one in the hills is the combined pasture land. This is continued until the farmer has his holdings consolidated into about five good-size fields.

In addition to consolidating the fragmented holdings, the farmers agree to build new roads in an orderly pattern so that every field can be reached by the road, thus avoiding the need for crossing someone else's land. New strips representing the roads built by the farmers are laid on the flannel.

As the new pattern of our farmer's land takes shape on the flannelgraph, the audience realizes how much more efficient this arrangement is than the old arrangement.

The flannelgraph which was developed in the workshop was demonstrated before the entire conference and many delegates expressed keen interest in the use of this simple visual aid in their countries to teach better farm and home practices. No expensive equipment is required; yet the story is made vivid and interesting.

The workshop participants thought a filmstrip might also be used in Greece as another way of getting the farmers interested in consolidation; so they designed a filmstrip of thirty frames. The pictures would tell the story of a farmer whose lands are scattered and of the hardships he has during a day's farming with this arrangement. Then at the market place he learns from a friend about a nearby village which has consolidated its land. He hears of all these advantages for the farmers there, and wonders what his work-day would be like under this plan. In his mind, he retraces his day and sees how much better consolidation would be for him. While the last picture of the filmstrip is being shown the farmer is saying to himself: "I think I would like to try this plan in my village. I will talk to the other farmers now and see what we can do."

FAREWELL IN MADISON

Edwin B. Fred

IT IS WITH much regret that we approach the end of these meetings at the University of Wisconsin. We have learned much from you who came so far to attend. We hope that in the exchange of ideas and experience you also have found something of value.

There has been no attempt here for any group to say "we have the answers," or to "sell" their ideas to the others.

If—as your host—we have served to stimulate free discussion, have provided basic materials for study, and have prompted thorough consideration of important problems, we are satisfied.

You have had freedom to express your points of view, to challenge others . . . or if you liked, to remain silent.

This is the spirit of inquiry which we enjoy here at Wisconsin; we are free to review old ideas; fearless in expressing new ones.

In this atmosphere of freedom, conflicting ideas can be put to exacting tests. And out of such tests, new truths grow.

Changes in land tenure practices, we know, can be worked out only within the framework of a culture. So in any discussion of needed changes, those who know a nation's history, government, economic system, educational program, and all the rest which makes its culture pattern must guide the discussion.

With representatives here from so many nations, we have had expert knowledge and experience to guide us. You have learned of the differences in countries which call for differences in solutions to common problems.

It may be that we have received more benefits from this conference than our visitors have, for the special information they have brought to us will provide the orientation and stimulus to new studies we shall undertake. I hope that this experience will help to broaden our training, research, and service to the world.

This conference has captured the imagination of people everywhere. We do not have to search far to learn why.

Everyone knows the vital place of land in human existence. The mere fact that this conference is being held has brought a broader and clearer meaning to the term "land tenure."

In the United States we usually think of land tenancy in terms of two parties—the owner and the operator. Recently we have given more consideration to a third party —the land itself.

But even this view is too narrow. All of us depend upon the land for our food, our clothing, and our shelter. Land is not just property owned and operated by individuals. Land and its use provide the basic resource for the prosperity and peace of nations and the family of nations. The state of the world today makes it abundantly clear that satisfactory land arrangements are basic to world peace.

This conference was built upon faith in the future. There were elements of faith in the willingness of the United States government to sponsor these sessions. There were elements of faith in the University of Wisconsin's interest in being host to the conference. And I salute the faith which has brought each of you many miles over land and sea to meet with other agricultural leaders in the shaping of a better future for mankind.

Let us take a closer look at some of the articles of faith on which this conference rests.

First, the belief that something can be done to improve living standards throughout the world. For many nations, where the acute terrors of famine are chronic, the first battle is a purely defensive one. For other nations—and we hope eventually for all—hunger has been conquered, but there are still other ways in which man's lot needs to be improved.

A second article of faith would be that change in farming practice has become inevitable. Technological advance gives the inspiration for change, by developing new crops, new kinds of livestock, new machines to increase production while using less manpower.

The third belief, which I think the participants in this conference share, is that as technology progresses and knowledge spreads, adjustments in some of the long-standing institutions—particularly those of land holding—will appear. Then these obstacles to progress will not loom so large.

Fourth, we believe that if there is no provision for peaceful change, the pressures will build up to an explosive force. Make no mistake, there is great power behind the moral belief that injustice exists and must be corrected. That power can be channelled constructively—or, like any other kind of great power, it can burn and blast and destroy.

This leads to a final article of faith— that the democratic way of making change is the peaceful and orderly way; that, in fact, peaceful adjustment of differences is the essence of democracy.

These, then, are the things that have brought you from the four corners of the earth:

1. A vision of a better way of life for your people.

2. A faith that by sharing ideas and experiences with men of good will from other cultures, you can do something to provide that better life.

3. A belief that the combined intelligence of free and inquiring minds will bring the wisest answer to the problems of humanity. A conference of this kind would be impossible in a society which tries to proclaim wisdom or truth by edict, and enforce it at gunpoint.

These, I think, are the qualities that you have brought to this conference, and they are what has made the conference so productive.

They are the reasons why I said, a moment ago, that your presence here has helped the University of Wisconsin. Every social scientist is inevitably, to some extent at least, a prisoner of his own culture. But if he is a good social scientist, he searches for larger truths than those of his own neighborhood or state or nation. That is why the University of Wisconsin is happy to open its doors to students from other lands. Your visit to Wisconsin enlarges that tradition. Any university would be helped by the presence of so earnest and energetic a group of mature scholars. We hope that you will return to Wisconsin.

I believe, too, that our country has gained from its participation in these sessions. We have our own problems of land tenure— much less acute than those of some other lands, but equally deserving of study. In the presence of representatives from nations whose agricultural history reaches back for thirty centuries, the Americans who have participated in your program have done so with humility. I should like to emphasize that we have viewed this conference as a meeting ground, a place for exchange of views and experiences, a conference from which each nation's scholars and policy-makers stood to gain as well as give.

A few days ago one of your number told of an imaginative and far-sighted program under which his country proposes to clear 50,000 acres of jungle land, put it to the plow, and turn it to agricultural production.

There is an analogy here with what the conference on world land tenure problems is undertaking. In the month you have been here, besides clearing away trees and under-brush from the land, you have prepared the seed bed—I hope we are now ready to sow the seed of new ideas and new ways of doing things and thus improve our present system of land tenure.

Between now and harvest time much remains to be done to insure a good crop. There may be ways that this University can serve you. If there are, I hope you will let us know.

The fruit of your work will be of vital concern to persons all over the world—the man who works the Burmese rice paddy, the Greek who tills a hillside vineyard, the Cuban cane grower, the Wisconsin dairy farmer.

I wish you well in your exceedingly important task.

INTERNATIONAL GROUP THINKING

A Statement at the Closing Session in Washington[1]

𝄢𝄢𝄢𝄢   *Henry C. Taylor*

Mr. Chairman and friends of farmers from many lands, it is a pleasure to meet with you and to contemplate the far-reaching effects which may result from the work you have been doing together at Wisconsin on the problem of land tenure reform. You have been doing group thinking. Group thinking is very different from debating. The participant in a debate emphasizes parts of the truth with the hope of making his opinion prevail. His will is bent on one con-clusion. In group thinking, the will of the participant is relaxed. He is content to let the conclusion be what it may and with zest co-operates with others in gathering facts, analyzing them, and scrutinizing every pos-sible meaning of the facts with the view of arriving at the whole truth. Debate often in-tensifies diversity of opinion, leads to con-flict in international matters, even to war. Group thinking leads to a common under-standing, harmony of ideas, and co-opera-tive effort.

I am sure you found a favorable atmos-phere for group thinking at the University of Wisconsin. Charles R. Van Hise, Presi-dent from 1903 to 1919, did much to create that atmosphere. To a professor who had a closed mind on certain subjects Van Hise said: "The true scholar is never dogmatical. He seeks the undiscovered facts and the un-thought-of hypothesis which may give a new interpretation of the known facts." Those engaged in group thinking work to-gether in searching for more facts. They try to think of and test all possible explanations of the facts.

Group thinking on land tenure and other agricultural problems may be significant in fields far beyond the immediate realm of the farmer. International group thinking re-garding rural affairs may provide the train-ing and set the example for applying the methods of group thinking to the more arduous tasks of resolving international political problems. Your work at Wisconsin in recent weeks has been a splendid example of international group thinking.

Do not be discouraged if, when you get home, you come to realize that few of the facts and few of the proposed solutions of land tenure problems correspond to and fit the needs in your own country. The important thing you have gotten out of the experience at Wisconsin will prove to be a method of approach and a clarified objective in making a fresh study of the problems faced by the farmers of your own country. You will need to work out solutions fitted to the peculiar needs of each country. Tenure problems are first of all local problems. They are problems of human relations— problems of applying the Golden Rule intelligently.

Whether the problems of land tenure and the various other problems of agricultural economics are approached from the standpoint of the individual farmer or from the point of view of the statesman, there is a unity in the facts and the problems to be studied if not in the opinions and points of view. The facts should be viewed from every angle by both the farmer and the statesman. This is true of choice of crops, intensity of culture, land tenure, size of farms, or of problems of prices and markets. In each case the factual setting to be studied is the same, whether viewed by the farmer or the statesman, although the things hoped for, the motives and aspirations may be different. Group thinking, with farmers and statesmen participating, may bring unity of purpose.

In many lands modernizing the instruments of agricultural production to enable each farmer to use more land and produce more food and raw material for clothing and thereby elevate the level of living is balked by the lack of available land. India and China, for example, became densely populated on the basis of the self-sufficing economy. The standard of living was based upon what could be produced locally. That meant a limited variety of food and clothing but it also meant a limited demand for land per family. How to modernize agricultural methods under the present circumstances in those countries is a problem for which the American experience does not provide the answer.

The people of the U.S. and Canada were fortunate in having a vast amount of unoccupied land of good quality available at the time when modern farm machinery and modern means of transportation made commercial agriculture possible on a broad scale. The northern part of the United States was being settled largely by self-sufficing farmers up to the middle of the past century. The farms were relatively small; the plow, the sickle or scythe, the cradle, the hoe, and the rake were the principal farm tools. With the coming of canals, railroads, and farm machinery farmers produced more and more for the market and improved their living conditions by buying more and more goods produced in factories. In 1860 my father started farming in southeastern Iowa on forty acres, less than thirty of which was cropland. He cut wheat with a cradle and hay with a scythe. He husked corn by hand. He had land enough to keep him busy. My mother had a loom on which she wove the cloth used for bedding and for clothing. It was a busy life but strictly limited to basic necessities. My father bought a McCormick combined reaper and mower. He acquired a two-horse corn cultivator. He then could use more land.

In 1862 the U.S. government commenced giving 160 acres of land to actual settlers. A neighbor living on an adjacent forty-acre tract decided to go West and take up a claim. My father bought that neighbor's land. Others decided to go West and get larger farms. My father bought their farms and thus provided them the money needed for making the move. With free land in Nebraska, land prices were very low in eastern Iowa. In the course of twenty years my father bought out nine neighbors and thus expanded his farm to 600 acres, half cropland and half pasture land. Cattle, horses, sheep, and hogs were produced largely for the market. Thus the transition from self-sufficing economy to commercial economy was easily made in the U.S. in the last half of the nineteenth century.

But the farmers of the U.S. are not without land problems today. Their major problem arises from the over-valuation of farm land. Now that good, free land is no longer available the competition for land is keen and the price of land is high. Farmers must now depend more largely upon renting land. The buying of a farm often must be postponed for many years. The problem of adjusting the relations of a landlord and tenant has become a vital one.

England is the classic land of tenant farmers. Many of the difficult problems that the farmers of England faced have been solved. We in the U.S. have studied the progress of the English system of land tenure, but in the main we are working out solutions fitted to our peculiar needs.

In the effort to solve farmers' problems agricultural economics has grown up in the U.S. We have learned that academic economic thinking and classroom teaching do not solve the farm problems. Action programs must be planned and made effective.

The story of agricultural economics in the United States is a story of action as well as of thought. In the telling of that story two-thirds of the space must be given to the creating of agencies to render services to farmers. Ideas without action are sterile. Action without knowledge and careful planning may do more harm than good.

In 1839 it was realized that farmers had to know the facts of supply and demand in order to secure fair prices for their products. Work was started to meet that need. The first U.S. census of agriculture was taken in 1840; the first crop estimate was made for the crop of 1841. This statistical work was gradually improved through the years and will continue to be improved. Production information was soon followed by price and market information. In due course, farm surveys and farm accounts gave the farmer a clearer view of the facts on his own farm. With knowledge of his costs and his markets the farmer was able to plan his farming more intelligently on the basis of probable prices in the future when the product would be ready for the market. The Agricultural Outlook Service of the U.S. Department of Agriculture was started in 1923 to aid the farmer in planning.

The Agricultural Extension Service made the Outlook Service one of its major projects. The farmers were taught to plan their operations in the light of costs of production and market conditions. That is a task the farmer can not do for himself without the fact-finding services of the government. The markets are too remote and the competitors in the markets are too widely scattered. Thus production information and market information provided by public agencies throw light on the farmer's pathway.

Please do not overlook the fact that government services for farmers have reached their present stage of development in the U.S. only after a century of thought and action, trial and error. In a country where services for farmers are largely undeveloped, a start should be made by doing well a few of the simpler things. Careful thought and patience, along with a persistent effort to adjust the service to the outstanding needs, will prove rewarding. Progress will come with experience and continued effort.

In developing public agencies to serve farmers, agricultural economists should thoroughly scrutinize the ideas which the agencies are to implement. The ideas on which government actions are based spring largely from the minds of men of action who see the national and world economy from a single and, most likely, a class-interest point of view. It is a function of the good economist to view ideas from every angle and help in refining them so that the actions to implement the ideas will promote the general welfare as well as advance the interest of any one group. The action groups have the following and the dynamic to put ideas into effect. These action groups sometimes call upon economists to help refine an idea and plan legislation to create an agency to implement the idea. This is a great opportunity if the economist adheres to right, ethical principles and can succeed in leading the action group to appreciate the advantage in the long run to securing their objectives through means fair to all the groups which make up the national economy. Though he can advise, the economist of the chair is rarely in a position to promote action.

Once an agency is established it should be studied carefully with a view to improving its service. In perfecting ideas and developing service agencies a world point of view should be kept in mind. A world view is essential to wise action, both private and public, in any given country. A world outlook service is a primary function of any agency which would serve the farmers of the world. International co-operation is essential to a full agricultural outlook service for farmers of any one country. Continued group thinking on an international basis is essential to the further improvement of that service. It is especially important that men of all nations jointly seek the truth, for only through a common understanding of the truth can the conditions of a peaceful world be created.

REPORT OF THE STEERING COMMITTEE

 Chairman, *Akram El-Ricaby*

THE MAJOR contribution of this conference is the realization that land tenure is a world problem and an extremely urgent one at that. If social justice is to be the foundation of democracy, land tenure needs the attention of the free world.

The excellent work of agencies of the United Nations in the field of land tenure and land reform is not unfamiliar to the conference. The report of the Economic and Social Council of the UN on land reform, dated September 21, 1951, for example, sets forth recommendations which most of the delegates have read and with which they are in general agreement. But we believe that the kind of conference we have had can prepare the way for the actual carrying out of such recommendations and has prepared the soil for greater international co-operation of land tenure problems. Here at the University of Wisconsin we have had an op-

portunity freely and openly to discuss our mutual problems, unhampered by national responsibilities, speaking always for ourselves alone, not for our governments. Further, this conference brought together a happy blend of administrative and academic people. The administrators brought hard, immediate, practical problems; the university people, research results and broad perspectives. In short, the conception of this conference was sound and its pattern must not be abandoned.

The committee used the dual criteria of economic efficiency and social justice and discovered that there was hardly any part of the world where the prevailing tenurial pattern satisfied these in a full measure. It also became convinced that there could not be efficiency without justice and there could be no justice without efficiency.

We found that unhealthy features in land

tenure are due either to basic backwardness of an economy or to institutional maladjustments, social, economic, and political. We realized that the land tenure problems had roots spread through the entire economy and the remedies had, therefore, to be sought both within and without agriculture. The problem of pressure and control of population, industrialization, distribution of wealth and income, tax, inheritance laws were as germane to our discussion as those of land reclamation, land consolidation, and landlord-tenant relations. We realized that the land tenure specialist may go wrong if he ignores the integral relation between agriculture, the rest of the economy and, indeed, the social order. We also realized the prime importance of education and communication in a land tenure program. Creating an ideal economic farming unit and putting it in the hands of an illiterate farmer bound to the old ways of agriculture by superstition and custom does little to solve the basic problem.

Some of the Major Problems

MALDISTRIBUTION OF OWNERSHIP

One feature of the land tenure problem which appears to be fairly ubiquitous is the concentration of ownership of land in a few hands. Whether the land is scarce or abundant, somehow it has become concentrated in the hands of a comparatively small class of large landholders, many of whom take little interest in cultivation. We have thus a queer phenomenon of a few large—and often badly managed—farms existing side by side with a very large number of small and uneconomic farms in many countries of the world. Purchase and redistribution of land either by sale, lease, or otherwise, has been a major plank of agrarian reform throughout its history. After World War II this program has received a fresh impetus. Land reform in Japan is an outstanding example of this. Similar measures are contemplated in India, in Pakistan, and in Formosa.

For a proper appreciation of these reform measures, it is necessary to emphasize that ownership rights in many countries, especially in the Orient, are of a dubious origin and legally and morally not well established. This, along with the exigencies of economic and political situations, determines the manner and extent of compensation given to the dispossessed owners. What distinguishes the democratic from the totalitarian approach to the question is whether or not the reform is sought to be accomplished by due process of law and is subject to judicial review. If the legislation authorizing purchase has been passed by a democratically constituted legislature and respects the person and individuality of the divested parties, the extent of compensation, though of course vital, becomes less crucial.

For the country which wishes to embark on a land purchase and redistribution program, there is much experience in various parts of the world on which to draw. There is experience in bond flotation and the financing arrangements, both in countries with security markets and without. There is also important experience in flexibly defining economic farming units under varying conditions of soil, climate, and market. Laws fixing limits on maximum size of holdings exist in several countries. Progressive taxation as a means of forcing neglected land or land owned by absentee landlords into the market exists as do arrangements to prevent excessive fragmentation of the redistributed land. There are also possible alternatives to land purchase and resale schemes which may, under some circumstances, free capital to be used for other important purposes.

Small and fragmented holdings constitute a major obstacle to efficient farming. And yet it is a universal phenomenon in all overpopulated countries. Strangely, however, it is also found in countries with a favorable man-land ratio. Whereas in the former, it is a symbol of overpopulation and under-development, in the latter it is an offshoot of faulty social and political arrangement and institutions.

A satisfactory solution of the problem has to contend with established law as well as custom and tradition such as those affecting inheritance laws, property rights, distribution of wealth and income. On the technical side, there is enough experience with land consolidation efforts and achievements in various parts of the world so that, if properly assimilated and articulated, it could be used to advantage with situational modifications. Once consolidation has been achieved, active training programs for the farmers as well as arrangements to prevent re-fragmentation, through the operation of inheritance laws, are required. Also required is a speeding up of consolidation work through the use of aerial photographs, streamlined procedures, speedier surveying, and the like.

The problem, however, assumes altogether different dimensions where even after consolidation the size of the individual unit remains too small and uneconomic. If there are limitations on the removal of surplus farm population to nonfarm occupations, solutions will have to be found within agriculture, at any rate for the short period. Co-operative farming is suggested as one possible remedy, with a varying degree of integration with local conditions. Though this does not "solve" the problem of full efficient use of resources, it does mitigate it to some extent.

CREDIT

If an enterprise has an efficient and an economic unit of operation, the problem of credit is not particularly difficult. It is only when the borrower is considered "uncreditworthy" by the normal financing agencies that a question of special and alternative arrangements springs up. Unfortunately, in many parts of the world, a large number of farmers are outside the pale of organized credit. This is especially true when substantial credit is needed to purchase land or capital equipment. Mere transfer of ownership rights from one class to another might not result in improved use of land, unless means are available in the new owners to increase their productive efficiency. The very process of agrarian reforms, such as the acquisition of new rights, etc., will set up pressure for additional funds, while their supply, on the other hand, is likely to contract to some extent by the enforcement of measures like restrictions on transfer and subletting of land, etc. The provision of suitable credit, therefore, assumes great importance in a plan for achieving any improved pattern of tenurial and land-use relationship. There are two major types of institutional agencies which could be organized to meet the situation —co-operatives or state-sponsored corporations. In some countries, the risks of financing the severely disadvantaged class of cultivators is so great that, without the active support of the state, co-operatives might find it difficult to finance them. In a democratic state, the objectives of government policy and of the co-operatives run parallel to a great extent. To the extent they do, there is no reason why each should not draw upon the other to achieve the common end.

Government-to-government loans from developed countries to underdeveloped countries are needed to start the flow of credit from state agencies to co-operatives (and other local lending institutions) and thence to the farmer. A state-sponsored corporation may thus, in certain circumstances, act as a central reservoir of loanable funds on which the co-operatives could draw in times of need.

There should, however, be proper safeguards for insuring that the credit supplied is used for the purpose for which it is given, viz., the land improvement. The provision of loans, therefore, internal as well as international, should be conditioned on the development of a well-organized mechanism for supervision and check at every stage of the application of funds, so that the credit granted the applicant may be both safe and productive. The organization of a full-fledged extension service side by side with the provision of credit under the authority of a Farm and Home Administration would be a step in the right direction.

It may be not only futile but a total waste to give credit to the uncreditworthy farmer without providing him with technical supervisors and assistance until he becomes qualified to carry on his home making and farming operations in a sound and rational manner. This will involve attention to tenure, technology, and provision of social services like health and education.

LANDLORD-TENANT RELATIONS

As already indicated, one of the most serious issues raised at the conference is the concentration of landownership in many underdeveloped countries. This has invariably given rise to systems of tenancy that have proven ruinous to farm workers and have brought about depressed conditions in agriculture. It has been emphasized that the ultimate goal in land tenure improvement is to secure the ownership of land for the tillers of the soil. While this has been accepted on broad principles as the ideal tenure system in free societies, farm tenancy has always a justifiable place in any system of progressive agriculture. A rational program of improving landlord-tenant relations is therefore necessary to raise the efficiency of farming, afford security, and to secure fair contractual arrangements to safeguard interests of tenants and land owners. Especially is this important, and the need very great, where tenants are in the category of share croppers such as those found in many countries of Asia, Latin America, the Mid-

dle East, and the USA. As a group they are generally ignorant, without much capital, hopelessly bound to the land because of debt, and, as a consequence, exploited, oppressed, and in dire poverty. Tenancy legislation is only one of the lines of improvement indicated. Education, health protection, social security, and provision of cheap and easy credit are other lines.

Experience in many countries in finding equitable landlord-tenant relations may be profitably utilized in undertaking programs of improvement of the tenant's status.

POSSIBILITIES OF CO-OPERATION

Co-operation is one of the issues raised in the search for improvement of tenure conditions in many countries. It would seem that where peasant farming has degenerated through fragmentation into small uneconomic farm units on account of high pressure of population on land leading to conditions like extortionate rents, low education and low literacy, high birth and death rates, poverty, disease, and debt, co-operative farming appears, prima facie, an attractive solution; but as experience has proved its limited success, in the absence of high character personnel leadership it may, in countries under those conditions be tried out on a pilot basis, and gradually extended if success warrants such extension.

RECLAMATION AND SETTLEMENT

In many countries strong efforts have been made since World War II to alleviate maladjustments in agriculture by reclaiming land and settling farmers on it. Programs in Venezuela, Chile, Egypt, Syria, Holland, Italy, and other countries are in point. Perhaps most dramatic and inspiring of all has been the program in Finland. Such projects not only permit experimentation with technological innovations like mapping by aerial photography and mechanized land clearance methods to make land more speedily available for settlement but also with land tenure and credit arrangements to prevent fragmentation, induce good husbandry, and permit land ownership without unduly burdensome debt.

Continuity for the Work Started

There are needs in the world that are great and urgent but which by their very nature cannot be effectively met by political organization, whether they be of diplomats connected with individual governments or international agencies like the United Nations. Land tenure is one of these, but there are many others. Universities and their technical staffs have an opportunity to render enormous service to world welfare and world peace in undertaking in these fields those types of services which the University of Wisconsin has done in land tenure.

We believe this pattern has much to commend itself and deserves widespread adaptation throughout the world.

Those of us who have attended the world land tenure conference at the University of Wisconsin have received much stimulation and have acquired many new ideas which we will take back with us to the problems which will face us at home. It would be tragic to permit this stimulation and inspiration to die with the termination of this conference. To prevent this and to provide for the continuity of the work started at the conference the steering committee makes the following recommendations:

1. There should be established at the University of Wisconsin a permanent central committee with both resident and corresponding members. The resident members shall be three professors on the staff of the University; the corresponding members shall be selected on a regional basis in a manner that may be prescribed by the resident members. The resident members, in the orderly discharge of the duties listed below, may from time to time constitute such executive

subcommittees as may be necessary to accomplish the objectives in view. This central committee shall be charged with the following duties: (a) to provide for a regular exchange of information between the countries represented at this conference and such other countries as may care to join in this activity, and in this connection to periodically publish a review of progress in land reform all over the world; (b) to create regional subcommittees with a view toward holding regional conferences to work with land tenure problems in the same objective manner that has characterized this conference; (c) to give continuing attention and encouragement to the trainee program recommended later in this report; (d) to encourage and support the building up and maintenance of an international land tenure lending library of the type later described; (e) to sponsor the exchange between countries of personnel expert in the handling of land tenure problems; (f) to recommend schemes for international assistance and research in the land tenure field; (g) to encourage in every way research in the land tenure field; (h) to collaborate to the greatest possible extent with the appropriate agencies of the United Nations, with the international conference of agricultural economists, and other international organizations to supplement the work already being done by them in the land tenure field; and (i) to do anything else necessary to give continuity to the crucially important work started at this conference.

2. As just suggested, the central committee should sponsor and encourage the holding of regional meetings on land tenure problems, each country to be consulted as to regional meetings in which it desires to participate. These regional sessions should be attended by representatives of countries where similar conditions and needs exist, such as the regions of the Near East, Southeast Asia, Latin America, etc. It may be pos-

sible to arrange for annual regional meetings to be held in rotation in different countries.

3. The trainee program started in connection with this conference should be continued for the indefinite future. This program should involve not only the training of non-Americans in American universities; it should also involve the training of Americans in other countries of the world. It is felt that the trainees who are now at the University of Wisconsin and those who come to that University in the future will provide the necessary continuing stimulus which will make it possible to continue the work of this conference through the central and regional committees above suggested. For example, the trainees now at the University might during the course of the present academic year prepare a detailed analysis of some of the major problems discussed at this conference, elaborating extensively upon the necessarily summary comments in the first part of this report. In subsequent years trainees going to and from America could provide the living nexus which would hold the world-wide interests of this conference together. The chief burden of providing most current information about land tenure and land reform programs in various parts of the world would fall upon these trainees who could also, perhaps, aid in the preparation of periodic reports with respect to such programs. The central committee should ensure that this trainee program is tied up closely with the research of the type mentioned in the next paragraph.

4. It is strongly urged that in its new library building about to become a reality, the University of Wisconsin maintain an up-to-date and world-wide land tenure library with facilities for the lending of land tenure materials to interested and reliable persons anywhere in the free world. If such a library is established, the steering committee feels confident that it can without quali-

fication promise for each delegate that he will keep this library supplied with the latest land tenure materials from his own country, or if cost considerations require it, to at least provide the library with a list of such materials.

5. A prime necessity is accelerated and broadened research in the land tenure field. We must have the facts if we are to act intelligently. This conference has disclosed clearly the existence of many problems common to two or more countries. Comparative land tenure research criss-crossing national boundaries is called for. This can best be accomplished by collaborative arrangements between universities within the same or in two or more countries. The central committee should offer its services in helping plan such research and in actually administering it and should also act as a stimulator of research, particularly comparative research. It should offer its services as a screening agent for international and other agencies in the field of international land tenure research.

It is suggested that priority may be given to the following fields of research: (a) the process of industrial development in underdeveloped territories, as exemplified, for instance, in the Tennessee Valley, taking into consideration the economic and sociological aspects and paying particular attention to the integration of industry and agriculture; (b) conditions influencing population trends in underdeveloped territories and ways and means for keeping population growth in check; (c) the development of supervised credit techniques as a means of improving the management efficiency of small holdings and raising the level of production, co-operative farming and other forms of joint organization, e.g., the proportional profit farm of Puerto Rico and the group farming techniques used in the Sudan and the Fiji Islands, as alternative measures for making the fullest use of resources and raising the level of production under conditions of heavy pressure of population on the land, and appropriate types of farming pending the creation of conditions which would enable family farms to be successfully established, and economic and social implications of mechanized farming in backward agriculture economies; (d) comparative analysis of land reform legislation and the effect of such legislation on agricultural production in the different countries.

6. Land Tenure problems should be given consideration on the programs of international conferences dealing with natural resources lest the work done at this conference and by the central committee might re-main confined to the purely academic sphere.

It is recommended that the results of the research and the solution which their committee may suggest should be examined, with a view to translating them into practice, by international conferences at the official and governmental level convened from time to time under the auspices of the FAO of the UN.

7. If called upon by any government or international agency for advice, the central committee should feel free to comment on proposed schemes for international research or assistance, financial, or otherwise, in the land tenure field.

NOTES & INDEX

Land Reform and Agricultural Development
(Pages 3–22)

1. This interpretation has grown out of the conference experience, and many suggestions from the conference have been incorporated. It has not seemed feasible, however, to try to tie these opening remarks to specific citations in the chapters which follow. Not only would such an attempt be cumbersome, but it would be impossible to acknowledge fully the debt to the conference participants.

2. For a summary and interpretation of the available statistics on land tenure see *Land Reform* (U.N. Publication II B 3, 1951).

3. See especially his *Legal Foundations of Capitalism* (New York, 1934).

4. John Stuart Mill, *Principles of Political Economy,* ed. Sir W. J. Ashley (London and New York, 1936).

5. See especially David Mitrany, *Marx Against the Peasant* (Chapel Hill, North Carolina, 1951).

6. John M. Brewster, "The Machine Process in Agriculture and Industry," *Journal of Farm Economics,* XXXII (1950), 69–81.

7. Einar Jensen, *Danish Agriculture: Its Economic Development* (Copenhagen, 1937). I am indebted to Mr. Don Kanel for reminding me of this particular quotation as well as for many other suggestions in this statement.

Issues in the Background of the Conference
(Pages 49–55)

1. War Department Pamphlet 31–170 (July 29, 1944).

2. A landed estate was defined as a farm having more than 100 hectares (247 acres) of agriculturally-used land.

3. *German Food Self-Sufficiency and Landed Estates* (Washington, D.C., 1945).

4. Joint Chiefs of Staff Directive No. 1067/6 (April 26, 1945).

5. Joint Chiefs of Staff Directive No. 1380/15 (November 3, 1945).

6. For an account of the development of U.S. agrarian policy in Japan see *Japanese Land Reform Program* (Tokyo: Report No. 127, Natural Resources Section, General Headquarters, Supreme Commander for the Allied Powers, 1950), from which this quotation is taken.

7. For Japan the interested reader will find valuable material in the following official reports: *Japanese Land Reform Program* (Tokyo:

Report No. 127, Natural Resources Section, General Headquarters, Supreme Commander for the Allied Powers, 1950); *The Japanese Village in Transition* (Tokyo: Report No. 136, SCAP, 1950); *Agricultural Land Reform Legislation* (Tokyo: Agricultural Land Bureau, Ministry of Agriculture and Forestry, 1949); and *Agricultural Land Reform Legislation Supplement* (Tokyo, 1951).

For discussion see the following articles: William M. Gilmartin and W. I. Ladejinsky, "The Promise of Agrarian Reform in Japan," *Foreign Affairs,* XXVI (1948), 312–24; Laurence I. Hewes, Jr., "On the Current Readjustment of Land Tenure in Japan," *Land Economics,* XXV (1949); Mark B. Williamson, "Land Reform in Japan," *Journal of Farm Economics,* XXXIII (1951); Arthur F. Raper, "Some Effects of Land Reform in Thirteen Japanese Villages," *Journal of Farm Economics,*

XXXIII (1951); W. I. Ladejinsky, "The Plow Outbids the Sword in Asia," *Country Gentleman*, (1951); and W. I. Ladejinsky, "Landlord Versus Tenant in Japan," *Foreign Agriculture*, XI (1947), 83–88, 121–28; "Land Reform Progress in Japan," *Foreign Agriculture*, XIII (1949), 38–41.

For Germany, official reports on military government efforts in implementing land tenure reforms in the U.S. zone are contained in the series of *Monthly Reports of the Military Governor, U.S. Zone* (Berlin, Germany). See especially the reports for the months subsequent to September, 1946, the date of military government approval of the Law for the Acquisition of Land for Settlement Purposes and for Land Reform for the U.S. Zone. See also the unpubl. diss. (University of Wisconsin, 1949) by Philip M. Raup, "Land Reform in Postwar Germany: The Soviet Zone Experiment."

8. The proceedings of this conference are available in *Caribbean Land Tenure Symposium* (Washington, D.C., 1946).

9. Joseph Ackerman and Marshall Harris, eds., *Family Farm Policy. Proceedings of a Conference on Family Farm Policy* (Chicago, 1947).

10. Included among the sponsoring agencies were the Home Missions Council of North America, the Federal Council of Churches of Christ in America, the International Council of Religious Education, the Rural Missions Cooperating Committee of the Foreign Missions Conference of North America, the Farm Foundation, and Agricultural Missions, Inc.

11. Marshall Harris and Joseph Ackerman, eds., *Agrarian Reform and Moral Responsibility. Report of an International Conference on the Rural Church and Farm Land Tenure* (New York, 1949), p. iv.

12. A careful account, written on the eve of the Communist seizure of power in China, is given by Chee Kwon Chun, "Agrarian Unrest and the Civil War in China," *Land Economics*, XXVI (1950). The same conclusion is forcefully presented by John King Fairbank, "The Problem of Revolutionary Asia," *Foreign Affairs*, XXIX (1950), 101–13.

13. See, for example, C. Clyde Mitchell, *Korea: Second Failure in Asia* (Washington, D.C., 1951). See also the articles in *The Reporter* magazine, especially the issues of September-December, 1950.

14. *New York Times*, Oct. 18, 1950.

15. Daniel W. Bell, Chief of Mission, *Report to the President of the United States by the Economic Survey Mission to the Philippines* (Washington, D.C., 1950). It is important to note here that action has been taken on the Bell report recommendation that a program of land redistribution be undertaken through the sale of large estates to small farmers. On Feb. 28, 1951, a Philippine Advisory Committee was created to study the problem and recommend implementing legislation. That committee's report has been published under the title *Report and Recommendation of the Advisory Committee on Large Estate Problems* (Manila, 1951).

16. Charles F. Brannan, "Agriculture and National Defense." Speech before the United States Department of Agriculture Outlook Conference, Washington, D.C., Oct. 30, 1951.

17. Speech before the United Nations General Assembly, Committee Two, Oct. 31, 1950. The full text is available in the *Congressional Record* for Dec. 5, 1950 (Appendix, pp. A 7897–98).

18. Charles F. Brannan, "Hope, an American Export." Speech before the annual meeting of the Association of Land Grant Colleges and Universities, Washington, D.C., Nov. 16, 1950.

19. "The Elements of Leadership," Minneapolis, Minn., 1950.

20. "Land and Liberty," Bismarck, N.D., 1950.

21. "Hemispheric Strength Through a Mutually Prosperous Agriculture," Montevideo, Uruguay, 1950.

22. The interim results of this review are available in *Family Farm Policy Review. Provisional Report and Tentative Recommendations of the Department of Agriculture's Family Farm Policy Review Subcommittee* (Washington, D.C., 1951).

23. "Beyond Today's Horizon." Opening Statement of Clarence J. McCormick, United States Member of the Council of FAO, Twelfth FAO Council Session, Rome, Italy, June 11, 1951.

The United Nations and Land Reform
(Pages 63–69)

1. This report was prepared by five experts appointed by the Secretary-General: Alberto Baltra Cortez, National University of Chile; D. R. Gadgil, Gokhale Institute of Politics and Economics, Poona, India; George Hakim, Lebanon; W. Arthur Lewis, University of Man- chester, England; and T. W. Schultz, University of Chicago.

2. *Land Reform: Defects in Agrarian Structure as Obstacles to Economic Development* (New York, 1951), pp. 28–34.

World Land Tenure Problems and the Food and Agriculture Organization
(Pages 69–77)

1. Since the presentation of this statement at the Wisconsin conference, FAO's technical assistance activities have expanded considerably. The total number of experts who have participated in missions between the initiation of the technical assistance program in July, 1950, and the end of 1952 was 565. As of Jan. 1, 1953, 315 experts were working in 50 countries.

2. A Central American seminar on agricultural credit was actually held in Guatemala during the period Sept.–Oct., 1952, sponsored by FAO with the co-operation of ECLA. Sixty representatives from fifteen countries participated.

3. Since the presentation of this paper the pertinent recommendations of the Sixth Session of the FAO Conference and the resulting FAO program of work in land tenure have appeared. These documents are added as Appendices to this statement.

The Land Tenure Situation in Iran
(Pages 95–100)

1. For detailed information about the plan, see *Report on Seven Year Development Plan for the Plan Organization of the Imperial Gov-* *ernment of Iran,* 5 Vols. (New York, 1949).

2. For the text of the order, see Royal Decree, dated BAHMAN 7th. 1329.

Major Aspects of Land Tenure and Rural Social Structure in Israel
(Pages 111–17)

1. This paper does not deal with the political problems connected with the abandonment of land by the Arab peasants.

2. There is another important colonizing institution in Israel, The Palestine Jewish Colonization Association (PJCA). It leases land under contracts very similar to those concluded between the Jewish National Fund and its tenant farmers.

3. The term "collective settlement" which is used for the "Kibbutz" in Israel has no connotation with other forms of collectivized agriculture as practiced in some countries. The Hebrew word "Kibbutz" means "group." Since the term "group settlement" is a somewhat vague expression, the term collective settlement or village has come in use in English descriptions in order to denote those settlements in which means of production are owned by the total of the community and in which there is

also a common household for all its members. The state has no rights of ownership, interference, or guidance in these settlements.

4. The economic problems of collective agriculture in Israel are aptly summarized in a recent article by Prof. Clarence Walter Ef-

roymson, "Collective Agriculture in Israel," *Journal of Political Economy*, LVIII (1950), 30–46.

5. The principle of exclusive self-labor has been temporarily abandoned following pressure of work and emergency conditions.

The Land Tenure Situation in Pakistan
(Pages 125–33)

1. The main cash crop of East Pakistan is jute, which is almost all exported in its raw state. Pakistan produces 75 per cent of the world's crop.

2. Alfred Marshall, *Principles of Economics,* 8th ed. (London, 1936), p. 644.

3. Hubert Calvert, *The Wealth and Welfare of the Punjab,* 2nd ed. (Lahore, 1936), p. 200.

4. *Ibid.*

Problems in Countries with Heavy Pressure of Population on Land: The Case of India
(Pages 134–46)

1. V. Balasubramanian, *A Policy for Agriculture* (New Delhi, Bombay, and London, 1945), p. 3.

2. *Report of the United Provinces of Agra and Ondh Zamindar Abolition Committee* (Allahabad, 1948), I, 388.

3. *We Build for Socialism* (Bombay, 1951), p. 8.

4. *The First Five Year Plan* (New Delhi, 1951), pp. 99–100.

5. Lazar Volin, "A Long-Drawn Question," *Foreign Agriculture,* XV (1951), 183–86.

6. *Measures for the Economic Development of Underdeveloped Countries* (New York, 1951), pp. 7–8, para. 17.

7. One crore equals 10 millions; 4.5 rupees equal 1 dollar (approximately).

The Attitude of the Malayan Peasant toward the Tenure Problem of Malaya, with Special Reference to the State of Kedah
(Pages 176–78)

1. Mr. Akib was able to attend a part of the conference in the course of his study of agricultural extension methods. In view of his intimate knowledge of his own state, he was invited to make these personal observations.

Farm Ownership and Tenancy in the Philippines
(Pages 180–88)

1. *Report and Recommendations of the Advisory Committee on Large Estates Problems* (Manila, 1951).

2. *Reports of the Special Committee on Land Settlement and Title Issuance and Clearance* (Manila, 1951).

The Population of Southeast Asia
(Pages 197–201)

1. United Nations Economic Commission for Asia and the Far East.

2. This résumé for Java follows closely segments of the analysis presented in Marshall C. Balfour, *Public Health and Demography in the Far East* (New York, 1950), pp. 89–97, and in "The Netherlands India," *Population Index*, VI (1940), 150–54.

3. A somewhat more expanded report is presented in Balfour, *Public Health* and in the article "The Philippines," *Population Index*, VIII (1942), 3–9.

4. A more detailed description of the Ceylonese situation was presented by the author in "Ceylon As a Demographic Laboratory: Preface to Analysis," *Population Index*, XV (1949), 293–304.

Some Problems of Land Tenure in Contemporary Africa
(Pages 231–39)

1. References: "Review of Economic Conditions in Africa," in *Supplement to World Economic Report,* 1949–50 (New York, 1951); C. K. Meek, *Land Law and Custom in the Colonies* (London, 1946).

Some Aspects of Land Tenure in Brazil
(Pages 283–89)

1. *A Estrutura da Economia Agropecuaria do Brasil* (Rio de Janeiro, 1940), p. 9.

2. This and the following data were taken from the 1940 Census of Agriculture of Brazil.

3. For more details on this point see João Gonçalves deSouza, "O Problema da Terra no Brasil," in *Revista de Pesquisas Economico-Sociais,* (Rio de Janeiro, 1949), pp. 112–45.

4. *Sinopse do Censo Agrícola* (Rio de Janeiro, 1948), p. 10.

5. See deSouza, "O Problema da Terra no Brasil," p. 141.

6. T. Lynn Smith, *Brazil: People and Institutions* (Baton Rouge, La., 1946), p. 527.

7. Henry W. Spiegel, *The Brazilian Economy* (Philadelphia, 1949), p. 165.

8. *Sinopse Preliminar do Censo Demográfico* (Rio de Janeiro, 1951).

9. "O Recenseamento de 1950," *Journal do Commercio* (Rio de Janeiro), March 11, 1951.

10. A recent publication shows that 500,000 mostly landless workers migrated from the northeast to the southern part of the country in the last five years.—Colombo de Souza, *Recuperação do Nordeste* (Fortaleza Ceará, 1951), p. 23. Cloves Canado in his mimeographed publication *Movimento Migratorio das Popualacoes Rurais nas Zonas da Mata de Minas* (n.p., 1950) estimates that in the last five years 100,000 people migrated from an area of Minas to neighboring states.

11. T. Lynn Smith says about this type: "At present the following system of *parceiro* or sharecropping is prevalent in Sao Paulo. The owner prepares the ground for the seed and in that condition it is turned over to the *parceiro.* The latter is responsible for the planting, the cultivating, and the harvesting processes. The product is divided in the field, each party to the contract being responsible for the transportation of his share. If insecticides are required, the proprietor furnishes the materials and the worker applies them. If fertilizers are used, the cost is shared equally. Generally the product

also is divided on a fifty-fifty basis."—Reprint from *Journal of Land and Public Utility Economics*, XX (1944), 194–201.

12. Jorge Zarur, *A Bacia do Médio São Fran-* *cisco: Uma Analise Regional* (Rio de Janeiro, 1946), p. 73.

13. João Gonçalves deSouza, *Relações do Homem Com a Terra Em 4 Communidades Rurais do Medio São Francisco* (Rio de Janeiro, 1950), p. 22.

SOCIAL WELFARE AND LAND TENURE PROBLEMS IN THE AGRARIAN REFORM PROGRAM OF VENEZUELA
(Pages 293–304)

1. Since, by law, only direct descendants of full Spanish parentage were allowed to wear mantles, it became the custom to refer to the wearers of the mantles as "mantuanos"—the highest social class in colonial Venezuela.

2. The rigid class structure, imposed by the law of 1571, was still in operation at the time of the rebellion. This law stipulated in fact that "no free negress, or slave, or mulatto could wear gold, pearls, or silk; but if the free negress or mulatto were married to a Spaniard she could wear gold and pearl earrings and a necklace, her skirt could be hemmed with velvet; she could neither wear nor carry a mantle made of crepe or any other material, she could only wear a short cloak that would reach down to her waist, otherwise she would suffer the penalty of losing her jewels, her silk dresses and her mantle."—Quoted by the Venezuelan historian, Jose Gil Fortoul, *Historia Constitu-* *cional de Venezuela,* 3rd ed. (Caracas, 1942), I, 78.

3. A white "criollo" is a person born in Venezuela of Spanish parents.

4. Part 1 was read by Dr. Antonio Manzano in Spanish before the conference; part 2 was read by Prof. George W. Hill in English.

5. To achieve the general goals required by the needs of the country the program of the Institute will be co-ordinated with production activities of other federal agencies, including the Venezuelan Development Corporation, the Agricultural and Livestock Bank, and the Ministry of Agriculture and Livestock. Each of these agencies has specialized production programs. The 1951/52 budget of the Development Corporation, for example, carries an appropriation of 6,400,000 dollars for an increased rice and corn production program, 9,600,000 dollars for sugar, and 3,085,000 dollars for livestock.

AGRICULTURAL CO-OPERATION IN MEXICO IN RELATION TO SMALL LANDHOLDINGS
(Pages 308–23)

1. At the beginning of 1947 the National Bank of Agricultural Credit changed its name to National Bank of Agricultural and Livestock Credit.

TENURE INNOVATIONS AND AGRICULTURAL PRODUCTION IN PUERTO RICO
(Pages 328–37)

1. A. D. Gayer, P. T. Homan, and E. K. Jones, *The Sugar Economy of Puerto Rico* (New York, 1938), p. 107.

2. S. L. Descartes, "Land Reform in Puerto Rico," *Journal of Land and Public Utility Economics,* XIX (1943), p. 397.

3. Ralph Will, "Activities of the Farm Security Administration in Puerto Rico," in

Caribbean Land Tenure Symposium (Washington, D.C., 1946), p. 179.

4. The master plan studies for the resettlement of squatters (agregados) point out that there are about 73,000 agregados families pending resettlement. It has been recommended that the program be developed in the municipalities of the coastal region where sugar cane is grown. This would cover about 56,000 agregados. The other 17,000 are those who live in the interior mountainous part of the island. The present program does not seem to be the solution to the problem of the agregado family in that region.

5. Mainly corn, beans, sweet potatoes, plantains, bananas, yams, and miscellaneous vegetables.

6. Mainly chickens, cattle, goats, swine, and rabbits.

SOCIAL SECURITY FOR LANDLESS WORKERS: THE EXPERIENCE OF BRAZIL
(Pages 337–40)

1. *La Securita Sociala* (Geneva, 1950), p. 6.

2. "Social Security in Agriculture," *International Labor Review*, LXI (1950), 168.

3. Law No. 3,200, April 19, 1941.

4. Alonso Caldas Brandao, *Legislação Trabalhista*, 3rd ed. (Rio de Janeiro, 1949), p. 17.

5. Law No. 738, June 13, 1951.

AN EVALUATION OF MEXICO'S PRINCIPAL TYPES OF FARM OPERATION AND OF THEIR SIGNIFICANCE TO OTHER LATIN AMERICAN COUNTRIES
(Pages 350–56)

1. Marco Antonio Durán, *Del Agrarismo a la Revolución Agrícola* (Mexico City, 1947), pp. 28–30, 51–53.

2. Durán, p. 85.

3. N. L. Whetten, *Rural Mexico* (Chicago, 1948), p. 195.

4. Whetten, Ch. X.

5. Durán, p. 85.

6. Instituto Agrario Nacional, *Turen* (Caracas, 1951).

7. Carl C. Taylor, *Rural Life in Argentina* (Baton Rouge, La., 1948), pp. 352–67.

8. Leo Waibel, "Uma Viagem de Reconhecimento ao Sul de Goiás," *Revista Brasileira de Geografia*, IX (1947), pp. 331–40.

PRINCIPLES OF TENURE IN ENGLAND AND WALES
(Pages 360–74)

1. *Proceedings of the Fourth International Conference of Agricultural Economists, Held at St. Andrews, Scotland, 30 August to 6 September, 1936* (London, 1937).

2. "Owners of Land 1872–3 (England and Wales)," *Great Britain Sessional Papers* (London, 1874), LXXII (72), Pts. 1 and 2.

3. It is true now that the 1941–43 National Farm Survey records indicate the name of the owner, and it would be possible to reconstruct ownership by estates by building up the areas of individual farms. This was done in 1947 for the Eastern Counties of England. See *Landownership in the Eastern Counties 1941: A Study of Distribution of Estates and the Statement of their Equipment* (Cambridge, 1947).

4. Arthur H. Johnson, *The Disappearance of the Small Landowner* (Oxford, 1909).

5. See Charles S. Orwin and W. R. Peel, *The*

Tenure of Agricultural Land, 2nd ed. (Cambridge, 1926). See also J. J. MacGregor, "Recent Land Tenure Changes in Mid-Devon," *Economica,* New Series, I (1934).

6. "Land Tenure and the Development of Agriculture," in *Proceedings of the Fourth International Conference of Agricultural Economists* (London, 1937), p. 90.

7. Alexander W. Menzies-Kitchin, *Land Settlement. A Report Prepared for the Carnegie United Kingdom Trustees* (Edinburgh, 1935).

8. This figure is not strictly comparable with that of 36 per cent quoted for 1927, since the former is based on all holdings over five acres

and the latter on all holdings over one acre.

9. C. S. Orwin, "Land Tenure in England," in *Proceedings of the First International Conference of Agricultural Economists* (n.p., 1929), p. 11.

10. *An Economic History of Modern Britain, 1850–1886* (Cambridge, 1932), II, 257.

11. G. Shaw Lefevre, *Agrarian Tenures in England, Ireland, and Scotland* (London, 1893), p. 52.

12. Charles Douglas, "The Policy of the Agricultural Act (1920)," *Transactions of the Highland and Agricultural Society of Scotland,* Series 33 (Edinburgh, 1921).

Land Tenure Issues in Western Europe Since the French Revolution
(Pages 374–83)

1. "Evolution of Land Tenure," *Journal of Proceedings of the Agricultural Economics Society,* IX (1951), 115–25.

The Italian Agrarain Reform
(Pages 390–400)

1. *La distribuzione della proprieta fondiaria in Italia,* 13 Vols. (Rome, 1948); Guiseppe Medici, *I tipi d'impresa nell'agricoltura Italiana* (Rome, 1951).

2. The figures of Table 1 are not strictly comparable with those of Tables 2 and 3. Those of Table 1 refer only to cultivated land on the total privately owned surface, including the land owned by institutions of a private character (welfare and church institutions or companies); those of Tables 2 and 3 refer to the total privately owned productive surface, including forests and pasture but excluding land owned by institutions.

3. In comparing Table 3 with Table 2, it is to be noted that 8.1 million hectares are attributed to cultivating owners from the holdings of less than fifty hectares.

4. The contract of "mezzadria" is typical for Central and Northern Italy. According to it, the owners install on each one of the family farms, into which their property is split, a cul-

tivating family who is obliged to provide all the needed work and to contribute half of the enterprise capital and of the expenses, obtaining as a compensation one-half of all the products of the farm. Similar but more complicated contracts are applied elsewhere in Italy with the name of "mezzadria" or "colonia parziaria." The cultivator with the contract of mezzadria is called mezzadro.

5. The figures given for Calabria in the table do not correspond to those given in the text because with the "extract" law there has been added to the original Sila district the district of Caulonia with a total surface of 30,000 hectares in which it will be possible to expropriate 5,000 hectares.

6. The figures given here refer to the time— October, 1951—at which this paper was presented.

7. Reference is to a movie on land reform in Calabria shown following the presentation of this paper.

Collectivization of Agriculture in Soviet Russia
(Pages 407–16)

1. See the excellent treatment of the subject by David Mitrany, *Marx Against the Peasant: A Study in Social Dogmatism* (Chapel Hill, North Carolina, 1951). See also Victor Chernov, *Marks i Engel's o Krestyanstve* (Moscow, 1906).

2. For a more detailed discussion, see Lazar Volin, *A Survey of Soviet Russian Agriculture,* United States Department of Agriculture Mono-

graph No. 5 (Washington, D.C., 1951), Ch. III.

3. The discussion from this point on follows in the main the author's article "The Turn of the Screw in Soviet Agriculture," *Foreign Affairs,* XXX (1952), 279–88.

4. Gustav Schmoller, "Grundriss der Allgemeinen," *Volkswirtschaftslehre,* I (1900), 520. Quoted in J. H. Clapham, *The Economic Development of France and Germany, 1815–1914* (Cambridge, 1921), p. 1.

The Land Settlement Program of Finland
(Pages 453–65)

1. Komiteanmietinto, July 19, 1943.

2. *Kansantaloudellinen Aikakauskirja* (Helsinki, 1946), p. 154.

3. Komiteanmietinto, Dec. 1, 1944.

4. *Asutustoiminnan Aikakauskirja* (Helsinki, 1952), I, 14–15.

5. *Ibid.,* pp. 16–17.

6. *Asutustoiminnan Aikakauskirja* (Helsinki, 1952), II, 6–9.

Appraising Experiences in the Resettlement of Populations
(Pages 472–74)

1. A member of the committee, Prof. K. H. Stone, presented areas of pioneer settlement in the world as mapped in the early 1930's and proposed that there is still a large total area of land in the world available for new settlement

on a commercial or subsistence basis. The suggestion to prepare and collect, through Prof. Stone, world maps showing areas of present new settlement and areas of potential settlement was warmly welcomed by the committee.

Financial Aspects of Land Reform in the Far East
(Pages 481–86)

1. Because of the limited time, I was unable to discuss the problems of the individual farmer in financing the purchase of a farm. These problems vary with the type of agriculture prevailing, the capital needed for operation, and the managerial and operating skills essential to success. When the problem of the individual farmer is included, a land reform program often needs to be supplemented with the following co-ordinated programs:

Measures to open up new investment opportunities.—This may mean a survey of basic resources and an industrial development program.

Measures to assist investment in local enterprises.—These would embrace tax concessions, preferential foreign exchange allocations, the right to cash land bonds at par value, requests for technical assistance in specialized fields, and, in cases of shortage of foreign exchange, the negotiation of loans or grants for development purposes.

An expanded education and extension service to enable the farmer to make full use of his new opportunity.—Where the landlord in the past has provided seed, fertilizer, and instruction as to the crops to be grown, not only farming guidance but supplementary credit may be needed. These conditions also apply when land development programs, as separate

from land reform programs, are considered.

A program of consolidation of holdings where fragmentation is a serious handicap to efficient operation.—This should also be associated with restriction on land transfers to prevent a recurrence of small holdings and tenancy. This is essential where there is serious population pressure. Unless such steps are taken a land reform program may result in only temporary benefits to the farmers.

DISCUSSION
(Pages 486-92)

1. Mr. Galbraith was chairman of the session at which the preceeding two papers by Messrs. Palmer and Bunce were presented and discussed.

EQUITABLE TENANCY ARRANGEMENTS IN THE UNITED STATES
(Pages 522-31)

1. *Illinois Bulletin 502.*
2. See Illinois mimeographed publication

AE2415, *Charging-off Fertilizer Costs.*

FRAGMENTATION OF LAND HOLDINGS AND MEASURES FOR CONSOLIDATION IN GREECE
(Pages 543-48)

1. References: *The Consolidation of Fragmented Agricultural Holdings* (Washington, D.C., 1950); Euthymios Papageorgiou, "Research in Farm Management and Its Usefulness for the Farmer," in *Science in Aid of Our Farmers* (Thessalonike, 1948).

REALLOCATION OF LAND IN THE NETHERLANDS
(Pages 548-54)

1. Paul Lamartine Yates, *Food Production in Western Europe* (London and New York, 1940).
2. Explanatory memorandum with the 1938 Reallotment Bill.

3. Radiocauserie Ministerie van Landbouw, Aug. 30, Oct. 25, 1946.
4. *Ibid.*
5. A. Rienks, "Ruilverkaveling," *De Pacht,* VII (1947).

ASPECTS OF CONSOLIDATION WORK IN THE NETHERLANDS
(Pages 554-58)

1. The article by Miss Vanderpol is published in this volume immediately preceding this paper. Another good article in English on this subject is to be found in A. Rienks, "The Replanning of Holdings in The Netherlands," *Farm Economist,* VI (1948).

Land Reform and Agricultural Production

(Pages 575–82)

1. Mr. Schickele presented this report with the following remark: "We claim no credit for this report. However, we must accept the onus of any omissions, misinterpretations, and errors that may be found, since it was not possible to have this report checked by the working party members. The chairman has tried to arrange in a systematic manner the observations, problems, and ideas expressed by the participants in order to highlight the issues which deserve utmost attention. He has attempted to point out the basic principles as they emerged from the discussion, which ran four afternoons and in which sixteen countries were represented. These principles appear to have wide applicability in many countries throughout the world. They should govern the planning and execution of land reform programs if agricultural production is not to suffer but to expand as a result of tenure improvements."

2. In the following, the term "rents or taxes" is used as a generic term to connote any payments, in cash or in kind, made by farmers for the use of the land or for its purchase or to the government for taxes.

3. The issues in this section came up toward the end of the last session of the working party and received hardly more than a scant mention. The chairman, therefore, assumes the responsibility for this part of the report.

Appraising the Adequacy of Land Tenure Systems for Agricultural Production

(Pages 583–89)

1. Theodore W. Schultz, "Land Reform: Community Preference and Production Possibilities." Paper presented at the Church and Agricultural Policy Conference, Haverford, Pa., June, 1951.

2. Rainer Schickele, "Effect of Tenure Systems on Agricultural Efficiency," *Journal of Farm Economics*, XXIII (1951), 185–207.

3. Earl O. Heady and Earl W. Kehrberg, *Relationship of Crop Share and Cash Leasing Systems to Farming Efficiency*, Research Bulletin 386, Agricultural Experiment Station, Iowa State College (Ames, Iowa, 1952).

4. Horace Belshaw, *Land Tenure and the Problem of Tenurial Reform in New Zealand* (Wellington, n.d.); Joseph Ackerman and Marshall Harris, eds., *Family Farm Policy. Proceedings of a Conference on Family Farm Policy* (Chicago, 1947), pp. 9–10, 405–26, 428, 480.

5. These optima naturally depend on environmental and economic conditions. What is wanted is an institutional structure which is in harmony with these conditions.

6. See the writer's unpubl. diss. (Cornell University, 1951), "Agricultural Development in Central Chile."

7. *Basic Problems of Plantation Labour* (Geneva, 1950).

8. Comment by Prof. L. W. Witt: "I have the feeling that if we think in terms of long sweeps of history, the present system of holdings [fragmentation] is the result of previous periods when technology did not discourage divided holdings. . . . The laggardness of the adjustment and unwillingness to take advantage of current opportunities may [present] serious 'historical lags' leading to severe social, economic and, above all, political problems."

9. *The Consolidation of Fragmented Agricultural Holdings* (Washington, D.C., 1950).

10. Paul V. Maris, "Farm Tenancy," in *Farmers in a Changing World, Yearbook of Agriculture, 1940* (Washington, D.C., 1940), p. 901.

11. It has been argued that "too much security" reduces agricultural efficiency by undue protection from competition.—Schickele, "Effect of Tenure Systems on Agricultural Efficiency," *op. cit.*, p. 197.

12. The greatest relevant practical problem is in measuring these contributions. For an attempt, see J. Lossing Buck, "Farm Tenancy in China," *Economic Facts* No. 33–34 (June–July, 1944).

13. Question by Prof. Rainer Schickele: "Is the synchronizing of the interests and desirable incentives of all the parties involved under tenancy an almost hopeless task unless the operator is given virtual freedom of management?"

14. Theodore W. Schultz, "How Efficient is American Agriculture?" *Journal of Farm Economics*, XXIX (1947), 644–58. For excellent statements summarizing the role of both vertical and horizontal mobility of resources, see *Measures for the Economic Development of Under-Developed Countries* (New York, 1951), Ch. III.

15. In economic terms this means a rate of capital investment which compared to other factors yields equimarginal returns.—Schickele, "Effect of Tenure Systems on Agricultural Efficiency," *op. cit.*

16. In a wider economic sense, the market effects of a change in the distribution of income also influence agriculture through a changed pattern of demand for nonagricultural goods.

17. *Monthly Bulletin of Agricultural Economics and Sociology*, XXVIII (1937) Nos. 2, 3, 4.

18. *Land Reform: Defects in Agrarian Structure As Obstacles to Economic Development* (New York, 1951); *Measures for the Economic Development of Under-Developed Countries* (New York, 1951).

The Possibilities of Co-operative Farming
(Pages 590–97)

1. The word co-operation is used here in its technical sense.

2. Claude F. Strickland, *Co-operation in India,* 3rd ed. (London, New York, and Bombay, 1938), pp. 15–16.

3. Lazar Volin, *A Survey of Soviet Russian Agriculture* (Washington, D.C., 1951), p. 23.

4. *Yearbook of Agricultural Cooperation,* (Oxford, 1950), p. 101.

5. Otto Schiller, "The Farming Co-operative: A New System of Farm Management," *Land Economics*, XXVII (1951), 2.

6. For details, see *Yearbook of Agricultural Cooperation,* (Oxford, 1950), pp. 130–43.

7. See Karl Brandt, "Otto Schiller's 'Farming Co-operatives': A Critical Appraisal," *Land Economics*, XXVII (1951), 105.

A Comparison of Collective and Co-operative Farming
(Pages 602–5)

1. This paper has been extracted from the review *Ost Europa*, I (1951). The term "collective" is used throughout in the sense of the Russian "kolkhoz."

Experiences in Operation of Farm Machinery Co-operatives in Germany
(Pages 618–23)

1. H. Hoechstetter, *Eigen-, Lohn- oder Gemeinschaftsschlepper für bäuerliche Familienbetriebe?* (Wolfratshausen, 1950).

2. W. Abel, *Maschine und Kleinbauerntum* (Hanover, 1951).

3. *Ibid.*

4. A. Münzinger, "Die bäuerliche Maschinengenossenschaft Hausern," *Schriften des RKTL*, LIV (1934).

5. Abel, *Maschine.*

The Principles of Public Land Management in the United States
(Pages 638–42)

1. A portion of a paper "Public Land Management in the United States" prepared for the use of the working party on public land management.

Taxation and Public Regulation of Private Land Uses
(Pages 642–45)

1. It was noted that in some South American countries uncultivated land is assessed at a higher rate than cultivated land to encourage cultivation.

2. Some South American members of the group pointed to a major obstacle here in that such forms of taxation can only be applied where cadastral surveys have been made. Many parts of under-developed countries have never been surveyed.

Cadastral Surveying As a Basic Tool in Land Management
(Pages 648–51)

1. This paper consists of excerpts from a more extensive paper of the same title prepared for the use of the working party on methods of title registration, cadastral and boundary surveys.

On the Making of Land Tenure Research Surveys
(Pages 652–59)

1. It is regretted that limitations of space permitted the inclusion of only one project statement in the proceedings of the conference.

The Function of Problem Formulation
(Pages 665–69)

1. Prepared as a supplement to the report of the working party on the methodology and value of land tenure research surveys, this paper is an attempt to give a more general statement of problem formulation than is presented in the workshop report and to draw out the implications of this approach for the kinds of research that need to be carried on.

2. For a full discussion of the relation between practical and scientific inquiry, see F. S. C. Northrop, *The Logic of the Sciences and the Humanities* (New York, 1948), especially Ch. IV.

The theories of any particular science are statements of the sequence of results following from a given action. The problems for further research arise from inconsistencies in these concepts. Their test proceeds by formulating inconsistent concepts into alternative statements of what would ensue and by checking those implications which would validate one of the alternative series of concepts. It may be possible to perform these tests by statistical manipulation of data. This test would be directed by the formulation of the problem.

Further, the theories of social sciences, as statements of possible actions, may be used when policy judgments are needed to overcome some problem which arises in the course of previous action. This provides a test of the validity of the concepts used, and it may raise the question of inconsistency of the reformulated concepts with the other theories of that science. Through the repercussion of such tests, all the concepts of a discipline can be maintained as the best available statements of possible alternatives, usable in practical situations. Thus the test of a scientific hypothesis is related to the practical question of what alternative actions can be undertaken.

3. See L. A. Salter, Jr., *A Critical Review of Research in Land Economics* (Minneapolis, Minn., 1948).

INFLUENCING RURAL PEOPLE
(Pages 673–83)

1. These workshops were under the direction of Charles E. Rogers, information consultant formerly with the Food and Agriculture Organization of the United Nations in Washington, D.C. He was assisted by Dorothy Cochran, of the information staff, North American Regional Office of FAO. The Department of Agricultural Journalism of the University of Wisconsin co-operated in the information workshops by providing the technical assistance of the staff members as well as facilities and resource materials.

INTERNATIONAL GROUP THINKING
(Pages 686–89)

1. This paper consists of a statement by Dr. Henry C. Taylor in Washington, D.C., at the closing session of the conference. Dr. Taylor, formerly Professor of Agricultural Economics at the University of Wisconsin, was the first Chief of the Bureau of Agricultural Economics, United States Department of Agriculture.